MATH 1000

Teacher's Guide

Author:
Alpha Omega Publications

Editor:
Alan Christopherson, M.S.

804 N. 2nd Ave. E.
Rock Rapids, IA 51246-1759

MATH 1000

LIFEPAC® Overview

MATH SCOPE & SEQUENCE

KINDERGARTEN

Lessons 1-40	Lessons 41-80	Lessons 81-120	Lessons 121-160
Directions – right, left, high, low, etc.	**Directions** – right, left, high, low, etc.	**Directions** – right, left, high, low, etc.	**Directions** – right, left, high, low, etc.
Comparisons – big, little, alike, different	**Comparisons** – big, little, alike, different	**Comparisons** – big, little, alike, different	**Comparisons** – big, little, alike, different
Matching	**Matching**	**Matching**	**Matching**
Cardinal Numbers – to 9	**Cardinal Numbers** – to 12	**Cardinal Numbers** – to 19	**Cardinal Numbers** – to 100
Colors – red, blue, green, yellow, brown, purple	**Colors** – orange	**Colors** – black, white	**Colors** – pink
Shapes – circle, square, rectangle, triangle	**Shapes** – circle, square, rectangle, triangle	**Shapes** – circle, square, rectangle, triangle	**Shapes** – circle, square, rectangle, triangle
Number Order	**Number Order**	**Number Order**	**Number Order**
Before and After	**Before and After**	**Before and After**	**Before and After**
Ordinal Numbers – to 9th	**Ordinal Numbers** – to 9th	**Ordinal Numbers** – to 9th	**Ordinal Numbers** – to 9th
Problem Solving	**Problem Solving**	**Problem Solving**	**Problem Solving**
	Number Words – to nine	**Number Words** – to nine	**Number Words** – to nine
	Addition – to 9	**Addition** – multiples of 10	**Addition** – to 10 and multiples of 10
		Subtraction – to 9	**Subtraction** – to 10
		Place Value	**Place Value**
		Time/Calendar	**Time/Calendar**
			Money
			Skip Counting – 2s, 5s, 10s
			Greater/Less Than

MATH SCOPE & SEQUENCE

	Grade 1	Grade 2	Grade 3
UNIT 1	NUMBER ORDER, ADD/SUBTRACT • Number order, skip count • Add, subtract to 9 • Story problems • Measurements • Shapes	NUMBERS AND WORDS TO 100 • Numbers and words to 100 • Operation symbols: +, –, =, >, < • Add and subtract • Place value and fact families • Story problems	ADD/SUB TO 18 AND PLACE VALUE • Digits, place value to 999 • Add and subtract • Linear measurements • Operation symbols: +, –, =, ≠, >, < • Time
UNIT 2	ADD/SUBTRACT TO 10, SHAPES • Add, subtract to 10 • Number words • Place value • Patterns, sequencing, estimation • Shapes	ADD/SUBTRACT AND EVEN/ODD • Numbers and words to 200 • Add, subtract, even and odd • Skip count 2s, 5s, and 10s • Ordinal numbers, fractions, and money • Shapes	CARRYING AND BORROWING • Fact families, patterns, and fractions • Add and subtract with carrying and borrowing • Skip count 2s, 5s, 10s • Money, shapes, lines • Even and odd
UNIT 3	FRACTIONS, TIME, AND SYMBOLS • Number sentences • Fractions • Story problems • Time and the = symbol • Oral directions	ADD WITH CARRYING TO THE 10'S PLACE • Add with carrying to the 10's place • Subtract • Flat shapes, money, A.M./P.M. • Rounding to the 10's place • Standard measurements	FACTS OF ADD/SUB AND FRACTIONS • Add 3 numbers w/ carrying • Coins, weight, volume, A.M./P.M. • Fractions • Skip count 3s, subtract w/ borrowing • Oral instructions
UNIT 4	ADD TO 18, MONEY, MEASUREMENT • Add to 18 • Skip count, even and odd • Money • Shapes and measurement • Place value	NUMBERS/WORDS TO 999, AND GRAPHS • Numbers and words to 999 • Addition, subtraction, and place value • Calendar • Measurements and solid shapes • Making change	ROUND, ESTIMATE, STORY PROBLEMS • Place value to 9,999 • Rounding to the 10's and estimating • Add and subtract fractions • Roman numerals • 1/4 inch
UNIT 5	COLUMN ADDITION AND ESTIMATION • Add three 1-digit numbers • Ordinal numbers • Time and number lines • Estimation and charts • Fractions	ADD/SUBTRACT TO THE 100'S PLACE • Data and bar graphs and shapes • Add and subtract to the 100's place • Skip count 3s and place value to the 100's place • Add fractions • Temperature	PLANE SHAPES AND SYMMETRY • Number sentences • Rounding to the 100's and estimation • Perimeter and square inch • Bar graph, symmetry, and even/odd rules • Temperature
UNIT 6	NUMBER WORDS TO 99 • Number words to 99 • Add two 2-digit numbers • Symbols: > and < • Fractions • Shapes	SUBTRACT WITH BORROWING FROM 10'S • Measurements • Time and money • Subtract w/ borrowing from the 10's place • Add and subtract fractions • Perimeter	MULTIPLICATION, LINES, AND ANGLES • Add and subtract to 9,999 • Multiples and multiplication facts for 2 • Area and equivalent fractions • Line graphs, segments, and angles • Money
UNIT 7	COUNT TO 200, SUBTRACT TO 12 • Number order and place value • Subtract to 12 • Operation signs • Estimation and time • Graphs	ADD WITH CARRYING TO THE 100'S PLACE • Add with carrying to the 100's place • Fractions as words • Number order in books • Rounding and estimation	ADD/SUB MIXED NUMBERS, PROBABILITY • Multiplication facts for 5 and missing numbers • Add and subtract mixed numbers • Subtract with 0s in the minuend • Circle graphs • Probability
UNIT 8	ADD/SUBTRACT TO 18 • Addition, subtract to 18 • Group counting • Fractions • Time and measurements • Shapes	VOLUME AND COIN CONVERSION • Addition, subtraction, and measurements • Group counting and "thinking" answers • Convert coins • Directions – north, south, east, and west • Length and width	MEASUREMENTS AND MULTIPLICATION • Multiplication facts for 3 & 10, multiples of 4 • Convert units of measurement • Decimals and directions • Picture graphs and missing addends • Length and width
UNIT 9	SENSIBLE ANSWERS • Fact families • Sensible answers • Subtract 2-digit numbers • Add three 2-digit numbers	AREA AND SQUARE MEASUREMENT • Area and square measurement • Add three 2-digit numbers with carrying • Add coins and convert to cents • Fractions and quarter-inches	MULT, METRICS, AND PERIMETER • Add and subtract whole numbers, fractions, and mixed numbers • Standard measurements and metrics • Operation symbols • Multiplication facts for 4
UNIT 10	ADDITION AND SUBTRACTION REVIEW • Addition, subtraction, and place value • Directions – north, south, east, and west • Fractions • Patterns	CARRYING AND BORROWING REVIEW • Rules for even and odd numbers • Round numbers to the 100's place • Digital clocks and sensible answers • Add three 3-digit numbers	PROBABILITY, UNITS, AND SHAPES • Addition and subtraction • Rounding to the 1,000's place and estimating • Probability, equations, and parentheses • Perimeter and area • Multiplication facts for 2, 3, 4, 5, and 10

MATH SCOPE & SEQUENCE

	Grade 4	Grade 5	Grade 6
UNIT 1	WHOLE NUMBERS AND FRACTIONS • Naming whole numbers • Naming fractions • Sequencing patterns • Numbers to 1,000	PLACE VALUE, ADDITION, AND SUBTRACTION • Place value • Rounding and estimating • Addition • Subtraction	WHOLE NUMBERS AND ALGEBRA • Whole numbers and their properties • Operations and number patterns • Algebra
UNIT 2	MULTIPLYING WHOLE NUMBERS • Operation symbols • Multiplication — 1-digit multipliers • Addition and subtraction of fractions • Numbers to 10,000	MULTIPLYING WHOLE NUMBERS AND DECIMALS • Multiplying whole numbers • Powers • Multiplying decimals	DATA ANALYSIS • Collecting and describing data • Organizing data • Displaying and interpreting data
UNIT 3	SEQUENCING AND ROUNDING • Multiplication with carrying • Rounding and estimation • Sequencing fractions • Numbers to 100,000	DIVIDING WHOLE NUMBERS AND DECIMALS • One-digit divisors • Two-digit divisors • Decimal division	DECIMALS • Decimal numbers • Multiplying and dividing decimal numbers • The metric system
UNIT 4	LINES AND SHAPES • Plane and solid shapes • Lines and line segments • Addition and subtraction • Multiplication with carrying	ALGEBRA AND GRAPHING • Expressions • Functions • Equations • Graphing	FRACTIONS • Factors and fractions • The LCM and fractions • Decimals and fractions
UNIT 5	DIVISION AND MEASUREMENTS • Division - 1-digit divisors • Families of facts • Standard measurements • Number grouping	MEASUREMENT • The metric system • The customary system • Time • Temperature	FRACTION OPERATIONS • Adding and subtracting fractions • Multiplying and dividing fractions • The customary system
UNIT 6	DIVISION, FACTORS, AND FRACTIONS • Division — 1-digit divisors with remainders • Factors and multiples • Improper and mixed fractions • Equivalent fractions	FACTORS AND FRACTIONS • Factors • Equivalent fractions • Fractions	RATIO, PROPORTION, AND PERCENT • Ratios • Proportions • Percent
UNIT 7	WHOLE NUMBERS AND FRACTIONS • Multiplication — 2-digit multipliers • Simplifying fractions • Averages • Decimals in money problems • Equations	FRACTION OPERATIONS • Like denominators • Unlike denominators • Multiplying fractions • Dividing fractions	PROBABILITY AND GEOMETRY • Probability • Geometry: Angles • Geometry: Polygons
UNIT 8	WHOLE NUMBERS AND FRACTIONS • Division — 1-digit divisors • Fractions and unlike denominators • Metric units • Whole numbers: +, –, x, ÷	DATA ANALYSIS AND PROBABILITY • Collecting data • Analyzing data • Displaying data • Probability	GEOMETRY AND MEASUREMENT • Plane figures • Solid figures
UNIT 9	DECIMALS AND FRACTIONS • Reading and writing decimals • Adding and subtracting mixed numbers • Cross multiplication • Estimation	GEOMETRY • Geometry • Classifying plane figures • Classifying solid figures • Transformations • Symmetry	INTEGERS AND TRANSFORMATIONS • Integers • Integer operations • Transformations
UNIT 10	ESTIMATION, CHARTS, AND GRAPHS • Estimation and data gathering • Charts and graphs • Review numbers to 100,000 • Whole numbers: +, –, x, ÷	PERIMETER, AREA, AND VOLUME • Perimeter • Area • Surface area • Volume	EQUATIONS AND FUNCTIONS • Equations • More equations and inequalities • Functions

MATH SCOPE & SEQUENCE

	Grade 7	Pre-algebra Grade 8	Algebra 1 Grade 9
UNIT 1	INTEGERS • Adding and Subtracting Integers • Multiplying and Dividing Integers • The Real Number System	THE REAL NUMBER SYSTEM • Relationships • Other Forms • Simplifying	VARIABLES AND NUMBERS • Variables • Distributive Property • Definition of signed numbers • Signed number operations
UNIT 2	FRACTIONS • Working with Fractions • Adding and Subtracting Fractions • Multiplying and Dividing Fractions	MODELING PROBLEMS IN INTEGERS • Equations with Real Numbers • Functions • Integers • Modeling with Integers	SOLVING EQUATIONS • Sentences and formulas • Properties • Solving equations • Solving inequalities
UNIT 3	DECIMALS • Decimals and Their Operations • Applying Decimals • Scientific Notation • The Metric System	MODELING PROBLEMS WITH RATIONAL NUMBERS • Number Theory • Solving Problems with Rational Numbers • Solving Equations and Inequalities	PROBLEM ANALYSIS AND SOLUTION • Words and symbols • Simple verbal problems • Medium verbal problems • Challenging verbal problems
UNIT 4	PATTERNS AND EQUATIONS • Variable Expressions • Patterns and Functions • Solving Equations • Equations and Inequalities	PROPORTIONAL REASONING • Proportions • Percents • Measurement/Similar Figures	POLYNOMIALS • Addition of polynomials • Subtraction of polynomials • Multiplication of polynomials • Division of polynomials
UNIT 5	RATIOS AND PROPORTIONS • Ratios, Rates, and Proportions • Using Proportions • Fractions, Decimals, and Percents	MORE WITH FUNCTIONS • Solving Equations • Families of Functions • Patterns	ALGEBRAIC FACTORS • Greatest common factor • Binomial factors • Complete factorization • Word problems
UNIT 6	PROBABILITY AND GRAPHING • Probability • Functions • Graphing Linear Equations • Direct Variation	MEASUREMENT • Angle Measures and Circles • Polygons • Indirect Measure	ALGEBRAIC FRACTIONS • Operations with fractions • Solving equations • Solving inequalities • Solving word problems
UNIT 7	DATA ANALYSIS • Describing Data • Organizing Data • Graphing Data and Making Predictions	PLANE GEOMETRY • Perimeter and Area • Symmetry and Reflections • Other Transformations	RADICAL EXPRESSIONS • Rational and irrational numbers • Operations with radicals • Irrational roots • Radical equations
UNIT 8	GEOMETRY • Basic Geometry • Classifying Polygons • Transformations	MEASURE OF SOLID FIGURES • Surface Area • Solid Figures • Volume • Volume of Composite Figures	GRAPHING • Equations of two variables • Graphing lines • Graphing inequalities • Equations of lines
UNIT 9	MEASUREMENT AND AREA • Perimeter • Area • The Pythagorean Theorem	DATA ANALYSIS • Collecting and Representing Data • Central Tendency and Dispersion • Frequency and Histograms • Box-and-Whisker Plots • Scatter Plots	SYSTEMS • Graphical solution • Algebraic solutions • Determinants • Word problems
UNIT 10	SURFACE AREA AND VOLUME • Solids • Prisms • Cylinders	PROBABILITY • Outcomes • Permutations and Combinations • Probability and Odds • Independent and Dependent Events	QUADRATIC EQUATIONS AND REVIEW • Solving quadratic equations • Equations and inequalities • Polynomials and factors • Radicals and graphing

MATH SCOPE & SEQUENCE

	Geometry Grade 10	Algebra 2 Grade 11	Pre-Calculus Grade 12
UNIT 1	A MATHEMATICAL SYSTEM • Points, lines, and planes • Definition of definitions • Geometric terms • Postulates and theorems	SETS, STRUCTURE, AND FUNCTION • Properties and operations of sets • Axioms and applications • Relations and functions • Algebraic expressions	RELATIONS AND FUNCTIONS • Ordered-pair numbers • Algebra of functions
UNIT 2	PROOF • Logic • Reasoning • Two-column proof • Paragraph proof	NUMBERS, SENTENCES, & PROBLEMS • Order and absolute value • Sums and products • Algebraic sentences • Number and motion problems	FUNCTIONS • Linear functions • Second-degree functions • Polynomial and special functions • Complex numbers
UNIT 3	ANGLES AND PARALLELS • Definitions and measurement • Relationships and theorems • Properties of parallels • Parallels and polygons	LINEAR EQUATIONS & INEQUALITIES • Graphs • Equations • Systems of equations • Inequalities	RIGHT TRIANGLE TRIGONOMETRY • Solving a right triangle • Unit circle and special angles • Reciprocal functions and identities • Radian measure
UNIT 4	CONGRUENCY • Congruent triangles • Corresponding parts • Inequalities • Quadrilaterals	POLYNOMIALS • Multiplying polynomials • Factoring • Operations with polynomials • Variations	GRAPHING AND INVERSE FUNCTIONS • Graphing • Sinusoidal functions • Inverse trigonometric functions • Trigonometric equations
UNIT 5	SIMILAR POLYGONS • Ratios and proportions • Definition of similarity • Similar polygons and triangles • Right triangle geometry	RADICAL EXPRESSIONS • Multiplying and dividing fractions • Adding and subtracting fractions • Equations with fractions • Applications of fractions	ANALYTIC TRIGONOMETRY • Trigonometric identities • Addition formulas • Double- and half-angle formulas • Products and sums
UNIT 6	CIRCLES • Circles and spheres • Tangents, arcs, and chords • Special angles in circles • Special segments in circles	REAL NUMBERS • Rational and irrational numbers • Laws of Radicals • Quadratic equations • Quadratic formula	TRIGONOMETRIC APPLICATIONS • Trigonometry of oblique triangles • Vectors
UNIT 7	CONSTRUCTION AND LOCUS • Basic constructions • Triangles and circles • Polygons • Locus meaning and use	QUADRATIC RELATIONS & SYSTEMS • Distance formulas • Conic sections • Systems of equations • Application of conic sections	POLAR COORDINATES • Polar equations • Complex numbers
UNIT 8	AREA AND VOLUME • Area of polygons • Area of circles • Surface area of solids • Volume of solids	EXPONENTIAL FUNCTIONS • Exponents • Exponential equations • Logarithmic functions • Matrices	QUADRATIC EQUATIONS • Circles and ellipses • Parabolas and hyperbolas • Translations
UNIT 9	COORDINATE GEOMETRY • Ordered pairs • Distance • Lines • Coordinate proofs	COUNTING PRINCIPLES • Progressions • Permutations • Combinations • Probability	COUNTING PRINCIPLES • Probability • Combinations and permutations • Sequences, series, and induction
UNIT 10	GEOMETRY REVIEW • Proof and angles • Polygons and circles • Construction and measurement • Coordinate geometry	REVIEW • Integers and open sentences • Graphs and polynomials • Fractions and quadratics • Exponential functions	CALCULUS • Limits • Slopes • Curves

STRUCTURE OF THE LIFEPAC CURRICULUM

The LIFEPAC curriculum is conveniently structured to provide one Teacher's Guide containing teacher support material with answer keys and ten student worktexts for each subject at grade levels 2 through 12. The worktext format of the LIFEPACs allows the student to read the textual information and complete workbook activities all in the same booklet. The easy-to-follow LIFEPAC numbering system lists the grade as the first number(s) and the last two digits as the number of the series. For example, the Language Arts LIFEPAC at the 6th grade level, 5th book in the series would be LAN0605.

Each LIFEPAC is divided into three to five sections and begins with an introduction or overview of the booklet as well as a series of specific learning objectives to give a purpose to the study of the LIFEPAC. The introduction and objectives are followed by a vocabulary section which may be found at the beginning of each section at the lower levels or in the glossary at the high school level. Vocabulary words are used to develop word recognition and should not be confused with the spelling words introduced later in the LIFEPAC. The student should learn all vocabulary words before working the LIFEPAC sections to improve comprehension, retention, and reading skills.

Each activity or written assignment in grades 2 through 12 has a number for easy identification, such as 1.1. The first number corresponds to the LIFEPAC section and the number to the right of the decimal is the number of the activity.

Teacher checkpoints, which are essential to maintain quality learning, are found at various locations throughout the LIFEPAC. The teacher should check 1) neatness of work and penmanship, 2) quality of understanding (tested with a short oral quiz), 3) thoroughness of answers (complete sentences and paragraphs, correct spelling, etc.), 4) completion of activities (no blank spaces), and 5) accuracy of answers as compared to the answer key (all answers correct).

The self test questions in grades 2 through 12 are also number-coded for easy reference. For example, 2.015 means that this is the 15th question in the self test of Section 2. The first number corresponds to the LIFEPAC section, the zero indicates that it is a self test question, and the number to the right of the zero the question number.

The LIFEPAC test is packaged at the center of each LIFEPAC. It should be removed and put aside before giving the booklet to the student for study.

Answer and test keys in grades 2 through 12 have the same numbering system as the LIFEPACs. The student may be given access to the answer keys (not the test keys) under teacher supervision so that they can score their own work.

A thorough study of the Scope & Sequence by the teacher before instruction begins is essential to the success of the student. The teacher should become familiar with expected skill mastery and understand how these grade-level skills fit into the overall skill development of the curriculum. The teacher should also preview the objectives that appear at the beginning of each LIFEPAC for additional preparation and planning.

TEST SCORING AND GRADING

Answer keys and test keys give examples of correct answers. They convey the idea, but the student may use many ways to express a correct answer. The teacher should check for the essence of the answer, not for the exact wording. Many questions are high level and require thinking and creativity on the part of the student. Each answer should be scored based on whether or not the main idea written by the student matches the model example. "Any Order" or "Either Order" in a key indicates that no particular order is necessary to be correct.

Most self tests and LIFEPAC tests at the lower elementary levels are scored at 1 point per answer; however, the upper levels may have a point system awarding 2 to 5 points for various answers or questions. Further, the total test points will vary; they may not always equal 100 points. They may be 78, 85, 100, 105, etc..

Example 1

58/72 **SCORE** ________ **TEACHER** ________ ________
initials date

Example 2

93/105 **SCORE** ________ **TEACHER** ________ ________
initials date

A score box similar to ex. 1 above is located at the end of each self test and on the front of the LIFEPAC test. The bottom score, 72, represents the total number of points possible on the test. The upper score, 58, represents the number of points your student will need to receive an 80% or passing grade. If you wish to establish the exact percentage that your student has achieved, find the total points of their correct answers and divide it by the bottom number (in this case 72). For example, if your student has a point total of 65, divide 65 by 72 for a grade of 90%. Referring to ex. 2, on a test with a total of 105 possible points, the student would have to receive a minimum of 84 correct points for an 80% or passing grade. If your student has received 93 points, simply divide the 93 by 105 for a percentage grade of 89%. Students who receive a score below 80% should review the LIFEPAC and retest using the appropriate Alternate Test found in the Teacher's Guide.

The following is a guideline to assign letter grades for completed LIFEPACs based on a maximum total score of 100 points.

Example:

LIFEPAC Test	=	60% of the Total Score (or percent grade)
Self Test	=	25% of the Total Score (average percent of self tests)
Reports	=	10% or 10* points per LIFEPAC
Oral Work	=	5% or 5* points per LIFEPAC

*Determined by the teacher's subjective evaluation of the student's daily work.

Example:

LIFEPAC Test Score	=	92%	92 × .60	=	55 points
Self Test Average	=	90%	90 × .25	=	23 points
Reports				=	8 points
Oral Work				=	4 points
TOTAL POINTS				=	90 points

Grade Scale based on point system:

100 – 94	=	A
93 – 86	=	B
85 – 77	=	C
76 – 70	=	D
Below 70	=	F

TEACHER HINTS AND STUDYING TECHNIQUES

LIFEPAC activities are written to check the level of understanding of the preceding text. The student may look back to the text as necessary to complete these activities; however, a student should never attempt to do the activities without reading (studying) the text first. Self tests and LIFEPAC tests are never open book tests.

Language arts activities (skill integration) often appear within other subject curriculum. The purpose is to give the student an opportunity to test their skill mastery outside of the context in which it was presented.

Writing complete answers (paragraphs) to some questions is an integral part of the LIFEPAC curriculum in all subjects. This builds communication and organization skills, increases understanding and retention of ideas, and helps enforce good penmanship. Complete sentences should be encouraged for this type of activity. Obviously, single words or phrases do not meet the intent of the activity, since multiple lines are given for the response.

Review is essential to student success. Time invested in review where review is suggested will be time saved in correcting errors later. Self tests, unlike the section activities, are closed book. This procedure helps to identify weaknesses before they become too great to overcome. Certain objectives from self tests are cumulative and test previous sections; therefore, good preparation for a self test must include all material studied up to that testing point.

The following procedure checklist has been found to be successful in developing good study habits in the LIFEPAC curriculum.

1. Read the introduction and Table of Contents.
2. Read the objectives.
3. Recite and study the entire vocabulary (glossary) list.
4. Study each section as follows:
   a. Read the introduction and study the section objectives.
   b. Read all the text for the entire section, but answer none of the activities.
   c. Return to the beginning of the section and memorize each vocabulary word and definition.
   d. Reread the section, complete the activities, check the answers with the answer key, correct all errors, and have the teacher check.
   e. Read the self test but do not answer the questions.
   f. Go to the beginning of the first section and reread the text and answers to the activities up to the self test you have not yet done.
   g. Answer the questions to the self test without looking back.
   h. Have the self test checked by the teacher.
   i. Correct the self test and have the teacher check the corrections.
   j. Repeat steps a–i for each section.
5. Use the **SQ3R** method to prepare for the LIFEPAC test.

   Scan the whole LIFEPAC.

   Question yourself on the objectives.

   Read the whole LIFEPAC again.

   Recite through an oral examination.

   Review weak areas.
6. Take the LIFEPAC test as a closed book test.
7. LIFEPAC tests are administered and scored under direct teacher supervision. Students who receive scores below 80% should review the LIFEPAC using the **SQ3R** study method and take the Alternate Test located in the Teacher's Guide. The final test grade may be the grade on the Alternate Test or an average of the grades from the original LIFEPAC test and the Alternate Test.

GOAL SETTING AND SCHEDULES

Each school must develop its own schedule, because no single set of procedures will fit every situation. The following is an example of a daily schedule that includes the five LIFEPAC subjects as well as time slotted for special activities.

Possible Daily Schedule

8:15	–	8:25	Pledges, prayer, songs, devotions, etc.
8:25	–	9:10	Bible
9:10	–	9:55	Language Arts
9:55	–	10:15	Recess (juice break)
10:15	–	11:00	Math
11:00	–	11:45	History & Geography
11:45	–	12:30	Lunch, recess, quiet time
12:30	–	1:15	Science
1:15	–		Drill, remedial work, enrichment*

***Enrichment:** *Computer time, physical education, field trips, fun reading, games and puzzles, family business, hobbies, resource persons, guests, crafts, creative work, electives, music appreciation, projects.*

Basically, two factors need to be considered when assigning work to a student in the LIFEPAC curriculum.

The first is time. An average of 45 minutes should be devoted to each subject, each day. Remember, this is only an average. Because of extenuating circumstances, a student may spend only 15 minutes on a subject one day and the next day spend 90 minutes on the same subject.

The second factor is the number of pages to be worked in each subject. A single LIFEPAC is designed to take three to four weeks to complete. Allowing about three to four days for LIFEPAC introduction, review, and tests, the student has approximately 15 days to complete the LIFEPAC pages. Simply take the number of pages in the LIFEPAC, divide it by 15 and you will have the number of pages that must be completed on a daily basis to keep the student on schedule. For example, a LIFEPAC containing 45 pages will require three completed pages per day. Again, this is only an average. While working a 45-page LIFEPAC, the student may complete only one page the first day if the text has a lot of activities or reports, but go on to complete five pages the next day.

Long-range planning requires some organization. Because the traditional school year originates in the early fall of one year and continues to late spring of the following year, a calendar should be devised that covers this period of time. Approximate beginning and completion dates can be noted on the calendar as well as special occasions such as holidays, vacations and birthdays. Since each LIFEPAC takes three to four weeks or 18 days to complete, it should take about 180 school days to finish a set of ten LIFEPACs. Starting at the beginning school date, mark off 18 school days on the calendar and that will become the targeted completion date for the first LIFEPAC. Continue marking the calendar until you have established dates for the remaining nine LIFEPACs making adjustments for previously noted holidays and vacations. If all five subjects are being used, the ten established target dates should be the same for the LIFEPACs in each subject.

TEACHING SUPPLEMENTS

The sample weekly lesson plan and student grading sheet forms are included in this section as teacher support materials and may be duplicated at the convenience of the teacher.

The student grading sheet is provided for those who desire to follow the suggested guidelines for assignment of letter grades as previously discussed. The student's self test scores should be posted as percentage grades. When the LIFEPAC is completed, the teacher should average the self test grades, multiply the average by .25, and post the points in the box marked self test points. The LIFEPAC percentage grade should be multiplied by .60 and posted. Next, the teacher should award and post points for written reports and oral work. A report may be any type of written work assigned to the student whether it is a LIFEPAC or additional learning activity. Oral work includes the student's ability to respond orally to questions which may or may not be related to LIFEPAC activities or any type of oral report assigned by the teacher. The points may then be totaled and a final grade entered along with the date that the LIFEPAC was completed.

The Student Record Book which was specifically designed for use with the Alpha Omega curriculum provides space to record weekly progress for one student over a nine-week period as well as a place to post self test and LIFEPAC scores. The Student Record Books are available through the current Alpha Omega catalog; however, unlike the enclosed forms these books are not for duplication and should be purchased in sets of four to cover a full academic year.

WEEKLY LESSON PLANNER

Week of:

Monday	Subject	Subject	Subject	Subject
Tuesday	Subject	Subject	Subject	Subject
Wednesday	Subject	Subject	Subject	Subject
Thursday	Subject	Subject	Subject	Subject
Friday	Subject	Subject	Subject	Subject

WEEKLY LESSON PLANNER

Week of:

Monday	Subject	Subject	Subject	Subject
Tuesday	Subject	Subject	Subject	Subject
Wednesday	Subject	Subject	Subject	Subject
Thursday	Subject	Subject	Subject	Subject
Friday	Subject	Subject	Subject	Subject

Student Name ______________________ Year ____________

Bible

LP	Self Test Scores by Sections 1	2	3	4	5	Self Test Points	LIFEPAC Test	Oral Points	Report Points	Final Grade	Date
01											
02											
03											
04											
05											
06											
07											
08											
09											
10											

History & Geography

LP	Self Test Scores by Sections 1	2	3	4	5	Self Test Points	LIFEPAC Test	Oral Points	Report Points	Final Grade	Date
01											
02											
03											
04											
05											
06											
07											
08											
09											
10											

Language Arts

LP	Self Test Scores by Sections 1	2	3	4	5	Self Test Points	LIFEPAC Test	Oral Points	Report Points	Final Grade	Date
01											
02											
03											
04											
05											
06											
07											
08											
09											
10											

Student Name ______________________ Year ____________

Math

LP	Self Test Scores by Sections 1	2	3	4	5	Self Test Points	LIFEPAC Test	Oral Points	Report Points	Final Grade	Date
01											
02											
03											
04											
05											
06											
07											
08											
09											
10											

Science

LP	Self Test Scores by Sections 1	2	3	4	5	Self Test Points	LIFEPAC Test	Oral Points	Report Points	Final Grade	Date
01											
02											
03											
04											
05											
06											
07											
08											
09											
10											

Spelling/Electives

LP	Self Test Scores by Sections 1	2	3	4	5	Self Test Points	LIFEPAC Test	Oral Points	Report Points	Final Grade	Date
01											
02											
03											
04											
05											
06											
07											
08											
09											
10											

INSTRUCTIONS FOR MATH

The LIFEPAC curriculum from grades 2 through 12 is structured so that the daily instructional material is written directly into the LIFEPACs. The student is encouraged to read and follow this instructional material in order to develop independent study habits. The teacher should introduce the LIFEPAC to the student, set a required completion schedule, complete teacher checks, be available for questions regarding both content and procedures, administer and grade tests, and develop additional learning activities as desired. Teachers working with several students may schedule their time so that students are assigned to a quiet work activity when it is necessary to spend instructional time with one particular student.

Math is a subject that requires skill mastery. But skill mastery needs to be applied toward active student involvement. Measurements require measuring cups, rulers, and empty containers. Boxes and other similar items help the study of solid shapes. Construction paper, beads, buttons, and beans are readily available and can be used for counting, base ten, fractions, sets, grouping, and sequencing. Students should be presented with problem situations and be given the opportunity to find their solutions.

Any workbook assignment that can be supported by a real world experience will enhance the student's ability for problem solving. There is an infinite challenge for the teacher to provide a meaningful environment for the study of math. It is a subject that requires constant assessment of student progress. Do not leave the study of math in the classroom.

This section of the Math Teacher's Guide includes the following teacher aids: Suggested and Required Material (supplies), Additional Learning Activities, Answer Keys, and Alternate LIFEPAC Tests.

The Teacher Notes section of the Teacher's Guide lists the required or suggested materials for the LIFEPACs and provides additional learning activities for the students. Additional learning activities provide opportunities for problem solving, encourage the student's interest in learning and may be used as a reward for good study habits.

MATH 1001

Unit 1: A Mathematical System

TEACHER NOTES

MATERIALS NEEDED FOR LIFEPAC	
Required	Suggested
(None)	• an instrument to make straight lines such as a ruler or straightedge

ADDITIONAL LEARNING ACTIVITIES

Section 1: Undefined Terms

1. On graph paper, have students make each of the following diagrams that represent tables. Dimensions should be written along the sides.

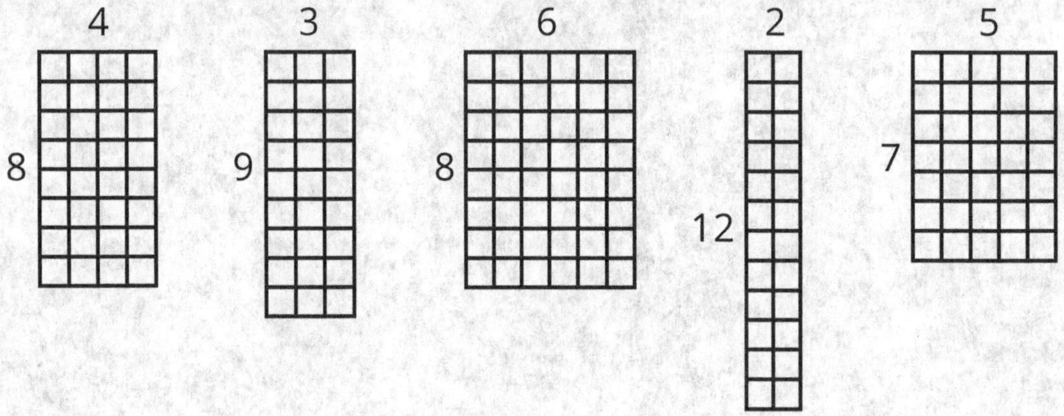

Have students draw the path a small ball would take for each table, starting at the lower left-hand corner, and moving the ball at a 45° angle with each side of the table. The ball always moves one unit up or down for one unit left or right. If the ball stops in a corner, mark the corner with a large dot. At that point the path of the ball terminates; otherwise, it continues rebounding at a 45° angle as it hits each side or end.

Do you think the ball will always end up in a corner?

If the ball starts from the lower left-hand corner, do you think it can stop in any of the four corners?

Section 2: Basic Definitions

1. Discuss these questions with your class.
   a. Can a ray have more than one name?
   b. Can a ray have two end points?
   c. How many line segments are in a line?
2. Have students draw the following figure. Ask them to determine the number of triangles of any size in the figure.

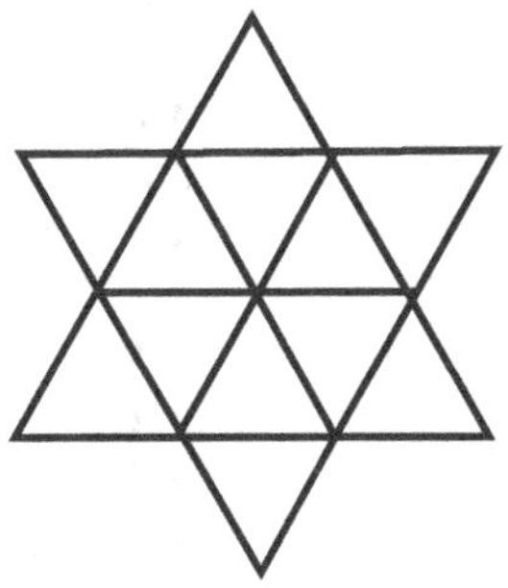

3. During their study of geometry, the students will be learning the definition of many terms. Encourage them to learn each new term as it is presented because later terms will be defined by using earlier terms. New terms will be defined as they need them in their study of geometry. Many of the definitions, theorems, and postulates in this unit will be needed in later units. Lists of these kept and maintained will be very helpful for future reference. The student should start a notebook now! Then as definitions, theorems, and postulates are given in the LIFEPAC they should be added to the notebook and used for reference.

Section 3: Geometric Statements

1. Discuss these questions with your class.
   a. Are any two points always collinear?
   b. Will any two noncollinear lines intersect?
   c. Do any postulates and theorems exist other than the ones used in the LIFEPAC?
2. Research Euclid, a Greek mathematician of 300 B.C., for whom Euclidean geometry is named.
3. Write several general statements such as "all rectangles have four sides." Then write several specific statements such as "a square has four equal sides." Devise a postulate or a theorem of your own. Remember that a postulate is a statement accepted without proof and that a theorem is a general statement that can be proved. Prove your theorem(s).

Administer the LIFEPAC Test.

The test is to be administered in one session. Give no help except with directions.
Evaluate the tests and review areas where the students have done poorly.
Review the pages and activities that stress the concepts tested.
If necessary, administer the Alternate LIFEPAC Test

ANSWER KEYS

SECTION 1

1.1 location or position
1.2 a dot
1.3 Example:

1.4 infinite number
1.5 none
1.6 no
1.7 points
1.8 straight
1.9 a. $\overleftrightarrow{AB}$
b. $\overleftrightarrow{CD}$
c. $\overleftrightarrow{EF}$
1.10 infinite number
1.11 A line exceeds indefinitely in both directions.
1.12 a. flat
b. points
1.13 a. plane *R*
b. plane *S*
c. plane *T*
1.14 infinitely long
1.15 no thickness
1.16 no

SELF TEST 1

1.01 plane (table top)
1.02 line (arrow)
1.03 planes (cover and pages of book)
1.04 points (marbles)
1.05 lines (parallel railroad tracks)
1.06 points (freckles)
1.07 e
1.08 c
1.09 a
1.010 b
1.011 f
1.012 d
1.013 $\overleftrightarrow{AC}$
1.014 a. intersects
b. *E*
1.015 point *T*
1.016 *B* or *R* (same plane)
1.017 a. $\overleftrightarrow{AC}$
b. line *x*
c. line *w*
1.018 *S*
1.019 *S*, *E*, *A*, *C*, *T*
1.020 *C*, *R*, *A*, *B*

SECTION 2

2.1 unacceptable (not restrictive enough)
2.2 unacceptable (not restrictive enough)
2.3 unacceptable (too restrictive)
2.4 acceptable
2.5 space
2.6 no (some are coplanar)
2.7 yes
2.8 a. S
Either order:
b. R
c. T
2.9 $UV + VW = UW$
2.10 false (they are coplanar)
2.11 true
2.12 true
2.13 false (they are coplanar)
2.14 true
2.15 true
2.16 true
2.17 false (the three points are not collinear)
2.18 true (definition of a plane)
2.19 true
2.20 no (do not have the same end point)
2.21 yes
2.22 Either order:
a. $\overrightarrow{AC}$
b. $\overrightarrow{AB}$
2.23 Any order:
a. $\overline{CA}$
b. $\overline{CB}$
c. $\overline{AB}$
d. $\overline{AD}$
2.24 yes
2.25 point B
2.26 opposite rays
2.27 midpoint of $\overline{CB}$
2.28 no (the figure formed is not a straight line)
2.29 no (the three points are not collinear)

SELF TEST 2

2.01 The points must be collinear.
2.02 Either order:
a. $\overline{SA} = \overline{AM}$
b. $\overline{SA} + \overline{AM} = \overline{SM}$
2.03 $GO + OD = GD$

2.04 no (point O is not necessarily in a position such that $GO = OD$)
2.05 $\overrightarrow{SA}$

2.06 midpoint

2.07 U is between N and S.

2.08 U is between N and S.

2.09 one

2.010 Any order:
$\overline{NU}$, $\overline{UT}$, and $\overline{NT}$

2.011 space
2.012 line
2.013 line
2.014 c
2.015 c
2.016 c
2.017 b
2.018 b
2.019 b
2.020 b
2.021 b
2.022 b
2.023 d
2.024 d

SECTION 3

3.1 Postulate 5: If two planes intersect, then their intersection is a line.
3.2 one
3.3 Postulate 2: Through any two different points, exactly one line exists.
3.4 a. no
b. Postulate 2: Through any two different points, exactly one line exists.
3.5 a. no
b. The three points cannot be on one line.
3.6 Postulate 1: Space contains at least four points not all in one plane.
3.7 Postulate 2: Through any two different points, exactly one line exists.
3.8 Postulate 3: Through any three points that are not on one line, exactly one plane exists.
3.9 Postulate 4: If two points lie in a plane, the line containing them lies in that plane.
3.10 Postulate 1: A plane contains at least three points not all on one line.
3.11 false (undefined terms are used to state some postulates)
3.12 false (a postulate does not require proof)
3.13 false (two planes intersect in exactly one line)
3.14 true
3.15 false (a plane must have at least 3 points)
3.16 false (the intersection of two planes is exactly one line)
3.17 the multiplication by one postulate
3.18 the commutative postulate for addition
3.19 the distributive postulate
3.20 the addition of zero postulate
3.21 the additive inverse postulate
3.22 the multiplication by one postulate
3.23 the addition of zero postulate
3.24 the commutative postulate of multiplication
3.25 the distributive postulate
3.26 the multiplicative inverse postulate
3.27 the addition postulate of inequality
3.28 the multiplication postulate of inequality
3.29 the multiplication postulate of inequality
3.30 the transitive postulate of equality
3.31 the symmetric postulate of equality
3.32 the comparison postulate
3.33 the multiplication postulate of inequality
3.34 the transitive postulate of inequality
3.35 the multiplication postulate of inequality
3.36 the reflexive postulate of equality
3.37 three collinear points
Example:

3.38 three noncollinear points
Example:

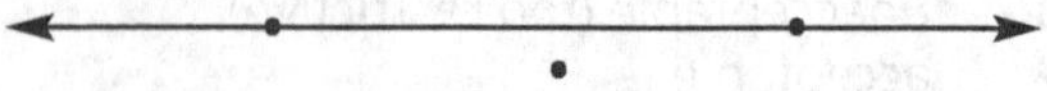

3.39 two intersecting lines
Example:

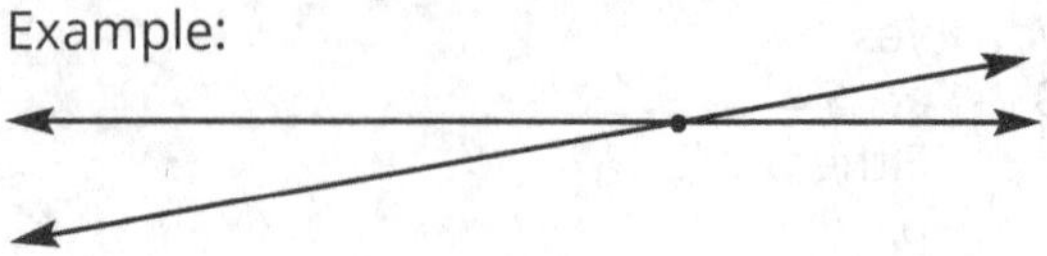

3.40 two nonintersecting lines
Example:

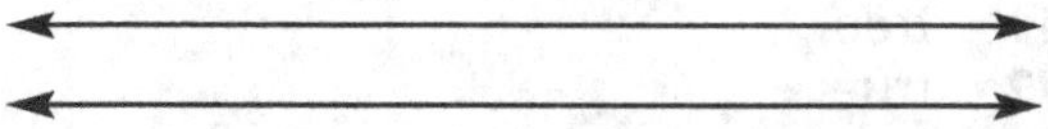

3.41 two intersecting planes
Example:

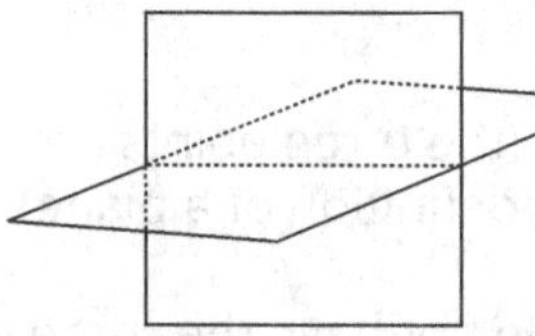

3.42 two nonintersecting planes
Example:

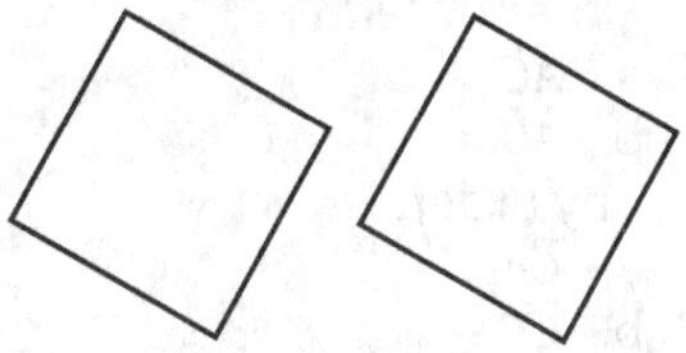

3.43 false (skew lines do not lie in one plane)
3.44 true
3.45 false (two intersecting lines lie in one plane)
3.46 false (three noncollinear points determine a plane)
3.47 true
3.48 They are the same point. Or, they are the point of intersection.

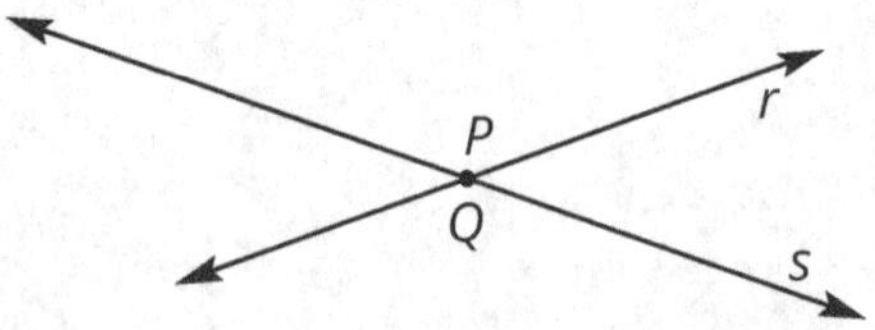

3.49 Theorem 1-1: If two lines intersect, then their intersection is exactly one point.

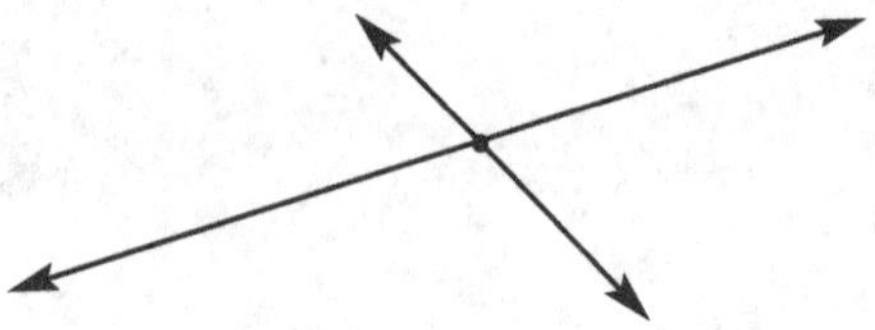

3.50 They lie in plane *N*.

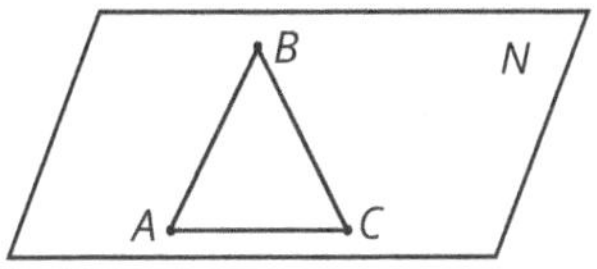

3.51 Postulate 4: If two points lie in a plane, the line containing them lies in that plane.
3.52 an infinite number
3.53 an infinite number
3.54 exactly one
3.55 exactly one
3.56 planes: *BCE*, *BEA*, *CED*, *AED*, *ABCD*, *ACE*, and *BDE*
3.57 the division property of equality
3.58 the multiplication property of equality
3.59 the subtraction property of equality
3.60 the addition property of equality
3.61 the multiplication property of equality
3.62 the addition property of equality
3.63 the multiplication property of equality
3.64 true
3.65 false (If $a + 2 < b + 3$, then $a < b + 1$.)
3.66 true
3.67 false (If $2 > -a$, then $a > -2$.)
3.68 the subtraction property of equality
3.69 the division property of equality
3.70 the addition property of equality
3.71 the subtraction property of equality
3.72 the division property of equality
3.73 the distributive postulate
3.74 the subtraction property of equality
3.75 the division property of equality
3.76 the distributive postulate
3.77 the subtraction property of equality
3.78 the subtraction property of equality
3.79 the division property of equality
3.80 the distributive postulate
3.81 the distributive postulate
3.82 the zero product property
3.83 the subtraction property of equality

SELF TEST 3

3.01 Example: line *l* intersects *m* at *P*.

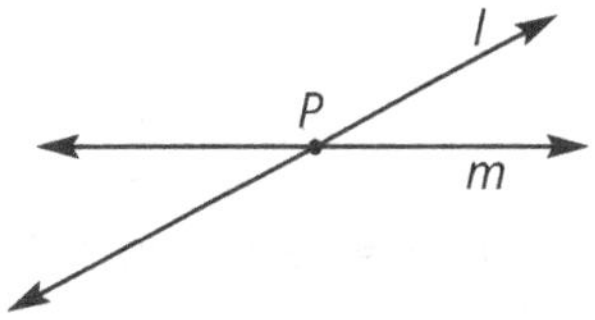

3.02 Example: Plane *A* contains line *l* and point *P*.

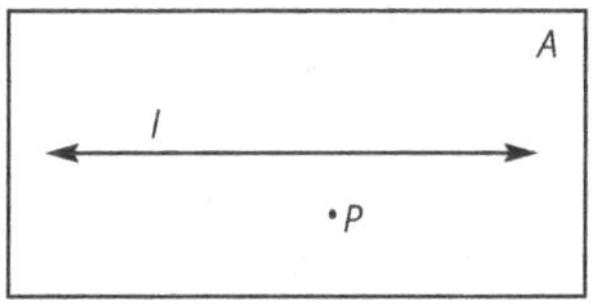

3.03 Example: Line *l* intersects line *m*; plane *A* contains both lines.

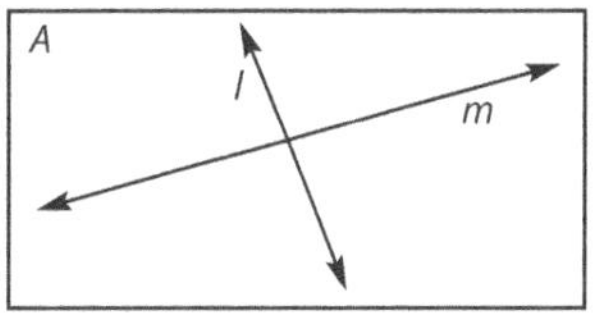

3.04 Example: $\overleftrightarrow{PQ}$, $\overleftrightarrow{PR}$, $\overleftrightarrow{PS}$, $\overleftrightarrow{QR}$, $\overleftrightarrow{QS}$, and $\overleftrightarrow{RS}$ are six different lines.

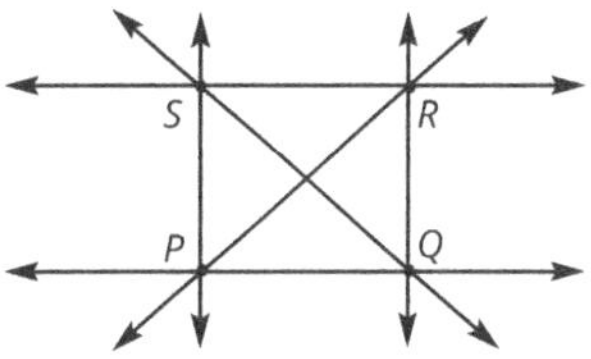

3.05 Example: *A*, *B*, *C*, and *D* are not all in one plane.

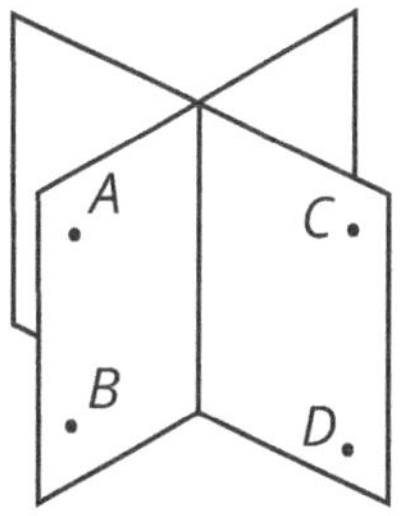

3.06 false (an undefined term can be used in a theorem)
3.07 true
3.08 false (two intersecting lines lie in one plane)
3.09 true
3.010 false (a segment has exactly two endpoints)
3.011 theorem
3.012 defined
3.013 postulate
3.014 line *AB*

3.015 line
3.016 b
3.017 d
3.018 c
3.019 a
3.020 Theorem 1-1: If two lines intersect, then their intersection is exactly one point.
3.021 Postulate 2: Through any two different points, exactly one line exists.
3.022 Postulate 4: If two points lie in a plane, the line containing them lies in that plane.
3.023 Postulate 5: If two planes intersect, then their intersection is a line.
3.024 the subtraction property of equality
3.025 the reflexive postulate of equality

LIFEPAC TEST

1. c
2. d
3. a
4. e
5. b
6. space
7. *A*

8. *BC*

9. midpoint

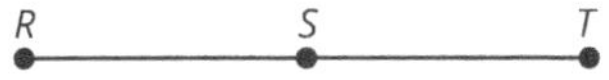

10. proof
11. prove
12. two
13. four
14. three

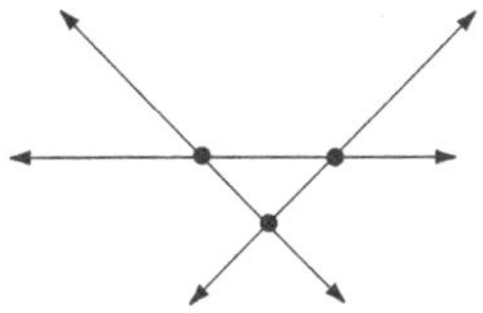

15. -*a*
16. lines *AB* and *CD* intersecting at point *P*

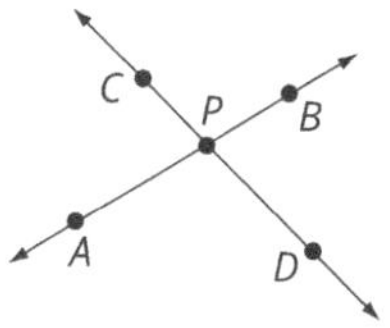

17. line *l* and point *Q* not on *l*, both in plane *T*

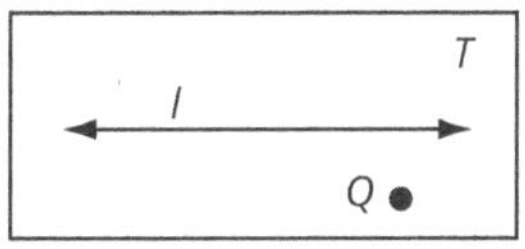

18. segment *UV* with midpoint *M*

19. collinear and coplanar points *A*, *B*, *C*, and *D*

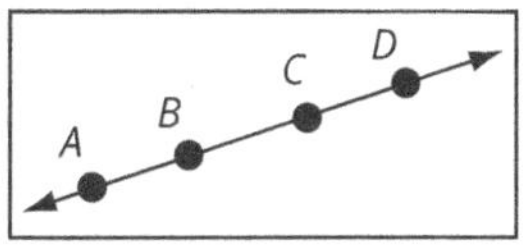

20. opposite rays $\overrightarrow{AC}$ and $\overrightarrow{AB}$

ALTERNATE LIFEPAC TEST

1. e
2. d
3. b
4. a
5. c
6. collinear
7. Either order:
   a. *P*
   b. *Q*
8. *RS*
9. midpoint
10. postulate
11. theorem
12. line
13. four
14. four
15. c
16.

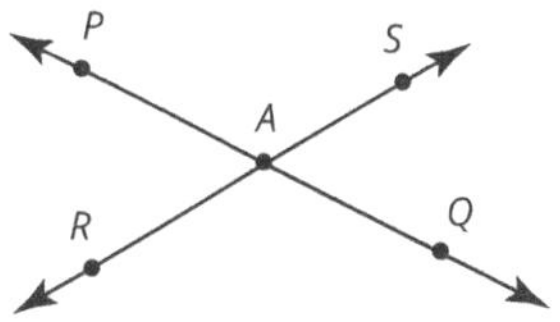

17.

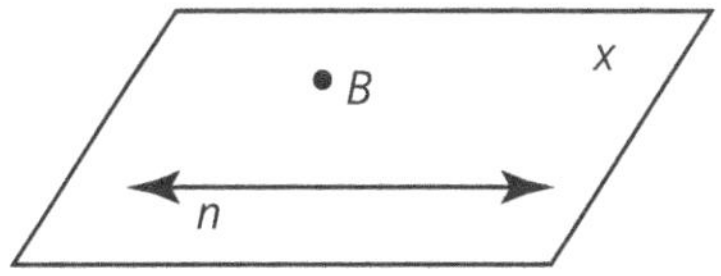

18.

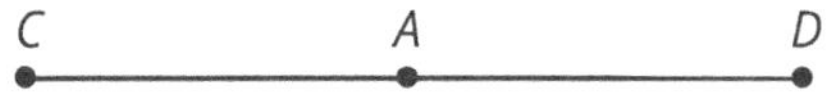

19.

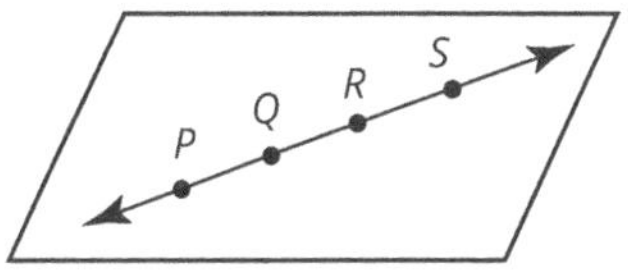

20.

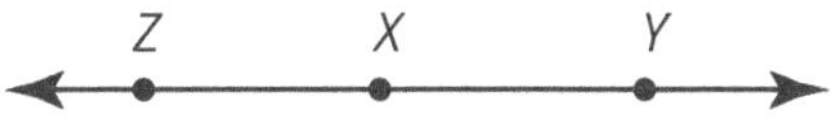

MATH 1001

ALTERNATE LIFEPAC TEST

NAME ______________________________

DATE ______________________________

SCORE ______________________________

54
68

After each model in Column I, write the matching term from Column II (each answer, 2 points).

	Column I		**Column II**
1.		______	a. $\overline{AB}$
2.		______	b. Point Q
3.		______	c. $AB + BC = AC$
4.		______	d. $\overleftrightarrow{AB}$
5.		______	e. $\overrightarrow{AB}$

Complete the following statements (each answer, 3 points).

6. Two or more points all on the same line are called ______________________ points.
7. The two end points of $\overline{PQ}$ are a. ____________ and b. ____________ .
8. If point P is between R and S, then $RP + PS$ = ____________________ .
9. If $AB = BC$ on AC, point B is called the ____________________ of $\overline{AC}$.
10. A ________________ is a statement we accept without proof.
11. A ________________ is a statement we must prove.
12. A ________________ contains at least two points.
13. Space contains at least ________________ points.
14. How many planes are determined by four noncoplanar points? ________________
15. ________________ + $(-c) = 0$.

Sketch and label the following conditions (each answer, 5 points).

16. Two lines, $\overleftrightarrow{PQ}$ and $\overleftrightarrow{RS}$, intersecting in a point *A*.

17. A line *n* and a point *B* not on *n* that are both in plane *X*.

18. A segment with midpoint *A* and end points *C* and *D*.

19. Collinear and coplanar points *P*, *Q*, *R*, and *S*.

20. Opposite rays $\overrightarrow{XY}$ and $\overrightarrow{XZ}$.

MATH 1002

Unit 2: Proofs

TEACHER NOTES

MATERIALS NEEDED FOR LIFEPAC	
Required	Suggested
• a ruler or a straightedge	(None)

ADDITIONAL LEARNING ACTIVITIES

Section 1: Logic

1. Let one student think of a statement (it may be true or false) and tell the group. Then let students, in turn, respond with the negation, conditional, contrapositive, converse, and inverse of the original statement. Students may alternate thinking of statements and responding with the other statements. Students may also tell whether their statement is true or false. The Compiled Truth Table from the LIFEPAC may be used if necessary.

Section 2: Reasoning

1. Discuss these questions with your class.
   a. Why is deductive reasoning more reliable than inductive reasoning?
   b. Can all definitions, postulates, and theorems be proved by deductive reasoning?
2. Have the class draw the following figure. Ask them to determine the number of squares of any size.

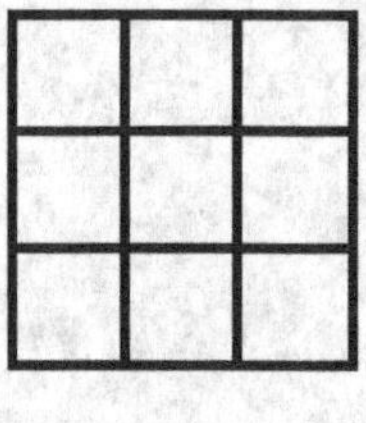

Next have the class draw the following figure. Ask them to determine the number of squares of any size.

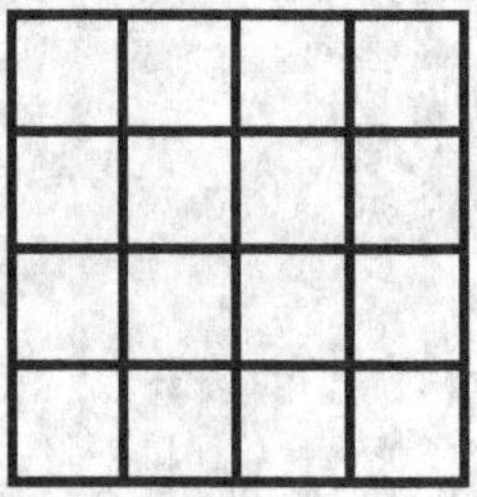

On the basis of the relationship between the size of the squares and their corresponding numbers of total squares, can the class state a hypothesis and a conclusion? Is this type of reasoning an example of inductive or deductive reasoning?

3. Have the students solve the following logic problem. A ship tied up in a harbor has a rope ladder hanging over its side. Each rung of the ladder is one inch in diameter and the rungs are eight inches apart, center to center. The ladder hangs down into the water, the water just covering the fifth rung from the bottom. If the tide rises at a uniform rate of twelve inches per hour, how many rungs will be submerged after two hours?

Section 3: Proof Formats

1. Discuss these questions with your class.
   a. In a two-column proof (direct proof), what happens when one of the statements is incorrect? when one of the reasons is incorrect?
   b. A postulate is a statement accepted without proof, and a theorem is a statement that can be proved. What are the reasons for accepting postulates to be true without proving them?
2. Prove the following statement in a direct proof (two-column proof) and then in an indirect proof (paragraph proof); then compare the two proofs. For the indirect proof, remember to write the *To Prove* and the *Given*.

$$3(x + 5) - 6 = 21$$

Administer the LIFEPAC Test.

The test is to be administered in one session. Give no help except with directions.
Evaluate the tests and review areas where the students have done poorly.
Review the pages and activities that stress the concepts tested.
If necessary, administer the Alternate LIFEPAC Test

ANSWER KEYS

SECTION 1

1.1 statement
1.2 statement
1.3 statement
1.4 statement
1.5 statement
1.6 not a statement (not a true or false statement)
1.7 not a statement (do not know what x represents)
1.8 no statement (Who is *he*?)
1.9 statement
1.10 statement
1.11 false (If p is true and q is false, then p and q is false.)
1.12 false (If p is true and q is false, then p and q is false.)
1.13 true (If p is true and q is true, then p and q is true.)
1.14 false (If p is false and q is false, then p and q is false.)
1.15 false (If p is false and q is false, then p and q is false.)
1.16 true (If p is true and q is true, then p and q is true.)
1.17 true (If p is true and q is true, then p and q is true.)
1.18 false (If p is false and q is true, then p and q is false.)
1.19 false (If p is false and q is true, then p and q is false.)
1.20 true (If p is true and q is true, then p and q is true.)
1.21 true (If p is true or q is true, then p or q is true.)
1.22 true (If p is true or q is false, then p or q is true.)
1.23 true (If p is false or q is true, then p or q is true.)
1.24 false (If p is false or q is false, then p or q is false.)
1.25 true (If p is true or q is true, then p or q is true.)
1.26 true (If p is true or q is true, then p or q is true.)
1.27 true (If p is true or q is false, then p or q is true.)
1.28 true (If p is true or q is true, then p or q is true.)
1.29 false (If p is false or q is false, then p or q is false.)
1.30 true (If p is false or q is true, then p or q is true.)
1.31 The grass is not green.
1.32 This rose is not white.
1.33 $5 + 4 \neq 90$
1.34 $5 \not> -5$
1.35 Geometry is not interesting.
1.36 A line has length.
1.37 All pigs are not fat. Or, not all pigs are fat.
1.38 My dog does not have fleas.
1.39 Two points do not determine a line.
1.40 A line does have a midpoint.
1.41 true (If p is true and q is true, then $p \rightarrow q$ is true.)
1.42 false (If p is true and q is false, then $p \rightarrow q$ is false.)
1.43 true (If p is false and q is true, then $p \rightarrow q$ is true.)
1.44 true (If p is false and q is false, then $p \rightarrow q$ is true.)
1.45 true (If p is false and q is false, then $p \rightarrow q$ is true.)
1.46 true (If p is false and q is true, then $p \rightarrow q$ is true.)
1.47 false (If p is true and q is false, then $p \rightarrow q$ is false.)
1.48 false (If p is true and q is false, then $p \rightarrow q$ is false.)
1.49 false (If p is true and q is false, then $p \rightarrow q$ is false.)
1.50 true (If p is true and q is true, then $p \rightarrow q$ is true.)
1.51 a. If $x > 7$, then $x > 5$.
b. true (If p is true and q is true, then $p \rightarrow q$ is true.)
1.52 a. If $x > 7$, then $x \not> 5$.
b. false (If p is true and q is false, then $p \rightarrow q$ is false.)
1.53 a. If $x \not> 7$, then $x > 5$.
b. true (If p is false and q is true, then $p \rightarrow q$ is true.)
1.54 a. If $x \not> 7$, then $x \not> 5$.
b. true (If p is false and q is false, then $p \rightarrow q$ is true.)
1.55 a. If $x > 5$, then $x > 7$.
b. true (If p is true and q is true, then $q \rightarrow p$ is true.)

1.56 a. If $x > 5$, then $x \ngtr 7$.
b. false (If p is false and q is true, then $q \rightarrow p$ is false.)

1.57 a. If $x \ngtr 5$, then $x > 7$.
b. true (If p is true and q is false, then $q \rightarrow p$ is true.)

1.58 a. If $x \ngtr 5$, then $x \ngtr 7$.
b. true (If p is false and q is false, then $q \rightarrow p$ is true.)

1.59 Converse: If two angles have the same vertex, then they are adjacent.

Inverse: If two angles are not adjacent, then the angles do not have the same vertex.

Contrapositive: If two angles do not have the same vertex, then the two angles are not adjacent.

1.60 Converse: If tomorrow is Wednesday, then today is Thursday.

Inverse: If today is not Thursday, then tomorrow is not Wednesday.

Contrapositive: If tomorrow is not Wednesday, then today is not Thursday.

1.61 Converse: If a polygon is a rectangle, then it is a square.

Inverse: If a polygon is not a square, then it is not a rectangle.

Contrapositive: If a polygon is not a rectangle, then it is not a square.

1.62 Converse: If the intersection of two lines is a point, then they intersect.

Inverse: If two lines do not intersect, then their intersection is not one point.

Contrapositive: If the intersection of two lines is not one point, then the two lines do not intersect.

1.63 Example:
Conditional: If Jack is the student's name, then the student is a male.

Converse: If the student is a male, then Jack is the student's name.

1.64 Example:
Conditional: If you work diligently, you will enjoy your job.

Converse: If you enjoy your job, you will work diligently.

1.65 This cannot be done because the conditional and the contrapositive have the same truth value.

SELF TEST 1

1.01 conjunction
1.02 disjunction
1.03 Either order:
a. conditional
b. implication
1.04 false (only two possibilities exist)
1.05 $q \rightarrow p$
1.06 $\sim r \rightarrow \sim s$
1.07 $\sim t \rightarrow \sim s$
1.08 true (If p is true and q is true, then $p \rightarrow q$ is true.)
1.09 true (If p is true or q is false, then p or q is true.)
1.010 false (If p is true and q is false, then p and q is false.)
1.011 false (If p is true and q is false, then $p \rightarrow q$ is false.)
1.012 true (If p is false and q is true, then $p \rightarrow q$ is true.)
1.013 true (If p is false and q is true, then $p \rightarrow q$ is true.)
1.014 false (If p is true and q is false, then $p \rightarrow q$ is false.)
1.015 false $(\sim(\sim p))$
1.016 Conditional and contrapositive (b) are equivalent.
1.017 Either order:
a. Converse (c) and
b. inverse (a) are equivalent.
1.018 a. If $-6 < 5$, then $3 < 2$.
b. false (If p is false and q is true, then $q \rightarrow p$ is false.)
1.019 a. If $3 \nless 2$, then $-6 \nless 5$.
b. false (If p is true and q is false, then $p \rightarrow q$ is false.)
1.020 a. If $-6 \nless 5$, then $3 \nless 2$.
b. true (If p is true and q is false, then $q \rightarrow p$ is true.)

SECTION 2

2.1 neither (both are the same length)
2.2 $\overline{BD}$
2.3 neither (both are the same length)
2.4 "Stop, look and listen."
2.5 yes
2.6 Examples:
A box in a corner, a box in front of a box, a box with the corner removed.
2.7 A woman is elected president.
2.8 A certain map uses four colors and has two regions colored alike that touch in more than one point.
2.9 Some numbers are less than 0, such as -2.
2.10 Allen gets a score below 90% on a test.
2.11 You are allergic to that fruit.
2.12 The rest will be snakes.
2.13 You will have a true-false test today.
2.14 Any number added to 0 equals that number.
2.15 Donald is the oldest.
2.16 No one is working.
2.17 Cathy's dad is fishing.
2.18 The figure is a square or a rhombus.
2.19 $x = 0$
2.20 Planes *R* and *S* intersect in a line.
2.21 Zelda lives in Zee.
2.22 My pet likes lettuce.
2.23 $SR + RT = ST$
2.24 The triangle does not have a right angle. (The conditional and the contrapositive are equivalent.)
2.25 No conclusion can be drawn. (Not enough information is given.)
2.26 Theorem 1-1: If two lines intersect, then their intersection is exactly one point.
2.27 Definition of bisector: A line that intersects the segment at its midpoint.
2.28 Definition of midpoint: The point on a segment that divides the segment into two equal segments.
2.29 Definition of betweenness: Three points are collinear and $AB + BC = AC$.
2.30 Postulate: If a plane contains a line, it contains the points of the line.

SELF TEST 2

2.01 deductive (general to specific)
2.02 inductive (specific to general)
2.03 deductive (general to specific)
2.04 deductive (general to specific)
2.05 neither (no reasoning)
2.06 $x = 2$ (the division property of equality)
2.07 $g = h$ (the division property of equality)
2.08 $t = 23$

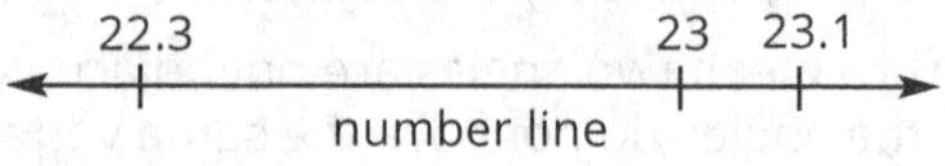

2.09 *q* is false (If *p* is true and *q* is false, then $p \rightarrow q$ is false.)
2.010 *q* is true (If p is true and q is true, then *p* and *q* is true.)
2.011 cannot
2.012 conjunction
2.013 disjunction
2.014 inductive (specific to general)
2.015 deductive (general to specific)
2.016 *q* (If *p* is true and *q* is true, then $p \rightarrow q$ is true.)
2.017 $2x + 2 = 11 - x$
$3x + 2 = 11$
Addition property of equality
2.018 $3x = 9$
Subtraction property of equality
2.019 $x = 3$
Division property of equality
2.020 If dogs do not scratch all night, then they do not have fleas.

SECTION 3

3.1 If two rays are opposite, then they form a straight line.

3.2 If Sam plays the piano, then Joe will sing.

3.3 If a man lives in Chicago, then he lives in Illinois.

3.4 If an angle exists, then it has exactly one bisector.

3.5 If you have a triangle, then the sum of the angles is 180°.

3.6 Example: *l* is parallel to *m* drawn through point *P*.

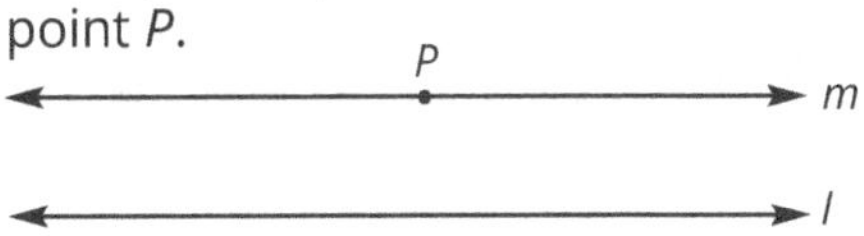

3.7 Example: Plane *R* is parallel to Plane *S*.
Planes *R* and *S* are cut by Plane *T*.
Line *l* is parallel to line *m*.

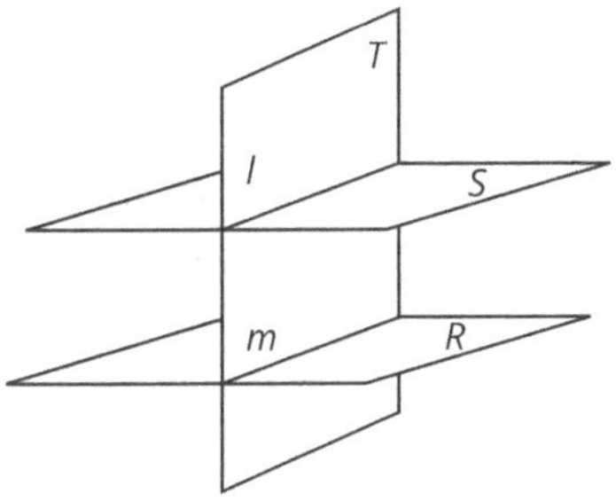

3.8 Example: In triangle *ABC*, ∠1 is equal to ∠2.
Side *AB* is equal to side *CB*.

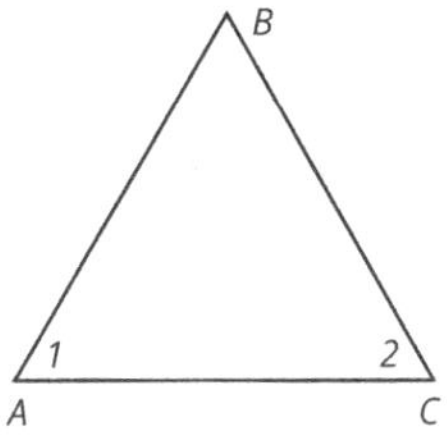

3.9 Example: In triangle *ABC*, segment *MN* joins midpoints *M* and *N* and is one-half the length of segment *AB*.

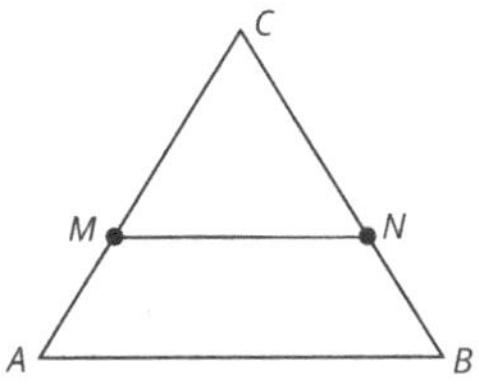

3.10 Example: Point *B* is between *A* and *C*.
AB + *BC* = *AC*.

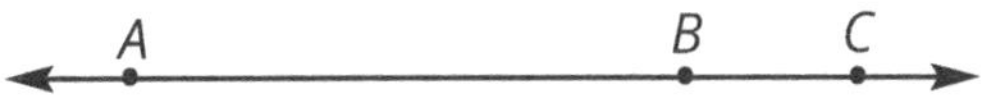

3.11 Given: Line *l*; point *P* not on *l*.

3.12 Given: Plane *R* is parallel to plane *S*; plane *T* cuts planes *R* and *S*.

3.13 Given: △*ABC* with ∠1 = ∠2.

3.14 Given: △*ABC* with midpoints *M* and *N*.

3.15 Given: Point *B* is between points *A* and *C*.

3.16 To Prove: *m* is parallel to *l*.

3.17 To Prove: *l* is parallel to *m*.

3.18 To Prove: *AB* = *BC*

3.19 To Prove: $MN = \frac{1}{2}AB$

3.20 To Prove: *AB* + *BC* = *AC*

1. **STATEMENT**
$12 - x = 20 - 5x$
REASON
Given

3.21 2. **STATEMENT**
$12 + 4x = 20$
REASON
Addition property of equality

3.22 3. **STATEMENT**
$4x = 8$
REASON
Subtraction property of equality

3.23 4. **STATEMENT**
$x = 2$
REASON
Division property of equality

1. **STATEMENT**
$2(x + 3) = 8$
REASON
Given

3.24 2. **STATEMENT**
$2x + 6 = 8$
REASON
Distributive postulate

3.25 3. **STATEMENT**
$2x = 2$
REASON
Subtraction property of equality

3.26 4. **STATEMENT**
$x = 1$
REASON
Division property of equality

1. **STATEMENT**
$x(x + 4) = x(x + 2) + 1$
REASON
Given

3.27 2. **STATEMENT**
$x^2 + 4x = x^2 + 2x + 1$
REASON
Distributive postulate

3.28 3. **STATEMENT**
$2x = 1$
REASON
Subtraction property of equality

3.29 4. **STATEMENT**
$x = \frac{1}{2}$
REASON
Division property of equality

3.30 1. **STATEMENT**
$x^2 + 6x + 2x + 12 = 0$
REASON
Given

3.31 2. **STATEMENT**
$x^2 + 8x + 12 = 0$
REASON
Substitution

3.32 3. **STATEMENT**
$(x + 6)(x + 2) = 0$
REASON
Distributive postulate

3.33 4. **STATEMENT**
$x + 6 = 0$ or $x + 2 = 0$
REASON
Zero product postulate

3.34 5. **STATEMENT**
$x = -6$ or $x = -2$
REASON
Subtraction property of equality

3.35 Apples do not make good pies.
3.36 The sun is not hot today.
3.37 $3 + 2 \neq 7$
3.38 A right angle does not measure less than 90°.
3.39 Seven is not a prime number.
3.40 A line does not contain at least 2 points.
3.41 Its square is not odd.
3.42 They intersect in more than one point.
3.43 Its leaves are not in groups of three.
3.44 $x = 4$
3.45 The sides opposite are equal.
3.46 Suppose $x \nless 25$, say $x = 26$. Then $2(26) < 50$ or $52 < 50$. This is a contradiction, so $x \nless 25$ is false and $x < 25$ is true.
3.47 A triangle cannot have two right angles. Suppose a triangle had two right angles. Then the sum of the angles would be more than 180°, but this fact contradicts the fact that the sum is 180°. Therefore, that a triangle cannot have two right angles is true.

SELF TEST 3

3.01 six
3.02 if-then
3.03 if
3.04 then
3.05 plan or analysis
3.06 always
3.07 always
3.08 always
3.09 never (both columns should have the same number of steps)
3.010 sometimes (only if the plan applies)
3.011 On $\overrightarrow{AB}$, AB is a given distance from end point A.

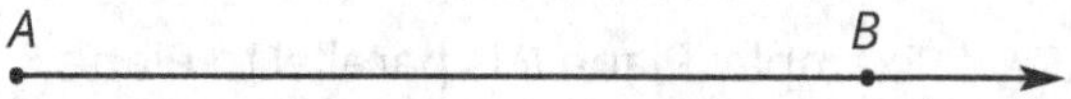

3.012 Point m is the only midpoint of AB.

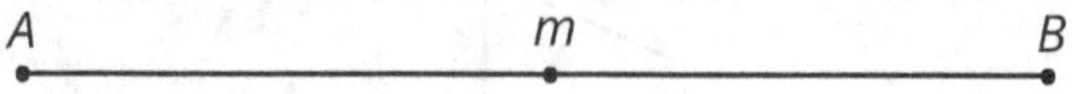

3.013 One plane through points A, B, and C.

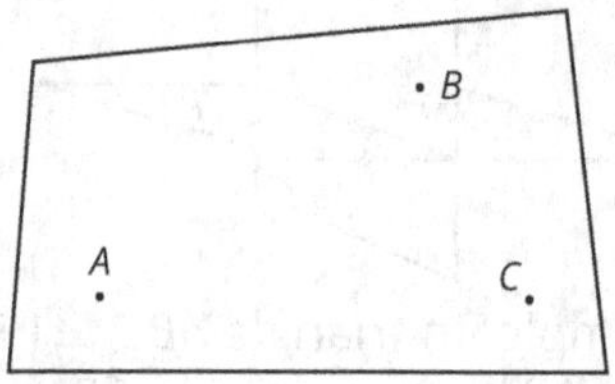

3.014 Jersey has a tail.
3.015 $\angle 1 = \angle 2$
3.016 S, O, N form a plane.
3.017 Bruce has no beans for supper tonight.

1. **STATEMENT**
$2x + x + 4 = -17$
REASON
Given

3.018 2. **STATEMENT**
$3x + 4 = -17$
REASON
Substitution

3.019 3. **STATEMENT**
$3x = -21$
REASON
Subtraction property of equality

3.020 4. **STATEMENT**
$x = -7$
REASON
Division property of equality

LIFEPAC TEST

1. b. disjunction
2. d. conditional
3. a. conjunction
4. d. conditional
5. b. disjunction
6. Converse: If two angles are complementary, then they add to 90°.
7. Inverse: If two angles do not add to 90°, then they are not complementary.
8. Contrapositive: If two angles are not complementary, then they do not add to 90°.
9. Converse: If the flowers bloom, then it rained.
10. Inverse: If it does not rain, then the flowers will not bloom.
11. Contrapositive: If the flowers do not bloom, then it did not rain.
12. inductive (specific to general)
13. deductive (general to specific)
14. deductive (general to specific)
15. inductive (specific to general)
16. never (If p is true and q is false, then $p \rightarrow q$ is false.)
17. always (If p is false or q is true, then p or q is true.)
18. always (If p is true and $\sim q$ is false, then $p \rightarrow \sim q$ is false.)
19. always (If p is false and q is false, then $p \rightarrow q$ is true.)
20. sometimes (p is sometimes true and sometimes false.)
21. Given: Triangle ABC with angle $B = 90°$
22. To Prove: $\angle A + \angle C = 90°$
23. Given: Paul is older than Bill; Fred is younger than Bill.
24. To Prove: Bill's age is between Paul's and Fred's.
25. Suppose $x = 2$; then $(2)^2 + 2 = 4$, which means $4 + 2 = 4$ or $6 = 4$. This is a contradiction because $4 = 4$. Therefore, $x = 2$ is false and $x \neq 2$ is true.

ALTERNATE LIFEPAC TEST

1. b. disjunction
2. a. conjunction
3. d. conditional
4. b. disjunction
5. c. negation
6. If tomorrow is Tuesday, then today is Monday.
7. If today is not Monday, then tomorrow is not Tuesday.
8. If tomorrow is not Tuesday, then today is not Monday.
9. If a polygon is a parallelogram, then it is a rectangle.
10. If a polygon is not a rectangle, then it is not a parallelogram.
11. If a polygon is not a parallelogram, then it is not a rectangle.
12. inductive (general to specific)
13. deductive (specific to general)
14. deductive (specific to general)
15. inductive (general to specific)
16. never
17. never
18. always
19. always
20. always
21. $\triangle ABC$ with $\angle A = \angle B$ (two angles of a triangle are equal)
22. $BC = AC$ (the sides opposite those angles are equal)
23. Sue is younger than Joan; Joan is younger than Jill.
24. Jill is the oldest of the three girls.
25. Suppose $x = 4$; then $3(4) - 2 = 7$, which means $12 - 2 = 7$ or $10 = 7$. This statement is a contradiction because $7 = 7$. Therefore, $x = 4$ is false and $x \neq 4$ is true.

MATH 1002

ALTERNATE LIFEPAC TEST

NAME ______________________

DATE ______________________

SCORE ______________________

71
88

Write the letter and the term that describes each statement (each answer, 2 points).

a. conjunction   b. disjunction   c. negation   d. conditional

1. ______________ All sides are equal or a square has three angles.

2. ______________ The grass is green and the sky is blue.

3. ______________ If a figure has three sides, then it is a triangle.

4. ______________ Geometry is hard or rabbits are white.

5. ______________ A triangle does not have six sides.

Write the converse, inverse, and contrapositive of these statements (each answer, 4 points).

If today is Monday, then tomorrow is Tuesday.

6. Converse: ______________________________

7. Inverse: ______________________________

8. Contrapositive: ______________________________

If a polygon is a rectangle, then it is a parallelogram.

9. Converse: ______________________________

10. Inverse: ______________________________

11. Contrapositive: ______________________________

Write *inductive* **or** *deductive* **to state which type of reasoning is used** (each answer, 2 points).

12. ________________ Sarah observes several robins' nests and comes to the conclusion that all robins' eggs are blue.

13. ________________ If a girl is a cheerleader at West High, then she must be a junior. Susan is a cheerleader at West High, so she is a junior.

14. ________________ All geometry students have studied algebra. Bob is a geometry student, so he has studied algebra.

15. ________________ Stanley looks at ten pennies and notices Lincoln's head on them. He decides that all pennies are Lincoln-head pennies.

Answer with *always, sometimes,* **or** *never* (each answer, 4 points).

16. When p is true and q is false, then p and q is ________________ true.

17. If p is true and q is false, then $p \rightarrow q$ is ________________ true.

18. If $p \rightarrow q$ is true and p is true, then q is ________________ true.

19. If p is true and q is true, then $\sim q \rightarrow \sim p$ is ________________ true.

20. If q is true and $\sim q$ is false, then $q \rightarrow \sim q$ is ________________ false.

Write the *Given* **and** *To Prove* **in the following proofs** (each answer, 4 points).

If two angles of a triangle are equal, the sides opposite those angles are equal.

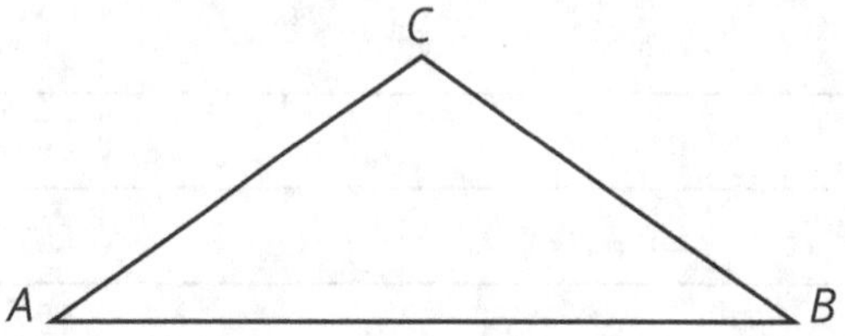

21. Given: ________________________________

22. To Prove: ________________________________

If Sue is younger than Joan and Joan is younger than Jill, then Jill is the oldest of the three girls.

23. Given: ________________________________

24. To Prove: ________________________________

Give an indirect proof of the following statement (10 points).

25. If $3x - 2 = 7$, then $x \neq 4$.

____

____

____

____

____

MATH 1003

Unit 3: Angles and Parallels

TEACHER NOTES

MATERIALS NEEDED FOR LIFEPAC	
Required	Suggested
• straightedge and protractor	(None)

ADDITIONAL LEARNING ACTIVITIES

Section 1: Angle Definitions and Measurement

1. Discuss these questions with your class.
   a. How many acute angles can be in a 90° angle? an obtuse angle?
   b. When do two acute angles equal a right angle? an obtuse angle?

Section 2: Angle Relationships and Theorems

1. Discuss these questions with your class.
   a. When are complementary angles equal? supplementary angles?
   b. When are vertical angles complementary? supplementary?
2. Review the essential differences between two-column proofs and paragraph proofs.
3. Have students draw the three squares in one continuous line without crossing any lines or taking the pencil off the paper.

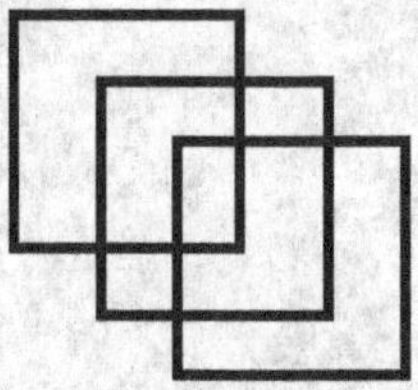

4. Given triangle *ABC*, have the students find the measure of $\angle DEB$.

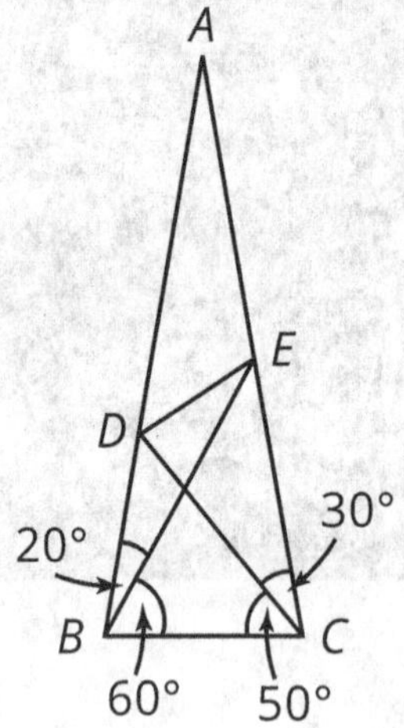

5. Have the student draw a set of angles such that *AO* and *DO* ⊥ *CF*, ∠*AOB* and ∠*BOC* are complementary and adjacent, ∠*ACF* and ∠*COD* are vertical angles, and $\overrightarrow{OE}$ and $\overrightarrow{OB}$ are opposite rays. Then have the student name all of the obtuse ∠'s, acute ∠'s, rt. ∠'s, complementary ∠'s, supplementary ∠'s, vertical ∠'s, and ⊥ lines.

Section 3: Parallels

1. Have the students find as many parallel lines, parallel planes, and transversals as possible in the classroom. Use the theorems in the LIFEPAC to prove that the lines and planes are parallel.
2. From the figure indicated, have the students remove exactly two matches so that exactly two squares remain.

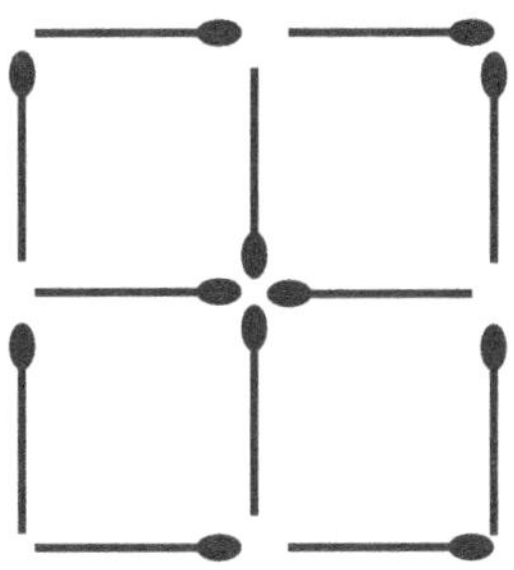

Section 4: Applying Parallels to Polygons

1. Have the class discuss which provides more information about triangles: classification by sides or classification by angles.
2. Have the students draw any triangle, quadrilateral, pentagon, hexagon, and octagon. Then have them measure the exterior angles of each figure and add the measures to see that the sum of the exterior angles is always 360°.
3. Let the student complete the following table. The left side of the table lists the classifications of triangles according to the number of equal sides they have. The top of the table lists the classifications of triangles according to the size of their angles.

	acute	obtuse	right	equiangular
scalene				
isosceles				
equilateral				

Then have the student draw and label an example of each possible combination. Not all combinations are possible.

Administer the LIFEPAC Test.

ANSWER KEYS

SECTION 1

1.1 $\angle 1$, $\angle S$, $\angle RST$, $\angle TSR$

1.2 S

1.3 $\overrightarrow{SR}$, $\overrightarrow{ST}$

1.4 $\overrightarrow{BA}$, $\overrightarrow{BC}$

1.5 B

1.6 $\angle CFD$, $\angle DFE$, $\angle CFE$

1.7 $\angle CFE$

1.8 $\overrightarrow{FD}$

1.9 $\overrightarrow{FD}$

1.10 $\angle AOD$, $\angle BOC$

1.11 $\angle AOB$, $\angle DOC$

1.12 a. and b.

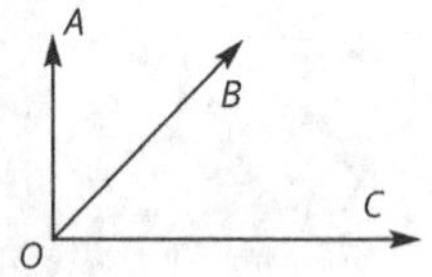

c. Acute and equal angles are formed.

1.13 a.

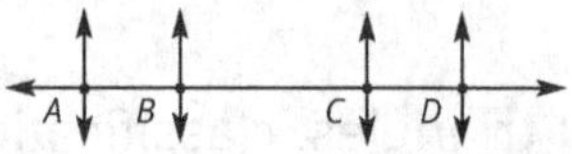

b. These lines are parallel to each other.

1.14 a. Example:

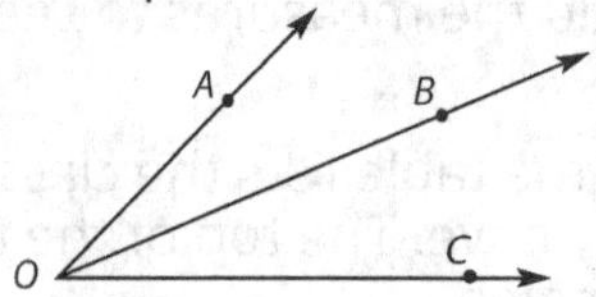

b. The sum of the measures of $\angle AOB$ and $\angle BOC$ equals the measure of $\angle AOC$.

1.15 a.

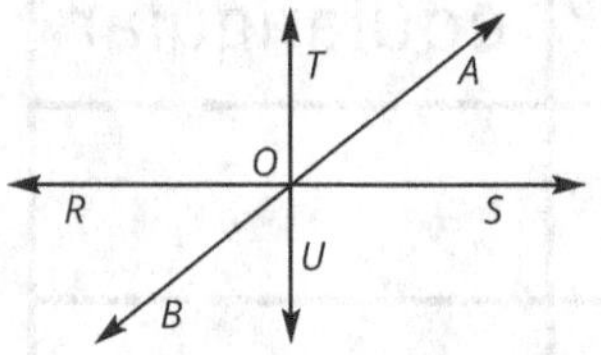

b. The measures of $\angle AOS$ and $\angle BOR$ are equal.

c. $\angle AOT$ and $\angle BOU$ are equal.

1.16 a. Examples:

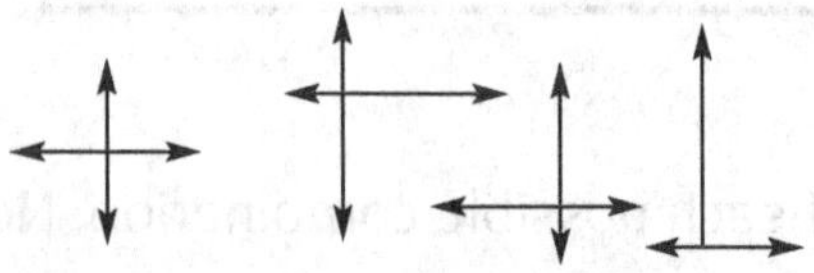

b. Right angles are formed.

1.17 a. Examples:

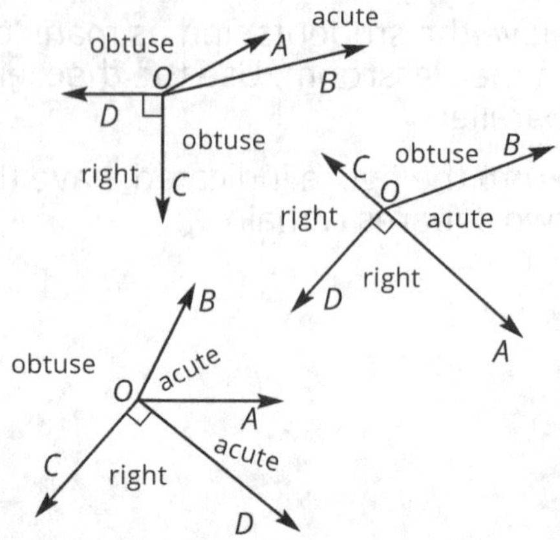

b. $\angle AOD$ can be obtuse, acute, or right.

1.18 90°

1.19 greater than 90° and less than 180°

1.20 less than 90°

1.21 a. $\angle AOX = 40°$

b. $\angle BOX = 60°$

c. $\angle BOA = |60 - 40| = 20°$

d. $\angle COB = |80 - 60| = 20°$

e. $\angle DOX = 120°$

f. $\angle BOE = |140 - 60| = 80°$

g. $\angle EOD = |140 - 120| = 20°$

h. $\angle AOD = |120 - 40| = 80°$

i. $\angle AOC = |80 - 40| = 40°$

1.22 $\angle BOA$, $\angle COB$, $\angle EOD$

1.23 $\angle AOX$, $\angle COA$, $\angle DOC$, or $\angle ZOE$

1.24 $\angle EOZ = |180 - 140| = 40°$
$\angle AOX = |40 - 0| = 40°$
yes

1.25 $\overrightarrow{OB}$

1.26 a. $\overrightarrow{OB}$

b. $\angle COB = |80 - 60| = 20°$
$\angle BOA = |60 - 40| = 20°$
yes

1.27 $\angle AOX$, $\angle AOB$, $\angle AOC$, $\angle AOD$, $\angle AOE$, $\angle AOZ$

1.28 $m\angle COX = m\angle AOX + m\angle COA$
$|80 - 0| = |40 - 0| + |80 - 40|$
$80 = 40 + 40$
$80° = 80°$
yes

1.29 $m\angle COB = |80 - 60| = 20°$
$m\angle BOA = |60 - 40| = 20°$
Yes, they are equal.

1.30 $\overrightarrow{OB}$ is the $\angle$ bisector of $\angle COA$.

1.31 Examples:

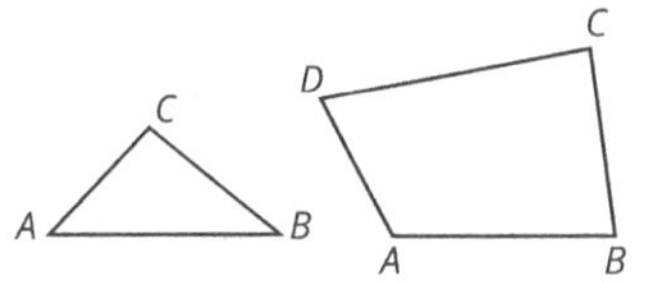

∠A = 55°
∠B = 47°
∠C = 78°
180°

The angles of any triangle add to 180°.

∠A = 115°
∠B = 75°
∠C = 90°
∠D = 80°
360°

The angles of any quadrilateral add to 360°.

1.32 $\frac{2}{3} \times \frac{60}{1} = \frac{120}{3} = 40'$

1.33 $\frac{45}{60} = \frac{5 \cdot 3 \cdot 3}{5 \cdot 3 \cdot 4} = \frac{3}{4}°$

1.34 $\frac{3}{4} \times \frac{60}{1} = \frac{180}{4} = 45''$

1.35 yes; 60″ = 1′ and 60′ = 1°

1.36 m ∠ROT = m ∠ROS + m ∠SOT
m ∠ROS = 20° 15′ 40″
m ∠SOT = 10° 12′ 30″
30° 27′ ~~70″~~
+ 1′ 60″ = 1′
m ∠ROT = 30° 28′ 10″

1.37 m ∠SOT = m ∠ROT – m ∠ROS
61 68
m ∠ROT = ~~62°~~ ~~8′~~ 12″
m ∠ROS = 41° 12′
m ∠SOT = 20° 56′ 12″

1.38 m ∠ROS = m ∠ROT – m ∠SOT
m ∠ROT = 48° 12′ 16″
m ∠SOT = 7° 5′ 8″
m ∠ROS = 41° 7′ 8″

1.39 m ∠ROT = m ∠ROS + m ∠SOT
m ∠ROS = 28° 4′ 16″
m ∠SOT = 31° 48′ 50″
59° 52′ ~~66″~~
+ 1′ 60″ = 1′
m ∠ROT = 59° 53′ 6″

1.40 m ∠SOT = m ∠ROT – m ∠ROS
m ∠ROT = 52° 52′ 52″
m ∠ROS = 15° 22′ 40″
m ∠SOT = 37° 30′ 12″

SELF TEST 1

1.01 Example:

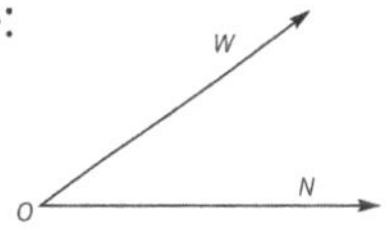

1.02 O

1.03 $\overrightarrow{OW}$, $\overrightarrow{ON}$

1.04

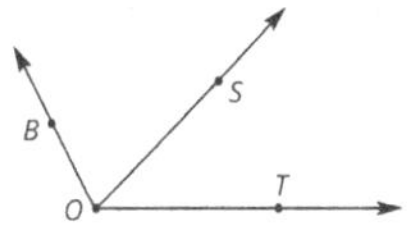

1.05

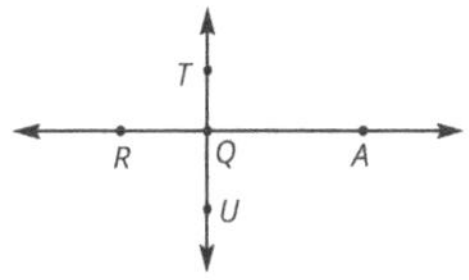

1.06 greater than 90° but less than 180°

1.07 less than 90°

1.08 m ∠CXA = m ∠BXA + m ∠CXB
m ∠BXA = 30° 20′
m ∠CXB = 40° 35′
m ∠CXA = 70° 55′

1.09 m ∠CXB = m ∠DXB – m ∠DXC
69 74 72
m ∠DXB = ~~70°~~ ~~15′~~ ~~12″~~
m ∠DXC = 30° 30′ 20″
m ∠CXB = 39° 44′ 52″

1.010 ∠DXA

1.011 m ∠DXA

1.012 no

1.013 no

1.014 20° 15′ 18″
30° 41′ 32″
2° 30′ 15″
52° 86′ ~~65″~~
+ 1
52° ~~87′~~ 5″
+ 1
53° 27′ 5″

1.015
49 100
60° ~~50′~~ ~~40″~~
30° 40′ 50″
30° 9′ 50″

1.016 Given

1.017 Addition property of equality

1.018 Angle addition theorem

1.019 Angle addition theorem

1.020 Substitution

SECTION 2

2.1 b
2.2 e
2.3 a
2.4 c
2.5 1. **STATEMENT**
∠2, ∠3 are complementary ∠'s;
∠1, ∠3 are complementary ∠'s.
REASON
Given

2. **STATEMENT**
m ∠2 + m ∠3 = 90°
m ∠1 + m ∠3 = 90°
REASON
Definition of complementary ∠'s

3. **STATEMENT**
m ∠1 + m ∠3 = m ∠2 + m ∠3
REASON
Substitution

4. **STATEMENT**
m ∠1 = m ∠2
REASON
Subtraction property of equality

2.6 ∠*APZ*, ∠*ZPB*
2.7 ∠*WPB*
2.8 ∠*APW*, ∠*WPZ*
2.9 $\overrightarrow{PA}$, $\overrightarrow{PB}$
2.10 ∠*APW*, ∠*BPZ*
2.11 ∠*APW*, ∠*WPB*
2.12 ∠*APW*, ∠*ZPB*
∠*APW*, ∠*APZ*
∠*WPZ*, ∠*WPB*
2.13 ∠*APZ*, ∠*ZPB*
2.14 m ∠*WPZ* = m ∠*APZ* – m ∠*APW*
= 90 – 20
= 70°
2.15 ∠*BCD*, ∠*CDA*
2.16 ∠*ABC*
2.17 ∠*BCA*, ∠*ACD*
2.18 ∠*ABC*
2.19 $\overline{BC}$, $\overline{AD}$
2.20 ∠*CAD*, ∠*ACD*
2.21 ∠*BCA*
2.22 m ∠*ABC* = 110°
180° – 110° = 70°
m ∠*BAD* = 40° + 30° = 70°
∠*BAD* is the supplement.

2.23 m ∠*CAB* = 40°
90 – 40 = 50
No angle has a measure of 50°.
2.24 no
2.25 m ∠*x* + m ∠*x* = 90
2m ∠*x* = 90
m ∠*x* = 45°
2.26 m ∠*x* + m ∠*x* = 180
2m ∠*x* = 180
m ∠*x* = 90°
2.27 Let *x* = first ∠ measure.
3*x* = second ∠ measure.
$x + 3x = 90°$
$4x = 90°$
$x = 22\frac{1}{2}°$
$3x = 67\frac{1}{2}°$
2.28 90° – 3*x*
2.29 $(3x - 10) + (2x + 20) = 90$
$5x + 10 = 90$
$5x = 80$
$x = 16$
$3x - 10 = 38°$
$2x + 20 = 52°$
2.30 $2x + 20 = 5x - 34$
$-3x = -54$
$x = 18$
$2x + 20 = 56°$
$5x - 34 = 56°$
2.31 Given
2.32 Exterior sides in opposite rays
2.33 Definition of supplementary ∠'s
2.34 Substitution
2.35 Vertical ∠'s are =
2.36 Substitution
2.37 Definition of supplementary ∠'s
2.38 1. **STATEMENT**
∠1, ∠2 are rt. ∠'s.
REASON
Given

2. **STATEMENT**
m∠1 = 90°
m∠2 = 90°
REASON
Definition of rt. ∠'s

3. **STATEMENT**
m∠1 = m∠2
REASON
Substitution

2.39 90°
2.40 30°
2.41 40°
2.42 no
2.43 yes
2.44 30°
2.45 90°
2.46 90°
2.47 180°
2.48 a. $\angle 1$ and $\angle 2$
b. $\angle 3$ and $\angle 4$
2.49 $m\angle 3 = 90° - m\angle 4$

89
~~90°~~ 60′
$m\angle 4 = \underline{20°\ 15'}$
$m\angle 3 = 69°\ 45'$

2.50 Theorem 3-1, angle addition theorem
2.51 Theorem 3-3, $\perp$'s form rt. $\angle$'s
2.52 Theorem 3-4, exterior sides in perpendicular lines
2.53 Theorem 3-2, exterior sides are opposite rays
2.54 Given
2.55 Exterior sides in $\perp$ lines
2.56 Definition of rt. $\angle$
2.57 Angle addition theorem
2.58 Substitution
2.59 Subtraction property of equality

SELF TEST 2

2.01 Example:

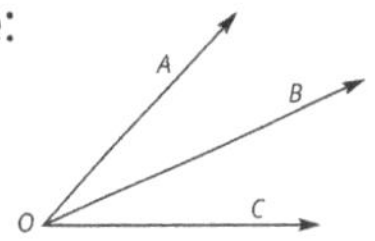

2.02

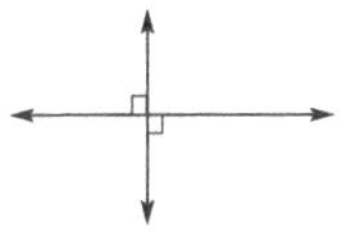

2.03 The angles are supplementary.
2.04 The angles are complementary.
2.05 They are equal to one another.
2.06 rt. $\angle$'s
2.07 equal
2.08 equal
2.09 The lines are perpendicular.
2.010 90°
2.011 180°
2.012 $m\angle B = 180° - m\angle A$

179
~~180°~~ 60′
$m\angle A = \underline{37°\ 15'}$
142° 45′

2.013 Vertical angles are equal; therefore, $m\angle D = m\angle C = 63°\ 15'\ 47''$.
2.014

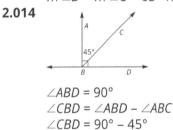

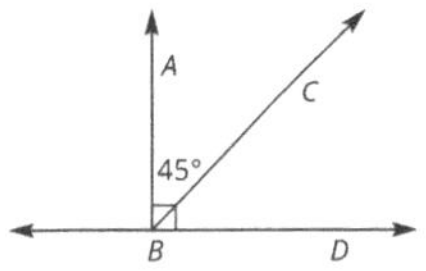

$\angle ABD = 90°$
$\angle CBD = \angle ABD - \angle ABC$
$\angle CBD = 90° - 45°$
$\angle CBD = 45°$

2.015

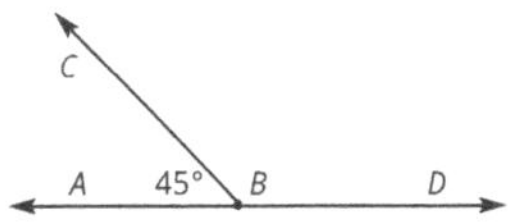

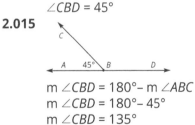

$m\angle CBD = 180° - m\angle ABC$
$m\angle CBD = 180° - 45°$
$m\angle CBD = 135°$

2.016 Vertical angles are equal; therefore, $\overline{BD}$ and $\overline{CA}$ are straight segments
$m\angle BOC = 180° - \angle BOA$
$m\angle BOC = 180° - 30°$
$m\angle BOC = 150°$
2.017 Given
2.018 Theorem 3-2, exterior sides in opposite rays
2.019 Definition of supplementary $\angle$'s
2.020 Substitution

SECTION 3

3.1 never
3.2 sometimes
3.3 sometimes
3.4 always
3.5 always
3.6 sometimes
3.7 sometimes
3.8 sometimes
3.9 sometimes
3.10 always

3.11
1. **STATEMENT**
   l | | *m*
   REASON
   Given
2. **STATEMENT**
   m ∠1 = m ∠3
   REASON
   If lines | | , corresponding ∠'s =.
3. **STATEMENT**
   m ∠2 = m ∠3
   REASON
   Vertical ∠'s =.
4. **STATEMENT**
   m ∠1 = m ∠2
   REASON
   Substitution

3.12 60°
3.13 60°
3.14 60°
3.15 120°
3.16 120°
3.17 120°
3.18 120°
3.19 Either order:
a. ∠2 and ∠3
b. ∠6 and ∠7
3.20 Either order:
a. ∠1 and ∠4
b. ∠5 and ∠8

3.21
1. **STATEMENT**
   a | | *b*, m ∠2 = m ∠3
   REASON
   Given
2. **STATEMENT**
   m ∠1 = m ∠2
   REASON
   P8: If lines | | , corresponding ∠'s =.
3. **STATEMENT**
   m ∠1 = m ∠3
   REASON
   Substitution

3.22
1. **STATEMENT**
   c | | *d*, m ∠4 = m ∠5
   REASON
   Given
2. **STATEMENT**
   m ∠4 = m ∠7
   REASON
   If lines | | , alternate interior ∠'s =.
3. **STATEMENT**
   m ∠5 = m ∠8
   REASON
   Vertical ∠'s =.
4. **STATEMENT**
   m ∠7 = m ∠8
   REASON
   Substitution

3.23
1. **STATEMENT**
   a | | *b*, *c* | | *d*
   REASON
   Given
2. **STATEMENT**
   m ∠1 = m ∠6
   REASON
   Vertical ∠'s =.
3. **STATEMENT**
   m ∠6 = m ∠8
   REASON
   Corresponding ∠'s =.
4. **STATEMENT**
   m ∠8 = m ∠16
   REASON
   Corresponding ∠'s =.
5. **STATEMENT**
   m ∠1 = m ∠16
   REASON
   Substitution

3.24
1. **STATEMENT**
   s | | *t*
   REASON
   Given

2. **STATEMENT**
   $\angle 5$, $\angle 7$ are supplementary
   REASON
   Exterior sides in opposite rays
3. **STATEMENT**
   m $\angle 5$ + m $\angle 7 = 180°$
   REASON
   Definition of supplementary $\angle$'s
4. **STATEMENT**
   m $\angle 1$ = m $\angle 5$
   REASON
   Corresponding $\angle$'s =.
5. **STATEMENT**
   m $\angle 1$ + m $\angle 7 = 180°$
   REASON
   Substitution
6. **STATEMENT**
   $\angle 1$, $\angle 7$ are supplementary
   REASON
   Definition of supplementary $\angle$'s

3.25
1. **STATEMENT**
   $s \mid\mid t$
   REASON
   Given
2. **STATEMENT**
   $\angle 1$, $\angle 3$ are supplementary
   REASON
   Exterior sides in opposite rays
3. **STATEMENT**
   m $\angle 1$ + m $\angle 3 = 180°$
   REASON
   Definition of supplementary $\angle$'s
4. **STATEMENT**
   m $\angle 1$ = m $\angle 5$
   REASON
   Corresponding $\angle$'s =.
5. **STATEMENT**
   m $\angle 5$ + m $\angle 3 = 180°$
   REASON
   Substitution
6. **STATEMENT**
   $\angle 3$, $\angle 5$ are supplementary
   REASON
   Definition of supplementary $\angle$'s

3.26
1. **STATEMENT**
   m $\angle 1$ = m $\angle 2$
   REASON
   Given
2. **STATEMENT**
   m $\angle 1$ = m $\angle 3$
   REASON
   Vertical $\angle$'s =.
3. **STATEMENT**
   m $\angle 2$ = m $\angle 3$
   REASON
   Substitution
4. **STATEMENT**
   $l \mid\mid m$
   REASON
   If corresponding $\angle$'s =, then lines are | |.

3.27 true
If 2 $\angle$'s have equal measure, then each has a measure of 28°; false.

3.28 false
If 2 $\angle$'s are equal, then they are both obtuse; false.

3.29 true
If $x = -5$, then $3 - 2x =$
$3 - 2(-5) =$
$3 + 10 = 13$; true

3.30 false
If $x = 5$, then $x^2 = 25$; true

3.31 false
If 2 $\angle$'s are not equal, then they are supplementary; false.

3.32 $\overline{AD} \mid\mid \overline{BC}$
3.33 $\overline{AD} \mid\mid \overline{BC}$
3.34 $\overline{AB} \mid\mid \overline{DC}$
3.35 none
3.36 $\overline{DC} \mid\mid \overline{AB}$
3.37 none
3.38 $\overline{AD} \mid\mid \overline{BC}$
3.39 $\overline{AD} \mid\mid \overline{BC}$
3.40 none
3.41 none
3.42 none
3.43 $\overline{DC} \mid\mid \overline{AB}$
3.44 none

3.45
1. **STATEMENT**
   m $\angle 2 = 122°$
   m $\angle 3 = 58°$
   REASON
   Given
2. **STATEMENT**
   $\angle 3$, $\angle 5$ are supplementary
   REASON
   Exterior sides in opposite rays

3. **STATEMENT**
   m $\angle 3$ + m $\angle 5$ = 180°
   REASON
   Definition of supplementary $\angle$'s
4. **STATEMENT**
   58° + m $\angle 5$ = 180°
   REASON
   Substitution
5. **STATEMENT**
   m $\angle 5$ = 122°
   REASON
   Subtraction property of equality
6. **STATEMENT**
   m $\angle 2$ = m $\angle 5$
   REASON
   Substitution
7. **STATEMENT**
   l | | *m*
   REASON
   If corresponding $\angle$'s =, then lines are | |.

3.46
1. **STATEMENT**
   m $\angle 6$ = m $\angle 8$, *b* | | *c*
   REASON
   Given
2. **STATEMENT**
   m $\angle 7$ = m $\angle 8$
   REASON
   If lines | | , corresponding $\angle$'s =.
3. **STATEMENT**
   m $\angle 6$ = m $\angle 7$
   REASON
   Substitution
4. **STATEMENT**
   a | | *b*
   REASON
   If alternate interior $\angle$'s =, then lines | |.

3.47
1. **STATEMENT**
   j | | *k*, m $\angle 1$ = m $\angle 3$
   REASON
   Given
2. **STATEMENT**
   m $\angle 1$ = m $\angle 2$
   REASON
   If lines | | , corresponding $\angle$'s =.
3. **STATEMENT**
   m $\angle 2$ = m $\angle 3$
   REASON
   Substitution
4. **STATEMENT**
   l | | *m*
   REASON
   If alternate interior $\angle$'s =, then lines | |.

3.48
1. **STATEMENT**
   $\angle A$, $\angle B$, $\angle C$, $\angle D$ are rt. $\angle$'s
   REASON
   Given
2. **STATEMENT**
   $\overline{DA} \perp \overline{AB}$, $\overline{DA} \perp \overline{DC}$, $\overline{CD} \perp \overline{AD}$, $\overline{AB} \perp \overline{AD}$
   REASON
   If rt. $\angle$'s formed, lines are $\perp$.
3. **STATEMENT**
   $\overline{AD}$ | | $\overline{BC}$, $\overline{AB}$ | | $\overline{DC}$
   REASON
   If two lines are $\perp$ to another line, they are | |.

3.49
1. **STATEMENT**
   m $\angle 1$ + m $\angle 5$ = 180°
   m $\angle 1$ + m $\angle 4$ = 180°
   REASON
   Given
2. **STATEMENT**
   m $\angle 1$ + m $\angle 5$ = m $\angle 1$ + m $\angle 4$
   REASON
   Substitution
3. **STATEMENT**
   m $\angle 5$ = m $\angle 4$
   REASON
   Subtraction property of equality
4. **STATEMENT**
   $\overrightarrow{YZ}$ | | $\overrightarrow{UV}$
   REASON
   If alternate interior $\angle$'s =, then lines | |.

3.50
1. **STATEMENT**
   $\angle 1$, $\angle 2$ are supplementary $\angle$'s
   REASON
   Given
2. **STATEMENT**
   m $\angle 1$ + m $\angle 2$ = 180°
   REASON
   Definition of supplementary $\angle$'s
3. **STATEMENT**
   $\angle 1$, $\angle 3$ are supplementary $\angle$'s
   REASON
   Exterior sides in opposite rays

4. **STATEMENT**
   m ∠1 + m ∠3 = 180°
   REASON
   Definition of supplementary ∠'s
5. **STATEMENT**
   m ∠1 + m ∠2 = m ∠1 + m ∠3
   REASON
   Substitution
6. **STATEMENT**
   m ∠2 = m ∠3
   REASON
   Subtraction property of equality
7. **STATEMENT**
   l || *m*
   REASON
   If alternate interior ∠'s =, then lines ||.

SELF TEST 3

3.01 no point in common
3.02 plane
3.03 parallel
3.04 equal
3.05 line
3.06 parallel
3.07 parallel
3.08 complementary
3.09 supplementary
3.010

$$\begin{array}{r} \scriptstyle 89 \quad 59 \qquad \\ \not{90}^\circ \ \not{60}' \ 60'' \\ -\ \underline{45^\circ \ 12' \ 10''} \\ 44^\circ \ 47' \ 50'' \end{array}$$

3.011 yes
3.012 no
3.013 yes
3.014 yes
3.015 yes
3.016 *l* || *m*
3.017 Theorem 3-12, alternate interior ∠'s =
3.018 ∠2 , ∠3 are supplementary
3.019 Definition of supplementary ∠'s
3.020 m ∠2 + m ∠1 = 180°
3.021 Definition of supplementary ∠'s
3.022 Given
3.023 Substitution
3.024 Definition of alternate interior ∠'s
3.025 *l* || *m*

SECTION 4

4.1 isosceles and equilateral

4.2 scalene

4.3 isosceles

4.4 isosceles

4.5 scalene

4.6 acute

4.7 right

4.8 obtuse

4.9 right

4.10 acute and equiangular

4.11 $m\angle 4 = m\angle 2 + m\angle 3$
$= 50 + 100$
$= 150°$

4.12 $m\angle 1 + m\angle 2 + m\angle 3 = 180°$
$30 + 45 + m\angle 3 = 180°$
$75 + m\angle 3 = 180°$
$m\angle 3 = 105°$

4.13 $m\angle 4 = m\angle 2 + m\angle 3$
$= a° + b°$

4.14 $m\angle 3 = m\angle 4 - m\angle 2$
$= 150 - 40$
$= 110°$

4.15 $m\angle 1 = 180° - (m\angle 2 + m\angle 3)$
$= 180° - (2x° + 5x°)$
$= 180° - 7°x$

4.16 $m\angle 1 + m\angle 2 + m\angle 3 = 180°$
$3x + 4x + 2x = 180°$
$9x = 180°$
$x = 20°$

4.17 $m\angle 2 + m\angle 3 = m\angle 4$
$\frac{4}{3}x + 20 = 2x$
$4x + 60 = 6x$
$60 = 2x$
$30° = x$

4.18 $m\angle 1 = 180° - m\angle 2$
$= 180° - 50°$
$= 130°$

4.19 $m\angle M + m\angle P + m\angle 2 = 180°$
$m\angle P = 180° - (m\angle M + m\angle 2)$
$= 180° - (90° + 30°)$
$= 180° - 120°$
$= 60°$

4.20 $m\angle M + m\angle P + m\angle 2 = 180°$
$90° + 2m\angle P = 180°$
$2m\angle P = 90°$
$m\angle P = 45°$

4.21 $m\angle M + m\angle P = m\angle 1$
$90° + 40° = m\angle 1$
$130° = m\angle 1$

4.22 a. $m\angle 1 = 180° - (m\angle P + m\angle O)$
$= 180° - (38° + 70°)$
$= 180° - 108°$
$m\angle 1 = 72°$
b. $m\angle 2 = m\angle P + m\angle O$
$= 38° + 70°$
$m\angle 2 = 108°$

4.23 a. $m\angle 2 = 180° - m\angle 1$
$= 180° - 46°$
$m\angle 2 = 134°$
b. $m\angle O = 180° - (m\angle 1 + m\angle P)$
$= 180° - (46° + 38°)$
$= 180° - 84°$
$m\angle O = 96°$

4.24 a. $m\angle P = 180° - (m\angle O + m\angle 1)$
$= 180° - (90° + 35°)$
$= 180° - 125°$
$m\angle P = 55°$
$m\angle 2 = m\angle O + m\angle P$
$= 90° + 55°$
$m\angle 2 = 145°$
b. $m\angle P = 55°$

4.25 a. $m\angle P = 180° - (m\angle O + m\angle 1)$
$= 180° - (90° + 63°)$
$= 180° - 153°$
$m\angle P = 27°$
$m\angle 2 = m\angle O + m\angle P$
$= 90° + 27°$
$m\angle 2 = 117°$
b. $m\angle P = 27°$

4.26 $m\angle O + m\angle P + m\angle 1 = 180°$
$m\angle O = m\angle P$; let $m\angle O + m\angle P = 2m\angle O$
$2m\angle O = 180° - m\angle 1$
$2m\angle O = 180° - 36°$
$2m\angle O = 144°$
$m\angle O = 72°$
$m\angle 2 = m\angle O + m\angle P = 2m\angle O$
$m\angle 2 = 144°$

4.27 through 4.31

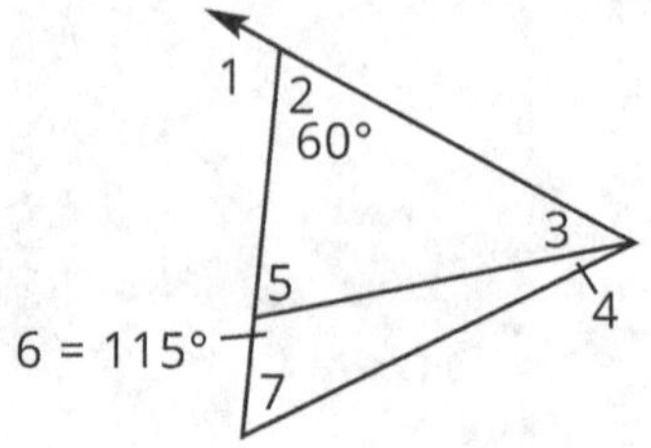

4.27 $\angle 1$ and $\angle 2$ are supplementary
$\angle 1 = 180° - m\angle 2$
$= 180° - 60°$
$m\angle 1 = 120°$

4.28 $120° = m\angle 3 + m\angle 5$
$120° = m\angle 3 + (180° - m\angle 6)$
$120° = m\angle 3 + (180° - 115°)$
$120° = m\angle 3 + 65°$
$120° - 65° = m\angle 3$
$55° = m\angle 3$

4.29 $m\angle 4 = 180 - (m\angle 6 + m\angle 7)$
$= 180° - (m\angle 6 + m\angle 3)$
$= 180° - (115° + 55°)$
$= 180° - 170°$
$m\angle 4 = 10°$

4.30 $\angle 5$ and $\angle 6$ are supplementary
$m\angle 5 = 180° - m\angle 6$
$= 180° - 115°$
$m\angle 5 = 65°$

4.31 $m\angle 7 = m\angle 3 = 55°$

4.32 through 4.36

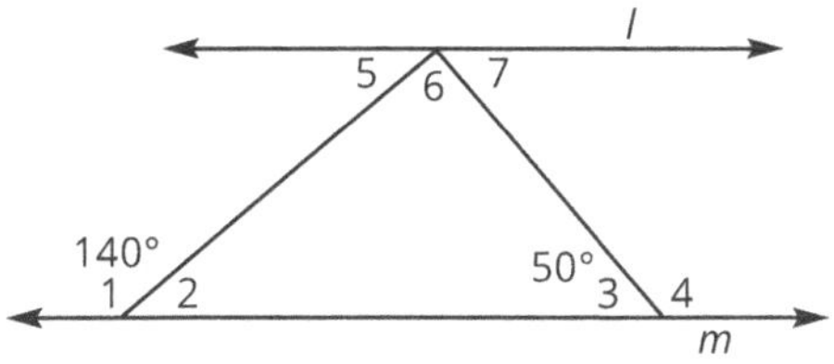

4.32 $\angle 1$ and $\angle 2$ are supplementary
$m\angle 2 = 180° - m\angle 1$
$= 180° - 140°$
$m\angle 2 = 40°$

4.33 $\angle 3$ and $\angle 4$ are supplementary
$m\angle 4 = 180° - m\angle 3$
$= 180° - 50°$
$m\angle 4 = 130°$

4.34 $m\angle 5 = 180° - (m\angle 6 + m\angle 7)$
$= 180° - (90° + 50°)$
$= 180° - 140°$
$m\angle 5 = 40°$

4.35 $m\angle 6 = 180° - (m\angle 2 + m\angle 3)$
$= 180° - (40° + 50°)$
$= 180° - 90°$
$m\angle 6 = 90°$

4.36 $\angle 3$ and $\angle 7$ are alternate interior $\angle$'s;
$m\angle 3 = m\angle 7$
$m\angle 7 = 50°$

4.37
1. **STATEMENT**
$\overline{JK} \perp \overline{MN}$
REASON
Given
2. **STATEMENT**
$\angle MKJ$ is rt. $\angle$
REASON
$\perp$'s form rt. $\angle$'s
3. **STATEMENT**
$\triangle MKJ$ is rt. $\triangle$
REASON
Definition of rt. $\triangle$
4. **STATEMENT**
$\angle 1$, $\angle 2$ are complementary
REASON
Acute $\angle$'s of rt. $\triangle$ are complementary.

4.38
1. **STATEMENT**
$m\angle 5 = m\angle 6$
REASON
Given
2. **STATEMENT**
$m\angle 1 = m\angle 2$
REASON
Vertical $\angle$'s are =
3. **STATEMENT**
$m\angle 3 = m\angle 4$
REASON
If 2 $\angle$'s of one $\triangle$ = 2 $\angle$'s of another $\triangle$, then third $\angle$'s are =.

4.39
1. **STATEMENT**
$\overline{AC} \perp \overline{CD}$, $\overline{DB} \perp \overline{AB}$
REASON
Given
2. **STATEMENT**
$\angle C$ is rt. $\angle$, $\angle B$ is rt. $\angle$
REASON
$\perp$'s form rt. $\angle$'s
3. **STATEMENT**
$m\angle C = m\angle B$
REASON
All rt. $\angle$'s are =
4. **STATEMENT**
$m\angle 1 = m\angle 2$
REASON
Vertical $\angle$'s are =

5. **STATEMENT**
m $\angle A$ = m $\angle D$
REASON
If 2 $\angle$'s of one $\triangle$ = 2 $\angle$'s of another $\triangle$, then third $\angle$'s are =.

4.40 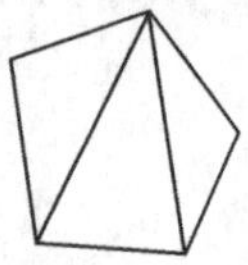 3 triangles

4.41 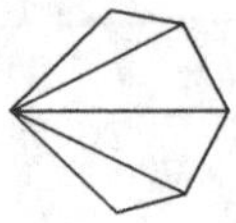 4 triangles

4.42 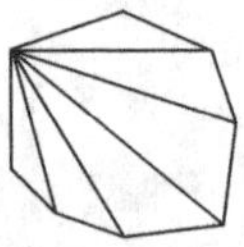 6 triangles

4.43 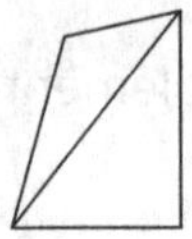 2 triangles

4.44 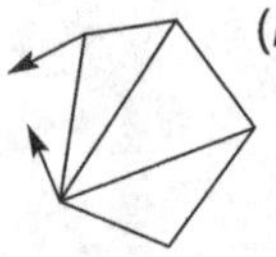 (n – 2) triangles

4.45 11 + 2 = 13 sides
4.46 (7 – 2)180 = 5(180) = 900°
4.47 (12 – 2)180 = 10(180) = 1,800°
4.48 (20 – 2)180 = 18(180) = 3,240°
4.49 (100 – 2)180 = 98(180)
= 17,640°
4.50 360 – (80 + 90 + 103) =
360 – 273 = 87°
4.51 360 ÷ 6 = 60°
4.52 360 ÷ 5 = 72°
4.53 $360 \div 16 = 22\frac{1}{2}°$
4.54 360 ÷ 90 = 4 sides
4.55 360 ÷ 72 = 5 sides
4.56 360 ÷ 1 = 360 sides
4.57 $\frac{(8-2)180}{8} = \frac{(6)180}{8} = 135°$
4.58 $\frac{(10-2)180}{10} = \frac{8(180)}{8} = 144°$
4.59 $\frac{(n-2)180°}{n}$
4.60 $\frac{(n-2)180}{n} = 60$
$180n - 360 = 60n$
$120n = 360$
$n = 3$ sides

SELF TEST 4

4.01 isosceles
4.02 scalene
4.03 180°
4.04 remote interior
4.05 pentagon
4.06 regular
4.07 parallel
4.08 180°
4.09 less than
4.010 complementary
4.011 acute, scalene
4.012 right, isosceles
4.013 acute, equilateral
4.014 obtuse, scalene
4.015 right, scalene
4.016 right, adjacent, supplementary
4.017 acute, adjacent, complementary
4.018 acute, vertical
4.019 right, vertical, supplementary
4.020 obtuse, adjacent

LIFEPAC TEST

1. Note: There may be more than one correct solution for the proof.

1. **STATEMENT**
   $\overleftrightarrow{AB} \perp \overleftrightarrow{CD}$
   REASON
   Given
2. **STATEMENT**
   m ∠1 = m ∠*COB*
   REASON
   Definition of ⊥ lines
3. **STATEMENT**
   m ∠*COB* = m ∠2 + m ∠3 + m ∠4
   REASON
   Angle addition theorem
4. **STATEMENT**
   m ∠1 = m ∠2 + m ∠3 + m ∠4
   REASON
   Substitution
5. **STATEMENT**
   m ∠3 = m ∠7
   REASON
   Vertical ∠'s are =.
6. **STATEMENT**
   m ∠1 = m ∠2 + m ∠4 + m ∠7
   REASON
   Substitution

2. Note: There may be more than one correct solution for the proof.

1. **STATEMENT**
   $\overline{AB} \parallel \overline{CD}$
   REASON
   Given
2. **STATEMENT**
   m ∠1 = m ∠2 + m ∠4
   REASON
   Exterior ∠ of △ = sum of remote interior ∠'s.
3. **STATEMENT**
   m ∠3 = m ∠4
   REASON
   If lines | |, alternate interior ∠'s =.
4. **STATEMENT**
   m ∠1 = m ∠2 + m ∠3
   REASON
   Substitution

3. true
4. true
5. false
6. true
7. false
8. false
9. d
10. c
11. b
12. a
13. e
14. f
15. at least 2
16. 2
17. regular
18. 3
19. An interior ∠ is supplementary to an exterior ∠.
An exterior ∠ = 180° – interior ∠
= 180° – 120°
= 60°
20. 90°
21. ∠1 = 90° – 50° = 40°

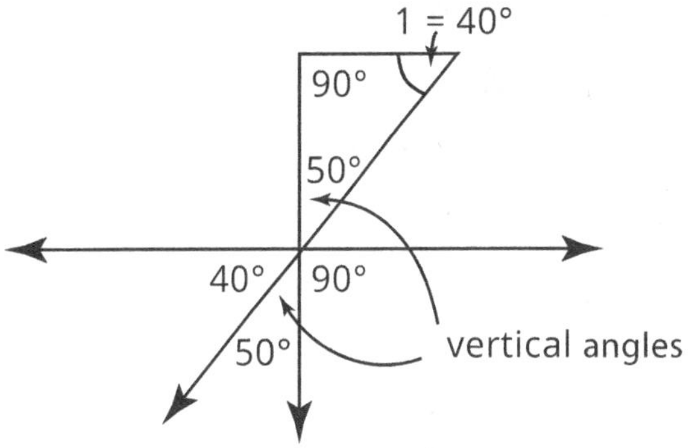

22. ∠1 = 60° (vertical ∠'s)

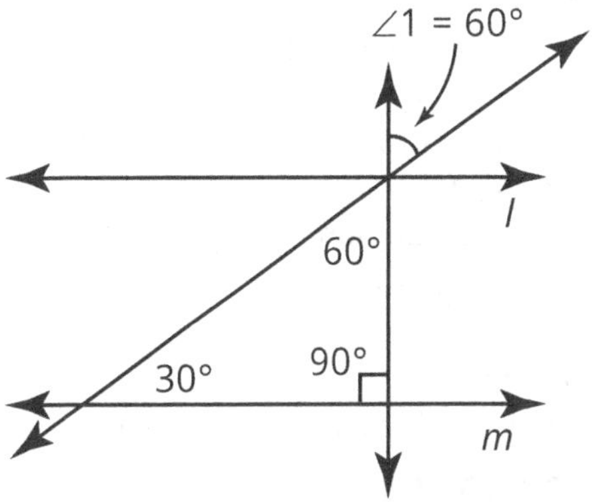

ALTERNATE LIFEPAC TEST

1. 1. **STATEMENT**
$l \parallel m$
REASON
Given

2. **STATEMENT**
$\angle 1 = \angle 3$; $\angle 2 = \angle 4$
REASON
If lines are $\parallel$, corresponding $\angle$'s =.

3. **STATEMENT**
$\angle 1$, $\angle 2$ are supplementary
$\angle 3$, $\angle 4$ are supplementary
REASON
Exterior sides in opposite rays

4. **STATEMENT**
$\angle 3 + \angle 4 = 180°$
REASON
Definition of supplementary $\angle$'s

5. **STATEMENT**
$\angle 1 + \angle 4 = 180°$
REASON
Substitution

6. **STATEMENT**
$\angle 1$, $\angle 4$ are supplementary
REASON
Definition of supplementary $\angle$'s

2. 1. **STATEMENT**
m $\angle 2$ = m $\angle 3$
REASON
Given

2. **STATEMENT**
$\angle 1$, $\angle 2$ are supplementary
$\angle 3$, $\angle 4$ are supplementary
REASON
Exterior sides in opposite rays

3. **STATEMENT**
m $\angle 1$ = m $\angle 4$
REASON
Two $\angle$'s supplementary to = $\angle$'s are =.

4. **STATEMENT**
$\angle 1$, $\angle 5$ are supplementary
REASON
Exterior sides in opposite rays

5. **STATEMENT**
$\angle 5$, $\angle 4$ are supplementary
REASON
Substitution

3. e or f
4. g
5. h
6. c
7. a
8. e
9. b
10. d
11. i
12. f
13. 360°
14. 360°
15. 180°
16. Either order:
a. $\angle D$
b. $\angle DCB$
17. $\angle B$
18. Either order:
a. $\angle BAC$
b. $\angle CAD$
19. $\angle BCA$
20. $\angle B$

MATH 1003

ALTERNATE LIFEPAC TEST

NAME ______________________

DATE ______________________

SCORE ______________________

105
131

Complete the following proofs (each answer, 4 points).

1. Given: $l \mid\mid m$

To Prove: ∠1 and ∠4 are supplementary.

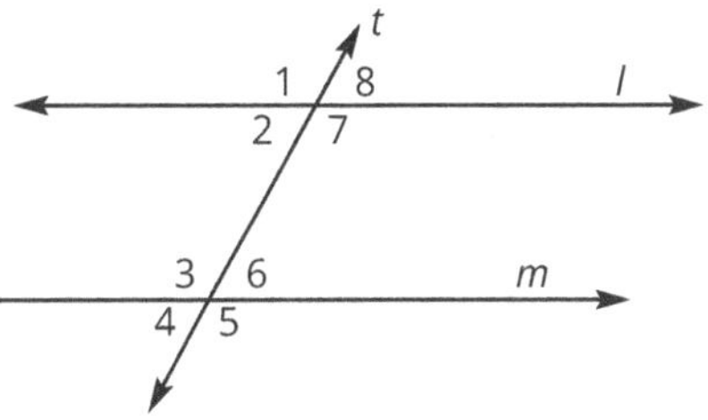

STATEMENT	REASON
1. ______	1. ______
2. ______	2. ______
3. ______	3. ______
4. ______	4. ______
5. ______	5. ______
6. ______	6. ______

2. Given: m ∠2 = m ∠3

To Prove: ∠5 and ∠4 are supplementary.

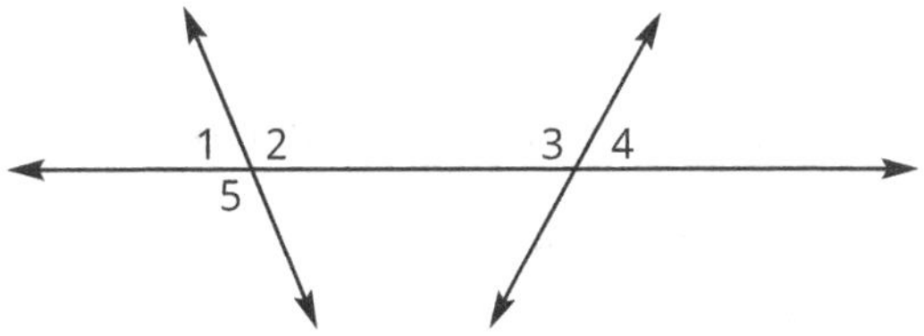

STATEMENT	REASON
1. ______	1. ______
2. ______	2. ______
3. ______	3. ______
4. ______	4. ______
5. ______	5. ______

Write the letter for the correct answer on the blank (each answer, 2 points).

3. ______ scalene △
4. ______ obtuse ∠
5. ______ acute △
6. ______ pentagon
7. ______ quadrilateral
8. ______ right △
9. ______ hexagon
10. ______ acute ∠
11. ______ octagon
12. ______ obtuse △

a. 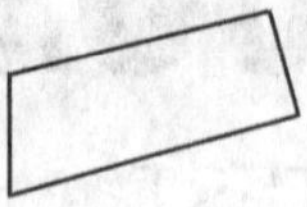

b. 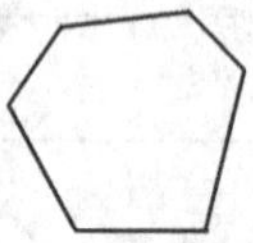

c. 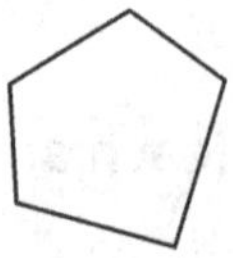

d. 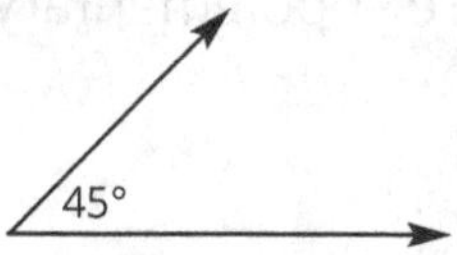

e. 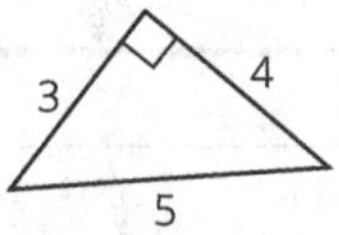

f. 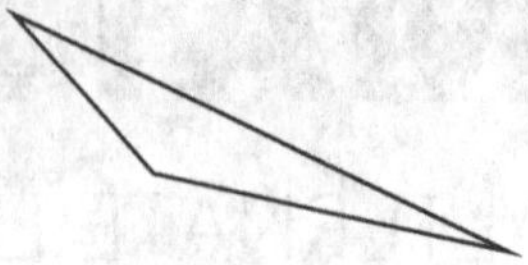

g. 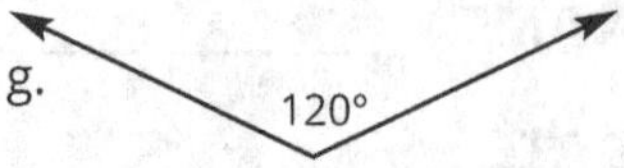

h. 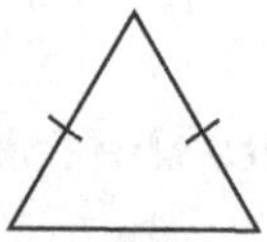

i. 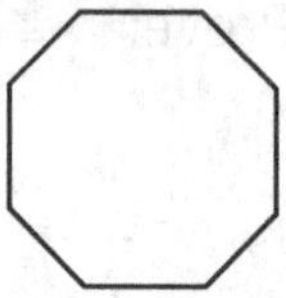

j. 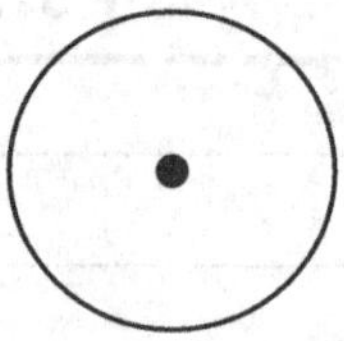

Complete the following statements (each answer, 3 points).

13. The sum of the angles of a quadrilateral is ____________________ .
14. The sum of the exterior angles, one at each vertex, of a pentagon is ____________________ .
15. The sum of the angles of a triangle is ____________________ .

Name the following angles. Use the figure given (each answer, 2 points).

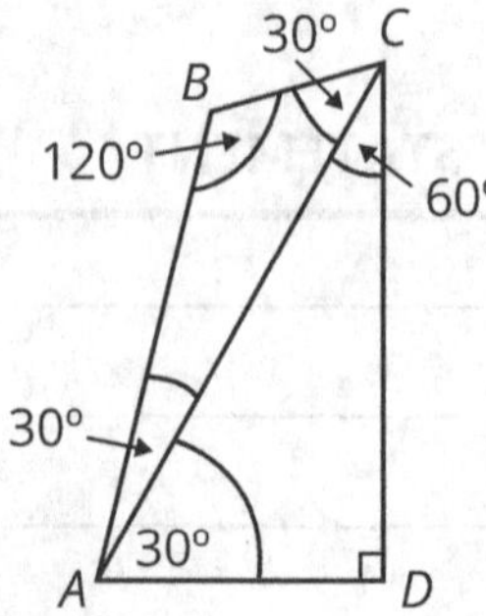

16. Two right angles:

    a. ________________ and b. ________________

17. An obtuse angle: ________________
18. Two equal adjacent angles:

    a. ________________ and b. ________________

19. A complement to angle *DAB*: ________________
20. A supplement to angle *DCA*: ________________

MATH 1004

Unit 4: Congruency

TEACHER NOTES

MATERIALS NEEDED FOR LIFEPAC	
Required	Suggested
• straightedge and protractor	(None)

ADDITIONAL LEARNING ACTIVITIES

Section 1: Triangles

1. Let one student read the "If" part of Postulate 11, 12, 13, or 14, or of Theorem 4-1, 4-2, 4-3, or 4-4. Then let a second student draw and label an appropriate figure to illustrate the postulate or theorem. Then let a third student say the "then" part of the postulate or theorem (without using the LIFEPAC). Repeat the procedure with each of the other postulates or theorems.
2. Draw any angle. Use only a compass and a straightedge to construct the bisector of the angle.

Section 2: Corresponding Parts

1. Discuss these questions with your class.
   a. If four lines in the same plane intersect at the same point, how many different pairs of vertical angles are formed?
   b. According to Theorem 4-5 in the LIFEPAC, the altitude to the base of an isosceles triangle bisects the base. When are all of the altitudes equal to all of the medians?
2. Let one student read Theorem 4-6 or 4-7 from the LIFEPAC. Then let another student draw and label an appropriate figure to illustrate the theorem. Repeat the procedure for the other theorem.
3. Let one student read the "If" part of Theorem 4-8 from the LIFEPAC. Then let a second student draw and label an appropriate figure to illustrate the theorem (representative figures are included in the LIFEPAC). Then let a third student say the "then" part of the theorem (without using the LIFEPAC).
4. Use a ruler and a protractor to construct a right triangle with a 45° angle and a right triangle with a 30° angle. What relationships can you discover about the various angles and sides of these right triangles?

Section 3: Inequalities

1. With your class, discuss what geometric figure is formed by any two coplanar, nonparallel lines cut by a transversal.
2. Let one student read the "If" part of Theorem 4-9, 4-10, 4-12, or 4-13 from the LIFEPAC. Then let a second student draw and label an appropriate figure (representative figures are included in the LIFEPAC with each theorem). Then let a third student say the "then" part of the theorem (without using the LIFEPAC). Repeat the procedure for each of the other theorems.

3. Let one student read Theorem 4-11 (triangle inequality theorem) from the LIFEPAC. Let another student draw an appropriate figure to illustrate the theorem. Then let a third student write three lengths for the sides of the triangle and check to be sure by adding all possible combinations of two sides that a triangle can be constructed with those measurements.

Section 4: Quadrilaterals

1. Discuss these questions with your class. How many diagonals can be drawn in a square? a regular pentagon? a regular hexagon? a regular *n*-gon?
2. Let one student read from the LIFEPAC Theorem 4-15, 4-20, 4-21, 4-22, 4-23, 4-24, or 4-25. Then let another student draw and label an appropriate figure to illustrate the theorem (representative figures are included in the LIFEPAC with each theorem). Repeat the procedure with each of the other theorems.
3. Let one student read the "If" part of Theorem 4-14, 4-16, 4-17, 4-18, or 4-19 from the LIFEPAC. Then let a second student draw and label an appropriate figure to illustrate the theorem (representative figures are included in the LIFEPAC with each theorem). Then let a third student say the "then" part of the theorem (without using the LIFEPAC). Repeat the procedure with each of the other theorems.
4. Draw all the diagonals of a pentagon. Find the number of triangles, quadrilaterals, pentagons, and trapezoids of any size that are formed.
5. Draw all the diagonals of a hexagon. Find the number of triangles, quadrilaterals, pentagons, and trapezoids of any size that are formed.

Administer the LIFEPAC Test.

The test is to be administered in one session. Give no help except with directions.
Evaluate the tests and review areas where the students have done poorly.
Review the pages and activities that stress the concepts tested.
If necessary, administer the Alternate LIFEPAC Test

ANSWER KEYS

SECTION 1

1.1 *S*
1.2 *R*
1.3 *T*
1.4 *R*
1.5 *K*
1.6 *O*
1.7 true
1.8 false
1.9 false
1.10 false
1.11 false
1.12 true
1.13 true
1.14 false
1.15 false
1.16 $\overline{AC}$
1.17 $\overline{BD}$
1.18 $\overline{AD}$
1.19 $\angle 2$
1.20 $\angle 4$
1.21 $\angle C$
1.22 $\overline{TU}$
1.23 $\overline{RU}$
1.24 $\overline{TR}$
1.25 $\angle 6$
1.26 $\angle 8$
1.27 $\angle S$
1.28 $\angle A$
1.29 $\angle W$
1.30 $\overline{SA}$
1.31 $\overline{SW}$
1.32 $\angle S$
1.33 $\overline{WA}$
1.34 SAS
1.35 SSS
1.36 AAS
1.37 SAS
1.38 SAS
1.39 ASA
1.40 AAS

1.41
1. **STATEMENT**
   $AM = MB$
   $DM = MC$
   REASON
   Given
2. **STATEMENT**
   $\angle 1 = \angle 2$
   REASON
   Vertical $\angle$'s are =.
3. **STATEMENT**
   $\triangle AMD \cong \triangle BMC$
   REASON
   SAS

1.42
1. **STATEMENT**
   $\overline{AD} \parallel \overline{BC}$
   $AD = BC$
   REASON
   Given
2. **STATEMENT**
   $\angle 1 = \angle 3$
   $\angle 2 = \angle 4$
   REASON
   If lines | |, alternate interior $\angle$'s =.
3. **STATEMENT**
   $\triangle ADM \cong \triangle BCM$
   REASON
   ASA

1.43
1. **STATEMENT**
   $RT = RU$
   $TS = US$
   REASON
   Given
2. **STATEMENT**
   $RS = RS$
   REASON
   Reflexive
3. **STATEMENT**
   $\triangle RST \cong \triangle RSU$
   REASON
   SSS

1.44
1. **STATEMENT**
   $CM \perp AB$
   $\angle 3 = \angle 4$
   REASON
   Given

2. **STATEMENT**
   $\angle 1 = \angle 2$
   REASON
   Definition of $\perp$ lines
3. **STATEMENT**
   $CM = CM$
   REASON
   Reflexive
4. **STATEMENT**
   $\triangle AMC \cong \triangle BMC$
   REASON
   ASA

1.45
1. **STATEMENT**
   $DC \parallel AB$
   $AD \parallel BC$
   REASON
   Given
2. **STATEMENT**
   $\angle 2 = \angle 3$
   $\angle 1 = \angle 4$
   REASON
   If lines $\parallel$, then alternate interior $\angle$'s =.
3. **STATEMENT**
   $AC = AC$
   REASON
   Reflexive
4. **STATEMENT**
   $\triangle ACD \cong \triangle CAB$
   REASON
   ASA

1.46 $BC = ST = 8$
1.47 $RT = AC = 12$
1.48 $\angle C = \angle T = 20°$
1.49 $\angle B = 180° - (\angle A + \angle C)$
$= 180° - (40° + 20°)$
$= 180° - 60°$
$= 120°$
1.50 $\angle S = \angle B = 120°$
1.51 $\angle R = \angle A = 40°$
1.52 $RS = AB = 6$
1.53 HA
1.54 LA
1.55 LA
1.56 LL
1.57 HL
1.58
1. **STATEMENT**
   $\angle 3$, $\angle 4$ are rt. $\angle$'s
   $RS = RT$
   REASON
   Given
2. **STATEMENT**
   $RZ = RZ$
   REASON
   Reflexive
3. **STATEMENT**
   $\triangle RZS \cong \triangle RZT$
   REASON
   HL

1.59
1. **STATEMENT**
   $\angle 3$, $\angle 4$ are rt. $\angle$'s
   $AX = BX$
   REASON
   Given
2. **STATEMENT**
   $CX = CX$
   REASON
   Reflexive
3. **STATEMENT**
   $\triangle AXC \cong \triangle BXC$
   REASON
   LL

1.60
1. **STATEMENT**
   $AB \perp BD$
   $AB \perp BC$
   $AC = AD$
   REASON
   Given
2. **STATEMENT**
   $\angle ABC$, $\angle ABD$ are rt. $\angle$'s
   REASON
   $\perp$'s form rt. $\angle$'s
3. **STATEMENT**
   $AB = AB$
   REASON
   Reflexive
4. **STATEMENT**
   $\triangle ABC \cong \triangle ABD$
   REASON
   HL

1.61
1. **STATEMENT**
   $\angle D$, $\angle B$ are rt. $\angle$'s
   $DC \parallel AB$
   REASON
   Given
2. **STATEMENT**
   $\angle 1 = \angle 2$
   REASON
   If lines $\parallel$, then alternate interior $\angle$'s =.

3. **STATEMENT**
   $AC = AC$
   REASON
   Reflexive
4. **STATEMENT**
   $\triangle ADC \cong \triangle CBA$
   REASON
   HA

1.62
1. **STATEMENT**
   $RS \perp ST$
   $RS \perp SQ$
   $\angle STR = \angle SQR$
   REASON
   Given
2. **STATEMENT**
   $RS = RS$
   REASON
   Reflexive
3. **STATEMENT**
   $\angle RST$, $\angle RSQ$ are rt. $\angle$'s
   REASON
   $\perp$'s form rt. $\angle$'s
4. **STATEMENT**
   $\triangle RST \cong \triangle RSQ$
   REASON
   LA

SELF TEST 1

1.01 $\angle W$
1.02 $\angle X$
1.03 $\angle Y$
1.04 WX
1.05 XY
1.06 WY
1.07 Either order:
a. JL
b. JK
1.08 Either order:
a. $\angle J$
b. $\angle K$
1.09 $\overline{JK}$
1.010 Either order (two possible sets of answers): JL and JK, or, KL and KJ
1.011 If two angles and the included side of one triangle are equal to two angles and the included side of another triangle, then the triangles are congruent.
1.012 If the hypotenuse and a leg of one right triangle are equal to the hypotenuse and leg of another right triangle, then the triangles are congruent.
1.013 If three sides of one triangle are equal to three sides of another triangle, then the triangles are congruent.
1.014 If a leg and an acute angle of one right triangle are equal to the corresponding parts of another right triangle, then the triangles are congruent.
1.015 If two sides and the included angle of one triangle are equal to two sides and the included angle of another triangle, then the triangles are congruent.

1.016 **STATEMENT**
$CA \parallel DB$; E is midpoint of $\overline{AD}$.
REASON
Given

1.017 **STATEMENT**
$\angle A = \angle D$
$\angle C = \angle B$
REASON
If lines | |, then alternate interior angles =.

1.018 **STATEMENT**
$EA = ED$
REASON
Definition of midpoint

1.019 **STATEMENT**
$\triangle AEC \cong \triangle BED$
REASON
AAS

1.020 SAS
1.021 HL
1.022 SSS
1.023 ASA
1.024 HA
1.025 ASA

SECTION 2

2.1
1. **STATEMENT**
$AB = CD$
$BC = DA$
REASON
Given
2. **STATEMENT**
$AC = AC$
REASON
Reflexive
3. **STATEMENT**
$\triangle ABC \cong \triangle CDA$
REASON
SSS
4. **STATEMENT**
$\angle B = \angle D$
REASON
CPCTE

2.2
1. **STATEMENT**
$AB = CD$
$\angle 1 = \angle 4$
REASON
Given
2. **STATEMENT**
$AC = AC$
REASON
Reflexive
3. **STATEMENT**
$\triangle ABC \cong \triangle CDA$
REASON
SAS
4. **STATEMENT**
$AD = CB$
REASON
CPCTE

2.3
1. **STATEMENT**
$\angle 1 = \angle 4$
$\angle 2 = \angle 3$
REASON
Given
2. **STATEMENT**
$AC = AC$
REASON
Reflexive
3. **STATEMENT**
$\triangle ABC \cong \triangle CDA$
REASON
ASA

4. **STATEMENT**
$AB = CD$
REASON
CPCTE

2.4

1. **STATEMENT**
$\angle 1 = \angle 4$
$\angle B = \angle D$
REASON
Given
2. **STATEMENT**
$AC = AC$
REASON
Reflexive
3. **STATEMENT**
$\triangle ABC \cong \triangle CDA$
REASON
AAS
4. **STATEMENT**
$AD = CB$
REASON
CPCTE

2.5

1. **STATEMENT**
$AB \mid\mid CD$
$AD \mid\mid CB$
REASON
Given
2. **STATEMENT**
$\angle 1 = \angle 4$
$\angle 2 = \angle 3$
REASON
If lines | |, then alternate interior $\angle$'s =.
3. **STATEMENT**
$AC = AC$
REASON
Reflexive
4. **STATEMENT**
$\triangle ABC \cong \triangle CDA$
REASON
ASA
5. **STATEMENT**
$AD = CB$
REASON
CPCTE

2.6

1. **STATEMENT**
$AB \mid\mid DC$
$AB = CD$
REASON
Given
2. **STATEMENT**
$\angle 1 = \angle 4$
REASON
If lines | |, then alternate interior $\angle$'s =.
3. **STATEMENT**
$AC = AC$
REASON
Reflexive
4. **STATEMENT**
$\triangle ABC \cong \triangle CDA$
REASON
SAS
5. **STATEMENT**
$\angle 2 = \angle 3$
REASON
CPCTE

2.7

1. **STATEMENT**
$AB = CD$
$AD = CB$
REASON
Given
2. **STATEMENT**
$AC = AC$
REASON
Reflexive
3. **STATEMENT**
$\triangle ABC \cong \triangle CDA$
REASON
SSS
4. **STATEMENT**
$\angle 1 = \angle 4$
REASON
CPCTE
5. **STATEMENT**
$\overline{DC} \mid\mid \overline{AB}$
REASON
If alternate interior $\angle$'s =, then lines | |.

2.8

1. **STATEMENT**
$\overline{TQ}$ bisects $\angle RTS$
$\angle R = \angle S$
REASON
Given
2. **STATEMENT**
$\angle 1 = \angle 2$
REASON
Definition of $\angle$ bisector

3. **STATEMENT**
   $TQ = TQ$
   REASON
   Reflexive
4. **STATEMENT**
   $\triangle RTQ \cong \triangle STQ$
   REASON
   AAS
5. **STATEMENT**
   $\angle 3 = \angle 4$
   REASON
   CPCTE
6. **STATEMENT**
   $\overline{TQ} \perp \overline{RS}$
   REASON
   Definition of $\perp$

2.9

1. **STATEMENT**
   $\overline{TQ}$ bisects $\overline{RS}$
   $RT = ST$
   REASON
   Given
2. **STATEMENT**
   $RQ = SQ$
   REASON
   Definition of bisector of segment
3. **STATEMENT**
   $TQ = TQ$
   REASON
   Reflexive
4. **STATEMENT**
   $\triangle RTQ \cong \triangle STQ$
   REASON
   SSS
5. **STATEMENT**
   $\angle 3 = \angle 4$
   REASON
   CPCTE
6. **STATEMENT**
   $\overline{TQ} \perp \overline{RS}$
   REASON
   Definition of $\perp$ bisector

2.10

1. **STATEMENT**
   $\overline{TQ}$ is $\perp$ bisector of RS
   REASON
   Given
2. **STATEMENT**
   $\angle 3 = \angle 4$
   $RQ = QS$
   REASON
   Definition of $\perp$ bisector
3. **STATEMENT**
   $TQ = TQ$
   REASON
   Reflexive
4. **STATEMENT**
   $\triangle RTQ \cong \triangle STQ$
   REASON
   SAS
5. **STATEMENT**
   $\angle R = \angle S$
   REASON
   CPCTE

2.11

1. **STATEMENT**
   $\angle 2 = \angle 3$
   $\angle 4 = \angle 5$
   REASON
   Given
2. **STATEMENT**
   $\angle 1 = \angle 3$
   REASON
   Vertical $\angle$'s are =
3. **STATEMENT**
   $\angle 1 = \angle 2$
   REASON
   Substitution
4. **STATEMENT**
   $VR = VR$
   REASON
   Reflexive
5. **STATEMENT**
   $\triangle VSR \cong \triangle VTR$
   REASON
   ASA
6. **STATEMENT**
   $RS = RT$
   REASON
   CPCTE

2.12

1. **STATEMENT**
   $\triangle ABC$, $\triangle DEF$ are rt. $\triangle$'s
   $AB = DE$
   $\angle A = \angle D$
   REASON
   Given

2. **STATEMENT**
$\triangle ABC \cong \triangle DEF$
REASON
LA

3. **STATEMENT**
$BC = EF$
REASON
CPCTE

2.13

1. **STATEMENT**
$\angle A$, $\angle B$ are rt. $\angle$'s
$AC = BD$
REASON
Given

2. **STATEMENT**
$\angle AMC = \angle BMD$
REASON
Vertical $\angle$'s are =

3. **STATEMENT**
$\triangle AMC \cong \triangle BMD$
REASON
LA

4. **STATEMENT**
$MC = MD$
REASON
CPCTE

2.14

1. **STATEMENT**
$\angle 1 = \angle 2$
$\angle 3 = \angle 4$
D midpoint of $\overline{BE}$
$BC = DE$
REASON
Given

2. **STATEMENT**
$BD = DE$
REASON
Definition of midpoint

3. **STATEMENT**
$BC = BD$
REASON
Substitution

4. **STATEMENT**
$\triangle ABD \cong \triangle EBC$
REASON
ASA

5. **STATEMENT**
$\angle A = \angle E$
REASON
CPCTE

2.15

1. **STATEMENT**
$\angle S = \angle T$
$RV = UV$
REASON
Given

2. **STATEMENT**
$\angle 1 = \angle 2$
REASON
Vertical $\angle$'s are =

3. **STATEMENT**
$\triangle RSV \cong \triangle UTV$
REASON
AAS

4. **STATEMENT**
$SR = TU$
REASON
CPCTE

2.16 *BCA*
2.17 *AED*
2.18 *BDA*
2.19 *BDC*
2.20 *BOC*
2.21 *AEC*
2.22 *AFC*
2.23 *AFB*
2.24 *EDF*
2.25 *EGD*
2.26 *EGC*
2.27 *EBC*
2.28 *DGC*
2.29 *DAC*
2.30 *EAD*
2.31 *CGB*

2.32

1. **STATEMENT**
$RM = SN$
$\angle MRS = \angle NSR$
REASON
Given

2. **STATEMENT**
$RS = RS$
REASON
Reflexive

3. **STATEMENT**
$\triangle MRS \cong \triangle NSR$
REASON
SAS

4. **STATEMENT**
$\angle RMS = \angle SNR$, $SM = RN$
REASON
CPCTE

2.33

1. **STATEMENT**
   $RM = SN$
   $SM = RN$
   REASON
   Given
2. **STATEMENT**
   $RS = RS$
   REASON
   Reflexive
3. **STATEMENT**
   $\triangle MRS \cong \triangle NSR$
   REASON
   SSS
4. **STATEMENT**
   $\angle RMS = \angle SNR$
   REASON
   CPCTE

2.34

1. **STATEMENT**
   $RT = ST$
   $MT = NT$
   REASON
   Given
2. **STATEMENT**
   $\angle T = \angle T$
   REASON
   Reflexive
3. **STATEMENT**
   $\triangle RTN \cong \triangle STM$
   REASON
   SAS
4. **STATEMENT**
   $\angle RNT = \angle SMT$
   REASON
   CPCTE

2.35

1. **STATEMENT**
   $RM = SN$
   $TM = TN$
   REASON
   Given
2. **STATEMENT**
   $\angle T = \angle T$
   REASON
   Reflexive
3. **STATEMENT**
   $RM + TM = SN + TN$
   REASON
   Addition property of equality
4. **STATEMENT**
   $RM + TM = RT$
   $SN + TN = ST$
   REASON
   Betweenness
5. **STATEMENT**
   $RT = ST$
   REASON
   Substitution
6. **STATEMENT**
   $\triangle RTN \cong \triangle STM$
   REASON
   SAS
7. **STATEMENT**
   $RN = SM$
   REASON
   CPCTE

2.36

1. **STATEMENT**
   $AD = BC$
   $BC \perp AE$
   $AD \perp BE$
   REASON
   Given
2. **STATEMENT**
   $\angle D$, $\angle C$ are rt. $\angle$'s
   REASON
   $\perp$'s form rt. $\angle$'s
3. **STATEMENT**
   $\angle E = \angle E$
   REASON
   Reflexive
4. **STATEMENT**
   $\triangle ADE \cong \triangle BCE$
   REASON
   LA
5. **STATEMENT**
   $\angle A = \angle B$
   REASON
   CPCTE

2.37

1. **STATEMENT**
   $CF = DF$
   $FC \perp AE$
   $FD \perp BE$
   REASON
   Given
2. **STATEMENT**
   $\angle C$, $\angle D$ are rt. $\angle$'s
   REASON
   $\perp$'s form rt. $\angle$'s

3. **STATEMENT**
$FE = FE$
REASON
Reflexive

4. **STATEMENT**
$\triangle FCE \cong \triangle FDE$
REASON
HL

5. **STATEMENT**
$\angle 1 = \angle 2$
REASON
CPCTE

2.38
1. **STATEMENT**
$AD \perp BE$
$BC \perp AE$
$AF = BF$
REASON
Given

2. **STATEMENT**
$\angle C$, $\angle D$ are rt. $\angle$'s
REASON
$\perp$'s form rt. $\angle$'s

3. **STATEMENT**
$\angle AFC = \angle BFD$
REASON
Vertical $\angle$'s are =.

4. **STATEMENT**
$\triangle AFC \cong \triangle BFD$
REASON
HA

5. **STATEMENT**
$AC = BD$
REASON
CPCTE

2.39 $\overline{CR}$
2.40 $\overline{AM}$
2.41 $\overline{BL}$
2.42 $\overline{BT}$
2.43 $\overline{AS}$
2.44 $\overline{CN}$
2.45 Q
2.46 P

2.47
1. **STATEMENT**
$AC = BC$
REASON
Given

2. **STATEMENT**
$\angle 1 = \angle 2$
REASON
Base $\angle$'s of isosceles $\triangle$ are =

3. **STATEMENT**
$\angle 2 = \angle 3$
REASON
Vertical $\angle$'s are =

4. **STATEMENT**
$\angle 1 = \angle 3$
REASON
Substitution

2.48
1. **STATEMENT**
$\angle 3 = \angle 1$
REASON
Given

2. **STATEMENT**
$\angle 3 = \angle 2$
REASON
Vertical $\angle$'s are =

3. **STATEMENT**
$\angle 1 = \angle 2$
REASON
Substitution

4. **STATEMENT**
$AC = BC$
REASON
If two $\angle$'s of $\triangle$ are =, sides opposite are =.

2.49
1. **STATEMENT**
$RA = RB$
$\overrightarrow{RS} \parallel \overline{AB}$
REASON
Given

2. **STATEMENT**
$\angle A = \angle B$
REASON
Base $\angle$'s of isosceles $\triangle$ are =

3. **STATEMENT**
$\angle A = \angle 2$
REASON
If lines | |, alternate interior $\angle$'s =.

4. **STATEMENT**
$\angle B = \angle 1$
REASON
If lines | |, corresponding $\angle$'s =.

5. **STATEMENT**
$\angle 1 = \angle 2$
REASON
Substitution

2.50 1. **STATEMENT**
$\overrightarrow{RS} \parallel \overline{AB}$
$\angle 1 = \angle 2$
REASON
Given

2. **STATEMENT**
$\angle B = \angle 1$
REASON
If lines | |, corresponding ∠'s =.

3. **STATEMENT**
$\angle A = \angle 2$
REASON
If lines | |, alternate interior ∠'s =.

4. **STATEMENT**
$\angle A = \angle B$
REASON
Substitution

5. **STATEMENT**
$RA = RB$
REASON
If two ∠'s of △ are =, sides opposite are =.

2.51 1. **STATEMENT**
$DF = EF$
REASON
Given

2. **STATEMENT**
$\angle 1 = \angle 2$
REASON
Base ∠'s of isosceles △ are =

3. **STATEMENT**
∠1, ∠3 are supplementary
∠2, ∠4 are supplementary
REASON
Exterior sides in opposite rays

4. **STATEMENT**
$\angle 3 = \angle 4$
REASON
Two ∠'s supplementary to equal ∠'s are equal.

2.52 1. **STATEMENT**
$\angle 3 = \angle 4$
REASON
Given

2. **STATEMENT**
∠1, ∠3 are supplementary
∠2, ∠4 are supplementary
REASON
Exterior sides in opposite rays

3. **STATEMENT**
$\angle 1 = \angle 2$
REASON
Two ∠'s supplementary to equal ∠'s are equal.

4. **STATEMENT**
$DF = EF$
REASON
If 2 ∠'s of △ are =, the sides opposite the ∠'s are =.

2.53 1. **STATEMENT**
$AR = AQ$
$RT = QS$
REASON
Given

2. **STATEMENT**
$\angle R = \angle Q$
REASON
Base ∠'s of isosceles △ are =

3. **STATEMENT**
$\triangle RAT \cong \triangle QAS$
REASON
SAS

4. **STATEMENT**
$\angle RAT = \angle QAS$
REASON
CPCTE

2.54 1. **STATEMENT**
$AR = AQ$
$\angle 1 = \angle 3$
REASON
Given

2. **STATEMENT**
$\angle R = \angle Q$
REASON
Base ∠'s of isosceles △ are =

3. **STATEMENT**
$\triangle ARS \cong \triangle AQT$
REASON
ASA

4. **STATEMENT**
$AS = AT$
REASON
CPCTE

2.55 1. **STATEMENT**
$\angle R = \angle Q$
$AS = AT$
REASON
Given

2. **STATEMENT**
   $\angle 5 = \angle 6$
   REASON
   Base $\angle$'s of isosceles $\triangle$ are =
3. **STATEMENT**
   $\angle 4$, $\angle 5$ are supplementary
   $\angle 6$, $\angle 7$ are supplementary
   REASON
   Exterior sides in opposite rays
4. **STATEMENT**
   $\angle 4 = \angle 7$
   REASON
   Two $\angle$'s supplementary to equal angles are =.
5. **STATEMENT**
   $\triangle RAS \cong \triangle QAT$
   REASON
   AAS
6. **STATEMENT**
   $RS = QT$
   REASON
   CPCTE

SELF TEST 2

2.01 $\angle XTY$
2.02 $\angle X$
2.03 $\angle XYT$
2.04 TX
2.05 XY
2.06 TY
2.07 $\angle E$
2.08 $\angle F$
2.09 $\angle FCE$
2.010 EF
2.011 FC
2.012 EC
2.013 $\triangle AFG$
2.014 $\triangle FCG$
2.015 $\triangle AFC$
2.016 $\triangle DCE$

2.017 **STATEMENT**
$\overline{AP} \parallel \overline{BC}$
$AD = CB$
REASON
Given

2.018 **STATEMENT**
$AC = AC$
REASON
Reflexive

2.019 **STATEMENT**
$\angle 2 = \angle 3$
REASON
If lines | |, alternate interior $\angle$'s =.

2.020 **STATEMENT**
$\triangle ACD \cong \triangle CAB$
REASON
SAS

2.021 **STATEMENT**
$\angle 1 = \angle 4$
REASON
CPCTE

2.022 **STATEMENT**
$\overline{AB} \parallel \overline{DC}$
REASON
If alternate interior $\angle$'s =, then lines | |.

2.023 **Given:**
$\triangle RAS$ is isosceles $\triangle$; AM is median

2.024 **To Prove:**
$\triangle RAM \cong SAM$

2.025 **STATEMENT**
$\triangle RAS$ is isosceles $\triangle$; *AM* is median
REASON
Given

2.026 **STATEMENT**
$AR = AS$
REASON
Definition of isosceles $\triangle$

2.027 **STATEMENT**
$AM = AM$
REASON
Reflexive

2.028 **STATEMENT**
$RM = MS$
REASON
Definition of median

2.029 **STATEMENT**
$\triangle RAM \cong SAM$
REASON
SSS

SECTION 3

3.1
1. **STATEMENT**
$\overline{PT} \perp \overleftrightarrow{RT}$
REASON
Given
2. **STATEMENT**
T is rt. $\angle$
REASON
$\perp$ forms rt. $\angle$
3. **STATEMENT**
$\angle T > \angle R$
REASON
Rt. $\angle$ is greater than acute $\angle$.
4. **STATEMENT**
$PR > PT$ or $PT < PR$
REASON
If two $\angle$'s of $\triangle \neq$, then side opposite larger $\angle$ is longer.

3.2 a. $\angle B$
b. $\angle A$
c. $\angle C$

3.3 a. $\angle T$
b. $\angle R$
c. $\angle S$

3.4 a. $\angle T$
b. $\angle M$
c. $\angle S$

3.5 a. $\angle B$
b. $\angle A$
c. $\angle C$

3.6 a. $\overline{MO}$
b. $\overline{MP}$
c. $\overline{PO}$

3.7 a. $\overline{DE}$
b. $\overline{OE}$
c. $\overline{OD}$

3.8 a. $\overline{NA}$
b. $\overline{MA}$
c. $\overline{MN}$

3.9 yes
3.10 yes
3.11 no; 2 yds. + 5 yds. $\ngtr$ 10 yds.
3.12 yes
3.13 no; 1mm + 2mm $\ngtr$ 3mm
3.14 yes
3.15 <
3.16 <
3.17 >
3.18 <
3.19 >
3.20 >

3.21 >

3.22 >

3.23 <

3.24
1. **STATEMENT**
   $BC = EF$
   REASON
   Given
2. **STATEMENT**
   $AC = AB + BC$
   REASON
   Betweenness
3. **STATEMENT**
   $AC > BC$
   REASON
   If $a = b + c$ and $c > 0$, then $a > b$.
4. **STATEMENT**
   $AC > EF$
   REASON
   Substitution

3.25
1. **STATEMENT**
   $\angle DBC = \angle RST$
   REASON
   Given
2. **STATEMENT**
   $\angle ABC = \angle DBC + \angle ABD$
   REASON
   Angle addition theorem
3. **STATEMENT**
   $\angle ABC > \angle DBC$
   REASON
   If $a = b + c$ and $c > 0$, then $a > b$.
4. **STATEMENT**
   $\angle ABC > \angle RST$
   REASON
   Substitution

3.26
1. **STATEMENT**
   $\triangle WXY$, $\angle 1$ an exterior $\angle$
   REASON
   Given
2. **STATEMENT**
   $\angle 1 = \angle 2 + \angle 3$
   REASON
   Exterior $\angle$ = sum of remote interior $\angle$'s
3. **STATEMENT**
   $\angle 1 > \angle 2$
   REASON
   If $a = b + c$ and $c > 0$, then $a > b$.

3.27
1. **STATEMENT**
   $WX > XY$
   REASON
   Given
2. **STATEMENT**
   $\angle 3 > \angle 4$
   REASON
   Angle opposite longer side is larger $\angle$.
3. **STATEMENT**
   $\angle 1 = \angle 3 + \angle 2$
   REASON
   Exterior $\angle$ = sum of remote interior $\angle$'s
4. **STATEMENT**
   $\angle 1 > \angle 3$
   REASON
   If $a = b + c$ and $c > 0$, then $a > b$.
5. **STATEMENT**
   $\angle 1 > \angle 4$
   REASON
   Transitive

3.28 **Given:** $\triangle ABC$ is rt. $\triangle$
To Prove: $AC > AB$
$AC > BC$

1. **STATEMENT**
   $\triangle ABC$ is rt. $\triangle$
   REASON
   Given
2. **STATEMENT**
   $\angle B$ is rt. $\angle$
   REASON
   Definition of rt. $\triangle$
3. **STATEMENT**
   $\angle B = 90°$
   REASON
   Definition of rt. $\angle$
4. **STATEMENT**
   $90° = \angle A + \angle C$
   REASON
   Acute $\angle$'s of rt. $\triangle$ are complementary.
5. **STATEMENT**
   $90° > \angle A$
   REASON
   If $a = b + c$ and $c > 0$, then $a > b$.
6. **STATEMENT**
   $\angle B > \angle A$
   REASON
   Substitution

7. **STATEMENT**
   $AC > BC$
   REASON
   Side opposite larger $\angle$ is longer.

8. **STATEMENT**
   $90° = \angle C + \angle A$
   REASON
   Commutative for addition

9. **STATEMENT**
   $90° > \angle C$
   REASON
   If $a = b + c$ and $c > 0$, then $a > b$.

10. **STATEMENT**
    $\angle B > \angle C$
    REASON
    Substitution

11. **STATEMENT**
    $AC > AB$
    REASON
    Side opposite larger angle is longer.

3.29 5 and 25
3.30 0 and 24
3.31 a. $|a - b|$
b. $a + b$
3.32 $>$
3.33 $>$
3.34 $<$
3.35 $>$
3.36 $>$
3.37 $<$
3.38 $>$
3.39 $<$
3.40 $=$
3.41 $=$
3.42 $<$
3.43 $<$
3.44 $>$
3.45 $>$
3.46 $=$
3.47 $=$
3.48 $<$
3.49 $>$
3.50 $>$
3.51 $=$
3.52 $<$
3.53 $<$
3.54 $>$
3.55 $<$
3.56 $=$

SELF TEST 3

3.01 > 0
3.02 longer
3.03 a. sides
b. sides
3.04 $<$
3.05 a. 5
b. 11
3.06 $>$
3.07 $>$
3.08 $<$
3.09 $<$
3.010 $>$
3.011 $=$
3.012 $=$
3.013 $\cong$

3.014 **STATEMENT**
$\angle A = \angle B$
M is midpoint of *AB*
REASON
Given

3.015 **STATEMENT**
$AM = MB$
REASON
Definition of midpoint

3.016 **STATEMENT**
$AC = BC$
REASON
Sides opposite = $\angle$'s are =.

3.017 **STATEMENT**
$\triangle AMC \cong \triangle BMC$
REASON
SAS

SECTION 4

4.1 Opposite sides of ▱ are ||.
4.2 Opposite sides of ▱ are =.
4.3 Opposite ∠'s of ▱ are =.
4.4 They are supplementary ∠'s.
4.5 ∠1 = ∠5, ∠2 = ∠6, ∠3 = ∠7, ∠4 = ∠8, ∠9 = ∠10
4.6 *RS* = *UT*, *RU* = *ST*, *RW* = *WT*, *UW* = *WS*
4.7 △*RSW* ≅ △*TUW*, △*RWU* ≅ △*TWS*, △*RST* ≅ △*TUR*, △*STU* ≅ △*URS*
4.8 180°
4.9 SSS

4.10
1. **STATEMENT**
   ABCD is ▱
   REASON
   Given
2. **STATEMENT**
   Draw diagonal *DB*
   REASON
   Auxiliary line
3. **STATEMENT**
   △*ABD* ≅ △*CDB*
   REASON
   Two ≅ △'s formed by diagonal
4. **STATEMENT**
   ∠*A* = ∠*C*
   REASON
   CPCTE

4.11
1. **STATEMENT**
   ABCD is ▱
   REASON
   Given
2. **STATEMENT**
   Draw diagonal *DB*
   REASON
   Auxiliary line
3. **STATEMENT**
   △*DAB* ≅ △*BCD*
   REASON
   Two ≅ △'s formed by diagonal
4. **STATEMENT**
   AB = *DC*, *AD* = *BC*
   REASON
   CPCTE

4.12
1. **STATEMENT**
   ▱*ABCD*
   REASON
   Given
2. **STATEMENT**
   BT = *TD*
   REASON
   Diagonals of ▱ bisect each other.
3. **STATEMENT**
   ∠1 = ∠2
   REASON
   Vertical ∠'s are =.
4. **STATEMENT**
   BC || *AD*
   REASON
   Definition of ▱
5. **STATEMENT**
   ∠3 = ∠4
   REASON
   If lines ||, then alternate interior ∠'s =.
6. **STATEMENT**
   △*BET* ≅ △*DFT*
   REASON
   ASA
7. **STATEMENT**
   ET = *FT*
   REASON
   CPCTE

4.13
1. **STATEMENT**
   ∠*A*, ∠*B*, and ∠*C* are rt. ∠'s
   REASON
   Given
2. **STATEMENT**
   DA ⊥ *AB*, *CB* ⊥ *AB*
   REASON
   If rt. ∠'s are formed, then lines are ⊥.
3. **STATEMENT**
   DA || *CB*
   REASON
   Two lines ⊥ to same line are ||.
4. **STATEMENT**
   DC ⊥ *BC*, *AB* ⊥ *BC*
   REASON
   If rt. ∠'s are formed, then lines are ⊥.
5. **STATEMENT**
   AB || *DC*
   REASON
   Two lines ⊥ to same line are ||.
6. **STATEMENT**
   ABCD is ▱
   REASON
   Definition of ▱

4.14 1. **STATEMENT**
RSTU is ▱
RSQP is ▱
REASON
Given

2. **STATEMENT**
$UT = RS$, $RS = PQ$
REASON
Opposite sides of ▱ are =.

3. **STATEMENT**
$PQ = UT$
REASON
Substitution

4.15 1. **STATEMENT**
$DO = OB$
$AO = OC$
REASON
Given

2. **STATEMENT**
$\angle DOC = \angle AOB$
REASON
Vertical ∠'s are =.

3. **STATEMENT**
$\triangle AOB \cong \triangle COD$
REASON
SAS

4. **STATEMENT**
$\angle 1 = \angle 2$
$AB = DC$
REASON
CPCTE

5. **STATEMENT**
$AB \parallel DC$
REASON
If alternate interior ∠'s are =, then | |.

6. **STATEMENT**
ABCD is ▱
REASON
If two sides = and | |, then ▱.

4.16 $\overline{UT}$

4.17 $VS \parallel UT$

$VS = \frac{1}{2}UT$

$= \frac{1}{2}(20)$

$= 10$

4.18 24

4.19 60°

4.20 180°

4.21 $\angle 3 = 180° - \angle 2$
$= 180° - 120°$
$= 60°$

4.22 $\overline{SM}$

4.23 $\overline{VM}$

4.24 $\overline{RT}$

4.25 $\overline{AB}$

4.26 $\overline{ST}$

4.27 $\overline{CB}$

4.28 $\overline{AB}$

4.29 $\overline{RT}$

4.30 paralellogram

4.31 through 4.34

$$\begin{aligned} 2(2x + 60) + 2(x + 30) &= 360 \\ 4x + 120 + 2x + 60 &= 360 \\ 6x + 180 &= 360 \\ 6x &= 180 \\ x &= 30° \end{aligned}$$

4.31 $\angle H = 2x + 60 = 120°$

4.32 $\angle A = x + 30 = 60°$

4.33 $\angle L = \angle H = 120°$

4.34 $\angle T = \angle A = 60°$

4.35 Either order:
a. $\overline{FL}$
b. $\overline{GA}$

4.36 Either order:
a. $\overline{GF}$
b. $\overline{AL}$

4.37 Either order:
a. $\angle G$
b. $\angle L$

4.38 Any order:
a. $\angle A$
b. $\angle X$
c. $\angle Z$

4.39 1. **STATEMENT**
ABEF is ▱
$EB \parallel DC$
REASON
Given

2. **STATEMENT**
$\overline{AF} \parallel \overline{BE}$
$\overline{FE} \parallel \overline{AB}$
REASON
Opposite sides of ▱ are =.

3. **STATEMENT**
$\overline{AF} \parallel \overline{CD}$
REASON
Transitive

4. **STATEMENT**
   $\overline{FD} \parallel \overline{AC}$
   REASON
   Part of $\overleftrightarrow{FE}$ and $\overleftrightarrow{AB}$
5. **STATEMENT**
   ACDF is ▱
   REASON
   Definition of ▱

4.40 **Given:** *RSTU* is rectangle
To Prove: *RT* = *US*

1. **STATEMENT**
   RSTU is rectangle
   REASON
   Given
2. **STATEMENT**
   RU = *TS*
   REASON
   Opposite sides of ▱ = (definition of rectangle).
3. **STATEMENT**
   RS = *RS*
   REASON
   Reflexive
4. **STATEMENT**
   $\angle S$, $\angle R$ are rt. ∠'s
   REASON
   Definition of rectangle
5. **STATEMENT**
   $\triangle RST \cong \triangle SRU$
   REASON
   LL
6. **STATEMENT**
   RT = *US*
   REASON
   CPCTE

4.41 **Given:** *ABCD* is rhombus
To Prove: $AC \perp DB$

1. **STATEMENT**
   ABCD is rhombus
   REASON
   Given
2. **STATEMENT**
   AD = *AB*
   REASON
   All sides of rhombus = (definition of rhombus).
3. **STATEMENT**
   DO = *OB*
   REASON
   Diagonals of ▱ bisect each other.
4. **STATEMENT**
   AO = *AO*
   REASON
   Reflexive
5. **STATEMENT**
   $\triangle DOA \cong \triangle BOA$
   REASON
   SSS
6. **STATEMENT**
   $\angle 1 = \angle 2$
   REASON
   CPCTE
7. **STATEMENT**
   $AC \perp DB$
   REASON
   Definition of ⊥ lines

4.42 **Given:** *ABCD* is rhombus
To Prove: *DB* bisects $\angle B$ and $\angle D$

1. **STATEMENT**
   ABCD is rhombus
   REASON
   Given
2. **STATEMENT**
   $\triangle ADB \cong \triangle CDB$
   REASON
   Diagonals of ▱ make ≅ △'s.
3. **STATEMENT**
   $\angle 1 = \angle 2$, $\angle 3 = \angle 4$
   REASON
   CPCTE
4. **STATEMENT**
   DB bisects $\angle B$ and $\angle D$
   REASON
   Definition of ∠ bisector

4.43 **Given:** *ABCD* is ▱, *AC* = *BD*
To Prove: *ABCD* is rectangle

1. **STATEMENT**
   ABCD is ▱
   AC = *BD*
   REASON
   Given

2. **STATEMENT**
   $\angle A = \angle C$
   $\angle B = \angle D$
   REASON
   Opposite $\angle$'s of ▱ are =.
3. **STATEMENT**
   $DA = CB$
   REASON
   Opposite sides of ▱ are =.
4. **STATEMENT**
   $AB = AB$
   REASON
   Reflexive
5. **STATEMENT**
   $\triangle DAB \cong \triangle CBA$
   REASON
   SSS
6. **STATEMENT**
   $\angle A = \angle B$
   REASON
   CPCTE
7. **STATEMENT**
   $\angle A + \angle B = 180°$
   REASON
   Interior $\angle$'s on same side of transversal are supplementary.
8. **STATEMENT**
   $2\angle A = 180°$
   REASON
   Substitution
9. **STATEMENT**
   $\angle A = 90°$
   REASON
   Division property of equality
10. **STATEMENT**
    $ABCD$ is rectangle
    REASON
    Definition of rectangle

4.44 **Given:** $AB = BC = CD = DA$
To Prove: $ABCD$ is rhombus

1. **STATEMENT**
   $AB = BC = CD = DA$
   REASON
   Given
2. **STATEMENT**
   $ABCD$ is ▱
   REASON
   Both pairs of opposite sides are =.
3. **STATEMENT**
   $ABCD$ is rhombus
   REASON
   Definition of rhombus

4.45 **Given:** $ABCD$ is rectangle
K, L, M, N are midpoints
To Prove: $KLMN$ is a parallelogram

1. **STATEMENT**
   $ABCD$ is rectangle
   K, L, M, N are midpoints
   REASON
   Given
2. **STATEMENT**
   Draw diagonal $\overline{AC}$
   REASON
   Auxiliary line
3. **STATEMENT**
   $\overline{NM} \parallel \overline{AC}$
   $NM = \frac{1}{2}AC$
   $\overline{KL} \parallel \overline{AC}$
   $KL = \frac{1}{2}AC$
   REASON
   Midpoint segment of $\triangle$ is || to third side and = $\frac{1}{2}$ third side.
4. **STATEMENT**
   $NM = KL$
   REASON
   Substitution
5. **STATEMENT**
   $\overline{NM} \parallel \overline{KL}$
   REASON
   Transitive
6. **STATEMENT**
   $KLMN$ is ▱
   REASON
   If two sides = and ||, then ▱.

4.46 false
4.47 true
4.48 false
4.49 true
4.50 true
4.51 true
4.52 false
4.53 true
4.54 true
4.55 HJ
4.56 $\angle GJI = \angle GHI = 120°$
4.57 $AB = DC = 12$

4.58 $\angle A$ or $\angle B$ or $\angle D$ or 90°

4.59 $ON = PO = 8$

4.60 $GH = HI = 16$

4.61 Either order:
a. H
b. J

4.62 $BD = AC = 20$

4.63 $PN = MO = 10$

4.64 <

4.65 $MN = \frac{1}{2}(RO + ES)$
$= \frac{1}{2}(10 + 6)$
$= \frac{1}{2}(16)$
$= 8$

4.66 $\frac{1}{2}(x + y)$

4.67 $MN = \frac{1}{2}(RO + ES)$
$24 = \frac{1}{2}(30 + ES)$
$48 = 30 + ES$
$ES = 18$

4.68 $MN = \frac{1}{2}(RO + ES)$
$24 = \frac{1}{2}(RO + 10)$
$48 = RO + 10$
$RO = 38$

4.69 a. $\angle Q = \angle P = 50°$
b. $\angle R = \frac{1}{2}[360° - (\angle P + \angle Q)]$
$= \frac{1}{2}[360° - (50 + 50)]$
$= \frac{1}{2}(260)$
$\angle R = 130°$
c. $\angle S = \angle R = 130°$

4.70 a. $\angle Q = \angle P = 60°$
b. $\angle R = \frac{1}{2}[360° - (\angle P + \angle Q)]$
$= \frac{1}{2}[360° - (60 + 60)]$
$= \frac{1}{2}(240)$
$\angle R = 120°$
c. $\angle S = \angle R = 120°$

4.71 a. $\angle S = \angle R = 100°$
b. $\angle P = \frac{1}{2}[360° - (\angle R + \angle S)]$
$= \frac{1}{2}[360° - (100 + 100)]$
$= \frac{1}{2}(160)$
$\angle P = 80°$
c. $\angle Q = \angle P = 80°$

4.72 a. $\angle Q = 180° - \angle S$
$= 180° - 120°$
$\angle Q = 60°$
b. $\angle R = \angle S = 120°$
c. $\angle P = \angle Q = 60°$

4.73 $QS = RP = 12$

4.74
1. **STATEMENT**
$AE = HD$
$AB = DC$
$\angle B = \angle C$
REASON
Definition of square
2. **STATEMENT**
$BC = BC$
REASON
Reflexive
3. **STATEMENT**
$\triangle ABC \cong \triangle DCB$
REASON
SAS
4. **STATEMENT**
$BD = AC$
REASON
CPCTE
5. **STATEMENT**
$\angle EAC = \angle HDB$
REASON
All rt. $\angle$'s =.
6. **STATEMENT**
$\triangle EAC \cong \triangle HDB$
REASON
SAS$\triangle$
7. **STATEMENT**
$HB = EC$
REASON
CPCTE

SELF TEST 4

4.01 median = $\frac{1}{2}(BO + TA)$

$= \frac{1}{2}(12 + 6)$

median = 9

4.02 Since *BOAT* is an isosceles trapezoid, $\angle B = \angle O$ and $\angle A = \angle T$.

$\angle B + \angle O + \angle A + \angle T = 360°$

$2\angle O + 2(130) = 360°$

$2\angle O = 100°$

$\angle O = 50°$

4.03 Any order:

a. *ATSR*

b. *RTSB*

c. *RTCS*

4.04 *R* is midpoint of *AB*; *S* is midpoint of *BC*

$RS = \frac{1}{2}AC$

$5 = \frac{1}{2}AC$

$AC = 10$

4.05 $P\ \triangle RST = RS + ST + TR$

$P\ \triangle ABC = AB + BC + CA$

$RS = \frac{1}{2}AC$

$ST = \frac{1}{2}BA$

$RT = \frac{1}{2}BC$

$P\ \triangle RST = \frac{1}{2}P\ \triangle ABC$

$= \frac{1}{2}(20)$

$P\ \triangle RST = 10$

4.06 *AC* and *BD* are the diagonals of ▱*ABCD*.

$AC = BD$

$10 = BD$

4.07 $BD = AC$

$BD = DE + BE$

$BE = \frac{1}{2}AC$

$= \frac{1}{2}(12)$

$BE = 6$

4.08 All sides of a rhombus are equal.

The diagonals of a rhombus bisect two angles of the rhombus.

$\therefore \angle 1 = \angle 2 = 25°$.

4.09 $\angle 1 = 35°, \therefore \angle 2 = 35°$

The diagonals of a rhombus are perpendicular.

$\therefore \angle 3 = 90°$.

$\angle 4 = 180° - (\angle 2 + \angle 3)$

$= 180° - (35° + 90°)$

$= 180° - 125°$

$\angle 4 = 55°$

4.010 $\angle 5 = \angle 1 = 20°$

4.011 All sides of a rhombus are equal.

$\therefore P = 4(5) = 20$

4.012 *UT*

4.013 *UX*

4.014 $\triangle TUR$

4.015 $\triangle UXR$

4.016 $\angle RTU$

4.017 $\angle R$

4.018 *QS*

4.019 $\triangle SRM$

4.020 >

4.021 <

4.022 =

4.023 HL

4.024 SAS

4.025 CPCTE

LIFEPAC TEST

1. HL
2. none
3. ASA
4. AAS
5. HA or AAS
6. SAS or LL
7. AAS
8. ASA
9. LA or AAS
10. SSS
11. Exterior sides in opposite rays
12. Given
13. Supplementary to equal ∠'s
14. Given
15. Reflexive
16. ASA
17. CPCTE
18. $\overline{DC}$
19. $\angle CBD = 180° - (\angle DCB + \angle CDB)$

    $= 180° - (37\frac{1}{2} + 37\frac{1}{2})°$

    $= 180° - 75°$

    $= 105°$

20. $\angle ADB = 180° - (\angle A + \angle ABD)$

    $= 180° - (60 + 60)°$

    $= 180° - 120°$

    $= 60°$

21. always
22. always
23. always
24. sometimes

ALTERNATE LIFEPAC TEST

1. SSS
2. none
3. HL
4. SAS
5. ASA
6. AAS
7. none
8. AAS
9. none
10. SAS
11. Given
12. If lines | |, alternate interior ∠'s are =.
13. Vertical ∠'s are =.
14. AAS
15. CPCTE
16. always
17. sometimes
18. always
19. never
20. always
21. >
22. >
23. >
24. <
25. $2" < x < 8"$

MATH 1004

ALTERNATE LIFEPAC TEST

NAME ______________________________

DATE ______________________________

SCORE ______________________________

56
70

Write *SSS, SAS, ASA, AAS, HL, LA, LL,* **or** *HA* **to indicate the method you would use to prove the two triangles congruent. If no method applies, write** *none* (each answer, 3 points).

1. __________

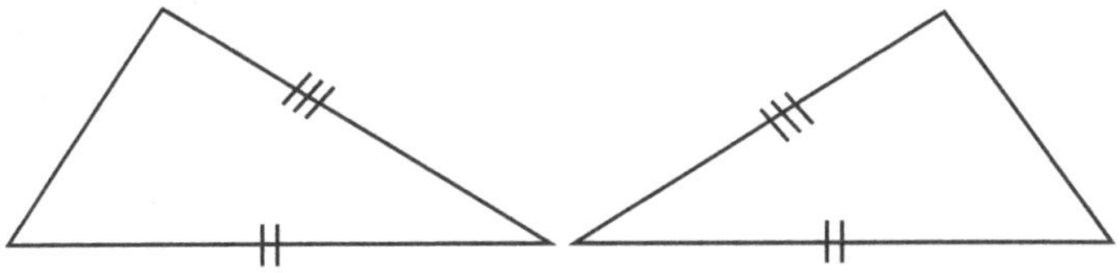

2. __________

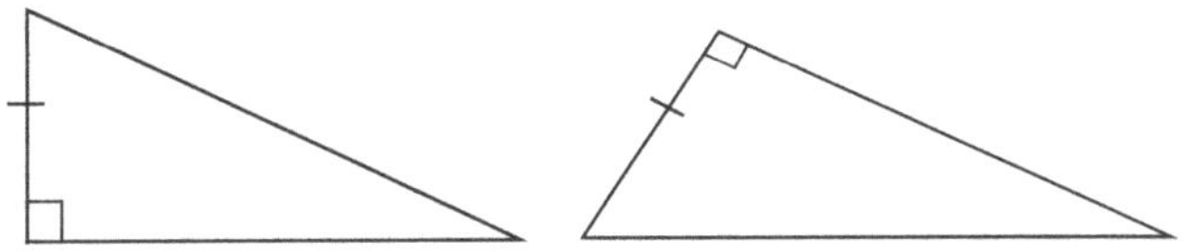

3. __________

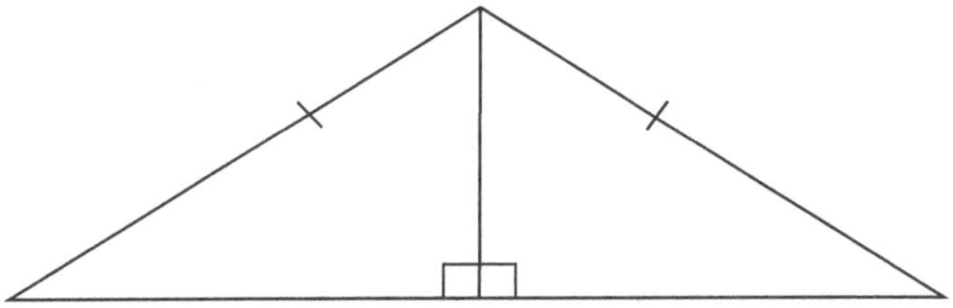

4. __________

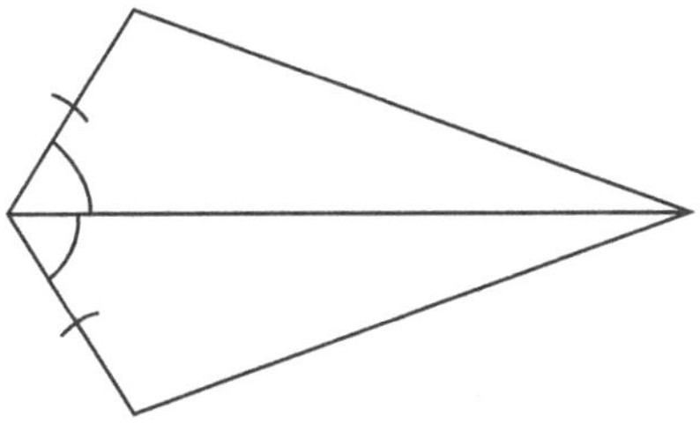

5. ____________

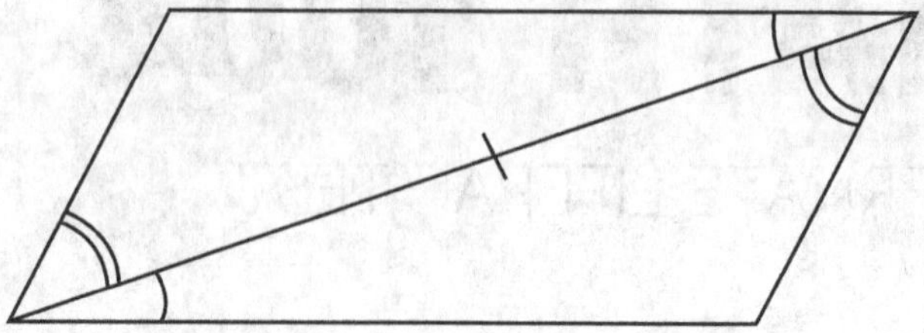

6. ____________

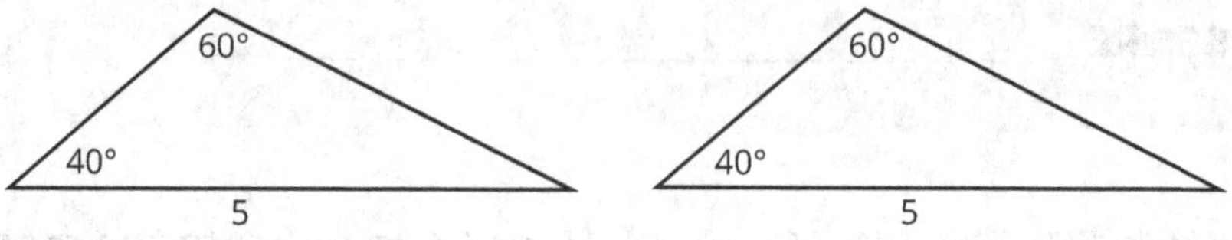

7. ____________

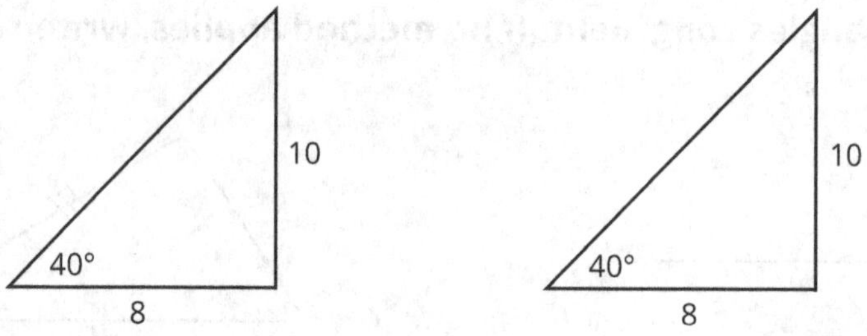

8. ____________

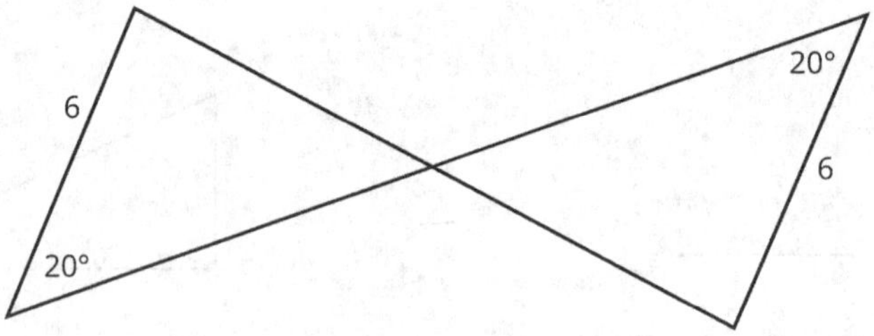

9. ____________

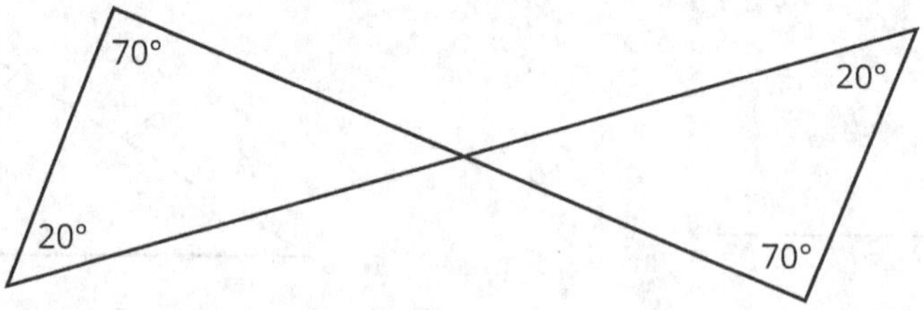

10. ____________

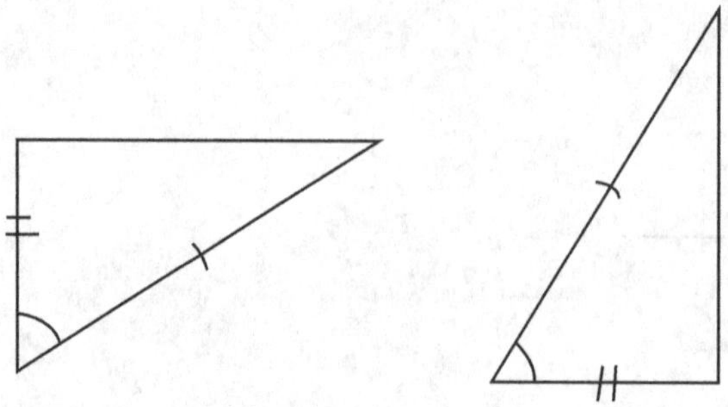

Write the reasons for this proof (each answer, 4 points).

Given: $\overline{AB} \parallel \overline{DE}$
$BC = CE$

To Prove: $AC = CD$

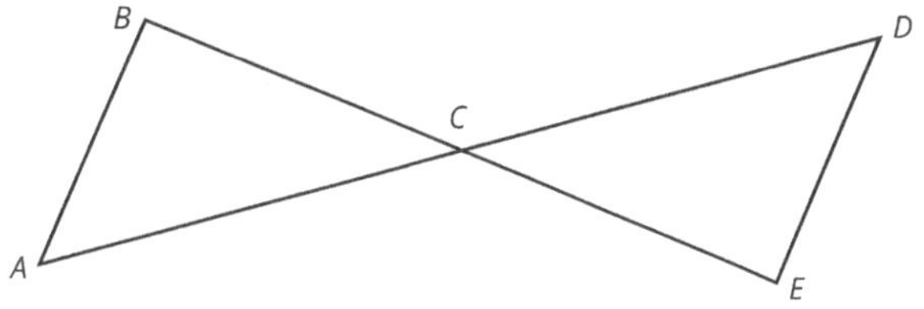

STATEMENT	REASON
11. $\overline{AB} \parallel \overline{DE}$, $BC = CE$	**11.** ______________________
12. $\angle A = \angle D$	**12.** ______________________
13. $\angle ACB = \angle DCE$	**13.** ______________________
14. $\triangle ABC \cong \triangle DEC$	**14.** ______________________
15. $AC = CD$	**15.** ______________________

Write *always, sometimes,* **or** *never* (each answer, 2 points).

16. If the diagonals are perpendicular and equal, then the quadrilateral is ______________ a rhombus.

17. If the opposite sides of a quadrilateral are equal, then the figure is ______________ a square.

18. If the opposite sides of a quadrilateral are parallel, then the figure is ______________ a parallelogram.

19. A trapezoid ______________ has both pairs of sides parallel.

20. If two sides of one triangle are equal to two sides of another and the included angles are equal, then the triangles are ______________ congruent.

Complete the following problems with <, >, or = (each answer, 4 points).

21. $AB < BC$

A ____ C

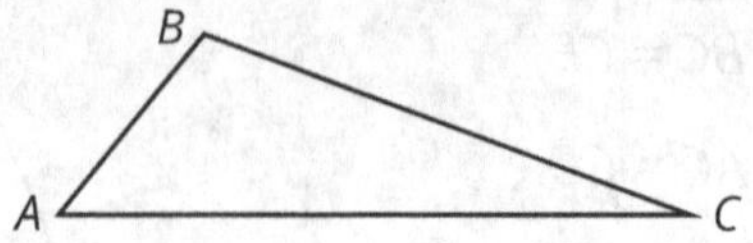

22. $\angle B > \angle C$

AC ____ AB

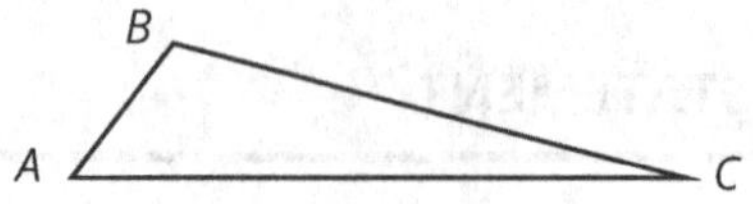

23. If $AB = DE$, $AC = DF$, and $\angle A > \angle D$,

then BC ____ EF.

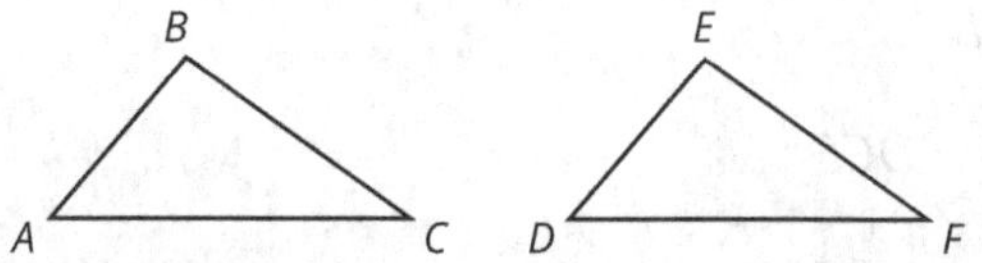

24. If $TR = YX$, $RS = XW$ and $TS > YW$,

then $\angle X$ ____ $\angle R$.

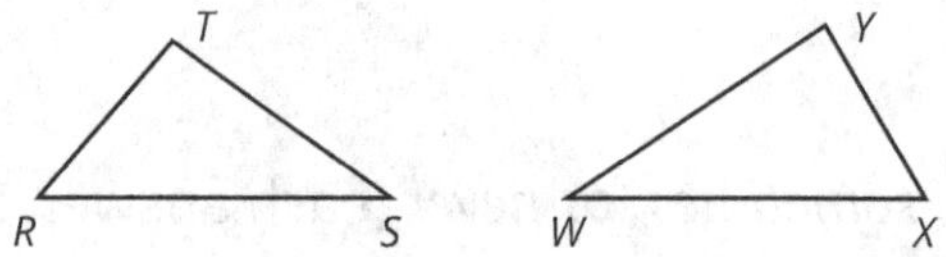

Answer the following question (4 points).

25. If two sides of a triangle have measures of 3" and 5", what range of size can the third side have? ________________________________

MATH 1005

Unit 5: Similar Polygons

TEACHER NOTES

MATERIALS NEEDED FOR LIFEPAC	
Required	Suggested
• straightedge, ruler, and protractor • trigonometric table for angles between 0° and 90° giving sine, cosine, and tangent ratios	(None)

ADDITIONAL LEARNING ACTIVITIES

Section 1: Principles of Algebra

1. The size of a motion picture on a screen is the square of the distance from the projector to the screen. Have the class determine the size of a picture at 4 ft.; 7 ft. The answer will be in square feet.

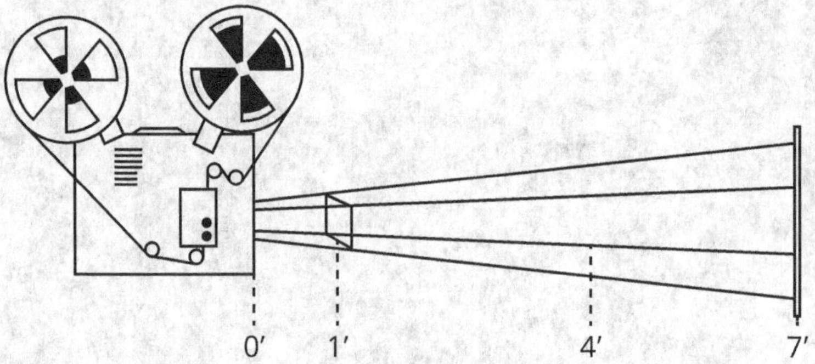

2. Two players may play the following proportion game. The first player names a proportion, but with one term missing. The second player must solve the proportion. If his answer is correct, he receives one point. Pencils and paper may be used. If a student is not sure of the correct answer of a problem, he should write out the problem and ask the teacher after the game. No points should be given for that round. A game consists of 35 points.

Example: First player: $\frac{8}{x} = \frac{3}{24}$

Second player: $24x = 24$, so $x = 1$

3. Locate a photograph of several people you know. The photograph should be a full-length shot of its subjects and should have relatively few people in it. Locate two or more persons in the photograph who are standing at the same distance from the camera. Find out and record the height of each of these persons. Then, from the photograph, measure the heights of these persons. Write the ratio of the scaled-down height of each person in the photograph to their respective actual height. Write the ratios as a proportion and check to see that they are equal.

   If one subject is farther away in the photograph than another subject, how does this distance affect the proportion? If you took a picture of two people of any height but at different distances from the camera and noted the distance from the camera to each person, would the ratios of each person's height in the photograph to their respective actual height make a true proportion (would the ratios be equal)?

Section 2: Similarity

1. Discuss these questions with your class.
   a. If 1 side of a pentagon (five-sided polygon) equals 1 side of another pentagon, are the pentagons similar?
   b. If 2 sides of a pentagon equal 2 sides of another pentagon, are the pentagons similar?
   c. If 3 sides of a pentagon equal 3 sides of another pentagon, are the pentagons similar?
   d. If 4 sides of a pentagon equal 4 sides of another pentagon, are the pentagons similar?
   e. If 5 sides of a pentagon equal 5 sides of another pentagon, are the pentagons similar?
2. Conduct a geometric mean bee (similar to a spelling bee) in which two numbers are said to each student in turn and the student finds the geometric mean between the two numbers. Or, the mean and one number may be given, and the student finds the missing number. Pencils and paper or a chalkboard may be used.
3. Observe your classroom, school, church, home, or other building for similar polygons. Tell how you know the polygons are similar based on definitions, postulates, and theorems.
4. Research the history and development of the Pythagorean Theorem.

Section 3: Right Triangles

1. Have the class draw the following figure to demonstrate proof of the Pythagorean Theorem.

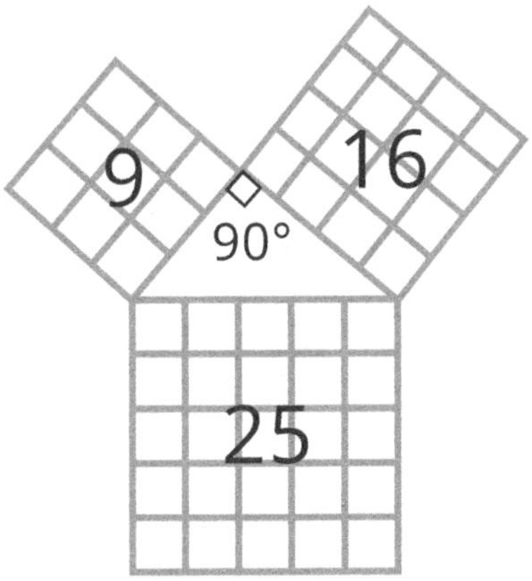

2. Two students may work together on this activity. Let the students go outside and locate or place a small marker on the ground at a distance of no more than 15 or 20 feet from the school building. Measure this distance. Draw a diagram and write each of the measurements on it (the diagram will probably be similar to the one in Problem 3.85 in the LIFEPAC). Then one student stands at a distance of no more than 10 or 15 feet past the marker (away from the school building). The other student measures this distance and writes it on the diagram. The first student measures the height of the student standing past the marker and writes it on the diagram. Then the students use similar triangles to compute the height of the school building.
3. This activity is an outside activity to be done at the student's home. Place a marker on the ground at a distance of no more than 15 or 20 feet from the house. Measure this distance. Draw a diagram and write each of the measurements on it (you may use the diagram in Problem 3.85 in the LIFEPAC as an example). Measure a distance of no more than 10 feet past the marker (away from the house). Write this distance and your height on the diagram. Then use similar triangles to compute the height of your house.
4. Measure the length of the shadow of a tree, school building, or any other object. Then measure the length of your shadow (you may need someone to measure for you). Use these measures and your height to find the height of the object.

Administer the LIFEPAC Test.

The test is to be administered in one session. Give no help except with directions.
Evaluate the tests and review areas where the students have done poorly.
Review the pages and activities that stress the concepts tested.
If necessary, administer the Alternate LIFEPAC Test

ANSWER KEYS

SECTION 1

1.1 $\frac{1}{2}$

1.2 $\frac{2}{3}$

1.3 $\frac{18}{29}$

1.4 $\frac{1}{2}$

1.5 $\frac{3}{4}$

1.6 $\frac{5}{9}$

1.7 $\frac{1}{2}$

1.8 3:5:7

1.9 $\frac{3}{5}$

1.10 $\frac{5}{3}$

1.11 $\frac{3}{3+5} = \frac{3}{8}$

1.12 $\frac{5}{3+5} = \frac{5}{8}$

1.13 $\frac{4}{5}$

1.14 $\frac{5}{4}$

1.15 $\frac{5}{4+5} = \frac{5}{9}$

1.16 $\frac{5-4}{5+4} = \frac{1}{9}$

1.17 $\frac{12}{6} = \frac{2}{1}$

1.18 $\frac{12}{12+6} = \frac{12}{18} = \frac{2}{3}$

1.19 $\frac{6}{12+6} = \frac{6}{18} = \frac{1}{3}$

1.20 $\frac{14}{14+7} = \frac{14}{21} = \frac{2}{3}$

1.21 $\frac{14+7}{14} = \frac{21}{14} = \frac{3}{2}$

1.22 $\frac{7}{14+7} = \frac{7}{21} = \frac{1}{3}$

1.23 $\frac{6}{10} = \frac{3}{5}$

1.24 $\frac{6}{6+10} = \frac{6}{16} = \frac{3}{8}$

1.25 $\frac{10}{6+10} = \frac{10}{16} = \frac{5}{8}$

1.26 $\frac{15}{9} = \frac{5}{3}$

1.27 $\frac{15}{9+15} = \frac{15}{24} = \frac{5}{8}$

1.28 $\frac{9+15}{6+10} = \frac{24}{16} = \frac{3}{2}$

1.29 Let x = first ∠
$2x$ = second ∠
$3x$ = third ∠

$x + 2x + 3x = 180$
$6x = 180$
$x = 30°$
$2x = 60°$
$3x = 90°$

1.30 60 feet = 720 inches
10 yards = 360 inches
$AB{:}BC{:}CD$ = 720:360:20 = 36:18:1

1.31 means: 4, 15
extremes: 3, 20

1.32 means: 7, 20
extremes: 5, 28

1.33 means: 11, x
extremes: 6, y

1.34 means: 9, 2
extremes: 3, 6

1.35 means: 2, 4
extremes: 1, 8

1.36 means: y, 3
extremes: x, 7

1.37 $\frac{x}{25} = \frac{2}{5}$
$5x = 50$
$x = 10$

1.38 $\frac{x}{6} = \frac{3}{2}$
$2x = 18$
$x = 9$

1.39 $\frac{9}{x} = \frac{3}{12}$
$3x = 108$
$x = 36$

1.40 $\frac{10}{7} = \frac{x}{5}$
$7x = 50$
$x = \frac{50}{7}$

1.41 $\frac{9}{x} = \frac{x}{4}$

$x^2 = 36$

$x = 6$ (only use positive values in ratios)

1.42 $\frac{\frac{1}{2}}{x} = \frac{\frac{2}{3}}{\frac{3}{4}}$

$\frac{2}{3}x = \frac{3}{8}$

$2x = \frac{9}{8}$

$x = \frac{9}{16}$

1.43 $\frac{x+3}{6} = \frac{5}{4}$

$4x + 12 = 30$

$4x = 18$

$x = \frac{18}{4} = \frac{9}{2}$

1.44 $\frac{x+1}{x+2} = \frac{2}{3}$

$2x + 4 = 3x + 3$

$2x + 1 = 3x$

$1 = x$

$x = 1$

1.45 $\frac{3}{2} = \frac{x}{4}$

$2x = 12$

$x = 6$

1.46 $2x = 3y$

$\frac{2x}{y} = 3$

$\frac{x}{y} = \frac{3}{2}$

1.47 $5x = 7y$

$\frac{5x}{y} = 7$

$\frac{x}{y} = \frac{7}{5}$

1.48 $\frac{x}{3} = \frac{y}{2}$

$2x = 3y$

$\frac{2x}{y} = 3$

$\frac{x}{y} = \frac{3}{2}$

1.49 $2x - 3y = 0$

$2x = 3y$

$\frac{2x}{y} = 3$

$\frac{x}{y} = \frac{3}{2}$

1.50 $x - 5y = 0$

$x = 5y$

$\frac{x}{y} = \frac{5}{1}$

1.51 Let x = first ∠

$5x$ = second ∠

$x + 5x = 90°$

$6x = 90°$

$x = 15°$

$5x = 75°$

1.52 Let $3x$ = first ∠

$7x$ = second ∠

$3x + 7x = 180$

$10x = 180$

$x = 18°$

$3x = 54°$

$7x = 126°$

1.53 Let $3x$ = first part

$5x$ = second part

$3x + 5x = 30$ in.

$8x = 30$ in.

$x = \frac{30}{8} = \frac{15}{4}$

$3x = 3(\frac{15}{4}) = \frac{45}{4} = 11\frac{1}{4}$ in.

$5x = 5(\frac{15}{4}) = \frac{75}{4} = 18\frac{3}{4}$ in.

1.54 Let $3x$ = first side

$4x$ = second side

$5x$ = third side

$3x + 4x + 5x = 48$ in.

$12x = 48$ in.

$x = 4$

$3x = 12$ in.

$4x = 16$ in.

$5x = 20$ in.

1.55 Let $2x$ = second side

$3x$ = third side

$8 + 2x + 3x = 18$ in.

$8 + 5x = 18$ in.

$5x = 10$ in.

$x = 2$

$2x = 4$ in.

$3x = 6$ in.

1.56 Denominator Sum
1.57 Cross Product
1.58 Numerator-Denominator Sum
1.59 Equivalent Forms
1.60 Denominator Difference
1.61 Cross Product

1.62 $\frac{x}{a} = \frac{b}{y}$ or $\frac{x}{b} = \frac{a}{y}$

1.63 $\frac{a}{x} = \frac{y}{b}$ or $\frac{b}{x} = \frac{y}{a}$

1.64 $\frac{x}{a} = \frac{b}{y}$ or $\frac{y}{a} = \frac{b}{x}$

1.65 $\frac{b}{x} = \frac{y}{a}$ or $\frac{b}{y} = \frac{x}{a}$

1.66 $\frac{y}{a} = \frac{b}{x}$ or $\frac{x}{a} = \frac{b}{y}$ or $\frac{x}{b} = \frac{a}{y}$ or $\frac{y}{b} = \frac{a}{x}$

1.67 $\frac{2}{x} = \frac{5}{y} = \frac{3}{5}$

$\frac{2}{x} = \frac{3}{5}$

$3x = 10$

$x = \frac{10}{3}$

$\frac{5}{y} = \frac{3}{5}$

$3y = 25$

$y = \frac{25}{3}$

1.68 $\frac{2}{x} = \frac{y}{4} = \frac{1}{4}$

$\frac{2}{x} = \frac{1}{4}$

$x = 8$

$\frac{y}{4} = \frac{1}{4}$

$4y = 4$

$y = 1$

1.69 $\frac{2}{3} = \frac{x}{6} = \frac{9}{y}$

$\frac{2}{3} = \frac{x}{6}$

$3x = 12$

$x = 4$

$\frac{2}{3} = \frac{9}{y}$

$2y = 27$

$y = \frac{27}{2}$

1.70 $\frac{2}{3} = \frac{4}{x}$

$2x = 12$

$x = 6$

1.71 $\frac{6}{2} = \frac{8}{x}$

$6x = 16$

$x = \frac{16}{6} = \frac{8}{3}$

1.72 $\frac{\frac{1}{2}}{\frac{2}{3}} = \frac{\frac{3}{4}}{x}$

$\frac{1}{2}x = \frac{1}{2}$

$x = 1$

1.73 $\frac{a + 1}{4} = \frac{2}{3}$

$3a + 3 = 8$

$3a = 5$

$a = \frac{5}{3}$

1.74 $\frac{a - 2}{3} = \frac{a}{4}$

$4a - 8 = 3a$

$a - 8 = 0$

$a = 8$

1.75 $\frac{a}{4} = \frac{9}{a}$

$a^2 = 36$

$a = 6$ (only use the positive value)

1.76 $\frac{XC}{AC}$

1.77 $\frac{AB + AC}{AC}$

1.78 $\frac{AB}{BX}$

1.79 $\frac{XC}{BX}$

1.80 $\frac{AX}{XB} = \frac{AY}{YC}$

$\frac{3}{4} = \frac{6}{YC}$

$3YC = 24$

$YC = 8$

1.81 $\frac{AX}{XB} = \frac{AY}{YC}$

$\frac{5}{4} = \frac{AY}{6}$

$4AY = 30$

$AY = \frac{30}{4} = \frac{15}{2}$

1.82 $\frac{AX}{XB} = \frac{AY}{YC}$

$\frac{AX}{4} = \frac{4}{8}$

$8AX = 16$

$AX = 2$

1.83 $\frac{AX}{XB} = \frac{AY}{YC}$

$\frac{7}{XB} = \frac{14}{4}$

$14XB = 28$

$XB = 2$

1.84 $\frac{4}{3}$

1.85 $\frac{5+7}{7} = \frac{12}{7}$

1.86 $\frac{5+7}{5} = \frac{12}{5}$

1.87 $\frac{3+4}{3} = \frac{7}{3}$

1.88 $\frac{2(3)}{3(4)} = \frac{6}{12} = \frac{1}{2}$

1.89 $\frac{4}{3}$

SELF TEST 1

1.01 division

1.02 $\frac{3}{4}$

1.03 3:4

1.04 same

1.05 are not

1.06 ratios

1.07 Cross Product

1.08 Numerator-Denominator Sum

1.09 p

1.010 Either order:

a. 6

b. 10

1.011 $\frac{6}{3} = \frac{2}{1}$

1.012 7 yards = 21 feet

$\frac{21}{6} = \frac{7}{2}$

1.013 $\frac{12}{100} = \frac{3}{25}$

1.014 $\frac{3}{9} = \frac{1}{3}$

1.015 $\frac{9}{3+9} = \frac{9}{12} = \frac{3}{4}$

1.016 $\frac{x}{7} = \frac{3}{5}$

$5x = 21$

$x = \frac{21}{5}$

1.017 $\frac{3}{8} = \frac{x}{32}$

$8x = 96$

$x = 12$

1.018 $\frac{5}{2x} = \frac{25}{4}$

$50x = 20$

$x = \frac{20}{50} = \frac{2}{5}$

1.019 $\frac{x}{3} = \frac{x+2}{5}$

$5x = 3x + 6$

$2x = 6$

$x = 3$

1.020 $\frac{16}{x} = \frac{x}{4}$

$x^2 = 64$

$x = 8$

1.021 $\frac{x+2}{2} = \frac{6+2}{2}$

$\frac{x+2}{2} = \frac{8}{2}$

$2x + 4 = 16$

$2x = 12$

$x = 6$

1.022 $\frac{TU}{TR} = \frac{UW}{RS}$

$\frac{3}{9} = \frac{UW}{15}$

$9UW = 45$

$UW = 5$

1.023 $\frac{TU}{TR} = \frac{WT}{ST}$

$\frac{3}{9} = \frac{4}{ST}$

$3ST = 36$

$ST = 12$

1.024 $WS = ST - WT$

$WS = 12 - 4$

$WS = 8$

1.025 $UR = TR - TU$

$UR = 9 - 3$

$UR = 6$

SECTION 2

2.1

1. **STATEMENT**
   $\triangle ABC \sim \triangle RST$
   $\triangle DEF \sim \triangle RST$
   REASON
   Given
2. **STATEMENT**
   $\angle A = \angle R$, $\angle D = \angle R$
   $\angle C = \angle T$, $\angle F = \angle T$
   REASON
   Definition of $\sim \triangle$'s
3. **STATEMENT**
   $\angle A = \angle D$, $\angle C = \angle F$
   REASON
   Transitive
4. **STATEMENT**
   $\triangle ABC \sim \triangle DEF$
   REASON
   AA

2.2 $\triangle BAC$

2.3 a. $\frac{BC}{DE}$

b. $\frac{AC}{AE}$

2.4 $\angle DEA$
2.5 $\angle B$
2.6 *c* and *h*; *a* and *d*; *e* and *f*
2.7 yes
2.8 no
2.9 no
2.10 yes
2.11 no

2.12

1. **STATEMENT**
   $k \parallel l$
   REASON
   Given
2. **STATEMENT**
   $\angle ADF = \angle EDB$
   REASON
   Vertical $\angle$'s =
3. **STATEMENT**
   $\angle FBE = \angle AFB$
   REASON
   If lines | |, alternate interior $\angle$'s =
4. **STATEMENT**
   $\triangle ADF \sim \triangle EDC$
   REASON
   AA theorem

2.13
1. **STATEMENT**
$k \parallel l$
REASON
Given
2. **STATEMENT**
$\angle C = \angle C$
REASON
Reflexive
3. **STATEMENT**
$\angle AFC = \angle BDC$
REASON
If lines ||, corresponding ∠'s are =
4. **STATEMENT**
$\triangle BCD \sim \triangle ACF$
REASON
AA theorem

2.14
1. **STATEMENT**
$\overline{DC} \perp \overline{CT}$
$\overline{PB} \perp \overline{CT}$
REASON
Given
2. **STATEMENT**
$\overline{DC} \parallel \overline{PB}$
REASON
Two lines ⊥ to same line are ||
3. **STATEMENT**
$\angle 1 = \angle 2$
REASON
If lines ||, alternate interior ∠'s are =.
4. **STATEMENT**
$\angle R = \angle R$
REASON
Reflexive
5. **STATEMENT**
$\angle 2 = \angle DVR$
REASON
Vertical ∠'s are =
6. **STATEMENT**
$\angle 1 = \angle DVR$
REASON
Substitution
7. **STATEMENT**
$\triangle SPR \sim \triangle VDR$
REASON
AA theorem

2.15 yes; SAS
2.16 no
2.17 no
2.18 yes; SSS
2.19 yes; SSS
2.20 no

2.21
1. **STATEMENT**
$\frac{BC}{CD} = \frac{AC}{CE}$
REASON
Given
2. **STATEMENT**
$\angle BCA = \angle ECD$
REASON
Vertical ∠'s are =
3. **STATEMENT**
$\triangle ACB \sim \triangle ECD$
REASON
SAS

2.22
1. **STATEMENT**
$\angle A = \angle D$
REASON
Given
2. **STATEMENT**
$\angle BCA = \angle ECD$
REASON
Vertical ∠'s are =
3. **STATEMENT**
$\triangle ACB \sim \triangle DCE$
REASON
AA theorem

2.23
1. **STATEMENT**
$GF = \frac{1}{2}GC$, $GE = \frac{1}{2}GD$
$EF = \frac{1}{2}DC$
REASON
Given
2. **STATEMENT**
$\frac{GF}{GC} = \frac{GE}{GD} = \frac{EF}{DC} = \frac{1}{2}$
REASON
Multiplication property of equality;
Substitution
3. **STATEMENT**
$\triangle GFE \sim \triangle GCD$
REASON
SSS

2.24
1. **STATEMENT**
$\overline{YZ} \parallel \overline{UV}$
REASON
Given

2. **STATEMENT**
   $\angle YXZ = \angle VXU$
   REASON
   Vertical $\angle$'s are =
3. **STATEMENT**
   $\angle YZV = \angle UVZ$
   REASON
   If lines | |, alternate interior $\angle$'s are =.
4. **STATEMENT**
   $\triangle XYZ \sim \triangle XUV$
   REASON
   AA theorem
5. **STATEMENT**
   $\frac{XY}{XU} = \frac{YZ}{VU}$
   REASON
   Definition of similar polygons

2.25

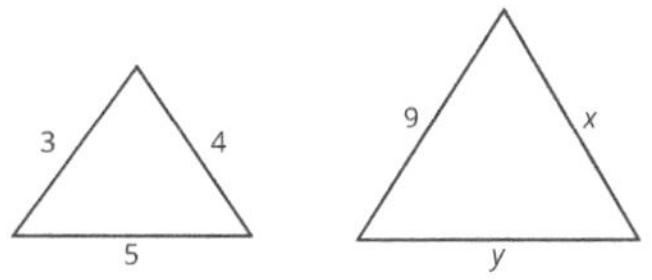

$\frac{y}{5} = \frac{x}{4} = \frac{9}{3}$

$\frac{x}{4} = \frac{9}{3}$

$3x = 36$

$x = 12$

$\frac{y}{5} = \frac{9}{3}$

$3y = 45$

$y = 15$

2.26

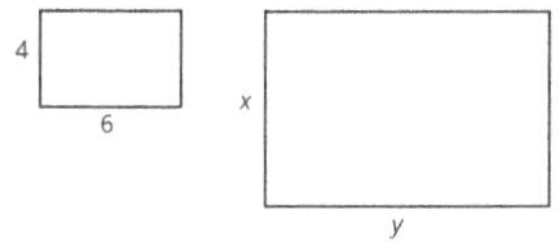

$\frac{P_1}{P_2} = \frac{2}{3} = \frac{s_1}{s_2}$

$\frac{2}{3} = \frac{4}{x}$

$2x = 12$

$x = 6$

$\frac{2}{3} = \frac{6}{y}$

$2y = 18$

$y = 9$

2.27 $P_1 = 20$

$P_2 = 28$

$\frac{P_1}{P_2} = \frac{s_1}{s_2}$

$\frac{20}{28} = \frac{4}{s_2}$

$20s_2 = 112$

$s_2 = \frac{112}{20} = \frac{28}{5} = 5\frac{3}{5}$

2.28 $\frac{P_1}{P_2} = \frac{s_1}{s_2}$

$\frac{30}{P_2} = \frac{12}{15}$

$12P_2 = 450$

$P_2 = 37\frac{1}{2}$

2.29 yes; symmetric property of similar polygons

2.30 a. $\frac{P_1}{P_2} = \frac{s_1}{s_2}$

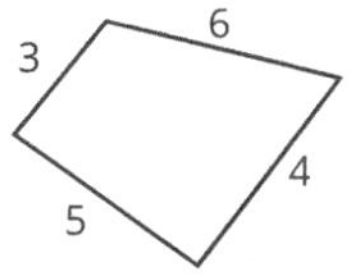

$\frac{P_1}{P_2} = \frac{3}{9}$

$\frac{P_1}{P_2} = \frac{1}{3}$

b. $\frac{5}{x} = \frac{1}{3}$

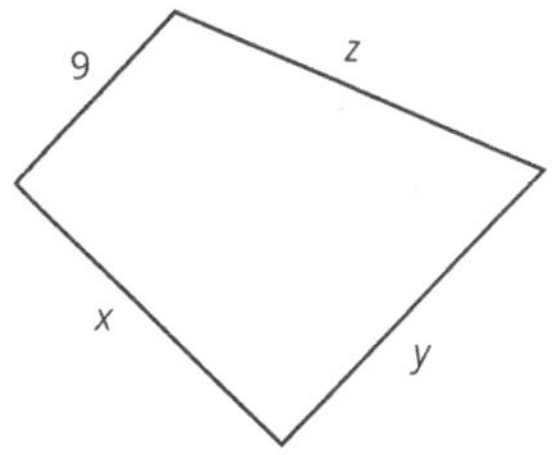

$x = 15$

$\frac{4}{y} = \frac{1}{3}$

$y = 12$

$\frac{6}{z} = \frac{1}{3}$

$z = 18$

2.31 $P_1 = 3 + 5 + 6 + 8 + 10 = 32$

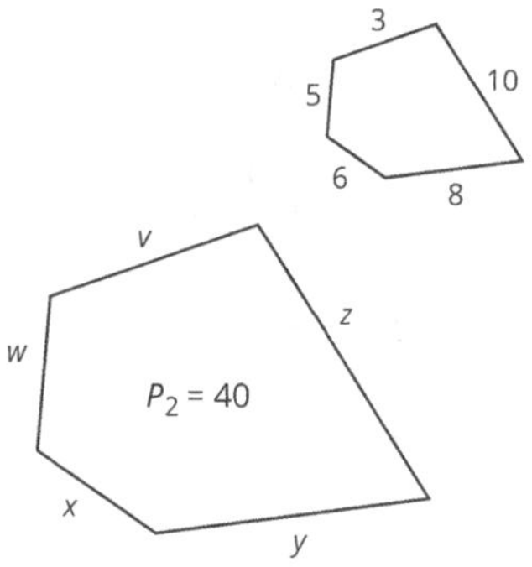

$\frac{P_1}{P_2} = \frac{32}{40} = \frac{4}{5}$

$\frac{4}{5} = \frac{3}{v}$

$4v = 15$

$v = \frac{15}{4}$

$\frac{4}{5} = \frac{5}{w}$

$4w = 25$

$w = \frac{25}{4}$

$\frac{4}{5} = \frac{6}{x}$

$4x = 30$

$x = \frac{30}{4} = \frac{15}{2}$

$\frac{4}{5} = \frac{8}{y}$

$4y = 40$

$y = 10$

$\frac{4}{5} = \frac{10}{z}$

$4z = 50$

$z = \frac{50}{4} = \frac{25}{2}$

2.32

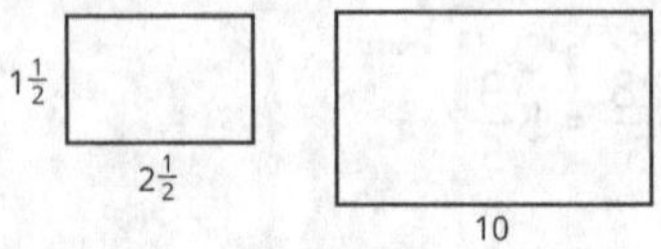

$$\frac{P_1}{P_2} = \frac{2\frac{1}{2}}{10}$$

$$\frac{8}{P_2} = \frac{2\frac{1}{2}}{10}$$

$$\frac{5}{2}P_2 = 80$$

$$P_2 = \frac{2}{5}(80)$$

$$P_2 = 32$$

2.33 $\frac{BC}{BX} = \frac{CD}{XY}$

$$\frac{10}{6} = \frac{CD}{4}$$

$$6CD = 40$$

$$CD = \frac{40}{6} = \frac{20}{3}$$

2.34 $\frac{ZY}{XY} = \frac{BC}{DC}$

$$BC = BX + XC$$

$$BC = ZY + XC$$

$$BC = 5 + 3$$

$$BC = 8$$

$$\frac{5}{XY} = \frac{8}{4}$$

$$8XY = 20$$

$$XY = \frac{20}{4} = \frac{5}{2}$$

2.35 $\frac{BX}{BZ} = \frac{BC}{DC}$

$$\frac{8}{3} = \frac{BC}{5}$$

$$3BC = 40$$

$$BC = \frac{40}{3}$$

$$XC = BC - BX$$

$$XC = \frac{40}{3} - 8$$

$$XC = \frac{40}{3} - \frac{24}{3}$$

$$XC = \frac{16}{3}$$

2.36 $\frac{BC}{BX} = \frac{BA}{BZ}$

$$\frac{12}{BX} = \frac{8}{3}$$

$$8BX = 36$$

$$BX = \frac{36}{8} = \frac{9}{2}$$

2.37 $\frac{BC}{YC} = \frac{AC}{XC}$

$$BC = BY + YC$$

$$BC = 4 + 7$$

$$BC = 11$$

$$\frac{11}{7} = \frac{AC}{10}$$

$$7AC = 110$$

$$AC = \frac{110}{7}$$

2.38 $\frac{BY}{YC} = \frac{AX}{XC}$

$$\frac{6}{10} = \frac{18}{XC}$$

$$6XC = 180$$

$$XC = 30$$

2.39 $\frac{BC}{YC} = \frac{AC}{XC}$

$$YC = BC - BY$$

$$YC = 20 - 5$$

$$YC = 15$$

$$\frac{20}{15} = \frac{18}{XC}$$

$$20XC = 270$$

$$XC = \frac{27}{2}$$

2.40 $\frac{BC}{AB} = \frac{YC}{XY}$

$$\frac{6}{AB} = \frac{4}{5}$$

$$4AB = 30$$

$$AB = \frac{30}{4} = \frac{15}{2}$$

2.41

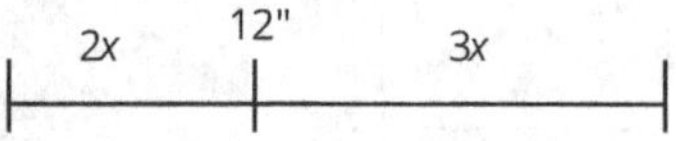

$$2x + 3x = 12$$

$$5x = 12$$

$$x = \frac{12}{5}$$

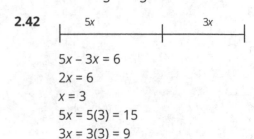

$$2x = 2(\frac{12}{5}) = \frac{24}{5}$$

$$3x = 3(\frac{12}{5}) = \frac{36}{5}$$

2.42

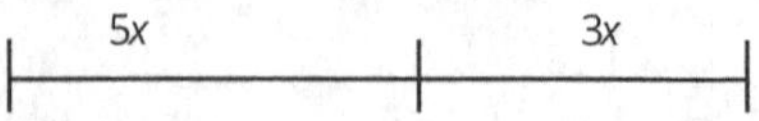

$$5x - 3x = 6$$

$$2x = 6$$

$$x = 3$$

$$5x = 5(3) = 15$$

$$3x = 3(3) = 9$$

2.43 $\frac{CR}{RA} = \frac{CS}{SB}$

$\frac{3}{5} = \frac{4}{SB}$

$3SB = 20$

$SB = \frac{20}{3}$

2.44 $\frac{CR}{RA} = \frac{CS}{SB}$

$\frac{2}{3} = \frac{CS}{10 - CS}$

$3CS = 20 - 2CS$

$5CS = 20$

$CS = 4$

2.45 $\frac{CR}{CA} = \frac{RS}{AB}$

$\frac{4}{10} = \frac{10}{AB}$

$4AB = 100$

$AB = 25$

2.46 $\frac{CR}{RA} = \frac{CS}{SB}$

$\frac{CR}{4} = \frac{9}{CR}$

$(CR)^2 = 36$

$CR = 6$

2.47 a. $\frac{AD}{DB} = \frac{AC}{BC}$

$\frac{AD}{7 - AD} = \frac{3}{5}$

$21 - 3AD = 5AD$

$21 = 8AD$

$\frac{21}{8} = AD$

$2\frac{5}{8} = AD$

b. $DB = AB - AD$

$DB = 7 - 2\frac{5}{8}$

$DB = 4\frac{3}{8}$

2.48 a. $\frac{AD}{DB} = \frac{AC}{BC}$

$\frac{AD}{10 - AD} = \frac{6}{6}$

$6AD = 60 - 6AD$

$12AD = 60$

$AD = 5$

b. $DB = AB - AD$

$DB = 10 - 5$

$DB = 5$

2.49 a. $\frac{AD}{DB} = \frac{AC}{BC}$

$\frac{AD}{10 - AD} = \frac{4}{8}$

$8AD = 40 - 4AD$

$12AD = 40$

$AD = \frac{40}{12} = \frac{10}{3} = 3\frac{1}{3}$

b. $DB = AB - AD$

$DB = 10 - 3\frac{1}{3}$

$DB = 6\frac{2}{3}$

2.50 a. $\frac{AD}{DB} = \frac{AC}{BC}$

$\frac{AD}{12 - AD} = \frac{3}{5}$

$5AD = 36 - 3AD$

$8AD = 36$

$AD = \frac{36}{8} = \frac{9}{2} = 4\frac{1}{2}$

b. $DB = AB - AD$

$DB = 12 - 4\frac{1}{2}$

$DB = 7\frac{1}{2}$

2.51 $\frac{6}{8} = \frac{9}{x}$

$6x = 72$

$x = 12$

$\frac{6}{14} = \frac{y}{21}$

$14y = 126$

$y = 9$

2.52 $\frac{12}{x} = \frac{10}{15}$

$10x = 180$

$x = 18$

$\frac{10}{25} = \frac{y}{20}$

$25y = 200$

$y = 8$

2.53 $\frac{x}{10} = \frac{30}{15}$

$15x = 300$

$x = 20$

$\frac{y}{12} = \frac{45}{15}$

$15y = 540$

$y = 36$

2.54 $\frac{x}{9} = \frac{4}{12}$

$12x = 36$

$x = 3$

$\frac{y}{12} = \frac{4}{16}$

$16y = 48$

$y = 3$

2.55 $\frac{x}{16} = \frac{6}{12}$

$12x = 96$

$x = 8$

$\frac{15}{y} = \frac{18}{12}$

$18y = 180$

$y = 10$

2.56 $\frac{x}{27} = \frac{16}{36}$

$36x = 432$

$x = 12$

$\frac{x}{y} = \frac{16}{20}$

$\frac{12}{y} = \frac{16}{20}$

$16y = 240$

$y = 15$

2.57 $\frac{x}{12} = \frac{x+6}{16}$

$16x = 12x + 72$

$4x = 72$

$x = 18$

2.58 $\frac{x}{x+7} = \frac{16}{22}$

$22x = 16x + 112$

$6x = 112$

$x = \frac{112}{6} = \frac{56}{3} = 18\frac{2}{3}$

2.59

1. **STATEMENT**
   $\overline{XA} \perp \overleftrightarrow{RS}$, $\angle 1 = \angle 2$
   REASON
   Given
2. **STATEMENT**
   $\angle 1$, $\angle 3$ are complementary
   $\angle 2$, $\angle 4$ are complementary
   REASON
   Adjacent ∠'s with exterior sides in ⊥'s are complementary
3. **STATEMENT**
   $\angle 3 = \angle 4$
   REASON
   Two ∠'s complementary to equal angles are equal
4. **STATEMENT**
   $\frac{BX}{XC} = \frac{AB}{AC}$
   REASON
   ∠ bisector proportion theorem

2.60

1. **STATEMENT**
   $\overline{XZ} \parallel \overline{BC}$, $\angle 1 = \angle 2$
   REASON
   Given
2. **STATEMENT**
   $YC = ZC$
   REASON
   Sides opposite = ∠'s are =
3. **STATEMENT**
   $\frac{AX}{XB} = \frac{AY}{YC}$
   REASON
   Segment || to side of △ divides other sides proportionally
4. **STATEMENT**
   $\frac{AX}{XB} = \frac{AY}{ZC}$
   REASON
   Substitution

2.61

1. **STATEMENT**
   $\overline{RS} \parallel \overline{BC}$, $\angle 1 = \angle 2$
   REASON
   Given
2. **STATEMENT**
   $\angle 2 = \angle 3$
   REASON
   If lines ||, alternate interior ∠'s =

3. **STATEMENT**
$\angle 1 = \angle 3$
REASON
Substitution

4. **STATEMENT**
$BR = RS$
REASON
Sides opposite = ∠' s are =

5. **STATEMENT**
$\frac{AR}{RB} = \frac{AS}{SC}$
REASON
Segment || to side of △ divides other sides proportionally

6. **STATEMENT**
$\frac{AR}{RS} = \frac{AS}{SC}$
REASON
Substitution

2.62 $\frac{2}{x} = \frac{x}{9}$
$x^2 = 18$
$\sqrt{x^2} = \sqrt{18}$
$x = 3\sqrt{2}$

2.63 $\frac{6}{x} = \frac{x}{3}$
$x^2 = 18$
$\sqrt{x^2} = \sqrt{18}$
$x = 3\sqrt{2}$

2.64 $\frac{8}{x} = \frac{x}{2}$
$x^2 = 16$
$\sqrt{x^2} = \sqrt{16}$
$x = 4$

2.65 $\frac{2}{x} = \frac{x}{6}$
$x^2 = 12$
$\sqrt{x^2} = \sqrt{12}$
$x = 2\sqrt{3}$

2.66 $\frac{x}{4} = \frac{5}{x}$
$x^2 = 20$
$\sqrt{x^2} = \sqrt{20}$
$x = 2\sqrt{5}$

2.67 $\frac{x}{3} = \frac{3}{x}$
$x^2 = 9$
$\sqrt{x^2} = \sqrt{9}$
$x = 3$

2.68 $\frac{2}{\sqrt{6}} = \frac{\sqrt{6}}{x}$
$2x = (\sqrt{6})^2$
$2x = 6$
$x = 3$

2.69 $\frac{12}{\sqrt{6}} = \frac{\sqrt{6}}{x}$
$12x = (\sqrt{6})^2$
$12x = 6$
$x = \frac{6}{12} = \frac{1}{2}$

2.70 $\frac{6}{\sqrt{6}} = \frac{\sqrt{6}}{x}$
$6x = (\sqrt{6})^2$
$6x = 6$
$x = 1$

2.71 $\frac{4}{\sqrt{6}} = \frac{\sqrt{6}}{x}$
$4x = (\sqrt{6})^2$
$4x = 6$
$x = \frac{6}{4} = \frac{3}{2}$

2.72 $\frac{2}{BD} = \frac{BD}{8}$
$(BD)^2 = 16$
$\sqrt{(BD)^2} = \sqrt{16}$
$BD = 4$

2.73 $\frac{3}{AB} = \frac{AB}{9}$
$(AB)^2 = 27$
$\sqrt{(AB)^2} = \sqrt{27}$
$AB = 3\sqrt{3}$

2.74 $\frac{DC}{BC} = \frac{BC}{DC + AD}$
$\frac{DC}{6} = \frac{6}{DC + 5}$
$(DC)^2 + 5DC = 36$
$(DC)^2 + 5DC - 36 = 0$
$(DC + 9)(DC - 4) = 0$
$DC + 9 = 0$ or $DC - 4 = 0$
$DC = -9, DC = 4$
$\therefore DC = 4$

2.75 $\frac{AD}{DB} = \frac{DB}{DC}$

$\frac{AD}{4} = \frac{4}{6}$

$6AD = 16$

$AD = \frac{16}{6} = \frac{8}{3} = 2\frac{2}{3}$

2.76 $\frac{AD}{AB} = \frac{AB}{AC}$

$AD = AC - DC$

$AD = 12 - 8$

$AD = 4$

$\frac{4}{AB} = \frac{AB}{12}$

$(AB)^2 = 48$

$\sqrt{(AB)^2} = \sqrt{48}$

$AB = 4\sqrt{3}$

2.77 $\frac{9}{x} = \frac{x}{4}$

$x^2 = 36$

$\sqrt{x^2} = \sqrt{36}$

$x = 6$

2.78 $\frac{4}{y} = \frac{y}{5}$

$y^2 = 20$

$\sqrt{y^2} = \sqrt{20}$

$y = 2\sqrt{5}$

2.79 $\frac{9}{z} = \frac{z}{5}$

$z^2 = 45$

$\sqrt{z^2} = \sqrt{45}$

$z = 3\sqrt{5}$

2.80 $\frac{4}{6} = \frac{6}{a}$

$4a = 36$

$a = 9$

2.81 $\frac{9}{b} = \frac{b}{4+9}$

$\frac{9}{b} = \frac{b}{13}$

$b^2 = 117$

$\sqrt{b^2} = \sqrt{117}$

$b = 3\sqrt{13}$

2.82 $\frac{4}{c} = \frac{c}{4+9}$

$\frac{4}{c} = \frac{c}{13}$

$c^2 = 52$

$\sqrt{c^2} = \sqrt{52}$

$c = 2\sqrt{13}$

2.83 $\overline{ST}$

2.84 S

2.85 $\overline{UT}$

2.86 $\overline{QU}$

2.87 $\overline{RS}$

2.88

1. **STATEMENT**
   $\overline{DB} \perp \overline{AC}$, $DB = n\ ADC$
   REASON
   Given
2. **STATEMENT**
   $\frac{AB}{DB} = \frac{DB}{BC}$
   REASON
   Altitude is geometric mean
3. **STATEMENT**
   $\frac{AB}{n} = \frac{n}{BC}$
   REASON
   Substitution
4. **STATEMENT**
   $AB \cdot BC = n^2$
   REASON
   POP

2.89

1. **STATEMENT**
   $\overline{SU} \perp \overline{RT}$, $RS = \sqrt{15}$ Right $\triangle RST$
   REASON
   Given
2. **STATEMENT**
   $\frac{RU}{RS} = \frac{RS}{RT}$
   REASON
   Leg of rt. $\triangle$ is geometric mean
3. **STATEMENT**
   $\frac{RU}{\sqrt{15}} = \frac{\sqrt{15}}{RT}$
   REASON
   Substitution
4. **STATEMENT**
   $RU \cdot RT = 15$
   REASON
   POP

2.90 $x^2 = 4^2 + 7^2$

2.91 $y^2 = 3^2 + 3^2$

2.92 $9^2 = a^2 + 5^2$

2.93 $8^2 = 4^2 + b^2$

2.94
$$\begin{aligned} 3^2 + 4^2 &\;?\; 5^2 \\ 9 + 16 &\;?\; 25 \\ 25 &= 25 \quad \text{yes} \end{aligned}$$

2.95
$$\begin{aligned} 4^2 + 5^2 &\;?\; 6^2 \\ 16 + 25 &\;?\; 36 \\ 41 &\neq 36 \quad \text{no} \end{aligned}$$

2.96
$$\begin{aligned} 6^2 + 8^2 &\;?\; 10^2 \\ 36 + 64 &\;?\; 100 \\ 100 &= 100 \quad \text{yes} \end{aligned}$$

2.97
$$\begin{aligned} 3^2 + 3^2 &\;?\; (3\sqrt{2})^2 \\ 9 + 9 &\;?\; 18 \\ 18 &= 18 \quad \text{yes} \end{aligned}$$

2.98
$$\begin{aligned} 5^2 + 12^2 &= c^2 \\ 25 + 144 &= c^2 \\ 169 &= c^2 \\ \sqrt{169} &= \sqrt{c^2} \\ 13 &= c \end{aligned}$$

2.99
$$\begin{aligned} 4^2 + 4^2 &= c^2 \\ 16 + 16 &= c^2 \\ 32 &= c^2 \\ \sqrt{32} &= \sqrt{c^2} \\ 4\sqrt{2} &= c \end{aligned}$$

2.100
$$\begin{aligned} 40^2 + b^2 &= 41^2 \\ 1{,}600 + b^2 &= 1{,}681 \\ b^2 &= 81 \\ \sqrt{b^2} &= \sqrt{81} \\ b &= 9 \end{aligned}$$

2.101
$$\begin{aligned} a^2 + 9^2 &= 16^2 \\ a^2 + 81 &= 256 \\ a^2 &= 175 \\ \sqrt{a^2} &= \sqrt{175} \\ a &= 5\sqrt{7} \end{aligned}$$

2.102
$$\begin{aligned} 8^2 + 15^2 &= c^2 \\ 64 + 225 &= c^2 \\ 289 &= c^2 \\ \sqrt{289} &= \sqrt{c^2} \\ 17 &= c \end{aligned}$$

2.103
$$\begin{aligned} 5^2 + 10^2 &= c^2 \\ 25 + 100 &= c^2 \\ 125 &= c^2 \\ \sqrt{125} &= \sqrt{c^2} \\ 5\sqrt{5} &= c \end{aligned}$$

2.104
$$\begin{aligned} 16^2 + b^2 &= 20^2 \\ 256 + b^2 &= 400 \\ b^2 &= 144 \\ \sqrt{b^2} &= \sqrt{144} \\ b &= 12 \end{aligned}$$

2.105
$$\begin{aligned} a^2 + 8^2 &= 12^2 \\ a^2 + 64 &= 144 \\ a^2 &= 80 \\ \sqrt{a^2} &= \sqrt{80} \\ a &= 4\sqrt{5} \end{aligned}$$

2.106

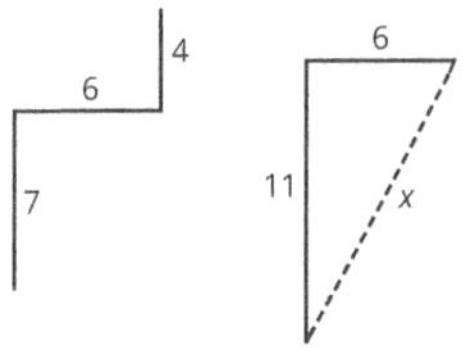

$$\begin{aligned} 11^2 + 6^2 &= x^2 \\ 121 + 36 &= x^2 \\ 157 &= x^2 \quad \text{same as} \\ \sqrt{157} &= \sqrt{x^2} \\ x &= \sqrt{157}\ \text{miles} \end{aligned}$$

2.107

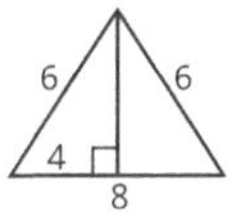

$$\begin{aligned} x^2 + 4^2 &= 6^2 \\ x^2 + 16 &= 36 \\ x^2 &= 20 \\ \sqrt{x^2} &= \sqrt{20} \\ x &= 2\sqrt{5}\ \text{in.} \end{aligned}$$

2.108

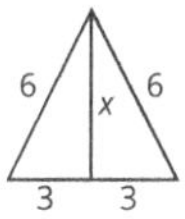

$$\begin{aligned} x^2 + 3^2 &= 6^2 \\ x^2 + 9 &= 36 \\ x^2 &= 27 \\ \sqrt{x^2} &= \sqrt{27} \\ x &= 3\sqrt{3}\ \text{ft.} \end{aligned}$$

2.109

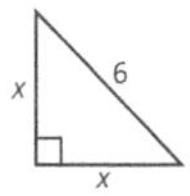

$$\begin{aligned} x^2 + x^2 &= 6^2 \\ 2x^2 &= 36 \\ x^2 &= 18 \\ \sqrt{x^2} &= \sqrt{18} \\ x &= 3\sqrt{2}\ \text{yd.} \end{aligned}$$

2.110 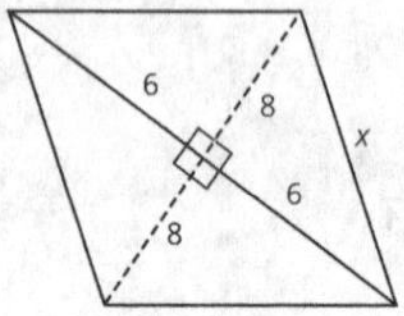

$$\begin{aligned} x^2 &= 6^2 + 8^2 \\ x^2 &= 36 + 64 \\ x^2 &= 100 \\ \sqrt{x^2} &= \sqrt{100} \\ x &= 10 \\ P &= 4(10) = 40 \end{aligned}$$

2.111 a. $5\sqrt{3}$

b. $2(5) = 10$

2.112 a. $\frac{2\sqrt{3}}{\sqrt{3}} = 2$

b. $2(2) = 4$

2.113 a. $\frac{12}{2} = 6$

b. $6\sqrt{3}$

2.114 a. $\frac{10}{2} = 5$

b. $5\sqrt{3}$

2.115 a. $7\sqrt{3}$

b. $2(7) = 14$

2.116 a. $\frac{3}{\sqrt{3}} = \frac{3}{\sqrt{3}} \cdot \frac{\sqrt{3}}{\sqrt{3}} = \frac{3\sqrt{3}}{3} = \sqrt{3}$

b. $2\sqrt{3}$

2.117 a. $\frac{8}{2} = 4$

b. $\frac{4}{2}\sqrt{3} = 2\sqrt{3}$

c. $AD = AB - DB$

$DB = \frac{4}{2} - 2$

$AD = 8 - 2 = 6$

d. $\frac{4}{2} = 2$

e. AC is hypotenuse of $\triangle ACD$.

$AC = 2(2\sqrt{3}) = 4\sqrt{3}$

2.118 a. $2(2) = 4$

b. $CD = \sqrt{3}DB$

$DB = \frac{CB}{2}$

$DB = \frac{2}{2} = 1$

$CD = \sqrt{3}(1) = \sqrt{3}$

c. $AD = AB - DB$

$AD = 4 - 1$

$AD = 3$

d. $\frac{2}{2} = 1$

e. AC is hypotenuse of $\triangle ACD$.

$AC = 2\sqrt{3}$

2.119 a. $AB = AD + DB$

$AD = \sqrt{3}(4\sqrt{3}) = 4(3) = 12$

$DB = \frac{4\sqrt{3}}{\sqrt{3}} = 4$

$AB = 12 + 4 = 16$

b. $2(4) = 8$

c. $\sqrt{3}(4\sqrt{3}) = 12$

d. $\frac{4\sqrt{3}}{\sqrt{3}} = 4$

e. AC is hypotenuse of $\triangle ACD$.

$AC = 2(4\sqrt{3}) = 8\sqrt{3}$

2.120 $CD = \frac{9}{\sqrt{3}} = \frac{9}{\sqrt{3}} \cdot \frac{\sqrt{3}}{\sqrt{3}} = \frac{9\sqrt{3}}{3} = 3\sqrt{3}$

$DB = \frac{3\sqrt{3}}{\sqrt{3}} = 3$

$BC = 2(3) = 6$

$AC = 2(3\sqrt{3}) = 6\sqrt{3}$

$AB = AD + DB = 9 + 3 = 12$

a. 12

b. 6

c. $3\sqrt{3}$

d. 3

e. $6\sqrt{3}$

2.121 $CD = \sqrt{3}(10\sqrt{3}) = 10(3) = 30$

$BC = 2(10\sqrt{3}) = 20\sqrt{3}$

$AD = 30\sqrt{3}$

$AC = 2(30) = 60$

$AB = 30\sqrt{3} + 10\sqrt{3} = 40\sqrt{3}$

a. $40\sqrt{3}$

b. $20\sqrt{3}$

c. 30

d. $30\sqrt{3}$

e. 60

2.122 $CD = \frac{8\sqrt{3}}{2} = 4\sqrt{3}$

$AD = \sqrt{3}(4\sqrt{3}) = 12$

$DB = \frac{4\sqrt{3}}{\sqrt{3}} = 4$

$BC = 2(4) = 8$

$AB = 12 + 4 = 16$

a. 16

b. 8

c. $4\sqrt{3}$

d. 12

e. 4

2.123 $6\sqrt{2}$"
2.124 $3\sqrt{2}(\sqrt{2}) = 6$"
2.125 $8\sqrt{2}$"
2.126 $6\sqrt{2}(\sqrt{2}) = 12$"
2.127 $\frac{12}{\sqrt{2}} = \frac{12}{\sqrt{2}} \cdot \frac{\sqrt{2}}{\sqrt{2}} = \frac{12\sqrt{2}}{2} = 6\sqrt{2}$ cm
2.128 $\frac{6\sqrt{2}}{\sqrt{2}} = 6$ cm
2.129 $\frac{8}{\sqrt{2}} = \frac{8}{\sqrt{2}} \cdot \frac{\sqrt{2}}{\sqrt{2}} = \frac{8\sqrt{2}}{2} = 4\sqrt{2}$ cm
2.130 $\frac{5\sqrt{6}}{\sqrt{2}} = \frac{5\sqrt{6}}{\sqrt{2}} \cdot \frac{\sqrt{2}}{\sqrt{2}} = \frac{5\sqrt{12}}{2} = \frac{5(2\sqrt{3})}{2} = 5\sqrt{3}$ cm
2.131 $16\sqrt{2}$"
2.132 $7\sqrt{3}(\sqrt{2}) = 7\sqrt{6}$
2.133 $5\sqrt{2}$"
2.134 $3\sqrt{2}(\sqrt{2}) = 2(3) = 6$
2.135 $\frac{12\sqrt{10}}{\sqrt{2}} = \frac{12\sqrt{10}}{\sqrt{2}} \cdot \frac{\sqrt{2}}{\sqrt{2}} = \frac{12\sqrt{20}}{2} = \frac{12(2\sqrt{5})}{2} =$
$12\sqrt{5}$ ft.
2.136 $\frac{15\sqrt{2}}{\sqrt{2}} = 15$ cm
2.137 $\frac{8}{\sqrt{2}} = \frac{8}{\sqrt{2}} \cdot \frac{\sqrt{2}}{\sqrt{2}} = \frac{8\sqrt{2}}{2} = 4\sqrt{2}$ miles
2.138 $\frac{\frac{1}{2}}{\sqrt{2}} = \frac{1}{2} \cdot \frac{1}{\sqrt{2}} = \frac{1}{2\sqrt{2}} = \frac{1}{2\sqrt{2}} \cdot \frac{\sqrt{2}}{\sqrt{2}} = \frac{\sqrt{2}}{2(2)} = \frac{\sqrt{2}}{4}$"
or $\frac{1}{4}\sqrt{2}$"

SELF TEST 2

2.01 equal
2.02 proportional
2.03 If two sides of one △ are proportional to two sides of another and included ∠'s are =, then the △'s are similar.
2.04 If three corresponding sides of one △ are proportional to three sides of another, then the △'s are similar.
2.05 the ratio of corresponding sides
2.06 proportionally
2.07 the ratio of corresponding sides
2.08 point
2.09 Pythagorean
2.010 twice
2.011 $\frac{4}{\sqrt{2}} = \frac{4}{\sqrt{2}} \cdot \frac{\sqrt{2}}{\sqrt{2}} = \frac{4\sqrt{2}}{2} = 2\sqrt{2}$
2.012 c

$$\begin{aligned} 4^2 + (3\sqrt{3})^2 &= (\sqrt{43})^2 \\ 16 + 27 &= 43 \\ 43 &= 43 \end{aligned}$$

2.013 Either order:
a. $\triangle TSX$
b. $\triangle RST$

2.014 $\frac{RX}{XT} = \frac{XT}{XS}$

$\frac{4}{XT} = \frac{XY}{9}$

$(XT)^2 = 36$

$\sqrt{(XT)^2} = \sqrt{36}$

$XT = 6$

2.015 $\frac{RX}{RT} = \frac{RT}{RS}$

$\frac{RX}{6} = \frac{6}{9}$

$9RX = 36$

$RX = 4$

2.016

$$\begin{aligned} 4^2 + 6^2 &= c^2 \\ 16 + 36 &= c^2 \\ 52 &= c^2 \\ \sqrt{52} &= \sqrt{c^2} \\ 2\sqrt{13} &= c \end{aligned}$$

2.017

$$\begin{aligned} 3^2 + b^2 &= 6^2 \\ 9 + b^2 &= 36 \\ b^2 &= 27 \\ \sqrt{b^2} &= \sqrt{27} \\ b &= 3\sqrt{3} \end{aligned}$$

2.018 $a^2 + 2^2 = (3\sqrt{2})^2$
$a^2 + 4 = 18$
$a^2 = 14$
$\sqrt{a^2} = \sqrt{14}$
$a = \sqrt{14}$

2.019 $RT = 2RX$
$RT = 2(3)$
$RT = 6$

2.020 $RX = \frac{RT}{2}$
$RX = \frac{8}{2}$
$RX = 4$
$TX = 4\sqrt{3}$

2.021 $TX = \sqrt{3}RX$
$TX = \sqrt{3}(2\sqrt{3})$
$TX = 2(3)$
$TX = 6$

2.022 $\frac{RX}{XS} = \frac{RT}{ST}$
$\frac{RX}{10 - RX} = \frac{4}{8}$
$8RX = 40 - 4RX$
$12RX = 40$
$RX = \frac{40}{12} = \frac{10}{3} = 3\frac{1}{3}$

2.023 $\frac{3}{XR} = \frac{TY}{6}$
$\frac{3}{XR} = \frac{XR}{6}$
$(XR)^2 = 18$
$\sqrt{(XR)^2} = \sqrt{18}$
$XR = 3\sqrt{2}$

2.024 $\frac{x - 4}{4} = \frac{3}{x}$
$x^2 - 4x = 12$
$x^2 - 4x - 12 = 0$
$(x + 2)(x - 6) = 0$
$x + 2 = 0$ or $x - 6 = 0$
$x = -2, x = 6$
$\therefore x = 6$

2.025 $\frac{2}{x} = \frac{x}{8}$
$x^2 = 16$
$\sqrt{x^2} = \sqrt{16}$
$x = 4$

SECTION 3

3.1 6
3.2 $\overline{QR}, \overline{TS}, \overline{BR}, \overline{CS}$
3.3 $\overline{AS}, \overline{BT}, \overline{CQ}, \overline{DR}$
3.4 90°
3.5 $\overline{QR}, \overline{TS}, \overline{DC}$
3.6 $QN = SL = 4$
3.7 $QT = RS = 6$
3.8 $KN = ST = 3$

3.9 $(QS)^2 = (QR)^2 + (RS)^2$
$(QS)^2 = 3^2 + 6^2$
$(QS)^2 = 9 + 36$
$(QS)^2 = 45$
$\sqrt{(QS)^2} = \sqrt{45}$
$QS = 3\sqrt{5}$

3.10 $(SM)^2 = (ST)^2 + (TM)^2$
$(SM)^2 = 3^2 + 4^2$
$(SM)^2 = 9 + 16$
$(SM)^2 = 25$
$\sqrt{(SM)^2} = \sqrt{25}$
$SM = 5$

3.11 $(RL)^2 = (RS)^2 + (SL)^2$
$(RL)^2 = 6^2 + 4^2$
$(RL)^2 = 36 + 16$
$(RL)^2 = 52$
$\sqrt{(RL)^2} = \sqrt{52}$
$RL = 2\sqrt{13}$

3.12 $(NS)^2 = (NQ)^2 + (QS)^2$
$(NS)^2 = 4^2 + (3\sqrt{5})^2$
$(NS)^2 = 16 + 45$
$(NS)^2 = 61$
$\sqrt{(NS)^2} = \sqrt{61}$
$NS = \sqrt{61}$

3.13 $(KT)^2 = (KR)^2 + (RT)^2$
$(KT)^2 = 4^2 + [(RS)^2 + (ST)^2]$
$(KT)^2 = 4^2 + 6^2 + 3^2$
$(KT)^2 = 16 + 36 + 9$
$(KT)^2 = 61$
$\sqrt{(KT)^2} = \sqrt{61}$
$KT = \sqrt{61}$

3.14 $d = \sqrt{2^2 + 3^2 + 6^2}$
$d = \sqrt{4 + 9 + 36}$
$d = \sqrt{49}$
$d = 7$

3.15 $d = \sqrt{5^2 + 4^2 + 2^2}$
$d = \sqrt{25 + 16 + 4}$
$d = \sqrt{45}$
$d = 3\sqrt{5}$

3.16 $d = \sqrt{3^2 + 3^2 + 2^2}$
$d = \sqrt{9 + 9 + 4}$
$d = \sqrt{22}$

3.17 $d = \sqrt{18^2 + 10^2 + 2^2}$
$d = \sqrt{324 + 100 + 4}$
$d = \sqrt{428}$
$d = 2\sqrt{107}$

3.18 $d = \sqrt{3^2 + 5^2 + 5^2}$
$d = \sqrt{9 + 25 + 25}$
$d = \sqrt{59}$

3.19 $d = e\sqrt{3}$
$d = 3\sqrt{3}$

3.20 $d = \sqrt{2^2 + 3^2 + 5^2}$
$d = \sqrt{4 + 9 + 25}$
$d = \sqrt{38}$

3.21 $\overline{PA}, \overline{PB}, \overline{PC}, \overline{PD}$
3.22 yes
3.23 yes
3.24 yes
3.25 yes
3.26 yes

3.27 $XY = \frac{1}{2}RS = \frac{1}{2}(6) = 3$

3.28 $PY = \sqrt{(PX)^2 + (XY)^2}$
$PY = \sqrt{4^2 + 3^2}$
$PY = \sqrt{16 + 9}$
$PY = \sqrt{25}$
$PY = 5$

3.29 $SY = \frac{1}{2}ST = \frac{1}{2}RS = \frac{1}{2}(6) = 3$

3.30 $ST = RS = 6$

3.31 $PS = \sqrt{(PY)^2 + (SY)^2}$
$PS = \sqrt{5^2 + 3^2}$
$PS = \sqrt{25 + 9}$
$PS = \sqrt{34}$

3.32 $PT = PS = \sqrt{34}$

3.33 $QS = RS\sqrt{2}$
$QS = 6\sqrt{2}$

3.34 $XT = XY\sqrt{2}$
$XT = 3\sqrt{2}$

3.35 $\frac{3}{5}$

3.36 $\frac{12}{13}$

3.37 $\frac{15}{17}$

3.38 $\frac{20}{29}$

3.39 a. $\frac{a}{c}$
b. $\frac{b}{c}$

3.40 a. $\frac{5}{10} = \frac{1}{2}$
b. $\frac{1}{2}\sqrt{3}$

3.41 a. $\frac{1}{2}\sqrt{2}$
b. $\frac{1}{2}\sqrt{2}$

3.42 $\sin 40° = \frac{x}{13}$

3.43 $\sin 25° = \frac{x}{18}$

3.44 $\sin 40° = \frac{x}{15}$

3.45 $\sin 20° = \frac{5}{x}$

3.46 $\sin 25° = \frac{6}{x}$

3.47 $\sin 80° = \frac{15}{x}$

3.48 $\sin 20° = \frac{x}{8}$
$0.342 = \frac{x}{8}$
$x = 8(0.342)$
$x = 2.736$
$x \doteq 2.7$

3.49 $\sin 50° = \frac{x}{12}$
$0.766 = \frac{x}{12}$
$x = 12(0.766)$
$x = 9.192$
$x \doteq 9.2$

3.50 $\sin 70° = \frac{x}{10}$
$0.9397 = \frac{x}{10}$
$x = 10(0.9397)$
$x = 9.397$
$x \doteq 9.4$

3.51 $\sin 48° = \frac{10}{x}$

$0.7431 = \frac{10}{x}$

$0.7431x = 10$

$x = \frac{10}{0.7431}$

$x = 13.4571...$

$x \doteq 13.5$

3.52 $\sin 15° = \frac{12}{x}$

$0.2588 = \frac{12}{x}$

$0.2588x = 12$

$x = \frac{12}{0.2588}$

$x = 46.3678...$

$x \doteq 46.4$

3.53 $\sin 35° = \frac{8}{x}$

$0.5736 = \frac{8}{x}$

$0.5736x = 8$

$x = \frac{8}{0.5736}$

$x = 13.947...$

$x \doteq 13.9$

3.54 $\sin \angle A = \frac{7}{10}$

$= 0.7000$

$\angle A \doteq 45°$

3.55 $\sin \angle A = \frac{3}{9}$

$= 0.3333$

$\angle A \doteq 19°$

3.56 $\sin \angle A = \frac{4}{20}$

$= 0.2000$

$\angle A \doteq 12°$

3.57 $\sin \angle A = \frac{12}{60}$

$= 0.2000$

$\angle A \doteq 12°$

3.58 $\sin \angle A = \frac{5}{7}$

$= 0.7143$

$\angle A \doteq 46°$

3.59 $\sin \angle A = \frac{2}{20}$

$= 0.1000$

$\angle A \doteq 6°$

3.60 $\cos 55° = \frac{x}{223}$

$0.5736 = \frac{x}{223}$

$x = 223(0.5736)$

$x = 127.9128$

$x \doteq 127.9$

3.61 $\cos 52° = \frac{x}{119}$

$0.6157 = \frac{x}{119}$

$x = 119(0.6157)$

$x = 73.2683$

$x \doteq 73.3$

3.62 $\cos 33° = \frac{1.2}{x}$

$0.8387 = \frac{1.2}{x}$

$0.8387x = 1.2$

$x = \frac{1.2}{0.8387}$

$x = 1.4307...$

$x \doteq 1.4$

3.63 $\cos 40° = \frac{x}{0.9}$

$0.766 = \frac{x}{0.9}$

$x = 0.9(0.766)$

$x = 0.6894$

$x \doteq 0.7$

3.64 $\cos 70° = \frac{x}{12.4}$

$0.342 = \frac{x}{12.4}$

$x = 12.4(0.342)$

$x = 4.2408$

$x \doteq 4.2$

3.65 $\cos 38° = \frac{24}{x}$

$0.788 = \frac{24}{x}$

$0.788x = 24$

$x = \frac{24}{0.788}$

$x = 30.4568...$

$x \doteq 30.5$

3.66 $\cos \angle A = \frac{14}{26}$

$= 0.5385$

$\angle A \doteq 57°$

3.67 $\cos \angle A = \frac{0.91}{1.2}$

$= 0.7583$

$\angle A \doteq 41°$

3.68 $\cos \angle A = \frac{75.5}{100}$

$= 0.7550$

$\angle A \doteq 41°$

3.69 $\cos \angle A = \frac{267}{391}$

$= 0.6829$

$\angle A \doteq 47°$

3.70 $\tan 20° = \frac{x}{10}$

$0.364 = \frac{x}{10}$

$x = 10(0.364)$

$x = 3.64$

$x \doteq 3.6$

3.71 $\tan 15° = \frac{5}{x}$

$0.2679 = \frac{5}{x}$

$0.2679x = 5$

$x = \frac{5}{0.2679}$

$x = 18.6636...$

$x \doteq 18.7$

3.72 $\tan 50° = \frac{x}{12}$

$1.1918 = \frac{x}{12}$

$x = 12(1.1918)$

$x = 14.3016$

$x \doteq 14.3$

3.73 $\tan 80° = \frac{x}{3}$

$5.6713 = \frac{x}{3}$

$x = 3(5.6713)$

$x = 17.0139$

$x \doteq 17.0$

3.74 $\tan 60° = \frac{x}{4}$

$0.7321 = \frac{x}{4}$

$x = 4(1.7321)$

$x = 6.9284$

$x \doteq 6.9$

3.75 $\tan 45° = \frac{6}{x}$

$1 = \frac{6}{x}$

$x = 6.0$

3.76 $\tan \angle A = \frac{3}{8}$

$= 0.3750$

$\angle A \doteq 21°$

3.77 $\tan \angle A = \frac{5}{8}$

$= 0.6250$

$\angle A \doteq 32°$

3.78 $\tan \angle A = \frac{6}{8}$

$= 0.7500$

$\angle A \doteq 37°$

3.79 $\tan \angle A = \frac{14}{7}$

$= 2.000$

$\angle A \doteq 63°$

3.80 $\tan \angle A = \frac{6}{6}$

$= 1.000$

$\angle A \doteq 45°$

3.81

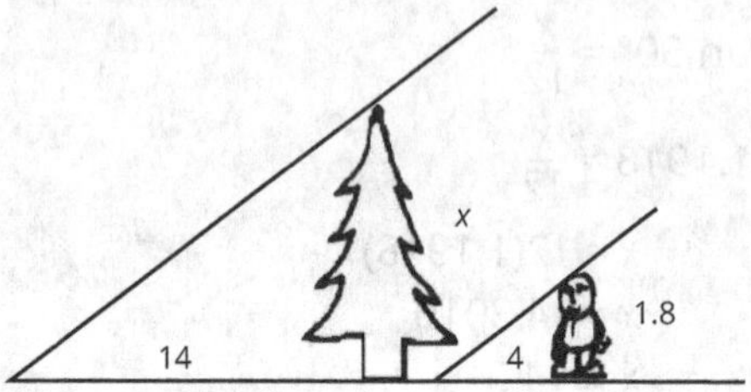

$\frac{x}{1.8} = \frac{14}{4}$

$4x = 25.2$

$x = 6.3$ m

3.82

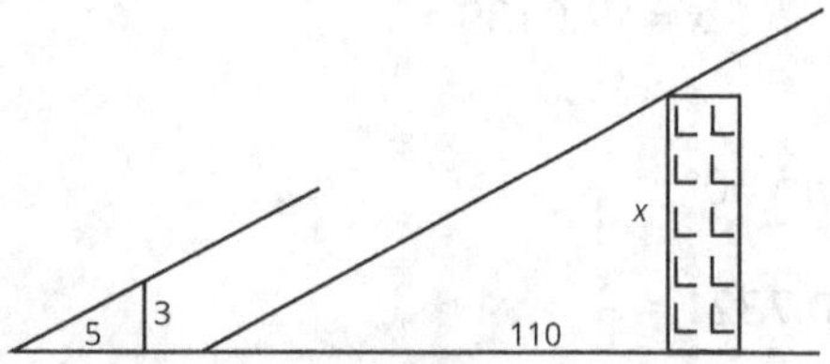

$\frac{3}{x} = \frac{5}{110}$

$5x = 330$

$x = 66$ m

3.83

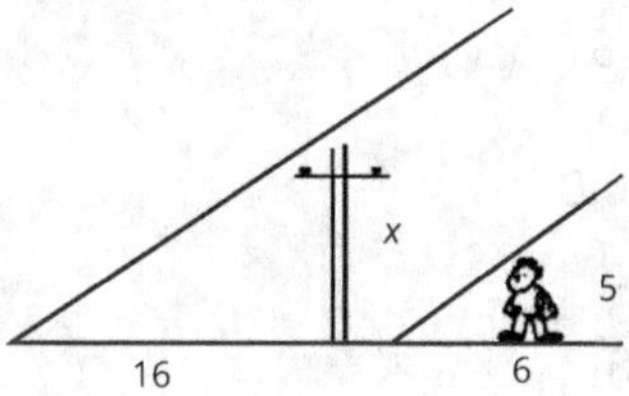

$\frac{x}{5} = \frac{16}{6}$

$6x = 80$

$x = \frac{80}{6} = \frac{40}{3} = 13\frac{1}{3}$ ft.

3.84 $\frac{a}{c} = \frac{b}{x} = \frac{d}{y}$

$\frac{9}{12} = \frac{15}{x} = \frac{7}{y}$

$\frac{9}{12} = \frac{15}{x}$

$9x = 180$

$x = 20$ ft.

$\frac{9}{12} = \frac{7}{y}$

$9y = 84$

$y = \frac{84}{9} = \frac{28}{3} = 9\frac{1}{3}$ ft.

3.85 $\frac{6}{x} = \frac{8}{16}$

$8x = 96$

$x = 12$ ft.

3.86

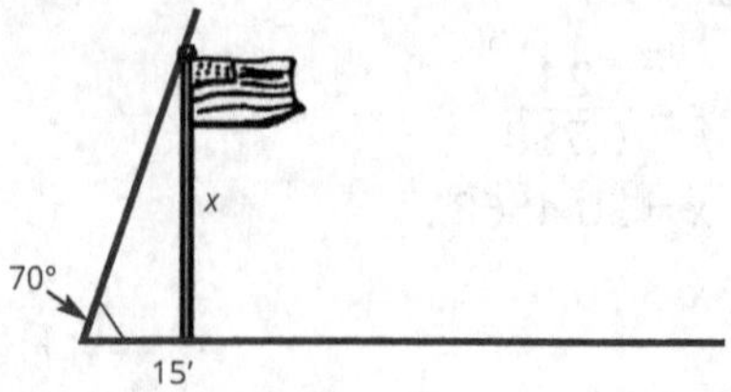

$\tan 70° = \frac{x}{15}$

$2.7475 = \frac{x}{15}$

$x = 15(2.7475)$

$x = 41.2125$

$x \doteq 41.2$ ft.

3.87

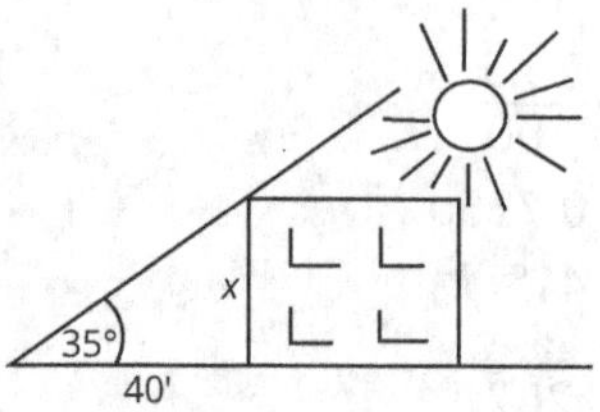

$\tan 35° = \frac{x}{40}$

$0.7002 = \frac{x}{40}$

$x = 40(0.7002)$

$x = 28.008$

$x \doteq 28$ ft.

3.88

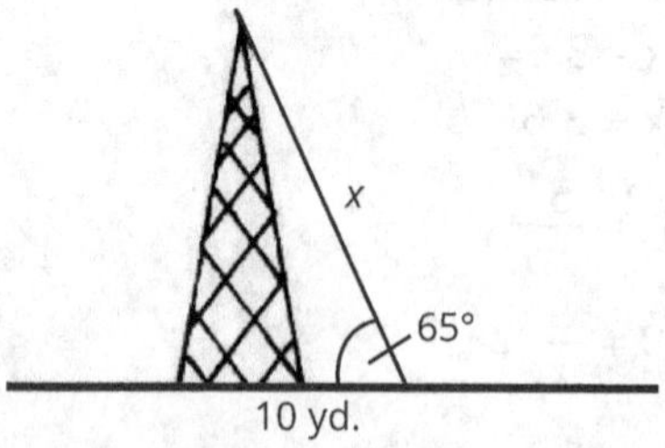

$\cos 65° = \frac{10}{x}$

$0.4226 = \frac{10}{x}$

$0.4226x = 10$

$x = \frac{10}{0.4226}$

$x = 23.663...$

$x \doteq 23.7$ yds.

3.89

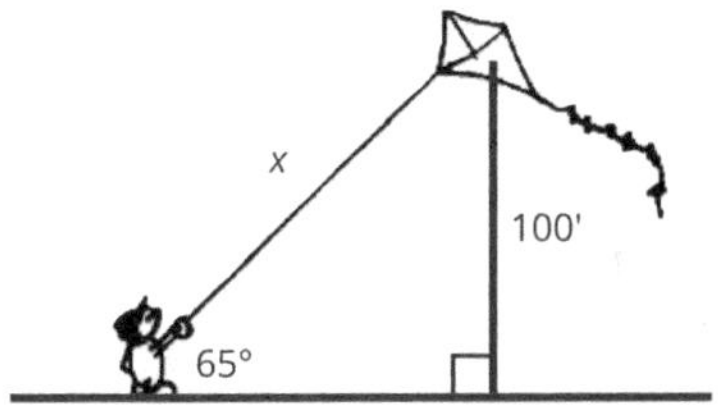

$\sin 65° = \frac{100}{x}$

$0.9063 = \frac{100}{x}$

$0.9063x = 100$

$x = \frac{100}{0.9063}$

$x = 110.3387...$

$x \doteq 110.3$ ft.

3.90

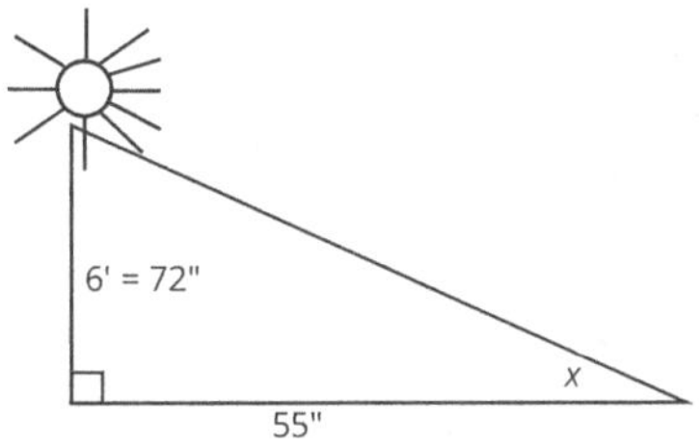

$\tan x = \frac{72}{55}$

$\tan x = 1.3091$

$x \doteq 53°$

3.91

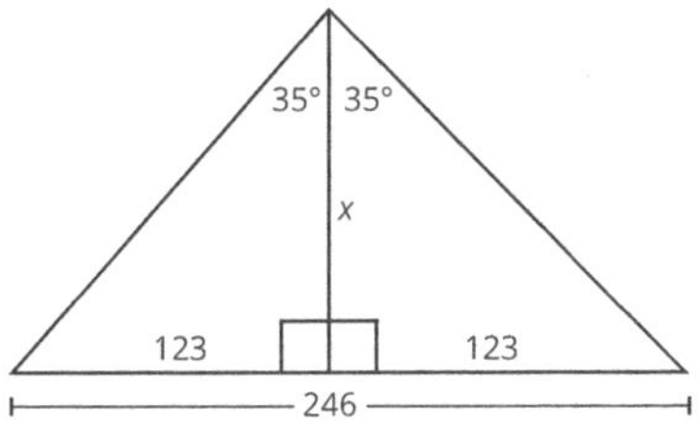

$\tan 35° = \frac{123}{x}$

$0.7002 = \frac{123}{x}$

$0.7002x = 123$

$x = \frac{123}{0.7002}$

$x = 175.6641$

$x \doteq 175.7$

3.92

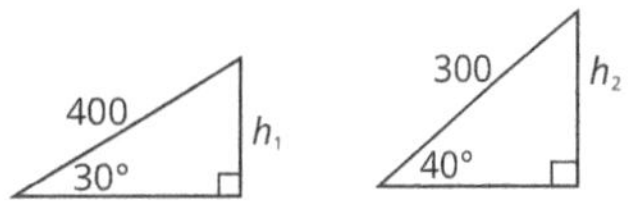

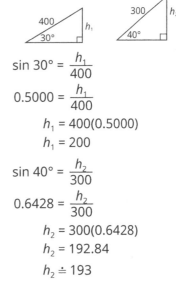

$\sin 30° = \frac{h_1}{400}$

$0.5000 = \frac{h_1}{400}$

$h_1 = 400(0.5000)$

$h_1 = 200$

$\sin 40° = \frac{h_2}{300}$

$0.6428 = \frac{h_2}{300}$

$h_2 = 300(0.6428)$

$h_2 = 192.84$

$h_2 \doteq 193$

The pilot rising 30° at 400 mph gains altitude 7 mph faster.

3.93

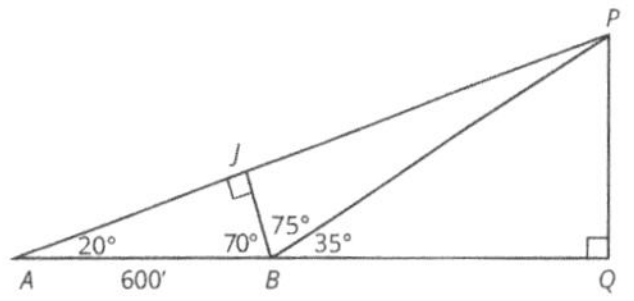

$\sin 20° = \frac{BJ}{600}$

$0.342 = \frac{BJ}{600}$

$BJ = 600(0.342)$

$BJ = 205.2$

$\cos 75° = \frac{205.2}{BP}$

$0.2588 = \frac{205.2}{BP}$

$0.2588BP = 205.2$

$BP = \frac{205.2}{0.2588}$

$BP = 792.8902...$

$BP \doteq 792.9$

$\sin 35° = \frac{PQ}{792.9}$

$0.5736 = \frac{PQ}{792.9}$

$PQ = 792.9(0.5736)$

$PQ = 454.80744$

$PQ \doteq 454.8$

height = 6,500 + 454.8 = 6,954.8 ft.

SELF TEST 3

3.01 never
3.02 sometimes
3.03 never
3.04 sometimes
3.05 always
3.06 never
3.07 always
3.08 sometimes
3.09 never
3.010 sometimes

3.011
$$\begin{aligned} 8^2 + 10^2 &= x^2 \\ 64 + 100 &= x^2 \\ 164 &= x^2 \\ \sqrt{164} &= \sqrt{x^2} \\ 2\sqrt{41} &= x \end{aligned}$$

3.012 $\tan y = \dfrac{8}{10}$

$\tan y = 0.8000$

$y \doteq 39°$

3.013 $\tan z = \dfrac{10}{8}$

$\tan z = 1.2500$

$z \doteq 51°$

3.014 $15 = 2x$

$\dfrac{15}{2} = x$

3.015 $y = \dfrac{\frac{15}{2}}{2}\sqrt{3}$

$y = \dfrac{15}{4}\sqrt{3}$

3.016 $z = \dfrac{15\sqrt{3}}{2}$

3.017 $a = \dfrac{\frac{15}{2}}{2}$

$a = \dfrac{15}{4}$

3.018 $b = 15 - \dfrac{15}{4}$

$b = \dfrac{60}{4} - \dfrac{15}{4}$

$b = \dfrac{45}{4}$

3.019 $d = \sqrt{8^2 + 4^2}$

$d = \sqrt{64 + 16}$

$d = \sqrt{80}$

$d = 4\sqrt{5}$

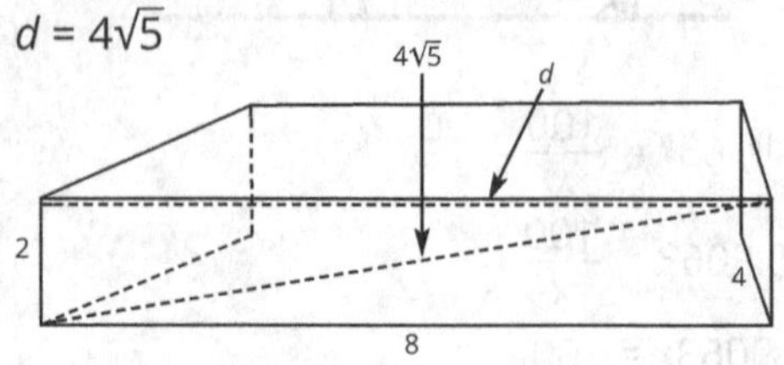

3.020 $d = \sqrt{(4\sqrt{5})^2 + 2^2}$

$d = \sqrt{80 + 4}$

$d = \sqrt{84}$

$d = 2\sqrt{21}$

3.021
$$\begin{aligned} (Py)^2 + 3^2 &= 6^2 \\ (Py)^2 + 9 &= 36 \\ (Py)^2 &= 27 \\ \sqrt{(Py)^2} &= \sqrt{27} \\ Py &= 3\sqrt{3} \end{aligned}$$

3.022
$$\begin{aligned} (Px)^2 + 3^2 &= (3\sqrt{3})^2 \\ (Px)^2 + 9 &= 27 \\ (Px)^2 &= 18 \\ \sqrt{(Px)^2} &= \sqrt{18} \\ Px &= 3\sqrt{2} \end{aligned}$$

3.023 $\sin 20° = \dfrac{x}{8}$

$0.342 = \dfrac{x}{8}$

$x = 8(0.342)$

$x = 2.736$

$x \doteq 2.7$

3.024 $\cos 20° = \dfrac{y}{8}$

$0.9397 = \dfrac{y}{8}$

$y = 8(0.9397)$

$y = 7.5176$

$y \doteq 7.5$

3.025 $\dfrac{h}{6} = \dfrac{20}{8}$

$8h = 120$

$h = \dfrac{120}{8}$

$h = 15$

LIFEPAC TEST

1. $\frac{5}{15} = \frac{1}{3}$

2. 2 hours = 120 minutes
$\frac{15}{120} = \frac{1}{8}$

3. $\frac{30}{6} = \frac{5}{1}$

4. $\frac{\frac{2}{3}}{\frac{3}{2}} = \frac{2}{3}(\frac{2}{3}) = \frac{4}{9}$

5. $\frac{x}{3} = \frac{5}{8}$
$8x = 15$
$x = \frac{15}{8} = 1\frac{7}{8}$

6. $\frac{3}{12} = \frac{x}{16}$
$12x = 48$
$x = \frac{48}{12}$
$x = 4$

7. $\frac{2}{x} = \frac{6}{2}$
$6x = 4$
$x = \frac{4}{6}$
$x = \frac{2}{3}$

8. a. $\frac{x}{5} = \frac{2}{3}$
$3x = 10$
$x = \frac{10}{3} = 3\frac{1}{3}$
b. $\frac{2}{3} = \frac{5}{y}$
$2y = 15$
$y = \frac{15}{2} = 7\frac{1}{2}$

9. Denominator Sum
10. Numerator-Denominator Sum
11. Cross Product
12. Equivalent Forms
13. a and d
14. a, b, and d

15. b
$4^2 + 5^2 = (\sqrt{41})^2$
$16 + 25 = 41$
$41 = 41$

16. $\frac{20}{x} = \frac{3}{9}$
$3x = 180$
$x = 60$ ft.

17. $\frac{P_1}{P_2} = \frac{s_1}{s_2}$
$\frac{P_1}{P_2} = \frac{3}{9}$
$\frac{P_1}{P_2} = \frac{1}{3}$

18. $5^2 + 8^2 = x^2$
$25 + 64 = x^2$
$89 = x^2$
$\sqrt{89} = \sqrt{x^2}$
$\sqrt{89} = x$

19. a. $\cos 60° = \frac{8}{x}$
$0.5000 = \frac{8}{x}$
$0.5000x = 8$
$x = \frac{8}{0.5000}$
$x = 16$
b. $\tan 60° = \frac{y}{8}$
$\sqrt{3} = \frac{y}{8}$
$y = 8\sqrt{3}$ or
$\tan 60° = \frac{y}{8}$
$1.7321 = \frac{y}{8}$
$y = 8(1.7321)$
$y = 13.8568$
$y \doteq 13.9$

20.

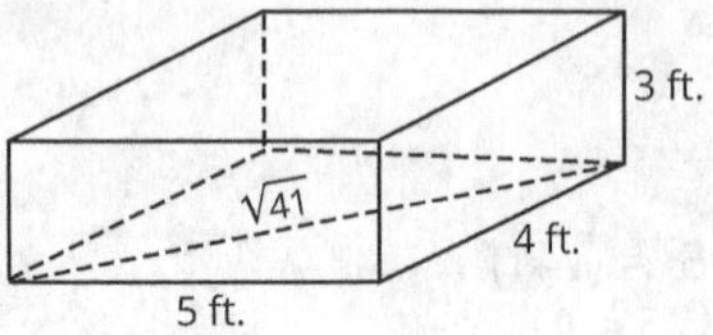

diagonal of base $= \sqrt{5^2 + 4^2}$
$= \sqrt{25 + 16}$
$= \sqrt{41}$

diagonal of solid $= \sqrt{3^2 + (41)^2}$
$= \sqrt{9 + 41}$
$= \sqrt{50}$
$= 5\sqrt{2}$

21. $3^2 + l^2 = 6^2$
$9 + l^2 = 36$
$l^2 = 27$
$\sqrt{l^2} = \sqrt{27}$
$l = 3\sqrt{3}$"

22. a. $\tan 45° = \frac{7}{x}$

$1 = \frac{7}{x}$

$x = 7$

b. $\sin 45° = \frac{7}{y}$

$\frac{\sqrt{2}}{2} = \frac{7}{y}$

$\frac{\sqrt{2}}{2}y = 7$

$y = \frac{7}{\frac{\sqrt{2}}{2}}$

$y = \frac{7(2)}{\sqrt{2}}$

$y = \frac{14}{\sqrt{2}} \cdot \frac{\sqrt{2}}{\sqrt{2}}$

$y = \frac{14\sqrt{2}}{2}$

$y = 7\sqrt{2}$ or

$\sin 45° = \frac{7}{y}$

$0.7071 = \frac{7}{y}$

$0.7071y = 7$

$y = \frac{7}{0.7071}$

$y = 9.8995$

$y \doteq 9.9$

23. $\tan 70° = \frac{x}{800}$

24. $\tan 80° = \frac{d}{30}$

25. 2 yards = 72 inches
5 ft. 6 in. = 66 inches
2 ft. = 24 inches

$\frac{h}{72} = \frac{66}{24}$

$24h = 4{,}752$

$h = \frac{4{,}752}{24}$

$h = 198$ in. $= 16\frac{1}{2}$ ft.

ALTERNATE LIFEPAC TEST

1. $\frac{x}{5} = \frac{6}{3}$

   $x(3) = 5(6)$

   $3x = 30$

   $x = \frac{30}{3} = 10$

2. $\frac{2x}{3} = \frac{8}{6}$

   $2x(6) = 3(8)$

   $12x = 24$

   $x = \frac{24}{12} = 2$

3. $1:8 = x:24$

   $8(x) = 1(24)$

   $8x = 24$

   $x = \frac{24}{8} = 3$

4. $3:x = x:4$

   $x(x) = 3(4)$

   $x^2 = 12$

   $x = \sqrt{12} = 2\sqrt{3}$

   $x = \sqrt{4 \cdot 3} = \sqrt{4} \cdot \sqrt{3} = 2\sqrt{3}$

5. $\frac{3}{4} = \frac{x+2}{5}$

   $3(5) = 4(x + 2)$

   $15 = 4x + 8$

   $7 = 4x$

   $x = \frac{7}{4}$

6. $\frac{8 \div 8}{24 \div 8} = \frac{1}{3}$

7. $\frac{40 \div 20}{60 \div 20} = \frac{2}{3}$

8. 1 foot = 12 inches; $\frac{1}{12}$

9. $\frac{16 \div 16}{64 \div 16} = \frac{1}{4}$

10. $\frac{50 \div 5}{5 \div 5} = \frac{10}{1}$

11. $\frac{AB}{AC} = \frac{BE}{CD}$

    $\frac{5}{10} = \frac{BE}{16}$

    $\frac{1}{2} = \frac{BE}{16}$

    $16 = 2BE$

    $BE = \frac{16}{2} = 8$

12. $\frac{AB}{AC} = \frac{EA}{DA}$

    $\frac{5}{10} = \frac{6}{DA}$

    $\frac{1}{2} = \frac{6}{DA}$

    $DA = 2(6) = 12$

13. $\frac{AB}{BC} = \frac{AE}{ED}$

    $BC = AC - AB$
    $BC = 10 - 5$
    $BC = 5$

    $\frac{5}{5} = \frac{6}{ED}$

    $\frac{1}{1} = \frac{6}{ED}$

    $ED = 6$

14. $BC = AC - AB$
    $BC = 10 - 5$
    $BC = 5$

15. $\triangle ABD \sim \triangle DBC$
16. $\triangle ABD \sim \triangle ADC$
17. $\triangle DBC \sim \triangle ADC$
18. $\frac{2}{5} = \frac{18}{x}$

    $2x = 5(18)$

    $2x = 90$

    $x = \frac{90}{2} = 45$ sq. ft.

19. $6\sqrt{3}$
20. 16
21. diagonal of base $= \sqrt{3^2 + 5^2}$
    $= \sqrt{9 + 25}$
    $= \sqrt{34}$

22. diagonal of rectangular solid

$= \sqrt{3^2 + 5^2 + 2^2}$

$= \sqrt{9 + 25 + 4}$

$= \sqrt{38}$

23.

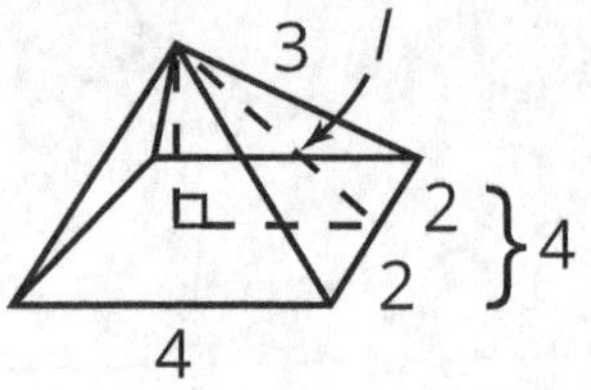

$$\begin{aligned}
\sqrt{l^2 + 2^2} &= 3 \\
\sqrt{l^2 + 4} &= 3 \\
(\sqrt{l^2 + 4})^2 &= 3^2 \\
l^2 + 4 &= 9 \\
l^2 &= 9 - 4 \\
l^2 &= 5 \\
\sqrt{l^2} &= \sqrt{5} \\
l &= \sqrt{5}
\end{aligned}$$

24. $\tan 60° = \frac{x}{80}$

25. $\tan 75° = \frac{x}{8}$

26. $\frac{x}{20} = \frac{3}{5}$

$x(5) = 20(3)$

$5x = 60$

$x = \frac{60}{5} = 12$ ft.

27. diagonal = $2\sqrt{3} = 5\sqrt{3}''$

28. $\frac{3}{x} = \frac{x}{12}$

$3(12) = x(x)$

$36 = x^2$

$x^2 = 36$

$\sqrt{x^2} = \sqrt{36}$

$x = 6$

MATH 1005

ALTERNATE LIFEPAC TEST

67/84

NAME ______________________________

DATE ______________________________

SCORE ______________________________

Solve the following proportions for *x* (each answer, 2 points).

1. $\frac{x}{5} = \frac{6}{3}$ — $x =$ ______________
2. $\frac{2x}{3} = \frac{8}{6}$ — $x =$ ______________
3. $1:8 = x:24$ — $x =$ ______________
4. $3:x = x:4$ — $x =$ ______________
5. $\frac{3}{4} = \frac{x+2}{5}$ — $x =$ ______________

Express the following ratios in simplest form (each answer, 2 points).

6. $8 to $24 ______________
7. 40° to 60° ______________
8. 1 inch to 1 foot ______________
9. 16 to 64 ______________
10. 50 to 5 ______________

Find the required numbers (each answer, 3 points).

Given: $\frac{AB}{AC} = \frac{BE}{CD} = \frac{EA}{DA}$

$AB = 5$ $CD = 16$ $AE = 6$ $AC = 10$

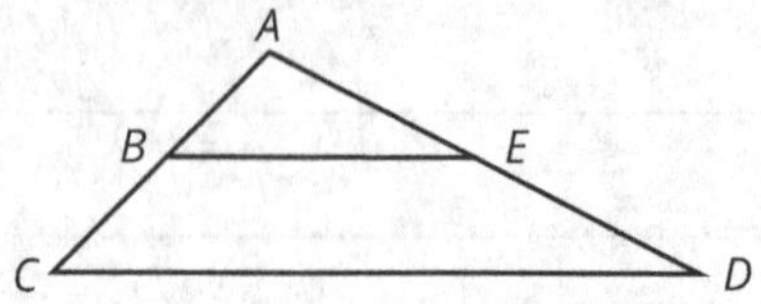

11. $BE =$ ____________

12. $DA =$ ____________

13. $ED =$ ____________

14. $BC =$ ____________

Name three pairs of similar triangles (each answer, 3 points).

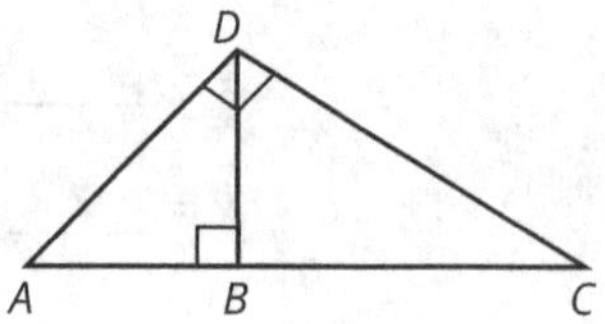

15. ____________ ~ ____________

16. ____________ ~ ____________

17. ____________ ~ ____________

Solve the following questions (each answer, 4 points).

18. The area of a triangle is 18 square feet. Find the area of a similar larger triangle if corresponding sides are 2 feet and 5 feet.

____

Given: rt. $\triangle ABC$

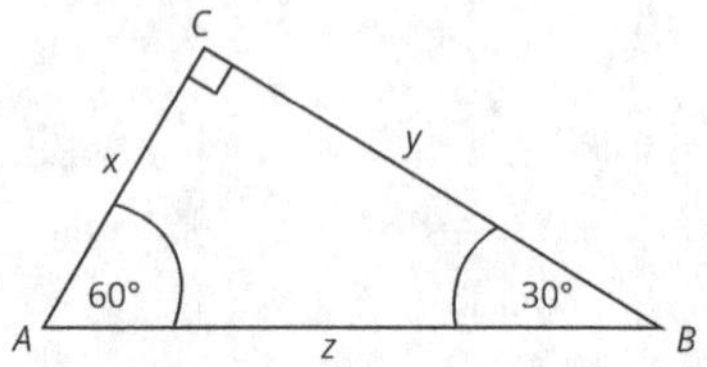

19. If $x = 6$, then $y =$ ________ .

20. If $x = 8$, then $z =$ ________ .

21. Find the diagonal of the base of the rectangular solid. ________________

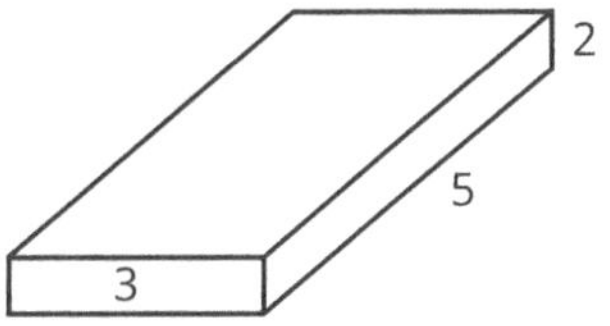

22. Find the diagonal of the rectangular solid. ________________

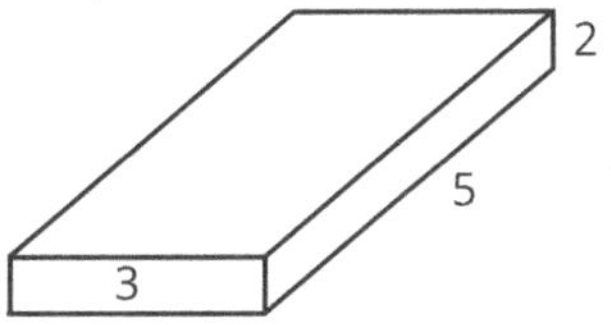

23. Find the slant height of the pyramid. ________________

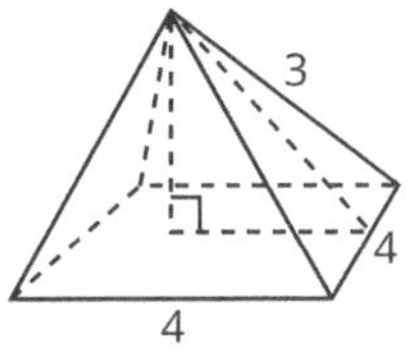

24. Write the equation to use to find the height of the kite. ____________________

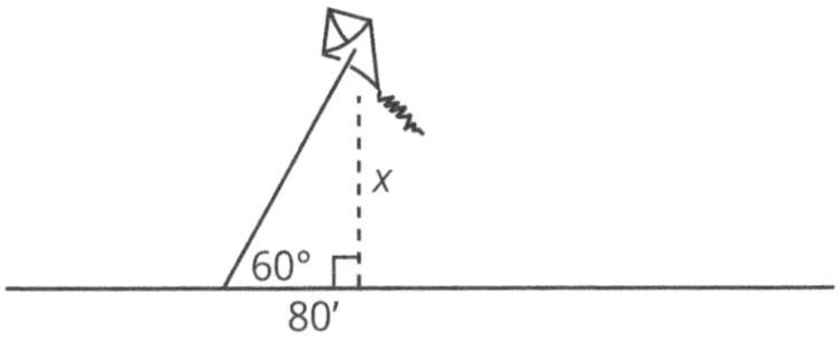

25. Write the equation to use to find the distance to shore. ____________________

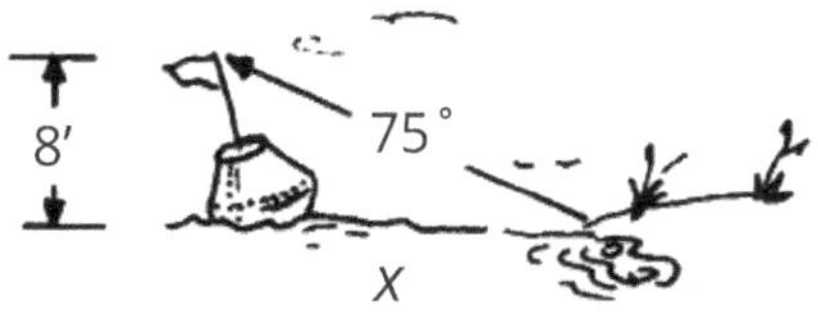

26. Find the height of the tree if the 3-ft. stick has a shadow of 5 ft. and the tree has a shadow of 20 ft. ____________________

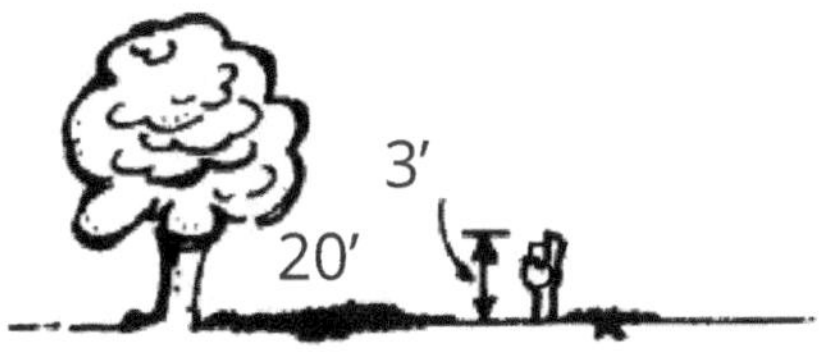

27. Find the diagonal of a cube whose edge is 5". ____________________

Solve the following problem (each answer, 3 points).

28. Given: $\frac{a}{x} = \frac{x}{b}$, $a = 3$, and $b = 12$

Find: the geometric mean. ____________________

MATH 1006

Unit 6: Circles

TEACHER NOTES

MATERIALS NEEDED FOR LIFEPAC	
Required	Suggested
• protractor, compass, and straightedge	(None)

ADDITIONAL LEARNING ACTIVITIES

Section 1: Circles and Spheres

1. Find Bible verses that refer to circles or spheres. The verses may be direct references to circles or spheres or they may be indirect references (such as a reference to a wheel). For each verse you find write the Bible reference (where the verse is located) and a phrase telling what the verse is about.

Section 2: Tangents, Arcs, and Chords

1. Discuss these questions with your class.
   a. What mechanical devices or machines use the concept of common internal tangents?
   b. What mechanical devices or machines use the concept of common external tangents?
2. Given the following tangent circles, have the students draw seven other systems that maintain a tangency relationship. Note: Relative size of circles may be changed.

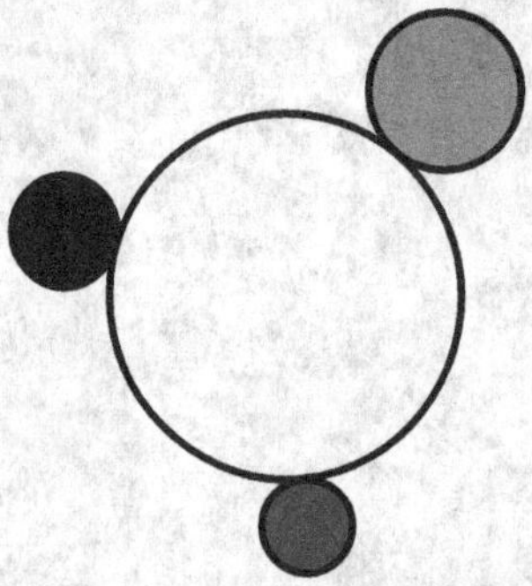

3. Have the students each draw a large circle. Mark off 18 equal arcs. To mark off 18 equal arcs, decide what the measure of each central angle will be. Then use a compass to mark off an arc on the circle. Use a compass to mark off the remaining 17 arcs. Label the end points of the arcs *A*, *B*, *C*, ... *R*. What is the measure of each arc? Have the students draw each of the following sets of chords (one set per circle). Each end point will have two lines drawn to it.

   $\{\overline{AI}, \overline{BJ}, \overline{CK}, \ldots \overline{RH}\}$

   $\{\overline{AH}, \overline{BI}, \overline{CJ}, \ldots \overline{RG}\}$

   $\{\overline{AG}, \overline{BH}, \overline{CI}, \ldots \overline{RF}\}$

   $\{\overline{AF}, \overline{BG}, \overline{CH}, \ldots \overline{RE}\}$

   $\{\overline{AE}, \overline{BF}, \overline{CG}, \ldots \overline{RD}\}$

4. Let one student read from the LIFEPAC the "If" part of Theorem 6-1, 6-2, 6-3, 6-4, 6-5, 6-6, 6-7, 6-8, 6-9, or Postulate 16. Then let a second student draw and label an appropriate figure to illustrate the theorem or postulate (representative figures are included in the LIFEPAC with each theorem and postulate). Then let a third student say the "then" part of the theorem or postulate (without using the LIFEPAC). Repeat the procedure with each of the other theorems or the postulate.

Section 3: Special Angles and Segments Related to Circles

1. Have the students draw three externally tangent circles the same size as shown. A straight line connects the centers of the circles. Then have the students find the length of $\overline{DE}$ in terms of $\overline{BC}$.

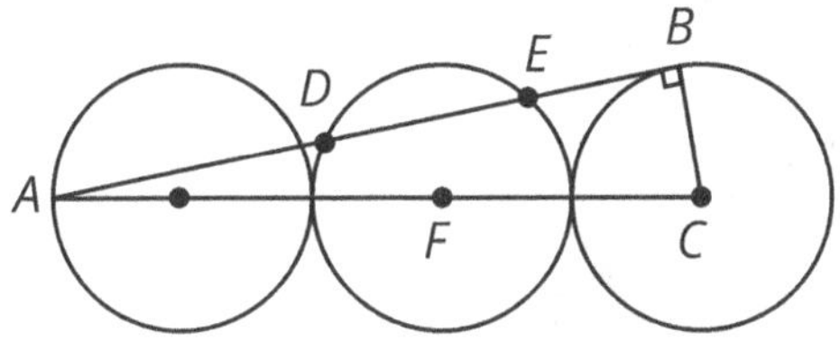

2. Let one student read from the LIFEPAC Theorem 6-10, 6-11, 6-12, 6-13, 6-14, or 6-15. Then let a second student draw and label an appropriate figure to illustrate the theorem (representative figures are included in the LIFEPAC with each theorem). Let a third student write all but one measurement in the figure (use a variable for the missing measurement). Then let a fourth student find the missing measurement by using the stated theorem. Repeat the procedure with each of the other theorems.

Example: First student: Theorem 6-10 says "the measure of an inscribed angle is equal to half the measure of its intercepted arc."

Second student: Draws and labels:

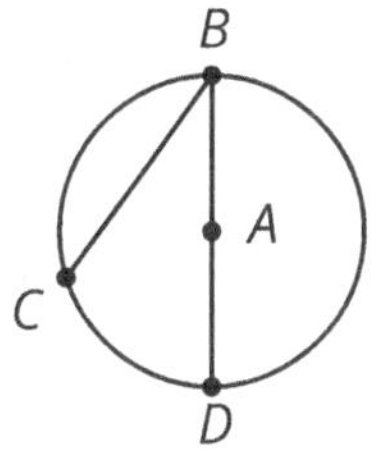

Third student:

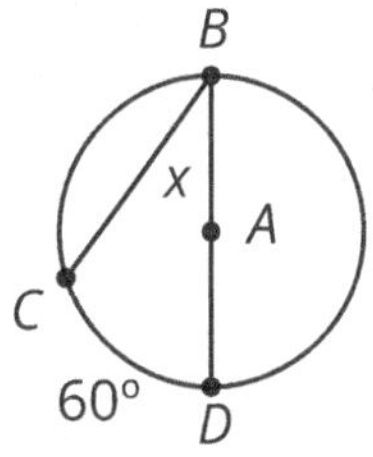

Fourth student: m $\angle CBA$ equals $\frac{1}{2}$ m $\overset{\frown}{CD}$;

m $\angle CBA = \frac{1}{2}(60°)$, which equals 30°.

3. Let one student read from the LIFEPAC the "If" part of Theorem 6-16, 6-17, or 6-18. Then let a second student draw and label an appropriate figure to illustrate the theorem (representative figures are included in the LIFEPAC with each theorem). Let a third student say the "then" part of the theorem (without using the LIFEPAC). Then let a fourth student, write all but one measurement in the figure (use a variable for the missing measurement). Then let a fifth student find the missing measurement by using the stated theorem. Repeat the procedure for each of the other theorems.

   Example: First student: Theorem 6-16 says "if two chords intersect in a circle."

   Second student: Draws and labels:

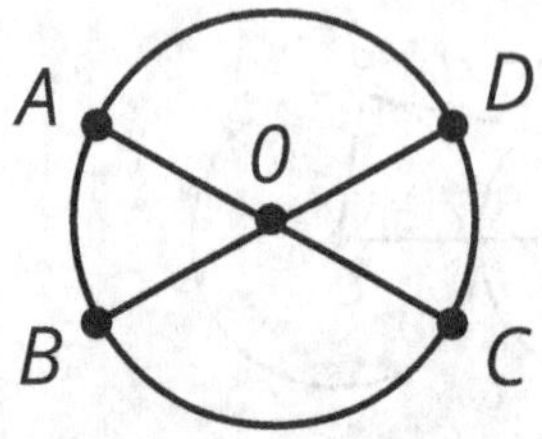

   Third student: (Then) the product of the lengths of the segments of one chord is equal to the product of the lengths of the other chord.

   Fourth student:

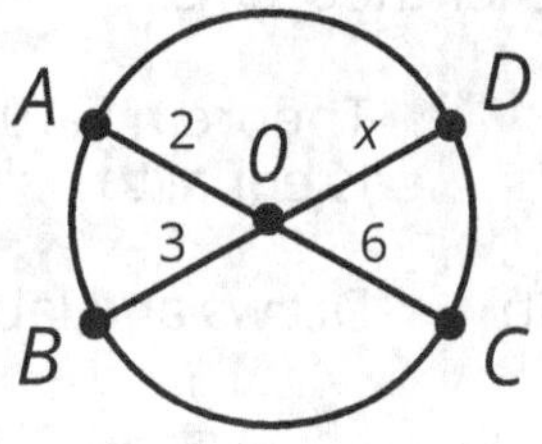

   Fifth student: Two times 6 equals 3 times x; 12 equals $3x$; $\frac{12}{3} = \frac{3x}{3}$, $4 = x$, which is the missing length.

Administer the LIFEPAC Test.

The test is to be administered in one session. Give no help except with directions.
Evaluate the tests and review areas where the students have done poorly.
Review the pages and activities that stress the concepts tested.
If necessary, administer the Alternate LIFEPAC Test

ANSWER KEYS

SECTION 1

1.1 $\overline{DK}$ and $\overline{DM}$
1.2 $\overline{EF}$
1.3 $\overline{BN}$ and $\overline{BH}$
1.4 C
1.5 $\overline{AE}$, $\overline{AG}$, $\overline{AF}$
1.6 5"
1.7 6"
1.8 A and D
1.9 A and D
1.10 none
1.11 $\overline{AB}$
1.12 $\overline{AC}$ or $\overline{AD}$
1.13 E, H, C, D, F, G
1.14 A, B, F, H
1.15 $BD = AC - AB = 6 - 4 = 2$
1.16 E, G
1.17 A
1.18 yes; $6 = 4 + 2$
1.19 $AC = AB + BD$
$20 = AB + 8$
$12 = AB$
1.20 $AC = AB + BD$
$AC = 7 + 7$
$AC = 14$
diameter = 2(14) = 28
1.21 R, S, T
1.22 $\overline{SD}$, $\overline{SJ}$, or $\overline{SE}$
1.23 $\overline{TF}$, $\overline{TH}$, $\overline{TG}$
1.24 $\overline{AB}$
1.25 S and T
1.26 $2 \cdot 4 = 8$
1.27 isosceles right triangle
1.28 T, I
1.29 A, B, C
1.30 8"

SELF TEST 1

1.01 center
1.02 center
1.03 two
1.04 concentric
1.05 equal
1.06 interior
1.07 sphere
1.08 equal
1.09 radii
1.010 concentric
1.011 2(2) = 4"
1.012 A and C
1.013 1 + 1 = 2"
1.014 D, X
1.015 $\angle JBM$, or $\angle KCG$
1.016 F, M, J
1.017 1 + 1 = 2"
1.018 $FB = MB = JB$
1.019 2(3) = 6"
1.020 no
1.021 through 1.025

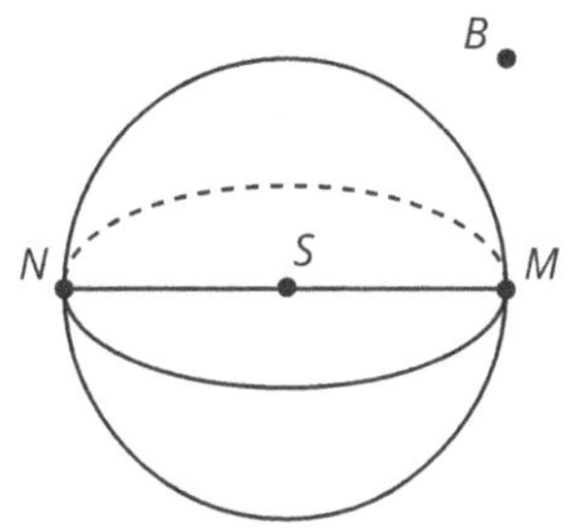

1.026 though 1.030

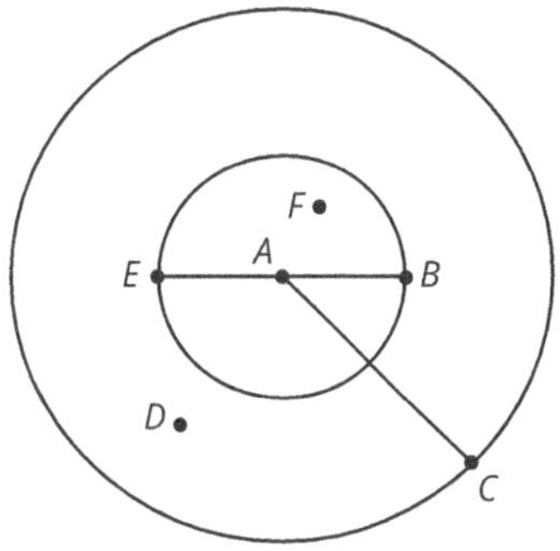

SECTION 2

2.1 *B*, *C*
2.2 *A*, *B*, or *A*, *C*
2.3 *B*, *C*
2.4 *A*, *B*, or *A*, *C*
2.5 no
2.6 a. 2
b. 1
c. 0
d. 0
e. 0
2.7 a. 2
b. 2
c. 2
d. 1
e. 0
2.8 a. infinite
b. infinite
c. infinite
d. 1
e. 0
2.9 a. infinite
b. infinite
c. infinite
d. infinite
e. 0

2.10
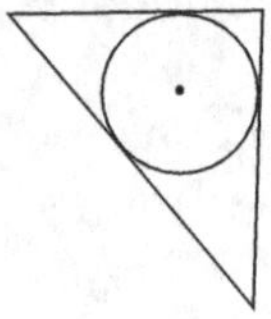

2.11
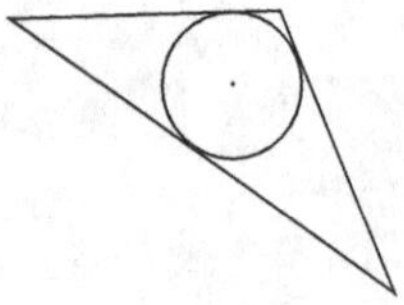

2.12
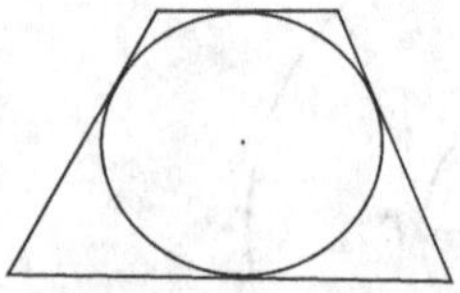

2.13
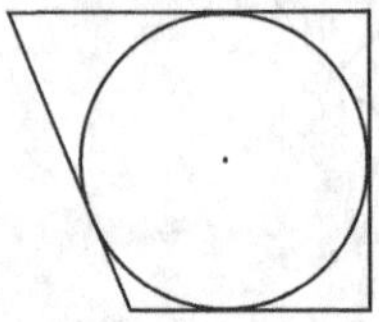

2.14 a.
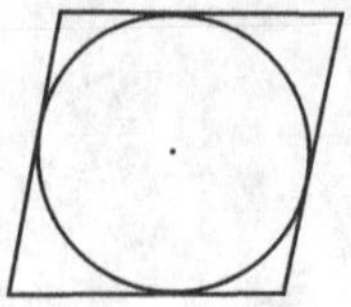

b. no

2.15 a.
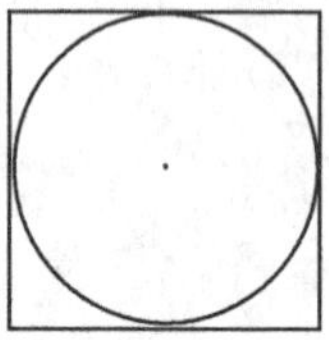

b. yes

2.16
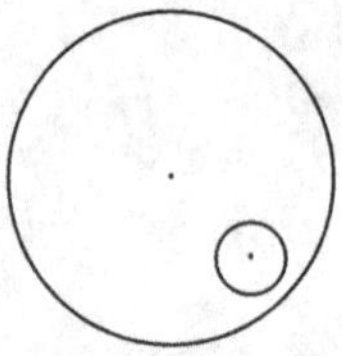

2.17
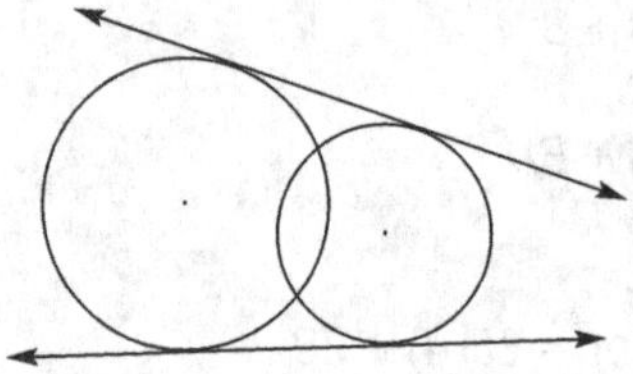

2.18
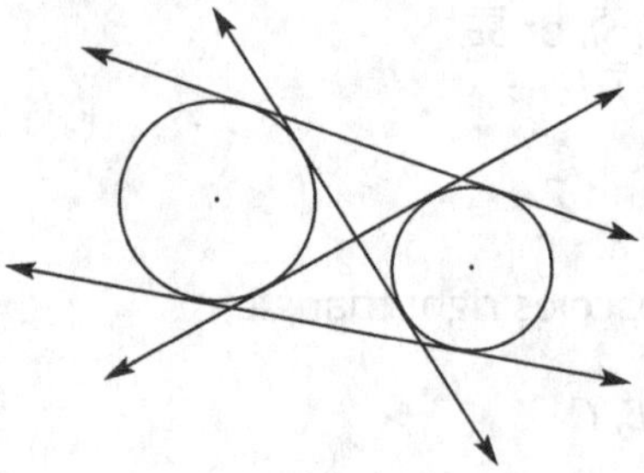

2.19
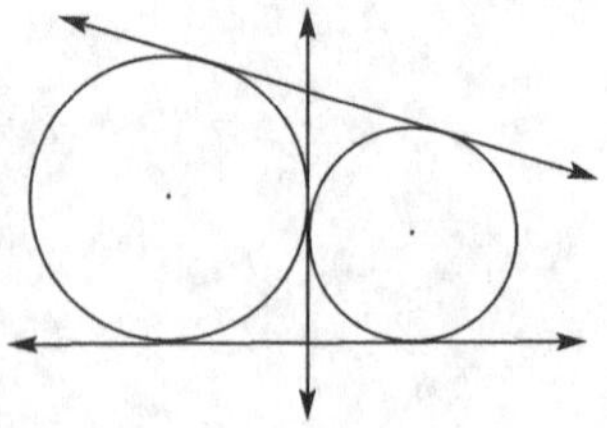

2.20
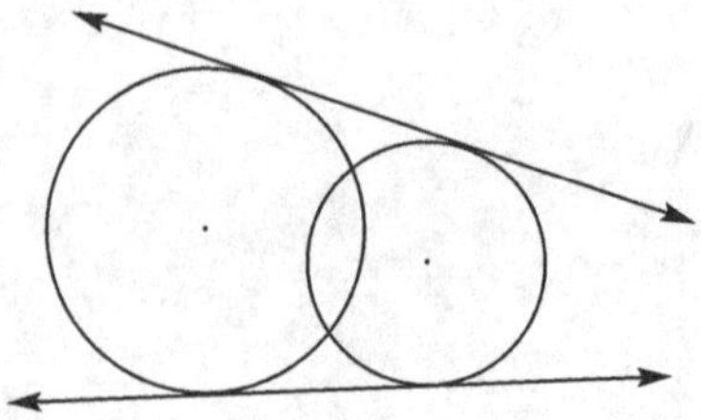

2.21

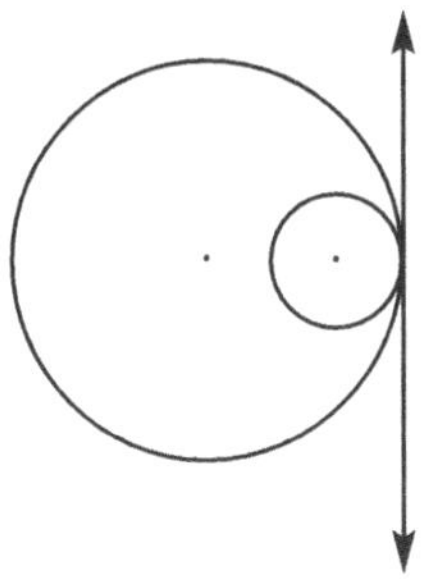

2.22 $\overline{RS}$, $\overline{RM}$, or $\overline{MS}$

2.23 $\overline{BC}$

2.24 M

2.25 It intersects the circle in two points.

2.26 $OP = 4 + 2 = 6$

2.27 a. 3

b. 4

c. $AB = OP - (OA + BP)$
$AB = 9 - (4 + 3)$
$AB = 9 - 7$
$AB = 2$

2.28 4

2.29 $(AP)^2 + (OA)^2 = (OP)^2$
$(AP)^2 + 6^2 = (6 + 4)^2$
$(AP)^2 + 36 = 100$
$(AP)^2 = 64$
$\sqrt{(AP)^2} = \sqrt{64}$
$AP = 8$

2.30 $(ON)^2 + (PN)^2 = (OP)^2$
$(ON)^2 + 15^2 = 17^2$
$(ON)^2 + 225 = 289$
$(ON)^2 = 64$
$\sqrt{(ON)^2} = \sqrt{64}$
$ON = 8$

2.31 no

2.32 no

2.33 90°

2.34 360° – 90° = 270°

2.35 $\overset{\frown}{ABC}$, $\overset{\frown}{ATC}$

2.36 $\overset{\frown}{AB}$, $\overset{\frown}{BR}$, $\overset{\frown}{RC}$, or $\overset{\frown}{BC}$

2.37 $\overset{\frown}{ATB}$, $\overset{\frown}{BAR}$, $\overset{\frown}{RAC}$, or $\overset{\frown}{BAC}$

2.38 a. $\overset{\frown}{AB}$

b. $\overset{\frown}{ACB}$

2.39 The triangle is equilateral, therefore, the segment is 8".

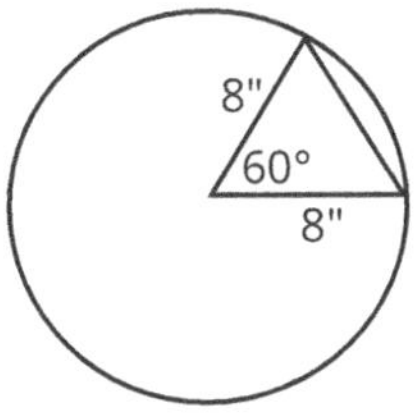

2.40

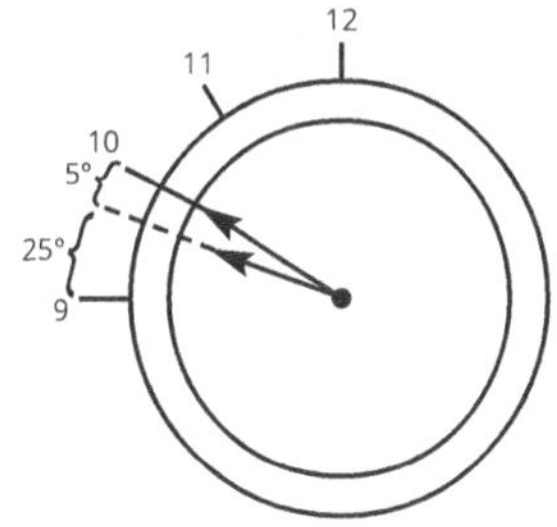

At 9:50 the hour hand is $\frac{50}{60} = \frac{5}{6}$ of the way from 9 to 10. The minute hand is on the 10.

$\frac{5}{6}$ of 30° = 25°

30° – 25° = 5°

2.41

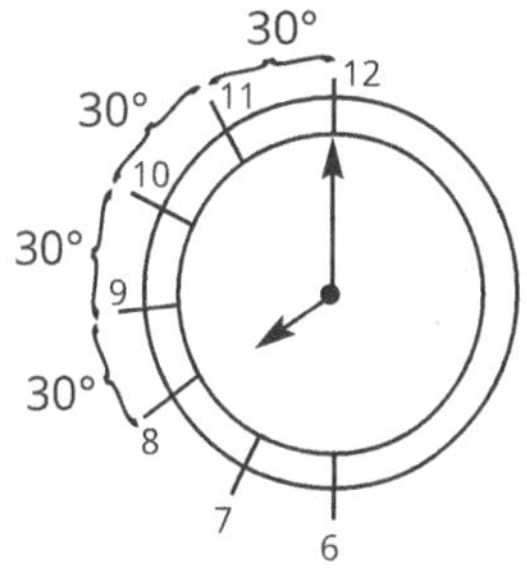

4(30°) = 120°

2.42

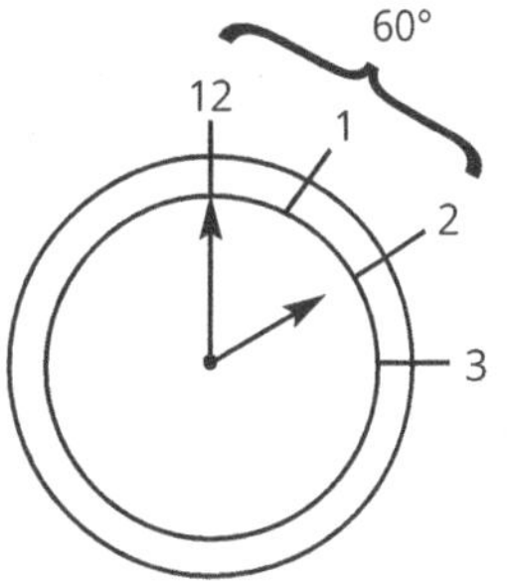

2(30°) = 60°

2.43

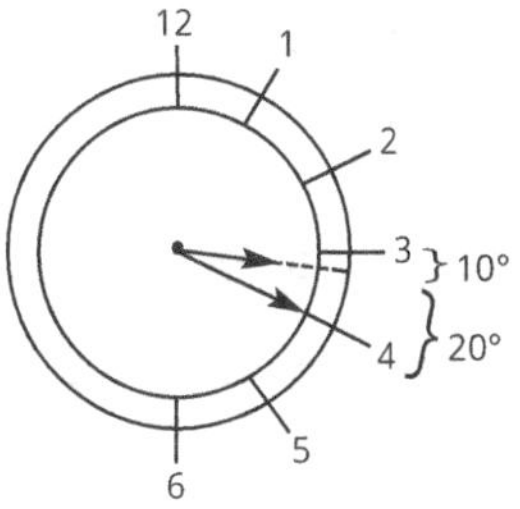

At 3:20 the hour hand is $\frac{20}{60} = \frac{1}{3}$ of the way from 3 to 4. The minute hand is on the 4.

$\frac{1}{3}$ of 30° = 10°

30° – 10° = 20°

2.44

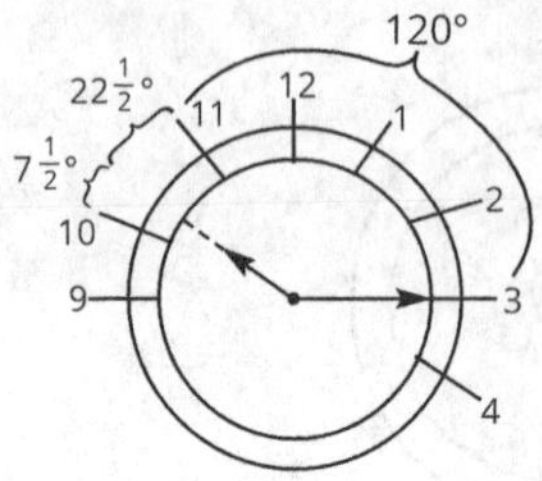

At 10:15 the hour hand has moved $\frac{15}{60} = \frac{1}{4}$ of the way from 10 to 11. The minute hand is on the 3.

$\frac{1}{4}$ of $30° = 7\frac{1}{2}°$

$30° - 7\frac{1}{2}° = 22\frac{1}{2}°$

$120° + 22\frac{1}{2}° = 142\frac{1}{2}°$

2.45

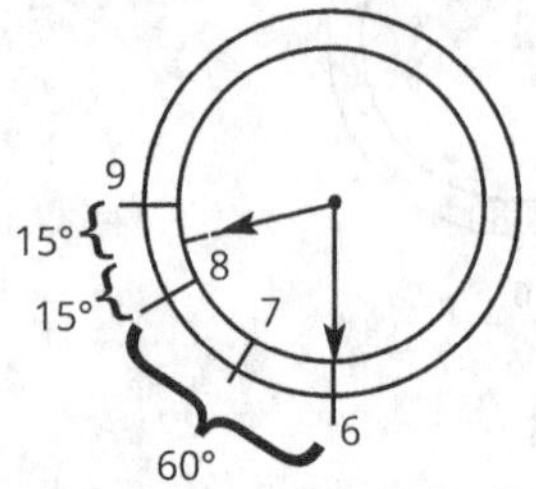

At 8:30 the hour hand is halfway between 8 and 9. The minute hand is on the 6.

$\frac{1}{2}$ of $30° = 15°$

$60° + 15° = 75°$

2.46

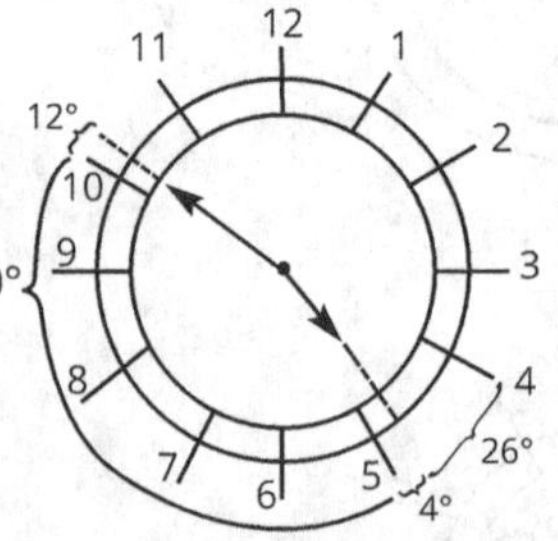

At 4:52 the hour hand is $\frac{52}{60} = \frac{13}{15}$ of the way from 4 to 5. The minute hand is $\frac{2}{5}$ of the way from 10 to 11.

$\frac{13}{15}$ of $30° = 26°$

$30° - 26° = 4°$

$\frac{2}{5}$ of $30° = 12°$

$150° + 4° + 12° = 166°$

2.47

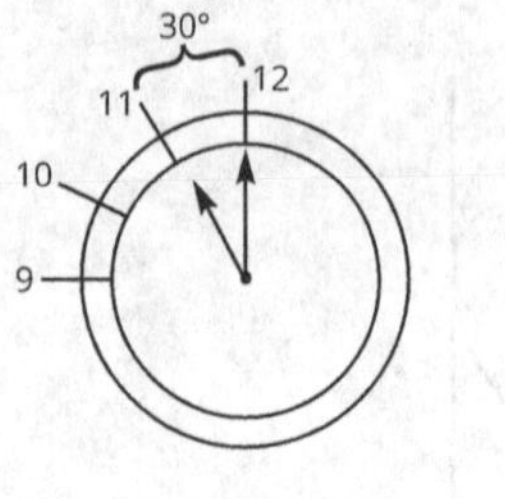

2.48

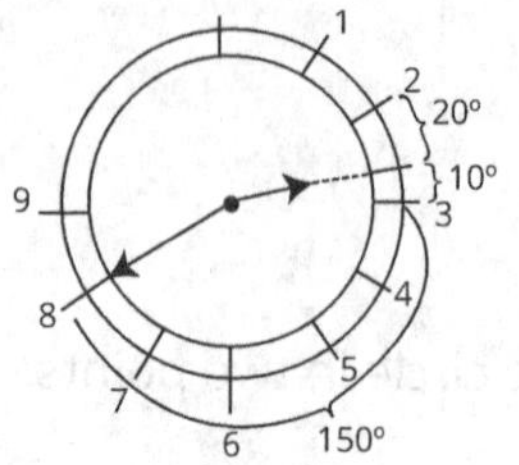

At 2:40 the hour hand is $\frac{40}{60} = \frac{2}{3}$ of the way from 2 to 3. The minute hand is on the 8.

$\frac{2}{3}$ of $30° = 20°$

$30° - 20° = 10°$

$150° + 10° = 160°$

2.49

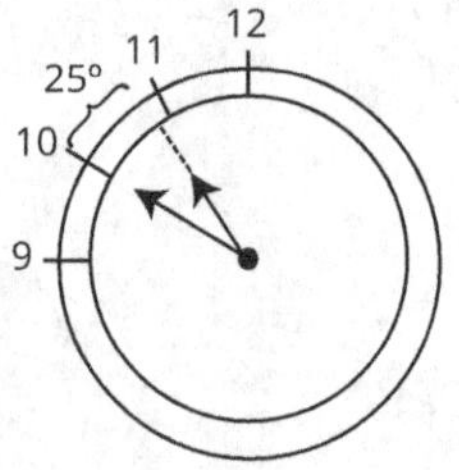

At 10:50 the hour hand is $\frac{50}{60} = \frac{5}{6}$ of the way from 10 to 11. The minute hand is on the 10.

$\frac{5}{6}$ of $30° = 25°$

2.50

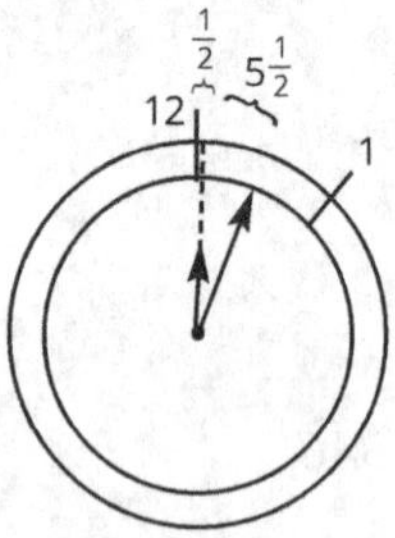

At 12:01 the hour hand is $\frac{1}{60}$ of the way from 12 to 1. The minute hand is $\frac{1}{5}$ of the way from 12 to 1.

$\frac{1}{60}$ of $30° = \frac{1}{2}°$

$\frac{1}{5}$ of $30° = 6°$

$6° - \frac{1}{2}° = 5\frac{1}{2}°$

2.51 $m\angle 2 = 180° - m\angle 1$
$= 180° - 100°$
$= 80°$

2.52 $m\angle 3 = m\widehat{BC} = 30°$

2.53 $m\angle 4 = 180° - m\angle 3$
$= 180° - 30°$
$= 150°$

2.54 $m\widehat{AD} = m\angle 1 = 100°$

2.55 $m\widehat{AC} = m\,AB + m\,BC$
$= m\angle 2 + m\angle BC$
$= 80° + 30°$
$= 110°$

2.56 $m\widehat{DC} = m\angle 4 = 150°$

2.57 $m\widehat{ADB} = 360° - m\angle 2$
$= 360° - 80°$
$= 280°$

2.58 180°

2.59 $m\widehat{DAC} = 360° - m\angle 4$
$= 360° - 150°$
$= 210°$

2.60 $m\widehat{CAB} = 360° - m\angle 3$
$= 360° - 30°$
$= 330°$

2.61 $\overline{RS}, \overline{WR}, \overline{WS}, \overline{SV}, \overline{WT}, \overline{RU}$

2.62 $\overleftrightarrow{WT}, \overleftrightarrow{VS}$

2.63 none

2.64 no

2.65 yes

2.66 $\overline{VS}, \overline{RU}$

2.67 $\overline{AS}, \overline{AR}, \overline{AV}, \overline{AU}$

2.68 Any three:
$\overline{MG}, \overline{MT}, \overline{MH}$, or $\overline{MC}$

2.69 Any three:
$\overline{HG}, \overline{JS}, \overline{CD}$, or $\overline{CT}$

2.70 $\overleftrightarrow{JS}, \overleftrightarrow{CD}$

2.71 $\overline{HG}$ or $\overline{CT}$

2.72 l

2.73 A polygon inscribed in a sphere is a polygon each of whose vertices is a point of the sphere.

2.74 Example:

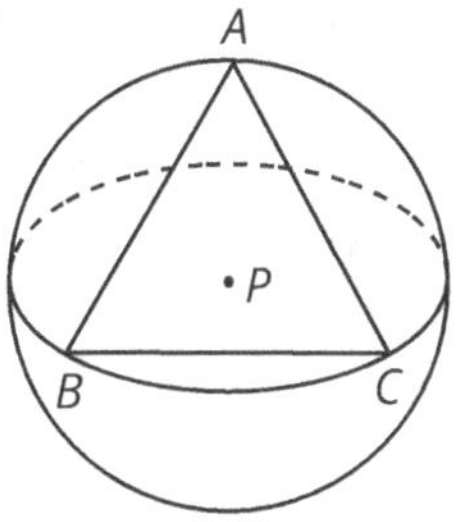

2.75 inscribed in the circle

2.76 circumscribed about the circle

2.77 neither

2.78 neither

2.79 neither

2.80
1. **STATEMENT**
   $\overline{AB}$ is the diameter of circle O
   $\overleftrightarrow{AC}$ and $\overleftrightarrow{BD}$ are tangents
   REASON
   Given
2. **STATEMENT**
   $\overline{AB} \perp \overline{AC}$
   $\overline{AB} \perp \overline{BD}$
   REASON
   Radius $\perp$ to tangent
3. **STATEMENT**
   $\overleftrightarrow{AC} \parallel \overleftrightarrow{BD}$
   REASON
   Two lines $\perp$ to same line are $\parallel$.

2.81
1. **Given**
2. **STATEMENT**
   $\overline{AR} \perp \overleftrightarrow{RS}$
   $\overline{BS} \perp \overleftrightarrow{RS}$
   REASON
   Radius $\perp$ to tangent
3. **STATEMENT**
   $\overline{AR} \parallel \overline{BS}$
   REASON
   Two lines $\perp$ to same line are $\parallel$.

2.82
1. **Given**
2. **STATEMENT**
   Draw $\overline{RA}, \overline{RB}, \overline{RP}$
   REASON
   Auxiliary lines
3. **STATEMENT**
   $RA = RB$
   REASON
   Radii of same $\odot$ are =.
4. **STATEMENT**
   $\overline{RP} = \overline{RP}$
   REASON
   Reflexive
5. **STATEMENT**
   $\overline{RA} \perp \overline{AP}, \overline{RB} \perp \overline{PB}$
   REASON
   Radii $\perp$ to tangent
6. **STATEMENT**
   rt. $\triangle RAP \cong$ rt. $\triangle RBP$
   REASON
   HL

7. **STATEMENT**
   $PA = PB$
   REASON
   CPCTE

2.83 1. **Given**
2. **STATEMENT**
   $\overline{RA} \perp \overline{AE}$, $\overline{SE} \perp \overline{AE}$
   REASON
   Radii ⊥ to tangent
3. **STATEMENT**
   $\overline{RA} \parallel \overline{SE}$
   REASON
   Two lines ⊥ to same line are | |.
4. **STATEMENT**
   $\angle R = \angle S$
   REASON
   If lines | |, alternate interior ∠'s are =.

2.84 1. **Given**
2. **STATEMENT**
   Draw $\overline{OA}$, $\overline{OB}$
   REASON
   Auxiliary lines
3. **STATEMENT**
   $\overline{OR} \perp \overline{AB}$
   REASON
   Radius ⊥ to tangent
4. **STATEMENT**
   $OR = OR$
   REASON
   Reflexive
5. **STATEMENT**
   $OA = OB$
   REASON
   Radii of same ⊙ are =.
6. **STATEMENT**
   rt. $\triangle AOR \cong$ rt. $\triangle BOR$
   REASON
   HL
7. **STATEMENT**
   $AR = RB$
   REASON
   CPCTE

2.85 1. **Given**
2. **STATEMENT**
   m $\overset{\frown}{RS}$ + m $\overset{\frown}{ST}$ = m $\overset{\frown}{RT}$
   m $\overset{\frown}{RT}$ + m $\overset{\frown}{TQ}$ = m $\overset{\frown}{RQ}$
   REASON
   Arc addition
3. **STATEMENT**
   m $\overset{\frown}{RS}$ + m $\overset{\frown}{ST}$ + m $\overset{\frown}{TQ}$ = m $\overset{\frown}{RQ}$
   REASON
   Substitution

2.86 1. **Given**
2. **STATEMENT**
   $OD = OC$; $OB = OA$
   REASON
   Radii of same ⊙ are =.
3. **STATEMENT**
   m $\angle DOB$ = m $\angle COA$
   REASON
   Vertical ∠'s are =.
4. **STATEMENT**
   $\triangle DOB \cong \triangle COA$
   REASON
   SAS
5. **STATEMENT**
   $BD = CA$
   REASON
   CPCTE

2.87 1. **STATEMENT**
   m $\angle XOY$ = m $\angle WOV$, m $\overset{\frown}{YZ}$ = m $\overset{\frown}{ZW}$
   REASON
   Given
2. **STATEMENT**
   m $\angle YOZ$ = m $\angle ZOW$
   REASON
   Central ∠'s = arcs.
3. **STATEMENT**
   m $\angle XOY$ + m $\angle YOZ$ = m $\angle WOV$ + m $\angle ZOW$
   REASON
   Addition property of equality
4. **STATEMENT**
   m $\angle XOZ$ = m $\angle ZOV$
   REASON
   Angle addition
5. **STATEMENT**
   m $\overset{\frown}{XZ}$ = m $\overset{\frown}{ZV}$
   REASON
   Measure of arc = measure of central ∠.

2.88 1. **STATEMENT**
   m $\overset{\frown}{TS}$ = 30°
   REASON
   Given
2. **STATEMENT**
   m $\angle SRT$ = 30°
   REASON
   Central ∠ = arc.

3. **STATEMENT**
   $\angle T = \angle W$
   REASON
   Base $\angle$ of isosceles $\triangle$'s are =.

4. **STATEMENT**
   m $\angle SRT$ = m $\angle T$ + m $\angle W$
   REASON
   Exterior $\angle$ = sum of remote interior $\angle$' s.

5. **STATEMENT**
   30° = 2(m $\angle T$)
   REASON
   Substitution

6. **STATEMENT**
   m $\angle T$ = 15°
   REASON
   Division

2.89 a. minor arc
b. $m\overset{\frown}{QR} = 180° - 48°$
$= 132°$

2.90 a. major arc
b. $m\overset{\frown}{QSP} = m\overset{\frown}{QR} + m\overset{\frown}{RS} + m\overset{\frown}{SP}$
$= 132° + 48° + 132°$
$= 312°$

2.91 a. semicircle
b. 180°

2.92 a. minor arc
b. $m\overset{\frown}{PQ} = m\overset{\frown}{RS} = 48°$

2.93 a. major arc
b. $m\overset{\frown}{PQS} = m\overset{\frown}{PQ} + m\overset{\frown}{QR} + m\overset{\frown}{RS}$
$= 48° + 132° + 48°$
$= 228°$

2.94 a. semicircle
b. 180°

2.95 Given: $m\overset{\frown}{AB} = m\overset{\frown}{CD}$
To Prove: m $\angle 1$ = m $\angle 2$

1. **STATEMENT**
   $\overset{\frown}{AB} = \overset{\frown}{CD}$
   REASON
   Given

2. **STATEMENT**
   m $\angle 1$ = $m\overset{\frown}{AB}$, m $\angle 2$ = $m\overset{\frown}{CD}$
   REASON
   Central $\angle$ = arc.

3. **STATEMENT**
   m $\angle 1$ = m $\angle 2$
   REASON
   Substitution

2.96 Given: $m\overset{\frown}{AB} = m\overset{\frown}{CD}$
To Prove: $m\,AB = m\,CD$

1. **STATEMENT**
   $\overset{\frown}{AB} = \overset{\frown}{CD}$
   REASON
   Given

2. **STATEMENT**
   Draw $\overline{OA}$, $\overline{OB}$, $\overline{OC}$, $\overline{OD}$.
   REASON
   Auxiliary lines

3. **STATEMENT**
   $OA = OC$, $OB = OD$
   REASON
   Radii of same $\odot$ are =.

4. **STATEMENT**
   m $\angle 1$ = m $\angle 2$
   REASON
   If $\frown$'s =, then central $\angle$'s =.

5. **STATEMENT**
   $\triangle AOB \cong \triangle DOC$
   REASON
   SAS

6. **STATEMENT**
   $AB = CD$
   REASON
   CPCTE

2.97

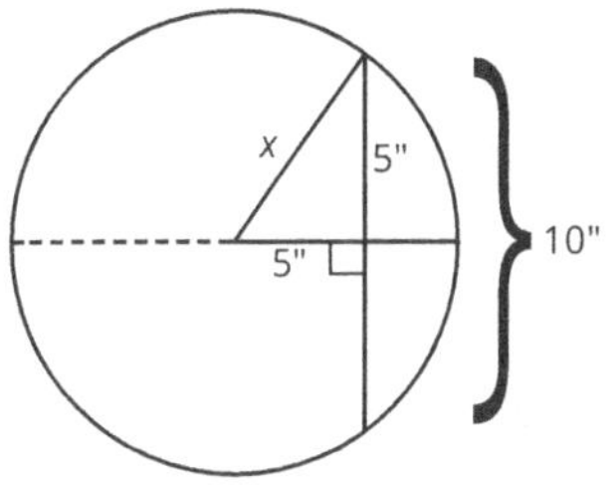

$x = 5\sqrt{2}$ in.

2.98

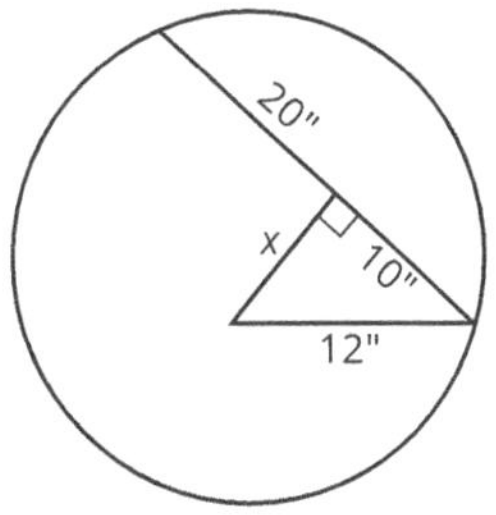

$$x^2 + 10^2 = 12^2$$
$$x^2 + 100 = 144$$
$$x^2 = 44$$
$$\sqrt{x^2} = \sqrt{44}$$
$$x = 2\sqrt{11} \text{ in.}$$

2.99

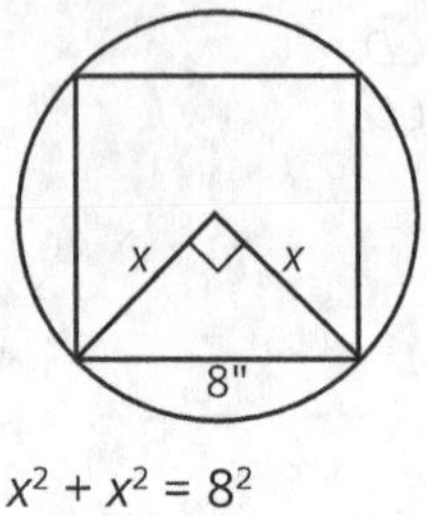

$x^2 + x^2 = 8^2$
$2x^2 = 64$
$x^2 = 32$
$\sqrt{x^2} = \sqrt{32}$
$x = 4\sqrt{2}$ in.

2.100 $AB = 2RB = 2(5) = 10$

2.101 $AR = \frac{1}{2}AB = \frac{1}{2}(12) = 6$

2.102 $(OB)^2 = (OR)^2 + (RB)^2$
$(OB)^2 = 3^2 + 4^2$
$(OB)^2 = 9 + 16$
$(OB)^2 = 25$
$\sqrt{(OB)^2} = \sqrt{25}$
$OB = 5$

2.103 $(OR)^2 + (RB)^2 = (OB)^2$
$(OR)^2 = (OB)^2 - (RB)^2$
$(OR)^2 = 10^2 - 8^2$
$(OR)^2 = 100 - 64$
$(OR)^2 = 36$
$\sqrt{(OR)^2} = \sqrt{36}$
$OR = 6$

2.104 $(OR)^2 + (RB)^2 = (OB)^2$
$(OR)^2 + (AR)^2 = (OB)^2$
$(OR)^2 = (OB)^2 - (AR)^2$
$(OR)^2 = 10^2 - 6^2$
$(OR)^2 = 100 - 36$
$(OR)^2 = 64$
$\sqrt{(OR)^2} = \sqrt{64}$
$OR = 8$

2.105 $(OR)^2 + (RB)^2 = (OB)^2$
$(OR)^2 + \frac{1}{2}(AB)^2 = (OB)^2$
$(OR)^2 + \frac{1}{2}(30)^2 = 17^2$
$(OR)^2 + (15)^2 = 17^2$
$(OR)^2 + 225 = 289$
$(OR)^2 = 64$
$\sqrt{(OR)^2} = \sqrt{64}$
$OR = 8$

2.106 $m\widehat{AC} = m\widehat{BC} = 20°$

2.107 $m\ BAC = 360° - m\ \angle BOC$
$= 360° - 30°$
$= 330°$

SELF TEST 2

2.01 yes
2.02 yes
2.03 no
2.04 yes
2.05 yes
2.06

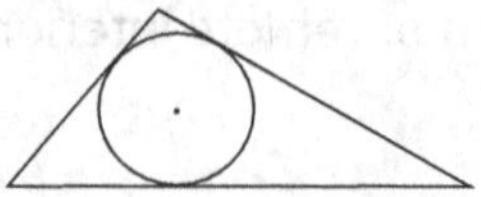

2.07

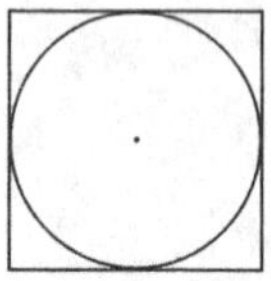

2.08

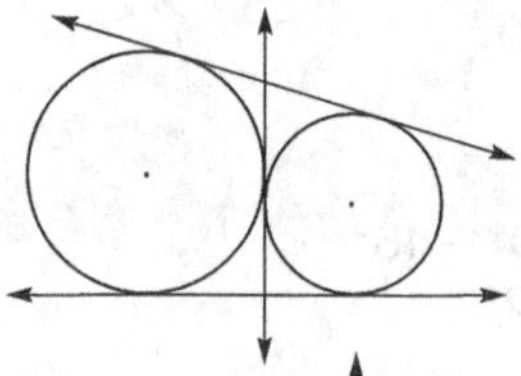

2.09

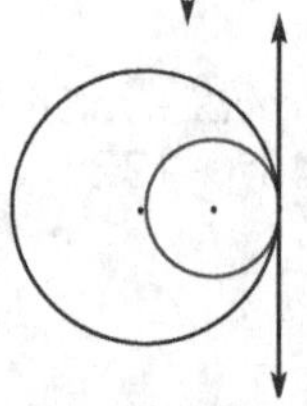

2.010

2.011

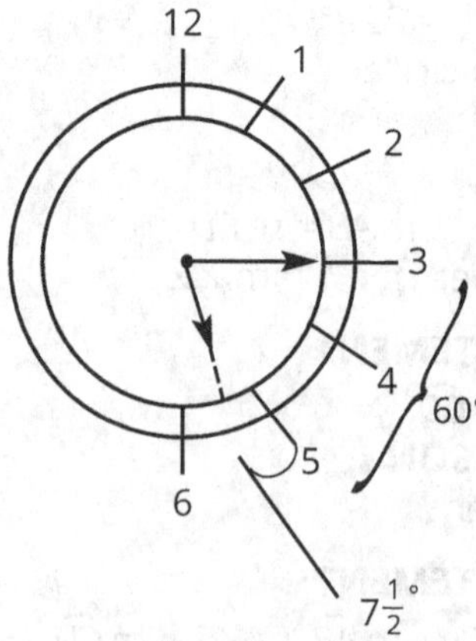

At 5:15 the hour hand is $\frac{15}{60} = \frac{1}{4}$ of the way from 5 to 6. The minute hand is on the 3.
$\frac{1}{4}$ of $30° = 7\frac{1}{2}°$
$60°$ of $7\frac{1}{2}° = 67\frac{1}{2}°$

2.012 $360° \div 12 = 30°$

2.013

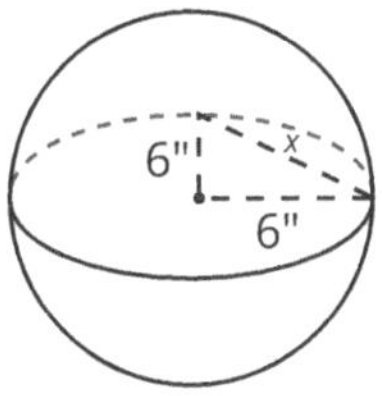

$x = 6\sqrt{2}$ "

2.014 $\overset{\frown}{AB}$

2.015 $\overline{AB}$

2.016 $m\ \overset{\frown}{DB} = m\ \angle DPB = 60°$

2.017
$m\ \overset{\frown}{AF} = m\ \overset{\frown}{AD}$
$m\ \overset{\frown}{AF} = 180° - m\ \overset{\frown}{DB}$
$110° = 180° - m\ \overset{\frown}{DB}$
$m\ \overset{\frown}{DB} + 110° = 180°$
$m\ \overset{\frown}{DB} = 70°$

2.018 Since $AC = CD = DB$, these segments are also equal to CP and PD. Triangle CPD is therefore equilateral and $m\ \angle CPD = 60°$.

2.019 t

2.020 $PB = PE + EB$; $PE = EB$
$PB = 2PE$
$= 2(3)$
$= 6$

2.021 **STATEMENT**
$\overline{RS} \perp \overline{TW}$
REASON
Given

2.022 **STATEMENT**
$m\ \overset{\frown}{TR} = m\ \overset{\frown}{RW}$
REASON
Diameter ⊥ to chord bisects major arc.

2.023 **STATEMENT**
$\overline{TR} = \overline{RW}$
REASON
If ⌒'s =, chords =.

2.024 **STATEMENT**
△*TRW* is isosceles.
REASON
Definition

SECTION 3

3.1

a. $m\ \overset{\frown}{BA} = 360° - (m\ \overset{\frown}{CDA} + m\ \overset{\frown}{BC})$
$= 360° - (260° + 30°)$
$= 360° - 290°$
$= 70°$

b. $m\ \overset{\frown}{CD} = 180° - (m\ \overset{\frown}{BA} + m\ \overset{\frown}{BC})$
$= 180° - (70° + 30°)$
$= 180° - 100°$
$= 80°$

c. $\angle BAD = \frac{1}{2}(m\ \overset{\frown}{BC} + m\ \overset{\frown}{CD})$
$= \frac{1}{2}(30° + 80°)$
$= \frac{1}{2}(110°)$
$= 55°$

d. $\angle BAC = \frac{1}{2} m\ \overset{\frown}{BC}$
$= \frac{1}{2}(30°)$
$= 15°$

e. $\angle CAD = \frac{1}{2} m\ \overset{\frown}{CD}$
$= \frac{1}{2}(80°)$
$= 40°$

3.2

a. $\angle BAD = \frac{1}{2} m\ \overset{\frown}{BD}$
$70° = \frac{1}{2} m\ \overset{\frown}{BD}$
$140° = m\ \overset{\frown}{BD}$

b. $m\ \overset{\frown}{BA} = 180° - m\ \overset{\frown}{BD}$
$= 180° - 140°$
$= 40°$

c. $\angle CAD = \frac{1}{2} m\ \overset{\frown}{CD}$
$= \frac{1}{2}(m\ \overset{\frown}{BD} - m\ \overset{\frown}{BC})$
$= \frac{1}{2}(140° - 50°)$
$= \frac{1}{2}(90°)$
$= 45°$

d. $\angle BAC = \angle BAD - \angle CAD$
$= 70° - 45°$
$= 25°$

3.3 a. $\frac{1}{2}\widehat{SV} = \angle U$
$\widehat{SV} = 2\angle U$
$= 2(70°)$
$= 140°$

$\angle VST = \frac{1}{2}m\,\widehat{SV}$
$= \frac{1}{2}(140°)$
$= 70°$

b. $\angle USV = 180° - (\angle USR + \angle VST)$
$= 180° - (50° + 70°)$
$= 180° - 120°$
$= 60°$

$\angle V = 180° - (\angle U + \angle USV)$
$= 180° - (70° + 60°)$
$= 180° - 130°$
$= 50°$

c. $\frac{1}{2}\widehat{SV} = \angle U$
$\widehat{SV} = 2\angle U$
$= 2(70°)$
$= 140°$

d. $\frac{1}{2}m\,\widehat{US} = \angle V$
$m\,\widehat{US} = 2\angle V$
$= 2(50°)$
$= 100°$

e. $\frac{1}{2}m\,\widehat{UV} = \angle USV$
$m\,\widehat{UV} = 2\angle USV$
$= 2(60°)$
$= 120°$

f. $\angle USV = 180° - (\angle USR + \angle VST)$
$= 180° - (50° + 70°)$
$= 180° - 120°$
$= 60°$

3.4 a. $\frac{1}{2}m\,\widehat{SUV} = \angle RSV$
$m\,\widehat{SUV} = 2\angle RSV$
$= 2(125°)$
$= 250°$

b. $m\,\widehat{SV} = 360° - m\,\widehat{SUV}$
$= 360° - 250°$
$= 110°$

c. $\angle TSV = \frac{1}{2}m\,\widehat{SV}$
$= \frac{1}{2}(110°)$
$= 55°$

d. $\angle U = \frac{1}{2}m\,\widehat{SV}$
$= \frac{1}{2}(110°)$
$= 55°$

3.5 a. 90°

b. $\angle ABD + \angle ADB = 180° - \angle BAD$
$= 180° - 90°$
$= 90°$

3.6 a. $\angle ADB = \frac{1}{2}AB$
$= \frac{1}{2}(120°)$
$= 60°$

b. $m\,\widehat{AD} = 180° - m\,\widehat{AB}$
$= 180° - 120°$
$= 60°$

c. $\angle ACD = \frac{1}{2}m\,\widehat{AD}$
$= \frac{1}{2}(60°)$
$= 30°$

3.7 a. $\angle ABD = 180° - (\angle BAD + \angle ADB)$
$= 180° - (90° + 70°)$
$= 180° - 160°$
$= 20°$

b. $\frac{1}{2}m\,\widehat{AB} = \widehat{ADB}$
$m\,\widehat{AB} = 2\angle ADB$
$= 2(70°)$
$= 140°$

c. $\frac{1}{2}m\,\widehat{AD} = \angle ABD$
$m\,\widehat{AD} = 2\angle ABD$
$= 2(20°)$
$= 40°$

3.8 a. $\frac{1}{2}m\,\widehat{DC} = \angle DBC$
$m\,\widehat{DC} = 2\angle DBC$
$= 2(40°)$
$= 80°$

b. $m\,\widehat{BC} = 180° - m\,\widehat{DC}$
$= 180° - 80°$
$= 100°$

c. $\angle ECB = \frac{1}{2}m\,\widehat{BC}$
$= \frac{1}{2}(100°)$
$= 50°$

d. $\angle DCF = \frac{1}{2} m\,\widehat{DC}$
$= \frac{1}{2}(80°)$
$= 40°$

e. $\angle BDC = \frac{1}{2} m\,\widehat{BC}$
$= \frac{1}{2}(100°)$
$= 50°$

3.9 a. $\angle Q = \frac{1}{2} m\,\widehat{TS}$
$= \frac{1}{2}(96°)$
$= 48°$

b. $\angle R = \frac{1}{2} m\,\widehat{TS}$
$= \frac{1}{2}(96°)$
$= 48°$

3.10 a. $\angle T = \frac{1}{2} m\,\widehat{QR}$
$= \frac{1}{2}(118°)$
$= 59°$

b. $\angle S = \frac{1}{2} m\,\widehat{QR}$
$= \frac{1}{2}(118°)$
$= 59°$

3.11 a. $\frac{1}{2} m\,\widehat{TS} = \angle Q$
$m\,\widehat{TS} = 2\angle Q$
$= 2(44°)$
$= 88°$

b. $\angle R = \frac{1}{2} m\,\widehat{TS}$
$= \frac{1}{2}(88°)$
$= 44°$

3.12 a. $\frac{1}{2} m\,\widehat{TS} = \angle Q$
$m\,\widehat{TS} = 2\angle Q$
$= 2(47°)$
$= 94°$

b. $\angle R = \frac{1}{2} m\,\widehat{TS}$
$= \frac{1}{2}(94°)$
$= 47°$

3.13 yes

3.14 $m\angle 1 = \frac{1}{2}(120°) = 60°$

3.15 $20° = \frac{1}{2}$ measure of intercepted arc of $\angle 1$
$40°$ = measure of intercepted arc of $\angle 1$
$\angle 1 = 40°$ (central $\angle$ = arc)

3.16 measure of intercepted arc of $\angle 1$
$= 360° - (150° + 130°)$
$= 360° - 280°$
$= 80°$

$\angle 1 = \frac{1}{2}$ measure of intercepted arc
$= \frac{1}{2}(80°)$
$= 40°$

3.17 measure of intercepted arc =
$360° - 274° = 86°$

$m\angle 1 = \frac{1}{2}$ measure of intercepted arc
$= \frac{1}{2}(86°)$
$= 43°$

3.18 $\frac{1}{2}$ measure of intercepted arc = $86°$
measure of intercepted arc
$= 2(86°)$
$= 172°$
measure of intercepted arc of $\angle 1$
measure of intercepted arc
$= 360° - 172°$
$= 188°$
$\angle 1 = \frac{1}{2}$ measure of intercepted arc
$= \frac{1}{2}(188°)$
$= 94°$

3.19 $90°$

3.20 measure of intercepted arc of $\angle 1$
$= 360° - (125° + 125°)$
$= 360° - 250°$
$= 110°$
$\angle 1 = \frac{1}{2}$ measure of intercepted arc
$= \frac{1}{2}(110°)$
$= 55°$

3.21 a. $m\angle 1 = \frac{1}{2}(50° + 30°)$
$= \frac{1}{2}(80°)$
$= 40°$

b. $m\angle 2 = 180° - m\angle 1$
$= 180° - 40°$
$= 140°$
c. $m\angle 3 = m\angle 1 = 40°$
d. $m\angle 4 = m\angle 2 = 140°$

3.22 $m\angle 2 = \frac{1}{2}(46° + 42°)$
$= \frac{1}{2}(88°)$
$= 44°$
$m\angle 4 = m\angle 2 = 44°$
$m\angle 1 = 180° - m\angle 2$
$= 180° - 44°$
$= 136°$
$m\angle 3 = m\angle 1 = 136°$

a. 136°
b. 44°
c. 136°
d. 44°

3.23 a. $m\angle 1 = \frac{1}{2}(36° + 40°)$
$= \frac{1}{2}(76°)$
$= 38°$
b. $m\angle 2 = 180° - 38° = 142°$
c. $m\angle 3 = m\angle 1 = 38°$
d. $m\angle 4 = m\angle 2 = 142°$

3.24 a. 78°
b. $m\angle 2 = 180° - m\angle 1$
$= 180° - 78°$
$= 102°$
c. $m\angle 3 = m\angle 1 = 78°$
d. $m\angle 4 = m\angle 2 = 102°$
e. $m\widehat{AB} = m\angle 2 = 102°$
f. $m\widehat{BC} = m\angle 3 = 78°$
g. $m\widehat{DC} = m\angle 4 = 102°$

3.25 $m\angle 3 = \frac{1}{2}(80° + 120°)$
$= \frac{1}{2}(200°)$
$= 100°$
$m\angle 4 = m\angle 3 = 100°$
$m\angle 1 = 180° - m\angle 3$
$= 180° - 100°$
$= 80°$
$m\angle 2 = m\angle 1 = 80°$

a. 80°
b. 80°
c. 100°
d. 100°

3.26 $40° = \frac{1}{2}(x + 41°)$
$80° = x + 41°$
$39° = x$

3.27 $89° = \frac{1}{2}(x + 88°)$
$178° = x + 88°$
$x = 90°$

3.28 $137° = \frac{1}{2}(x + 94°)$
$274° = x + 94°$
$x = 180°$

3.29 $50° = \frac{1}{2}(x + x)$
$100° = x + x$
$100° = 2x$
$x = 50°$

3.30 $120° = \frac{1}{2}(x + 2x)$
$240° = 3x$
$x = 80°$

3.31 $180° - 37° = \frac{1}{2}(x + 5 + x - 5)$
$180° - 37° = \frac{1}{2}(2x)$
$143° = \frac{1}{2}(2x)$
$x = 143°$

3.32

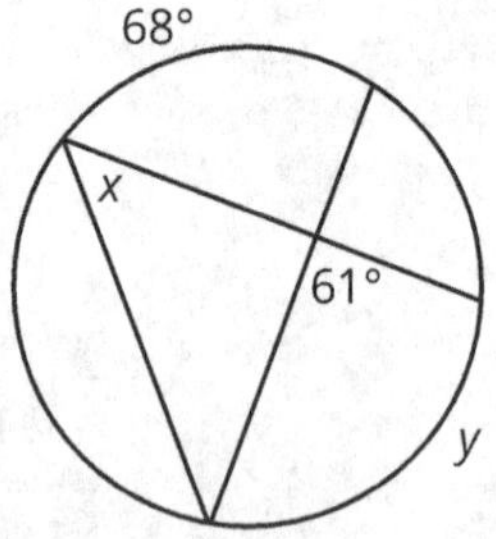

$x = \frac{1}{2}y$
$61° = \frac{1}{2}(y + 68°)$
$122° = y + 68°$
$54° = y$
$x = \frac{1}{2}(54°)$
$x = 27°$

3.33

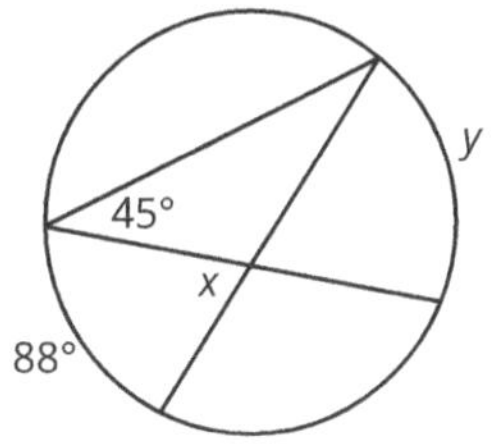

$x = \frac{1}{2}(88° + y)$

$y = 2(45°)$

$y = 90°$

$x = \frac{1}{2}(88° + 90°)$

$x = \frac{1}{2}(178°)$

$x = 89°$

3.34 $\angle 1 = \frac{1}{2}(100° - 30°)$

$\angle 1 = \frac{1}{2}(70°)$

$\angle 1 = 35°$

3.35 $\angle 1 = \frac{1}{2}(140° - 40°)$

$\angle 1 = \frac{1}{2}(100°)$

$\angle 1 = 50°$

3.36 $\angle 1 = \frac{1}{2}(280° - 60°)$

$\angle 1 = \frac{1}{2}(220°)$

$\angle 1 = 110°$

3.37 $\angle 1 = \frac{1}{2}(300° - 60°)$

$\angle 1 = \frac{1}{2}(240°)$

$\angle 1 = 120°$

3.38 $\angle 1 = \frac{1}{2}(20° - 10°)$

$\angle 1 = \frac{1}{2}(10°)$

$\angle 1 = 5°$

3.39 $28° = \frac{1}{2}(114° - x)$

$56° = 114° - x$

$x = 58°$

3.40 $30° = \frac{1}{2}(x - 40°)$

$60° = x - 40°$

$x = 100°$

3.41 $x = \frac{1}{2}(x + 60° - 20°)$

$x = \frac{1}{2}(x + 40°)$

$2x = x + 40°$

$x = 40°$

3.42 $x = \frac{1}{2}[x + 114° - (x + 50°)]$

$x = \frac{1}{2}[64°]$

$2x = 64°$

$x = 32°$

3.43 $70° = \frac{1}{2}[(360° - x) - x]$

$70° = \frac{1}{2}[360° - 2x]$

$140° = 360° - 2x$

$2x = 220°$

$x = 110°$

3.44 $90° = \frac{1}{2}[x - (360° - x)]$

$90° = \frac{1}{2}[2x - 360°]$

$180° = 2x - 360°$

$2x = 540°$

$x = 270°$

3.45 $m\,\widehat{ED} = 180° - (m\,\widehat{BA} + m\,\widehat{AE})$
$= 180° - (68° + 53°)$
$= 180° - 121°$
$= 59°$

$m\angle 1 = \frac{1}{2}(m\,\widehat{BA} + m\,\widehat{ED})$

$= \frac{1}{2}(68° + 59°)$

$= \frac{1}{2}(127°)$

$= 63\frac{1}{2}°$

3.46 $m\,\widehat{CD} = 180° - (m\,\widehat{BC})$
$= 180° - 72°$
$= 108°$

$m\angle 2 = \frac{1}{2}(m\,\widehat{BA} + m\,\widehat{CB} + m\,\widehat{CD})$

$= \frac{1}{2}(68° + 72° + 108°)$

$= \frac{1}{2}(248°)$
$= 124°$

3.47 $m\angle 3 = \frac{1}{2}m\overset{\frown}{ED}$
$= \frac{1}{2}(59°)$
$= 29\frac{1}{2}°$

3.48 $m\angle 4 = \frac{1}{2}(m\overset{\frown}{CB} + m\overset{\frown}{CD})$
$= \frac{1}{2}(72° + 108°)$
$= \frac{1}{2}(180°)$
$= 90°$

3.49 $m\angle 5 = \frac{1}{2}m\overset{\frown}{CD}$
$= \frac{1}{2}(108°)$
$= 54°$

3.50 $m\angle 6 = \frac{1}{2}(m\overset{\frown}{AE} + m\overset{\frown}{BCD})$
$= \frac{1}{2}(53° + 180°)$
$= \frac{1}{2}(233°)$
$= 116\frac{1}{2}°$

3.51 $m\angle 7 = m\overset{\frown}{BA} + m\overset{\frown}{AE}$
$= 68° + 53°$
$= 121°$

3.52 90°

3.53 $2 \cdot x = 3 \cdot 6$
$2x = 18$
$x = 9$

3.54 $12 \cdot x = 9 \cdot 4$
$12x = 36$
$x = 3$

3.55 $\frac{8}{2} = \frac{x}{2}$
$x^2 = 16$
$\sqrt{x^2} = \sqrt{16}$
$x = 4$

3.56 $\frac{x}{6} = \frac{6}{3}$
$3x = 36$
$x = 12$

3.57 $2 \cdot x = 3 \cdot 4$
$2x = 12$
$x = 6$

3.58 $\frac{x+2}{6} = \frac{6}{2}$
$2x + 4 = 36$
$2x = 32$
$x = 16$

3.59 $4(x + 4) = 3(8)$
$4x + 16 = 24$
$4x = 8$
$x = 2$

3.60 $cx = ab$
$x = \frac{ab}{c}$

3.61 $AM \cdot MB = CM \cdot MD$
$7 \cdot 6 = 8 \cdot MD$
$8MD = 42$
$MD = \frac{42}{8} = \frac{21}{4} = 5\frac{1}{4}$
$CD = CM + MD$
$CD = 8 + 5\frac{1}{4}$
$CD = 13\frac{1}{4}$

3.62 $AM \cdot MB = CM \cdot DM$
$AM(AB - AM) = 8 \cdot 6$
$AM(16 - AM) = 48$
$16AM - (AM)^2 = 48$
$(AM)^2 - 16AM + 48 = 0$
$(AM - 12)(AM - 4) = 0$
$AM - 12 = 0$ or $AM - 4 = 0$
$AM = 12$ $AM = 4$

3.63 $AM \cdot MB = CM \cdot MD$
$AM(AB - AM) = CM(CD - CM)$
$8(16 - 8) = CM(20 - CM)$
$64 = 20CM - (CM)^2$
$(CM)^2 - 20CM + 64 = 0$
$(CM - 16)(CM - 4) = 0$
$CM - 16 = 0$ or $CM - 4 = 0$
$CM = 16$ $CM = 4$

3.64 $AM \cdot MB = CM \cdot MD$
$AM(AB - AM) = (CD - MD)MD$
$AM(12 - AM) = (12 - 3)3$
$12AM - (AM)^2 = 27$
$(AM)^2 - 12AM + 27 = 0$
$(AM - 9)(AM - 3) = 0$
$AM - 9 = 0$ or $AM - 3 = 0$
$AM = 9$ $AM = 3$

3.65 $\frac{PB}{PA} = \frac{PA}{PE}$
$\frac{BE + PE}{PA} = \frac{PA}{PE}$
$\frac{BE + 4}{6} = \frac{6}{4}$
$4(BE + 4) = 36$
$4BE + 16 = 36$
$4BE = 20$
$BE = 5$

3.66
$$\frac{PC}{PA} = \frac{PA}{PD}$$
$$\frac{DC + PD}{PA} = \frac{PA}{PD}$$
$$\frac{7\sqrt{2} + 5\sqrt{2}}{PA} = \frac{PA}{5\sqrt{2}}$$
$$\frac{12\sqrt{2}}{PA} = \frac{PA}{5\sqrt{2}}$$
$$(PA)^2 = 120$$
$$\sqrt{(PA)^2} = \sqrt{120}$$
$$PA = 2\sqrt{30}$$

3.67
$$\frac{BP}{PA} = \frac{PA}{EP}$$
$$\frac{BP}{PA} = \frac{PA}{BP - BE}$$
$$\frac{BP}{10} = \frac{10}{BP - 21}$$
$$BP(BP - 21) = 10(10)$$
$$(BP)^2 - 21BP = 100$$
$$(BP)^2 - 21BP - 100 = 0$$
$$(BP - 25)(BP + 4) = 0$$
$BP - 25 = 0$ or $BP + 4 = 0$

$BP = 25$ or $BP = -4$; not acceptable

$\therefore BP = 25$

3.68
$$PC \cdot PD = PB \cdot PE$$
$$6 \cdot 4 = (x + 5) \cdot x$$
$$24 = x^2 + 5x$$
$$x^2 + 5x - 24 = 0$$
$$(x + 8)(x - 3) = 0$$
$x + 8 = 0$

$x = -8$; not acceptable

or $x - 3 = 0$

$x = 3$

$\therefore x = 3$

3.69

1. **STATEMENT**
   $PA = PB$
   REASON
   Given
2. **STATEMENT**
   $\frac{PA}{PC} = \frac{PB}{PD}$
   REASON
   Two secant segments theorem
3. **STATEMENT**
   $\frac{PA}{PC} = \frac{PA}{PD}$
   REASON
   Substitution
4. **STATEMENT**
   $PA \cdot PC = PA \cdot PD$
   REASON
   POP
5. **STATEMENT**
   $PC = PD$
   REASON
   Division property of equality

3.70

1. **STATEMENT**
   $\overline{AB}$ is diameter, $\overline{BC}$ is tangent to circle O.
   REASON
   Given
2. **STATEMENT**
   $\angle A = \angle A$
   REASON
   Reflexive
3. **STATEMENT**
   $\angle CBA$ is rt. $\angle$
   REASON
   Radius $\perp$ to tangent
4. **STATEMENT**
   $\angle BXA = 90°$
   REASON
   Inscribed in semicircle
5. **STATEMENT**
   $\angle CBA = \angle BXA$
   REASON
   All rt. $\angle$'s =.
6. **STATEMENT**
   $\triangle AXB \cong \triangle ABC$
   REASON
   AA

SELF TEST 3

3.01 inscribed
3.02 tangent
3.03 90°
3.04 $\frac{1}{2}(\widehat{XPQ} - \widehat{XQ})$
3.05 equal
3.06 central ∠'s
3.07 90°
3.08 half the sum of the intercepted arcs
3.09 half the difference of the intercepted arcs
3.010 bisects
3.011 $\overline{BT}$, $\overline{BU}$, or $\overline{BD}$
3.012 $\overline{RS}$
3.013 $\overleftrightarrow{CD}$
3.014 ∠*DBU*
3.015 no
3.016 $\frac{1}{2}(\widehat{BG} + \widehat{CD})$
3.017 $\frac{1}{2}(\widehat{CD} - \widehat{GE})$
3.018 $\frac{1}{2}(\text{m}\widehat{CD} + \text{m}\widehat{BG}) = \angle DFC$

$\frac{1}{2}(55° + \text{m}\widehat{BG}) = 40°$

$55° + \text{m}\widehat{BG} = 80°$

$\text{m}\widehat{BG} = 25°$

3.019 $\frac{1}{2}(\text{m}\widehat{CD} - \text{m}\widehat{GE}) = \text{m}\ \angle A$

$\frac{1}{2}(55° - \text{m}\widehat{GE}) = 15°$

$55° - \text{m}\widehat{GE} = 30°$

$\text{m}\widehat{GE} = 25°$

3.020 right
3.021 $2 \cdot HD = 3 \cdot 7$

$2HD = 21$

$HD = \frac{21}{2} = 10\frac{1}{2}$

3.022 $\frac{12}{x} = \frac{x}{3}$

$x^2 = 36$

$\sqrt{x^2} = \sqrt{36}$

$x = 6$

3.023 $x \cdot 10 = 5 \cdot 8$

$10x = 40$

$x = 4$

3.024 $\frac{16}{8} = \frac{8}{x}$

$16x = 64$

$x = 4$

3.025 $(5 + 3)3 = (x + 2)2$

$8(3) = (x + 2)2$

$24 = 2x + 4$

$20 = 2x$

$x = 10$

LIFEPAC TEST

1. r

2. s

3. $\perp$

4. J

5. 3

6. If chords are =, then arcs are =.

7. If arcs are =, then chords are =.

8. Diameter $\perp$ to chord bisects the chord.

9. $A = \frac{1}{2} m\overset{\frown}{BCD}$

$m\overset{\frown}{BCD} = 360° - m\overset{\frown}{BD}$
$= 360° - 150°$
$= 210°$

$\angle A = \frac{1}{2}(210°)$
$= 105°$

10. $m\angle C = \frac{1}{2} m\overset{\frown}{BD}$

$m\angle BDR = \frac{1}{2} m\overset{\frown}{BD}$

$m\angle BDR = m\angle C = 63°$

11. $m\overset{\frown}{DC} = 360° - m\,DAC$

$\frac{1}{2} m\overset{\frown}{DAC} = m\angle RDC$

$\frac{1}{2} m\overset{\frown}{DAC} = 120°$

$m\overset{\frown}{DAC} = 2(120°)$

$m\overset{\frown}{DAC} = 240°$

$m\overset{\frown}{DC} = 360° - 240° = 120°$

12. $\angle 1 = \frac{1}{2}(m\overset{\frown}{VU} - m\overset{\frown}{ST})$
$= \frac{1}{2}(80° - 40°)$
$= \frac{1}{2}(40°)$
$= 20°$

13. $m\angle 2 = \frac{1}{2}(m\overset{\frown}{UV} + m\overset{\frown}{ST})$
$= \frac{1}{2}(70° + 30°)$
$= \frac{1}{2}(100°)$
$= 50°$

14. $m\angle 3 = \frac{1}{2}(m\overset{\frown}{VB} - m\overset{\frown}{BS})$
$= \frac{1}{2}(60° - 30°)$
$= \frac{1}{2}(30°)$
$= 15°$

15. $\frac{1}{2}(m\overset{\frown}{UV} - m\overset{\frown}{ST}) = m\angle 1$

$\frac{1}{2}(m\overset{\frown}{UV} - 20°) = 30°$

$m\overset{\frown}{UV} - 20° = 60°$

$m\overset{\frown}{UV} = 80°$

16. 40°

17. $\overset{\frown}{AC}$

18. $m\overset{\frown}{BC} = 180° - (m\angle 1 + m\angle 3)$
$= 180° - (20° + 20°)$
$= 180° - 40°$
$= 140°$

19. $m\overset{\frown}{ABC} = 180° - m\angle 3$
$= 180° - 30°$
$= 150°$

20. $5 \cdot x = 10 \cdot 4$
$5x = 40$
$x = 8$

21. $\frac{8+4}{x} = \frac{x}{4}$

$\frac{12}{x} = \frac{x}{4}$

$x^2 = 48$

$\sqrt{x^2} = \sqrt{48}$

$x = 4\sqrt{3}$

22. $(5 + 4)4 = (x + 3)3$
$(9)4 = (x + 3)3$
$36 = 3x + 9$
$27 = 3x$
$9 = x$

23. $x \cdot x = 2 \cdot 6$
$x^2 = 12$
$\sqrt{x^2} = \sqrt{12}$
$x = 2\sqrt{3}$

24.

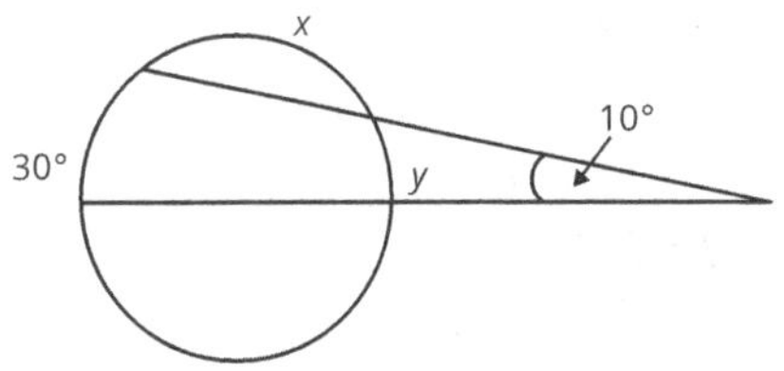

$10° = \frac{1}{2}(30° - y)$
$20° = 30° - y$
$y = 10°$

$x = 180° - (30° - 10°)$
$= 180° - 40°$
$= 140°$

25. $\frac{1}{2}$ measure of intercepted arc = 98°
measure of intercepted arc = 2(98°) = 196°
measure of intercepted arc of
$x = 360° - 196° = 164°$
$\angle x = \frac{1}{2}(164°) = 82°$

ALTERNATE LIFEPAC TEST

1. $\overline{OA}$ or $\overline{OB}$ or $\overline{OD}$
2. $\overrightarrow{AC}$
3. $\overline{AB}$
4. $\overleftrightarrow{BD}$
5. $\angle ABD$ or $\angle ODB$
6. $\angle DOB$ or $\angle DOA$
7. 2
8. 2
9. *S*
10. *S*
11. $\overset{\frown}{RAS}$ is a semicircle; therefore, $m\overset{\frown}{RAS} = 180°$.
12. The measure of a minor arc equals the measure of the central angle;
$m\overset{\frown}{AR} = m\angle 1 = 50°$.
13. The measure of a minor arc equals the measure of the central angle;
$m\angle 2 = m\overset{\frown}{RB} = 48°$.
14. $m\angle 1 = 180° - m\angle AOS$
$m\angle AOS = m\overset{\frown}{AS}$
$m\angle 1 = 180° - m\overset{\frown}{AS}$
$m\angle 1 = 180° - 126°$
$m\angle 1 = 54°$
15. $m\overset{\frown}{ASB} = m\overset{\frown}{AS} + m\overset{\frown}{SB}$
$m\overset{\frown}{AS} = 180° - m\overset{\frown}{AR}$
$m\overset{\frown}{AR} = m\angle 1 = 47°$
$m\overset{\frown}{AS} = 180° - 47°$
$m\overset{\frown}{AS} = 133°$
Since $m\overset{\frown}{AR} = m\overset{\frown}{RB}$, $m\overset{\frown}{SB} = m\overset{\frown}{AS}$.
$m\overset{\frown}{ASB} = 133° + 133°$
$m\overset{\frown}{ASB} = 266°$
16. Since $m\overset{\frown}{BC} = m\overset{\frown}{DE}$, $BC = DE$; $BC = 7$.
17. $DE = BC$
$m\overset{\frown}{DE} = m\overset{\frown}{BC}$
$m\overset{\frown}{DE} = 70°$
18. Since $BC = DE$, $AX = AY = 5$.
19. Since $AX = AY$, $BC = DE$.
$BX = \frac{1}{2}BC$
$BX = \frac{1}{2}DE = \frac{1}{2}(4) = 2$
20. $m\overset{\frown}{AB} = \frac{1}{2}m\overset{\frown}{BD}$
$m\overset{\frown}{AB} = \frac{1}{2}(100°)$
$m\overset{\frown}{AB} = 50°$
21. $m\overset{\frown}{AD} = m\overset{\frown}{AB}$
$m\overset{\frown}{BC} = 180° - m\overset{\frown}{AB}$
$m\overset{\frown}{BC} = 180° - m\overset{\frown}{AD}$
$m\overset{\frown}{BC} = 180° - 40°$
$m\overset{\frown}{BC} = 140°$
22. Draw auxiliary line *PD* to form rt. $\triangle PXD$.
$XD = \frac{1}{2}BD$
$XD = \frac{1}{2}(16)$ $\quad XD = 8$
$PD = \sqrt{6^2 + 8^2}$
$PD = \sqrt{36 + 64}$
$PD = \sqrt{100}$ $\quad PD = 10$
23. Use Theorem 6-11.
$x = \frac{1}{2}(360° - 250°)$
$x = \frac{1}{2}(110°)$
$x = 55°$
24. $20 = \frac{1}{2}(x + 10)$
$40 = x + 10$
$40 - 10 = x$
$30 = x$
$x = 30°$
25. $(6 + 4)(4) = (8)(x)$
$(10)(4) = 8x$
$40 = 8x$
$\frac{40}{8} = \frac{8x}{8}$
$5 = x$
26. The hour hand is $\frac{28}{60}$, or $\frac{7}{15}$, of the way from 1 to 2: $\frac{7}{15}$ of 30° = $\frac{7}{\cancel{15}} \times \frac{\cancel{30}}{1} = 14°$. The minute hand is $\frac{3}{5}$ of the way from 5 to 6: $\frac{3}{5}$ of 30° = $\frac{3}{5} \times \frac{\cancel{30}}{1} = 18°$. The total arc is 16° + 90° + 18° = 124°. The angle formed by the hands of the clock at 1:28 is 124°.

1:28

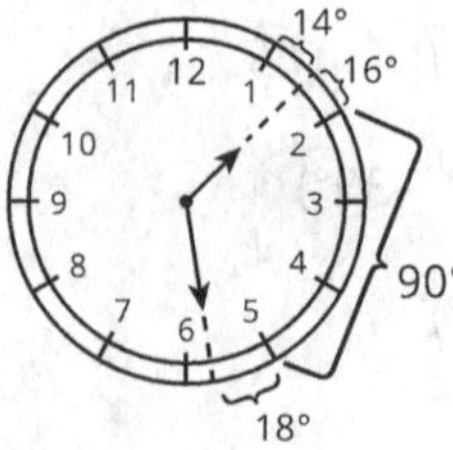

MATH 1006

ALTERNATE LIFEPAC TEST

NAME ______________________________

DATE ______________________________

SCORE ______________________________

63
78

Refer to the figure to name the following parts (each answer, 3 points).

Given: point *O* is center

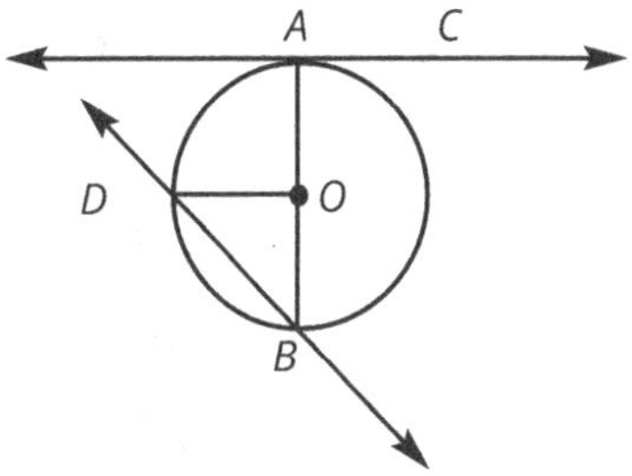

1. a radius ______________________
2. a tangent ______________________
3. a diameter ______________________
4. a secant ______________________
5. an inscribed angle ______________________
6. a central angle ______________________

Refer to the figure to complete the following items (each answer, 3 points).

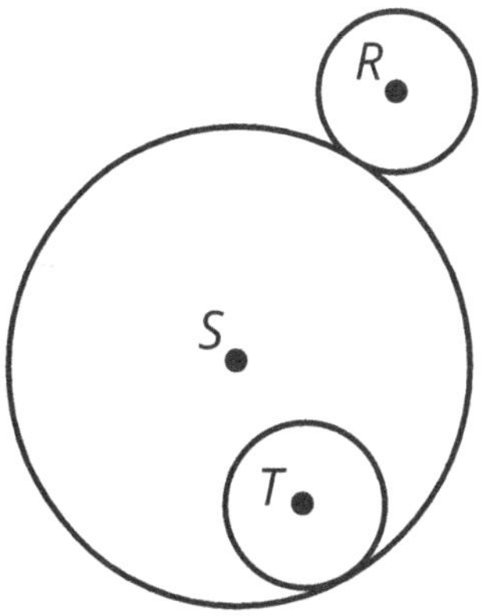

7. The number of common external tangents that can be drawn common to circle *S* and circle *R* is ____________ .
8. The number of common internal tangents that can be drawn common to circle *T* and circle *R* is ____________ .
9. Circle *T* is internally tangent to circle ____________ .
10. Circle *R* is externally tangent to circle ____________ .

Refer to the figures to complete the following items (each answer, 3 points).

Given: RS diameter

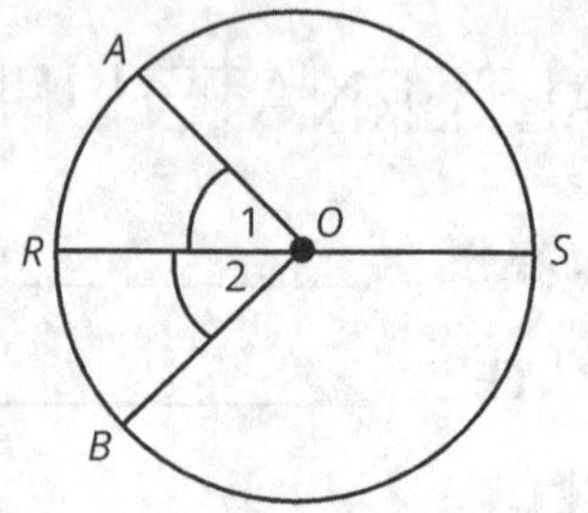

11. $m\overset{\frown}{RAS}$ = ____________

12. If $m\angle 1 = 50°$, then $m\overset{\frown}{AR}$ = ____________ .

13. If $m\overset{\frown}{RB} = 48°$, then $m\angle 2$ = ____________ .

14. If $m\overset{\frown}{AS} = 126°$, then $m\angle 1$ = ____________ .

15. If $m\overset{\frown}{AR} = m\overset{\frown}{RB}$ and $m\angle 1 = 47°$, then $m\overset{\frown}{ASB}$ = ____________ .

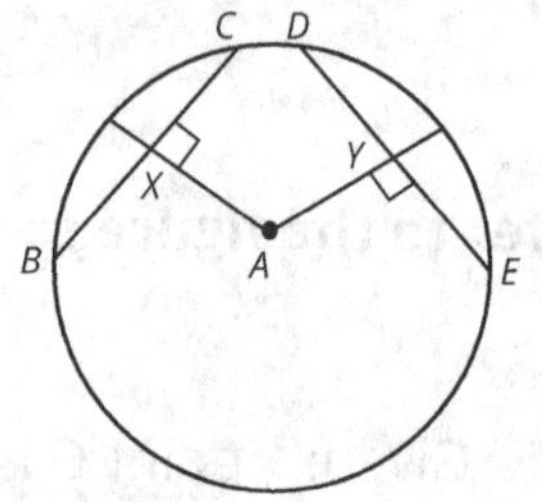

16. If $DE = 7$ and $m\overset{\frown}{BC} = m\overset{\frown}{DE}$, then BC = ____________ .

17. If $m\overset{\frown}{BC} = 70°$ and $DE = BC$, then $m\overset{\frown}{DE}$ = ____________ .

18. If $BC = DE$ and $AX = 5$, then AY = ____________ .

19. If $AX = AY$ and $DE = 4$, then BX = ____________ .

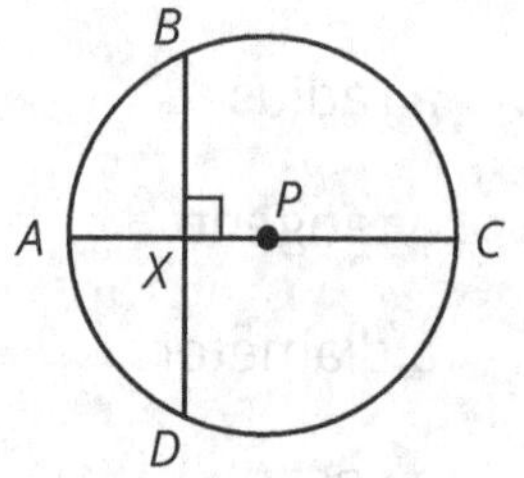

20. If $m\overset{\frown}{BD} = 100°$, then $m\overset{\frown}{AB}$ = ____________ .

21. If $m\overset{\frown}{AD} = 40°$, then $m\overset{\frown}{BC}$ = ____________ .

22. If $BD = 16$ and $PX = 6$, then PD = ____________ .

Find x in the given figures (each answer, 3 points).

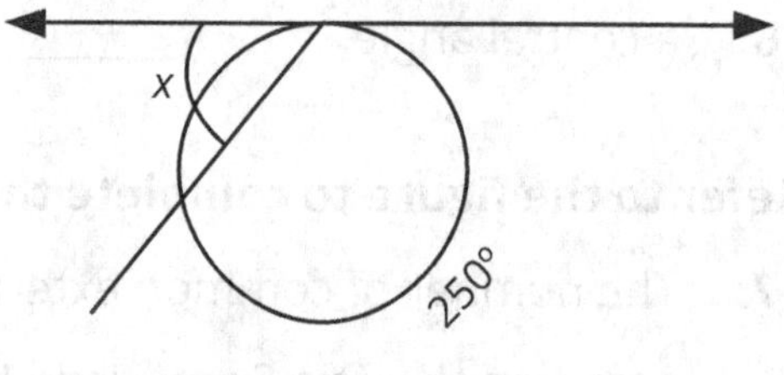

23. x = ____________

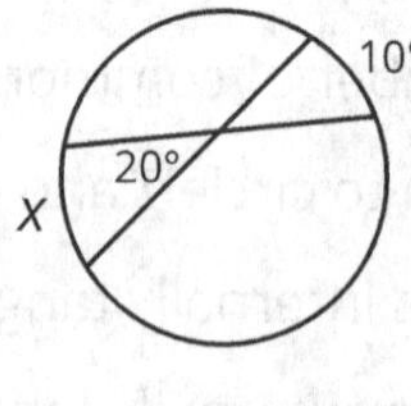

24. x = ____________

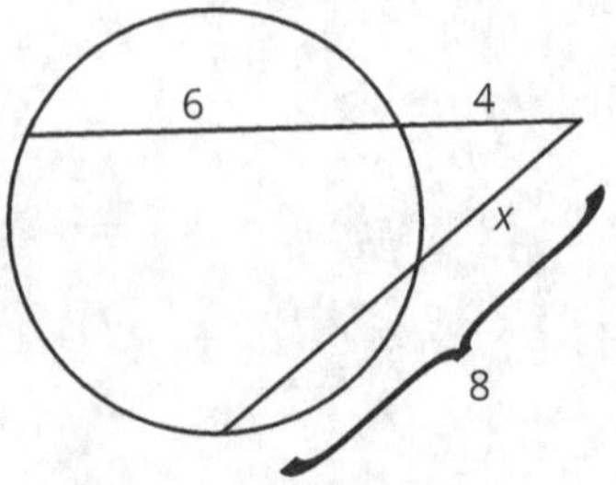

25. x = ____________

Work the following problem (3 points).

26. Find the angle formed by the hands of a clock.

____

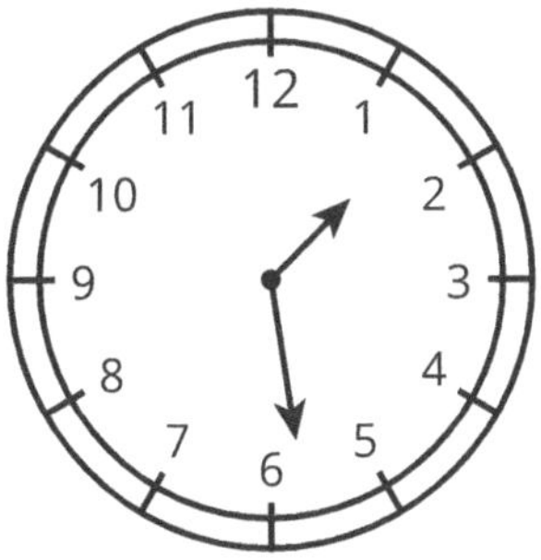

1:28

MATH 1007

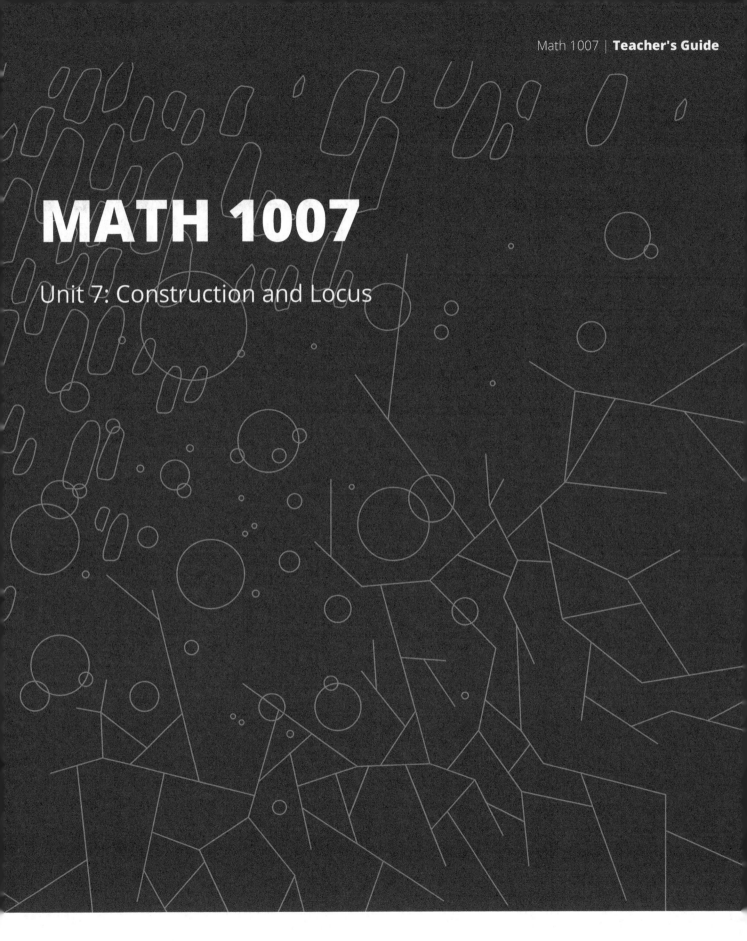

Unit 7: Construction and Locus

TEACHER NOTES

MATERIALS NEEDED FOR LIFEPAC	
Required	Suggested
• compass and straightedge	(None)

ADDITIONAL LEARNING ACTIVITIES

Section 1: Basic Construction

1. Write the equation $\frac{a}{b} = \frac{c}{x}$ on the chalkboard. Then write a proportion such as $\frac{4}{8} = \frac{7}{x}$ on the chalkboard. Let the class tell what they think the length of *x* will be in inches. Now let a student come to the chalkboard to draw the fourth proportional *x* (the LIFEPAC explains how to make this construction). Have the student copy a 4-inch segment for *a*, an 8-inch segment for *b*, and a 7-inch segment for *c*. After the fourth proportional *x* has been found, let the same student measure the length of *x* with a yardstick; the length should be 14 inches.
2. This activity is recommended for the more advanced student. On a sheet of paper construct a circle with the given segment as radius.

3. Label the center of the circle *O*. From the center of the circle, construct four angles each with measure equal to the given angle.

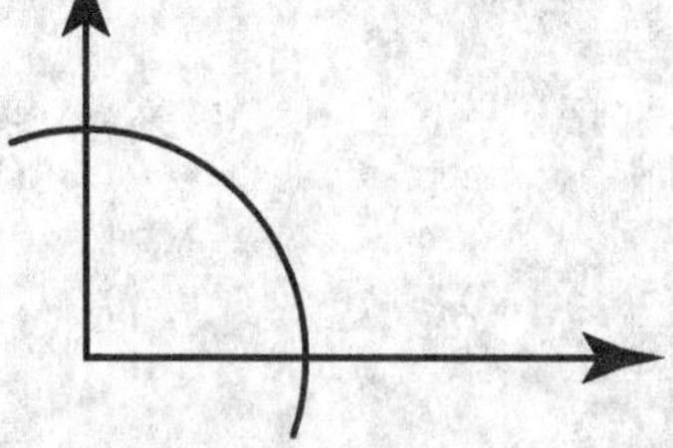

4. Label the end points of the angles on the circle *A*, *B*, *C*, and *D*. Now bisect $\angle AOB$, $\angle BOC$, $\angle COD$, and $\angle AOD$. Label the end points on the circle *J*, *K*, *L*, and *M*. Next construct the perpendicular bisectors of $\overline{OJ}$, $\overline{OK}$, $\overline{OL}$, and $\overline{OM}$; extend the bisectors to the circle. Label the points at which the bisectors intersect each other *W*, *X*, *Y*, and *Z*. Last, construct tangents to the circle at point *A*, point *B*, point *C*, and point *D*.

Section 2: Figure Construction

1. Let one student choose a triangle, median of a triangle, or altitude of a triangle to be constructed. If necessary, he also constructs any lengths or angles to be used for the construction and labels any drawings. Then let a second student construct and label the triangle, median, or altitude as specified.

   Example: First student: Says to construct a median of a triangle. Then he constructs and labels the triangle.

   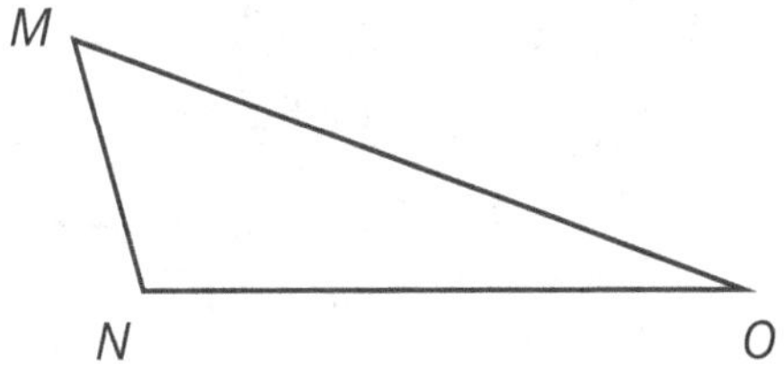

   Second student: Constructs and labels the median.

   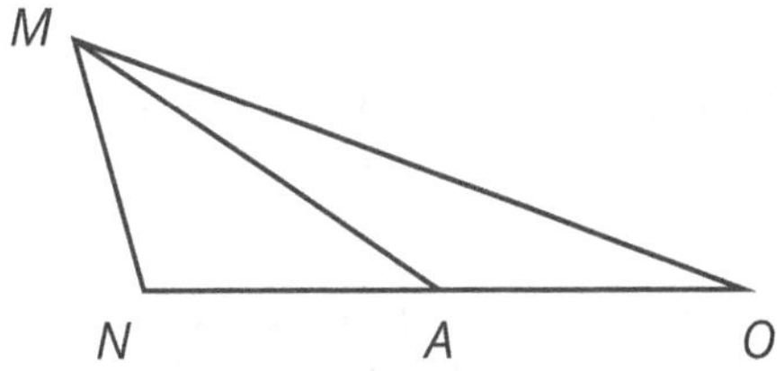

   One of the medians is $\overline{MA}$.

2. Based on your knowledge of the number of degrees in a circle and polygon construction, construct a regular nonagon (9-sided figure); a regular decagon (10-sided figure); a regular dodecagon (12-sided figure). Construct each polygon with each side equal to *r*.

Section 3: Locus

1. Discuss with your class how the Archimedean spiral is formed as a locus of points moving around a fixed point, or pole. The points increase in distance from the pole in arithmetic sequence.
2. Have the students construct a donut by using thirty-six positions of a circle as it rolls around a base circle of the same size. Note: drawing is schematic only.

3. Have the students construct a cardioid by drawing a base circle and a number of other circles that are centered on the base circle and pass through a fixed point on that circle. Note: drawing is schematic only.

4. Have one student think of and sketch a locus. Then have another student describe the locus. Let the students take turns sketching and describing the loci.

Administer the LIFEPAC Test.

The test is to be administered in one session. Give no help except with directions.
Evaluate the tests and review areas where the students have done poorly.
Review the pages and activities that stress the concepts tested.
If necessary, administer the Alternate LIFEPAC Test

ANSWER KEYS

SECTION 1

1.1 through 1.10

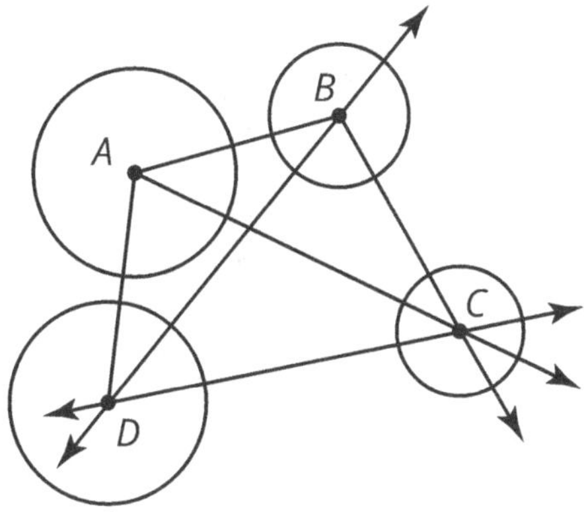

1.11 through 1.13

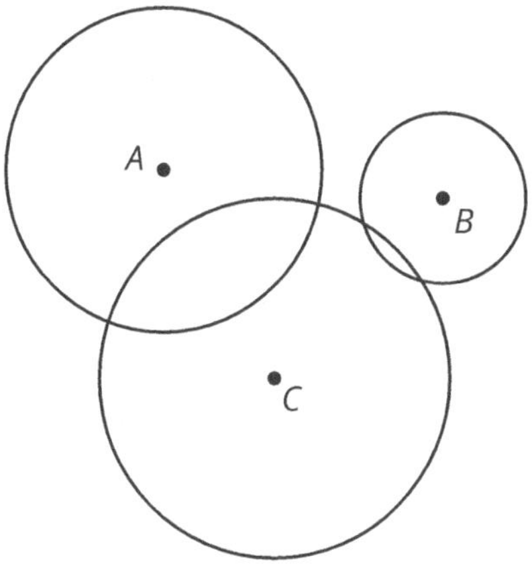

1.14 through 1.16

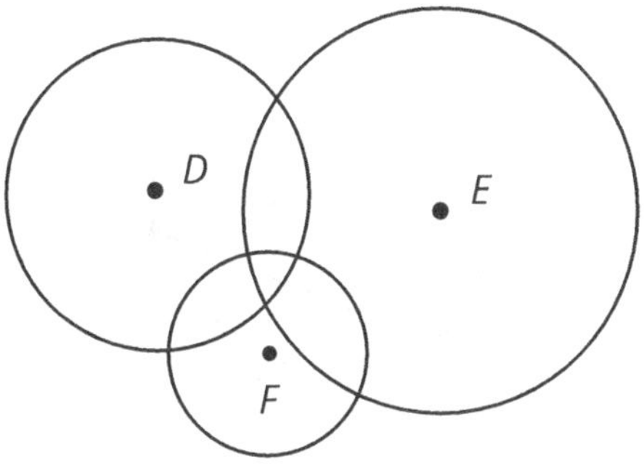

1.17

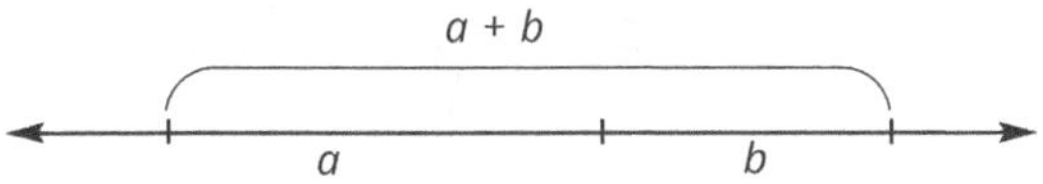

1.18

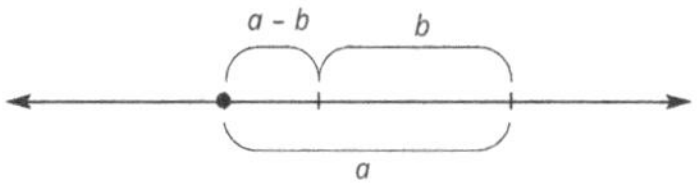

1.19

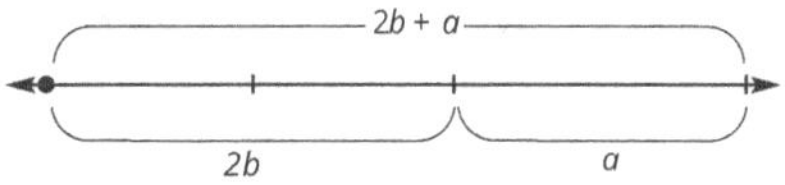

1.20

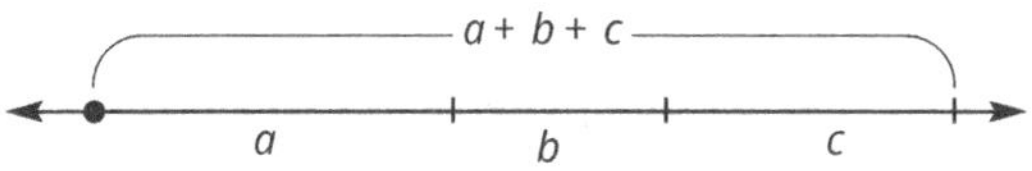

1.21

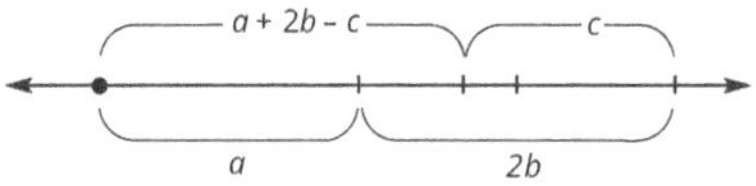

1.22

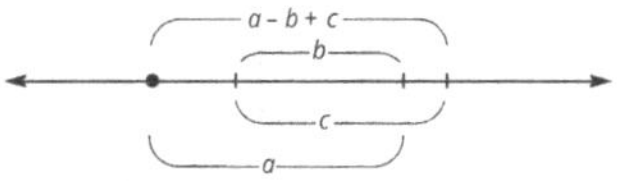

1.23

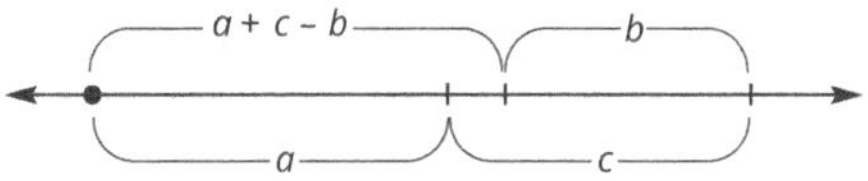

1.24

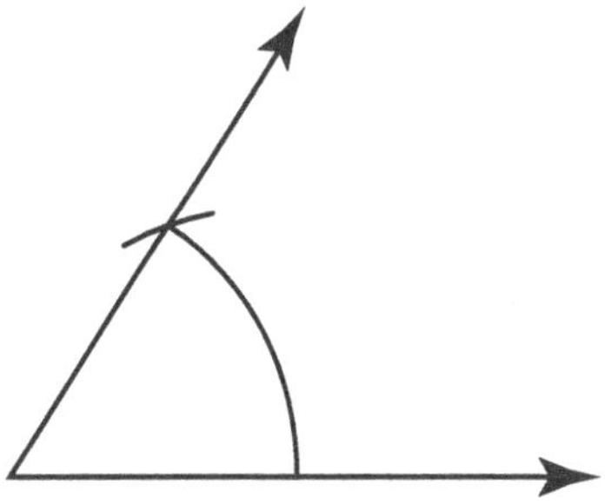

1.25

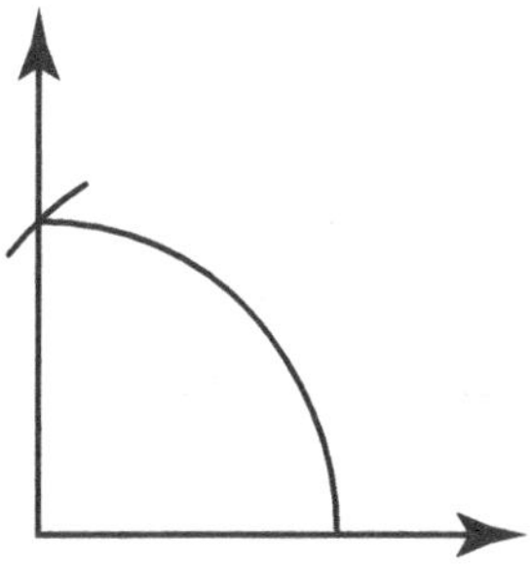

1.26

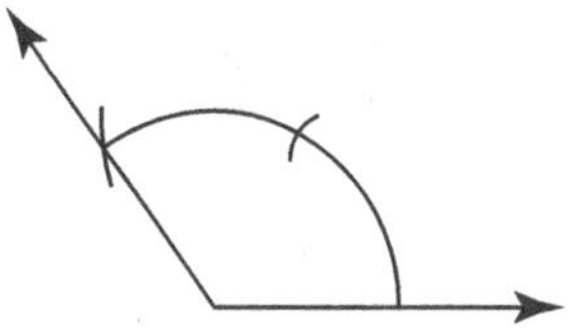

1.27

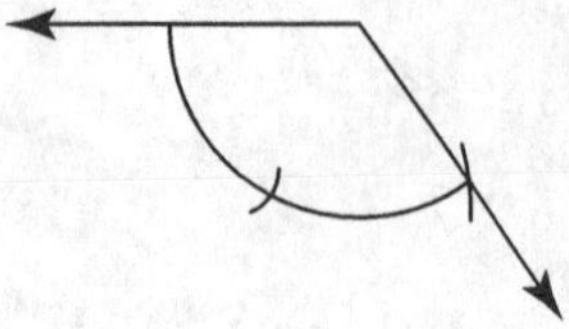

1.28

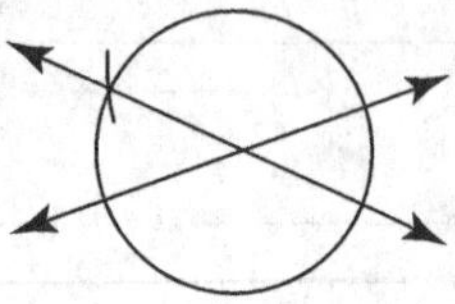

1.29

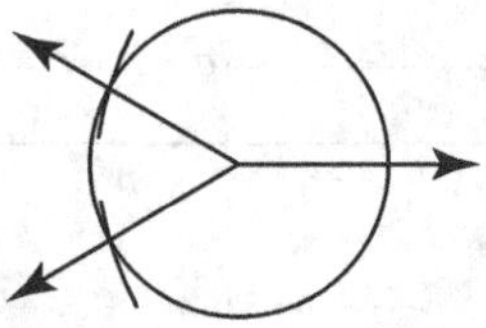

1.30

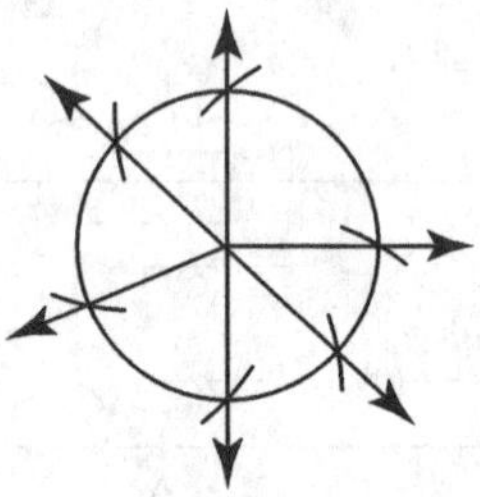

1.31

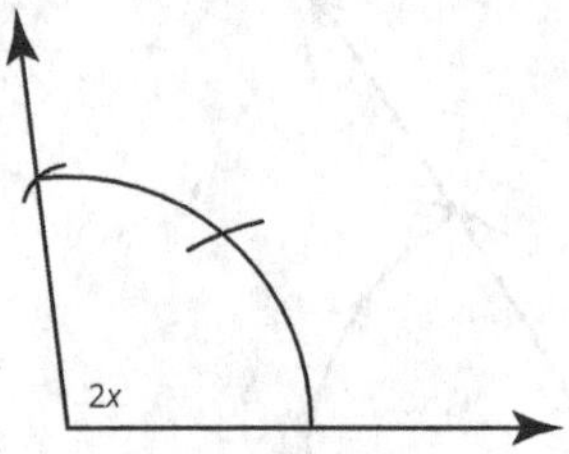

1.32

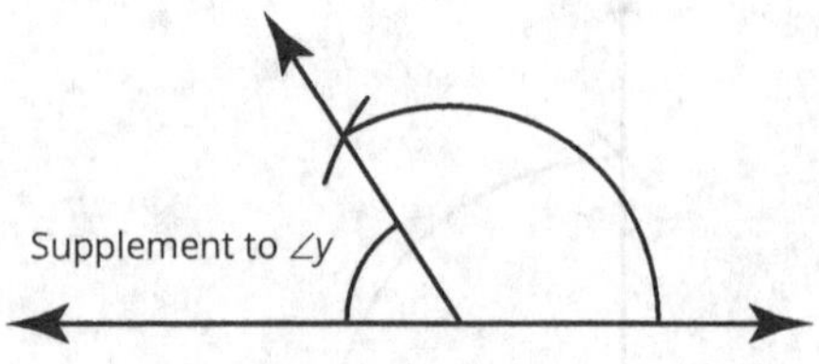

1.33

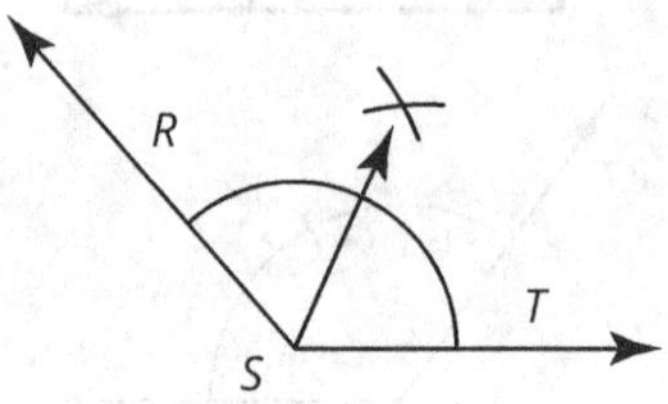

1.34

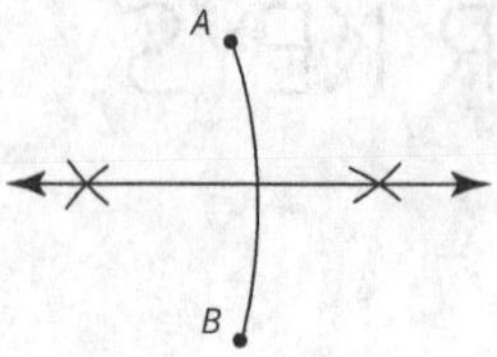

1.35

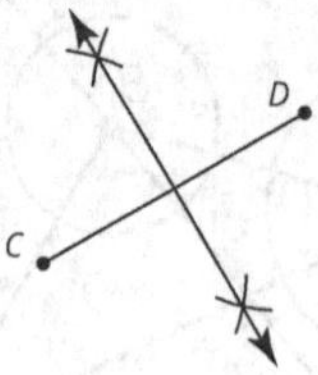

1.36

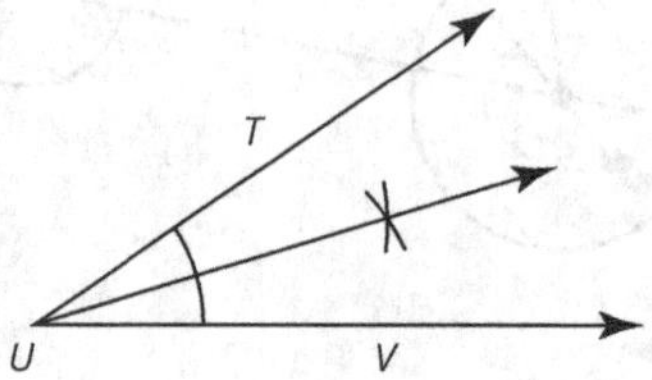

1.37

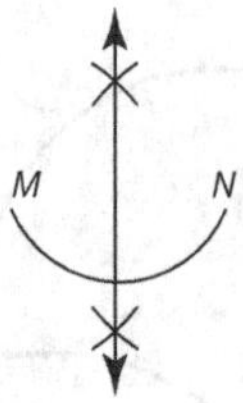

1.38

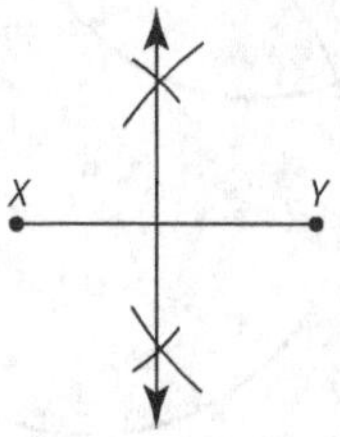

1.39

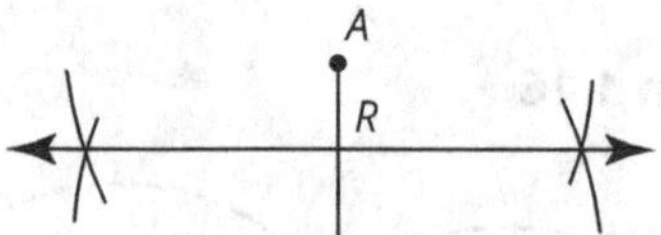

1.40

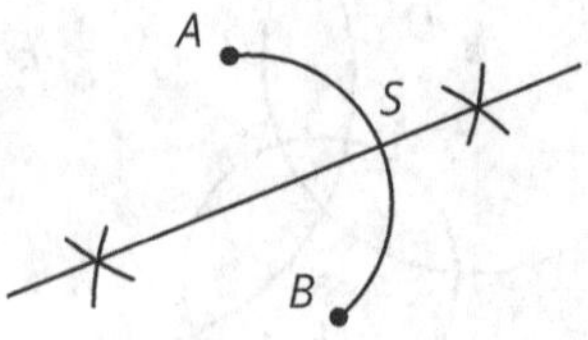

1.41

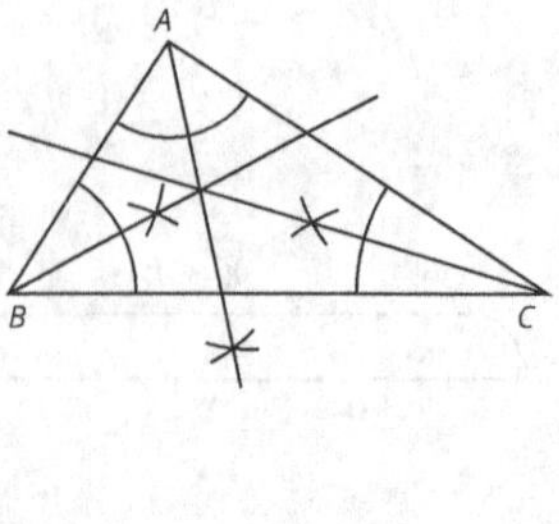

1.42 The point of intersection is the center of a circle that contains the arc.

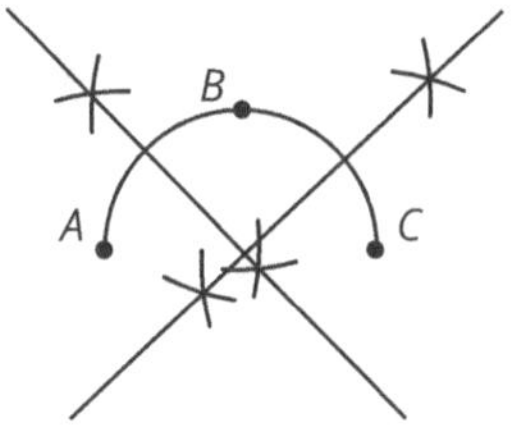

1.43

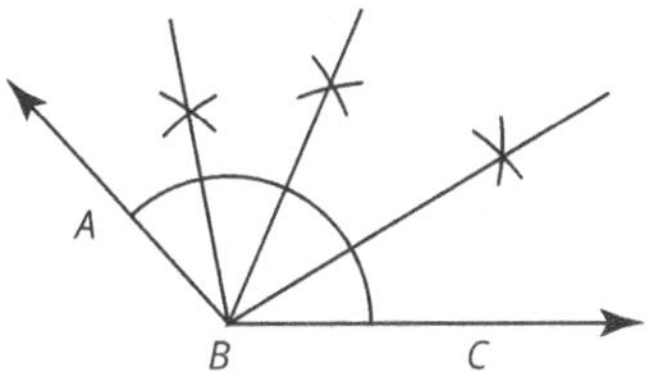

1.44

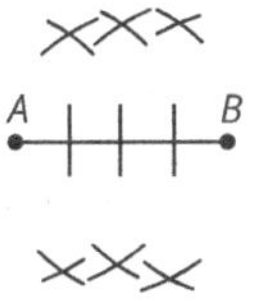

1.45

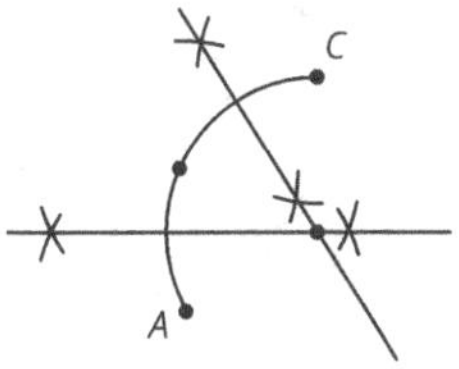

1.46

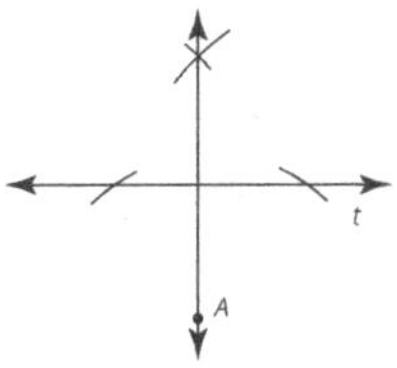

1.47

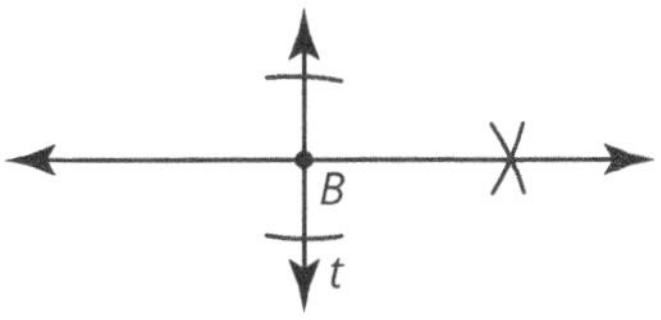

1.48

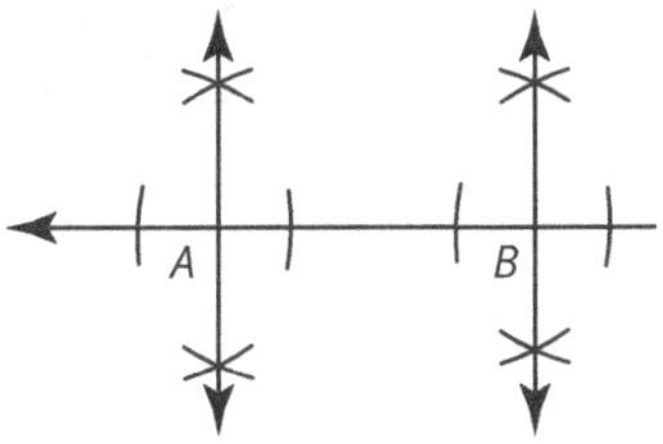

1.49

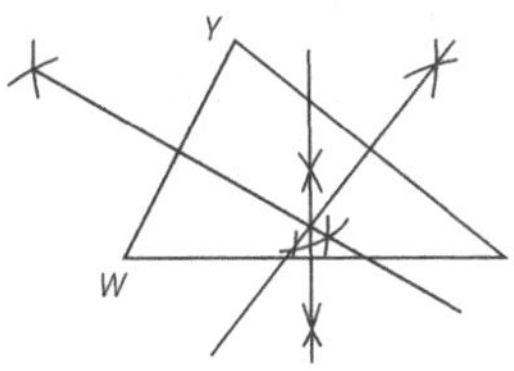

1.50

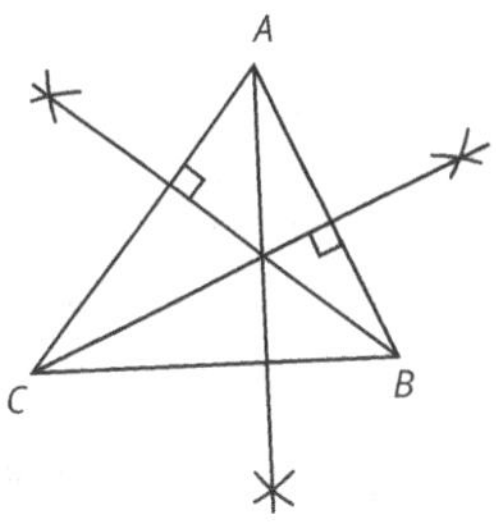

Yes, the perpendiculars intersect in one point.

1.51

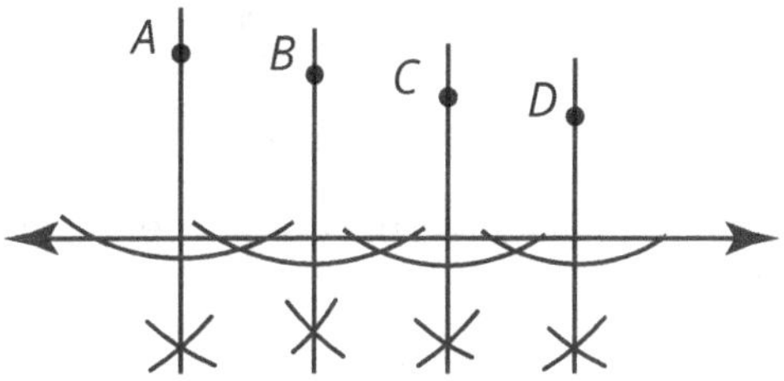

The lines are all parallel.

1.52

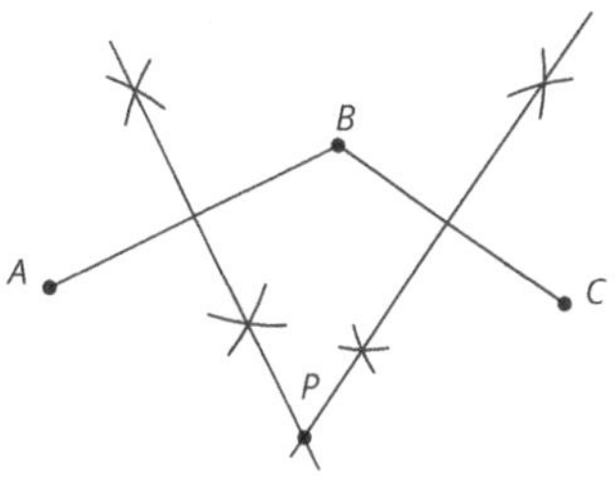

PA, *PB*, and *PC* are equal.

1.53

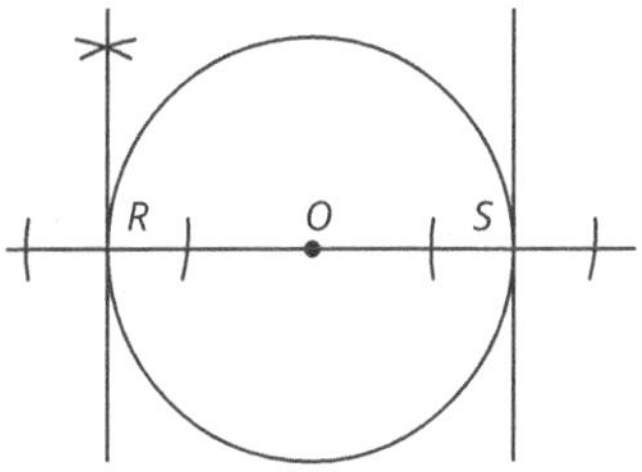

1.54

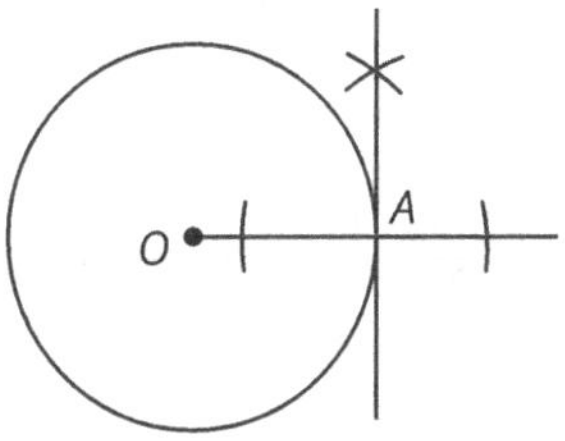

1.55

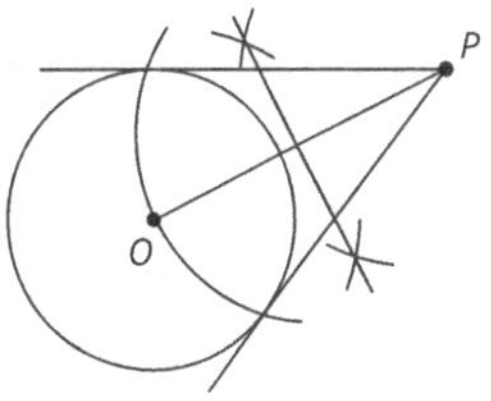

1.56

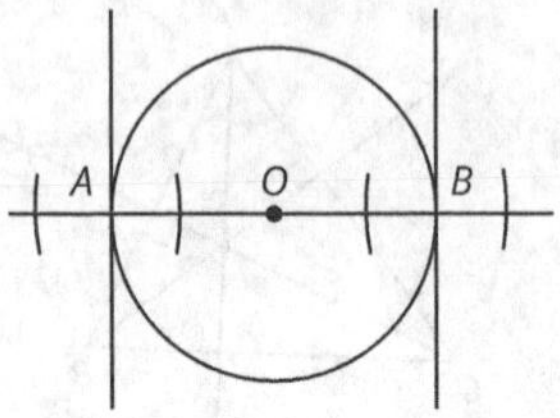

The two tangents are parallel.

1.57

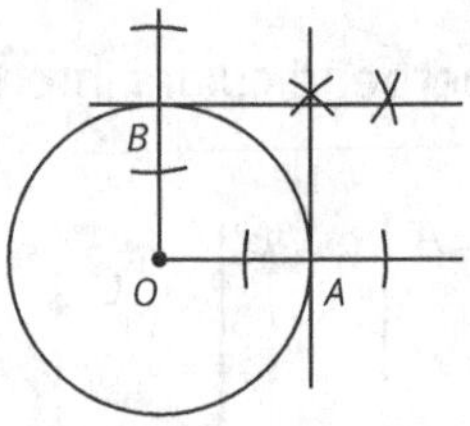

The two tangents are perpendicular.

1.58

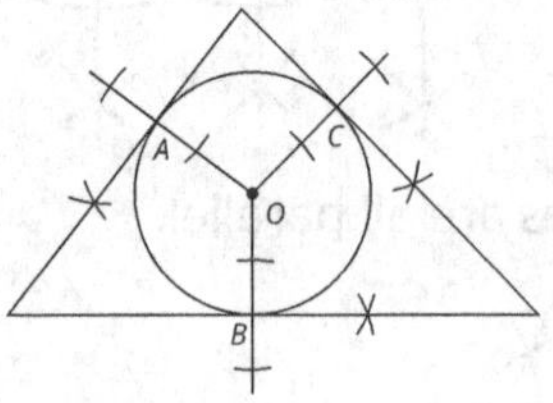

The sides of the triangle are tangents to the circle.

1.59

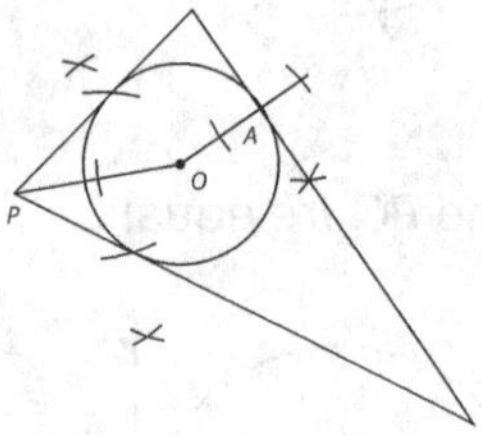

The circle is inscribed in the triangle.

1.60

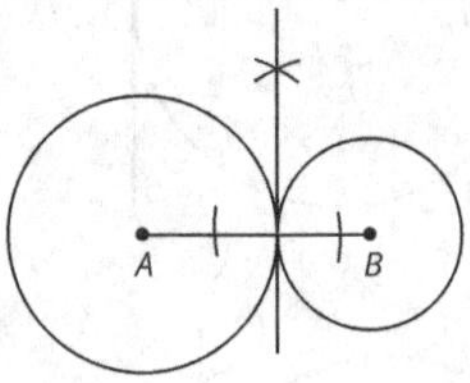

1.61

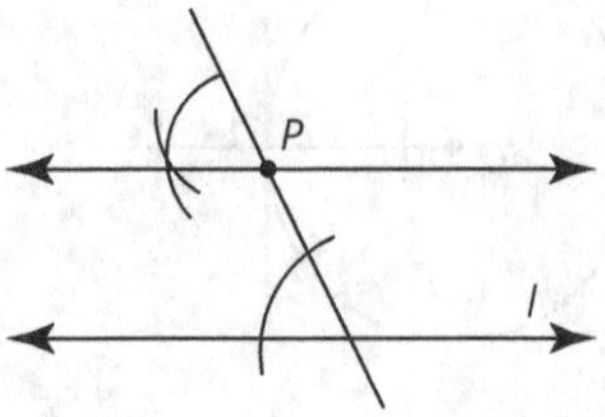

1.62

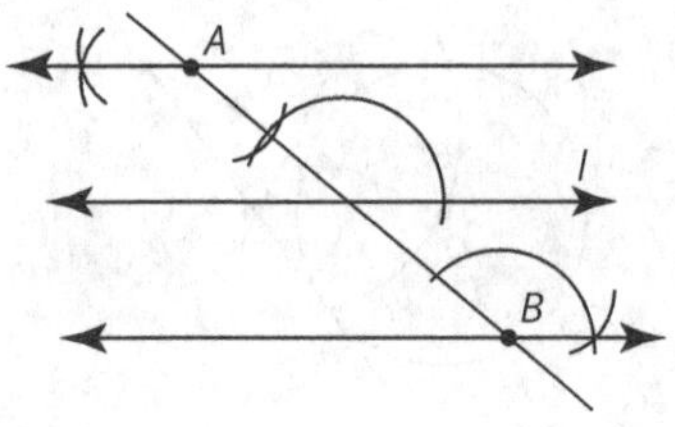

The lines constructed are parallel.

1.63

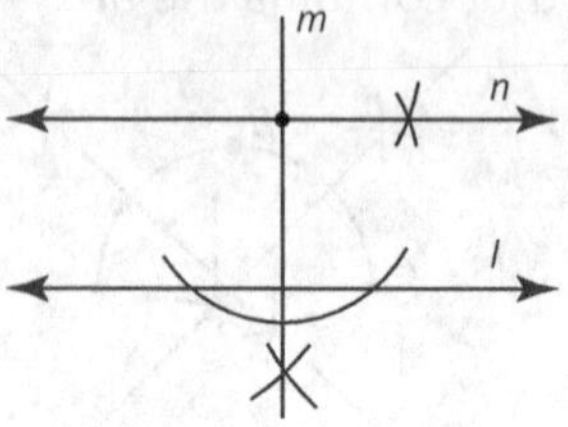

m and *n* are perpendicular.

1.64

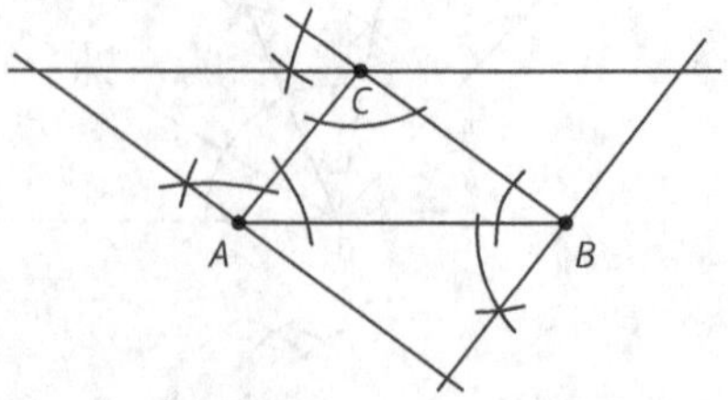

The two triangles are similar.

1.65 Example:

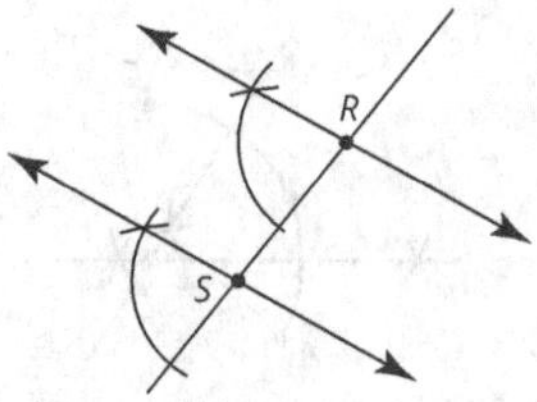

1.66

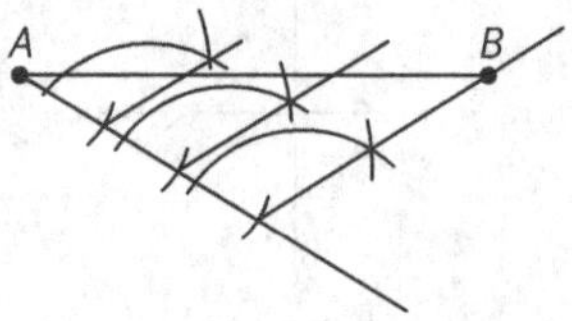

1.67

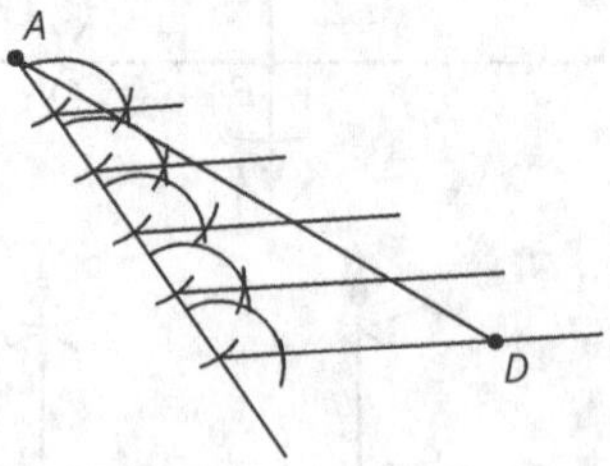

1.68

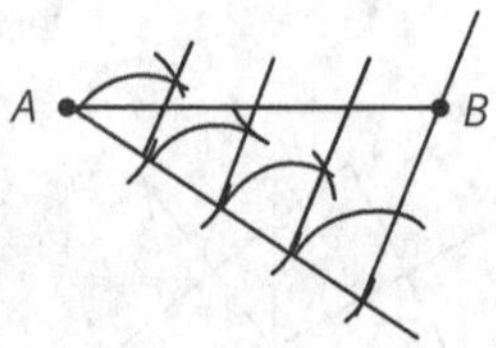

1.69

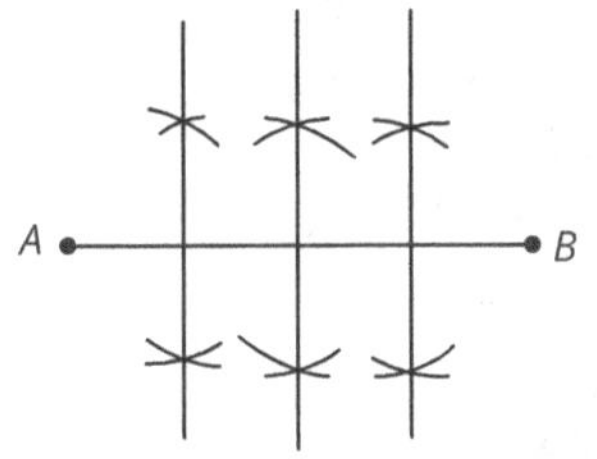

1.70

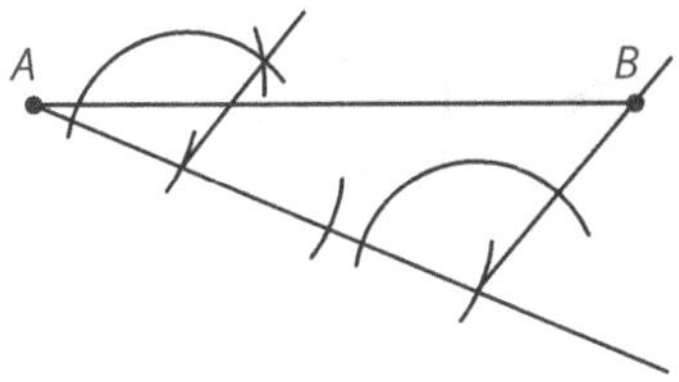

1.71

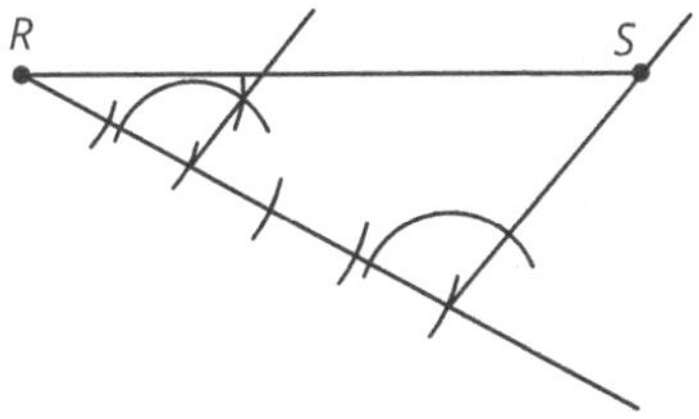

1.72

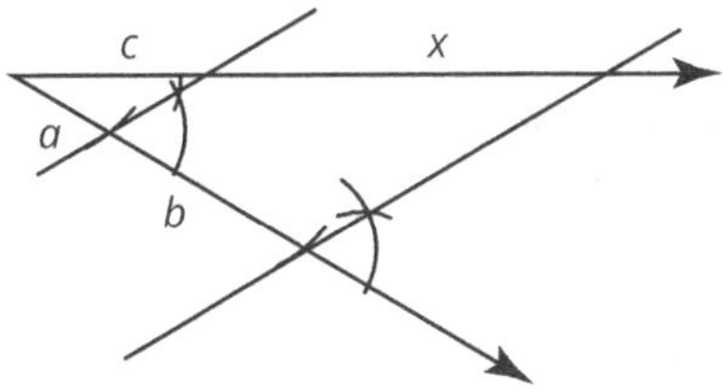

1.73

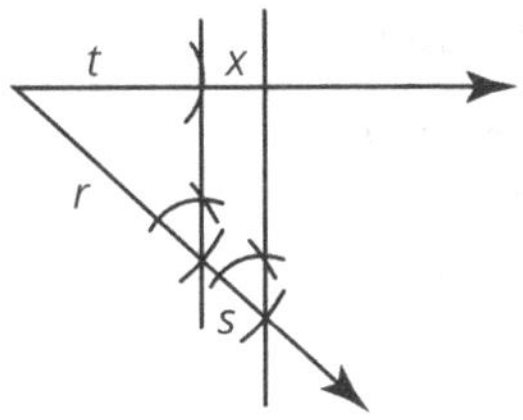

1.74

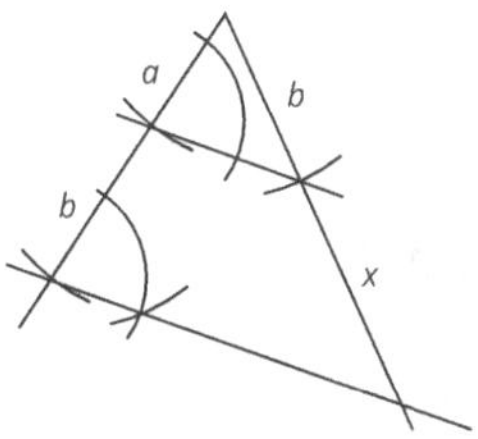

1.75

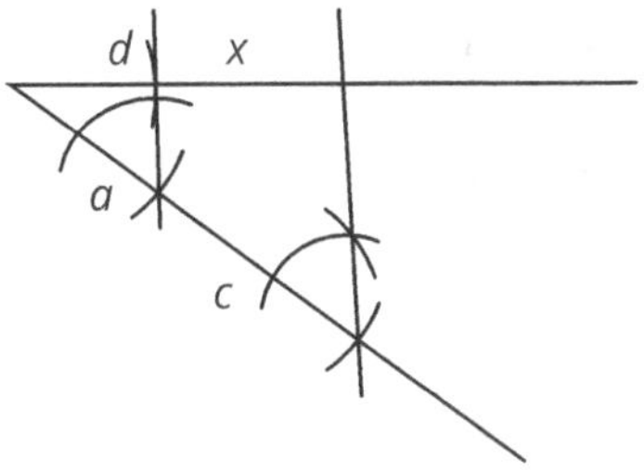

1.76

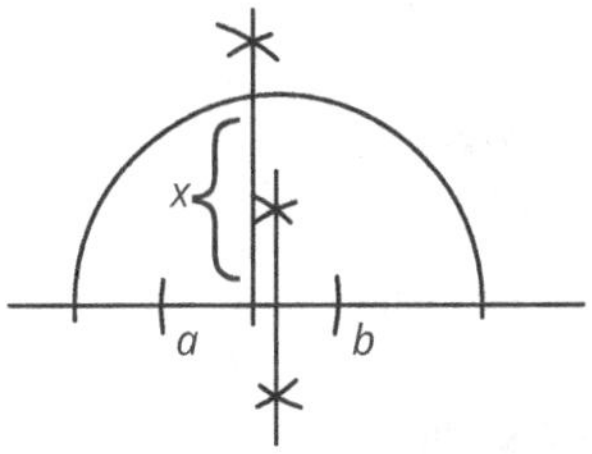

1.77

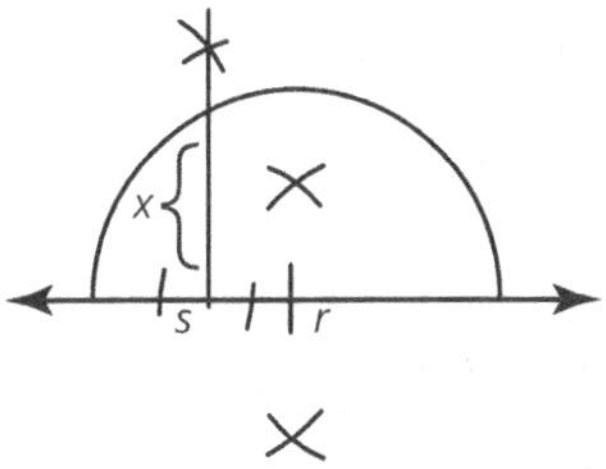

1.78

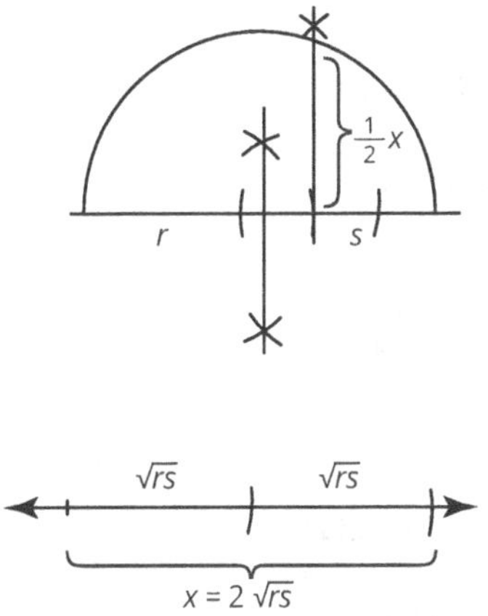

1.79

1. **STATEMENT**
   $\overline{AB}$
   REASON
   Given
2. **STATEMENT**
   $AX = BX = AY = BY$
   REASON
   Same radii
3. **STATEMENT**
   $XY = XY$
   REASON
   Reflexive
4. **STATEMENT**
   $\triangle XAY \cong \triangle XBY$
   REASON
   SSS
5. **STATEMENT**
   $\angle 1 = \angle 2$
   REASON
   CPCTE
6. **STATEMENT**
   $XM = XM$
   REASON
   Reflexive
7. **STATEMENT**
   $\triangle AXM \cong \triangle BXM$
   REASON
   SAS
8. **STATEMENT**
   $AM = MB$
   REASON
   CPCTE
9. **STATEMENT**
   M is midpoint of $\overline{AB}$
   REASON
   Definition of midpoint
10. **STATEMENT**
    $\overleftrightarrow{XY}$ bisects $\overline{AB}$
    REASON
    Definition of bisector

1.80

1. **STATEMENT**
   $\angle ABC$
   REASON
   Given
2. **STATEMENT**
   $BX = BY, XD = YD$
   REASON
   Same radii
3. **STATEMENT**
   $BD = BD$
   REASON
   Reflexive
4. **STATEMENT**
   $\triangle BXD \cong \triangle BYD$
   REASON
   SSS
5. **STATEMENT**
   $\angle 1 = \angle 2$
   REASON
   CPCTE
6. **STATEMENT**
   $\overrightarrow{BD}$ bisects $\angle ABC$
   REASON
   Definition of $\angle$ bisector

1.81

1. **STATEMENT**
   $\widehat{AB}$
   REASON
   Given
2. **STATEMENT**
   $BX = BY = AX = AY$
   REASON
   Same radii
3. **STATEMENT**
   $XY = XY$
   REASON
   Reflexive
4. **STATEMENT**
   $\triangle AXY \cong \triangle BXY$
   REASON
   SSS
5. **STATEMENT**
   $\angle 1 = \angle 2$
   REASON
   CPCTE
6. **STATEMENT**
   $XP = XP$
   REASON
   Reflexive

7. **STATEMENT**
$\triangle AXP \cong \triangle BXP$
REASON
SAS

8. **STATEMENT**
$AP = PB$
REASON
CPCTE

9. **STATEMENT**
$\overset{\frown}{AP} = \overset{\frown}{PB}$
REASON
If chords are =, then arcs are =.

10. **STATEMENT**
$\overleftrightarrow{XY}$ bisects $\overset{\frown}{AB}$
REASON
Definition of a bisector

1.82

1. **STATEMENT**
Circle *O*; point *A*
REASON
Given

2. **STATEMENT**
$\angle OXA$ is right $\angle$.
REASON
Angle inscribed in semicircle is a right $\angle$.

3. **STATEMENT**
$\overline{OX} \perp \overline{AX}$
REASON
If right $\angle$'s are formed, lines are $\perp$.

4. **STATEMENT**
$\overleftrightarrow{AX}$ is tangent to circle *O*
REASON
Line $\perp$ to radius at its outer end point is tangent to the circle.

1.83

1. **STATEMENT**
line *m*, point *P* not on *m*
REASON
Given

2. **STATEMENT**
$\angle 1 = \angle 2$
REASON
By Construction 2

3. **STATEMENT**
$m \parallel n$
REASON
If corresponding $\angle$'s =, then lines $\parallel$.

1.84

1. **STATEMENT**
$\overline{AB}$
REASON
Given

2. **STATEMENT**
$AW = WX = XY$
REASON
Same radii

3. **STATEMENT**
$\angle W = \angle X = \angle Y$
REASON
By Construction 2

4. **STATEMENT**
$\overline{DW} \parallel \overline{EX} \parallel \overline{BY}$
REASON
If corresponding $\angle$'s =, then lines $\parallel$.

5. **STATEMENT**
$\frac{AD}{AW} = \frac{DE}{WX} = \frac{EB}{XY}$
REASON
Lines $\parallel$ to side of $\triangle$ divide other sides proportionally.

6. **STATEMENT**
$AD = DE = EB$
REASON
Division property of equality

SELF TEST 1

1.01

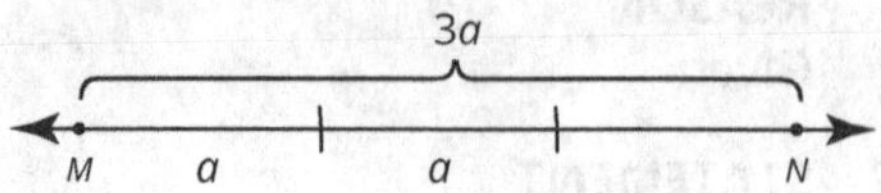

1.02

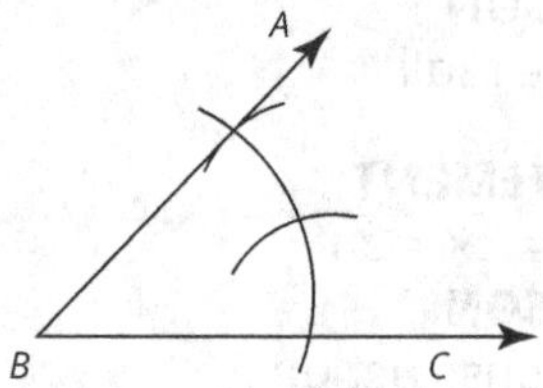

1.03

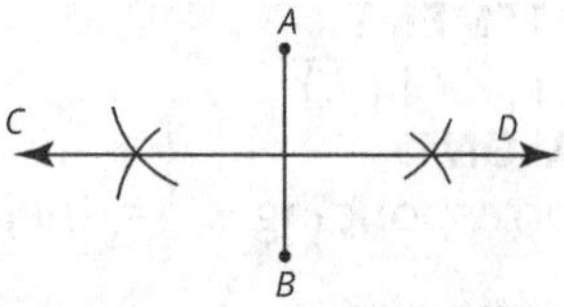

1.04

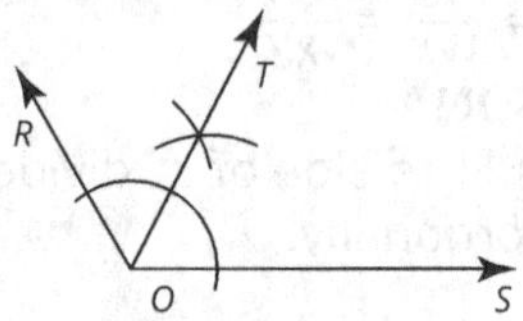

1.05

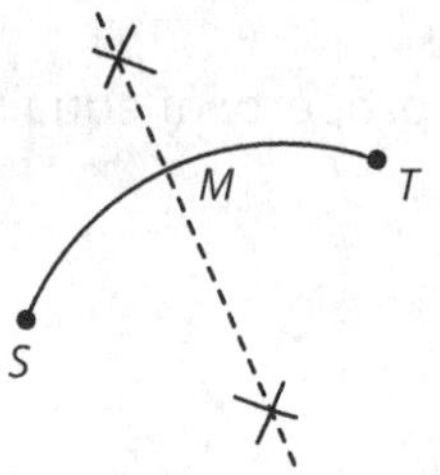

1.06

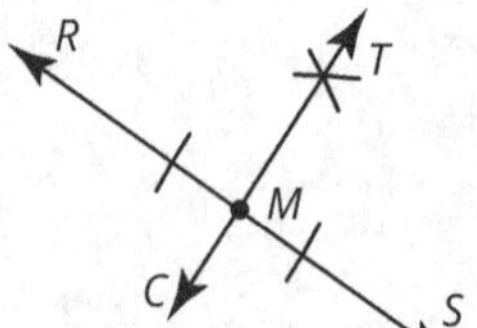

1.07

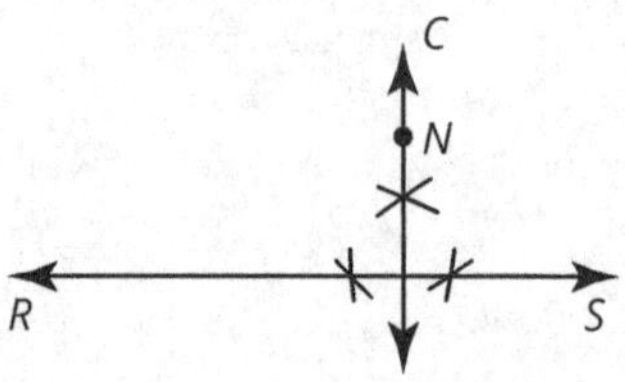

1.08

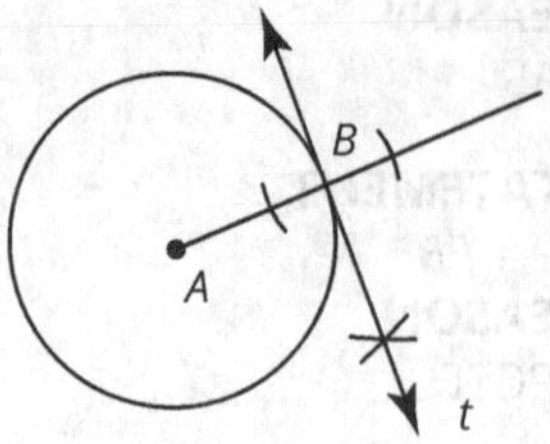

1.09

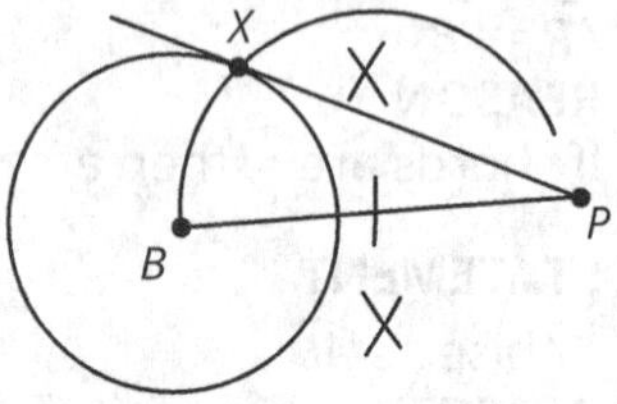

1.010

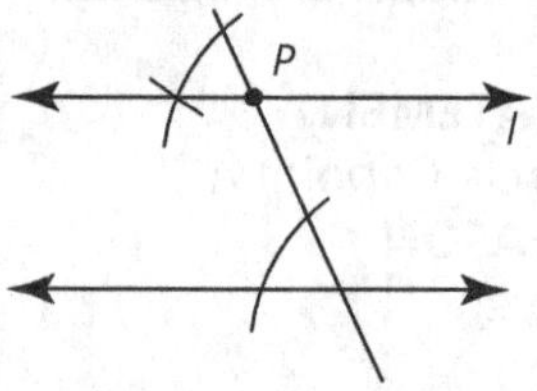

1.011

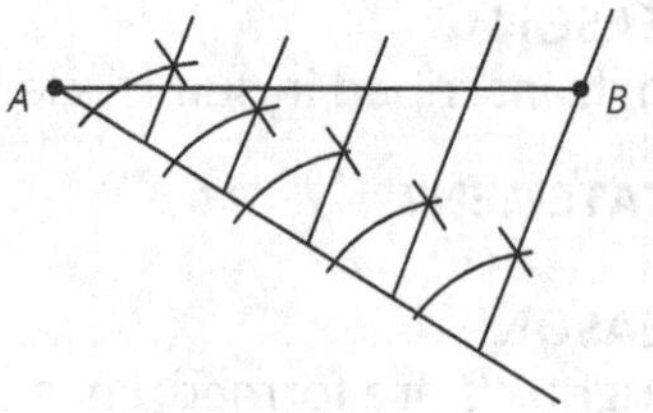

1.012

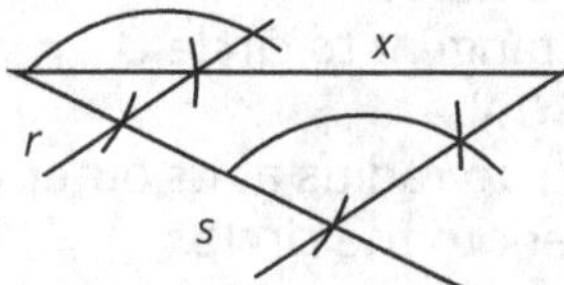

1.013

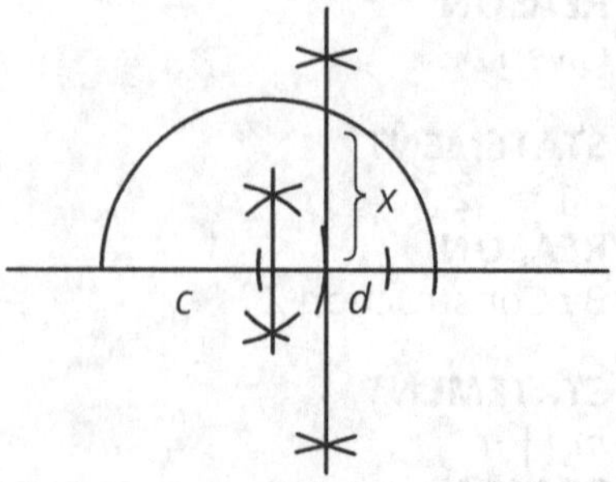

SECTION 2

2.1

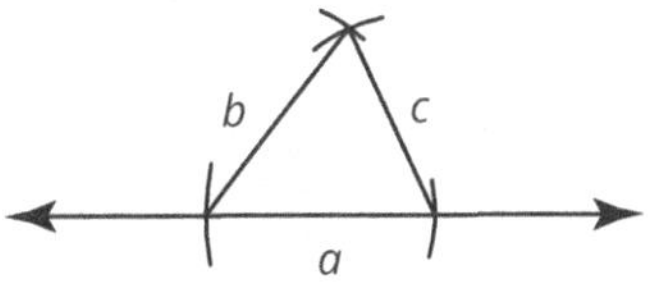

2.2

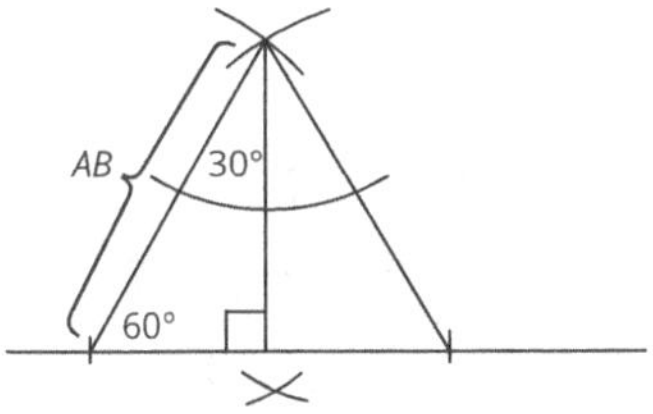

2.3

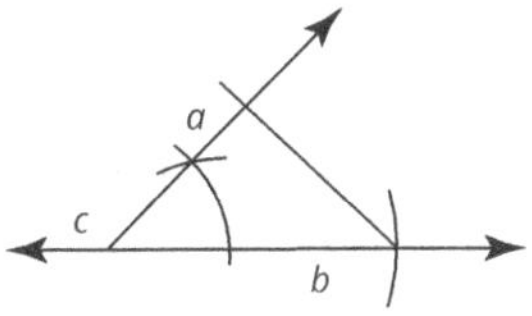

2.4

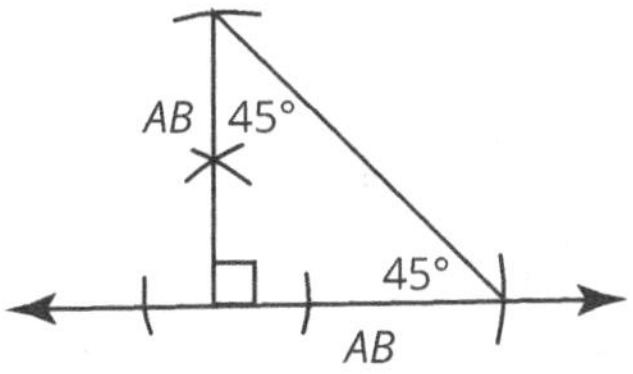

2.5

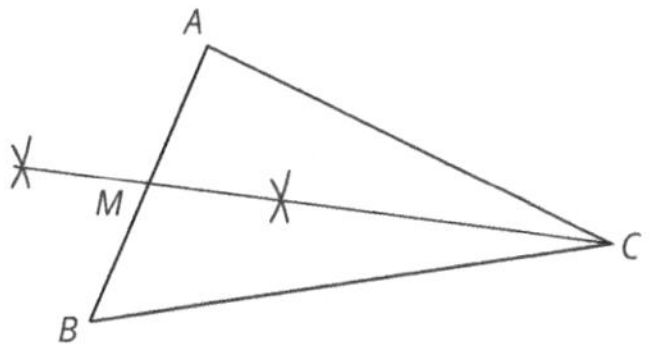

2.6

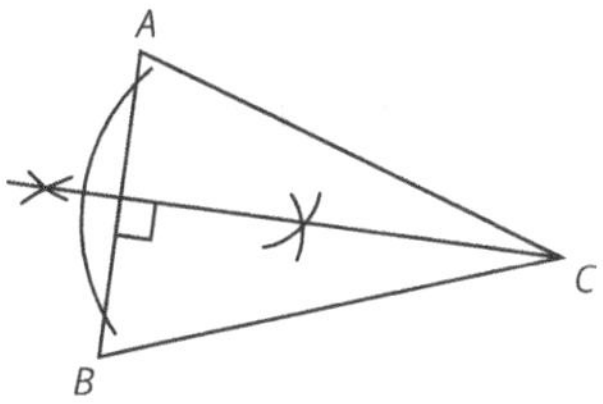

2.7

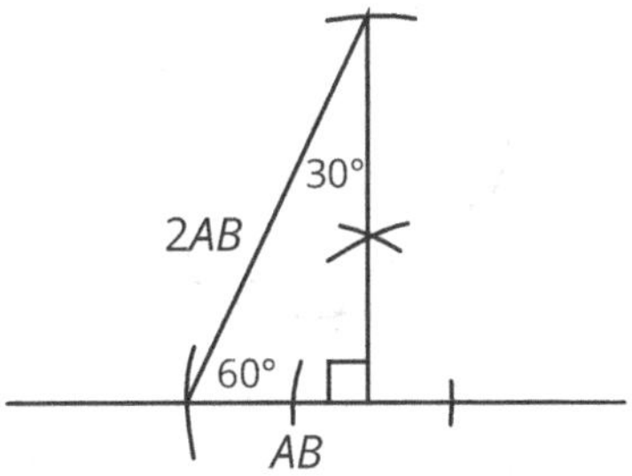

2.8

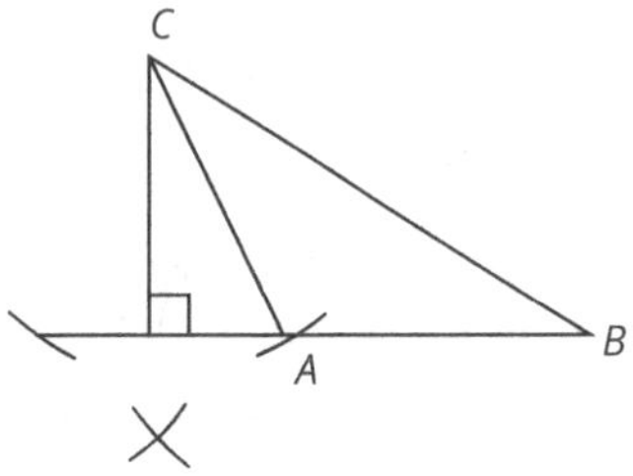

2.9

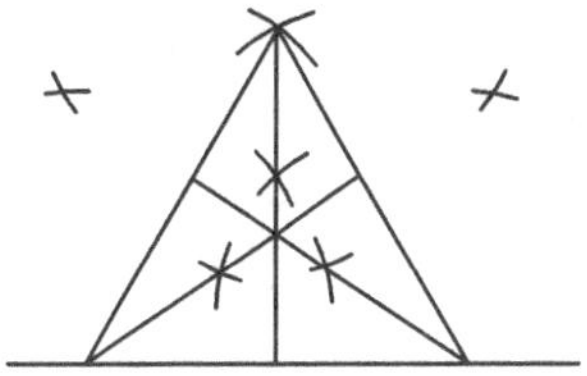

2.10

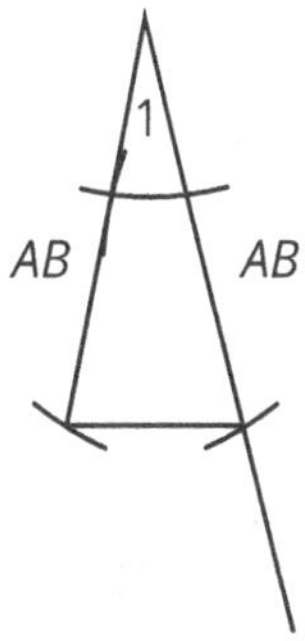

2.11

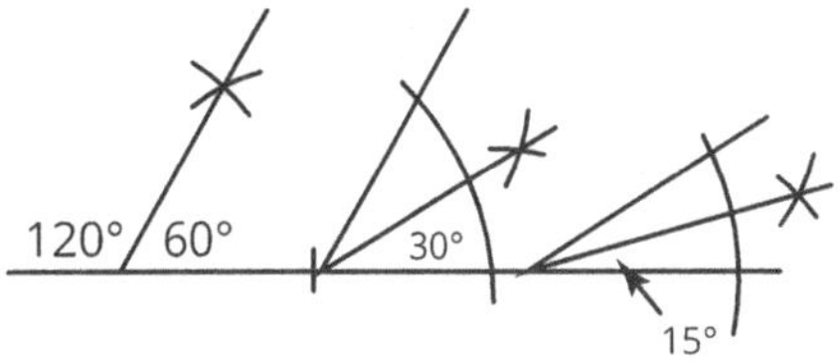

2.12

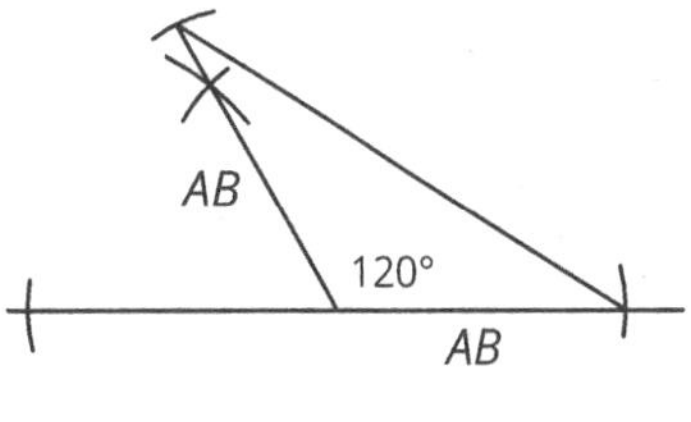

2.13 The altitudes intersect at the right-angle vertex.

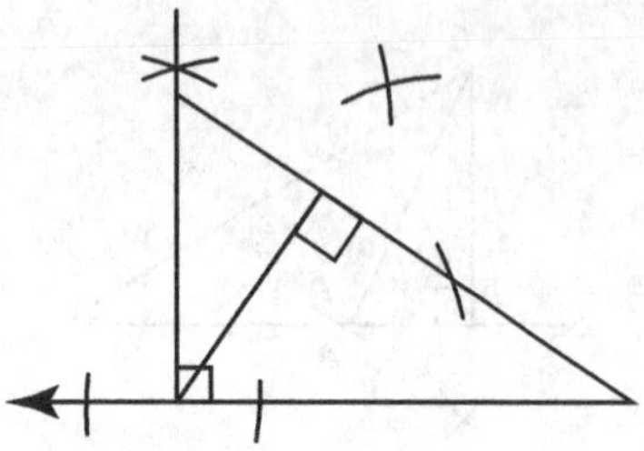

2.14 The altitudes intersect in the interior of the triangle.

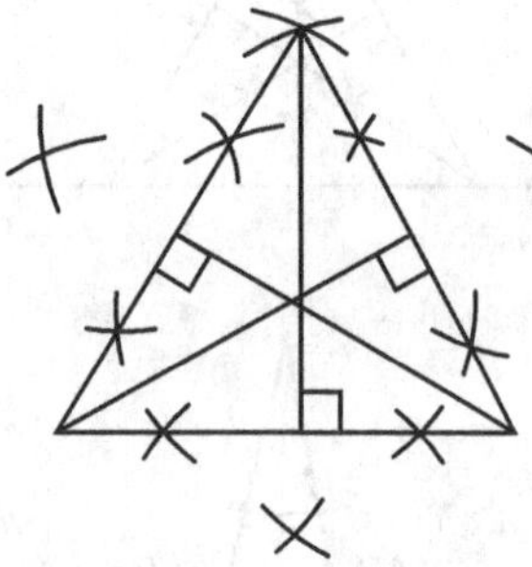

2.15 The altitudes intersect in the exterior of the triangle.

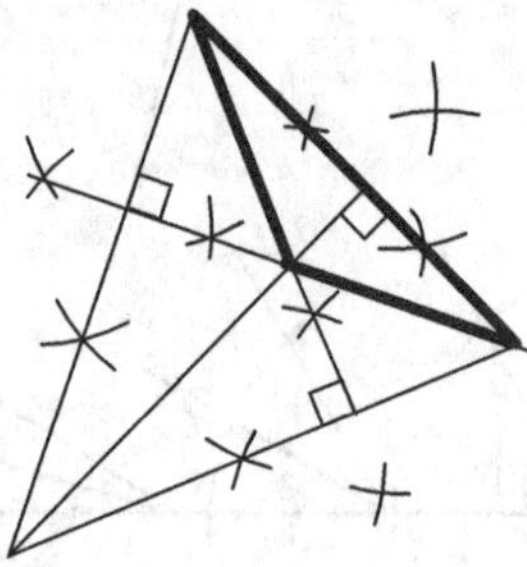

2.16

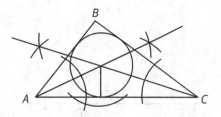

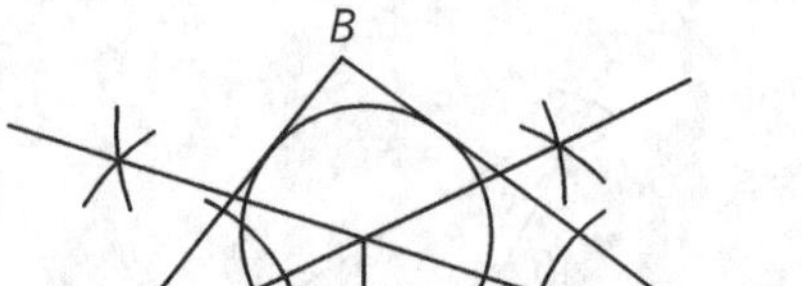

2.17

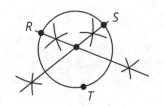

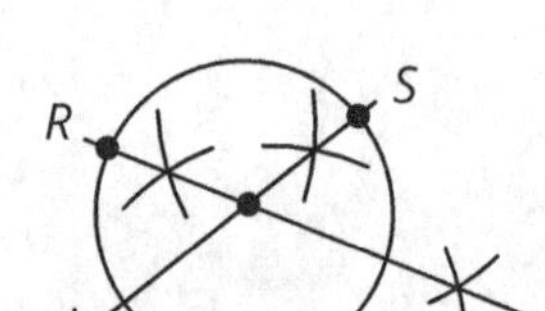

2.18

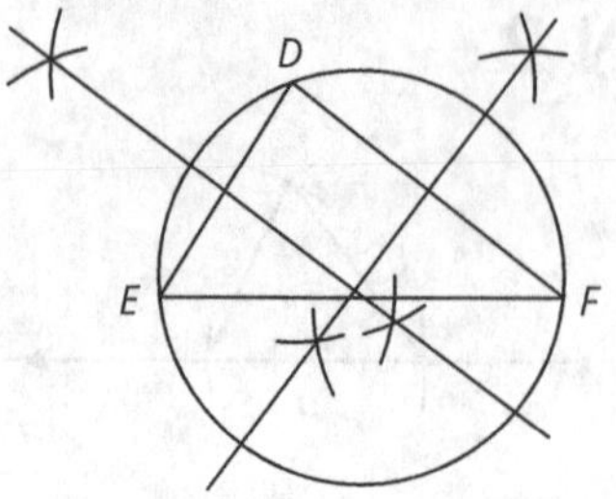

2.19

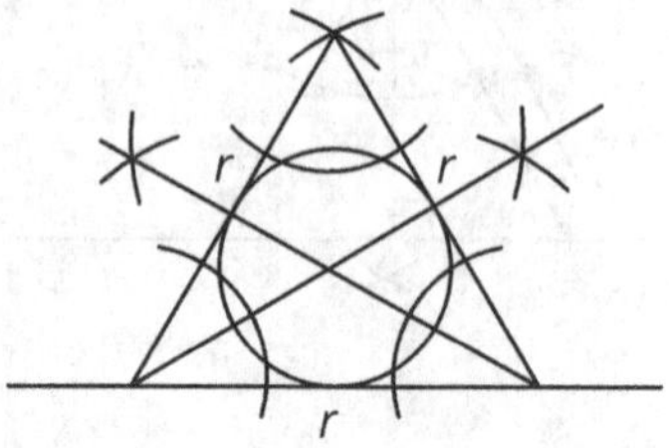

2.20
a. The hypotenuse is the diameter.
b. Bisect the hypotenuse

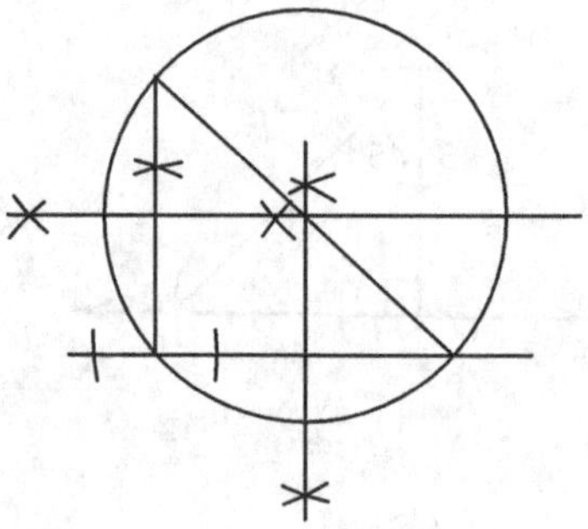

2.21

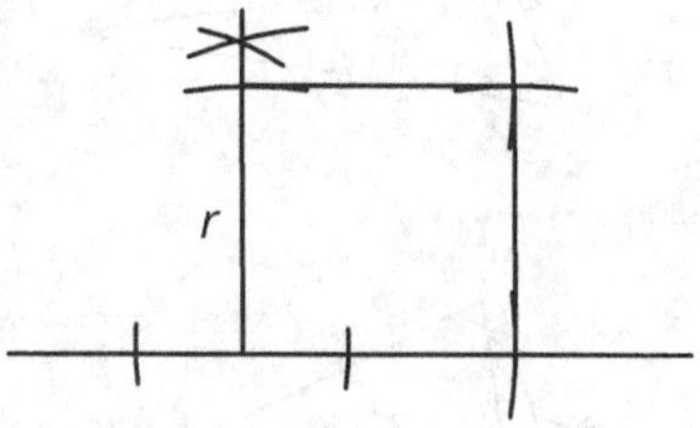

2.22

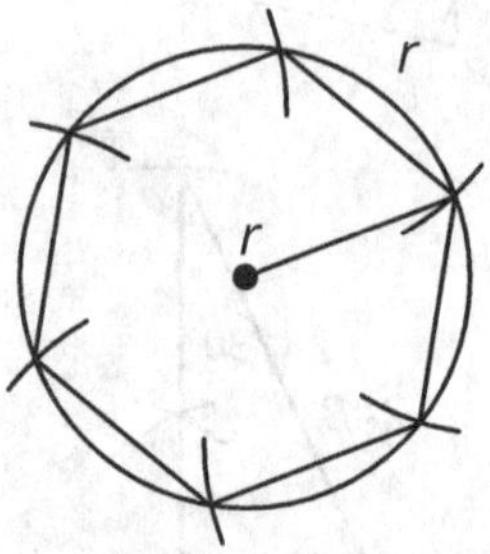

2.23

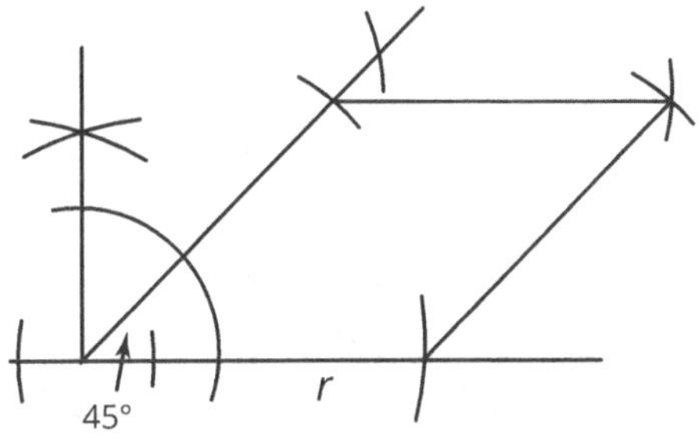

2.24

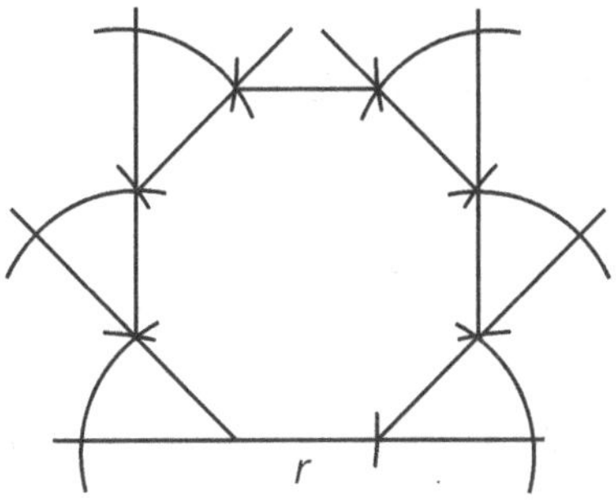

2.25

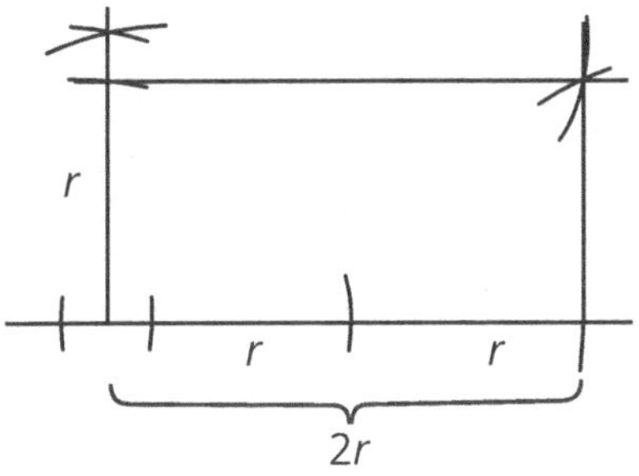

2.26

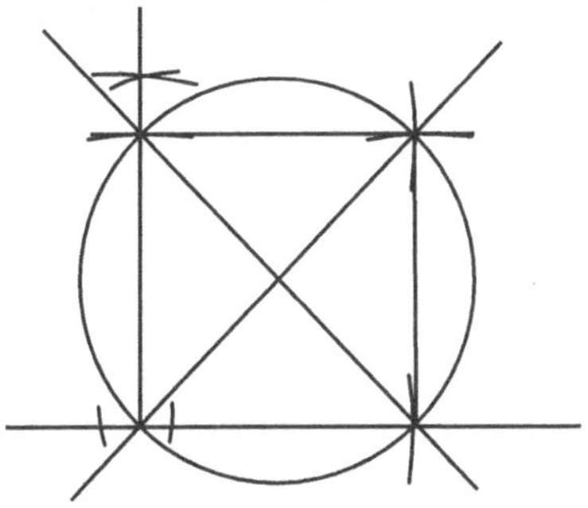

2.27 a. Six equilateral triangles are formed.
b. Join six equilateral triangles.

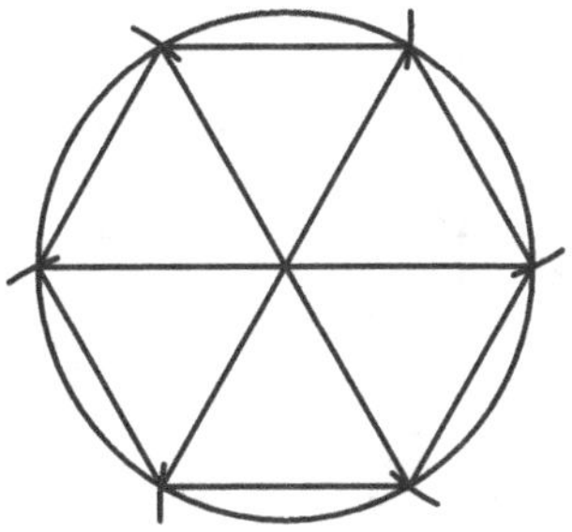

2.28 Two squares are formed.

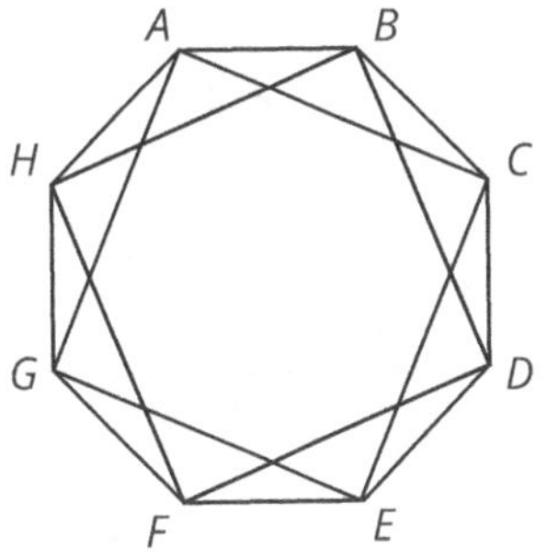

2.29
1. **STATEMENT**
Side = a
REASON
Given

2. **STATEMENT**
$AB = BC = CD = DE = EF = FA = a$
REASON
Same radii

3. **STATEMENT**
$\triangle AOB$, $\triangle BOC$, $\triangle COD$, and so on are equilateral.
REASON
All sides are equal to a.

4. **STATEMENT**
$\angle 1 = \angle 2 = \angle 3 \ldots = \angle 12$
REASON
All $\angle$'s of equilateral $\triangle$ are =.

5. **STATEMENT**
$\angle 2 + \angle 3 = \angle 4 + \angle 5 = \angle 6 + \angle 7 = \angle 8 + \angle 9 = \angle 10 + \angle 11 = \angle 12 + \angle 1$
REASON
Addition property of equality

6. **STATEMENT**
$\angle A = \angle B = \angle C = \angle D = \angle E = \angle F$
REASON
$\angle$ addition and substitution

7. **STATEMENT**
Polygon *ABCDEF* is a regular hexagon.
REASON
Definition of regular hexagon

SELF TEST 2

2.01

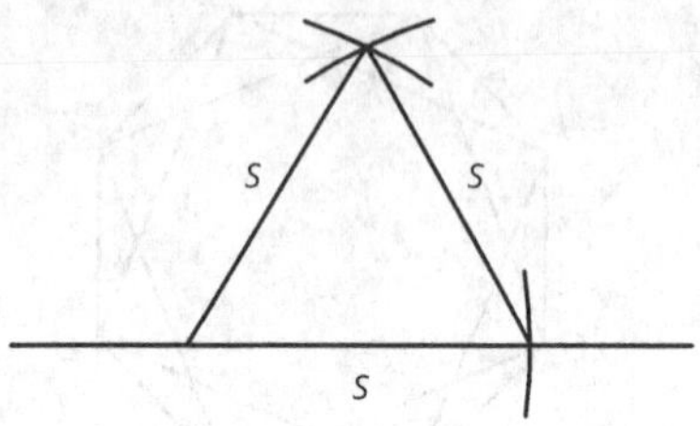

2.02

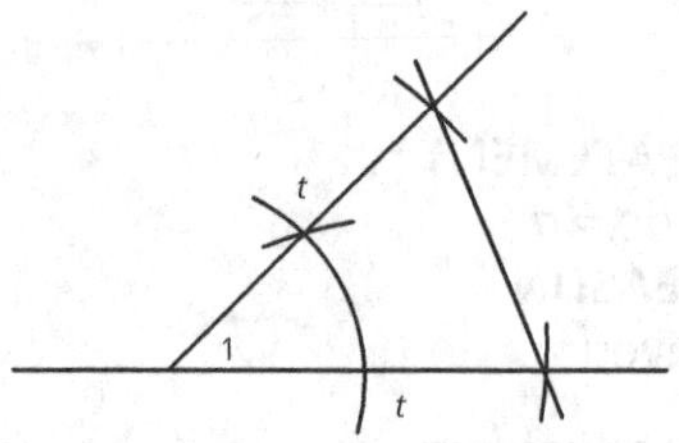

2.03

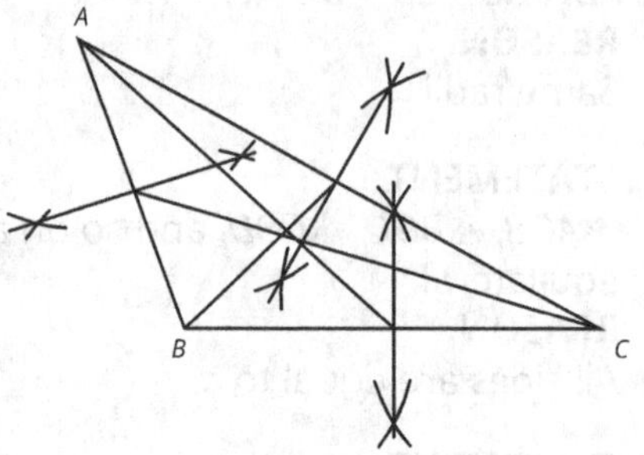

2.04

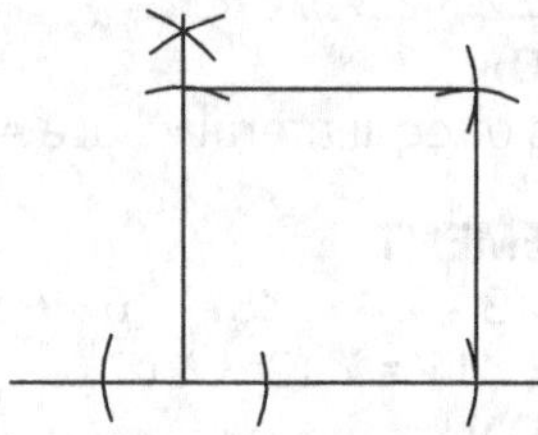

2.05

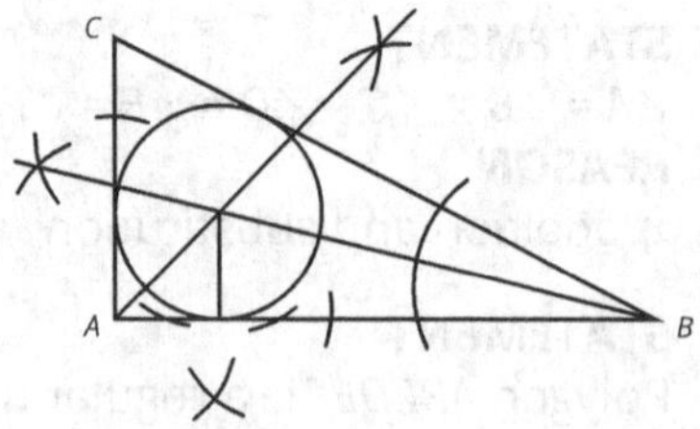

2.06

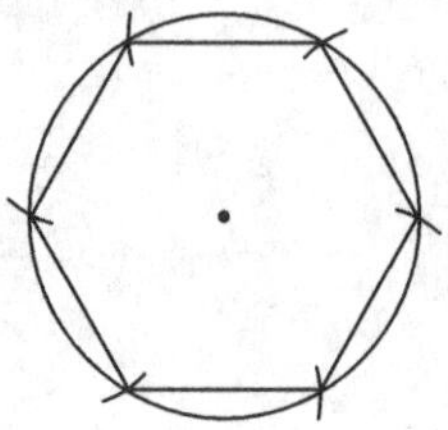

2.07

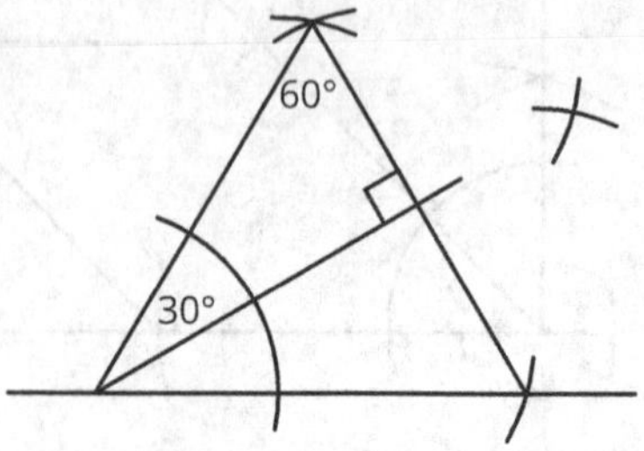

2.08 $\overline{CE}$ is altitude to $\overline{DE}$
$\overline{DE}$ is altitude to $\overline{CE}$

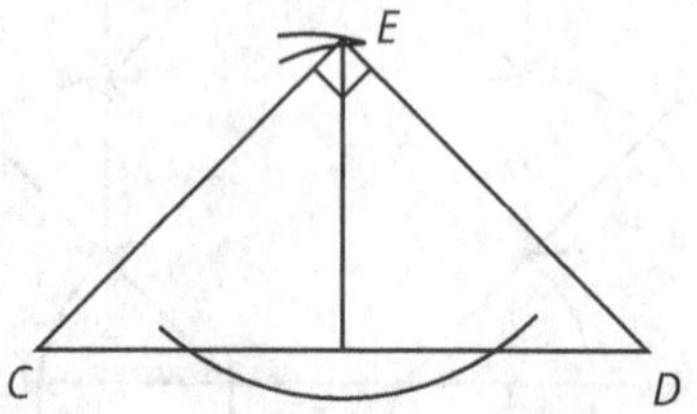

2.09

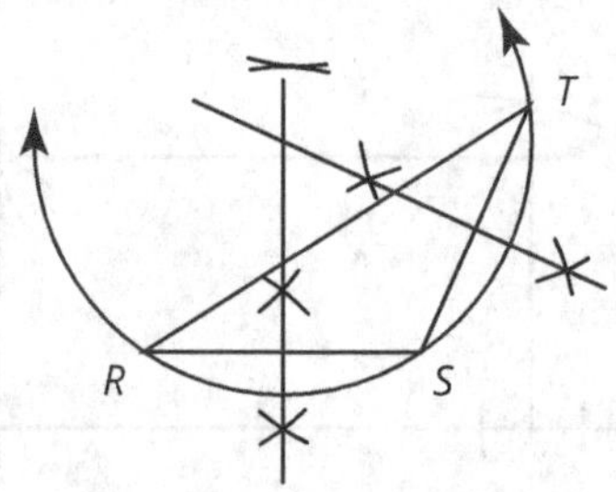

2.010

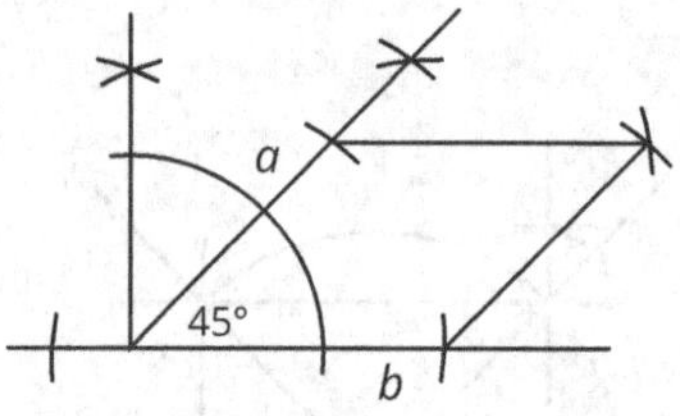

2.011

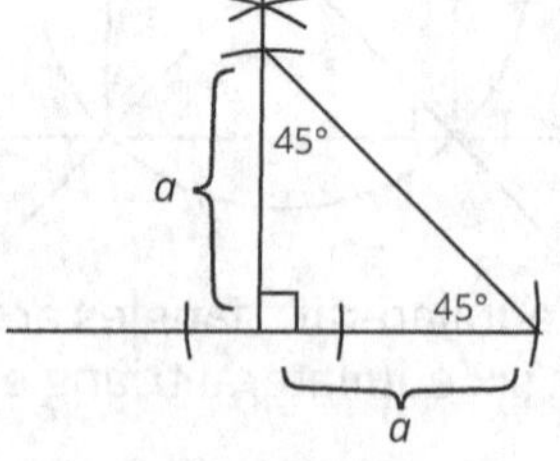

2.012

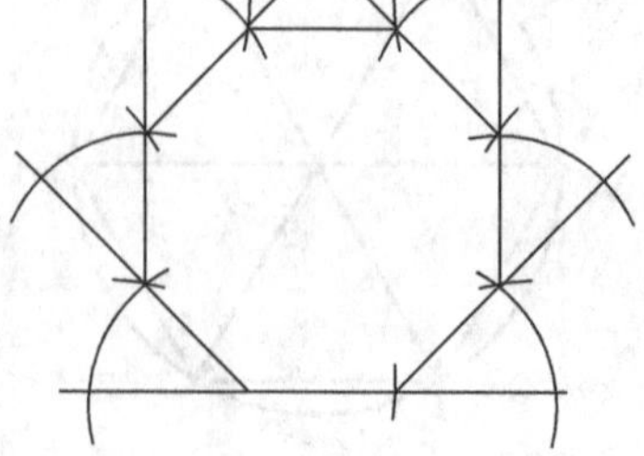

SECTION 3

3.1 A circle with center at *P* and radius of 2".

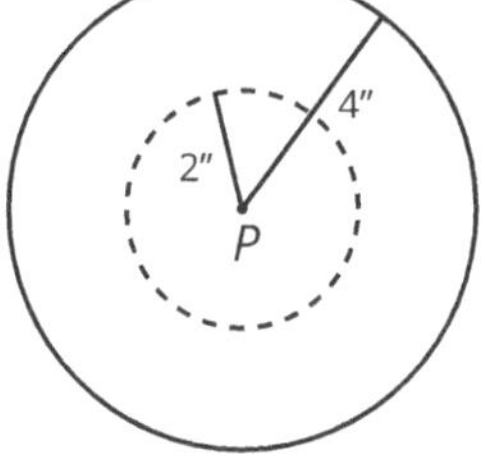

3.2 A pair of parallel lines 12" apart, one on each side of *t*.

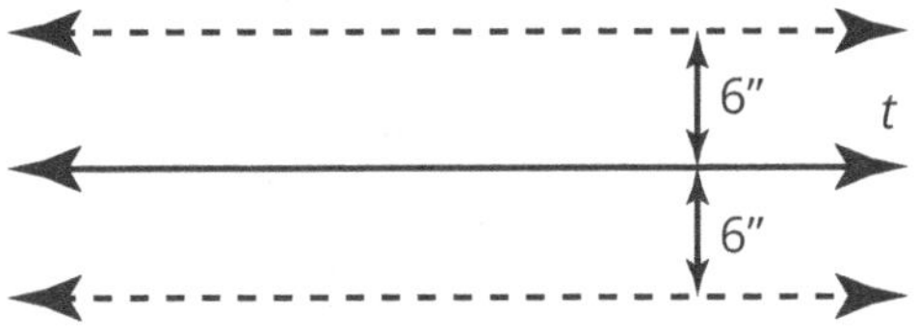

3.3 A line parallel to the given lines and midway between them.

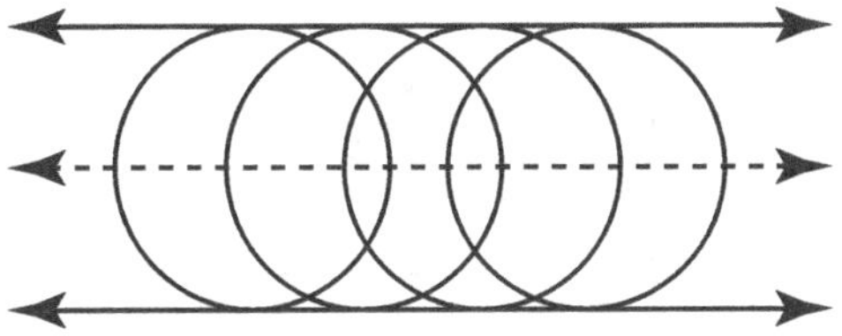

3.4 A ray that is the bisector of the given angle.

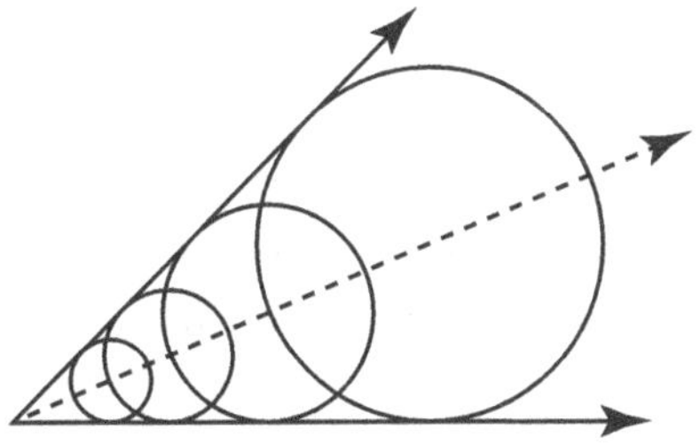

3.5 A cylinder with radius of 3".

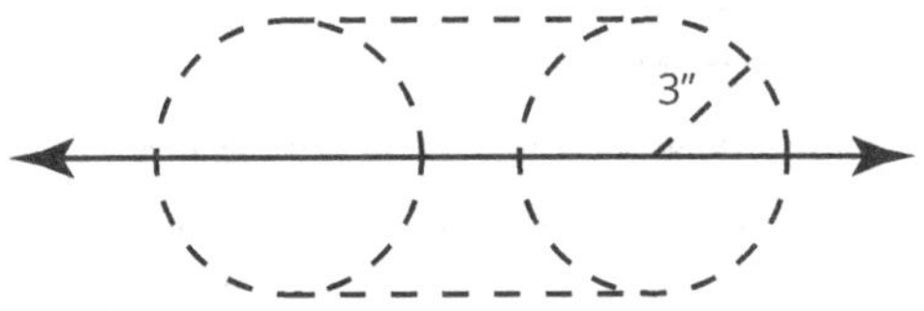

3.6 A circle concentric with the given circles with radius of 6".

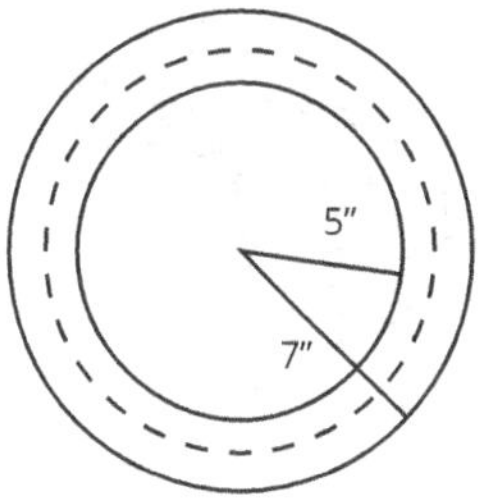

3.7 Two perpendicular lines that bisect the vertical angles formed.

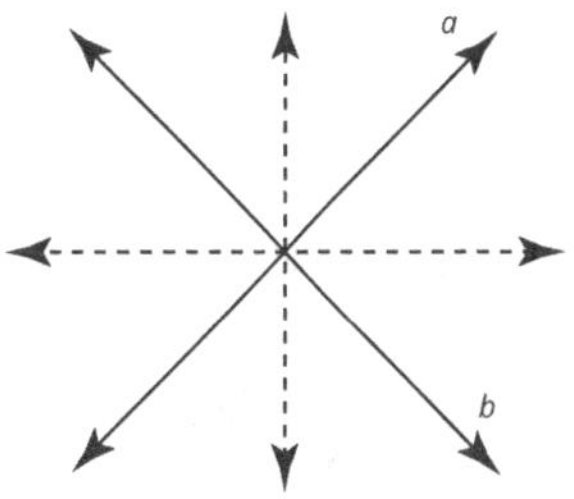

3.8 A circle with radius of 2" and center at *P*.

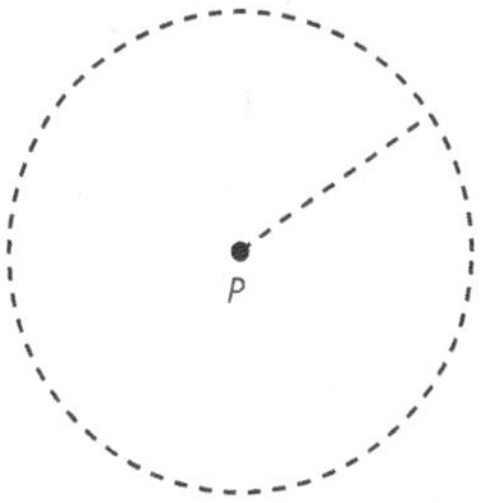

3.9 A ray that is the bisector of the angle.

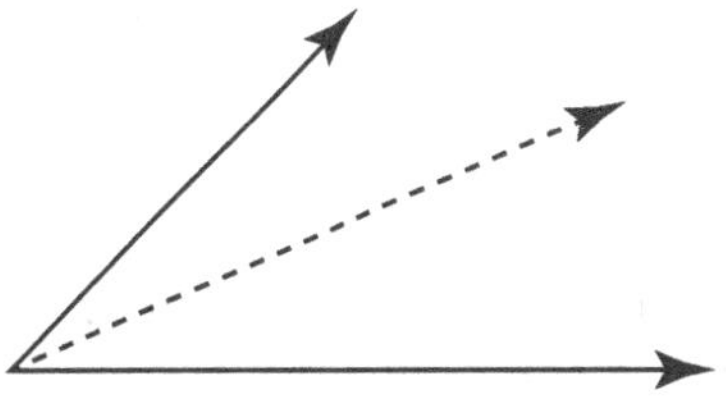

3.10 Two parallel planes 6" apart, both parallel to *R*.

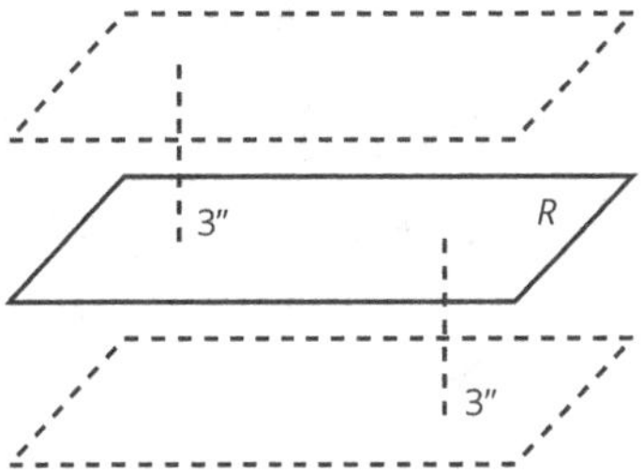

3.11 A line that is the perpendicular bisector of $\overline{RS}$.

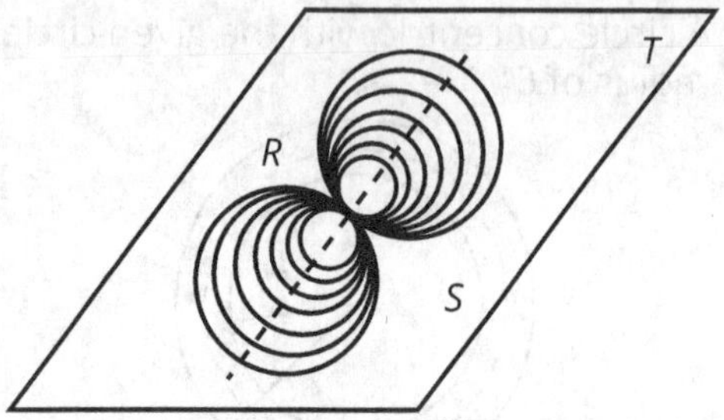

3.12 Two perpendicular lines that are the bisectors of the vertical angles formed.

3.13 Two concentric circles with radii 7" and 3".

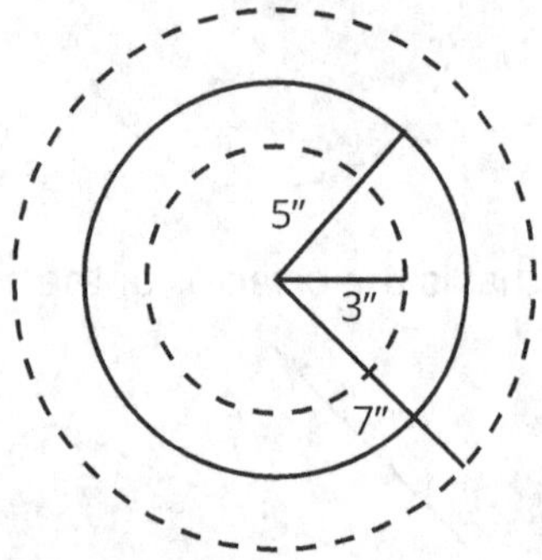

3.14 A sphere concentric with the larger sphere and having a radius of 4.

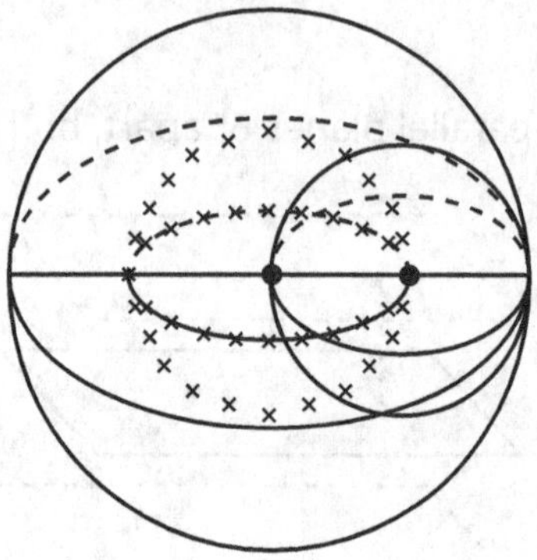

3.15

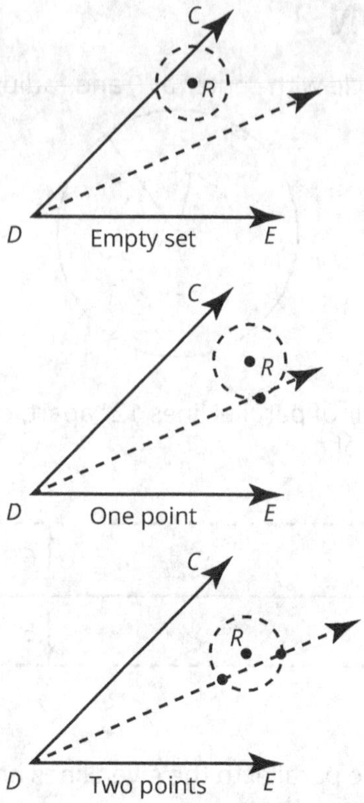

3.16

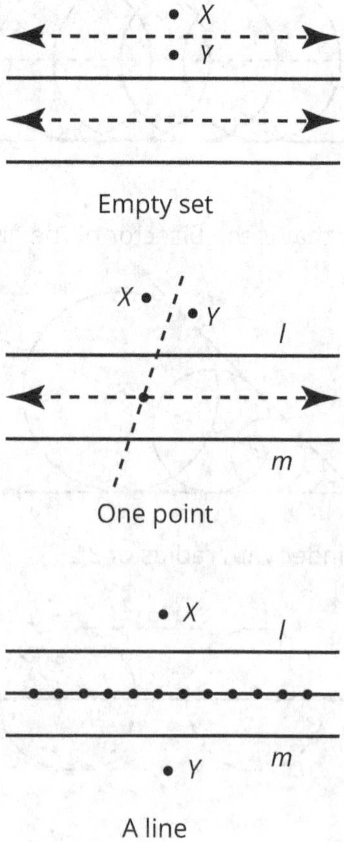

3.17

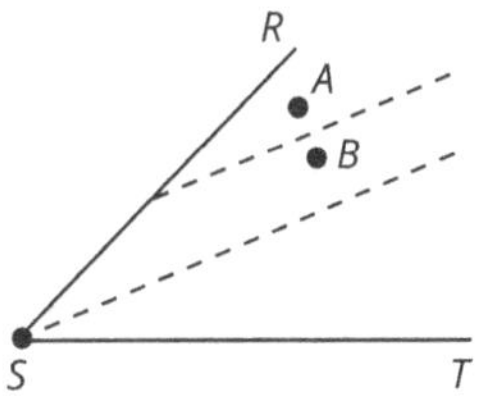

Empty set

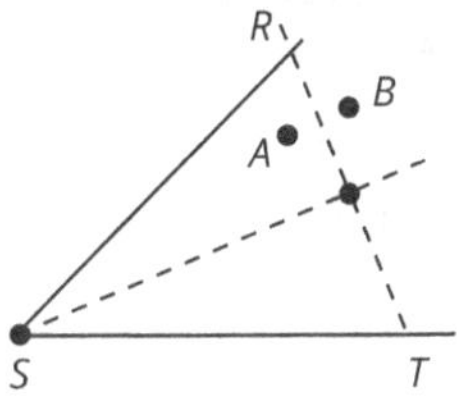

One point

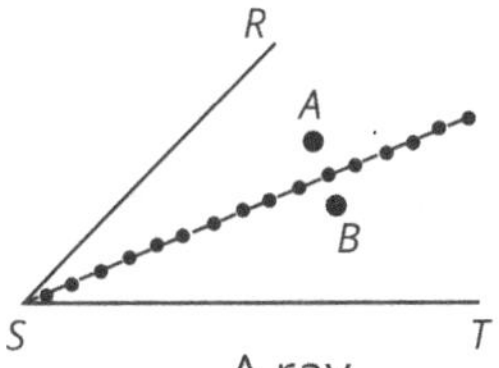

A ray

3.18

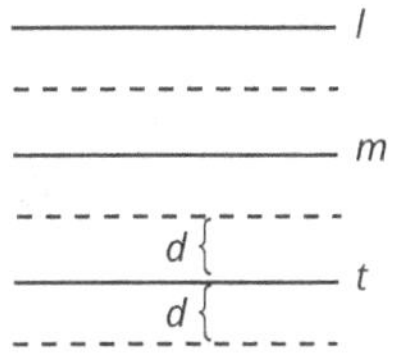

Empty set

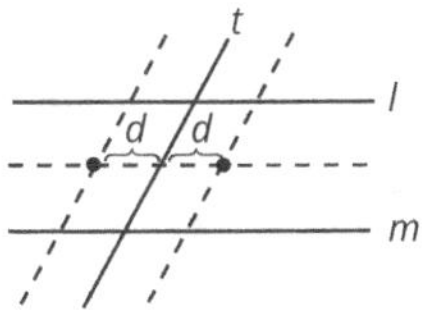

Two points

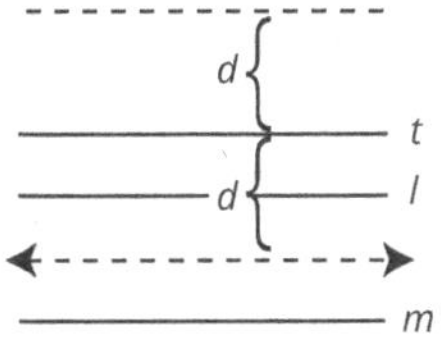

A line

3.19

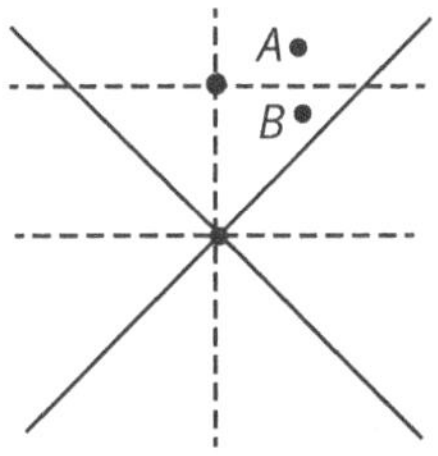

One point

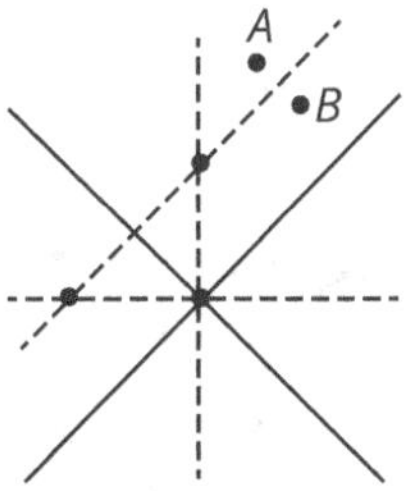

Two points

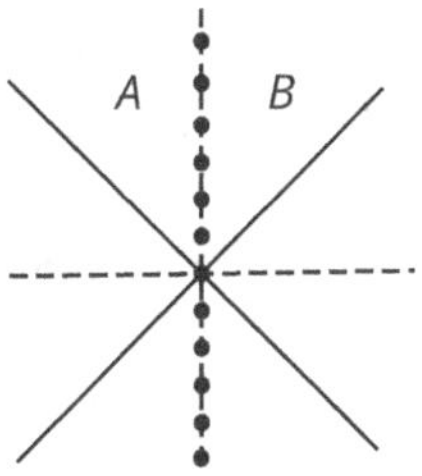

A line

3.20

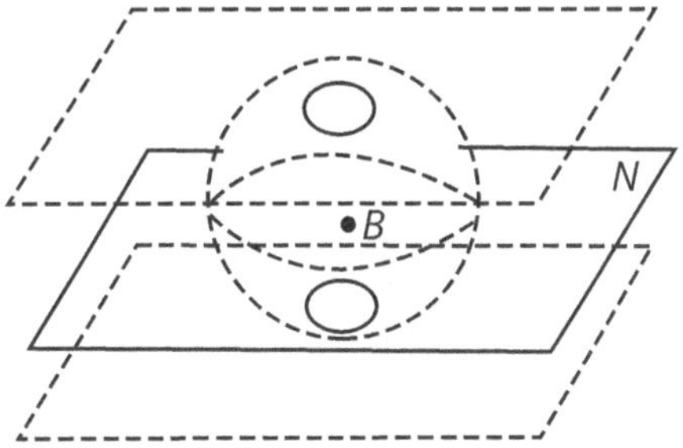

Two circles

3.21

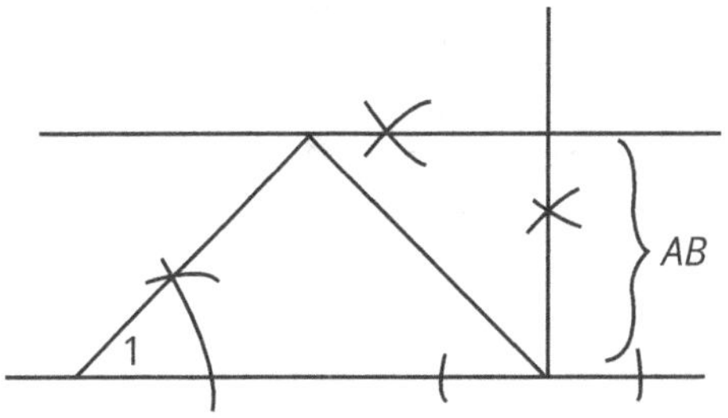

3.22

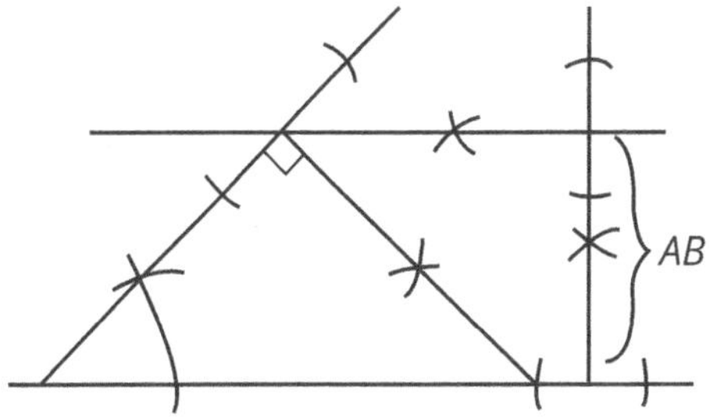

3.23

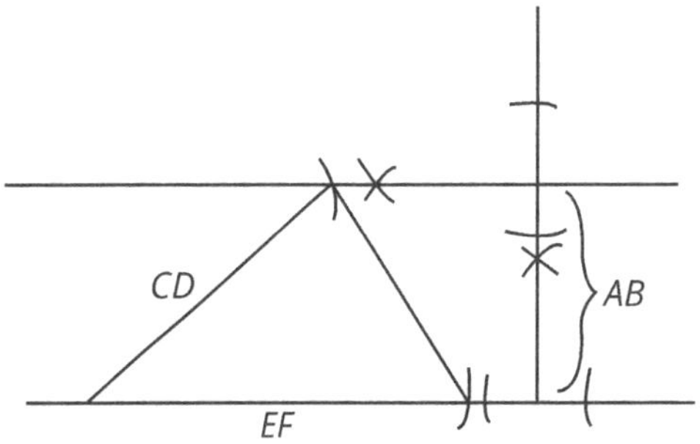

3.24

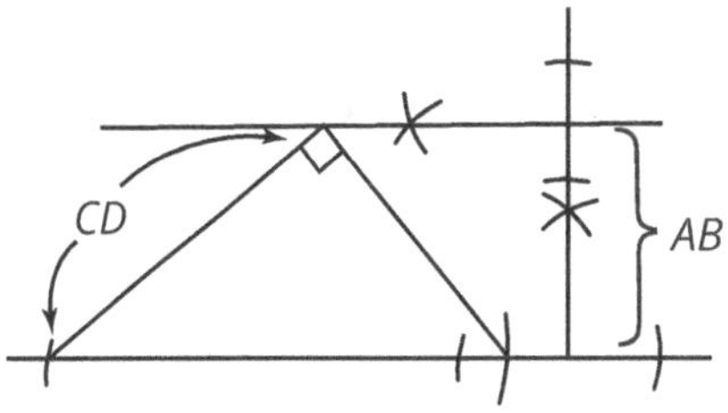

3.25

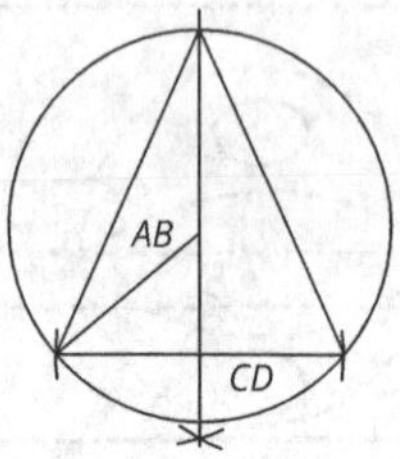

3.26

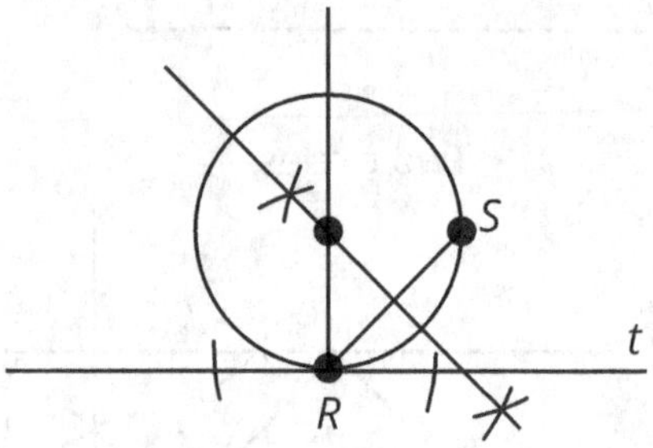

3.27 a.

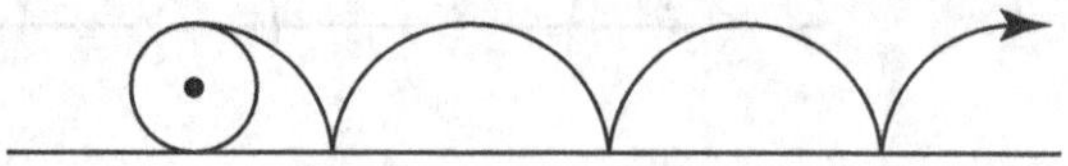

b.

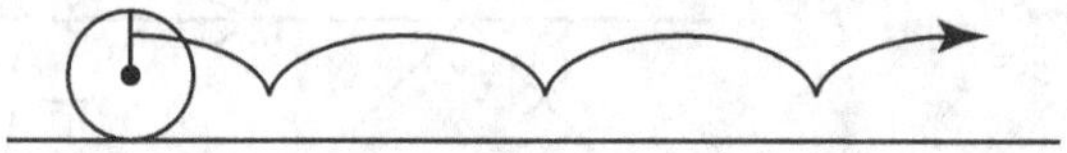

c.

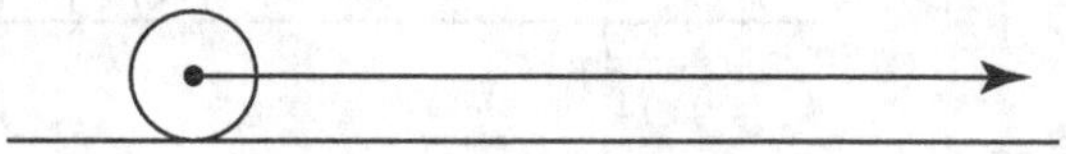

SELF TEST 3

3.01 A plane parallel to the floor and 1 foot above it.

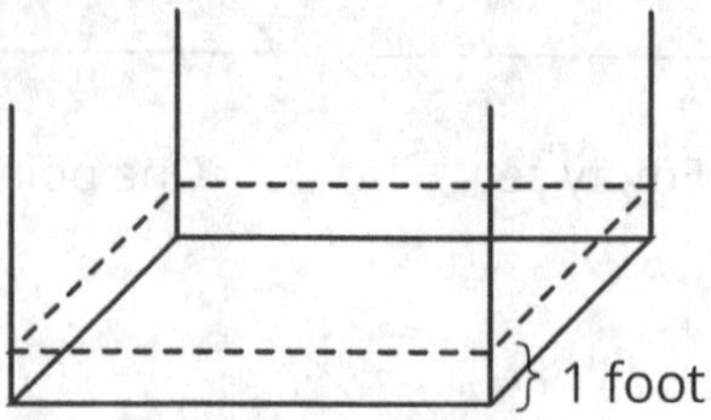

3.02 Two parallel lines 12" apart, both parallel to *t*.

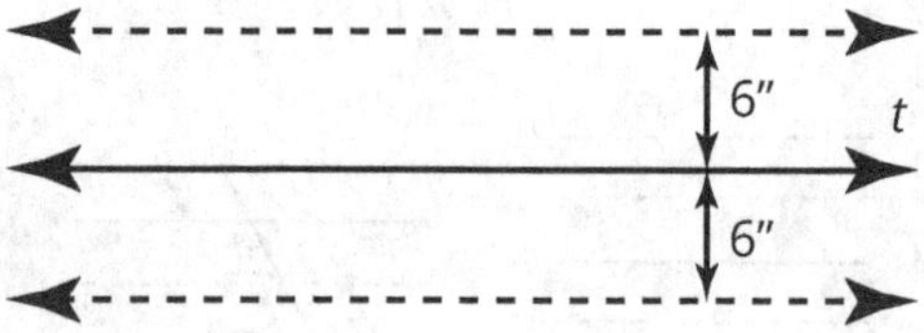

3.03 A line perpendicular to the plane of the square, passing through the intersection of the diagonals.

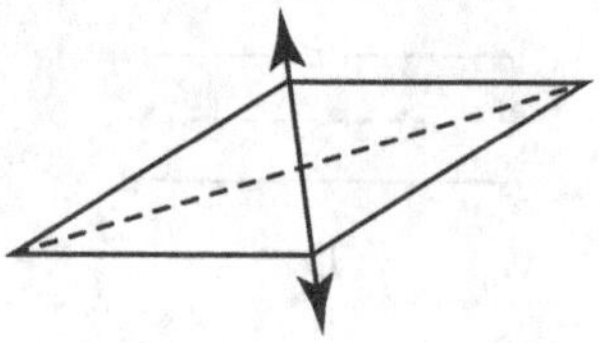

3.04 A plane parallel to and midway between the two given planes.

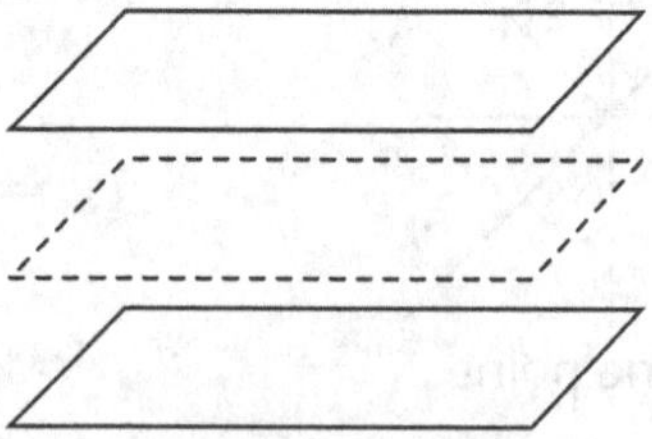

3.05 A line parallel to and midway between the given lines.

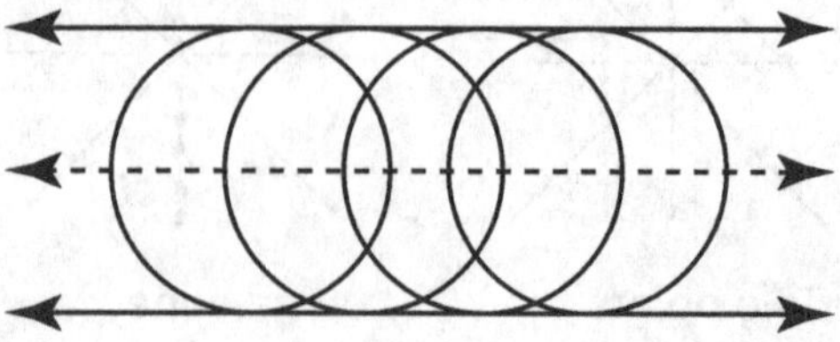

3.06 Empty set, One point, One line
3.07 Empty set, One point, One line
3.08 Empty set, One point, Two points
3.09 Empty set, One point, A circle
3.010 Empty set, One point, Two points, Three points, Four points
3.011 Empty set, One point, A circle
3.012

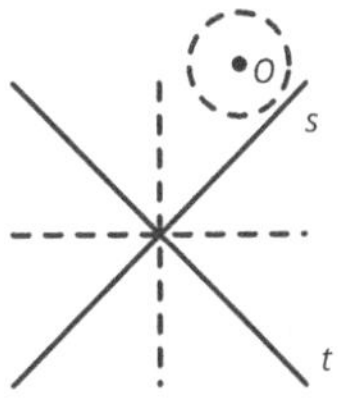

Empty set

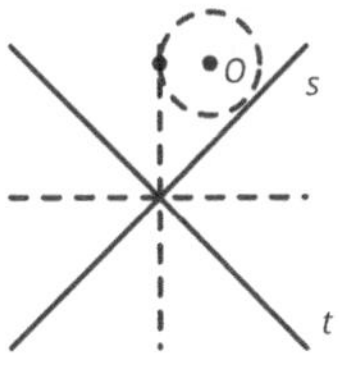

One point

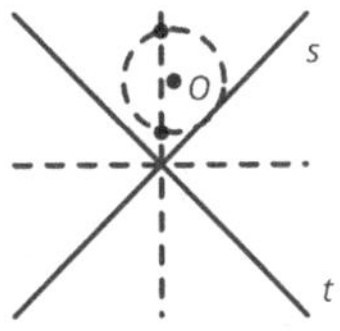

Two points

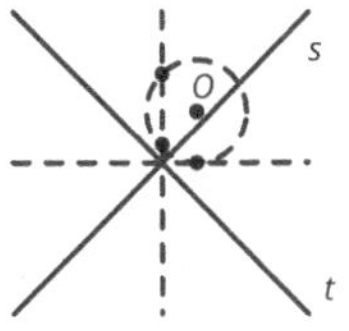

Three points

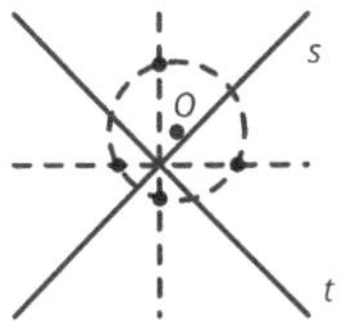

Four points

3.013

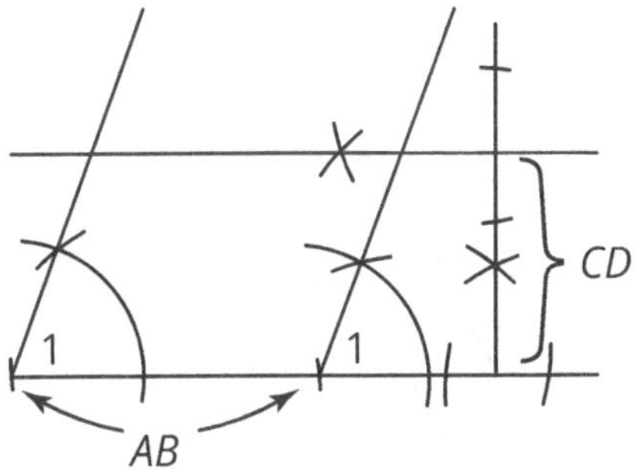

3.014

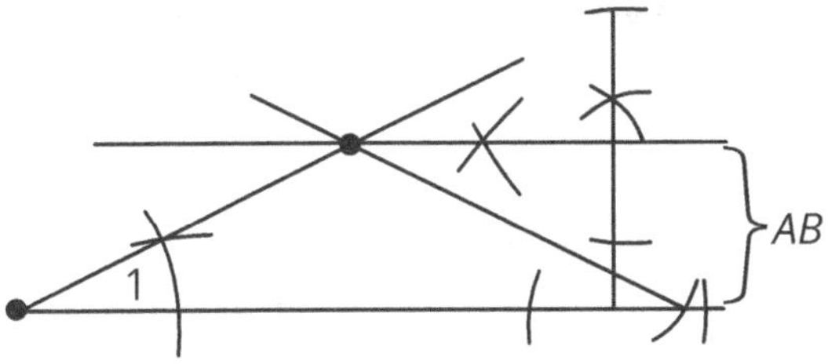

3.015

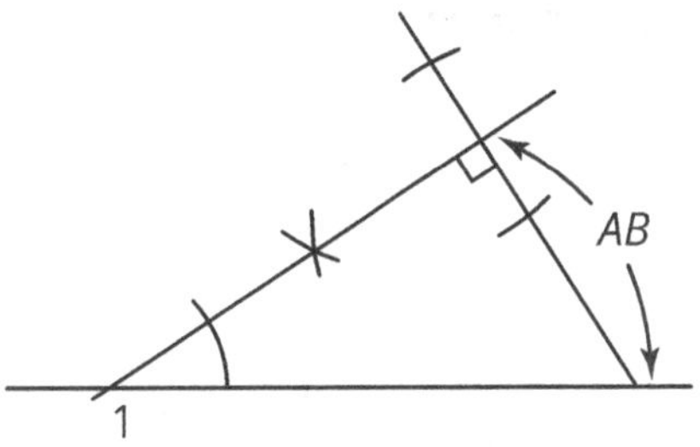

LIFEPAC TEST

1.

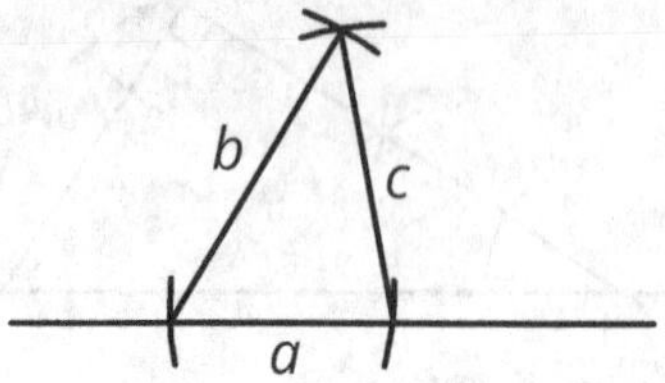

2.

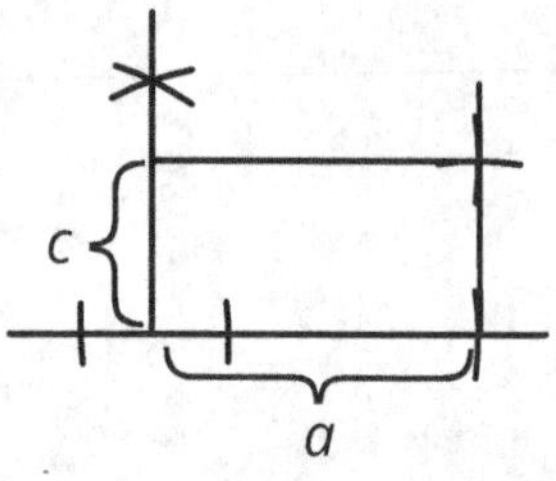

3.

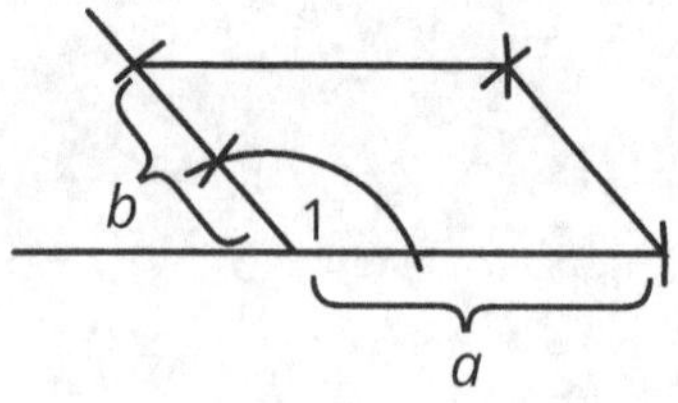

4.

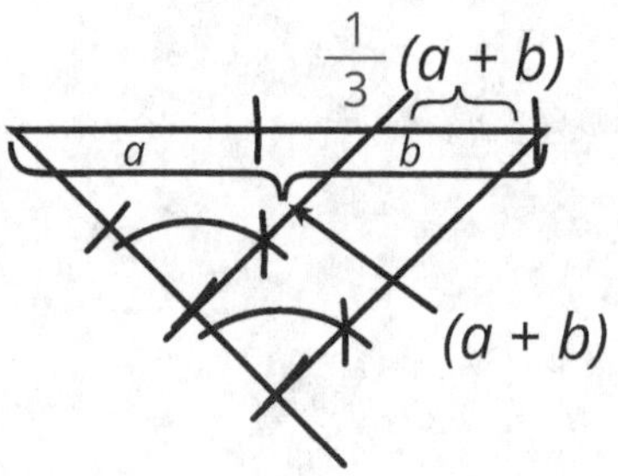

5.

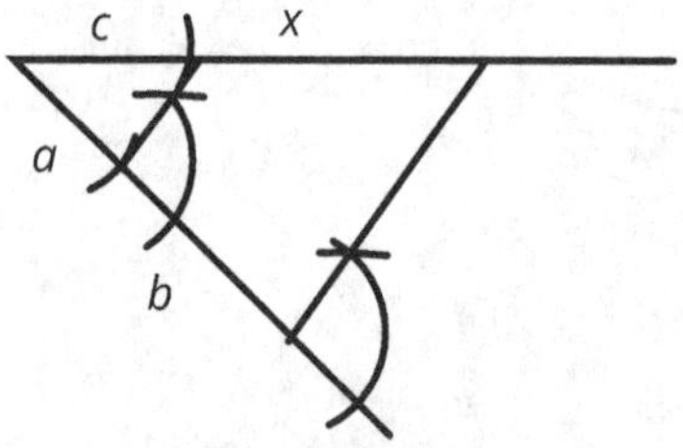

6.

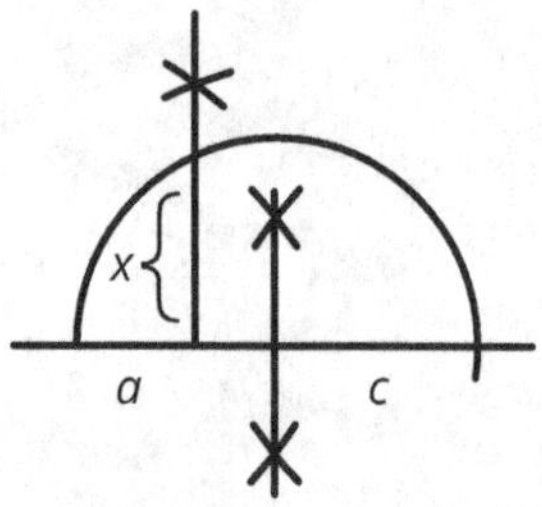

7.

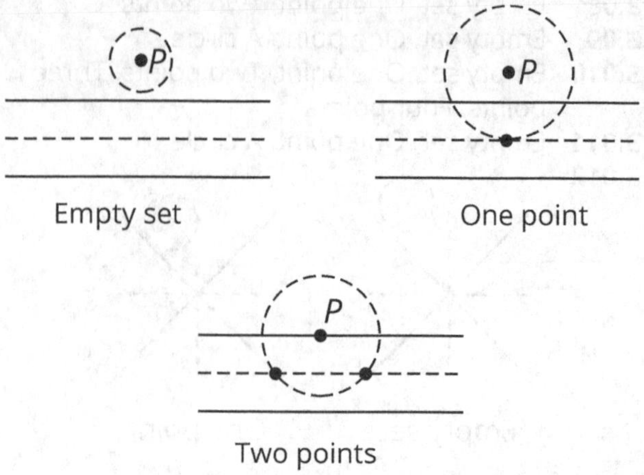

8.

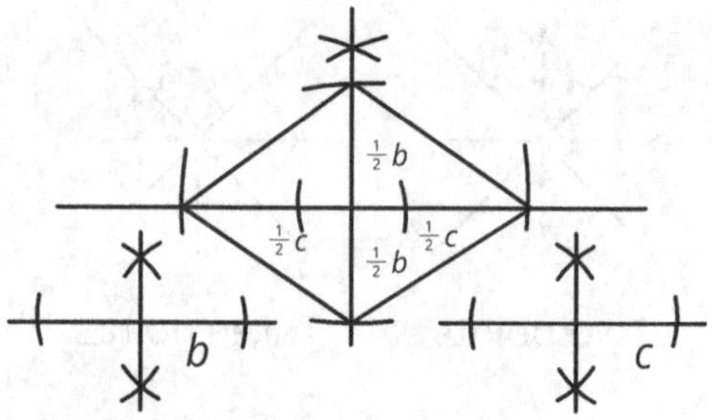

9. A part of a plane 4 ft. by 8 ft. and 3 inches above the table

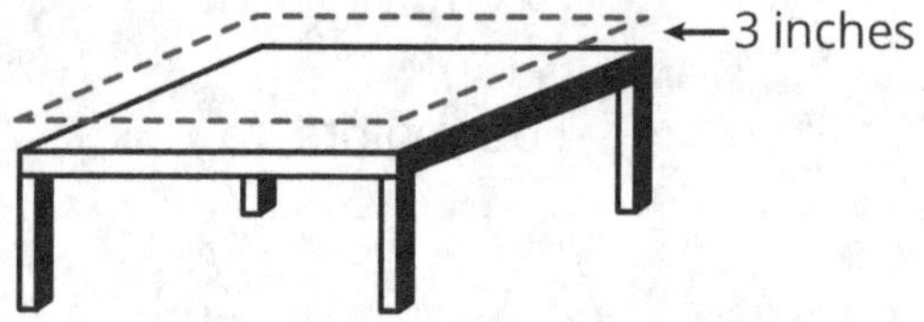

10.

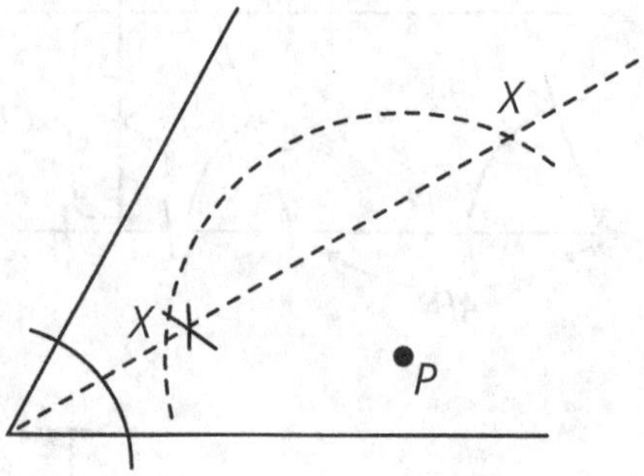

ALTERNATE LIFEPAC TEST

1.

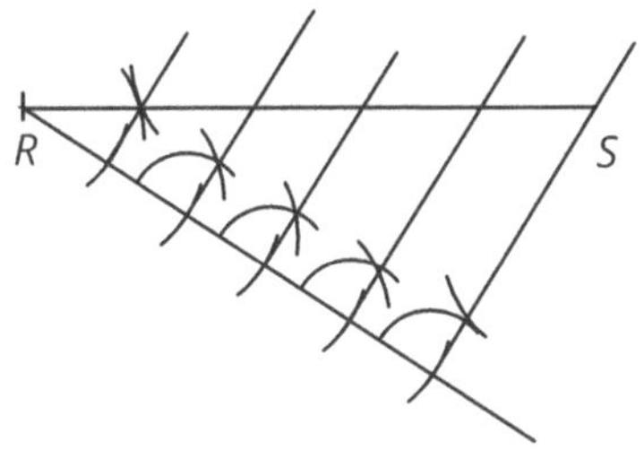

2.

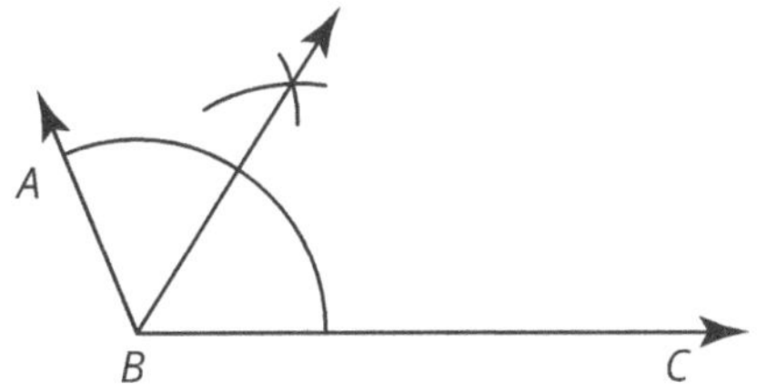

3.

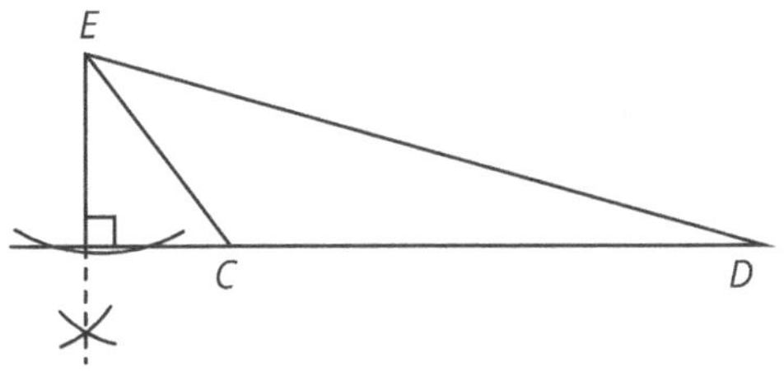

4.

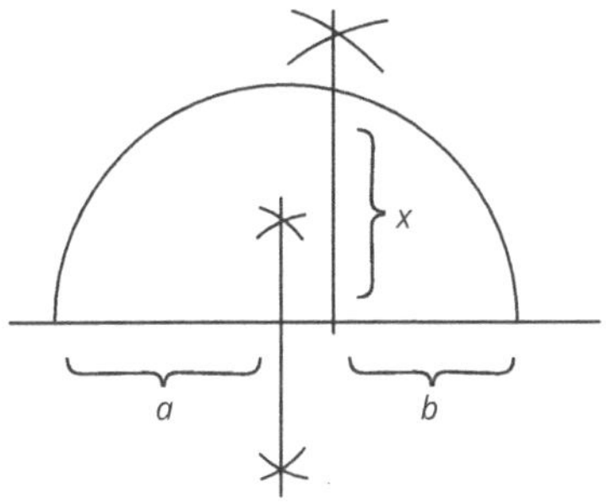

5.

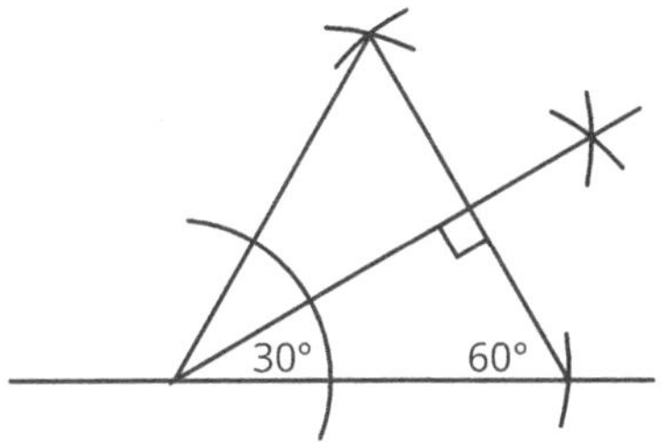

6.

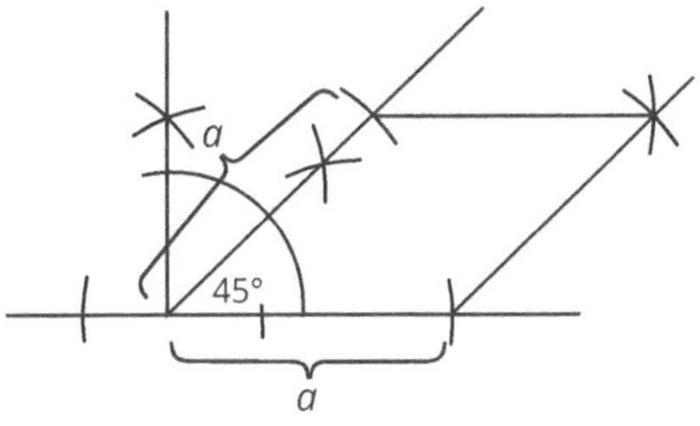

7.

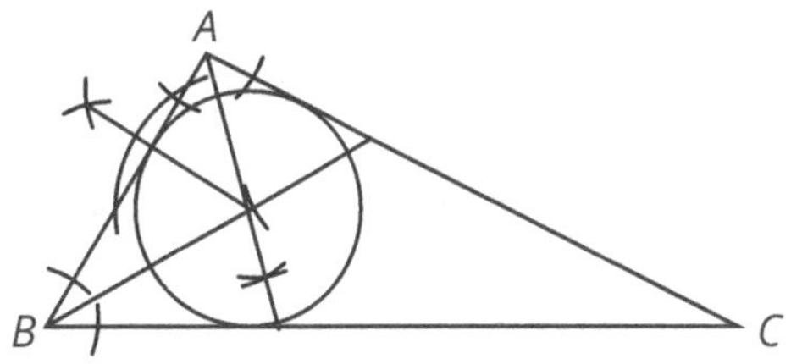

8.

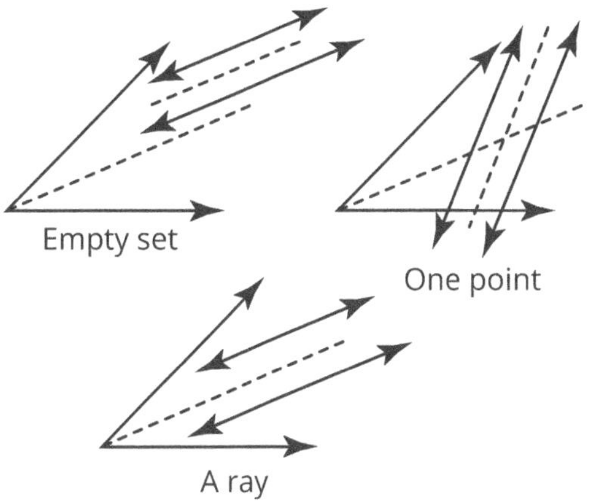

9.

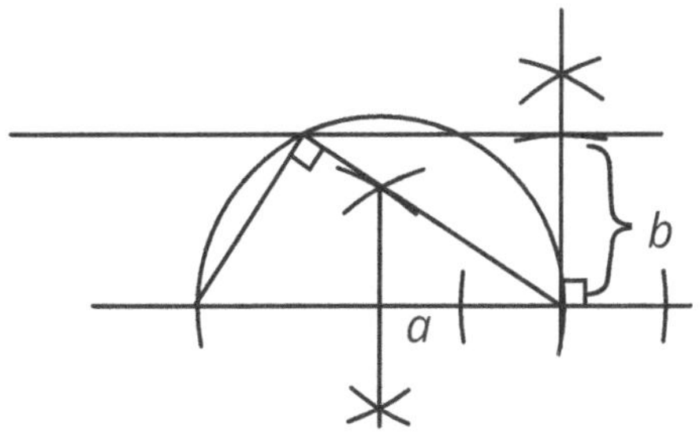

10.

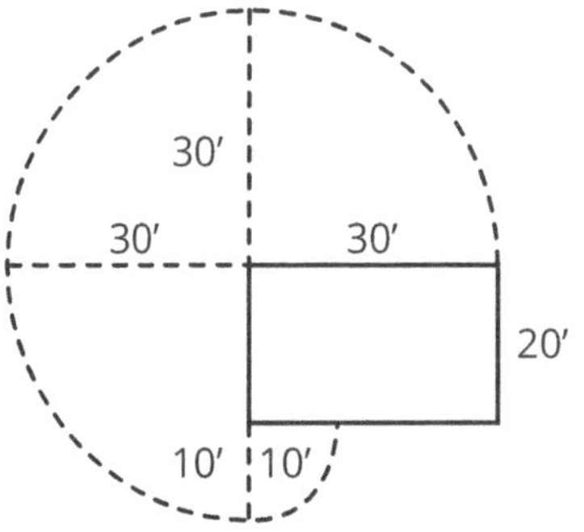

The locus is the interior of three-quarters of a circle with a 30-foot radius, plus one-quarter of a circle with a 10-foot radius.

MATH 1007

ALTERNATE LIFEPAC TEST

NAME ______________________________

DATE ______________________________

SCORE ______________________________

40/50

Complete the following items. Use only straightedge and compass for constructions and leave all construction arcs on your paper (each numbered item, 5 points).

1. Divide *RS* into five equal parts.

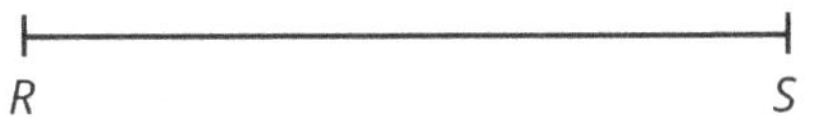

2. Bisect ∠*ABC*.

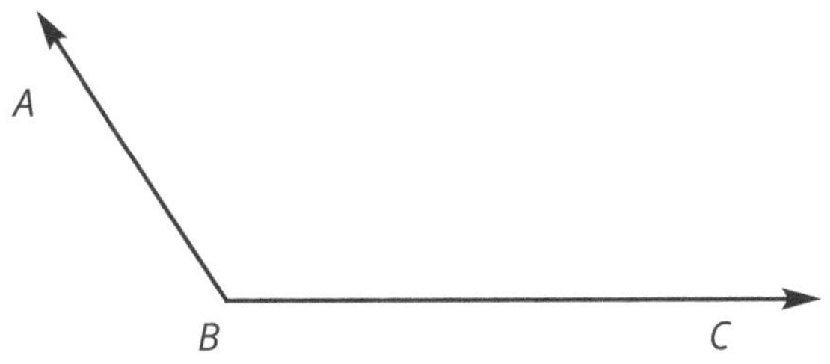

3. Construct the altitude to *CD*.

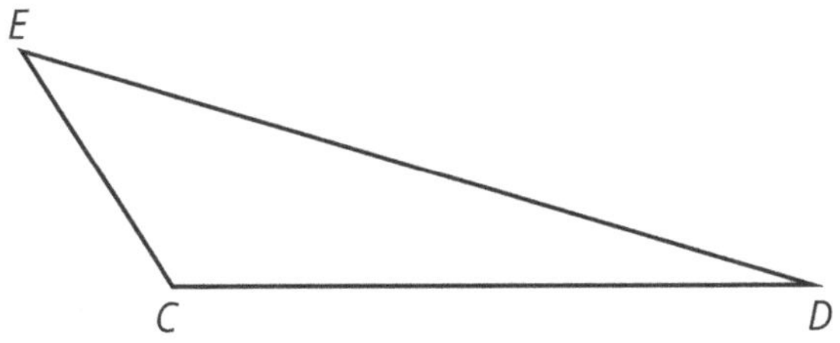

4. Construct x so that $x = \sqrt{ab}$

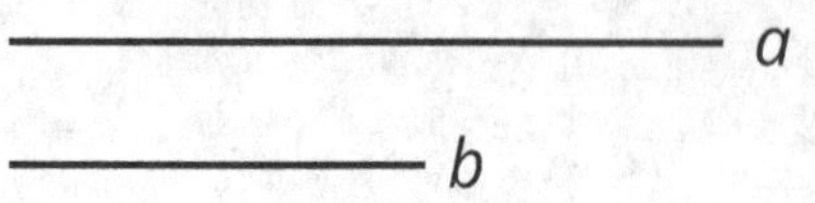

5. Construct a 30°-60°-90° triangle.

6. Construct a rhombus with a 45° angle and a side equal to a.

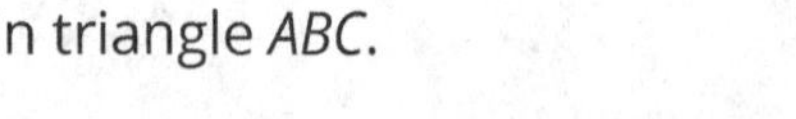

7. Inscribe a circle in triangle ABC.

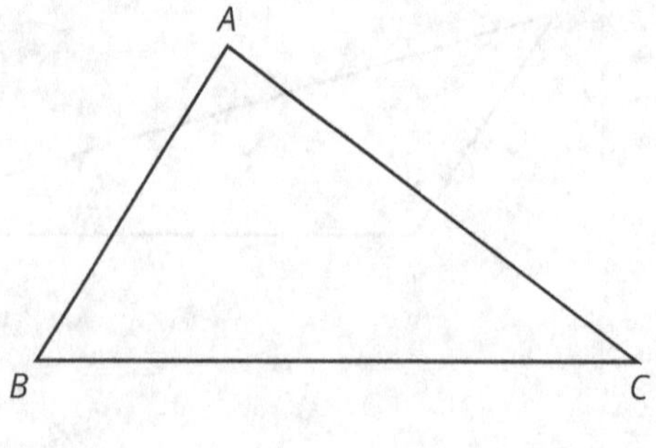

8. What is the locus of points in a plane equidistant from the side's of an angle and equidistant from two parallel lines? Show all solutions.

9. Construct a right triangle with hypotenuse equal to *a* and altitude to the hypotenuse equal to *b*.

a

b

10. A barn has dimensions of 20 by 30 feet.
A cow is tied to an outside corner of the barn by a rope 30 feet long.
What is the locus of points where the cow may graze? Make a sketch and describe.

MATH 1008

Unit 8: Area and Volume

TEACHER NOTES

MATERIALS NEEDED FOR LIFEPAC	
Required	Suggested
• protractor, compass, and straightedge	(None)

ADDITIONAL LEARNING ACTIVITIES

Section 1: Polygons

1. Discuss these questions with your class.
   a. How do the areas of an equilateral triangle, a square, a regular pentagon, a regular hexagon, and a regular octagon compare if each one has the same length side? Use a convenient length such as 6 inches to find the answer.
   b. If you double the length of the side of an equilateral triangle, how does the area of the smaller triangle compare with the area of the larger triangle?
   c. If you double the length of the side of a square, how does the area of the smaller square compare with the area of the larger square?
   d. What do you notice about the area comparisons in the preceding questions (b) and (c)?
2. People who get lost in a desert invariably do so because instead of walking in a straight line they walk in a large circle and eventually come back to their starting point without realizing it. The reason a person walks in a large circle without realizing it is that a person's legs are never exactly the same length, and so the steps he takes with his left foot and right foot are slightly different. An exaggerated diagram is shown following this activity.

   The radius of the circle in which a person walks is a function of the difference between the lengths of his steps and approximates $r = \frac{24}{d}$, where r is the radius of the circle in feet and d is the difference between the lengths of steps in inches. Suppose the steps a person takes with his left foot are $\frac{1}{16}$" longer than the steps he takes with his right foot. Have the class compute the radius of the circle the person would walk if he were blindfolded.

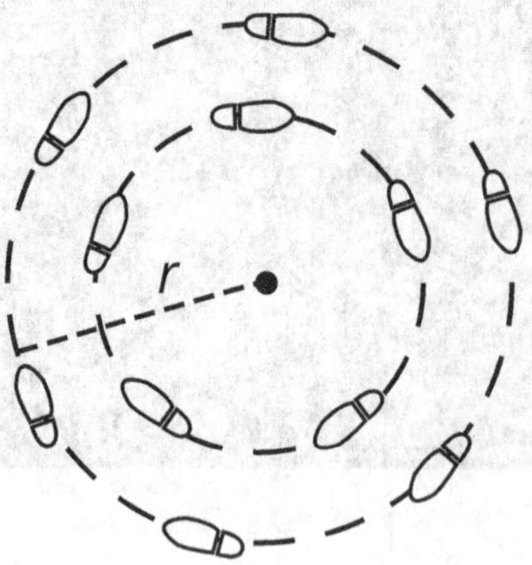

3. Have the class copy the dodecagon shown following this activity. Then have them draw 4 line segments in the dodecagon as shown. Note that the dodecagon is now divided into six parts. Point out to the class that the resulting figure has line symmetry and that one of the six parts seems to be an equilateral triangle. Have the class cut the six pieces apart with scissors and try to rearrange them to form a square (it can be done!).

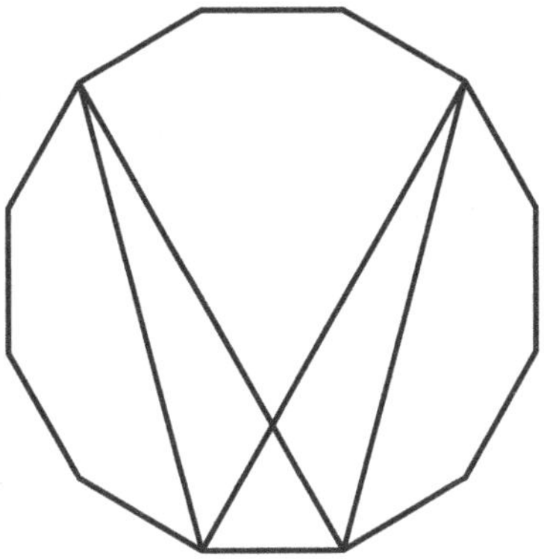

Section 2: Circles

1. Ask a biology teacher at your school to explain to the class how biologists use π to compute bacterial growth.
2. Invite an actuary (a person who estimates risks, rates, premiums, and other factors for insurance companies) to come and explain to the class how π is used to compute probabilities.
3. Let one student at a time work on this activity. Write the division problem $7\overline{)22.00}$ at the top of a long sheet of paper. The fraction $\frac{22}{7}$ is an approximation for π. Let each student take turns dividing the problem. Emphasize that each student should be as accurate as possible and should check his work carefully since the work of each student depends on the previous work. Each student may want to check the problem before he continues working on it to be sure the answers are correct.
4. Research the history of pi; use concordances, encyclopedias, books, online resources, and magazine articles.

Section 3: Solids

1. Compare the lateral area of a cube with side equal to 1 to the lateral area of a square-based pyramid with sides of base equal to 1 and slant height equal to 1. Then compare the total area of the same cube (side equal to 1) to the lateral area of the same square-based pyramid (sides of base equal to 1 and slant height equal to 1).
2. Ask the class if, based on their comparisons of the lateral areas and total areas of the cube and square-based pyramid, they think the volume of the cube compared to the volume of the pyramid will have the same ratio as the previous comparisons. Then have the class find the volume of the cube (side equal to 1) and the volume of the pyramid (sides of base equal to 1 and slant height equal to 1). Ask the class why the ratio of the volume of the cube to the volume of the pyramid is not the same ratio as the ratio of the lateral areas and the ratio of the total area.

Administer the LIFEPAC Test.

ANSWER KEYS

SECTION 1

1.1 Examples:

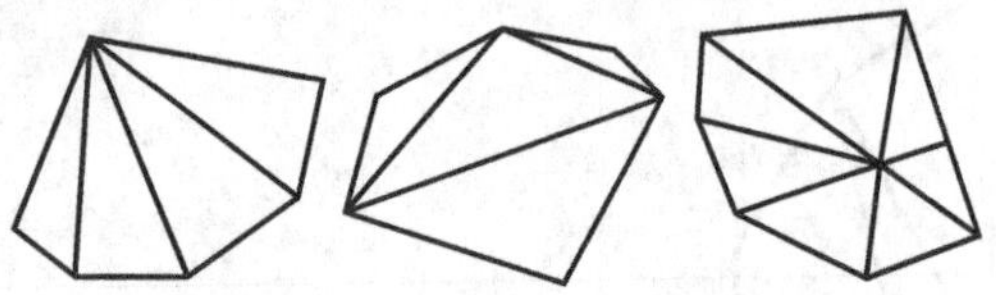

1.2 a. $3 + 5 + 8 + 2 = 18$
b. $3 + 3 + 3 + 3 + 3 + 3 = 18$
c. $2 + 2 + 2 + 2 + 2 + 2 + 2 + 2 = 16$
d. $2 + 5 + 3 + 7 + 9 + 6 = 32$

1.3 20 square inches

1.4 c., e., and f.

1.5 no

1.6 yes

1.7 They are =. Two $\cong \triangle$'s are formed.
P18 says their areas are =.

1.8 yes

1.9 yes

1.10 no

1.11 $12(8) = 96$ sq. in.

1.12 $7^2 = 49$ sq. ft.

1.13 a. $\frac{1}{2}(2) = 1$ sq. ft.
b. $6(24) = 144$ sq. in.

1.14 $16 \div 8 = 2$ cm

1.15 $\sqrt{25} = 5$ ft.

1.16 $12(12) = 144$ sq. in.

1.17 $A = bh$

$8\frac{3}{4} = 3\frac{1}{2}h$

$8\frac{3}{4} \div 3\frac{1}{2} = h$

$\frac{35}{4}(\frac{2}{7}) = h$

$\frac{5}{2} = h$

$h = 2\frac{1}{2}$ ft.

1.18 $A = 15(20) = 300$ sq. ft.
$\frac{300}{9} = 33\frac{1}{3}$ sq. yds.

1.19 $2(36)(15) = 1{,}080$ sq. ft.
$1{,}080 \div 100 = 10.8$ shingling squares
$10.8(70) = \$756$

1.20 $6(300) = 1{,}800$ sq. ft.
$1{,}800 \div 400 = 4.5$ gallons

1.21 a. $18(4) = 72$ sq. cm
b. $18(2) + 18(2) = 36 + 36 = 72$ sq. cm
c. $4(2) + 4(2) = 8 + 8 = 16$ sq. cm

1.22

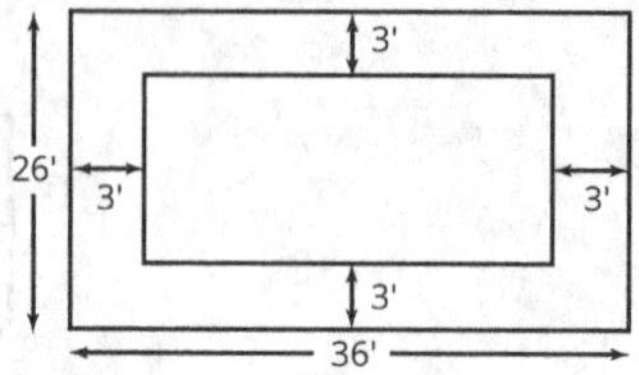

$2(26)(3) =$	156
$2(30)(3) =$	+ 180
	336 sq. ft. or
$26(36) =$	936
$20(30) =$	− 600
	336 sq. ft.

1.23

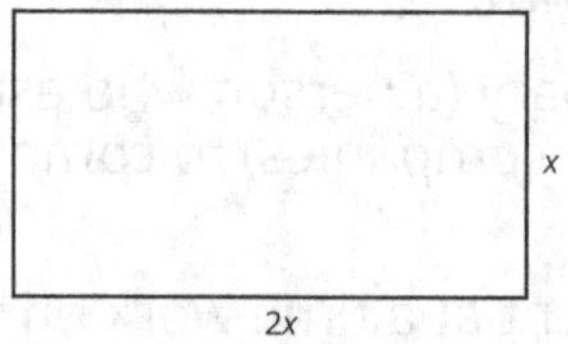

$2x(x) = 50$
$2x^2 = 50$
$x^2 = 25$
$\sqrt{x^2} = \sqrt{25}$
$x = 5$ yds.
$2x = 2(5) = 10$ yds.

1.24 $(2)(2)(3) = 12$ sq. ft.
$12 \div 9 = 1\frac{1}{3}$ sq. yds.

1.25

$20(10) =$	200
$30(40) =$	1,200
$15(20) =$	+ 300
	1,700 sq. ft.
$150(100) =$	15,000 sq. ft.

15,000
− 1,700
13,300 sq. ft. of grass

1.26 $3\frac{1}{2}(\frac{3}{4}) = \frac{7}{2}(\frac{3}{4}) = \frac{21}{8} = 2\frac{5}{8}$ sq. ft.

1.27 $8(4) = 32$ sq. in.

1.28 $1\frac{1}{2}(\frac{1}{2}) = \frac{3}{2}(\frac{1}{2}) = \frac{3}{4}$ sq. ft.

1.29 x yards = $3x$ feet
$3x(y) = 3xy$ sq. ft.

For Problems 1.30 through 1.33 refer to the following figure where $\overline{AD}$ is the hypotenuse of $\triangle ADX$.

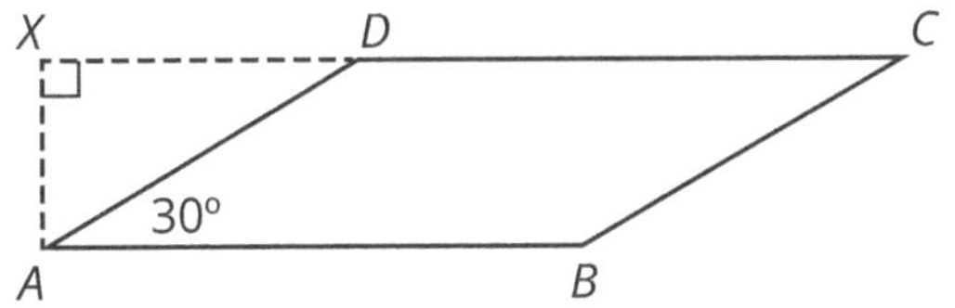

1.30
$A = bh$
$h = AX$
$AX = \frac{1}{2}(AD)$
$= \frac{1}{2}(6)$
$= 3$ in.
$A = 10(3) = 30$ sq. in.

1.31 $6(3\sqrt{3}) = 18\sqrt{3}$ sq. ft.

1.32
$A = bh$
$h = AX$
$AX = \frac{1}{2}(AD)$
$= \frac{1}{2}(4\sqrt{3})$
$= 2\sqrt{3}$ in.
$A = 8(2\sqrt{3}) = 16\sqrt{3}$ sq. in.

1.33 $4\sqrt{2}(3) = 12\sqrt{2}$ sq. ft.

1.34

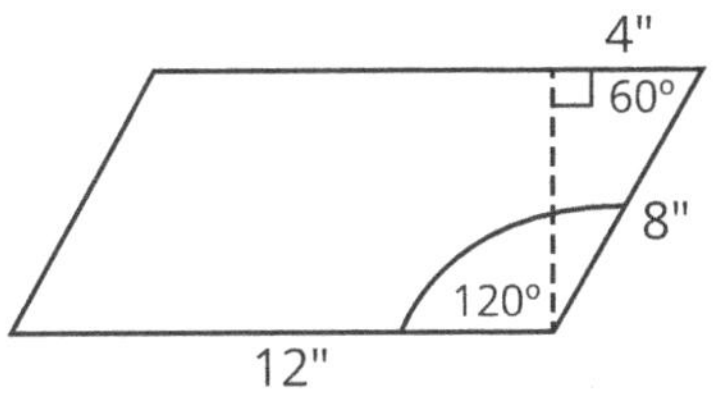

$12(4\sqrt{3}) = 48\sqrt{3}$ sq. in.

1.35

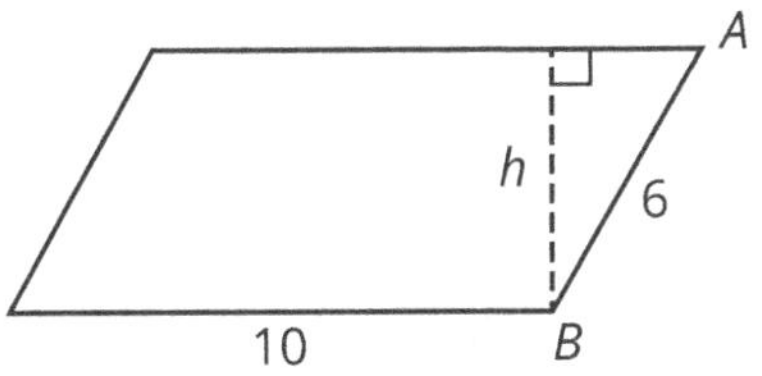

$A = bh$
$30\sqrt{2} = 10h$
$3\sqrt{2} = h$

$\therefore \angle A = 45°$
$\angle B = 180° - 45° = 135°$

1.36
a. $A = bh$
$A = \frac{b}{3}(3h)$
divided by 3

b. $A = bh$
$A = (2b)\frac{h}{2}$
multiply by 2

1.37 The diagonals of a rhombus divide it into 4 congruent right triangles. The base of one triangle equals $\frac{1}{2}d_1$ of the rhombus and its height equals $\frac{1}{2}d_2$. Therefore, the area of one of the triangles equals $\frac{1}{2}(\frac{1}{2}d_1)(\frac{1}{2}d_2)$.
The area of the rhombus $= 4(\frac{1}{2})(\frac{1}{2}d_1)(\frac{1}{2}d_2)$
$= \frac{4}{8}d_1d_2$
$= \frac{1}{2}d_1d_2$

1.38
$A = \frac{1}{2}bh$
$A = \frac{1}{2}(4)(6)$
$= 12$ sq. in.

1.39
$A = \frac{1}{2}bh$
$10 = \frac{1}{2}(b)(5)$
$20 = 5b$
$\frac{20}{5} = b$
4 in. $= b$

1.40
$A = \frac{1}{2}bh$
$12 = \frac{1}{2}(5)h$
$24 = 5h$
$\frac{24}{5}$ ft. $= h$

1.41
$A = \frac{1}{2}bh$
$= \frac{1}{2}(2\sqrt{3})(3\sqrt{3})$
$= \frac{1}{2}(18)$
$= 9$ sq. in.

1.42 $A = \frac{1}{2}bh$
$= \frac{1}{2}(6)(4)$
$= 12$ sq. in.

1.43 $c^2 = a^2 + b^2$
$13^2 = 5^2 + b^2$
$169 = 25 + b^2$
$144 = b^2$
$\sqrt{144} = \sqrt{b^2}$
$12 = b$
$A = \frac{1}{2}bh$
$= \frac{1}{2}(12)(5)$
$= 30$ sq. ft.

1.44 $c^2 = a^2 + b^2$
$6^2 = a^2 + 2^2$
$36 = a^2 + 4$
$32 = a^2$
$\sqrt{32} = \sqrt{a^2}$
$4\sqrt{2} = a$
$A = \frac{1}{2}bh$
$= \frac{1}{2}(4\sqrt{2})(2)$
$= 4\sqrt{2}$ sq. in.

1.45 $c^2 = a^2 + b^2$
$4^2 = (2\sqrt{3})^2 + b^2$
$16 = 12 + b^2$
$4 = b^2$
$\sqrt{4} = \sqrt{b^2}$
$2 = b$
$A = \frac{1}{2}bh$
$= \frac{1}{2}(2\sqrt{3})(2)$
$= 2\sqrt{3}$ sq. ft.

1.46 $A = \frac{1}{2}bh$
$= \frac{1}{2}(5\sqrt{2})(4\sqrt{2})$
$= 20$ sq. cm

1.47 a. $p = 3s$
$= 3(6)$
$= 18$ in.

b. $A = \frac{1}{4}s^2\sqrt{3}$
$= \frac{1}{4}(6)^2(\sqrt{3})$
$= \frac{1}{4}(36)(\sqrt{3})$
$= 9\sqrt{3}$ sq. in.

1.48 a. $p = 3s$
$= 3(5)$
$= 15$ in.

b. $A = \frac{1}{4}s^2\sqrt{3}$
$= \frac{1}{4}(5)^2(\sqrt{3})$
$= \frac{1}{4}(25)(\sqrt{3})$
$= \frac{25}{4}\sqrt{3}$ sq. in.

1.49 a. $p = 3s$
$12 = 3s$
4 ft. $= s$

b. $A = \frac{1}{4}s^2\sqrt{3}$
$= \frac{1}{4}(4)^2(\sqrt{3})$
$= \frac{1}{4}(16)(\sqrt{3})$
$= 4\sqrt{3}$ sq. ft.

1.50 a. $A = \frac{1}{4}s^2\sqrt{3}$
$9\sqrt{3} = \frac{1}{4}s^2\sqrt{3}$
$36\sqrt{3} = s^2\sqrt{3}$
$36 = s^2$
$\sqrt{36} = \sqrt{s^2}$
6 ft. $= s$

b. $p = 3s$
$= 3(6)$
$= 18$ ft.

1.51 a. $p = 3s$
$30 = 3s$
10 ft. $= s$

b. $A = \frac{1}{4}s^2\sqrt{3}$
$= \frac{1}{4}(10)^2(\sqrt{3})$
$= \frac{1}{4}(100)(\sqrt{3})$
$= 25\sqrt{3}$ sq. ft.

1.52

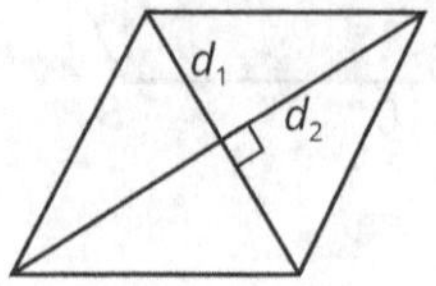

$A = \frac{1}{2}d_1d_2$
$= \frac{1}{2}(9)(12)$
$= 54$ sq. ft.

1.53

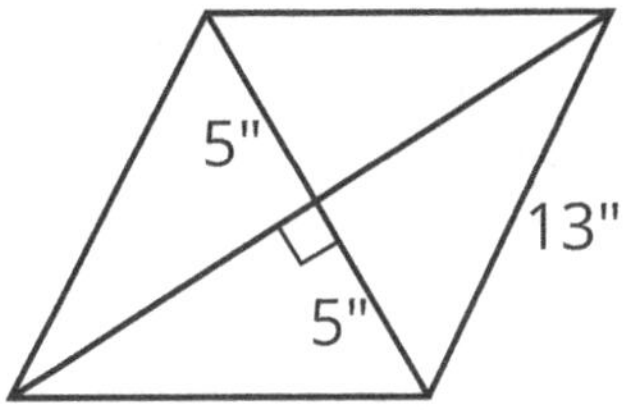

$13^2 = 5^2 + (\frac{d}{2})^2$

$169 = 25 + (\frac{d}{2})^2$

$144 = (\frac{d}{2})^2$

$\sqrt{144} = \sqrt{(\frac{d}{2})^2}$

$12 = \frac{d}{2}$

$24 = d$

$A = \frac{1}{2}d_1d_2$

$= \frac{1}{2}(10)(24)$

$= 120$ sq. in.

1.54

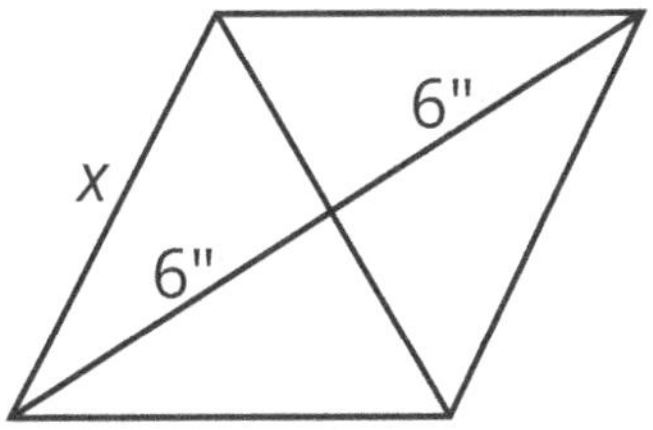

$x^2 = 6^2 + (\frac{x}{2})^2$

$x^2 = 36 + \frac{x^2}{4}$

$\frac{3x^2}{4} = 36$

$x^2 = 36(\frac{4}{3})$

$x^2 = 48$

$\sqrt{x^2} = \sqrt{48}$

$x = 4\sqrt{3}$

$A = \frac{1}{2}d_1d_2$

$= \frac{1}{2}(12)(4\sqrt{3})$

$= 24\sqrt{3}$ sq. in.

1.55 $A = \frac{1}{2}h(b_1 + b_2)$

$= \frac{1}{2}(4)(10 + 6)$

$= 2(16)$

$= 32$

1.56 $A = \frac{1}{2}h(b_1 + b_2)$

$18 = \frac{1}{2}(2)(6 + b_2)$

$18 = 6 + b_2$

$12 = b_2$

1.57 $A = \frac{1}{2}h(b_1 + b_2)$

$12 = \frac{1}{2}(3)(b_1 + 5)$

$24 = 3(b_1 + 5)$

$24 = 3b_1 + 15$

$9 = 3b_1$

$\frac{9}{3} = b_1$

$3 = b_1$

1.58 $A = \frac{1}{2}h(b_1 + b_2)$

$24 = \frac{1}{2}(h)(5 + 3)$

$24 = \frac{1}{2}(h)(8)$

$48 = 8h$

$6 = h$

1.59 $A = \frac{1}{2}h(b_1 + b_2)$

$= \frac{1}{2}(1)(\frac{1}{2} + \frac{1}{4})$

$= \frac{1}{2}(\frac{3}{4})$

$= \frac{3}{8}$

1.60 $A = \frac{1}{2}h(b_1 + b_2)$

$4\sqrt{6} = \frac{1}{2}(h)(5\sqrt{2} + 3\sqrt{2})$

$4\sqrt{6} = \frac{1}{2}(h)(8\sqrt{2})$

$4\sqrt{6} = 4\sqrt{2}h$

$\frac{4\sqrt{6}}{4\sqrt{2}} = h$

$\sqrt{3} = h$

1.61

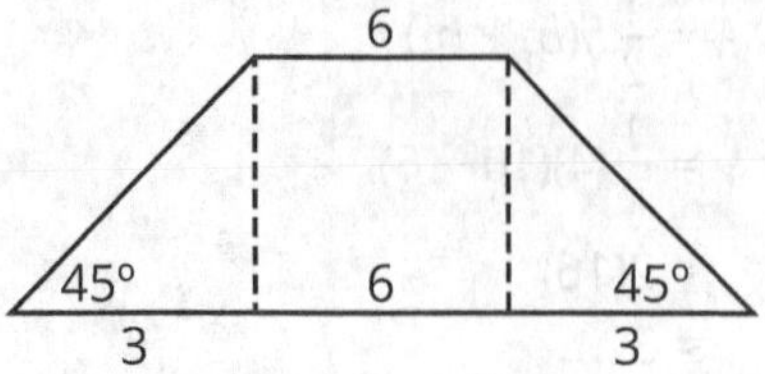

$A = \frac{1}{2}h(b_1 + b_2)$

$= \frac{1}{2}(h)(12 + 6)$

$= \frac{1}{2}(3)(18)$

$= 27$

1.62

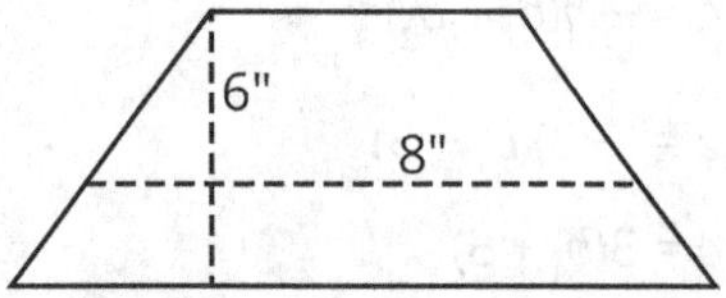

$A = \frac{1}{2}h(b_1 + b_2)$

$m = \frac{1}{2}(b_1 + b_2)$

$A = hm$

$= (6)(8)$

$= 48$ sq. in.

1.63

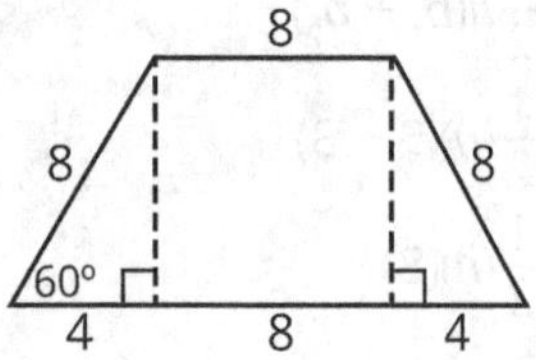

$A = \frac{1}{2}h(b_1 + b_2)$

$= \frac{1}{2}(4\sqrt{3})(16 + 8)$

$= \frac{1}{2}(4\sqrt{3})(24)$

$= 48\sqrt{3}$

1.64

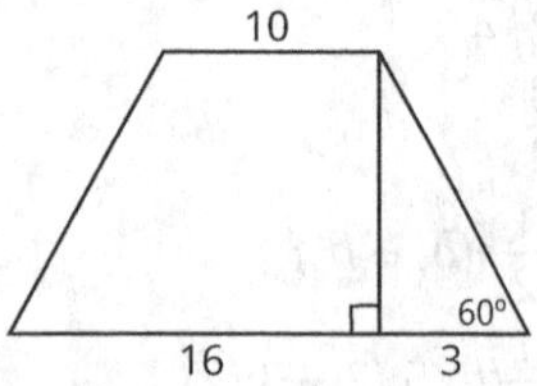

$A = \frac{1}{2}h(b_1 + b_2)$

$= \frac{1}{2}(3\sqrt{3})[(16 + 3) + 10]$

$= \frac{1}{2}(3\sqrt{3})(29)$

$= \frac{87\sqrt{3}}{2}$

1.65

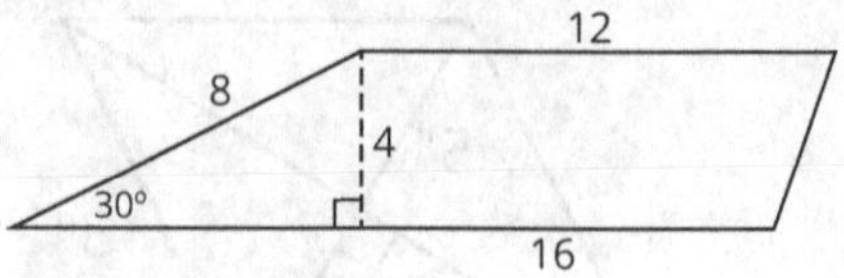

$A = \frac{1}{2}h(b_1 + b_2)$

$= \frac{1}{2}(4)(16 + 12)$

$= \frac{1}{2}(4)(28)$

$= 56$

1.66

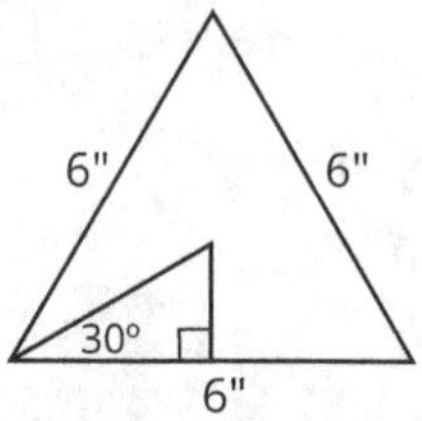

$A = \frac{1}{2}ap$

$= \frac{1}{2}(\sqrt{3})(18)$

$= 9\sqrt{3}$ sq. in.

1.67

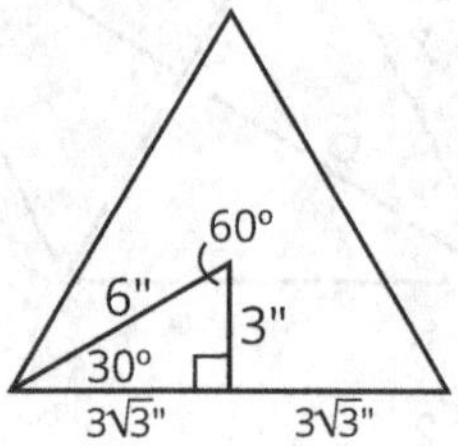

$A = \frac{1}{2}ap$

$= \frac{1}{2}(3)(18\sqrt{3})$

$= 27\sqrt{3}$ sq. in.

1.68

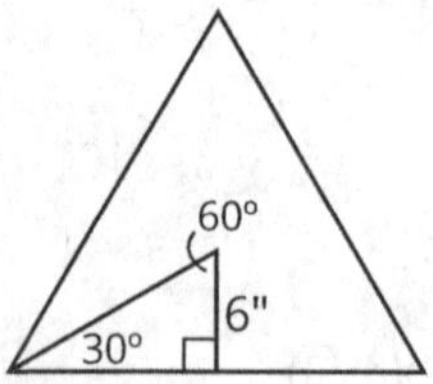

$A = \frac{1}{2}ap$

$= \frac{1}{2}(6)(36\sqrt{3})$

$= 108\sqrt{3}$ sq. in.

1.69

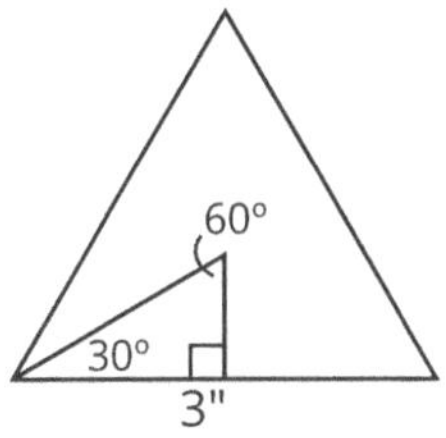

$A = \frac{1}{2}ap$

$= \frac{1}{2}(\frac{1}{2}\sqrt{3})(9)$

$= \frac{9}{4}\sqrt{3}$ sq. in.

1.70

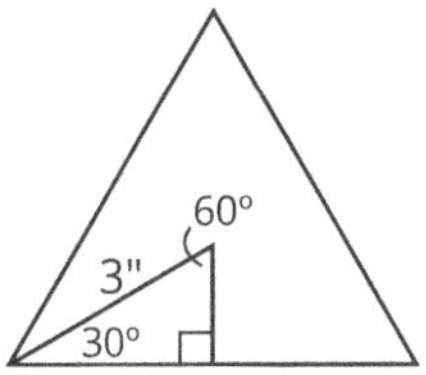

$A = \frac{1}{2}ap$

$= \frac{1}{2}(\frac{3}{2})9\sqrt{3}$

$= \frac{27}{4}\sqrt{3}$ sq. in.

1.71

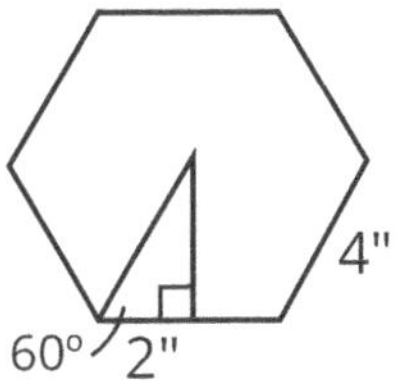

$A = \frac{1}{2}ap$

$= \frac{1}{2}(2\sqrt{3})(24)$

$= 24\sqrt{3}$ sq. in.

1.72

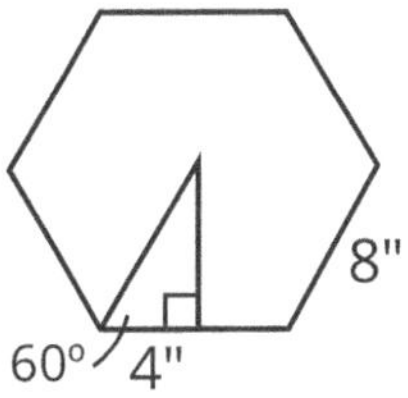

$p = 48"$
$s = 8"$

$A = \frac{1}{2}ap$

$= \frac{1}{2}(4\sqrt{3})(48)$

$= 96\sqrt{3}$ sq. in.

1.73

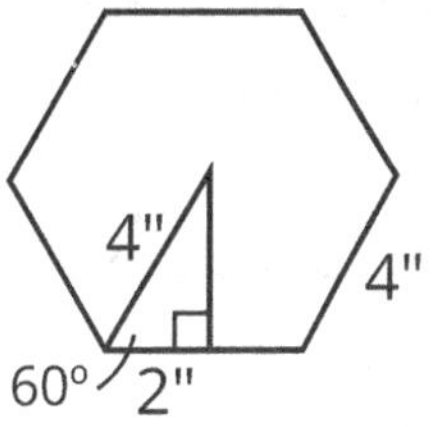

$A = \frac{1}{2}ap$

$= \frac{1}{2}(2\sqrt{3})(24)$

$= 24\sqrt{3}$

1.74

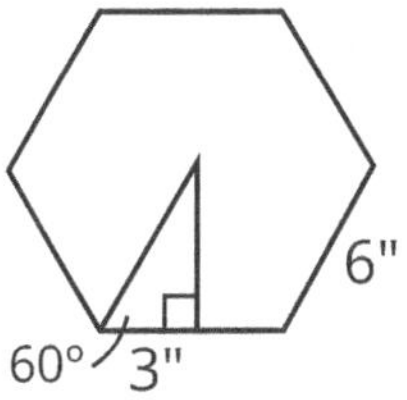

$A = \frac{1}{2}ap$

$= \frac{1}{2}(3\sqrt{3})(36)$

$= 54\sqrt{3}$ sq. in.

1.75 $p = 8(10) = 80$

$A = \frac{1}{2}ap$

$= \frac{1}{2}(K)(80)$

$= 40K$

1.76

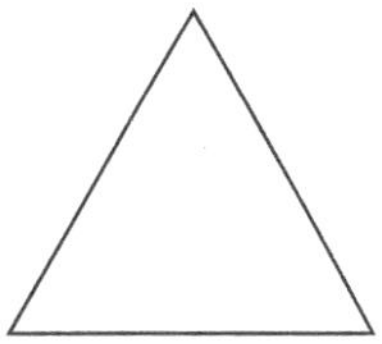

$p = 36$
$s = 12$

$A = \frac{1}{4}s^2\sqrt{3}$

$= \frac{1}{4}(12)^2(\sqrt{3})$

$= \frac{1}{4}(144)(\sqrt{3})$

$= 36\sqrt{3}$

$A = 36\sqrt{3}$

A hexagon is 6 equilateral triangles.

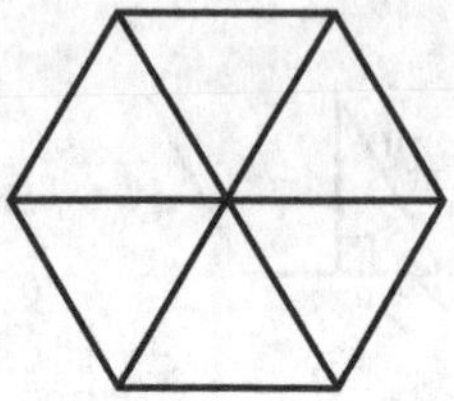

$A = 6(\frac{1}{4}s^2\sqrt{3})$

$36\sqrt{3} = \frac{3s^2\sqrt{3}}{2}$

$72\sqrt{3} = 3s^2\sqrt{3}$

$24 = s^2$

$\sqrt{24} = \sqrt{s^2}$

$2\sqrt{6}$ in. $= s$

1.77 $\frac{A}{A'} = (\frac{s}{s'})^2$

$\frac{50}{100} = (\frac{s}{s'})^2$

$\frac{1}{2} = (\frac{s}{s'})^2$

$\sqrt{\frac{1}{2}} = \sqrt{(\frac{s}{s'})^2}$

$\sqrt{\frac{1}{2}} = \frac{s}{s'}$

$\frac{s}{s'} = \frac{\sqrt{2}}{2}$

1.78 $\frac{A}{A'} = (\frac{s}{s'})^2$

$\frac{90}{A'} = (\frac{15}{9})^2$

$\frac{90}{A'} = (\frac{5}{3})^2$

$\frac{90}{A'} = \frac{25}{9}$

$25A' = 810$

$A' = 32.4$ sq. in.

1.79 $\frac{A}{A'} = (\frac{s}{s'})^2$

$\frac{196}{A'} = (\frac{4}{8})^2$

$\frac{196}{A'} = (\frac{1}{2})^2$

$\frac{196}{A'} = \frac{1}{4}$

$A' = 784$ sq. in.

1.80 $\frac{A}{A'} = (\frac{s}{s'})^2$

$\frac{1}{9} = (\frac{3}{s'})^2$

$\sqrt{\frac{1}{9}} = \sqrt{(\frac{3}{s'})^2}$

$\frac{1}{3} = \frac{3}{s'}$ $s' = 9$

$\frac{1}{9} = (\frac{4}{s'})^2$

$\sqrt{\frac{1}{9}} = \sqrt{(\frac{4}{s'})^2}$

$\frac{1}{3} = \frac{4}{s'}$ $s' = 12$

$\frac{1}{9} = (\frac{5}{s'})^2$

$\sqrt{\frac{1}{9}} = \sqrt{(\frac{5}{s'})^2}$

$\frac{1}{3} = \frac{5}{s'}$ $s' = 15$

$\frac{1}{9} = (\frac{6}{s'})^2$

$\sqrt{\frac{1}{9}} = \sqrt{(\frac{6}{s'})^2}$

$\frac{1}{3} = \frac{6}{s'}$ $s' = 18$

1.81 $\frac{A}{A'} = (\frac{s}{s'})^2$

$\frac{36}{64} = (\frac{s}{s'})^2$

$\sqrt{\frac{36}{64}} = \sqrt{(\frac{s}{s'})^2}$

$\frac{6}{8} = \frac{s}{s'}$

$\frac{s}{s'} = \frac{3}{4}$

1.82

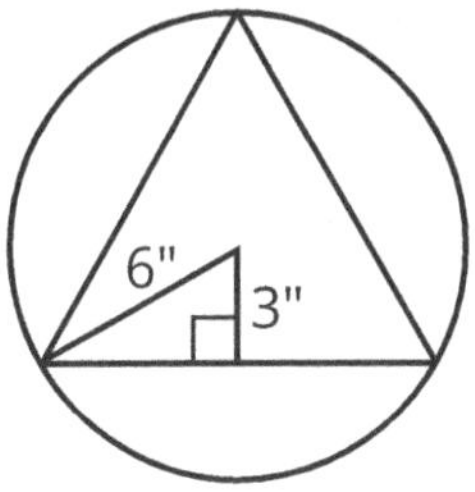

$A_I = \frac{1}{4}(6\sqrt{3})^2(\sqrt{3})$

$= \frac{1}{4}(108)(\sqrt{3})$

$= 27\sqrt{3}$ sq. in.

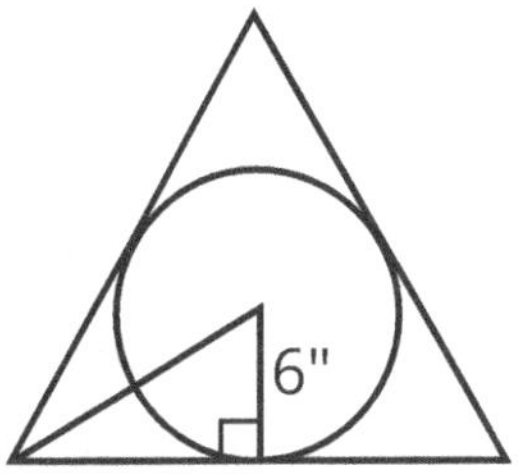

$A_C = \frac{1}{4}(12\sqrt{3})^2(\sqrt{3})$

$= \frac{1}{4}(432)(\sqrt{3})$

$= 108\sqrt{3}$ sq. in.

$\frac{A_I}{A_C} = \frac{27\sqrt{3}}{108\sqrt{3}} = \frac{1}{4}$ or 1:4.

1.83 $\frac{A}{A'} = (\frac{s}{s'})^2$

$= (\frac{2}{4})^2 = \frac{4}{16} = \frac{1}{4}$ or 1:4.

1.84 $\frac{A}{A'} = (\frac{s}{s'})^2$

$= (\frac{2}{3})^2 = \frac{4}{9}$ or 4:9.

1.85 $\frac{A}{A'} = (\frac{s}{s'})^2$

$= (\frac{3}{5})^2 = \frac{9}{25}$ or 9:25.

SELF TEST 1

1.01 e
1.02 e
1.03 b
1.04 g or e or c
1.05 f or e
1.06 c
1.07 a
1.08 d or a

1.09 $A = \frac{1}{2}ap$

$A = \frac{1}{2}(k)(15)$

$A = \frac{15}{2}k$

1.010

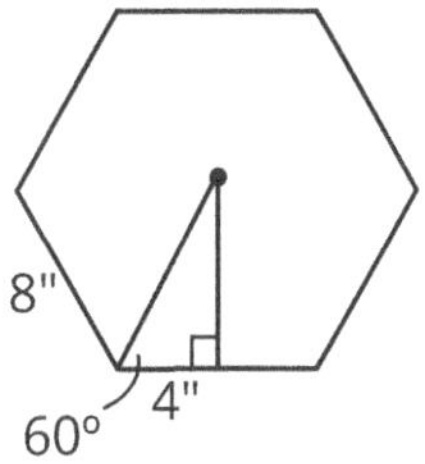

$A = \frac{1}{2}ap$

$A = \frac{1}{2}(4\sqrt{3})(48)$

$A = 96\sqrt{3}$ sq. in.

1.011 $A = \frac{1}{2}bh$

$A = \frac{1}{2}(10)(16)$

$A = 80$ sq. in.

1.012

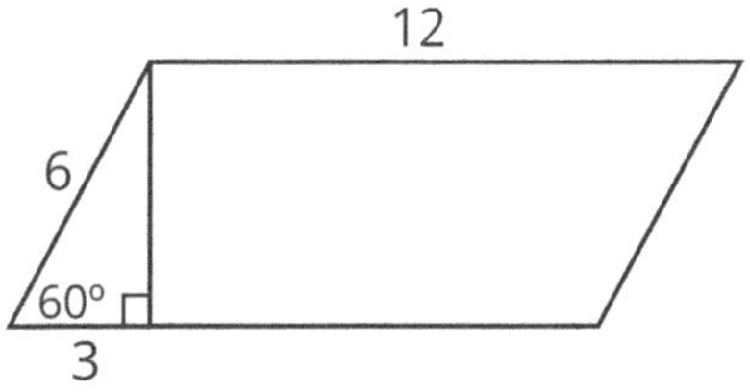

$A = bh$
$A = 12(3\sqrt{3})$
$A = 36\sqrt{3}$

1.013 $A = \frac{1}{2}h(b_1 + b_2)$

$A = \frac{1}{2}(10)(8 + 16)$

$A = \frac{1}{2}(10)(24)$

$A = 120$

1.014 $A = \frac{1}{4}s^2\sqrt{3}$

$A = \frac{1}{4}(6)^2(\sqrt{3})$

$A = \frac{1}{4}(36)(\sqrt{3})$

$A = 9\sqrt{3}$ sq. in.

1.015 $\frac{A}{A'} = (\frac{8}{10})^2 = (\frac{4}{5})^2 = \frac{16}{25}$ or 16:25

1.016

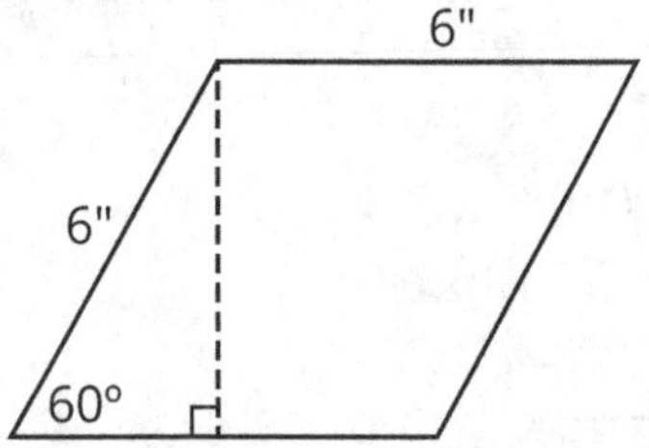

$A = bh$

$A = 6(3\sqrt{3})$

$A = 18\sqrt{3}$ sq. in.

1.017

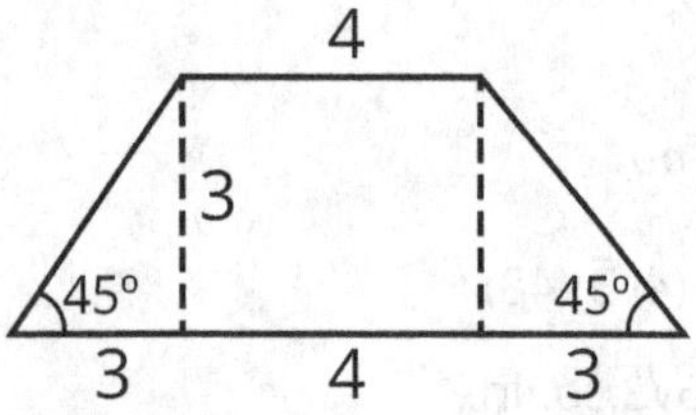

$A = \frac{1}{2}h(b_1 + b_2)$

$A = \frac{1}{2}(3)(10 + 4)$

$A = \frac{1}{2}(3)(14)$

$A = 21$

1.018 $A = bh$

$A = 3.5(1.7)$

$A = 5.95\ cm^2$

1.019 $A = \frac{1}{2}bh$

$A = \frac{1}{2}(16)(8)$

$A = 64$ sq. in.

1.020 $A = s^2$

$A = (3.2)^2$

$A = 10.24$ sq. in.

1.021 $A = bh$

$A = 10(6)$

$A = 60$

1.022 $A_{walls} = bh$

$A = (24 + 20 + 24 + 20)(10)$

$A = (88)(10)$

$A = 880$ sq. ft.

$A_{\triangle's} = 2(\frac{1}{2}bh)$

$A = 2[\frac{1}{2}(20)(5)]$

$A = 100$ sq. ft.

Total area = 880 + 100 = 980 sq. ft.

Two costs = 980 × 2 = 1,960 sq. ft. to cover

1,960 ÷ 350 = 5.6 gal. ≐ 6 gal.

SECTION 2

2.1 $C = 2\pi r$
$= 2\pi(5)$
$= 10\pi$ in.

2.2 $C = 2\pi r$
$= 2\pi(7)$
$= 14\pi$ ft.

2.3 $C = 2\pi r$
$= 2\pi(3\frac{1}{2})$
$= 7\pi$ cm

2.4 $C = 2\pi r$
$= 2\pi(3\frac{1}{4})$
$= \frac{13}{2}\pi$ in.

2.5 $C = 2\pi r$
$= 2\pi(\frac{x}{2})$
$= \pi x$ mi.

2.6 $C = 2\pi r$
$= 2\pi(36)$
$= 72\pi$ in.

2.7 $C = 2\pi r$
$= 2(3.14)(4)$
$= 25.12 \doteq 25$ in.

2.8 $C = 2\pi r$
$= 2(3.14)(6)$
$= 37.68 \doteq 38$ ft.

2.9 $C = 2\pi r$
$= 2(3.14)(5.1)$
$= 32.028 \doteq 32.0$ cm

2.10 $C = 2\pi r$
$= 2(3.14)(4.6)$
$= 28.888 \doteq 28.9$ in.

2.11 $C = 2\pi r$
$= 2(3.14)(3.21)$
$= 20.1588 \doteq 20.16$ ft.

2.12 $C = 2\pi r$
$= 2(3.14)(6.53)$
$= 41.0084 \doteq 41.01$ cm

2.13 $C = 2\pi r$
$12\pi = 2\pi r$
$\frac{12\pi}{2\pi} = r$
6 in. $= r$

2.14 $C = 2\pi r$
$15\pi = 2\pi r$
$\frac{15\pi}{2\pi} = r$
$\frac{15}{2}$ ft. $= r$

2.15 $C = 2\pi r$
$6\sqrt{2}\pi = 2\pi r$
$\frac{6\sqrt{2}\pi}{2\pi} = r$
$3\sqrt{2}$ in. $= r$

2.16 $C = 2\pi r$
$5\sqrt{3}\pi = 2\pi r$
$\frac{5\sqrt{3}\pi}{2\pi} = r$
$\frac{5}{2}\sqrt{3}$ cm $= r$

2.17 $C = 2\pi r$
$8t\pi = 2\pi r$
$\frac{8t\pi}{2\pi} = r$
$4t$ ft. $= r$

2.18 $C = 2\pi r$
$\pi = 2\pi r$
$\frac{\pi}{2\pi} = r$
$\frac{1}{2}$ yd. $= r$

2.19

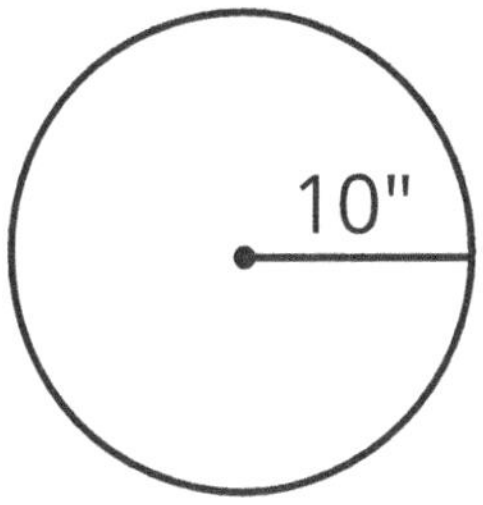

$C = 2\pi r$
$= 2\pi(10)$
$= 20\pi$
$20\pi(10) = 200\pi$ inches

2.20 $66 \div 6 = 11$ ft. per revolution
$C = 2\pi r$
$11 = 2(\frac{22}{7})r$
$77 = 2(22)r$
$77 = 44r$
$\frac{77}{44} = r$
$\frac{7}{4}$ ft. $= r$

2.21 $C_c = 2\pi r$

$= 2\pi(\frac{1}{2})(\sqrt{2})$

$= \sqrt{2}\pi$

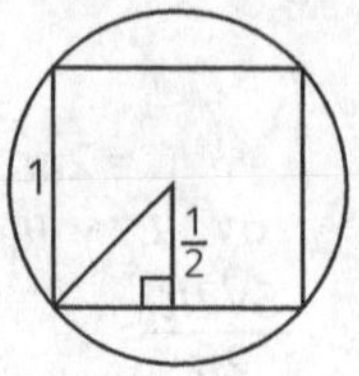

$C_i = 2\pi r$

$= 2\pi(\frac{1}{2})$

$= \pi$

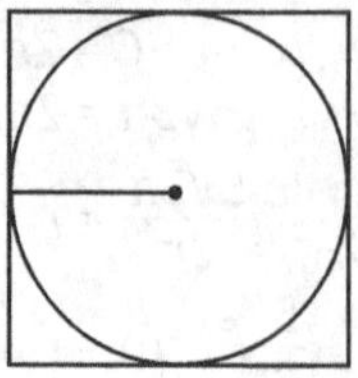

$\frac{C_c}{C_i} = \frac{\sqrt{2}\pi}{\pi}$

$= \frac{\sqrt{2}}{1}$ or $\sqrt{2}:1$

2.22

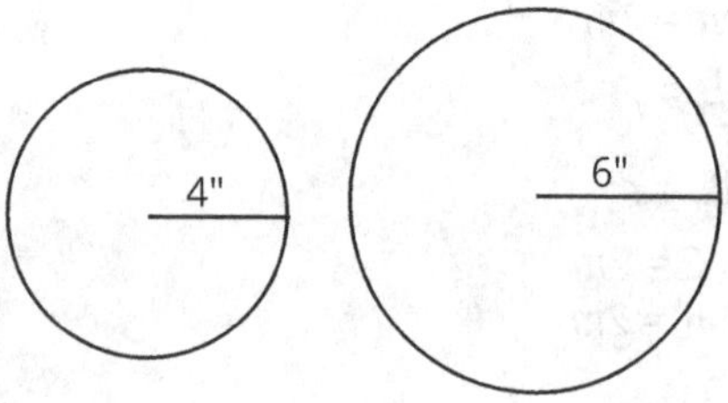

$C_1 = 2\pi r$
$C_1 = 2\pi(4)$
$C_1 = 8\pi$

$C_2 = 2\pi r$
$C_2 = 2\pi(6)$
$C_2 = 12\pi$

$C_3 = C_1 + C_2 = 20\pi$
$C_3 = 2\pi r$
$20\pi = 2\pi r$
10 in. $= r$

2.23 $C_1 = 2\pi r$
$= 2\pi(5)$
$= 10\pi$ in.

$C_2 = 2\pi r$
$= 2\pi(\frac{11}{2})$
$= 11\pi$ in.

$C_2 - C_1 = 11\pi - 10\pi$
$= \pi$
$= 3.14$ in.

2.24 $C_1 = 2\pi r$
$= 2\pi(40)$
$= 2(3.14)(40)$
$= 80(3.14)$
$= 251.2$ ft.
$\times\ 10$
$= 2{,}512$ ft.

2.24 cont'd

$C_2 = 2\pi r$
$= 2\pi(41)$
$= 2(3.14)(41)$
$= 82(3.14)$
$= 257.48$ ft.
$\times\ 10$
$= 2{,}574.8$ ft.
$-\ 2{,}512$ ft.
$=$ 62.8 ft. farther

2.25 $A = \pi r^2$
$= 3.14(6)^2$
$= 3.14(36)$
$= 113.04$

2.26 $A = \pi r^2$
$= 3.14(4)^2$
$= 3.14(16)$
$= 50.24$

2.27 $A = \pi r^2$
$= 3.14(2)^2$
$= 3.14(4)$
$= 12.56$

2.28 $A = \pi r^2$
$= 3.14(5)^2$
$= 3.14(25)$
$= 78.5$

2.29 $A = \pi r^2$
$= 3.14(6)^2$
$= 3.14(36)$
$= 113.04$

2.30 $A = \pi r^2$
$= 3.14(6.5)^2$
$= 3.14(42.25)$
$= 132.665$

2.31 $C = 2\pi r$
$8\pi = 2\pi r$
$4 = r$
$A = \pi r^2$
$= \pi(4)^2$
$= 16\pi$

2.32 $C = 2\pi r$
$3\pi = 2\pi r$
$\frac{3\pi}{2\pi} = r$
$\frac{3}{2} = r$
$A = \pi r^2$
$= \pi(\frac{3}{2})^2$
$= \frac{9}{4}\pi$

2.33

$$C = 2\pi r$$
$$4\sqrt{3}\pi = 2\pi r$$
$$\frac{4\sqrt{3}\pi}{2\pi} = r$$
$$2\sqrt{3} = r$$

$$A = \pi r^2$$
$$= \pi(2\sqrt{3})^2$$
$$= 12\pi$$

2.34

$$A = \pi r^2$$
$$36\pi = \pi r^2$$
$$36 = r^2$$
$$\sqrt{36} = \sqrt{r^2}$$
$$r = 6$$

$$C = 2\pi r$$
$$= 2\pi(6)$$
$$= 12\pi$$

2.35

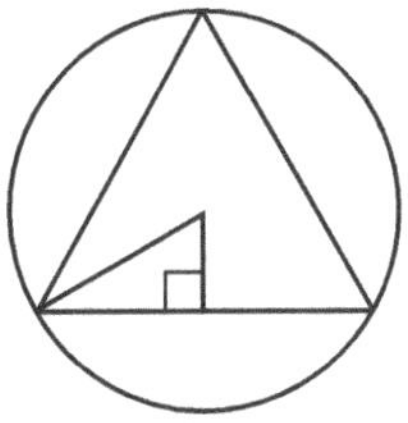

$$A = \pi r^2$$
$$= \pi(6\sqrt{3})^2$$
$$= 108\pi$$

2.36

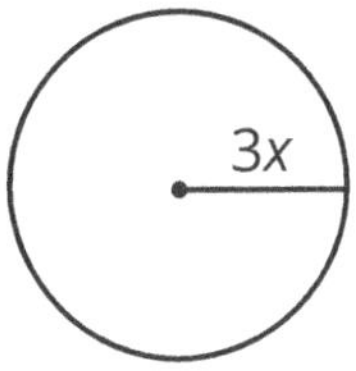

$$A = \pi r^2$$
$$27\pi = \pi(3x)^2$$
$$27\pi = 9x^2\pi$$
$$\frac{27\pi}{9\pi} = x^2$$
$$3 = x^2$$
$$\sqrt{3} = x$$

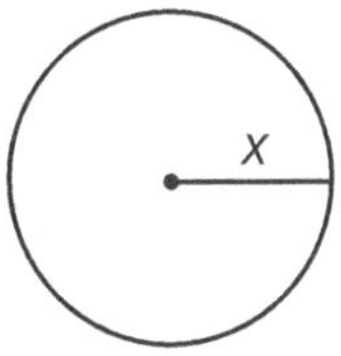

$$x = \sqrt{3}$$
$$A = \pi r^2$$
$$= \pi(\sqrt{3})^2$$
$$= 3\pi$$

2.37

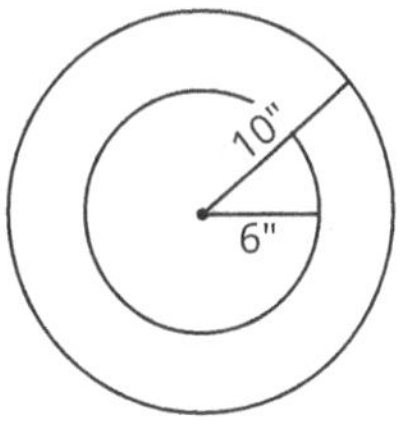

$$A_L = \pi r^2$$
$$= \pi(10)^2$$
$$= 100\pi$$
$$A_S = \pi r^2$$
$$= \pi(6)^2$$
$$= 36\pi$$
$$A_L - A_S = 100\pi - 36\pi$$
$$= 64\pi$$

2.38

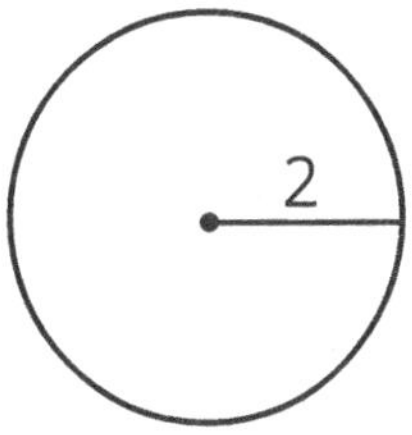

$$A = \pi r^2$$
$$= \pi(2)^2$$
$$= 4\pi$$

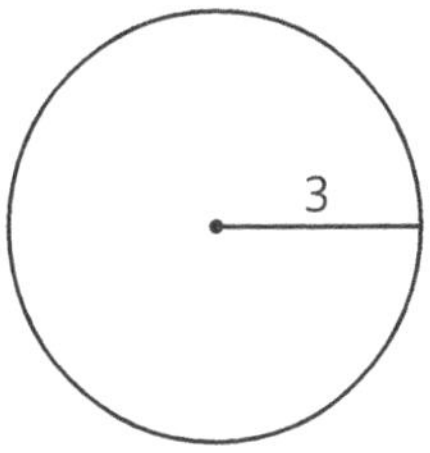

$$A = \pi r^2$$
$$= \pi(3)^2$$
$$= 9\pi$$

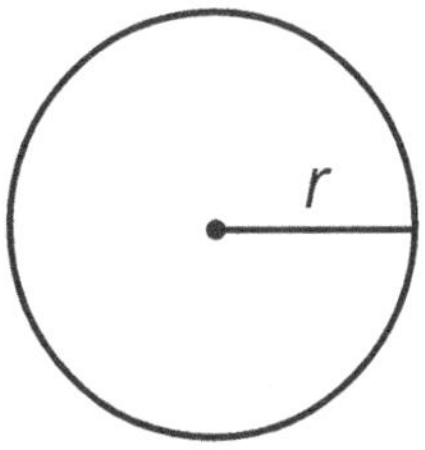

$$A = 4\pi + 9\pi = 13\pi$$
$$A = \pi r^2$$
$$13\pi = \pi r^2$$
$$\frac{13\pi}{\pi} = r^2$$
$$13 = r^2$$
$$\sqrt{13} = \sqrt{r^2}$$
$$\sqrt{13} = r$$

2.39

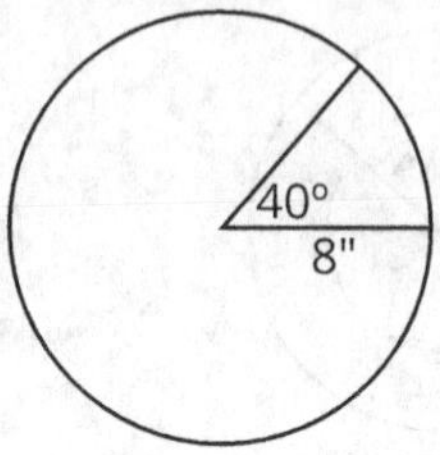

$$\text{length of arc} = \frac{40°}{360°}(2\pi)(8)$$
$$= \frac{1}{9}(16\pi)$$
$$= \frac{16}{9}\pi \text{ in.}$$

2.40

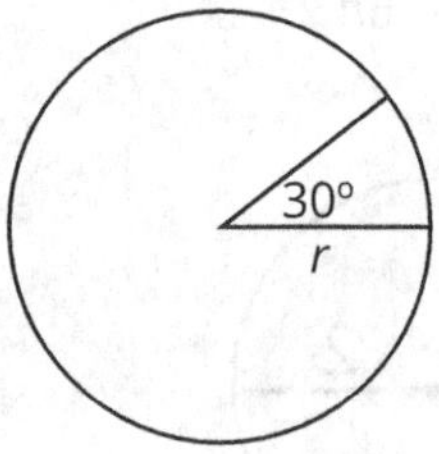

$$\text{length of arc} = \frac{m}{360°}(2\pi r)$$
$$2\pi = \frac{30°}{360°}(2\pi r)$$
$$2\pi = \frac{1}{12}(2\pi r)$$
$$2\pi = \frac{1}{6}\pi r$$
$$\frac{2\pi(6)}{\pi} = r$$
$$12 \text{ in.} = r$$

2.41

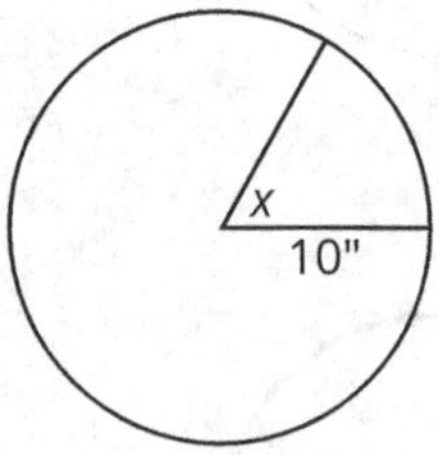

$$\text{length of arc} = \frac{m}{360°}(2\pi r)$$
$$4\pi = \frac{x}{360°}(2\pi)(10)$$
$$4\pi = \frac{x}{360°}(20\pi)$$
$$4\pi = \frac{\pi}{18}x$$
$$4\pi(\frac{18}{\pi}) = x$$
$$x = 72°$$

2.42

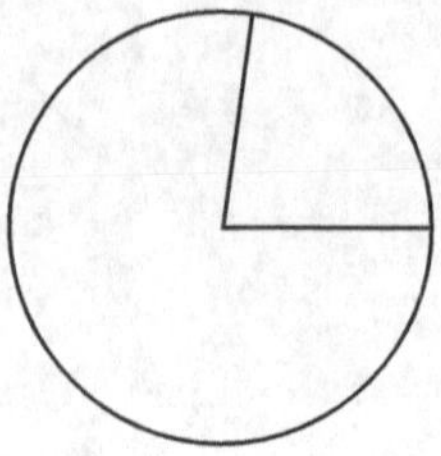

$$\text{length of arc} = \frac{m}{360°}(2\pi r)$$
$$\text{length of arc} = \frac{80°}{360°}(2\pi)(26)$$
$$= \frac{2}{9}(52\pi)$$
$$= \frac{104}{9}\pi \text{ in.}$$

2.43

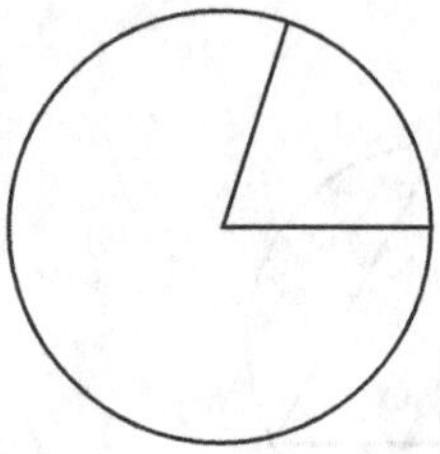

$$\text{length of arc} = \frac{m}{360°}(2\pi r)$$
$$12\pi = \frac{x}{360°}(2\pi)(10)$$
$$12\pi = \frac{x}{360°}(20\pi)$$
$$12\pi = \frac{\pi x}{18}$$
$$12\pi(\frac{18}{\pi}) = x$$
$$216° = x$$

2.44

a. $\frac{1}{360}$

b. $\frac{30}{360} = \frac{1}{12}$

c. $\frac{45}{360} = \frac{1}{8}$

d. $\frac{60}{360} = \frac{1}{6}$

e. $\frac{90}{360} = \frac{1}{4}$

2.45

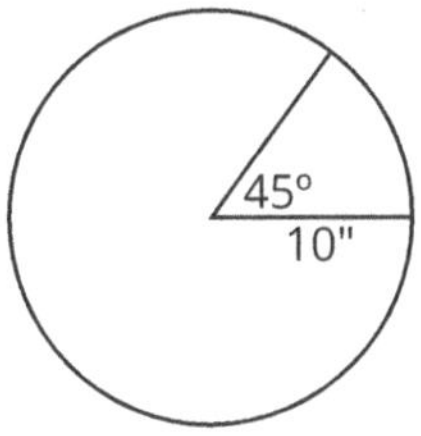

$$\text{area of sector} = \frac{m}{360°}(\pi r^2)$$
$$A = \frac{45°}{360°}(\pi)(10)^2$$
$$= \frac{45°}{360°}(100\pi)$$
$$= \frac{1}{8}(100\pi)$$
$$= \frac{25}{2}\pi \text{ sq. in.}$$

2.46

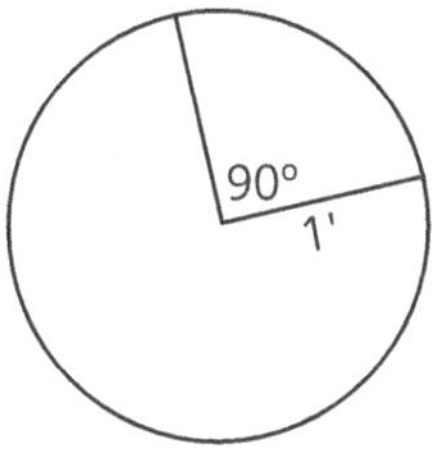

$$\text{area of sector} = \frac{m}{360°}(\pi r^2)$$
$$A = \frac{90°}{360°}(\pi)(1)^2$$
$$= \frac{1}{4}\pi \text{ sq. ft.}$$

2.47

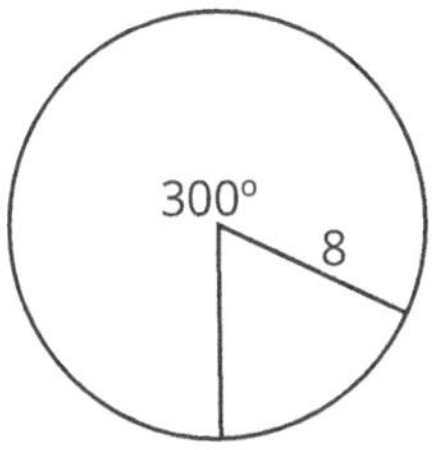

$$\text{area of sector} = \frac{m}{360°}(\pi r^2)$$
$$A = \frac{300°}{360°}(\pi)(8)^2$$
$$= \frac{5}{6}(64\pi)$$
$$= \frac{160}{3}\pi$$

2.48

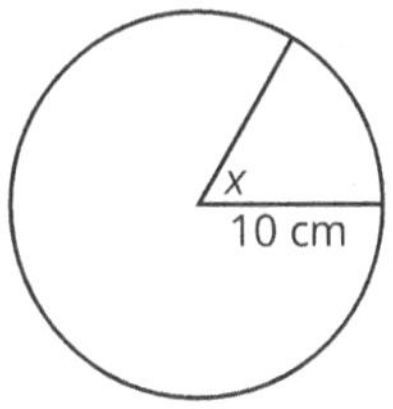

$$\text{area of sector} = \frac{m}{360°}(\pi r^2)$$
$$40\pi = \frac{x}{360°}(\pi)(10)^2$$
$$40\pi = \frac{x}{360°}(100\pi)$$
$$40\pi(\frac{360}{\pi}) = 100x$$
$$14{,}400 = 100x$$
$$\frac{14{,}400}{100} = x$$
$$144° = x$$

2.49

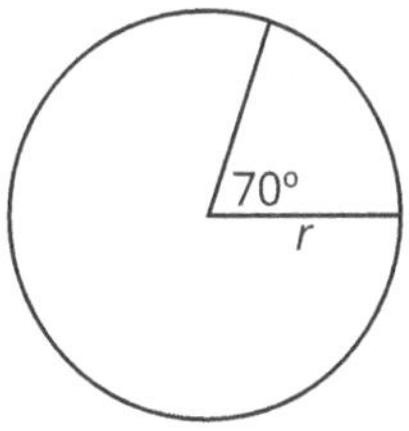

$$\text{area of sector} = \frac{m}{360°}(\pi r^2)$$
$$7\pi = \frac{70°}{360°}(\pi r^2)$$
$$7(360) = 70r^2$$
$$360 = \frac{70r^2}{7}$$
$$360 = 10r^2$$
$$\frac{360}{10} = r^2$$
$$36 = r^2$$
$$\sqrt{36} = \sqrt{r^2}$$
$$6 \text{ ft.} = r$$

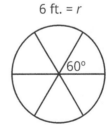

2.50

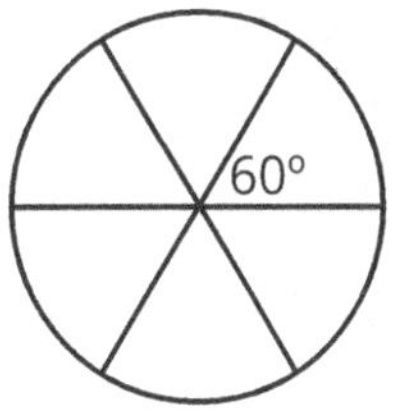

$$\text{area of sector} = \frac{m}{360°}(\pi r^2)$$
$$A = \frac{60°}{360°}(\pi)(5)^2$$
$$= \frac{1}{6}(25\pi)$$
$$= \frac{25}{6}\pi \text{ sq. in.}$$

2.51

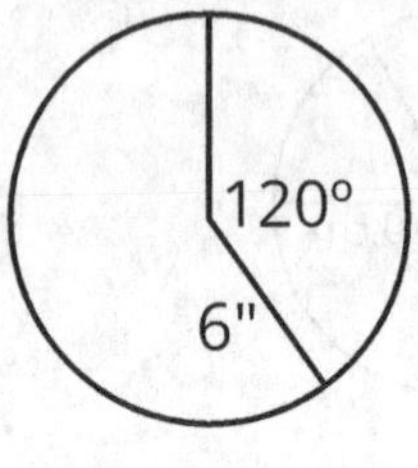

area of sector = $\frac{m}{360°}(\pi r^2)$

$A = \frac{120°}{360°}(\pi)(6)^2$

$= \frac{1}{3}(36\pi)$

$= 12\pi$ sq. in.

2.52

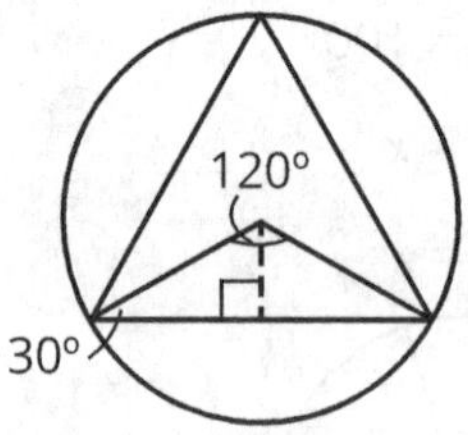

area of sector = $\frac{m}{360°}(\pi r^2)$

$A = \frac{120°}{360°}(\pi)(2)^2$

$= \frac{1}{3}(4\pi)$

$= \frac{4}{3}\pi$

2.53

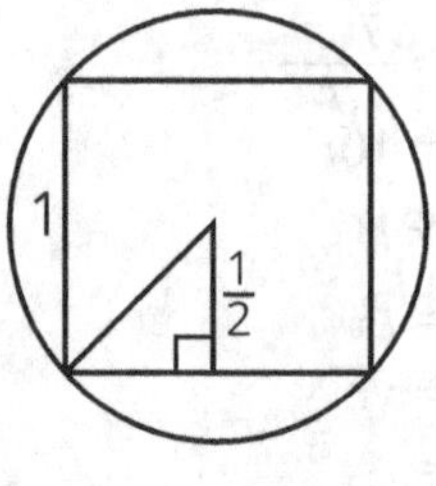

area of sector = $\frac{m}{360°}(\pi r^2)$

$A = \frac{90°}{360°}(\pi)(3)^2$

$= \frac{1}{4}(9\pi)$

$= \frac{9}{4}\pi$

2.54

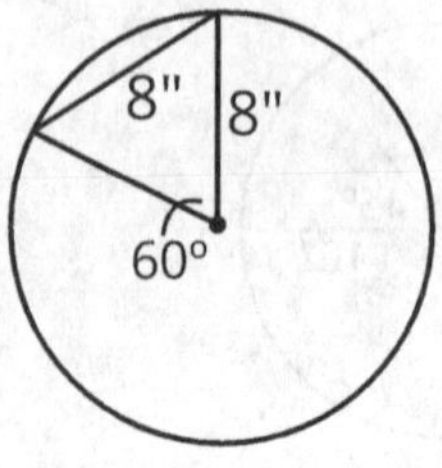

area of segment = area of sector – area of triangle

$A = \frac{60°}{360°}(\pi)(8)^2 - \frac{1}{2}(8)(4\sqrt{3})$

$= \frac{1}{6}(64\pi) - 4(4\sqrt{3})$

$= \frac{64\pi}{6} - 16\sqrt{3}$

$= (\frac{32}{3}\pi - 16\sqrt{3})$ sq. in.

2.55

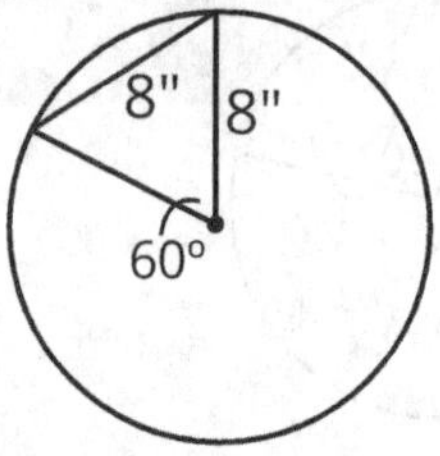

area of larger segment = area of circle – area of smaller segment

$A = (8)^2(\pi) - (\frac{32}{3}\pi - 16\sqrt{3})$

$= 64\pi - \frac{32}{3}\pi + 16\sqrt{3}$

$= (\frac{160}{3}\pi + 16\sqrt{3})$ sq. in.

2.56

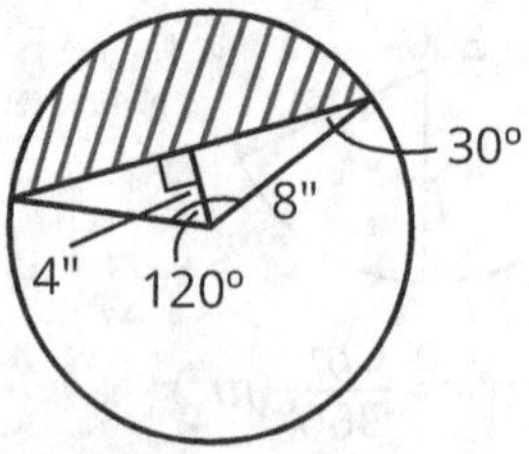

area of segment = area of sector – area of triangle

$A = \frac{120°}{360°}(\pi)(8)^2 - \frac{1}{2}(8\sqrt{3})(4)$

$= \frac{1}{3}(64\pi) - (4\sqrt{3})(4)$

$= (\frac{64}{3}\pi - 16\sqrt{3})$ sq. in.

2.57

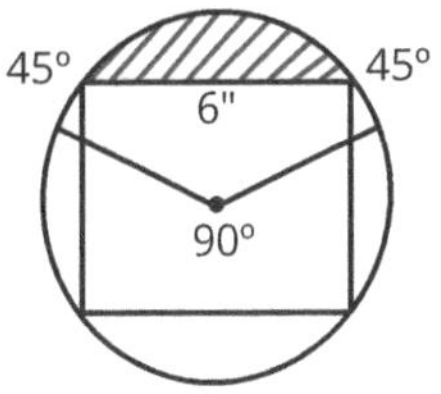

area of segment = area of sector – area of triangle

$A = \frac{90°}{360°}(\pi)(3\sqrt{2})^2 - \frac{1}{2}(3\sqrt{2})(3\sqrt{2})$

$= \frac{1}{4}(18\pi) - \frac{1}{2}(18)$

$= (\frac{9}{2}\pi - 9)$ sq. in.

2.58

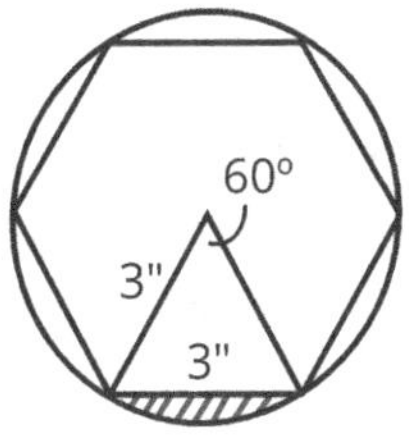

area of segment = area of sector – area of triangle

$A = \frac{60°}{360°}(\pi)(3)^2 - \frac{1}{4}(3)^2(\sqrt{3})$

$= \frac{1}{6}(9\pi) - \frac{1}{4}(9\sqrt{3})$

$= \frac{9}{6}\pi - \frac{9}{4}\sqrt{3}$

$= (\frac{3}{2}\pi - \frac{9}{4}\sqrt{3})$ sq. in.

2.59

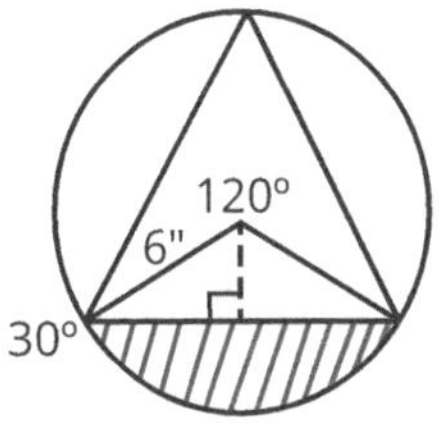

area of segment = area of sector – area of triangle

$A = \frac{120°}{360°}(\pi)(6)^2 - \frac{1}{2}(6\sqrt{3})(3)$

$= \frac{1}{3}(36\pi) - (3\sqrt{3})(3)$

$= (12\pi - 9\sqrt{3})$ sq. in.

2.60 $A = A_{triangle} - 3A_{sectors}$

$= \frac{1}{4}(6)^2(\sqrt{3}) - 3(\frac{60°}{360°})(\pi)(3)^2$

$= \frac{1}{4}(36)(\sqrt{3}) - 3(\frac{1}{6})(\pi)(9)$

$= 9\sqrt{3} - \frac{1}{2}(9\pi)$

$= 9\sqrt{3} - \frac{9}{2}\pi$

2.61 $A = A_{square} - A_{sector}$

$= 6^2 - \frac{90°}{360°}(\pi)(6)^2$

$= 36 - \frac{1}{4}(\pi)(36)$

$= 36 - \frac{36}{4}\pi$

$= 36 - 9\pi$

2.62

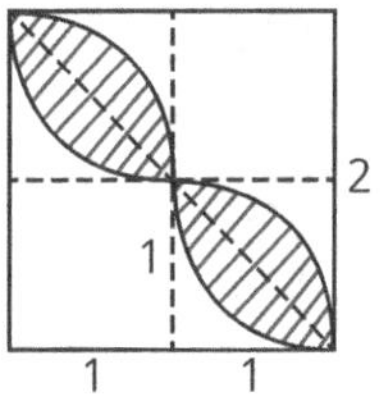

$A = 4$ times area of a segment

= 4(area of sector – area of triangle)

$= 4[\frac{90°}{360°}(\pi)(1)^2 - \frac{1}{2}(1)(1)]$

$= 4[\frac{1}{4}(\pi)(1) - \frac{1}{2}]$

$= 4[\frac{\pi}{4} - \frac{1}{2}]$

$= \pi - 2$

2.63

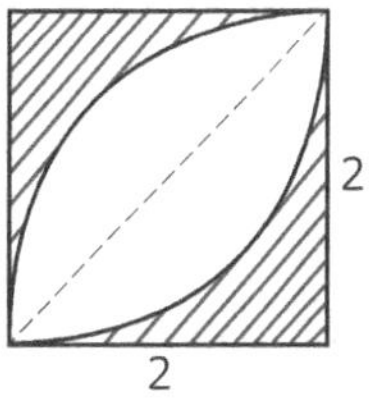

$A = A_{square} - 2$ segments

$= A_{square}$ – (area of sector – area of triangle)

$= 2^2 - 2[\frac{90°}{360°}(\pi)(2)^2 - \frac{1}{2}(2)(2)]$

$= 2^2 - 2[\frac{1}{4}(\pi)(4) - 1(2)]$

$= 4 - 2(\pi - 2)$

$= 4 - 2\pi + 4$

$= 8 - 2\pi$

2.64

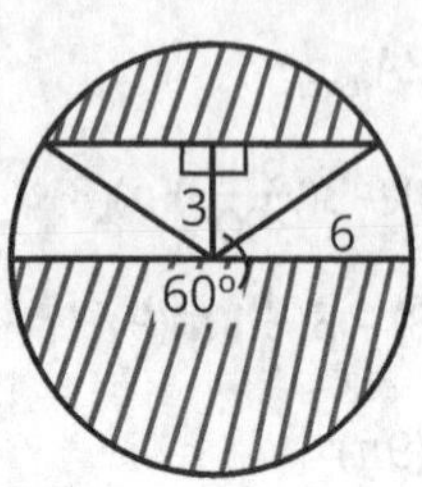

$A = \frac{1}{2}$ area of $\odot$ + area of segment

$= \frac{1}{2}$ area of $\odot$ + area of sector – area of $\triangle$

$= \frac{1}{2}(\pi)(6)^2 + \frac{120°}{360°}(\pi)(6)^2 - \frac{1}{2}(6\sqrt{3})(3)$

$= \frac{1}{2}(\pi)(36) + \frac{1}{3}\pi(36) - 3\sqrt{3}(3)$

$= 18\pi + 12\pi - 9\sqrt{3}$

$= 30\pi - 9\sqrt{3}$

2.65

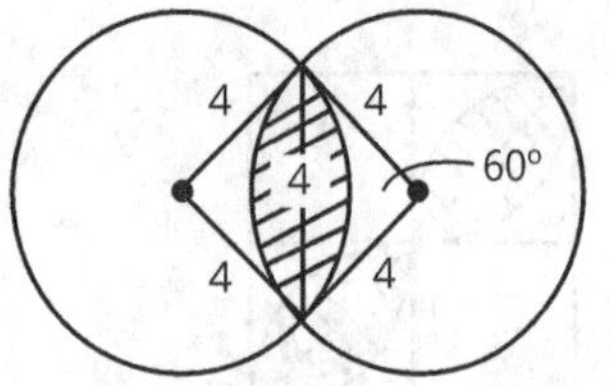

$A = 2(\text{area of segment})$

$= 2(\text{area of sector} - \text{area of triangle})$

$= 2[\frac{60°}{360°}(\pi)(4)^2 - \frac{1}{4}(4)^2(\sqrt{3})]$

$= 2[\frac{1}{6}\pi(16) - \frac{1}{4}(16\sqrt{3})]$

$= 2(\frac{16}{6}\pi - 4\sqrt{3})$

$= 2(\frac{8}{3}\pi - 4\sqrt{3})$

$= \frac{16}{3}\pi - 8\sqrt{3}$

2.66

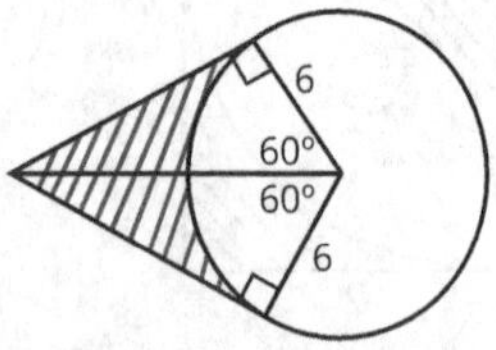

$A = 2(\text{area of rt.} \triangle - \text{area of sector})$

$= 2[\frac{1}{2}(6\sqrt{3})(6)] - \frac{120°}{360°}\pi(6)^2$

$= 2[3\sqrt{3}(6)] - \frac{1}{3}\pi(36)$

$= 2(18\sqrt{3}) - 12\pi$

$= 36\sqrt{3} - 12\pi$

SELF TEST 2

2.01

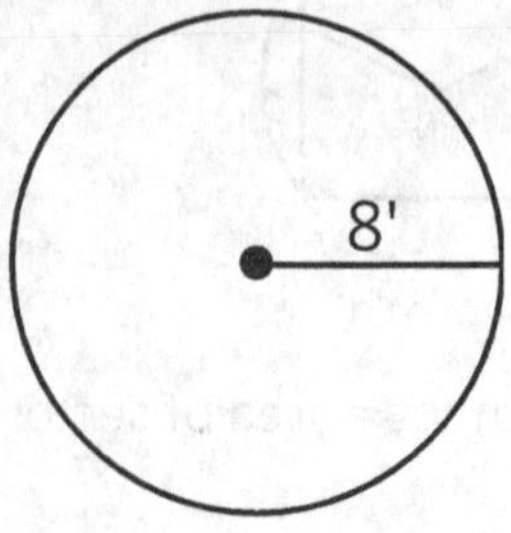

$A = \pi r^2$

$A = 3.14(8)^2$

$A = 3.14(64)$

$A = 200.96$ sq. ft.

2.02

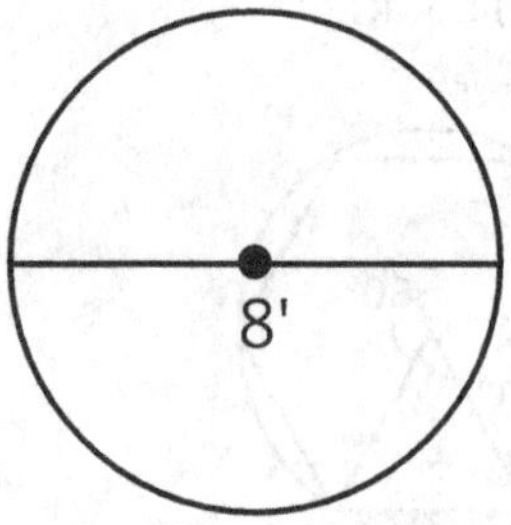

$C = 2\pi r$

$C = 2\pi(4)$

$C = 8\pi$ ft.

2.03

$A_{rectangle} = 2(11)$

$A = 22$

$A_{circle} = \pi r^2$

$22 = \pi r^2$

$22 = \frac{22}{7}r^2$

$22(\frac{7}{22}) = r^2$

$7 = r^2$

$\sqrt{7} = \sqrt{r^2}$

$r = \sqrt{7}$ ft.

2.04

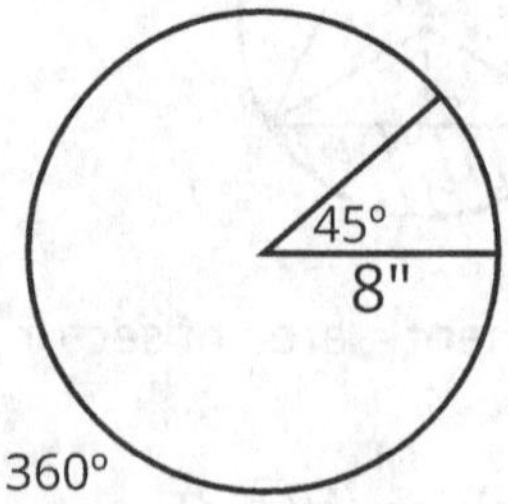

360°

$A = \frac{m}{360°}\pi r^2$

$A = \frac{45°}{360°}\pi(8)^2$

$A = \frac{1}{8}\pi(64)$

$A = 8\pi$ sq. in.

2.05 length of arc $= \frac{m}{360°}(2\pi r)$

$= \frac{45°}{360°}(2\pi)(8)$

$= \frac{1}{8}(2\pi)(8)$

$= 2\pi$ in.

2.06

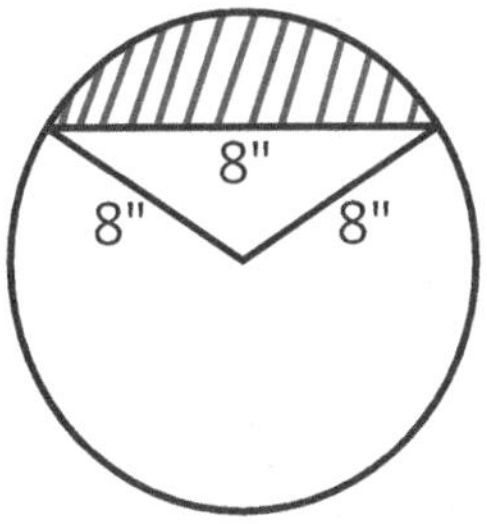

area of segment = area of sector – area of triangle

$A = \frac{60°}{360°}\pi(8)^2 - \frac{1}{4}(8)^2(\sqrt{3})$

$= \frac{1}{6}\pi(64) - \frac{1}{4}(64)(\sqrt{3})$

$= (\frac{32}{3}\pi - 16\sqrt{3})$ sq. in.

2.07

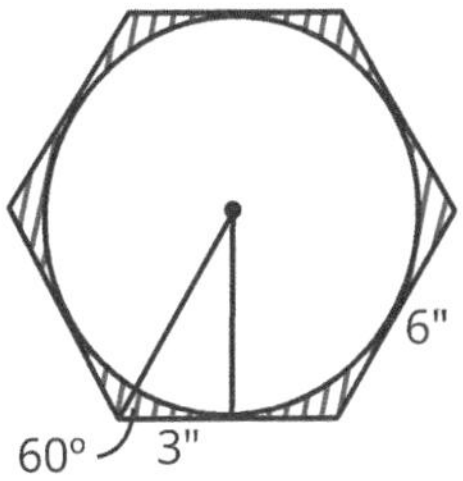

$A = A_{hex.} - A_{\odot}$

$A_{hex.} = \frac{1}{2}ap$

$= \frac{1}{2}(3\sqrt{3})(36)$

$= 54\sqrt{3}$

$A_{\odot} = \pi r^2$

$= \pi(3\sqrt{3})^2$

$= 27\pi$

$A = (54\sqrt{3} - 27\pi)$ sq. in.

2.08 $A = 2(\text{area of sector})$

$= 2[\frac{60°}{360°}\pi(4)^2]$

$= 2[\frac{1}{6}\pi(16)]$

$= 2(\frac{16}{6}\pi)$

$= \frac{16}{3}\pi$

2.09 $A = A_{large\odot} - A_{small\odot}$

$= \pi(6)^2 - \pi(3)^2$

$= 36\pi - 9\pi$

$= 27\pi$

2.010

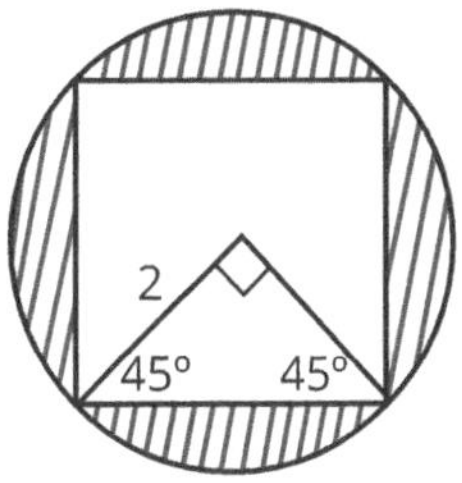

$A = A_{\odot} - A_{square}$

$= \pi(2)^2 - (2\sqrt{2})^2$

$= 4\pi - 8$

2.011

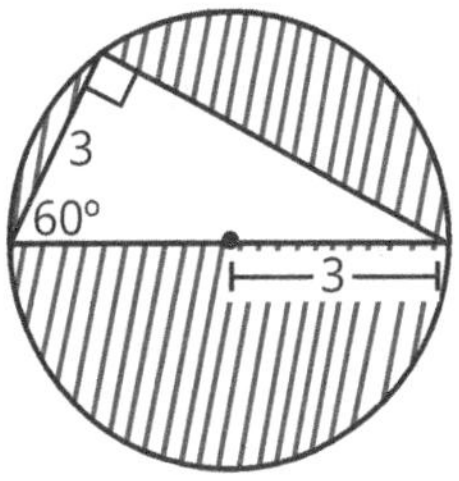

$A = A_{\odot} - A_{\triangle}$

$= \pi(3)^2 - \frac{1}{2}(3)(3\sqrt{3})$

$= 9\pi - \frac{9}{2}\sqrt{3}$

2.012 $A = 2(\text{area of triangle})$

$A = 2(\frac{1}{2})(4)(4)$

$A = 16$

2.013 b
2.014 e
2.015 c
2.016 d
2.017 a
2.018 g
2.019 f
2.020 h or b

SECTION 3

3.1 a. $L.A. = ph$
$= 10(5)$
$= 50$ sq. ft.

b. $T.A. = ph + 2B$
$= 50 + 2(6)$
$= 50 + 12$
$= 62$ sq. ft.

c. $V = Bh$
$= 6(5)$
$= 30$ cu. ft.

3.2 a. $L.A. = ph$
$= 9(6)$
$= 54$ sq. in.

b. $T.A. = ph + 2B$
$= 54 + 2(\frac{1}{4})(3)^2(\sqrt{3})$
$= 54 + 2(\frac{1}{4})(9\sqrt{3})$
$= 54 + (\frac{9}{2}\sqrt{3})$ sq. in.

c. $V = Bh$
$= (\frac{9}{4}\sqrt{3})(6)$
$= \frac{27}{2}\sqrt{3}$ cu. in.

3.3 a. $L.A. = ph$
$= 20(6)$
$= 120$ sq. in.

b. $T.A. = ph + 2B$
$= 120 + 2(\frac{1}{2})(k)(20)$
$= (120 + 20k)$ sq. in.

c. $V = Bh$
$= (\frac{1}{2})(k)(20)(6)$
$= 60k$ cu. in.

3.4 a. $c^2 = a^2 + b^2$
$c^2 = 4^2 + 6^2$
$c^2 = 16 + 36$
$c^2 = 52$
$\sqrt{c^2} = \sqrt{52}$
$c = 2\sqrt{13}$
$L.A. = ph$
$= (10 + 2\sqrt{13})(8)$
$= (80 + 16\sqrt{13})$ sq. ft.

b. $T.A. = L.A. + 2B$
$= 80 + 16\sqrt{13} + 2(\frac{1}{2})(4)(6)$
$= 80 + 16\sqrt{13} + 24$
$= (104 + 16\sqrt{13})$ sq. ft.

c. $V = Bh$
$= 12(8)$
$= 96$ cu. ft.

3.5 a. $L.A. = ph$
$= 48(12)$
$= 576$ sq. in.

b. $T.A. = ph + 2B$
$= 576 + 2(12)^2$
$= 576 + 2(144)$
$= 576 + 288$
$= 864$ sq. in.

c. $V = Bh$
$= 144(12)$
$= 1{,}728$ cu. in.

3.6

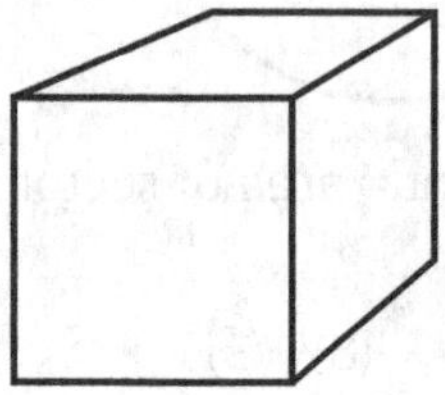

$T.A. = 96$
$A_{face} = 96 \div 6$
$= 16$ sq. in.
$A = s^2$
$16 = s^2$
$\sqrt{16} = \sqrt{s^2}$
$4 = s$
$V = Bh$
$= 16(4)$
$= 64$ cu. in.

3.7

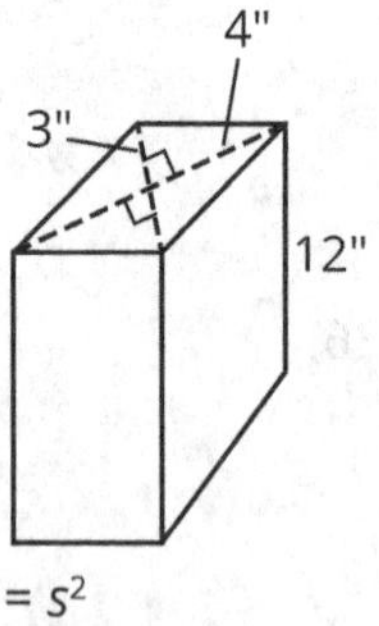

$4^2 + 3^2 = s^2$
$16 + 9 = s^2$
$25 = s^2$
$\sqrt{25} = \sqrt{s^2}$
$s = 5$

a. $V = Bh$
$= (24)(12)$
$= 288$ cu. in.

b. $L.A. = ph$
$= 20(12)$
$= 240$ sq. in.

3.8
$V = 300$ cu. in.
$h = 6$ in.
$V = Bh$
$300 = B(6)$
$\frac{300}{6} = B$
50 sq. in. $= B$

3.9
$L.A. = 88$ sq. ft.
$h = 16$ ft.
$L.A. = ph$
$88 = p(16)$
$\frac{88}{16} = p$
5.5 ft. $= p$

3.10
$V_{wall} = Bh$
$= 20(1)(6)$
$= 120$ cu. ft.
$\times\ 1{,}728$
$207{,}360$ cu. in.
$\times\ 10\%$
$20{,}736$ cu. in. of mortar
$207{,}360$
$-\ 20{,}736$
$186{,}624$ cu. in. of wall

$V_{one\ brick} = Bh$
$= 8(4)(2)$
$= 64$ cu. in.

$186{,}624 \div 64 = 2{,}916$ bricks

3.11
a. $L.A. = \frac{1}{2}pl$
$l = \sqrt{1^2 + 3^2}$
$= \sqrt{1 + 9}$
$= \sqrt{10}$
$L.A. = \frac{1}{2}(8)(\sqrt{10})$
$= 4\sqrt{10}$

b. $T.A. = \frac{1}{2}pl + B$
$= 4\sqrt{10} + 2^2$
$= 4\sqrt{10} + 4$

c. $V = \frac{1}{3}Bh$
$= \frac{1}{3}(4)(3)$
$= 4$

3.12
a. $L.A. = \frac{1}{2}pl$
$L.A. = \frac{1}{2}(24)(6)$
$= 72$

b.
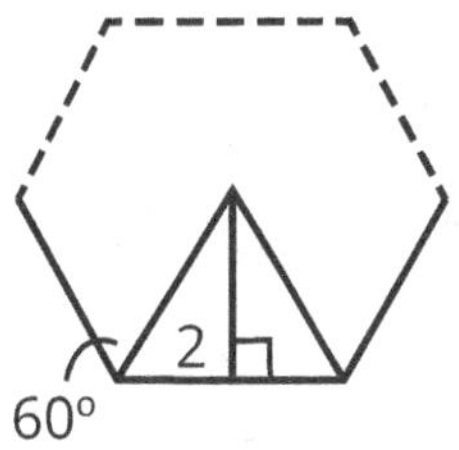

$T.A. = \frac{1}{2}pl + B$
$= 72 + \frac{1}{2}(2\sqrt{3})(24)$
$= 72 + 24\sqrt{3}$

c.
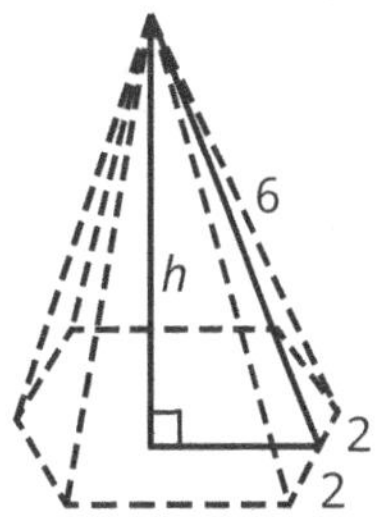

$V = \frac{1}{3}Bh$
$h^2 + (2\sqrt{3})^2 = 6^2$
$h^2 + 12 = 36$
$h^2 = 24$
$\sqrt{h^2} = \sqrt{24}$
$h = 2\sqrt{6}$

$V = \frac{1}{3}(24\sqrt{3})(2\sqrt{6})$
$= 16\sqrt{18}$
$= 48\sqrt{2}$

3.13
a.
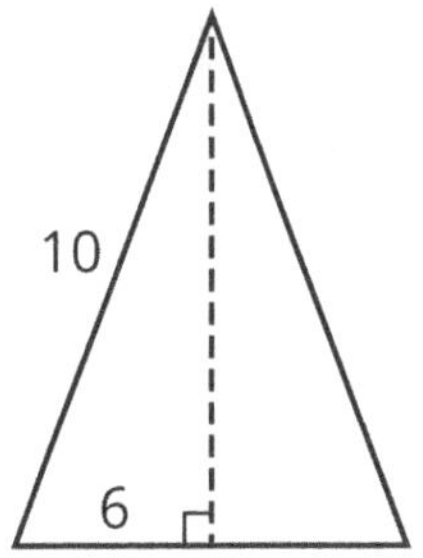

$L.A. = \frac{1}{2}pl$
$l^2 + 6^2 = 10^2$
$l^2 + 36 = 100$
$l^2 = 64$

$\sqrt{l^2} = \sqrt{64}$

$l = 8$

$L.A. = \frac{1}{2}(36)(8)$

$= 144$

b. $T.A. = \frac{1}{2}pl + B$

$= 144 + \frac{1}{4}(12)^2(\sqrt{3})$

$= 144 + \frac{1}{4}(144)(\sqrt{3})$

$= 144 + 36\sqrt{3}$

c.

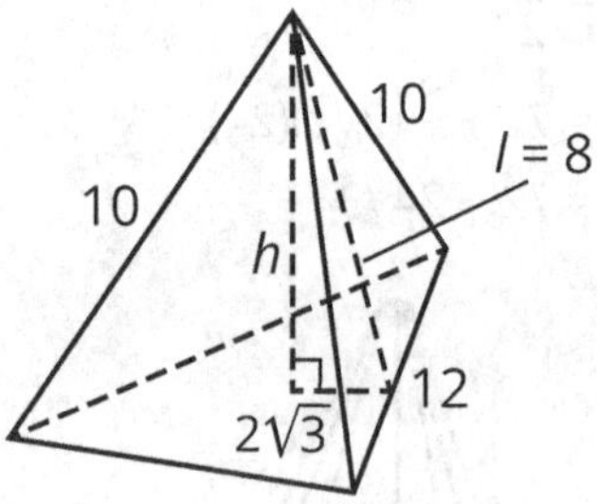

$V = \frac{1}{3}Bh$

$h^2 + (2\sqrt{3})^2 = 8^2$

$h^2 + 12 = 64$

$h^2 = 52$

$\sqrt{h^2} = \sqrt{52}$

$h = 2\sqrt{13}$

$V = \frac{1}{3}(36\sqrt{3})(2\sqrt{13})$

$= 24\sqrt{39}$

3.14 a.

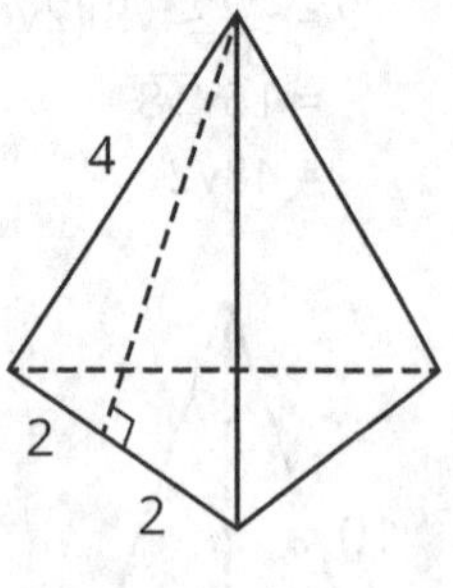

$L.A. = \frac{1}{2}pl$

$l^2 + 2^2 = 4^2$

$l^2 + 4 = 16$

$l^2 = 12$

$\sqrt{l^2} = \sqrt{12}$

$l = 2\sqrt{3}$

$L.A. = \frac{1}{2}(12)(2\sqrt{3})$

$= 12\sqrt{3}$

b. $T.A. = \frac{1}{2}pl + B$

$= 12\sqrt{3} + \frac{1}{4}(4)^2(\sqrt{3})$

$= 12\sqrt{3} + \frac{1}{4}(16\sqrt{3})$

$= 12\sqrt{3} + 4\sqrt{3}$

$= 16\sqrt{3}$

c.

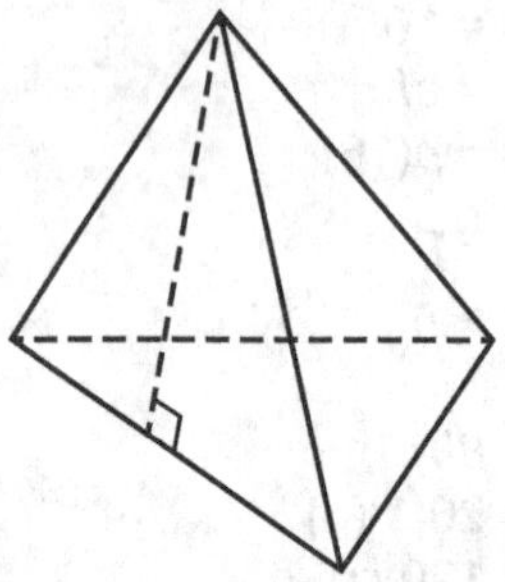

$V = \frac{1}{3}Bh$

$h^2 + (\frac{2\sqrt{3}}{3})^2 = (2\sqrt{3})^2$

$h^2 + \frac{12}{9} = 12$

$h^2 + \frac{4}{3} = 12$

$h^2 = \frac{32}{3}$

$\sqrt{h^2} = \sqrt{\ }$

$h = \frac{\sqrt{32}}{\sqrt{3}}$

$h = \frac{4\sqrt{2}}{\sqrt{3}} \cdot \frac{\sqrt{3}}{\sqrt{3}}$

$h = \frac{4\sqrt{6}}{3}$

$V = \frac{1}{3}(4\sqrt{3})(\frac{4\sqrt{6}}{3})$

$= \frac{16\sqrt{18}}{9}$

$= \frac{16(3\sqrt{2})}{9}$

$= \frac{16}{3}\sqrt{2}$

3.15 a.

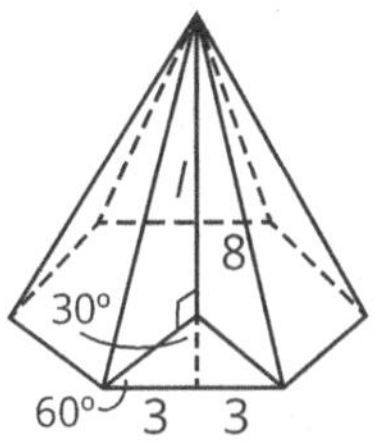

$L.A. = \frac{1}{2}pl$

$l = \sqrt{8^2 + (3\sqrt{3})^2}$

$= \sqrt{64 + 27}$

$= \sqrt{91}$

$L.A. = \frac{1}{2}(36)(\sqrt{91})$

$= 18\sqrt{91}$

b. $T.A. = \frac{1}{2}pl + B$

$= 18\sqrt{91} + \frac{1}{2}(3\sqrt{3})36$

$= 18\sqrt{91} + 54\sqrt{3}$

c. $V = \frac{1}{3}Bh$

$= \frac{1}{3}(54\sqrt{3})(8)$

$= 144\sqrt{3}$

3.16 $V = \frac{1}{3}Bh$

$= \frac{1}{3}(24\sqrt{3})(6\sqrt{3})$

$= 48\sqrt{9}$

$= 144$

3.17 $V = \frac{1}{3}Bh$

$32 = \frac{1}{3}(16)h$

$96 = 16h$

$\frac{96}{16} = h$

$6 \text{ in.} = h$

3.18

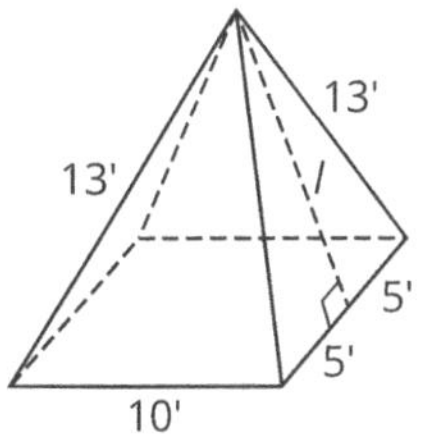

$L.A. = \frac{1}{2}pl$

$l^2 + 5^2 = 13^2$

$l^2 + 25 = 169$

$l^2 = 144$

$\sqrt{l^2} = \sqrt{144}$

$l = 12$

$L.A. = \frac{1}{2}(40)(12)$

$= 240$

$T.A. = \frac{1}{2}pl + B$

$= 240 + 100$

$= 340$ sq. ft.

3.19

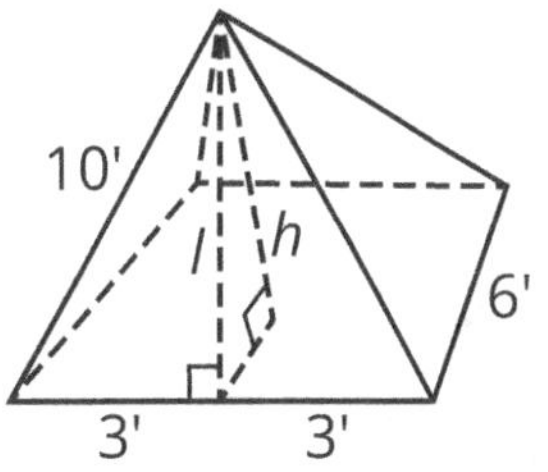

$V = \frac{1}{3}Bh$

$l^2 + 3^2 = 10^2$

$l^2 + 9 = 100$

$l^2 = 91$

$\sqrt{l^2} = \sqrt{91}$

$l = \sqrt{91}$

$h^2 + 3^2 = l^2$

$h^2 + 3^2 = (\sqrt{91})^2$

$h^2 + 9 = 91$

$h^2 = 82$

$\sqrt{h^2} = \sqrt{82}$

$h = \sqrt{82}$

$V = \frac{1}{3}Bh$

$= \frac{1}{3}(36)(\sqrt{82})$

$= 12\sqrt{82}$ cu. ft.

3.20

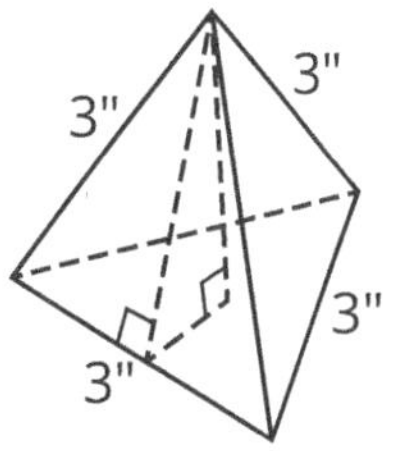

$V = \frac{1}{3}Bh$

$l^2 + (\frac{3}{2})^2 = 3^2$

$l^2 + \frac{9}{4} = 9$

$l^2 = \frac{27}{4}$

$\sqrt{l^2} = \sqrt{\frac{27}{4}}$

$l = \frac{3\sqrt{3}}{2}$

$h^2 + (\frac{\sqrt{3}}{2})^2 = l^2$

$h^2 + (\frac{\sqrt{3}}{2})^2 = (\frac{3\sqrt{3}}{2})^2$

$h^2 + \frac{3}{4} = \frac{27}{4}$

$h^2 = \frac{24}{4}$

$h^2 = 6$

$\sqrt{h^2} = \sqrt{6}$

$h = \sqrt{6}$

$V = \frac{1}{3}(\frac{1}{4})(3)^2(\sqrt{3})(\sqrt{6})$

$= \frac{1}{3}(\frac{1}{4})(9)(\sqrt{3})(\sqrt{6})$

$= \frac{3}{4}\sqrt{18}$

$= \frac{9\sqrt{2}}{4}$ cu. in.

3.21 a. $L.A. = 2\pi rh$
$= 2\pi(4)(5)$
$= 40\pi$

b. $T.A. = 2\pi rh + 2\pi r^2$
$= 40\pi + 2\pi(4)^2$
$= 40\pi + 2\pi(16)$
$= 40\pi + 32\pi$
$= 72\pi$

c. $V = \pi r^2 h$
$= \pi(4)^2(5)$
$= \pi(16)(5)$
$= 80\pi$

3.22 a. $L.A. = 2\pi rh$
$= 2\pi(2)(4)$
$= 16\pi$

b. $T.A. = 2\pi rh + 2\pi r^2$
$= 16\pi + 2\pi(2)^2$
$= 16\pi + 2\pi(4)$
$= 16\pi + 8\pi$
$= 24\pi$

c. $V = \pi r^2 h$
$= \pi(2)^2(4)$
$= \pi(4)(4)$
$= 16\pi$

3.23 a. $L.A. = 2\pi rh$
$= 2\pi(2)(3)$
$= 12\pi$

b. $T.A. = 2\pi rh + 2\pi r^2$
$= 12\pi + 2\pi(2)^2$
$= 12\pi + 2\pi(4)$
$= 12\pi + 8\pi$
$= 20\pi$

c. $V = \pi r^2 h$
$= \pi(2)^2(3)$
$= \pi(4)(3)$
$= 12\pi$

3.24 a. $L.A. = 2\pi rh$
$= 2\pi(1)(1)$
$= 2\pi$

b. $T.A. = 2\pi rh + 2\pi r^2$
$= 2\pi + 2\pi(1)^2$
$= 2\pi + 2\pi$
$= 4\pi$

c. $V = \pi r^2 h$
$= \pi(1)^2(1)$
$= \pi$

3.25 a. $L.A. = 2\pi rh$
$= 2\pi(6)(20)$
$= 240\pi$

b. $T.A. = 2\pi rh + 2\pi r^2$
$= 240\pi + 2\pi(6)^2$
$= 240\pi + 2\pi(36)$
$= 240\pi + 72\pi$
$= 312\pi$

c. $V = \pi r^2 h$
$= \pi(6)^2(20)$
$= \pi(36)(20)$
$= 720\pi$

3.26 $C = 2\pi r$
$16\pi = 2\pi r$
$\frac{16\pi}{2\pi} = r$
$8 = r$
$V = \pi r^2 h$
$= \pi(8)^2(6)$
$= \pi(64)(6)$
$= 384\pi$ cu. in.

3.27 $L.A. = 2\pi rh$
$70\pi = 2\pi(5)h$
$70\pi = 10\pi h$
$\frac{70\pi}{10\pi} = h$
7 in. $= h$

3.28

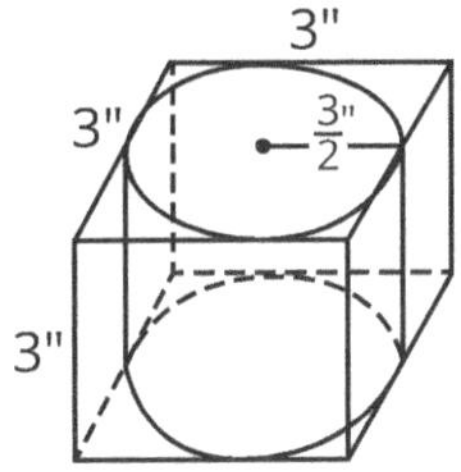

$V = \pi r^2 h$

$= \pi(\frac{3}{2})^2(3)$

$= \pi(\frac{9}{4})(3)$

$= \frac{27}{4}\pi$ cu. in.

3.29 $V = \pi r^2 h$

$320\pi = \pi r^2(5)$

$\frac{320\pi}{5\pi} = r^2$

$64 = r^2$

$\sqrt{64} = \sqrt{r^2}$

8 in. $= r$

3.30 $V_T = \pi r^2 h$

$= \pi(3)^2(2)$

$= \pi(9)(2)$

$= 18\pi$ cu. in.

$V_S = \pi r^2 h$

$= \pi(2)^2(3)$

$= \pi(4)(3)$

$= 12\pi$ cu. in.

The tuna can contains more food.

3.31 a. $h^2 + r^2 = l^2$

$5^2 + 3^2 = l^2$

$25 + 9 = l^2$

$34 = l^2$

$\sqrt{34} = \sqrt{l^2}$

$l = \sqrt{34}$

b. $L.A. = \pi rl$

$= \pi(3)(\sqrt{34})$

$= 3\sqrt{34}\pi$

c. $T.A. = \pi rl + \pi r^2$

$= 3\sqrt{34}\pi + \pi(3)^2$

$= 3\sqrt{34}\pi + 9\pi$

d. $V = \frac{1}{3}\pi r^2 h$

$= \frac{1}{3}\pi(3)^2(5)$

$= \frac{1}{3}\pi(9)(5)$

$= 15\pi$

3.32 a. $h^2 + r^2 = l^2$

$h^2 + 6^2 = 10^2$

$h^2 + 36 = 100$

$h^2 = 64$

$\sqrt{h^2} = \sqrt{64}$

$h = 8$

b. $L.A. = \pi rl$

$= \pi(6)(10)$

$= 60\pi$

c. $T.A. = \pi rl + \pi r^2$

$= 60\pi + \pi(6)^2$

$= 60\pi + 36\pi$

$= 96\pi$

d. $V = \frac{1}{3}\pi r^2 h$

$= \frac{1}{3}\pi(6)^2(8)$

$= \frac{1}{3}\pi(36)(8)$

$= 96\pi$

3.33 a. $L.A. = \pi rl$

$12\pi = \pi(2)l$

$\frac{12\pi}{2\pi} = l$

$6 = l$

b. $h^2 + r^2 = l^2$

$h^2 + 2^2 = 6^2$

$h^2 + 4 = 36$

$h^2 = 32$

$\sqrt{h^2} = \sqrt{32}$

$h = 4\sqrt{2}$

c. $T.A. = \pi rl + \pi r^2$

$= \pi(2)(6) + \pi(2)^2$

$= 12\pi + 4\pi$

$= 16\pi$

d. $V = \frac{1}{3}\pi r^2 h$

$= \frac{1}{3}\pi(2)^2(4\sqrt{2})$

$= \frac{1}{3}\pi(4)(4\sqrt{2})$

$= \frac{16}{3}\sqrt{2}\pi$

3.34 Note: must find *b* before *a* can be determined

b. $V = \frac{1}{3}\pi r^2 h$

$100\pi = \frac{1}{3}\pi(5)^2 h$

$100\pi = \frac{1}{3}\pi 25h$

$\frac{100\pi}{\pi}(\frac{3}{25}) = h$

$12 = h$

a. $h^2 + r^2 = l^2$
$12^2 + 5^2 = l^2$
$144 + 25 = l^2$
$169 = l^2$
$\sqrt{169} = \sqrt{l^2}$
$13 = l$

c. $L.A. = \pi rh$
$= \pi(5)(13)$
$= 65\pi$

d. $T.A. = \pi rl + \pi r^2$
$= 65\pi + \pi(5)^2$
$= 65\pi + 25\pi$
$= 90\pi$

3.35 a. $L.A. = \pi rl$
$8\pi = \pi r(4)$
$\frac{8\pi}{4\pi} = r$
$2 = r$

b. $h^2 + r^2 = l^2$
$h^2 + 2^2 = 4^2$
$h^2 + 4 = 16$
$h^2 = 12$
$\sqrt{h^2} = \sqrt{12}$
$h = 2\sqrt{3}$

c. $T.A. = \pi rl + \pi r^2$
$= 8\pi + \pi(2)^2$
$= 8\pi + 4\pi$
$= 12\pi$

d. $V = \frac{1}{3}\pi r^2 h$
$= \frac{1}{3}\pi(2)^2(2\sqrt{3})$
$= \frac{1}{3}\pi(4)(2\sqrt{3})$
$= \frac{8}{3}\sqrt{3}\pi$

3.36 $T.A. = \pi rl + \pi r^2$
$24\pi = \pi(3)l + \pi(3)^2$
$24\pi = 3\pi l + 9\pi$
$15\pi = 3\pi l$
$\frac{15\pi}{3\pi} = l$
$5" = l$
$h^2 + r^2 = l^2$
$h^2 + 3^2 = 5^2$
$h^2 + 9 = 25$
$h^2 = 16$
$\sqrt{h^2} = \sqrt{16}$
$h = 4"$
$V = \frac{1}{3}\pi r^2 h$
$= \frac{1}{3}\pi(3)^2(4)$
$= \frac{1}{3}\pi(9)(4)$
$= 12\pi$

3.37

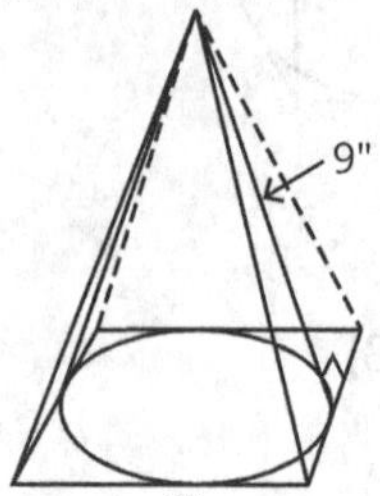

$h^2 + r^2 = l^2$
$h^2 + 3^2 = 9^2$
$h^2 + 9 = 81$
$h^2 = 72$
$\sqrt{h^2} = \sqrt{72}$
$h = 6\sqrt{2}$
$V = \frac{1}{3}\pi r^2 h$
$= \frac{1}{3}\pi(3)^2(6\sqrt{2})$
$= \frac{1}{3}\pi(9)(6\sqrt{2})$
$= 18\sqrt{2}\pi$

3.38 $V_{cube} = Bh$
$= 4(2)$
$= 8$ cu. in.
$V_{cone} = \frac{1}{3}\pi r^2 h$
$8 = \frac{1}{3}\pi(3)^2 h$
$8 = \frac{1}{3}\pi(9)h$
$8 = 3\pi h$
$h = \frac{8}{3\pi}$ in.

3.39 $V = \frac{1}{3}\pi r^2 h$
$= \frac{1}{3}\pi(5)^2(12)$
$= \frac{1}{3}\pi(25)(12)$
$= 100\pi$ cu. ft.

3.40 $L.A. = \pi rl$
$h^2 + r^2 = l^2$
$12^2 + 5^2 = l^2$
$144 + 25 = l^2$
$169 = l^2$
$\sqrt{169} = \sqrt{l^2}$
$l = 13$

$L.A. = 3.14(5)(13)$
$= 204.1$ sq. ft.

$204.1 \div 15 \doteq 13.6$

Fourteen skins are needed.

3.41 $S = 4\pi r^2$
$= 4\pi(4)^2$
$= 4\pi(16)$
$= 64\pi$ sq. in.

$V = \frac{4}{3}\pi r^3$
$= \frac{4}{3}\pi(4)^3$
$= \frac{4}{3}\pi(64)$
$= \frac{256}{3}\pi$ cu. in.

3.42 a.

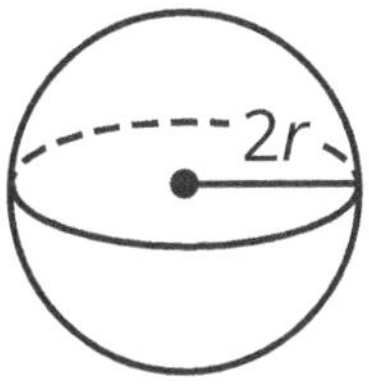

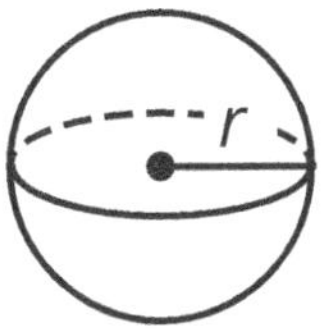

$S_1 = 4\pi(2r)^2$
$= 4\pi(4r^2)$
$= 16\pi r^2$
$\frac{S}{S_1} = \frac{4\pi r^2}{16\pi r^2} = \frac{1}{4}$

b. $V = \frac{4}{3}\pi r^3$
$V_1 = \frac{4}{3}\pi(2r)^3$
$= \frac{4}{3}\pi 8r^3$
$\frac{V}{V_1} = \frac{\frac{4}{3}\pi r^2}{\frac{4}{3}\pi 8r^3} = \frac{1}{8}$

3.43

$V = \frac{4}{3}\pi r^3$
$= \frac{4}{3}(\frac{22}{7})(7)$
$= \frac{4}{3}(\frac{22}{7})(\frac{343}{1})$
$= 1{,}437\frac{1}{3}$ cu. ft.

3.44 $S = 4\pi r^2$
$= 4\pi(2)^2$
$= 4\pi(4)$
$= 16\pi$ sq. in.

3.45 a. $V = \frac{4}{3}\pi r^3$
$288\pi = \frac{4}{3}\pi r^3$
$288\pi(\frac{3}{4\pi}) = r^3$
$216 = r^3$
$\sqrt[3]{216} = \sqrt[3]{r^3}$
$r = 6"$

b. $V = \frac{4}{3}\pi r^3$
$144\pi = \frac{4}{3}\pi r^3$
$144\pi(\frac{3}{4\pi}) = r^3$
$108 = r^3$
$\sqrt[3]{108} = \sqrt[3]{r^3}$
$r = \sqrt[3]{108}"$

3.46 $S = 4\pi r^2$
$16\pi = 4\pi r^2$
$\frac{16\pi}{4\pi} = r^2$
$4 = r^2$
$\sqrt{4} = \sqrt{r^2}$
$r = 2$ in.
$V = \frac{4}{3}\pi r^3$
$= \frac{4}{3}\pi(2)^3$
$= \frac{4}{3}\pi(8)$
$= \frac{32}{3}\pi$ cu. in.

3.47 $V = \frac{4}{3}\pi r^3$
$288\pi = \frac{4}{3}\pi r^3$
$288\pi(\frac{3}{4\pi}) = r^3$
$216 = r^3$
$\sqrt[3]{216} = \sqrt[3]{r^3}$
$r = 6$

$S = 4\pi r^2$
$= 4\pi(6)^2$
$= 4\pi(36)$
$= 144\pi$

3.48

$$V_1 = \frac{4}{3}\pi r^3$$
$$= \frac{4}{3}\pi(6)^3$$
$$= \frac{4}{3}\pi(216)$$
$$= 288\pi$$
$$V_2 = \frac{4}{3}\pi r^3$$
$$= \frac{4}{3}\pi(5)^3$$
$$= \frac{4}{3}\pi(125)$$
$$= \frac{500}{3}\pi$$
$$V_1 - V_2 = \frac{864}{3}\pi - \frac{500}{3}\pi = \frac{364}{3}\pi \text{ cu. in.}$$

3.49

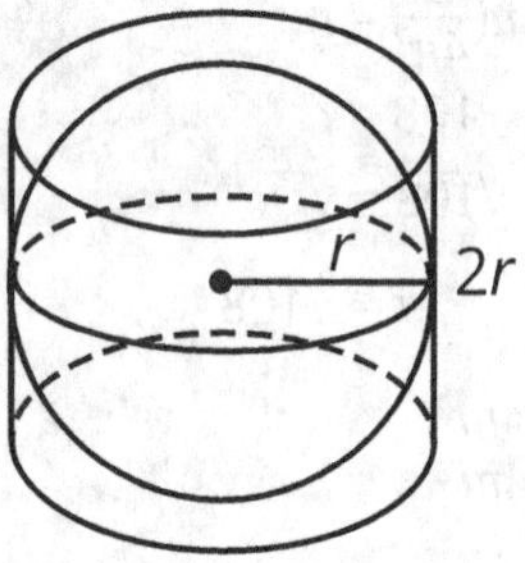

$$S_{sphere} = 4\pi r^2$$
$$L.A._{cylinder} = 2\pi rh$$
$$= 2\pi r(2r)$$
$$= 4\pi r^2$$

3.50

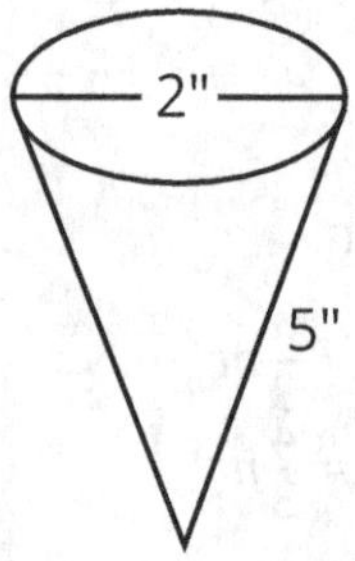

$$V = \frac{1}{3}Bh$$
$$= \frac{1}{3}\pi r^2 h$$
$$= \frac{1}{3}\pi(1)^2(5)$$
$$= \frac{5}{3}\pi$$

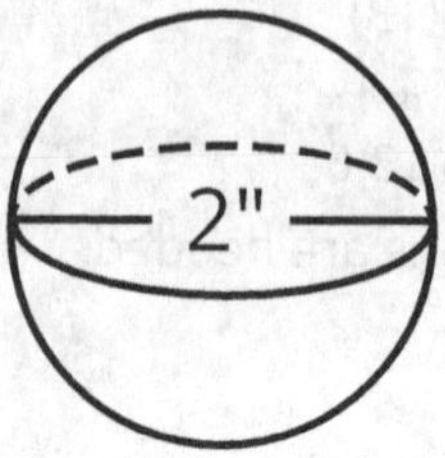

$$V = \frac{4}{3}\pi r^3$$
$$= \frac{4}{3}\pi(1)^3$$
$$= \frac{4}{3}\pi$$

The cone is $\frac{1}{3}\pi$ larger than the scoop of ice cream; therefore, the cone will not overflow.

SELF TEST 3

3.01 e
3.02 c
3.03 a
3.04 b
3.05 d
3.06 b
3.07 e
3.08 c
3.09 d
3.010 a
3.011 g
3.012 f
3.013 h or b
3.014 a. $L.A. = ph$
$= 16(6)$
$= 96$ sq. ft.

b. $T.A. = ph + 2B$
$= 96 + 2(15)$
$= 96 + 30$
$= 126$ sq. ft.

c. $V = Bh$
$= 15(6)$
$= 90$ cu. ft.

3.015 a.

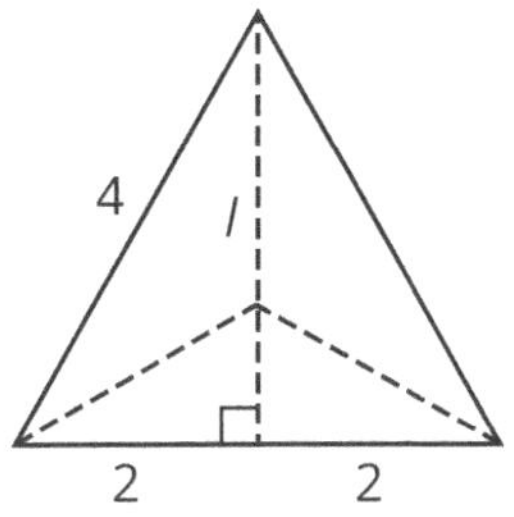

$$L.A. = \frac{1}{2}pl$$
$$l^2 + 2^2 = 4^2$$
$$l^2 + 4 = 16$$
$$l^2 = 12$$
$$\sqrt{l^2} = \sqrt{12}$$
$$l = 2\sqrt{3}$$
$$L.A. = \frac{1}{2}(12)(2\sqrt{3})$$
$$= 6(2\sqrt{3})$$
$$= 12\sqrt{3}$$

b. $T.A. = \frac{1}{2}pl + B$
$$= 12\sqrt{3} + \frac{1}{4}(4)^2(\sqrt{3})$$
$$= 12\sqrt{3} + \frac{1}{4}(16)(\sqrt{3})$$
$$= 12\sqrt{3} + 4\sqrt{3}$$
$$= 16\sqrt{3}$$

3.015 cont'd

c.

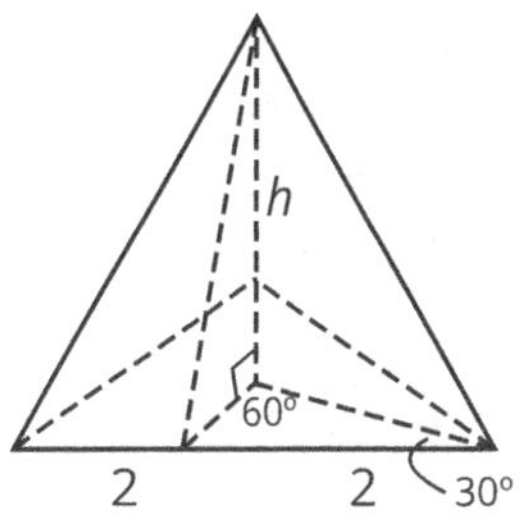

$$V = \frac{1}{3}Bh$$
$$h^2 + (\frac{2\sqrt{3}}{3})^2 = (2\sqrt{3})^2$$
$$h^2 + \frac{12}{9} = 12$$
$$h^2 + \frac{4}{3} = 12$$
$$h^2 = \frac{32}{3}$$
$$\sqrt{h^2} = \sqrt{\frac{32}{3}}$$
$$h = \frac{\sqrt{32}}{\sqrt{3}} = \frac{4\sqrt{2}}{\sqrt{3}} \cdot \frac{\sqrt{3}}{\sqrt{3}} = \frac{4\sqrt{6}}{3}$$
$$V = \frac{1}{3}(4\sqrt{3})(\frac{4\sqrt{6}}{3})$$
$$= \frac{16\sqrt{18}}{9}$$
$$= \frac{16(3\sqrt{2})}{9}$$
$$= \frac{16\sqrt{2}}{3}$$

3.016 a. $L.A. = \pi rl$
$$l = \sqrt{6^2 + 8^2}$$
$$= \sqrt{36 + 64}$$
$$= \sqrt{100}$$
$$= 10$$
$L.A. = \pi(6)(10)$
$= 60\pi$ sq. in.

b. $T.A. = \pi rl + \pi r^2$
$= 60\pi + \pi(6)^2$
$= 60\pi + 36\pi$
$= 96\pi$ sq. in.

c. $V = \frac{1}{3}\pi r^2 h$
$$= \frac{1}{3}\pi(6)^2(8)$$
$$= \frac{1}{3}\pi(36)(8)$$
$= 96\pi$ cu. in.

3.017 a. $L.A. = 2\pi rh$
$= 2\pi(3)(10)$
$= 60\pi$ sq. in.

b. $T.A. = 2\pi rh + 2\pi r^2$
$= 60\pi + 2\pi(3)^2$
$= 60\pi + 2\pi(9)$
$= 60\pi + 18\pi$
$= 78\pi$ sq. in.

c. $V = \pi r^2 h$
$= \pi(3)^2(10)$
$= \pi(9)(10)$
$= 90\pi$ cu. in.

3.018 $S = 4\pi r^2$
$= 4\pi(8)^2$
$= 4\pi(64)$
$= 256\pi$ sq. in.

$V = \frac{4}{3}\pi r^3$
$= \frac{4}{3}\pi(8)^3$
$= \frac{4}{3}\pi(512)$
$= \frac{2,048}{3}\pi$ cu. in.

LIFEPAC TEST

1. $A = lw$
$= 4(2)$
$= 8$

2. $L.A. = ph$
$= 12(3)$
$= 36$

3. $T.A. = L.A. + 2B$
$= 36 + 2(8)$
$= 36 + 16$
$= 52$

4. $V = Bh$
$= 8(3)$
$= 24$

5. $l = \sqrt{5^2 + 12^2}$
$= \sqrt{25 + 144}$
$= \sqrt{169}$
$= 13$

6. $L.A. = \frac{1}{2}pl$
$= \frac{1}{2}(40)(13)$
$= 260$

7. $T.A. = L.A. + B$
$= 260 + 100$
$= 360$

8. $V = \frac{1}{3}Bh$
$= \frac{1}{3}(100)(12)$
$= 400$

9. $L.A. = 2\pi rh$
$= 2\pi(4)(6)$
$= 48\pi$

10. $T.A. = L.A. + 2B$
$= 48\pi + 2\pi r^2$
$= 48\pi + 2\pi(4)^2$
$= 48\pi + 2\pi(16)$
$= 48\pi + 32\pi$
$= 80\pi$

11. $V = \pi r^2 h$
$= \pi(4)^2(6)$
$= \pi(16)(6)$
$= 96\pi$

12. $l = \sqrt{5^2 + 11^2}$
$= \sqrt{25 + 121}$
$= \sqrt{146}$

13. $L.A. = \pi rl$
$= \pi(5)(\sqrt{146})$
$= 5\sqrt{146}\pi$

14. $T.A. = L.A. + B$
$= 5\sqrt{146}\pi + \pi r^2$
$= 5\sqrt{146}\pi + \pi(5)^2$
$= 5\sqrt{146}\pi + 25\pi$

15. $V = \frac{1}{3}\pi r^2 h$
$= \frac{1}{3}\pi(5)^2(11)$
$= \frac{1}{3}\pi(25)(11)$
$= \frac{275}{3}\pi$

16. $S = 4\pi r^2$
$= 4\pi(3)^2$
$= 4\pi(9)$
$= 36\pi$

17. $V = \frac{4}{3}\pi r^3$
$= \frac{4}{3}\pi(3)^3$
$= \frac{4}{3}\pi(27)$
$= 36\pi$

18. $A = \pi r^2$
$= \pi(6)^2$
$= 36\pi$

19. $A_O - AXB = \frac{AB}{360°}\pi r^2$
$= \frac{60°}{360°}\pi(6)^2$
$= \frac{1}{6}\pi(36)$
$= 6\pi$

20. $A_{AXB} = A_{sector} - A_{\triangle}$
$= 6\pi - \frac{s^2}{4}\sqrt{3}$
$= 6\pi - \frac{6^2}{4}\sqrt{3}$
$= 6\pi - \frac{36}{4}\sqrt{3}$
$= 6\pi - 9\sqrt{3}$

21. $C = 2\pi r$
$= 2\pi(6)$
$= 12\pi$

22. Apothem is long leg of 30°-60°-90° △.
$a = 4\sqrt{3}$.

23. Radius is same length as side of hexagon.
$r = 8$.

24. central $\angle = \frac{360°}{m} = \frac{360°}{6} = 60°$

25. $A = \frac{1}{2}ap$
$= \frac{1}{2}(4\sqrt{3})(48)$
$= 2\sqrt{3}(48)$
$= 96\sqrt{3}$

ALTERNATE LIFEPAC TEST

1. $A = bh$
$A = 3(6)$
$A = 18$ sq. in.

2. $A = s^2$
$A = 4^2$
$A = 4(4)$
$A = 16$ sq. in.

3.

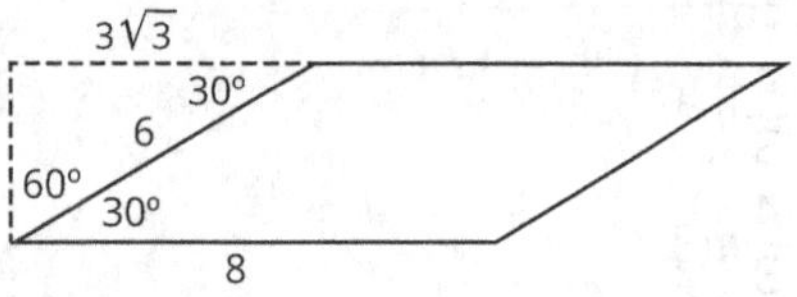

$h = 3$
$A = bh$
$A = 8(3)$
$A = 24$

4. $P = 4s$
$6 = 4s$
$\frac{6}{4} = \frac{4s}{4}$
$s = \frac{3}{2}$
$A = s^2$
$A = (\frac{3}{2})^2$
$A = \frac{3}{2}(\frac{3}{2})$
$A = \frac{9}{4}$ sq. ft. or $2\frac{1}{4}$ sq. ft.

5. $A = \frac{1}{2}(b_1 + b_2)$
$A = \frac{1}{2}(4)(6 + 8)$
$A = 2(14)$
$A = 28$ sq. in.

6. $P = 5(6)$
$P = 30$
$A = \frac{1}{2}ap$
$A = \frac{1}{2}(K)(30)$
$A = 15K$

7. $P = 6s$
$24 = 6s$
$\frac{24}{6} = \frac{6s}{6}$
$s = 4$

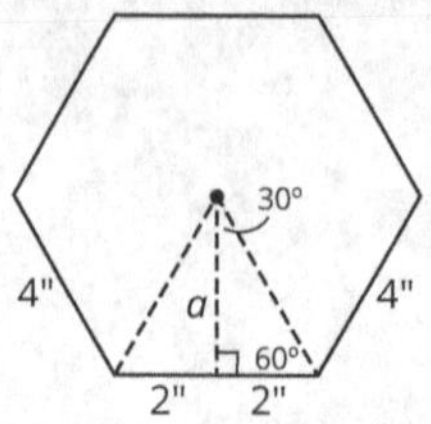

$a = 2\sqrt{3}$
$A = \frac{1}{2}ap$
$A = \frac{1}{2}(2\sqrt{3})(24)$
$A = 24\sqrt{3}$ sq. in.

8. $A = \frac{1}{4}s^2\sqrt{3}$
$A = \frac{1}{4}(6)^2(\sqrt{3})$
$A = \frac{1}{4}(36)(\sqrt{3})$
$A = 9\sqrt{3}$ sq. in.

9. $C = 2\pi r$
$C = 2\pi(4)$
$C = 8\pi$ in.

10. $A = \pi r^2$
$A = \pi(4)^2$
$A = \pi(4)(4)$
$A = 16\pi$ sq. in.

11. $A = \frac{m\overset{\frown}{}}{360}(\pi r^2)$
$A = \frac{90}{360}(\pi)(4)^2$
$A = \frac{\overset{1}{\cancel{90}}}{\underset{4}{\cancel{360}}}(\pi)(4)(4)$
$A = \frac{1}{\underset{1}{\cancel{4}}}(\pi)(\cancel{16})^{4}$
$A = 4\pi$ sq. in.

12.

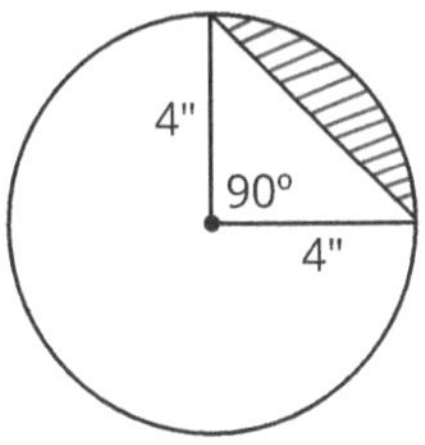

Area of sector = $\frac{90}{360}(\pi)(4)^2$

$= \frac{\overset{1}{\cancel{90}}}{\underset{4}{\cancel{360}}}(\pi)(4)(4)$

$= \frac{1}{\underset{1}{\cancel{4}}}(\pi)(\overset{4}{\cancel{16}})$

$= 4\pi$

Area of triangle = $\frac{1}{2}bh$

$= \frac{1}{2}(4)(4)$

$= \frac{1}{2}(16)$

$= 8$

Area of segment = $(4\pi - 8)$ sq. in.

13. $V = bh$
$V = (6 \cdot 4)(2)$
$V = (24)(2)$
$V = 48$ cu. in.

14. $T.A. = ph + 2B$
$p = 2(6) + 2(4)$
$p = 12 + 8$
$p = 20$

$h = 2$

$B = 6(4)$
$B = 24$

$T.A. = 20(2) + 2(24)$
$T.A. = 40 + 48$
$T.A. = 88$ sq. in.

15. $S = 4\pi r^2$
$S = 4\pi(3)^2$
$S = 4\pi(3)(3)$
$S = 4\pi(9)$
$S = 36\pi$ sq. in.

16. $V = \frac{4}{3}\pi r^3$

$V = \frac{4}{3}\pi(3)^3$

$V = \frac{4}{3}\pi(3)(3)(3)$

$V = \frac{4}{\underset{1}{\cancel{3}}}\pi(\overset{9}{\cancel{27}})$

$V = 36\pi$ cu. in.

17. $C = \pi d$
$C = \pi(8)$
$C = 8\pi$ in.

18. $A = \pi r^2$

$r = \frac{1}{2}(8)$

$r = 4$
$A = \pi(4)^2$
$A = \pi(4)(4)$
$A = 16\pi$ sq. in.

19. $V = \pi r^2 h$

$r = \frac{1}{2}(8)$

$r = 4$
$V = \pi(4)^2(4)$
$V = \pi(4)(4)(4)$
$V = 64\pi$ cu. in.

20.

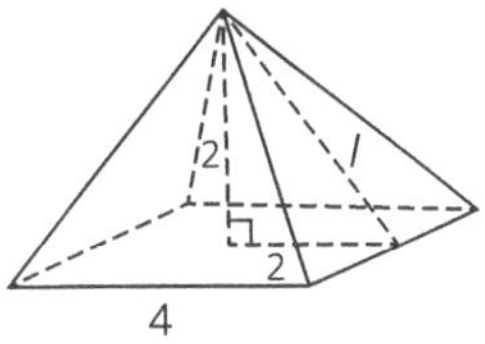

Use the Pythagorean Theorem.
$l = \sqrt{2^2 + 2^2}$
$l = \sqrt{4 + 4}$
$l = \sqrt{8}$
$l = \sqrt{4 \cdot 2} = \sqrt{4} \cdot \sqrt{2}$
$l = 2\sqrt{2}$

21. $A = s^2$
$A = 4^2$
$A = (4)(4)$
$A = 16$

22. $V = \frac{1}{3}Bh$

$V = \frac{1}{3}(4 \cdot 4)(2)$

$V = \frac{1}{3}(16)(2)$

$V = \frac{1}{3}(32)$

$V = \frac{32}{3}$ or $10\frac{2}{3}$

23. Use the Pythagorean Theorem.

$l = \sqrt{3^2 + 4^2}$

$l = \sqrt{9 + 16}$

$l = \sqrt{25}$

$l = 5$

24. $L.A. = \pi rl$

$L.A. = \pi(3)(5)$

$L.A. = 15\pi$

25. $V = \frac{1}{3}\pi r^2 h$

$V = \frac{1}{3}\pi(3)^2(4)$

$V = \frac{1}{3}\pi(3)(3)(4)$

$V = \frac{1}{\cancel{3}_1}\pi(\cancel{9}^3)(4)$

$V = 12\pi$

MATH 1008

ALTERNATE LIFEPAC TEST

NAME ______________________________

DATE ______________________________

SCORE ______________________________

80 / 100

Find the area of each of these quadrilaterals (each answer, 4 points).

1. A rectangle with length 3" and width 6". ______________________
2. A square with side 4 inches long. ______________________
3. A parallelogram with sides 8 and 6, and with an angle measure of 30°. ______________________
4. A square with perimeter 6 feet. ______________________
5. A trapezoid with bases 6" and 8" having a height of 4". ______________________

Find the area of each of these regular polygons (each answer, 4 points).

6. A pentagon with sides of 6 and apothem of *K*. ______________________
7. A hexagon with perimeter of 24". ______________________
8. A triangle with side equal to 6". ______________________

Find the following measures for a circle with radius equal to 4" and with a central angle equal to 90° (each answer, 4 points).

9. Circumference ______________________
10. Area ______________________
11. Area of smaller sector ______________________
12. Area of smaller segment ______________________

Find the following measures for these figures (each answer, 4 points).

13. Volume ______________________

14. Total area ______________________

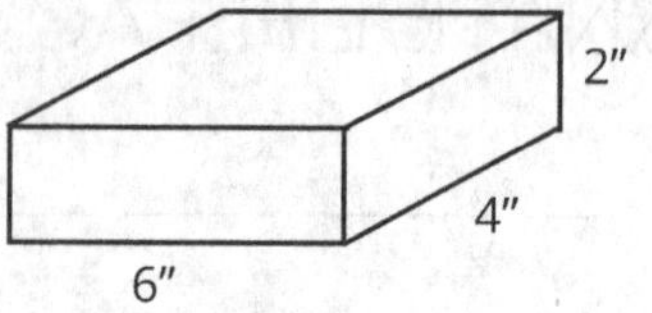

15. Surface area ______________________

16. Volume ______________________

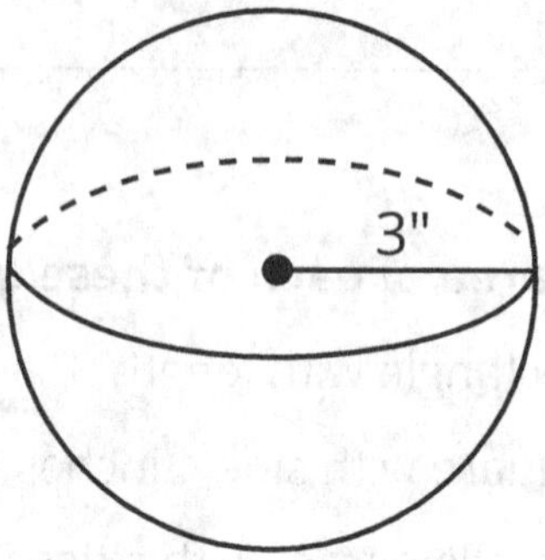

17. Circumference of base ______________________

18. Area of base ______________________

19. Volume ______________________

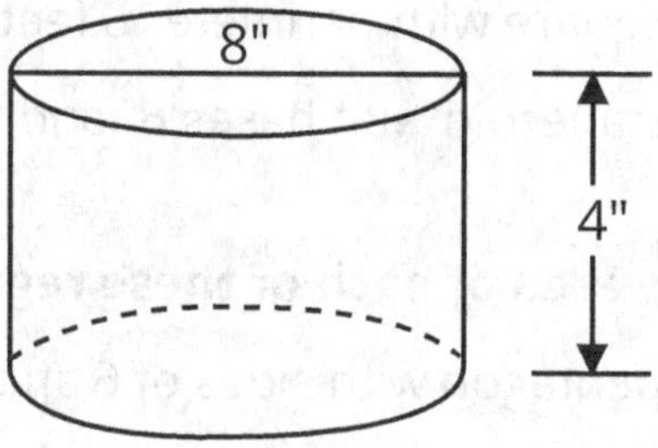

20. Slant height ______________________

21. Area of base ______________________

22. Volume ______________________

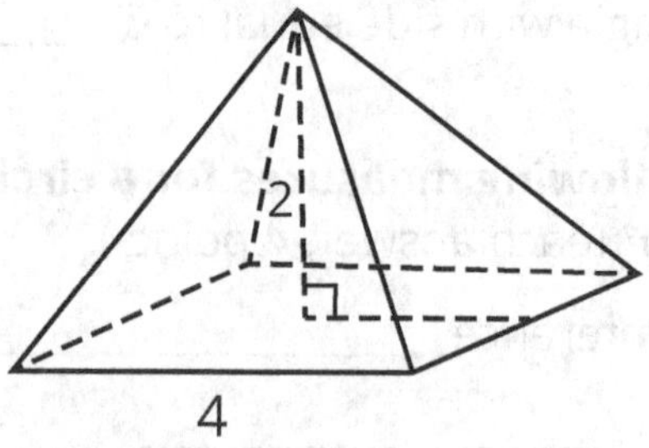

23. Slant height ______________________

24. Lateral area ______________________

25. Volume ______________________

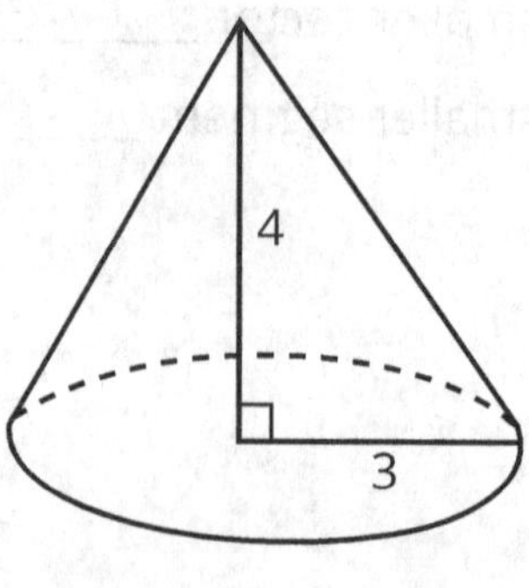

MATH 1009

Unit 9: Coordinate Geometry

TEACHER NOTES

MATERIALS NEEDED FOR LIFEPAC	
Required	Suggested
• protractor and straightedge	(None)

ADDITIONAL LEARNING ACTIVITIES

Section 1: Ordered Pairs

1. Discuss these questions with your class.

   What kind(s) of symmetry does a prism have? a pyramid? a cylinder? a cone? a sphere?

2. Let the students play "Battleship," a game that involves finding coordinates to "sink" the other player's battleships. The commercial game may be used or you may wish to make your own.

   To make a "Battleship" game board, acquire a small piece of plywood or other suitable material, (no larger than a foot square). Cut the plywood in half (for two sides of the game board for two players). Mark off $\frac{1}{4}$" lengths along each of the sides of both boards. Connect the lines to form $\frac{1}{4}$-" squares. At the intersection of each of the lines, drill a small hole. Paint a light-colored line down the middle of each board and across the middle of each board to represent the *x*- and *y*-axes. With a stencil or freehand, paint a small letter *x* at the top of each vertical line and paint a small letter *y* to the right of each horizontal line. Varnish the game boards and let dry. Acquire or make 12 or 14 small pegs ($\frac{1}{4}$" in diameter by 1" high), 6 or 7 for each player. On the top of each of two of the pegs, paint the letter *A*; the letter *B*; the letter *C*; the letter *D*; the letter *E*; the letter *F*; and the letter *G*. Each player plays with one set of pegs labeled *A* through *G* (or *A* through *F*).

   To play, each player must not see the other player's board (a partition may be placed between the game boards and the boards hinged together, or the students may sit not facing each other). Each player chooses six (or seven) holes on his game board in which to place his pegs. The first player names a point (any point) by a coordinate, such as (2, -4), on the second player's board. If the second player has a peg in the position named, he must remove it. If he does not have a peg there, he names a point on the first player's board. If the first player has a peg in the position named, he must remove it. If he does not have a peg there, he names another point on the second player's board. The play continues until one of the players has lost all his pegs.

Section 2: Distance

1. Water pressure in the ocean is a function of depth. Have the students copy the following table and plot a graph demonstrating the relationship.

Depth (in miles)	1	2	3	4	5
Pressure (in tons/sq. in.)	1.5	2.3	3.45	4.6	5.75

Section 3: Lines

1. The number of chirps that a cricket makes in a minute is a function of the surrounding temperature. The formula is $t = \frac{n}{4} + 40$, where t represents the temperature in °F and n is the number of cricket chirps in one minute. Have the students copy the following table and use the formula to find the missing numbers. Then have them graph the result.

n	40	60	80	100	120	140
t	50	____	____	____	____	75

2. Mark Twain once made a strange prediction about the future of the Mississippi River. The river is constantly changing course from wide bends to more direct paths, resulting in "cutoffs." As a result, the length of the Mississippi becomes shorter and shorter. Twain passed on these observations: "The Mississippi between Cairo and New Orleans was 1,215 miles long 176 years ago. It was 1,180 after the cutoff of 1722 ... its length is only 973 miles at present (1875)." Have students plot these points on a graph. They will note that the points seem to lie along a straight line. If the students extend the line until it intersects the time axis, the line appears that sometime about the year 2600 not much of a river will be left. What is wrong with this reasoning?
3. On a sheet of graph paper, mark an origin (0, 0). Then draw the following points, curves, and lines with a compass and straightedge.

Points: (3, 7), (7, 7), and (5, 5)

Curves: the lower three-fourths of the circle whose equation is $(x - 5)^2 + (y - 5)^2 = 25$; end points are (1, 8) and (9, 8)

the upper half of the circle with center (3, 7), $r = \frac{1}{2}$

the upper half of the circle with center (7, 7), $r = \frac{1}{2}$

the lower half of the circle whose equation is $(x - 5)^2 + (y - 4)^2 = \frac{25}{4}$; end points are on the line $y = 4$ (draw only the half-circle)

the curve with center (3, 3) and whose end points are on the lines $x = 2$ and $x = 3$ (draw only the curve)

the curve with center (7, 3) and whose end points are on the lines $x = 7$ and $x = 8$ (draw only the curve)

the left half of the circle with center (0, 6), $r = 1$

the right half of the circle with center (10, 6), $r = 1$

the left half of the circle with center (0, 6), $r = \frac{1}{3}$

the right half of the circle with center (10, 6), $r = \frac{1}{3}$

Lines: $y = 8$; end points are (-2, 8) and (12, 8)

$y = 10$; end points are (-2, 10) and (2, 10)

$m = 0$; end points are (8, 10) and (12, 10)

line || to $y = 8$; end points are (2, 12) and (8, 12)

line has no slope; equation is $x = 2$; end points are (2, 10) and (2, 12)

line has no slope; equation is $x = 8$; end points are (8, 10) and (8, 12)

line $\perp$ to $y = 8$; end points are (-2, 8) and (-2, 10)

line $\perp$ to $y = 10$; end points are (12, 8) and (12, 10)

What figure did you draw?

Section 4: Proofs by Coordinate Methods

1. Prove that the opposite sides of a square are equal. Prove that the opposite sides of a rhombus are equal. Prove that the opposite sides of a parallelogram are equal. Are the proofs the same? Why or why not?
2. Prove that the diagonals of a square are equal. Prove that the diagonals of a rectangle are equal. Prove that the diagonals of a rhombus are equal. Are the proofs the same? Why or why not?

Administer the LIFEPAC Test.

The test is to be administered in one session. Give no help except with directions.
Evaluate the tests and review areas where the students have done poorly.
Review the pages and activities that stress the concepts tested.
If necessary, administer the Alternate LIFEPAC Test

ANSWER KEYS

SECTION 1

1.1

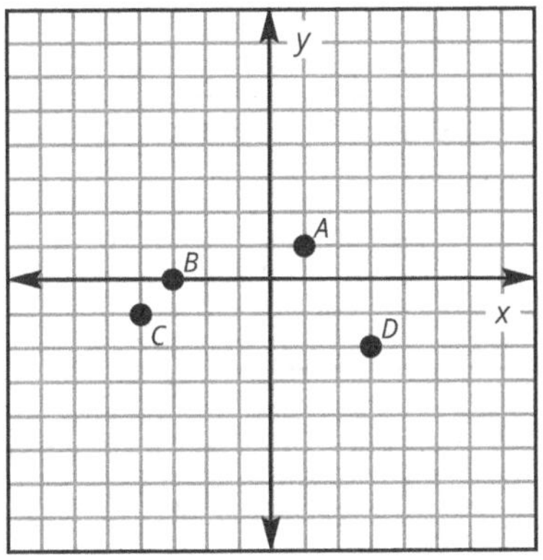

1.2

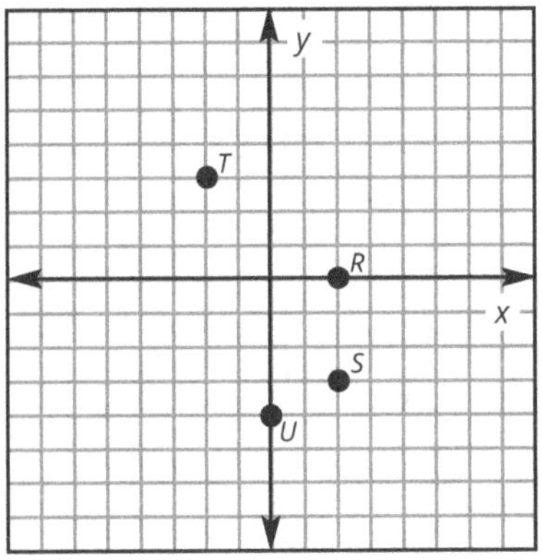

1.3 Triangle

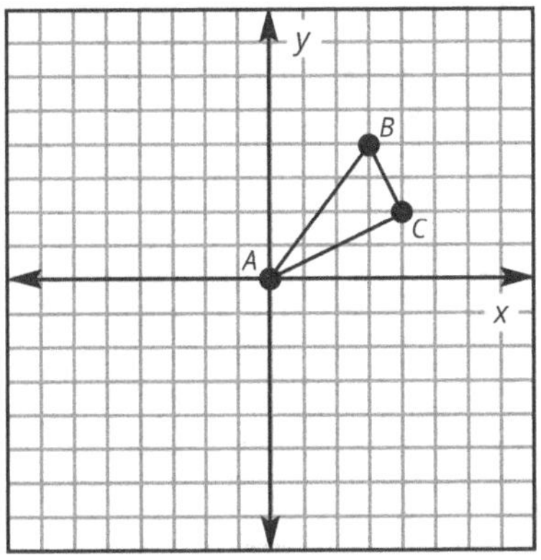

1.4 Rectangle

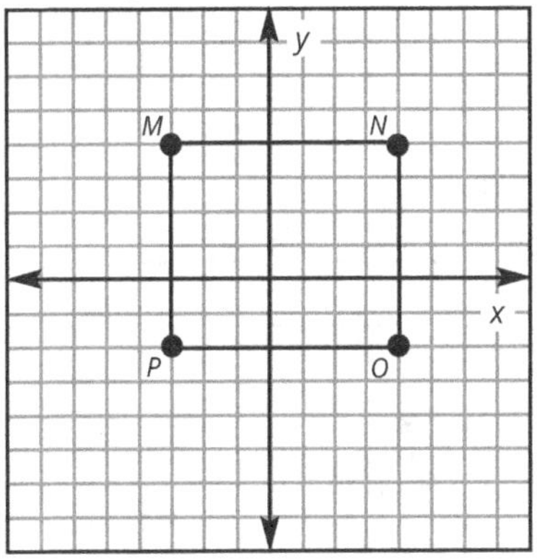

1.5 Trapezoid

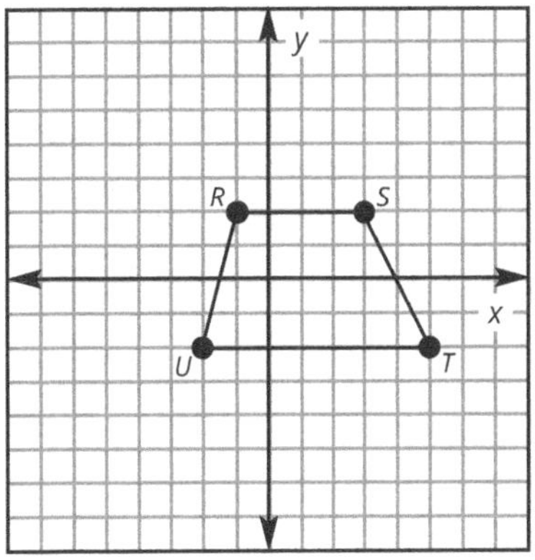

1.6 Square

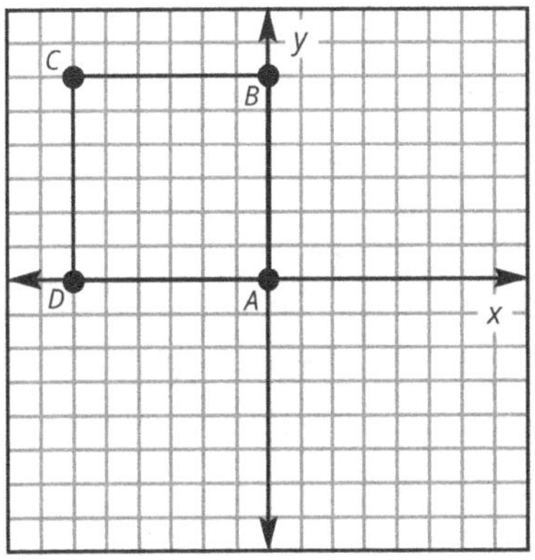

1.7

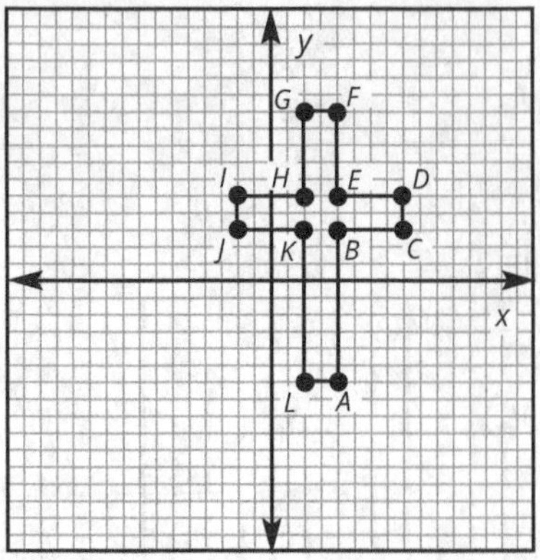

1.8

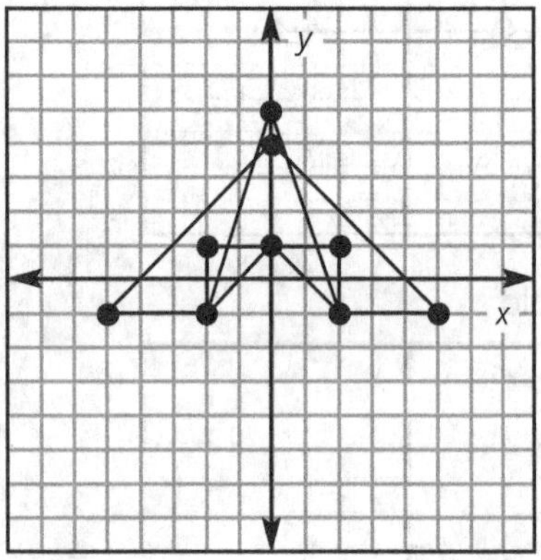

1.9 *A* (-4, -2)
B (2, -4)
C (4, -2)
D (2, 5)
E (-1, 1)
F (-5, 0)
G (4, 2)
H (0, -5)

1.10 (5, 6)

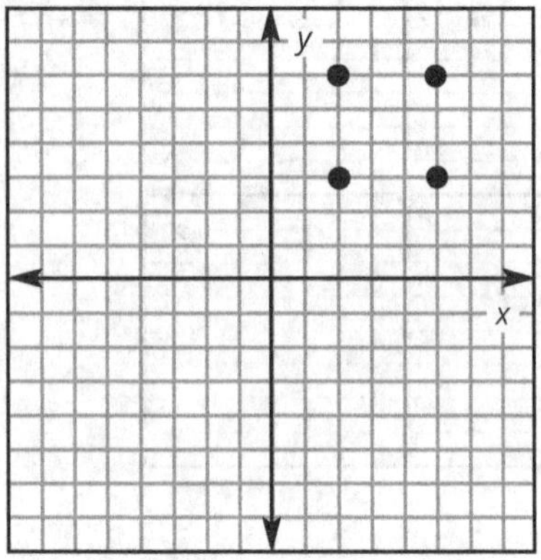

1.11 (6, 2)

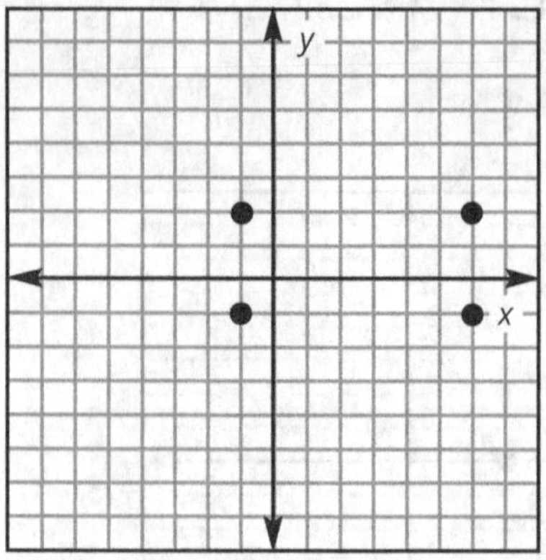

1.12 (5, 4)

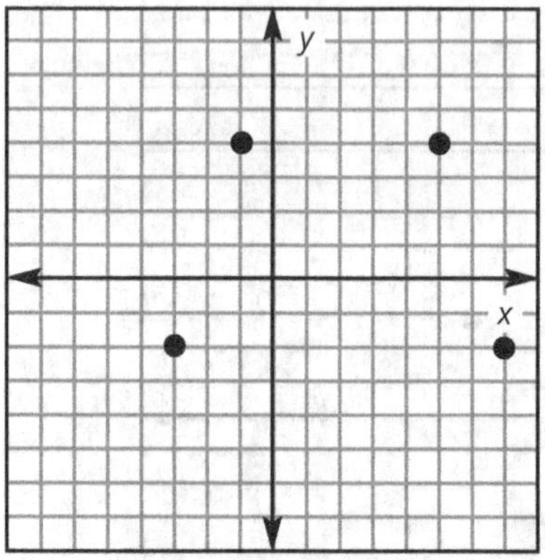

1.13 Either order:

a. (11, -2), (11, 6)
b. (-5, -2), (-5, 6)

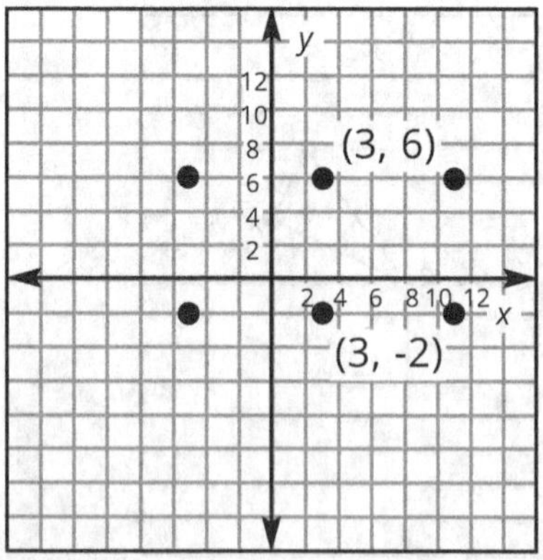

1.14 *A* (-4, -1)
B (2, -1)
C (6, 1)
D (6, 5)
E (3, 8)
F (-1, 6)
G (-4, 3)
H (2, 3)

1.15 *A* (0, 2)
B (3, 5)
C (6, 2)
D (6, -4)
E (0, -4)
F (3, -2)
G (4, 0)
H (4, 2)
I (2, 2)
J (2, 0)

1.16 Teacher check

1.17 line, plane

1.18 line, plane

1.19 line, plane

1.20 line, plane

1.21 line, plane

1.22 none

1.23 point, line, plane

1.24 none

1.25 line, plane

1.26 point, line, plane

1.27 line, plane

1.28 line, plane

1.29 none

1.30

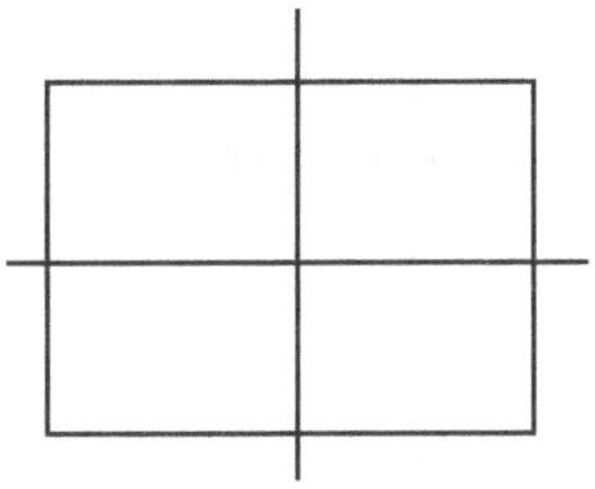

1.31

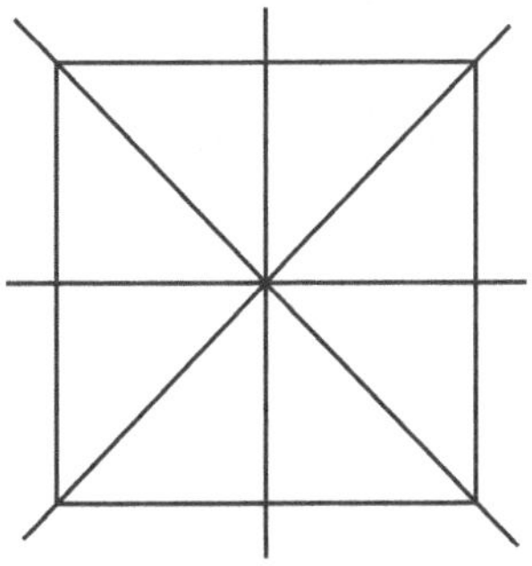

1.32

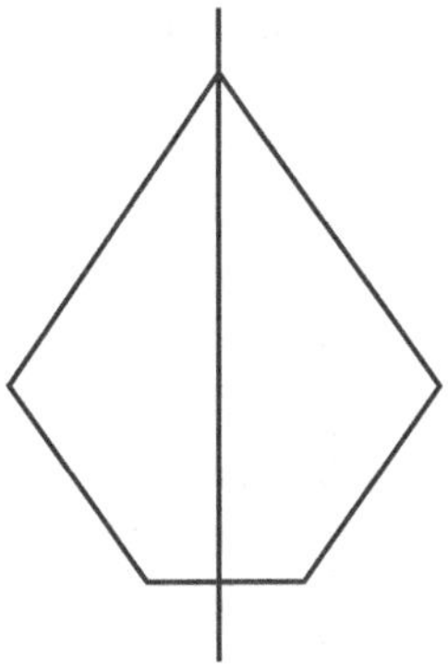

1.33 none

1.34

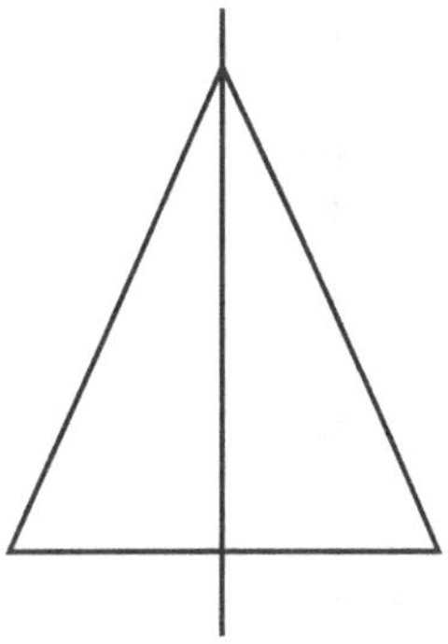

1.35

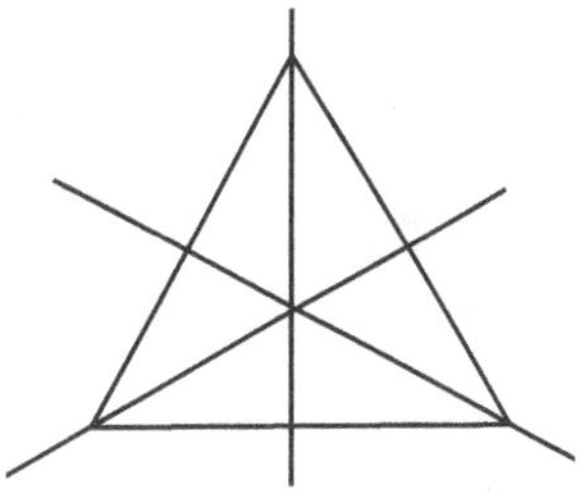

equilateral

1.36 a. (2, 1)

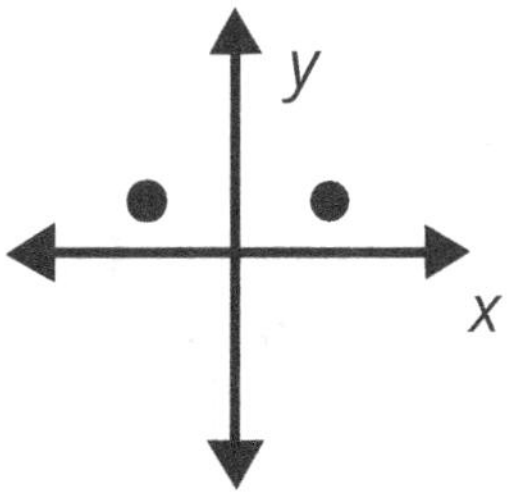

b. (3, -3)

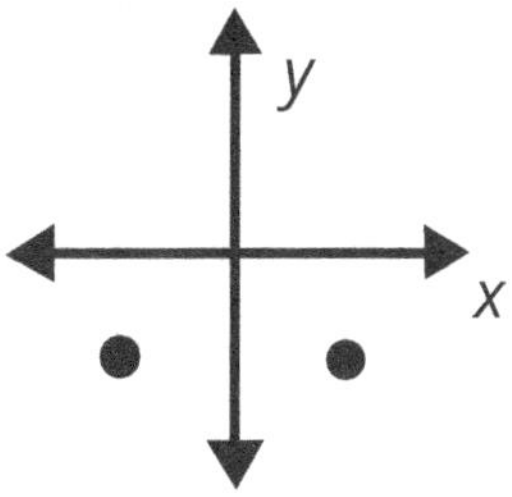

c. (-4, 2)

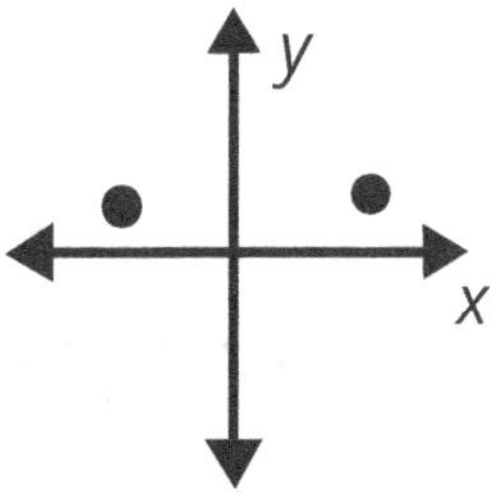

d. (-3, -1)

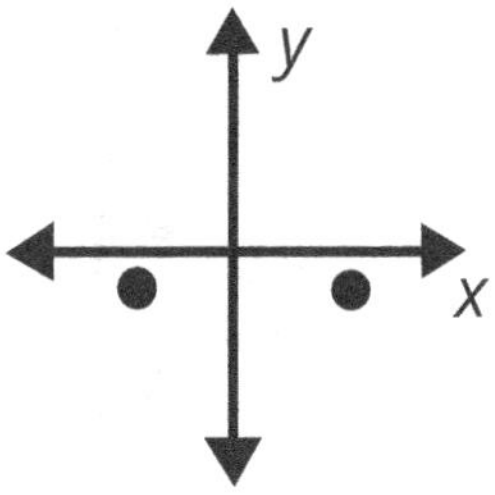

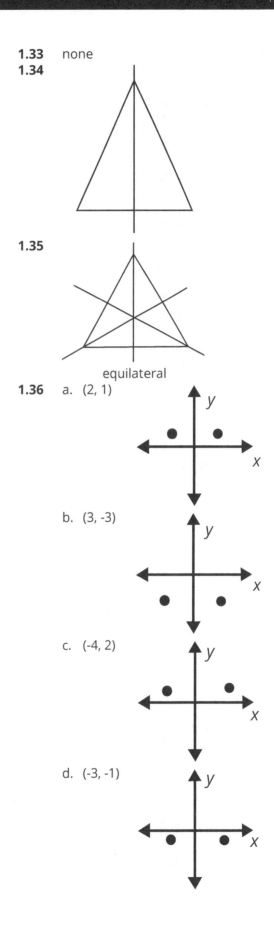

1.37 a. (4, -3)

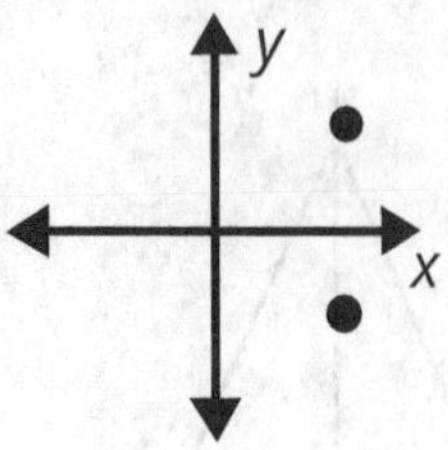

b. (4, -1)

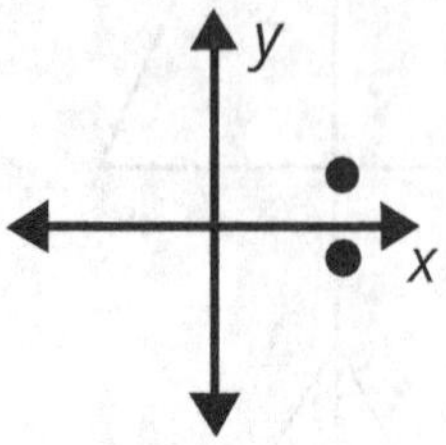

c. (-3, -5)

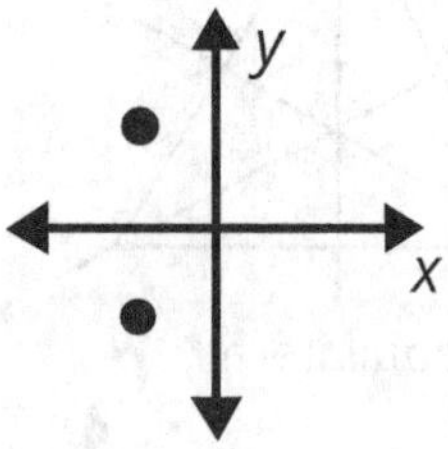

d. (-3, 2)

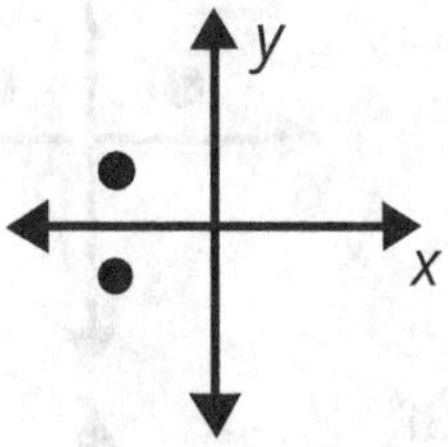

1.38 a. (0, 3)

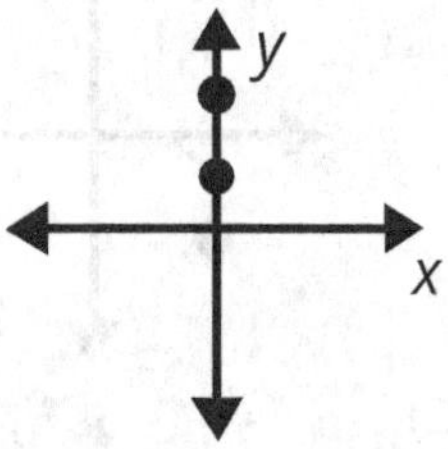

b. (3, -1)

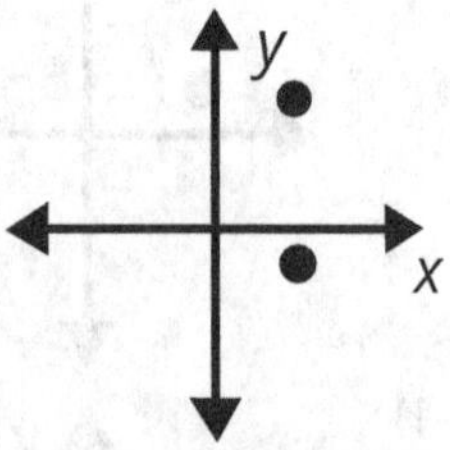

c. (-2, 5)

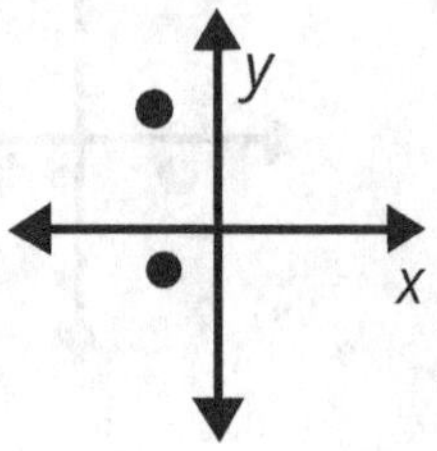

d. (-4, 1)

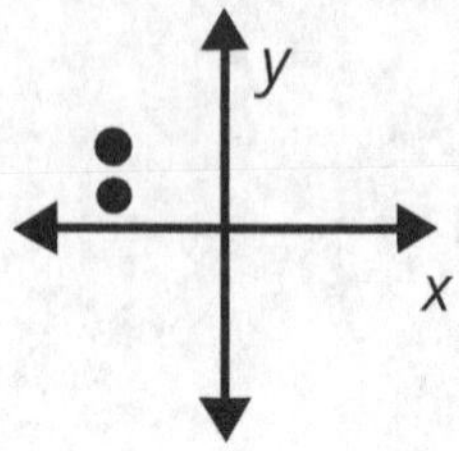

1.39 a. (-5, 0)

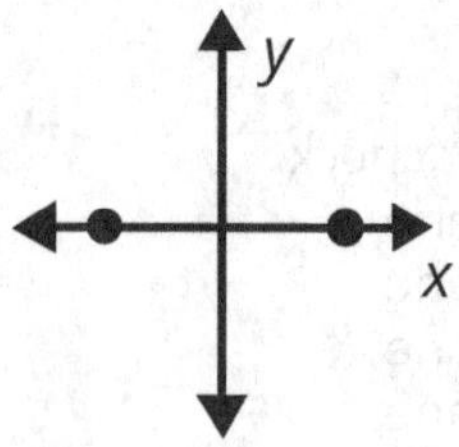

b. (0, -2)

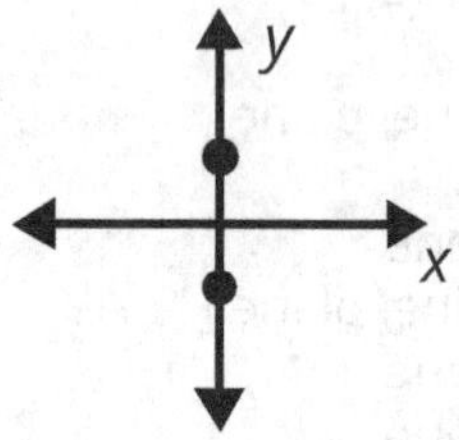

c. (-3, -3)

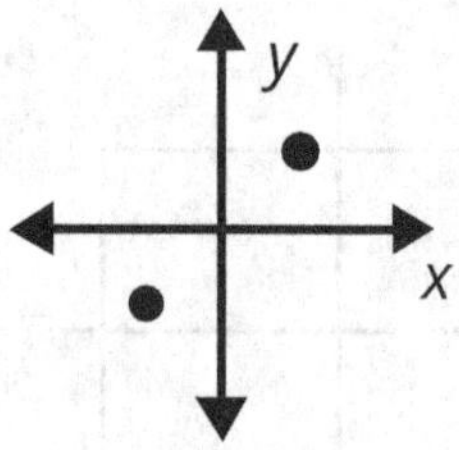

d. (-2, 2)

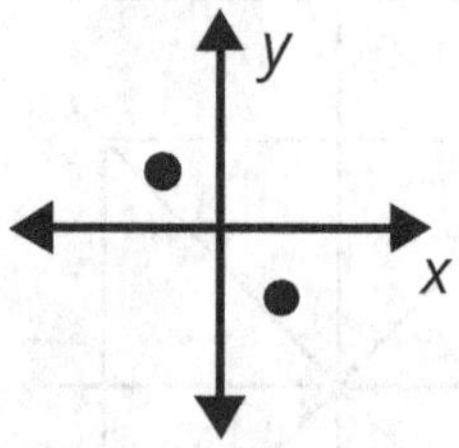

1.40 a. (0, 4)

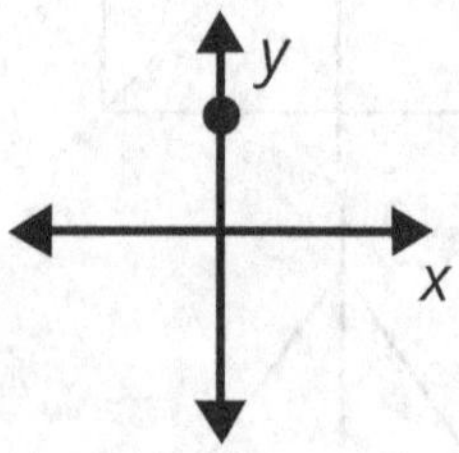

b. (0, 6)

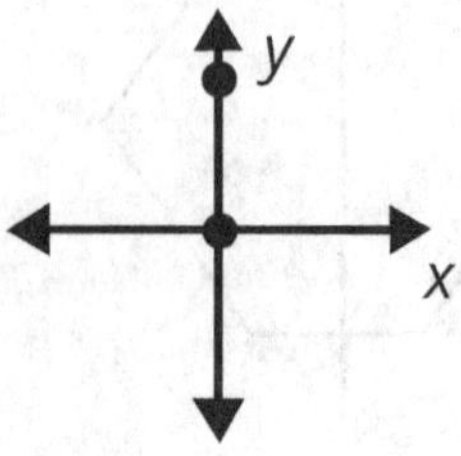

c. (1, 7)

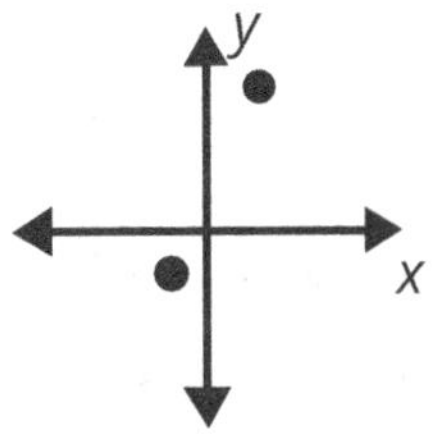

d. (-3, 3)

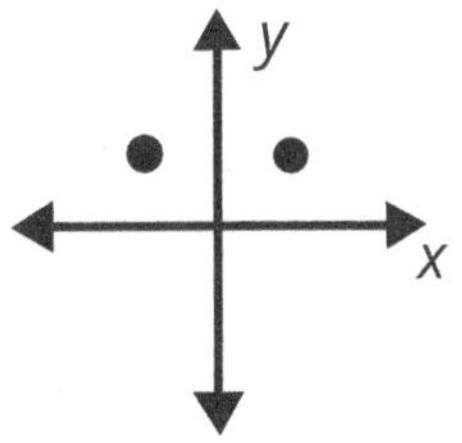

1.41 a. (3, 5)

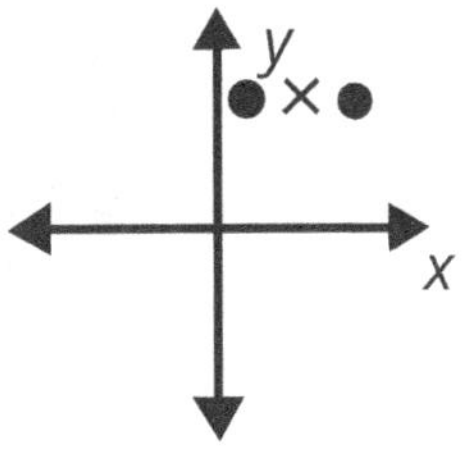

b. (-1, 5)

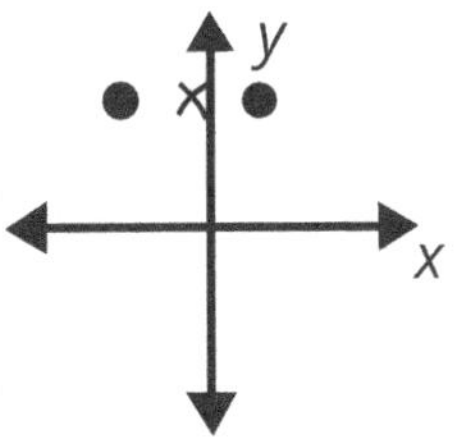

c. (0, 0)

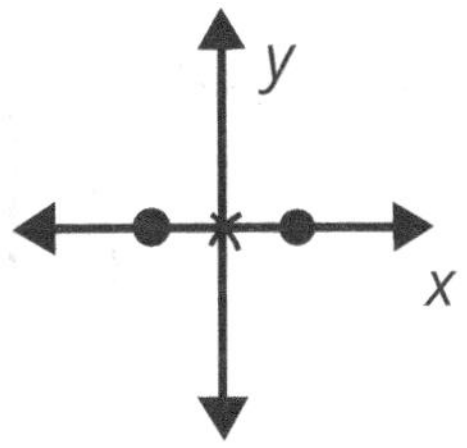

1.42

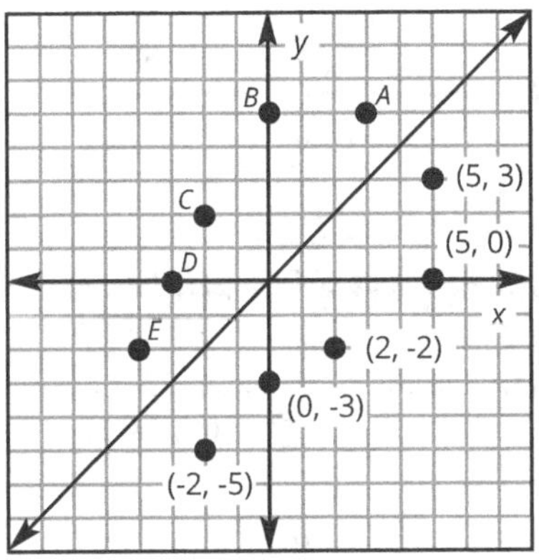

1.43

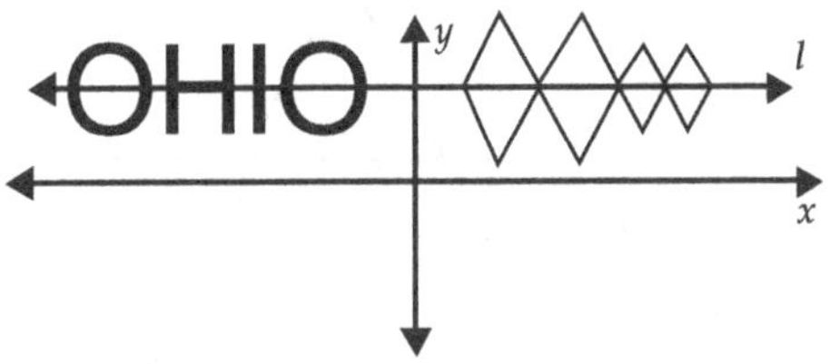

1.44

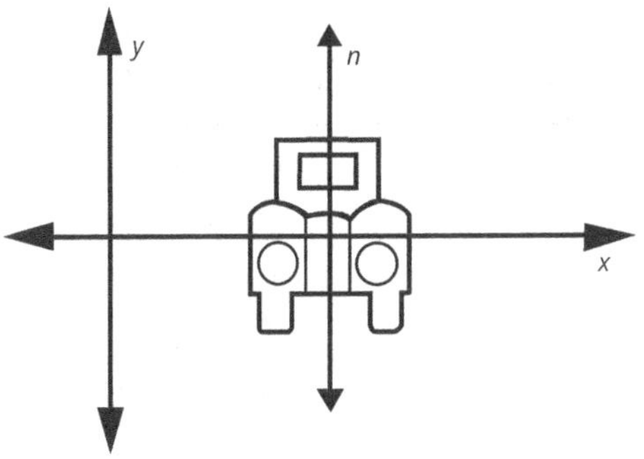

1.45

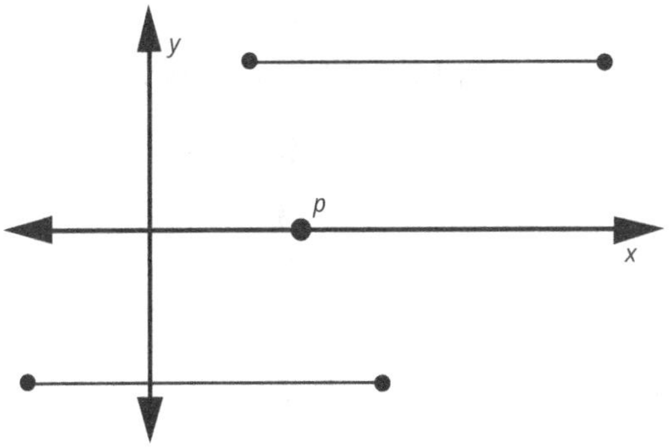

1.46

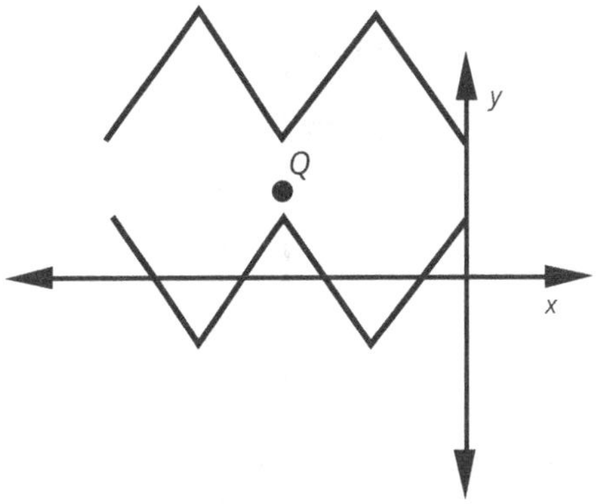

1.47

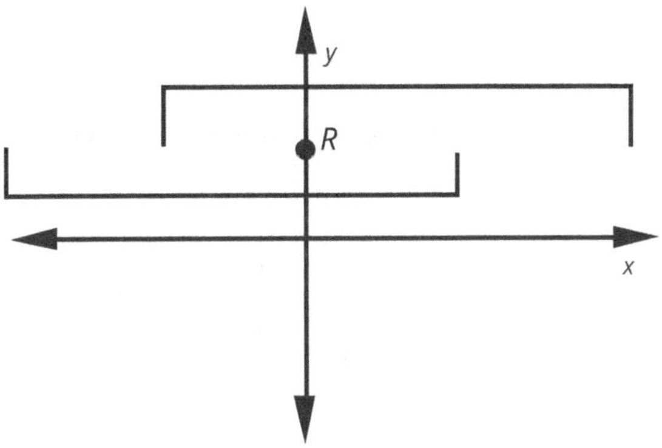

1.48

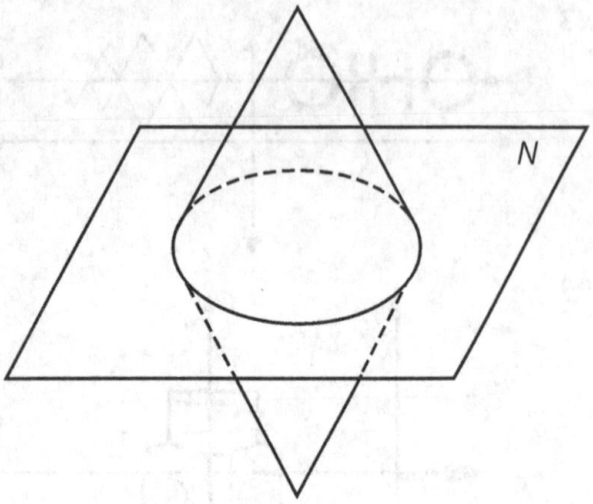

1.49

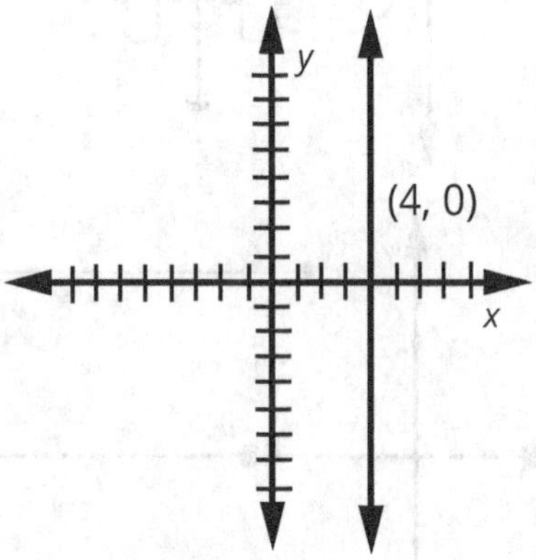

1.50

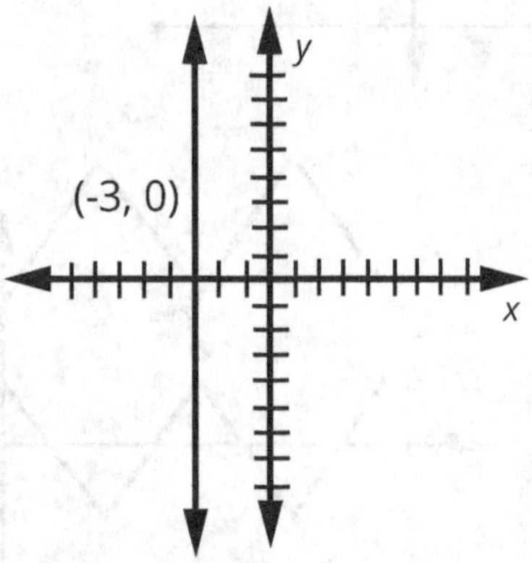

1.51

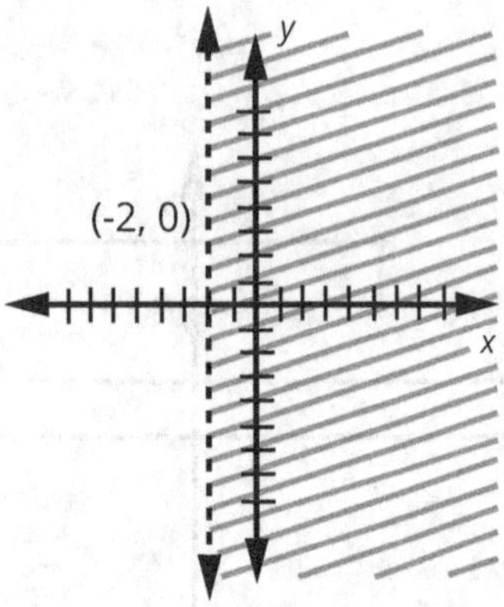

1.52

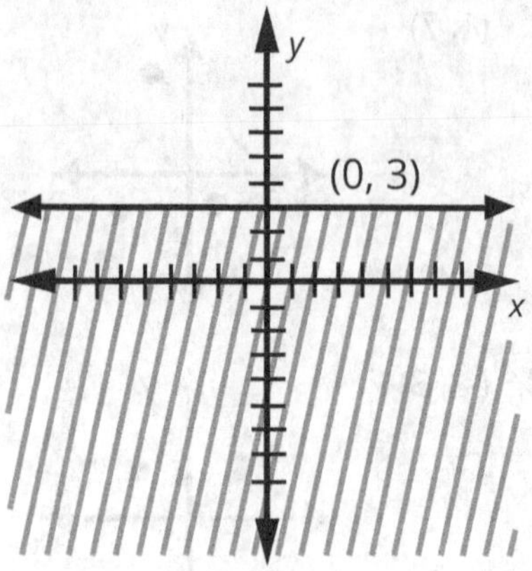

1.53

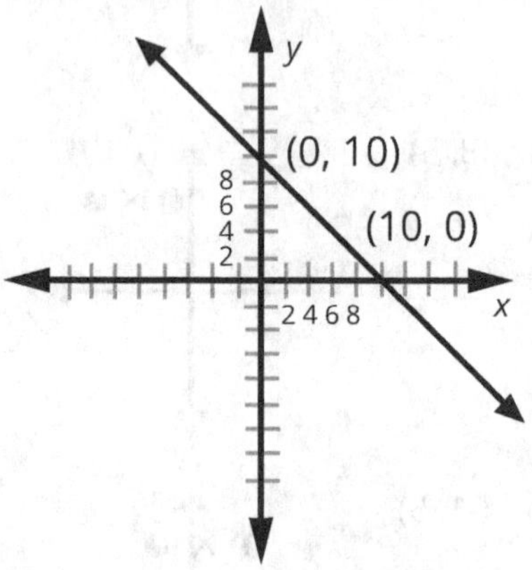

1.54

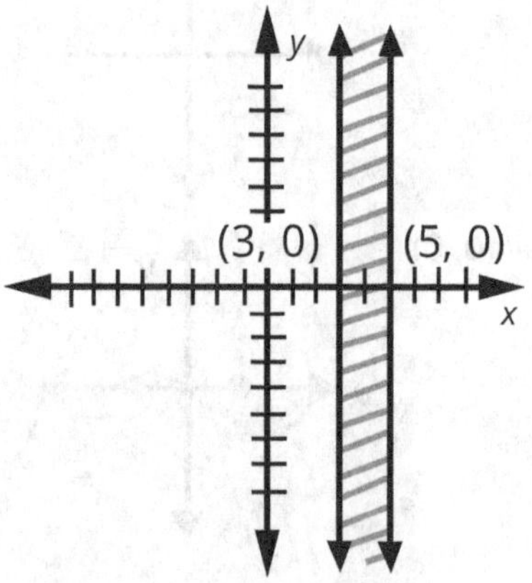

1.55

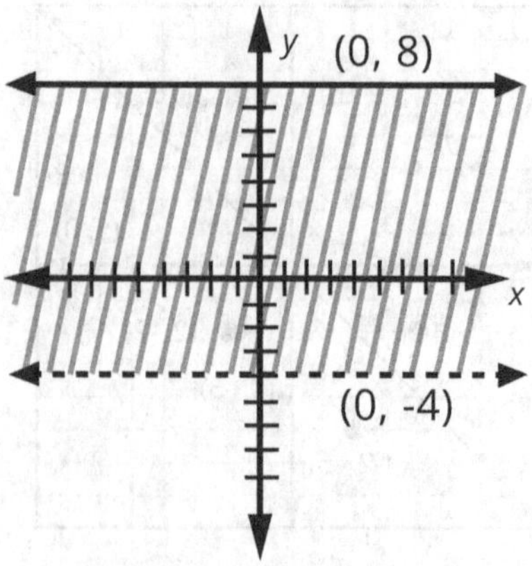

1.56

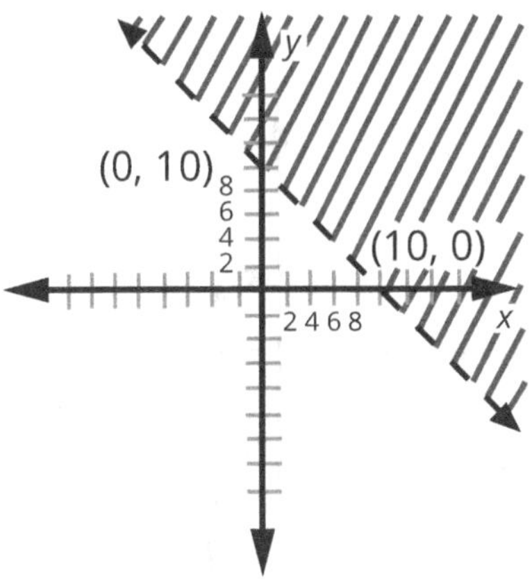

1.57

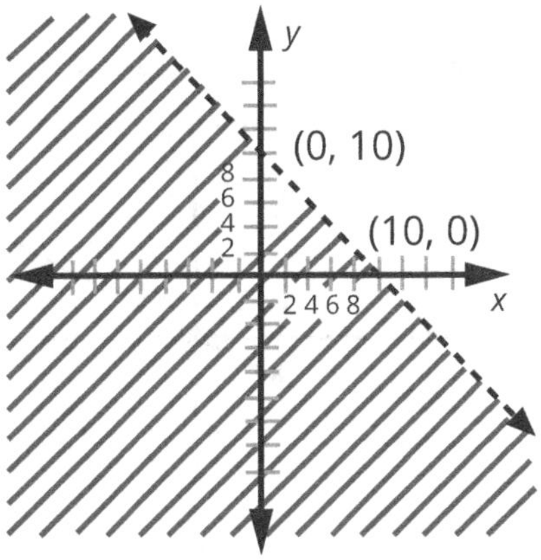

1.58

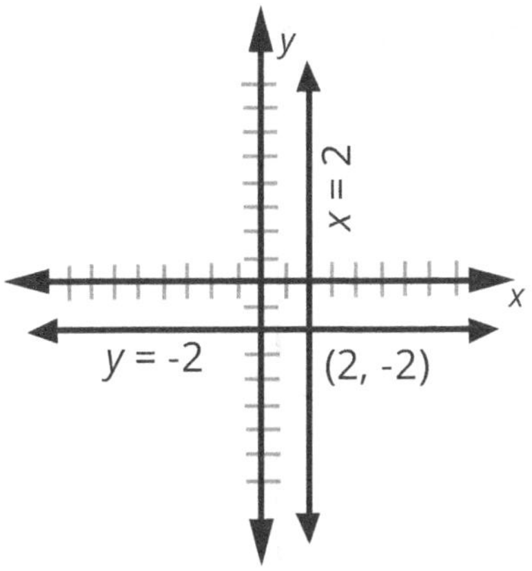

1.59

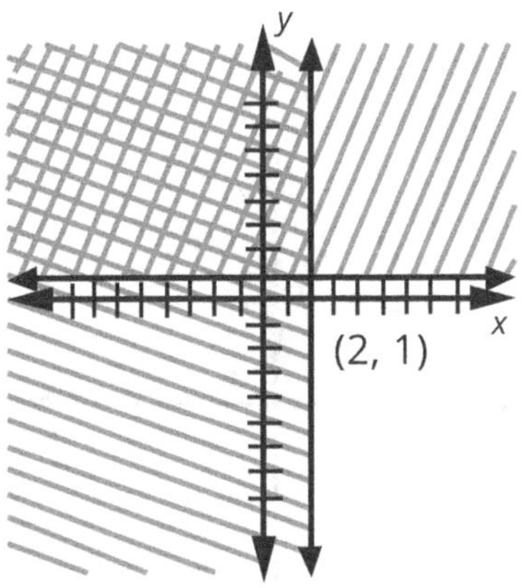

1.60

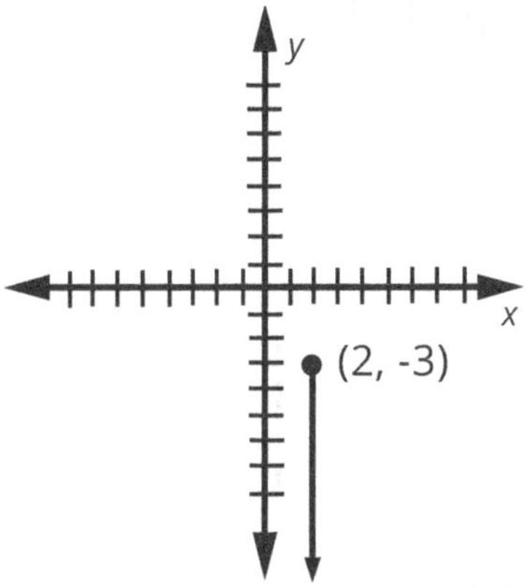

1.61

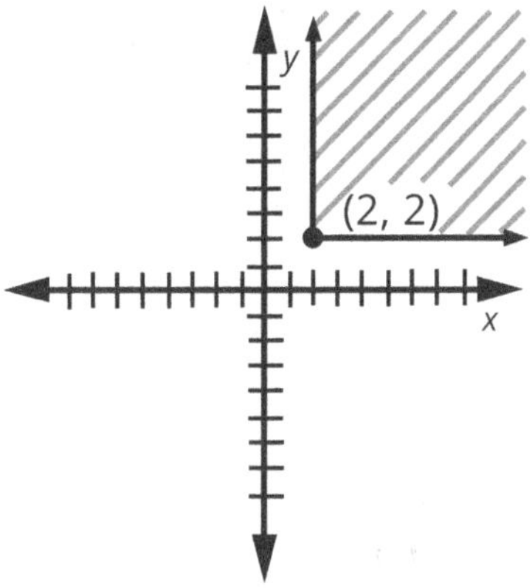

1.62

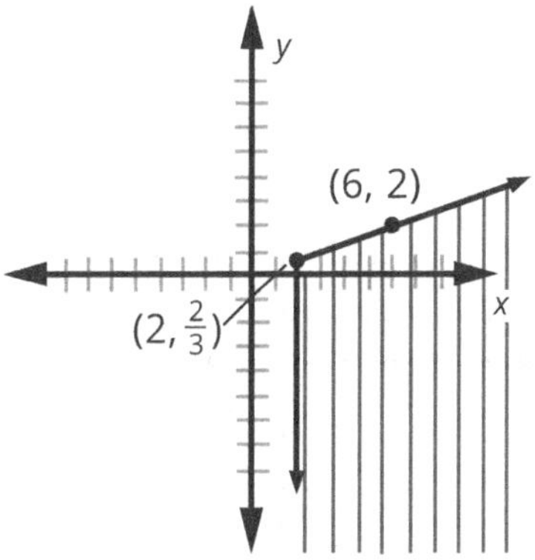

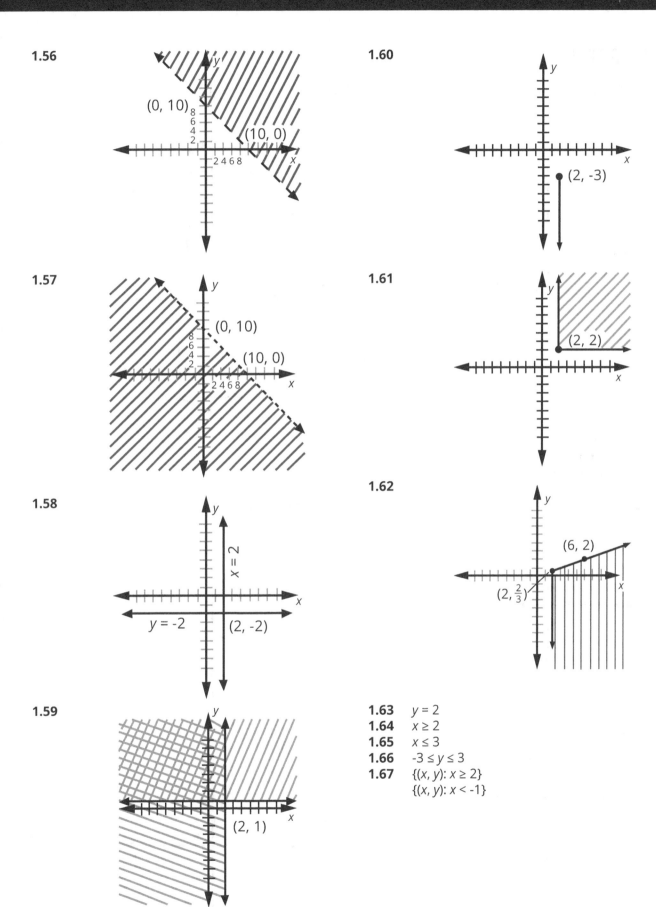

1.63 $y = 2$
1.64 $x \geq 2$
1.65 $x \leq 3$
1.66 $-3 \leq y \leq 3$
1.67 $\{(x, y): x \geq 2\}$
$\{(x, y): x < -1\}$

SELF TEST 1

1.01 *A* (-5, -5)
B (2, -3)
C (2, 4)
D (-2, 1)
E (-1, 4)

1.02

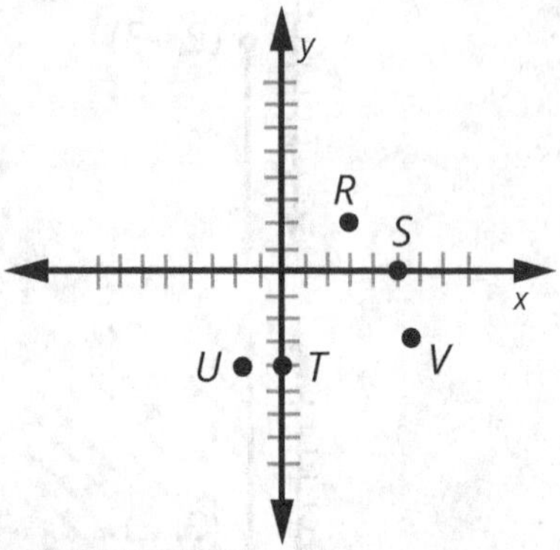

1.03 a. I
b. IV
c. III
d. II
e. I

1.04 line, plane
1.05 line, plane
1.06 point, line, plane
1.07 point, line, plane
1.08 point

1.09

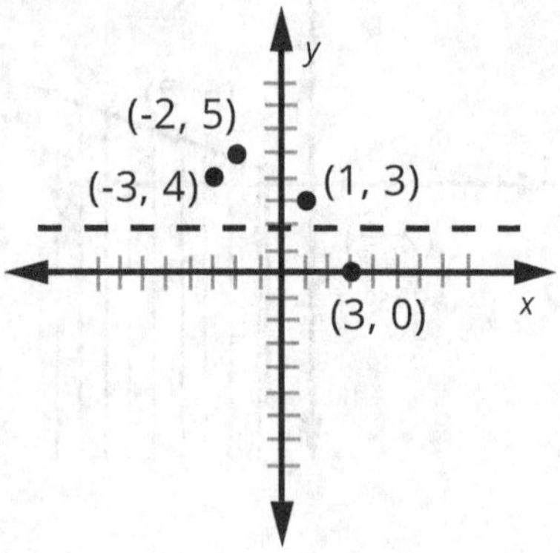

1.010

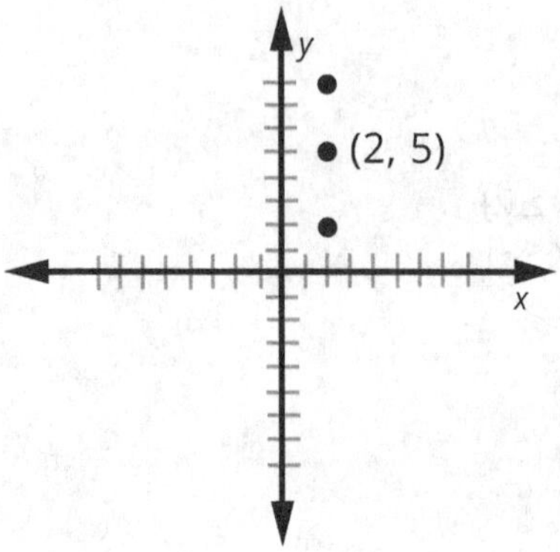

1.011

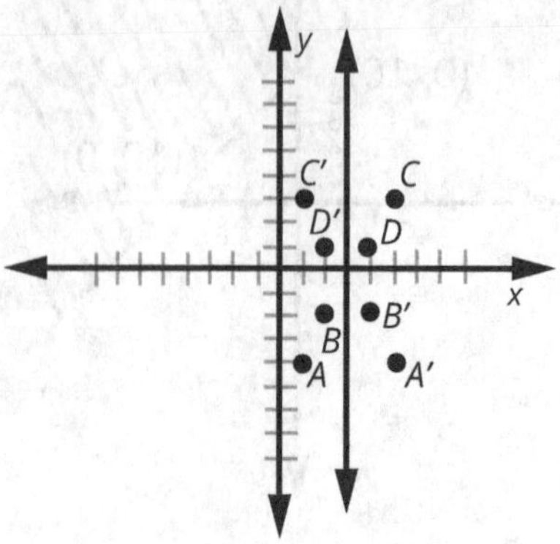

1.012 $x = 2y$
Some points are (-6, -3), (-4, -2), (0, 0), and (2, 1).

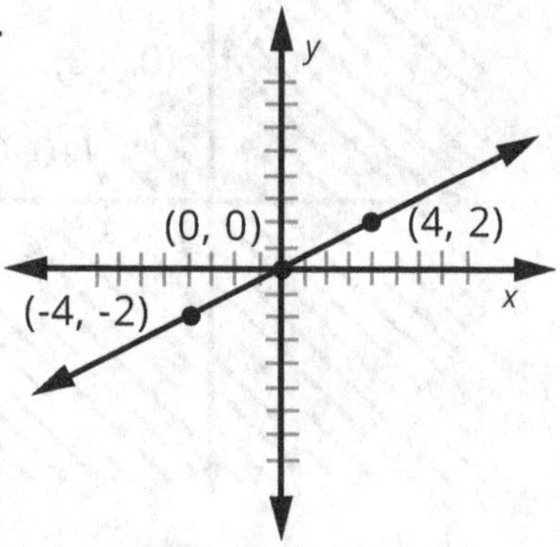

1.013 Two possibilities:

(4, -1)

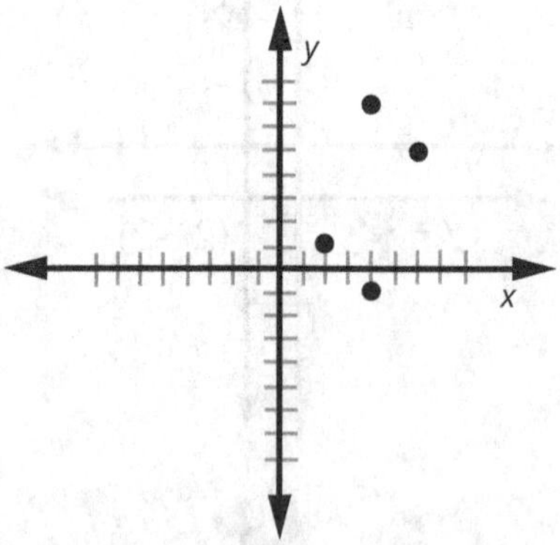

(0, 3)

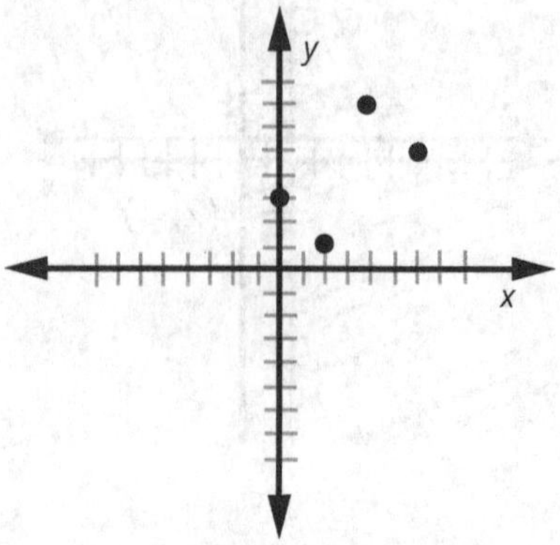

1.014 x-intercept: $x - 0 = 8$

$x = 8$

$(8, 0)$

y-intercept: $0 - y = 8$

$-y = 8$

$y = -8$

$(0, -8)$

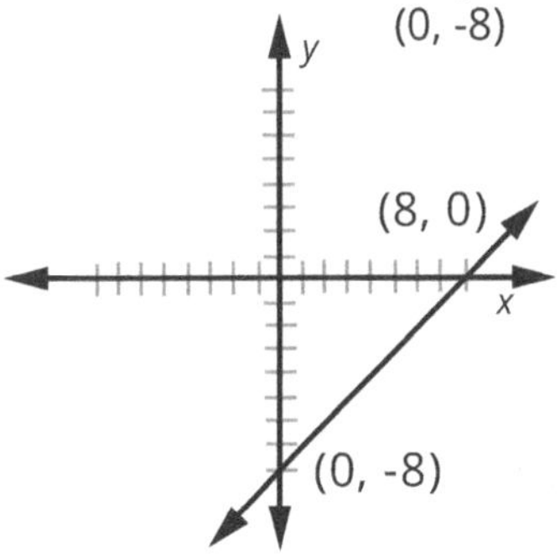

1.015

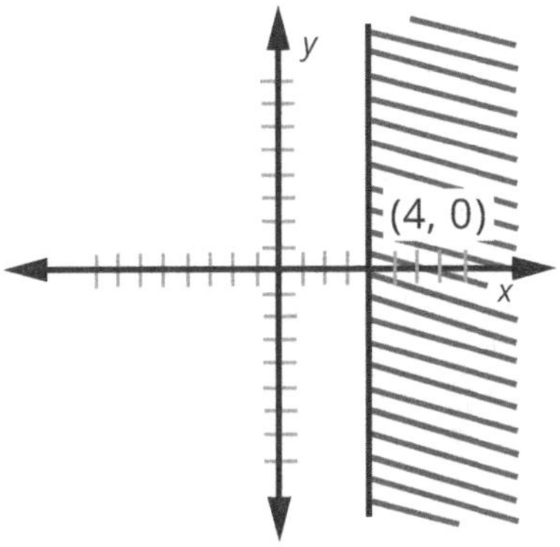

1.016

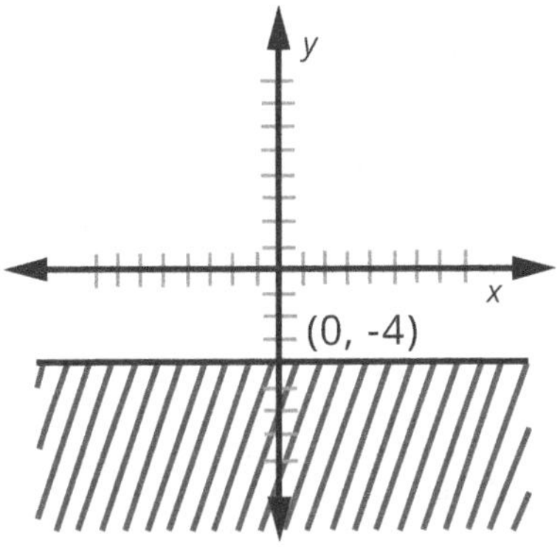

1.017

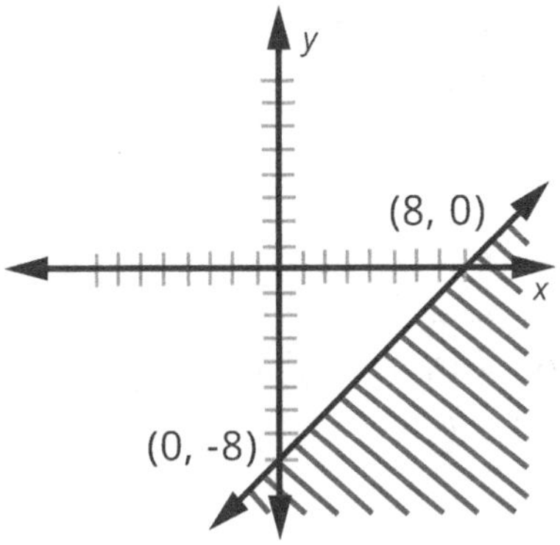

1.018 Solution graph:

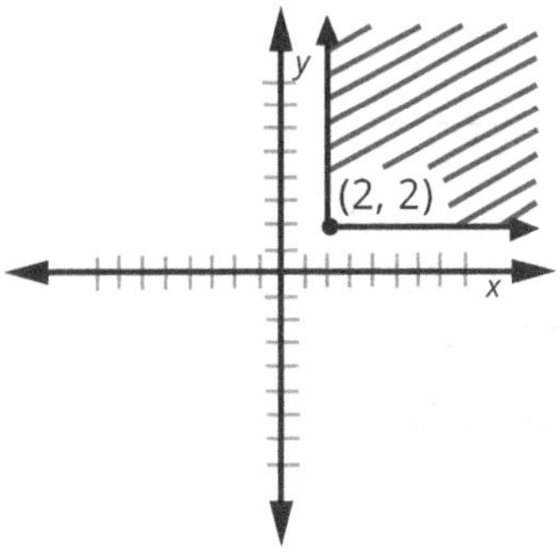

1.019

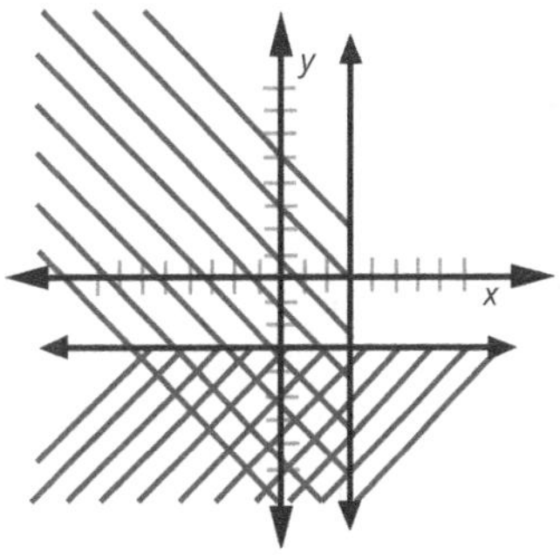

Solution graph:

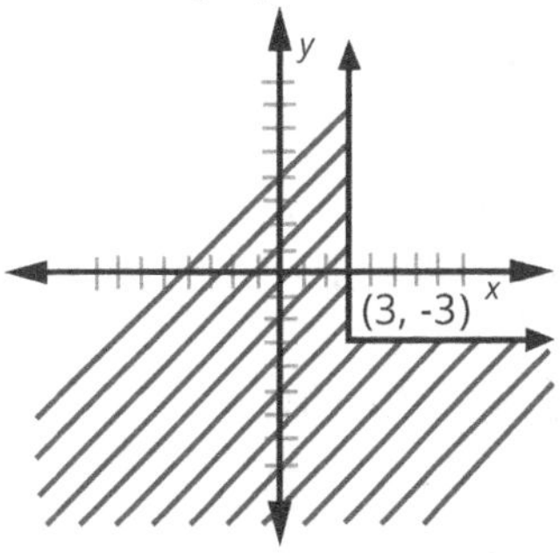

1.020

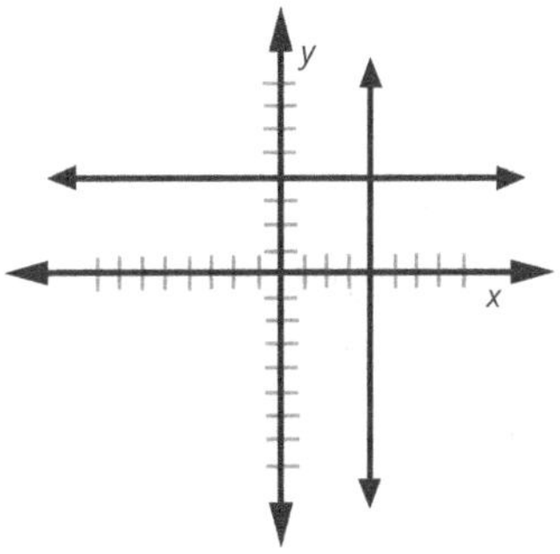

Solution graph:

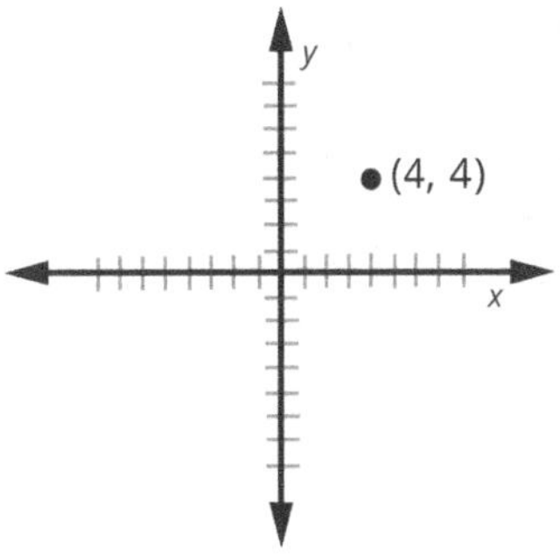

SECTION 2

2.1 $d = \sqrt{(2-6)^2 + (5-8)^2}$
$= \sqrt{(-4)^2 + (-3)^2}$
$= \sqrt{16 + 9} = \sqrt{25} = 5$

2.2 $d = \sqrt{(3-6)^2 + (4-8)^2}$
$= \sqrt{(-3)^2 + (-4)^2}$
$= \sqrt{9 + 16} = \sqrt{25} = 5$

2.3 $d = \sqrt{(-3-9)^2 + [2-(-3)]^2}$
$= \sqrt{(-12)^2 + 5^2}$
$= \sqrt{144 + 25} = \sqrt{169} = 13$

2.4 $d = \sqrt{(0-5)^2 + (6-12)^2}$
$= \sqrt{(-5)^2 + (-6)^2}$
$= \sqrt{25 + 36} = \sqrt{61}$

2.5 $d = \sqrt{(-3-0)^2 + (-4-0)^2}$
$= \sqrt{(-3)^2 + (-4)^2}$
$= \sqrt{9 + 16} = \sqrt{25} = 5$

2.6 $d = \sqrt{(0-9)^2 + (-6-6)^2}$
$= \sqrt{(-9)^2 + (-12)^2}$
$= \sqrt{81 + 144} = \sqrt{225} = 15$

2.7 $d = \sqrt{(4-7)^2 + (1-5)^2}$
$= \sqrt{(-3)^2 + (-4)^2}$
$= \sqrt{9 + 16} = \sqrt{25} = 5$

2.8 $d = \sqrt{(-3-3)^2 + (-6-2)^2}$
$= \sqrt{(-6)^2 + (-8)^2}$
$= \sqrt{36 + 64} = \sqrt{100} = 10$

2.9 $d = \sqrt{[2-(-10)]^2 + (3-12)^2}$
$= \sqrt{12^2 + (-9)^2}$
$= \sqrt{144 + 81} = \sqrt{225} = 15$

2.10 $d = \sqrt{(2-5)^2 + (2-5)^2}$
$= \sqrt{(-3)^2 + (-3)^2}$
$= \sqrt{9 + 9} = \sqrt{18} = 3\sqrt{2}$

2.11 $d = \sqrt{[0-(-5)]^2 + (5-0)^2}$
$= \sqrt{5^2 + 5^2} = \sqrt{25 + 25}$
$= \sqrt{50} = 5\sqrt{2}$

2.12 $d = \sqrt{(3-4)^2 + (4-7)^2}$
$= \sqrt{(-1)^2 + (-3)^2}$
$= \sqrt{1 + 9} = \sqrt{10}$

2.13 $d = \sqrt{(-1-1)^2 + (-1-3)^2}$
$= \sqrt{(-2)^2 + (-4)^2}$
$= \sqrt{4 + 16} = \sqrt{20} = 2\sqrt{5}$

2.14 $d = \sqrt{(-3-0)^2 + (0-\sqrt{7})^2}$
$= \sqrt{(-3)^2 + (7)^2}$
$= \sqrt{9 + 7} = \sqrt{16} = 4$

2.15 $d = \sqrt{(a-2a)^2 + (b-2b)^2}$
$= \sqrt{(-a)^2 + (-b)^2}$
$= \sqrt{a^2 + b^2}$

2.16 $AB = \sqrt{(3-6)^2 + (5-9)^2}$
$= \sqrt{(-3)^2 + (-4)^2}$
$= \sqrt{9 + 16} = \sqrt{25} = 5$
$BC = \sqrt{(6-2)^2 + (9-6)^2}$
$= \sqrt{4^2 + 3^2}$
$= \sqrt{16 + 9} = \sqrt{25} = 5$
$AC = \sqrt{(3-2)^2 + (5-6)^2}$
$= \sqrt{1^2 + (-1)^2}$
$= \sqrt{1 + 1} = \sqrt{2}$
isosceles

2.17 $RS = \sqrt{(1-3)^2 + (3-1)^2}$
$= \sqrt{(-2)^2 + 2^2}$
$= \sqrt{4 + 4} = \sqrt{8} = 2\sqrt{2}$
$ST = \sqrt{(3-5)^2 + (1-2)^2}$
$= \sqrt{(-2)^2 + (-1)^2}$
$= \sqrt{4 + 1} = \sqrt{5}$
$RT = \sqrt{(1-5)^2 + (3-2)^2}$
$= \sqrt{(-4)^2 + 1^2}$
$= \sqrt{16 + 1} = \sqrt{17}$
scalene

2.18 $WX = \sqrt{[5-(-2)]^2 + [-5-(-2)]^2}$
$= \sqrt{7^2 + (-3)^2}$
$= \sqrt{49 + 9} = \sqrt{58}$
$XY = \sqrt{(-2-8)^2 + (-2-2)^2}$
$= \sqrt{(-10)^2 + (-4)^2}$
$= \sqrt{100 + 16} = \sqrt{116} = 2\sqrt{29}$
$WY = \sqrt{(5-8)^2 + (-5-2)^2}$
$= \sqrt{(-3)^2 + (-7)^2}$
$= \sqrt{9 + 49} = \sqrt{58}$
isosceles

2.19 $PQ = \sqrt{(0-6)^2 + (0-0)^2}$
$= \sqrt{(-6)^2 + 0^2}$
$= \sqrt{36} = 6$
$QR = \sqrt{(6-3)^2 + (0-3\sqrt{3})^2}$
$= \sqrt{3^2 + (-3\sqrt{3})^2}$
$= \sqrt{9 + 27} = \sqrt{36} = 6$
$PR = \sqrt{(0-3)^2 + (0-3\sqrt{3})^2}$
$= \sqrt{(-3)^2 + (-3\sqrt{3})^2}$
$= \sqrt{9 + 27} = \sqrt{36} = 6$
equilateral

2.20 $RL = \sqrt{(7-3)^2 + (0-4)^2}$
$= \sqrt{4^2 + (-4)^2}$
$= \sqrt{16 + 16} = \sqrt{32} = 4\sqrt{2}$
$LM = \sqrt{(3-2)^2 + [4-(-1)]^2}$
$= \sqrt{1^2 + 5^2}$
$= \sqrt{1 + 25} = \sqrt{26}$
$RM = \sqrt{(7-2)^2 + [0-(-1)]^2}$
$= \sqrt{5^2 + 1^2}$
$= \sqrt{25 + 1} = \sqrt{26}$
isosceles

2.21

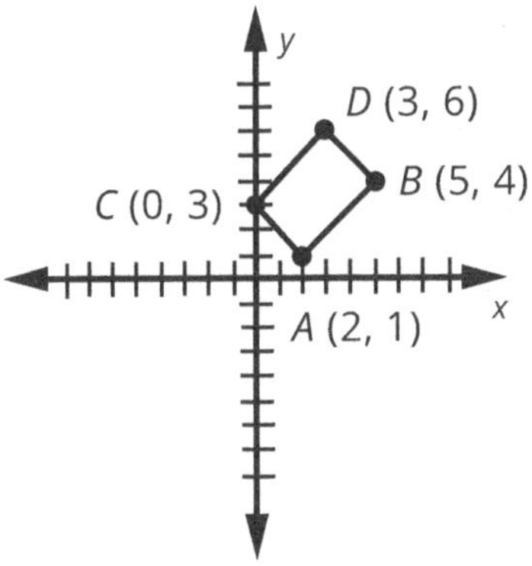

length = AB
$= \sqrt{(2-5)^2 + (1-4)^2}$
$= \sqrt{(-3)^2 + (-3)^2}$
$= \sqrt{9 + 9} = \sqrt{18} = 3\sqrt{2}$
width = AC
$= \sqrt{(2-0)^2 + (1-3)^2}$
$= \sqrt{(2)^2 + (-2)^2}$
$= \sqrt{4 + 4} = \sqrt{8} = 2\sqrt{2}$

2.22

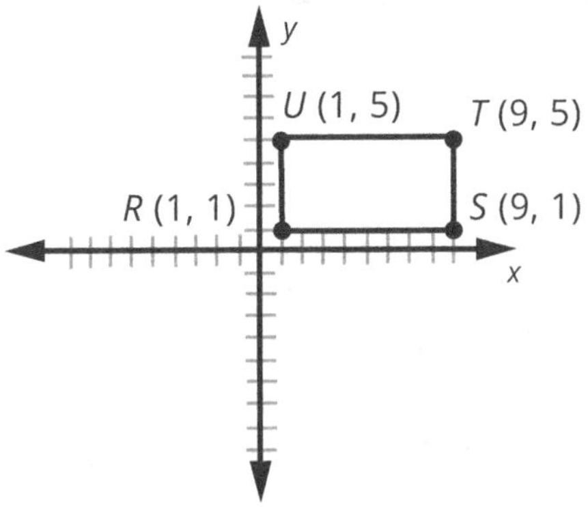

length = $RS = |9 - 1| = |8| = 8$
width = $UR = |5 - 1| = |4| = 4$

2.23

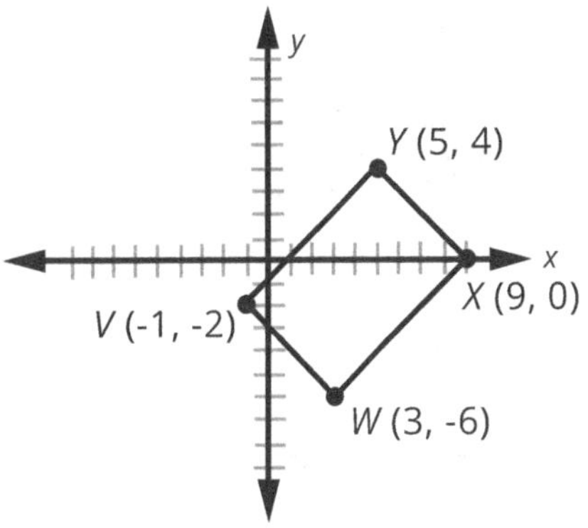

length = VY
$= \sqrt{(-1-5)^2 + (-2-4)^2}$
$= \sqrt{(-6)^2 + (-6)^2}$
$= \sqrt{36 + 36} = \sqrt{72} = 6\sqrt{2}$
width = VW
$= \sqrt{(-1-3)^2 + [-2-(-6)]^2}$
$= \sqrt{(-4)^2 + 4^2}$
$= \sqrt{16 + 16} = \sqrt{32} = 4\sqrt{2}$

2.24

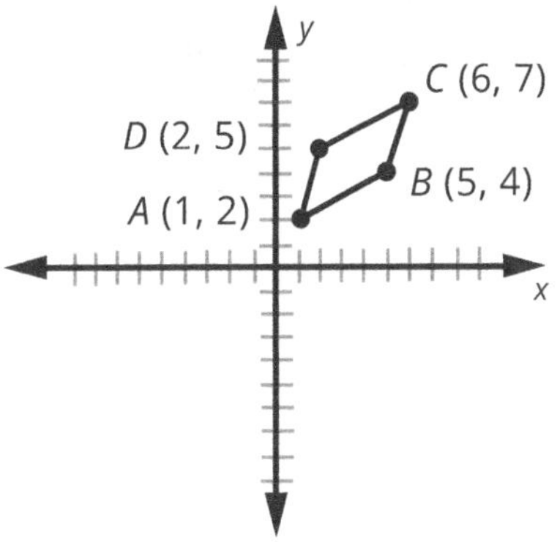

length = AB
$= \sqrt{(1-5)^2 + (2-4)^2}$
$= \sqrt{(-4)^2 + (-2)^2}$
$= \sqrt{16 + 4} = \sqrt{20} = 2\sqrt{5}$
width = AD
$= \sqrt{(1-2)^2 + (2-5)^2}$
$= \sqrt{(-1)^2 + (-3)^2}$
$= \sqrt{1 + 9} = \sqrt{10}$
$p = 2l + 2w$
$= 2(2\sqrt{5}) + 2\sqrt{10}$
$= 4\sqrt{5} + 2\sqrt{10}$
$d_1 = AC = \sqrt{(1-6)^2 + (2-7)^2}$
$= \sqrt{(-5)^2 + (-5)^2}$
$= \sqrt{25 + 25} = \sqrt{50} = 5\sqrt{2}$
$d_2 = BD = \sqrt{(5-2)^2 + (4-5)^2}$
$= \sqrt{3^2 + (-1)^2}$
$= \sqrt{9 + 1} = \sqrt{10}$

2.25

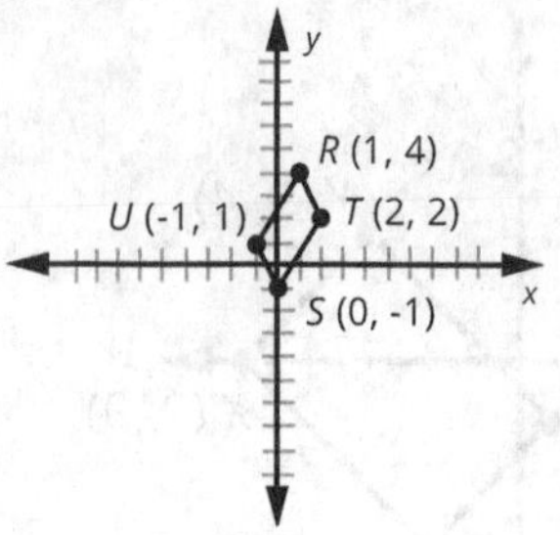

$$\begin{aligned}
\text{length} &= ST \\
&= \sqrt{(0-2)^2 + (-1-2)^2} \\
&= \sqrt{(-2)^2 + (-3)^2} \\
&= \sqrt{4+9} = \sqrt{13} \\
\text{width} &= RT \\
&= \sqrt{(1-2)^2 + (4-2)^2} \\
&= \sqrt{(-1)^2 + 2^2} \\
&= \sqrt{1+4} = \sqrt{5} \\
p &= 2l + 2w \\
&= 2\sqrt{13} + 2\sqrt{5} \\
d_1 = RS &= \sqrt{(1-0)^2 + [4-(-1)]^2} \\
&= \sqrt{1^2 + 5^2} \\
&= \sqrt{1+25} = \sqrt{26} \\
d_2 = TU &= \sqrt{[2-(-1)]^2 + (2-1)^2} \\
&= \sqrt{3^2 + 1^2} \\
&= \sqrt{9+1} = \sqrt{10}
\end{aligned}$$

2.26

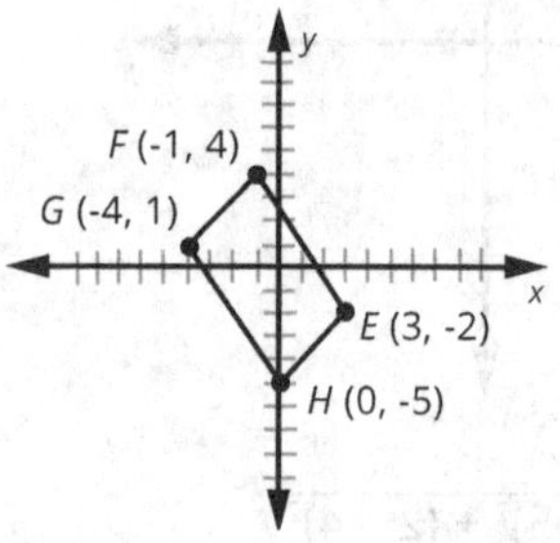

$$\begin{aligned}
\text{length} &= GH \\
&= \sqrt{(-4-0)^2 + [1-(-5)]^2} \\
&= \sqrt{(-4)^2 + 6^2} \\
&= \sqrt{16+36} = \sqrt{52} = 2\sqrt{13} \\
\text{width} &= EH \\
&= \sqrt{(3-0)^2 + [-2-(-5)]^2} \\
&= \sqrt{3^2 + 3^2} \\
&= \sqrt{9+9} = \sqrt{18} = 3\sqrt{2} \\
p &= 2l + 2w \\
&= 2(2\sqrt{13}) + 2(3\sqrt{2}) \\
&= 4\sqrt{13} + 6\sqrt{2} \\
d_1 = FH &= \sqrt{(-1-0)^2 + [4-(-5)]^2} \\
&= \sqrt{(-1)^2 + 9^2} \\
&= \sqrt{1+81} = \sqrt{82} \\
d_2 = EG &= \sqrt{[3-(-4)]^2 + (-2-1)^2} \\
&= \sqrt{7^2 + (-3)^2} \\
&= \sqrt{49+9} = \sqrt{58}
\end{aligned}$$

2.27

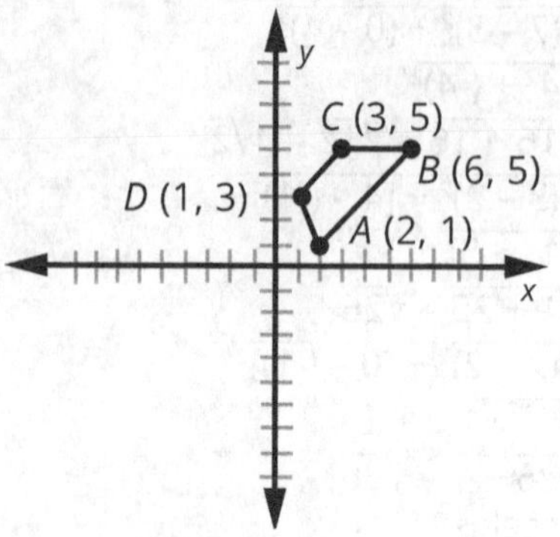

$$\begin{aligned}
AB &= \sqrt{(2-6)^2 + (1-5)^2} \\
&= \sqrt{(-4)^2 + (-4)^2} \\
&= \sqrt{16+16} = \sqrt{32} = 4\sqrt{2} \\
BC &= \sqrt{(6-3)^2 + (5-5)^2} \\
&= \sqrt{3^2 + 0^2} = \sqrt{9} = 3 \\
CD &= \sqrt{(3-1)^2 + (5-3)^2} \\
&= \sqrt{2^2 + 2^2} \\
&= \sqrt{4+4} = \sqrt{8} = 2\sqrt{2} \\
AD &= \sqrt{(2-1)^2 + (1-3)^2} \\
&= \sqrt{1^2 + (-2)^2} \\
&= \sqrt{1+4} = \sqrt{5} \\
P &= 4\sqrt{2} + 3 + 2\sqrt{2} + \sqrt{5} \\
&= 6\sqrt{2} + \sqrt{5} + 3
\end{aligned}$$

2.28

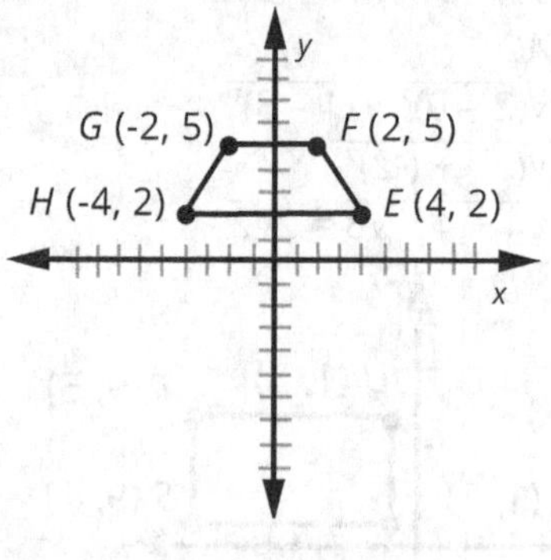

$$\begin{aligned}
EF &= \sqrt{(4-2)^2 + (2-5)^2} \\
&= \sqrt{2^2 + (-3)^2} \\
&= \sqrt{4+9} = \sqrt{13} \\
FG &= |2-(-2)| = |2+2| = |4| = 4 \\
GH &= \sqrt{[-2-(-4)]^2 + (5-2)^2} \\
&= \sqrt{2^2 + 3^2} \\
&= \sqrt{4+9} = \sqrt{13} \\
EH &= |4-(-4)| = |4+4| = |8| = 8 \\
P &= \sqrt{13} + 4 + \sqrt{13} + 8 \\
&= 12 + 2\sqrt{13}
\end{aligned}$$

2.29

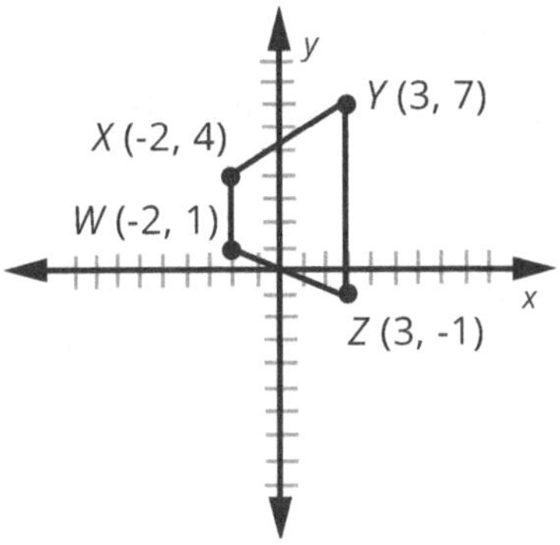

$WX = |1 - 4| = |-3| = 3$
$XY = \sqrt{(-2 - 3)^2 + (4 - 7)^2}$
$= \sqrt{(-5)^2 + (-3)^2}$
$= \sqrt{25 + 9} = \sqrt{34}$
$YZ = |7 - (-1)| = |7 + 1| = |8| = 8$
$WZ = \sqrt{(-2 - 3)^2 + [1 - (-1)]^2}$
$= \sqrt{(-5)^2 + 2^2}$
$= \sqrt{25 + 4} = \sqrt{29}$
$P = 3 + \sqrt{34} + 8 + \sqrt{29}$
$= 11 + \sqrt{34} + \sqrt{29}$

2.30 $h = 5, k = 2, r = 3$
$(x - h)^2 + (y - k)^2 = r^2$
$(x - 5)^2 + (y - 2)^2 = 3^2$
$(x - 5)^2 + (y - 2)^2 = 9$

2.31 $h = 3, k = -2, r = 5$
$(x - h)^2 + (y - k)^2 = r^2$
$(x - 3)^2 + [y - (-2)]^2 = 5^2$
$(x - 3)^2 + (y + 2)^2 = 25$

2.32 $r = 4$
$x^2 + y^2 = r^2$
$x^2 + y^2 = 4^2$
$x^2 + y^2 = 16$

2.33 $h = 0, k = 4, r = \sqrt{3}$
$(x - h)^2 + (y - k)^2 = r^2$
$(x - 0)^2 + (y - 4)^2 = (\sqrt{3})^2$
$x^2 + (y - 4)^2 = 3$

2.34 $h = -3, k = 0, r = \sqrt{5}$
$(x - h)^2 + (y - k)^2 = r^2$
$[x - (-3)]^2 + (y - 0)^2 = (\sqrt{5})^2$
$(x + 3)^2 + y^2 = 5$

2.35 a. $\underline{(3, 7)}$
b. $r = \sqrt{49} = 7$

2.36 a. $\underline{(5, -3)}$
b. $r = \sqrt{25} = 5$

2.37 a. $(x + 2)^2 + y^2 = 10$
$(x + 2)^2 + (y - 0)^2 = 10$
$\underline{(-2, 0)}$
b. $\sqrt{10}$

2.38 a. $x^2 + y^2 = 16$
$(x - 0)^2 + (y - 0)^2 = 16$
$\underline{(0, 0)}$
b. $r = \sqrt{16} = 4$

2.39 a. $\underline{(-3, 6)}$
b. $r = \sqrt{24} = 2\sqrt{6}$

2.40 a. $x^2 + (y - 3)^2 = 8$
$(x - 0)^2 + (y - 3)^2 = 8$
$\underline{(0, 3)}$
b. $r = \sqrt{8} = 2\sqrt{2}$

2.41 $(3 - 5)^2 + (2 + 3)^2 \ ? \ 25$
$(-2)^2 + 5^2 \ ? \ 25$
$4 + 25 \ ? \ 25$
$29 > 25$
exterior

2.42 $(2 - 5)^2 + (3 + 3)^2 \ ? \ 25$
$(-3)^2 + 6^2 \ ? \ 25$
$9 + 36 \ ? \ 25$
$45 > 25$
exterior

2.43 $(-2 - 5)^2 + (4 + 3)^2 \ ? \ 25$
$(-7)^2 + 7^2 \ ? \ 25$
$49 + 49 \ ? \ 25$
$98 > 25$
exterior

2.44 $(5 - 5)^2 + (-3 + 3)^2 \ ? \ 25$
$0^2 + 0^2 \ ? \ 25$
$0 < 25$
interior

2.45 $(5 - 5)^2 + (2 + 3)^2 \ ? \ 25$
$0^2 + 5^2 \ ? \ 25$
$25 = 25$
on the circle

2.46 $(0 - 5)^2 + (-3 + 3)^2 \ ? \ 25$
$(-5)^2 + 0^2 \ ? \ 25$
$25 = 25$
on the circle

2.47 Center = $\underline{(-2, 2)}$
$r = \sqrt{25} = 5$

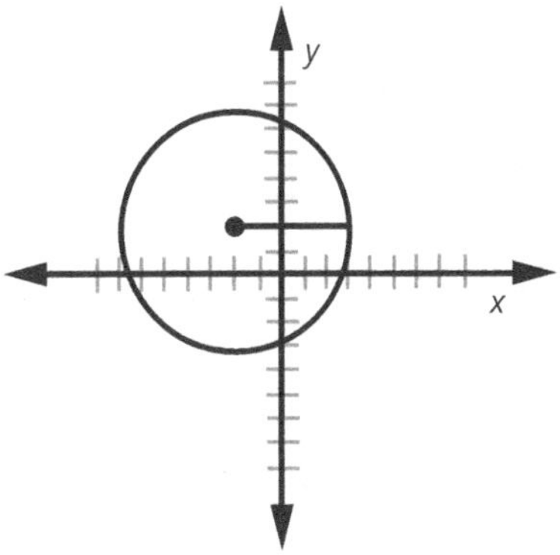

2.48 Center = (3, 0)
$r = \sqrt{4} = 2$

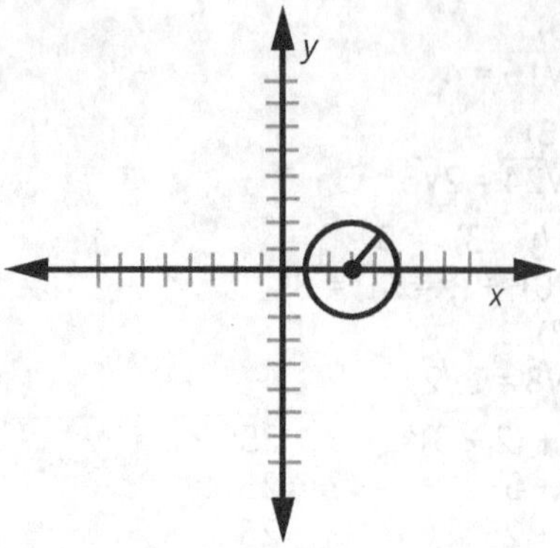

2.49 Center = (0, 0)
$r = \sqrt{16} = 4$

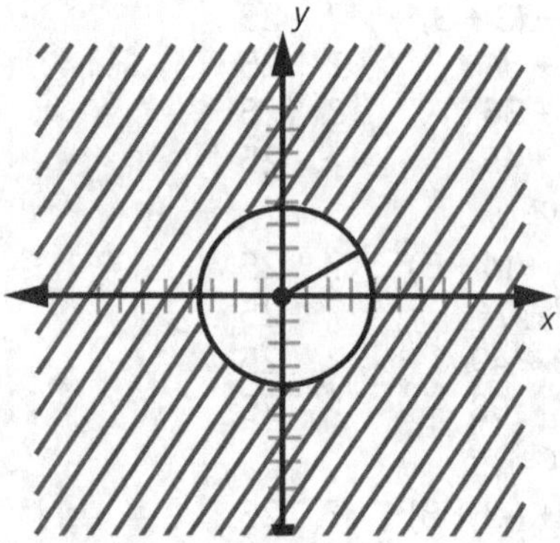

2.50 Center = (-1, 3)
$r = \sqrt{4} = 2$

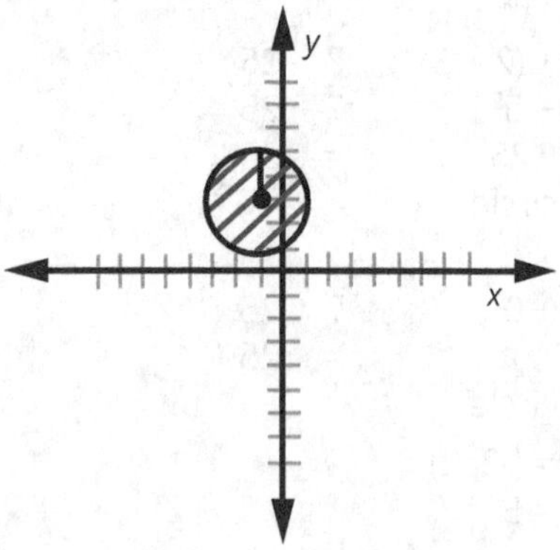

2.51 $M = (\frac{-2+3}{2}, \frac{0+5}{2}) = (\frac{1}{2}, \frac{5}{2})$

2.52 $M = (\frac{8+5}{2}, \frac{2+6}{2}) = (\frac{13}{2}, 4)$

2.53 $M = (\frac{-4+10}{2}, \frac{8+6}{2}) = (3, 7)$

2.54 $M = (\frac{0-16}{2}, \frac{-16+0}{2}) = (-8, -8)$

2.55 $M = (\frac{-8+12}{2}, \frac{8+4}{2}) = (2, 6)$

2.56
$-2 = \frac{1}{2}(3 + x_1)$
$-4 = 3 + x_1$ (multiply by 2)
$-4 - 3 = x_1$
$-7 = x_1$
$0 = \frac{1}{2}(5 + y_1)$
$0 = 5 + y_1$ (multiply by 2)
$0 - 5 = y_1$
$-5 = y_1$
(-7, -5)

2.57
$8 = \frac{1}{2}(5 + x_1)$
$16 = 5 + x_1$ (multiply by 2)
$16 - 5 = x_1$
$11 = x_1$
$2 = \frac{1}{2}(6 + y_1)$
$4 = 6 + y_1$ (multiply by 2)
$4 - 6 = y_1$
$-2 = y_1$
(11, -2)

2.58
$-4 = \frac{1}{2}(10 + x_1)$
$-8 = 10 + x_1$ (multiply by 2)
$-8 - 10 = x_1$
$-18 = x_1$
$8 = \frac{1}{2}(6 + y_1)$
$16 = 6 + y_1$ (multiply by 2)
$16 - 6 = y_1$
$10 = y_1$
(-18, 10)

2.59
$0 = \frac{1}{2}(-16 + x_1)$
$0 = -16 + x_1$ (multiply by 2)
$0 + 16 = x_1$
$16 = x_1$
$-16 = \frac{1}{2}(0 + y_1)$
$-32 = 0 + y_1$ (multiply by 2)
$-32 = y_1$
(16, -32)

2.60
$-8 = \frac{1}{2}(12 + x_1)$
$-16 = 12 + x_1$ (multiply by 2)
$-16 - 12 = x_1$
$-28 = x_1$
$8 = \frac{1}{2}(4 + y_1)$
$16 = 4 + y_1$ (multiply by 2)
$16 - 4 = y_1$
$12 = y_1$
(-28, 12)

2.61 $M_{AB} = (\frac{4+1}{2}, \frac{-1+4}{2}) = (\frac{5}{2}, \frac{3}{2})$

$M_{BC} = (\frac{-1+4}{2}, \frac{-4-1}{2}) = (\frac{3}{2}, -\frac{5}{2})$

$M_{CD} = (\frac{-4-1}{2}, \frac{1-4}{2}) = (-\frac{5}{2}, -\frac{3}{2})$

$M_{AD} = (\frac{-4+1}{2}, \frac{1+4}{2}) = (-\frac{3}{2}, \frac{5}{2})$

2.62 $M_{AB} = (\frac{5+0}{2}, \frac{7+0}{2}) = (\frac{5}{2}, \frac{7}{2})$

$M_{BC} = (\frac{3+5}{2}, \frac{9+7}{2}) = (\frac{8}{2}, \frac{16}{2}) = (4, 8)$

$M_{AC} = (\frac{3+0}{2}, \frac{9+0}{2}) = (\frac{3}{2}, \frac{9}{2})$

2.63 a. $M_{AC} = (\frac{-1+1}{2}, \frac{-4+4}{2}) = (\frac{0}{2}, \frac{0}{2}) = (0, 0)$

$M_{BD} = (\frac{-4+4}{2}, \frac{1-1}{2}) = (\frac{0}{2}, \frac{0}{2}) = (0, 0)$

b. The midpoints of the two diagonals are the same point.

2.64 $M_{AB} = (\frac{-3+5}{2}, \frac{1-1}{2}) = (\frac{2}{2}, \frac{0}{2}) = (1, 0)$

$d = |5 - 0| = |5| = 5$

$M_{BC} = (\frac{1-3}{2}, \frac{5+1}{2}) = (\frac{-2}{2}, \frac{6}{2}) = (-1, 3)$

$d = \sqrt{(-1-5)^2 + [3-(-1)]^2}$

$d = \sqrt{(-6)^2 + 4^2}$

$d = \sqrt{36+16} = \sqrt{52} = 2\sqrt{13}$

$M_{AC} = (\frac{1+5}{2}, \frac{5-1}{2}) = (\frac{6}{2}, \frac{4}{2}) = (3, 2)$

$d = \sqrt{[3-(-3)]^2 + (2-1)^2}$

$d = \sqrt{(6)^2 + 1^2}$

$d = \sqrt{36+1} = \sqrt{37}$

2.65 Sides: $M_{AB} = (\frac{3-2}{2}, \frac{6+5}{2}) = (\frac{1}{2}, \frac{11}{2})$

$M_{BC} = (\frac{4+3}{2}, \frac{1+6}{2}) = (\frac{7}{2}, \frac{7}{2})$

$M_{CD} = (\frac{-1+4}{2}, \frac{0+1}{2}) = (\frac{3}{2}, \frac{1}{2})$

$M_{AD} = (\frac{-1-2}{2}, \frac{0+5}{2}) = (-\frac{3}{2}, \frac{5}{2})$

Diagonals: $M_{AC} = (\frac{4-2}{2}, \frac{1+5}{2}) = (\frac{2}{2}, \frac{6}{2}) = (1, 3)$

$M_{BD} = (\frac{-1+3}{2}, \frac{0+6}{2}) = (\frac{2}{2}, \frac{6}{2}) = (1, 3)$

2.66 $M_{AB} = (\frac{8-1}{2}, \frac{4+1}{2}) = (\frac{7}{2}, \frac{5}{2})$

$= (\frac{\frac{7}{2}-1}{2}, \frac{\frac{5}{2}+1}{2}) = (\frac{\frac{5}{2}}{2}, \frac{\frac{7}{2}}{2}) = (\frac{5}{4}, \frac{7}{4})$

$= (\frac{8+\frac{7}{2}}{2}, \frac{4+\frac{5}{2}}{2}) = (\frac{\frac{23}{2}}{2}, \frac{\frac{13}{2}}{2}) = (\frac{23}{4}, \frac{13}{4})$

2.67 $M_{RS} = (\frac{4-2}{2}, \frac{2+2}{2}) = (\frac{2}{2}, \frac{4}{2}) = (1, 2)$

$d = |4-(-2)| = |4+2| = |6| = 6$

$r = \frac{1}{2}d = \frac{1}{2} \cdot 6 = 3$

$(x-1)^2 + (y-2)^2 = 3^2$

$(x-1)^2 + (y-2)^2 = 9$

2.68

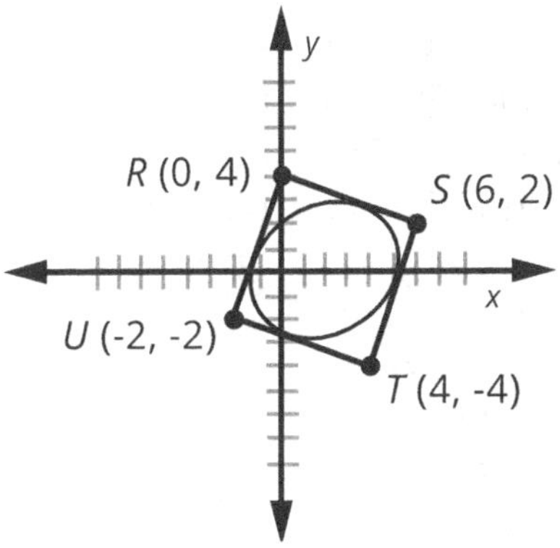

$M_{RT} = \text{ctr.} = (\frac{4+0}{2}, \frac{-4+4}{2}) = (\frac{4}{2}, \frac{0}{2}) = (2, 0)$

$r = \frac{d}{2} = \frac{RS}{2} = \frac{1}{2}\sqrt{(0-6)^2 + (4-2)^2}$

$= \frac{1}{2}\sqrt{(-6)^2 + 2^2}$

$= \frac{1}{2}\sqrt{36+4} = \frac{1}{2}\sqrt{40}$

$= \frac{1}{2}\sqrt{4 \cdot 10}$

$= \sqrt{10}$

Equation: $(x-2)^2 + (y-0)^2 = (\sqrt{10})^2$

$(x-2)^2 + y^2 = 10$

SELF TEST 2

2.01 $AB = \sqrt{[5 - (-3)]^2 + (8 - 4)^2}$
$= \sqrt{8^2 + 4^2}$
$= \sqrt{64 + 16} = \sqrt{80}$
$= \sqrt{5 \cdot 16} = \sqrt{5}\sqrt{16} = 4\sqrt{5}$

2.02 $RS = \sqrt{(-1 - 8)^2 + (0 - 6)^2}$
$= \sqrt{(-9)^2 + (-6)^2}$
$= \sqrt{81 + 36} = \sqrt{117} = 3\sqrt{13}$

2.03 $WX = \sqrt{(-6 - 6)^2 + (-8 - 8)^2}$
$= \sqrt{(-12)^2 + (-16)^2}$
$= \sqrt{144 + 256} = \sqrt{400} = 20$

2.04 $CT = \sqrt{[0 - (-6)]^2 + [4 - (-3)]^2}$
$= \sqrt{6^2 + 7^2} = \sqrt{36 + 49} = \sqrt{85}$

2.05 $(x - 5)^2 + (y - 6)^2 = 3^2$
$(x - 5)^2 + (y - 6)^2 = 9$

2.06 $(x - 7)^2 + [y - (-3)]^2 = (\sqrt{7})^2$
$(x - 7)^2 + (y + 3)^2 = 7$

2.07 $(x - 0)^2 + (y - 8)^2 = 8^2$
$x^2 + (y - 8)^2 = 64$

2.08 $[x - (-2)]^2 + [y - (-5)]^2 = 1^2$
$(x + 2)^2 + (y + 5)^2 = 1$

2.09 a. (-3, 5)
b. $r = \sqrt{25} = 5$

2.010 a. (3, 5)
b. $r = \sqrt{8} = \sqrt{2 \cdot 4} = \sqrt{2}\sqrt{4} = 2\sqrt{2}$

2.011 a. (-5, -7)
b. $r = \sqrt{16} = 4$

2.012 a. (4, 0)
b. $r = \sqrt{12} = \sqrt{3 \cdot 4} = \sqrt{3}\sqrt{4} = 2\sqrt{3}$

2.013 $(8 + 2)^2 + (4 - 3)^2 \quad ? \quad 81$
$10^2 + 1^2 \quad ? \quad 81$
$100 + 1 \quad ? \quad 81$
$101 \quad > \quad 81$
exterior

2.014 $(3 + 2)^2 + (0 - 3)^2 \quad ? \quad 81$
$5^2 + (-3)^2 \quad ? \quad 81$
$25 + 9 \quad ? \quad 81$
$34 \quad < \quad 81$
interior

2.015 $(6 + 2)^2 + (3 - 3)^2 \quad ? \quad 81$
$8^2 + 0^2 \quad ? \quad 81$
$64 + 0 \quad ? \quad 81$
$64 \quad < \quad 81$
interior

2.016 $(-2 + 2)^2 + (12 - 3)^2 \quad ? \quad 81$
$0^2 + 9^2 \quad ? \quad 81$
$0 + 81 \quad ? \quad 81$
$81 \quad = \quad 81$
on the circle

2.017 $M = (\frac{2 + 6}{2}, \frac{3 + 11}{2}) = (\frac{8}{2}, \frac{14}{2}) = (4, 7)$

2.018 $M = (\frac{0 + 12}{2}, \frac{5 - 5}{2}) = (\frac{12}{2}, \frac{0}{2}) = (6, 0)$

2.019 $M = (\frac{-3 - 8}{2}, \frac{-7 - 4}{2}) = (-\frac{11}{2}, -\frac{11}{2})$

2.020 $M = (\frac{5 - 5}{2}, \frac{5 - 5}{2}) = (\frac{0}{2}, \frac{0}{2}) = (0, 0)$

2.021 $M_{AB} = (\frac{-1 + 3}{2}, \frac{-2 + 6}{2}) = (\frac{2}{2}, \frac{4}{2}) = (1, 2)$
$d = \sqrt{(1 - 1)^2 + (2 - 0)^2}$
$= \sqrt{0^2 + 2^2} = \sqrt{0 + 4} = \sqrt{4} = 2$

$M_{BC} = (\frac{3 + 1}{2}, \frac{6 + 0}{2}) = (\frac{4}{2}, \frac{6}{2}) = (2, 3)$
$d = \sqrt{[2 - (-1)]^2 + [3 - (-2)]^2}$
$= \sqrt{3^2 + 5^2}$
$= \sqrt{9 + 25} = \sqrt{34}$

$M_{AC} = (\frac{-1 + 1}{2}, \frac{-2 + 0}{2}) = (\frac{0}{2}, \frac{-2}{2}) = (0, -1)$
$d = \sqrt{(0 - 3)^2 + (-1 - 6)^2}$
$= \sqrt{(-3)^2 + (-7)^2}$
$= \sqrt{9 + 49} = \sqrt{58}$

2.022 $m_{RS} = \frac{7 - 3}{2 - 0} = \frac{4}{2} = 2$
$m_{ST} = \frac{7 - 7}{8 - 2} = \frac{0}{6} = 0$
$m_{TU} = \frac{3 - 7}{12 - 8} = \frac{-4}{4} = -1$
$m_{RU} = \frac{3 - 3}{12 - 0} = \frac{0}{12} = 0$
$\overline{ST} \parallel \overline{RU}$; ∴ median goes from *RS* to *TU*.
$M_{RS} = (\frac{0 + 2}{2}, \frac{3 + 7}{2}) = (\frac{2}{2}, \frac{10}{2}) = (1, 5)$
$M_{TU} = (\frac{8 + 12}{2}, \frac{7 + 3}{2}) = (\frac{20}{2}, \frac{10}{2}) = (10, 5)$
$d = \sqrt{(10 - 1)^2 + (5 - 5)^2}$
$= \sqrt{9^2 + 0^2} = \sqrt{81 + 0}$
$= \sqrt{81} = 9$

2.023 center: (0, -4)

2.024 $d_{RT} = \sqrt{(1 - 8)^2 + (-1 - 5)^2}$
$= \sqrt{(-7)^2 + (-6)^2}$
$= \sqrt{49 + 36} = \sqrt{85}$
$d_{SU} = \sqrt{(6 - 3)^2 + (1 - 3)^2}$
$= \sqrt{3^2 + (-2)^2}$
$= \sqrt{9 + 4} = \sqrt{13}$
$\sqrt{13}$ is length of shorter diagonal

2.025 line, plane
2.026 line, plane
2.027 none
2.028 point, line, plane
2.029 none
2.030 line, plane
2.031 (4, 4)
2.032 (-4, -2)
2.033 (3, -6)
2.034 (-4, 6)
2.035 (1, 5)

SECTION 3

3.1 $m = \frac{8-2}{7-3} = \frac{6}{4} = \frac{3}{2}$

3.2 $m = \frac{0-4}{5-0} = -\frac{4}{5}$

3.3 $m = \frac{4-(-1)}{0-2} = \frac{4+1}{0-2} = -\frac{5}{2}$

3.4 $m = \frac{5-8}{-2-3} = \frac{-3}{-5} = \frac{3}{5}$

3.5 $m = \frac{1-(-4)}{3-1} = \frac{-1+4}{3-1} = \frac{3}{2}$

3.6 $m = \frac{-2-(-2)}{7-3} = \frac{-2+2}{7-3} = \frac{0}{4} = 0$

3.7 $m = \frac{b-0}{a-0} = \frac{b}{a}$

3.8 $m = \frac{0-d}{d-0} = \frac{-d}{d} = -1$

3.9 $m = \frac{(c+d)-(c-d)}{(c-d)-(c+d)}$
$= \frac{c+d-c+d}{c-d-c-d} = \frac{2d}{-2d} = -1$

3.10 $m = \frac{4-2}{3-1} = \frac{2}{2} = 1$

3.11
$\frac{3}{5} = \frac{y-2}{8-3}$
$\frac{3}{5} = \frac{y-2}{5}$
$3(5) = 5(y-2)$ (cross-multiply)
$3 = y - 2$
$3 + 2 = y$
$5 = y$

3.12
$5 = \frac{2-y}{-4-0}$
$5 = \frac{2-y}{-4}$
$\frac{5}{1} = \frac{2-y}{-4}$
$5(-4) = 1(2-y)$ (cross-multiply)
$-20 = 2 - y$
$-20 - 2 = -y$
$-22 = -y$
$22 = y$

3.13
$-\frac{7}{2} = \frac{-5-2}{x-13}$
$-\frac{7}{2} = \frac{-7}{x-13}$
$-7 = \frac{-14}{x-13}$ (multiply by 2)
$\frac{-7}{1} = \frac{-14}{x-13}$
$-7(x-13) = 1(-14)$ (cross-multiply)
$-7x + 91 = -14$
$-7x = -14 - 91$
$-7x = -105$
$x = 15$ (divide by -7)

3.14 $2 = \frac{10-0}{5-x}$

$\frac{2}{1} = \frac{10}{5-x}$

$2(5-x) = 1(10)$ (cross-multiply)

$10 - 2x = 10$

$-2x = 10 - 10$

$2x = 0$

$x = 0$

3.15 $j = \frac{y-b}{c-a}$

$\frac{j}{1} = \frac{y-b}{c-a}$

$j(c-a) = 1(y-b)$ (cross-multiply)

$j(c-a) = y - b$

$j(c-a) + b = y$

3.16 $m_{RS} = \frac{4-1}{2-(-1)} = \frac{4-1}{2+1} = \frac{3}{3} = 1$

$m_{ST} = \frac{8-4}{6-2} = \frac{4}{4} = 1$

$m_{PT} = \frac{8-1}{6-(-1)} = \frac{8-1}{6+1} = \frac{7}{7} = 1$

yes

3.17 $m_{CD} = \frac{4-(-1)}{3-1} = \frac{4+1}{3-1} = \frac{5}{2}$

$m_{DE} = \frac{8-4}{5-3} = \frac{4}{2} = 2$

$m_{CE} = \frac{8-(-1)}{5-1} = \frac{8+1}{5-1} = \frac{9}{4}$

no

3.18 $m_{WX} = \frac{2-4}{6-4} = \frac{-2}{2} = -1$

$m_{XY} = \frac{16-2}{-8-6} = \frac{14}{-14} = -1$

$m_{WY} = \frac{16-4}{-8-4} = \frac{12}{-12} = -1$

yes

3.19 $m_{AB} = \frac{10-0}{-2-3} = \frac{10}{-5} = -2$

$m_{BC} = \frac{5-10}{0-(-2)} = \frac{5-10}{0+2} = -\frac{5}{2}$

$m_{AC} = \frac{5-0}{0-3} = -\frac{5}{3}$

no

3.20 $m_{PQ} = \frac{0-3}{2-0} = -\frac{3}{2}$

$m_{QR} = \frac{-3-0}{4-2} = -\frac{3}{2}$

$m_{PR} = \frac{-3-3}{4-0} = \frac{-6}{4} = -\frac{3}{2}$

yes

3.21 $m_{AB} = \frac{4-0}{2-0} = \frac{4}{2} = 2$

$m_{BC} = \frac{4-4}{5-2} = \frac{0}{3} = 0$

$m_{CD} = \frac{0-4}{4-5} = \frac{-4}{-1} = 4$

$m_{DA} = \frac{0-0}{0-4} = \frac{0}{-4} = 0$

3.22 $m_{RS} = \frac{6-0}{-2-(-4)} = \frac{6-0}{-2+4} = \frac{6}{2} = 3$

$m_{ST} = \frac{4-6}{4-(-2)} = \frac{4-6}{4+2} = \frac{-2}{6} = -\frac{1}{3}$

$m_{TU} = \frac{-2-4}{2-4} = \frac{-6}{-2} = 3$

$m_{UR} = \frac{0-(-2)}{-4-2} = \frac{0+2}{-4-2} = \frac{2}{-6} = -\frac{1}{3}$

3.23 $m_{MN} = \frac{4-0}{2-0} = \frac{4}{2} = 2$

$m_{NP} = \frac{4-4}{8-2} = \frac{0}{6} = 0$

$m_{PQ} = \frac{0-4}{12-8} = \frac{-4}{4} = -1$

$m_{QM} = \frac{0-0}{0-12} = \frac{0}{-12} = 0$

3.24 $m_{PQ} = \frac{5-3}{3-1} = \frac{2}{2} = 1$

$m_{QR} = \frac{2-5}{6-3} = \frac{-3}{3} = -1$

$m_{RP} = \frac{3-2}{1-6} = -\frac{1}{5}$

3.25 $M_{QR} = (\frac{6+3}{2}, \frac{2+5}{2}) = (\frac{9}{2}, \frac{7}{2})$

[to (1, 3)]

$m = \frac{\frac{7}{2}-3}{\frac{9}{2}-1} = \frac{\frac{7}{2}-\frac{6}{2}}{\frac{9}{2}-\frac{2}{2}} = \frac{\frac{1}{2}}{\frac{7}{2}} = \frac{1}{7}$

$M_{PR} = (\frac{6+1}{2}, \frac{2+3}{2}) = (\frac{7}{2}, \frac{5}{2})$

[to (3, 5)]

$m = \frac{\frac{5}{2}-5}{\frac{7}{2}-3} = \frac{\frac{5}{2}-\frac{10}{2}}{\frac{7}{2}-\frac{6}{2}} = \frac{-\frac{5}{2}}{\frac{1}{2}} = \frac{-5}{1} = -5$

$M_{PQ} = (\frac{3+1}{2}, \frac{5+3}{2}) = (\frac{4}{2}, \frac{8}{2}) = (2, 4)$

[to (6, 2)]

$m = \frac{4-2}{2-6} = \frac{2}{-4} = -\frac{1}{2}$

3.26 $k \perp m$ because $\frac{2}{3}(-\frac{3}{2}) = -1$

$l \perp n$ because $-4(\frac{1}{4}) = -1$

3.27 $m_{AB} = \frac{2-(-2)}{-4-(-5)} = \frac{2+2}{-4+5} = \frac{4}{1} = 4$

$m_{BC} = \frac{5-2}{4-(-4)} = \frac{5-2}{4+4} = \frac{3}{8}$

$m_{CD} = \frac{1-5}{3-4} = \frac{-4}{-1} = 4$

$m_{AD} = \frac{1-(-2)}{3-(-5)} = \frac{1+2}{3+5} = \frac{3}{8}$

$m_{AB} = m_{CD}$; $\therefore \overline{AB} \parallel \overline{CD}$.

$m_{BC} = m_{AD}$; $\therefore \overline{BC} \parallel \overline{AD}$.

3.28 a. $m_{AB} = \frac{2-0}{9-16} = -\frac{2}{7}$

$m_{BC} = \frac{0-2}{0-9} = \frac{-2}{-9} = \frac{2}{9}$

$m_{AC} = \frac{0-0}{0-16} = \frac{0}{-16} = 0$

b. altitudes are perpendicular:

$m_{AB} = \frac{7}{2}$

$m_{BC} = -\frac{9}{2}$

m_{AC} = no slope

3.29 $m_{AC} = \frac{2-2}{4-(-2)} = \frac{2-2}{4+2} = \frac{0}{6} = 0$

$m_{BD} = \frac{4-(-2)}{2-2} = \frac{4+2}{2-2} = \frac{6}{0}$ = no slope

$\therefore$ diagonals are $\perp$

3.30 $m_1 = \frac{d-0}{c-0} = \frac{d}{c}$

$m_2 = \frac{c-0}{-d-0} = -\frac{c}{d}$

$\therefore$ lines are $\perp$

3.31 $m_{AB} = \frac{5-1}{3-2} = \frac{4}{1} = 4$; $m_{alt} = -\frac{1}{4}$

$m_{BC} = \frac{2-5}{7-3} = -\frac{3}{4}$; $m_{alt} = \frac{4}{3}$

$m_{AC} = \frac{2-1}{7-2} = \frac{1}{5}$; $m_{alt} = -5$

3.32 $m_{RS} = \frac{3-0}{6-0} = \frac{3}{6} = \frac{1}{2}$

$m_{ST} = \frac{5-3}{5-6} = \frac{2}{-1} = -2$

$m_{TU} = \frac{2-5}{-1-5} = \frac{-3}{-6} = \frac{1}{2}$

$m_{RU} = \frac{2-0}{-1-0} = \frac{2}{-1} = -2$

$\overline{RS} \parallel \overline{TU}$

$\overline{ST} \parallel \overline{RU}$

$\overline{RS} \perp \overline{ST}$

$\overline{RS} \perp \overline{RU}$

$\overline{TU} \perp \overline{ST}$

$\overline{TU} \perp \overline{RU}$

3.33 $m_{RS} = \frac{-1-(-3)}{4-1} = \frac{-1+3}{4-1} = \frac{2}{3}$

$m_{ST} = \frac{2-(-1)}{2-4} = \frac{2+1}{2-4} = -\frac{3}{2}$

$m_{TU} = \frac{-2-2}{-4-2} = \frac{-4}{-6} = \frac{2}{3}$

$m_{RU} = \frac{-2-(-3)}{-4-1} = \frac{-2+3}{-4-1} = -\frac{1}{5}$

$\overline{RS} \parallel \overline{TU}$

$\overline{RS} \perp \overline{ST}$

$\overline{TU} \perp \overline{ST}$

3.34 $m_{RS} = \frac{2-(-5)}{8-(-1)} = \frac{2+5}{8+1} = \frac{7}{9}$

$m_{ST} = \frac{5-2}{5-8} = \frac{3}{-3} = -1$

$m_{TU} = \frac{-2-5}{-4-5} = \frac{-7}{-9} = \frac{7}{9}$

$m_{RU} = \frac{-2-(-5)}{-4-(-1)} = \frac{-2+5}{-4+1} = \frac{3}{-3} = -1$

$\overline{RS} \parallel \overline{TU}$

$\overline{ST} \parallel \overline{RU}$

3.35 $m_{RS} = \frac{-2-1}{1-(-1)} = \frac{-2-1}{1+1} = -\frac{3}{2}$

$m_{ST} = \frac{0-(-2)}{4-1} = \frac{0+2}{4-1} = \frac{2}{3}$

$m_{TU} = \frac{3-0}{3-4} = \frac{3}{-1} = -3$

$m_{RU} = \frac{3-1}{3-(-1)} = \frac{3-1}{3+1} = \frac{2}{4} = \frac{1}{2}$

$\overline{RS} \perp \overline{ST}$

3.36 a. $m_{AB} = \frac{4-1}{3-0} = \frac{3}{3} = 1$

$m_{BC} = \frac{1-4}{6-3} = \frac{-3}{3} = -1$

$m_{CD} = \frac{-3-1}{3-6} = \frac{-4}{-3} = \frac{4}{3}$

$m_{AD} = \frac{1+3}{0-3} = \frac{4}{-3} = -\frac{4}{3}$

no special quadrilateral because only $\overline{AB} \perp \overline{BC}$

b. $m_{AC} = \frac{1-1}{6-0} = \frac{0}{6} = 0$

$m_{BD} = \frac{-3-4}{3-3} = \frac{-7}{0}$ = no slope

yes

3.37 $m_{AB} = \frac{1-1}{7-2} = \frac{0}{5} = 0$

$m_{BC} = \frac{4-1}{2-7} = -\frac{3}{5}$

$m_{AC} = \frac{4-1}{2-2} = \frac{3}{0}$ = no slope

yes, because $\overline{AB} \perp \overline{AC}$

3.38 $m_{RS} = \frac{-1-(-3)}{3-1} = \frac{-1+3}{3-1} = \frac{2}{2} = 1$

$m_{ST} = \frac{-7-(-1)}{5-3} = \frac{-7+1}{5-3} = \frac{-6}{2} = -3$

$m_{RT} = \frac{-7-(-3)}{5-1} = \frac{-7+3}{5-1} = \frac{-4}{4} = -1$

yes, because $\overline{RS} \perp \overline{RT}$

3.39 $m_{GH} = \frac{0-3}{9-7} = -\frac{3}{2}$

$m_{HI} = \frac{-1-0}{5-9} = \frac{-1}{-4} = \frac{1}{4}$

$m_{GI} = \frac{-1-3}{5-7} = \frac{-4}{-2} = 2$

no, because no ⊥'s

3.40 $m_{JK} = \frac{3-2}{-1-2} = -\frac{1}{3}$

$m_{KL} = \frac{-1-3}{-2-(-1)} = \frac{-1-3}{-2+1} = \frac{-4}{-1} = 4$

$m_{JL} = \frac{-1-2}{-2-2} = \frac{-3}{-4} = \frac{3}{4}$

no, because no ⊥'s

3.41 $m_{PQ} = \frac{2-1}{3-0} = \frac{1}{3}$

$m_{QR} = \frac{-4-2}{5-3} = \frac{-6}{2} = -3$

$m_{PR} = \frac{-4-1}{5-0} = \frac{-5}{5} = -1$

yes, because $\overline{PQ} \perp \overline{QR}$

3.42 $m = \frac{2-1}{5-4} = \frac{1}{1} = 1$

$y - 1 = 1(x - 4)$

$y - 1 = x - 4$

$y = x - 4 + 1$

$y = x - 3$

$-x + y = -3$ or $x - y = 3$

3.43 $m = \frac{-6-3}{-6-3} = \frac{-9}{-9} = 1$

$y - 3 = 1(x - 3)$

$y - 3 = x - 3$

$y = x - 3 + 3$

$y = x - 0$

$-x + y = 0$ or $x - y = 0$

3.44 $m = \frac{-4-0}{4-0} = \frac{-4}{4} = -1$

$y - 0 = -1(x - 0)$

$y = -x + 0$

$x + y = 0$

3.45 $m = \frac{-4-2}{8-6} = \frac{-6}{2} = -3$

$y - 2 = -3(x - 6)$

$y - 2 = -3x + 18$

$y = -3x + 18 + 2$

$y = -3x + 20$

$3x + y = 20$

3.46 $m = \frac{0-6}{6-0} = \frac{-6}{6} = -1$

$y - 6 = -1(x - 0)$

$y - 6 = -x + 0$

$y = -x + 6$

$x + y = 6$

3.47 $m = \frac{1-2}{5-(-2)} = \frac{1-2}{5+2} = -\frac{1}{7}$

$y - 2 = -\frac{1}{7}(x + 2)$

$y - 2 = -\frac{1}{7}x - \frac{2}{7}$

$y = -\frac{1}{7}x - \frac{2}{7} + 2$

$\frac{1}{7}x + y = \frac{12}{7}$

$x + 7y = 12$ (multiply by 7)

3.48 $m = \frac{5-6}{1-4} = \frac{-1}{-3} = \frac{1}{3}$

$y - 6 = \frac{1}{3}(x - 4)$

$y - 6 = \frac{1}{3}x - \frac{4}{3}$

$y = \frac{1}{3}x - \frac{4}{3} + 6$

$-\frac{1}{3}x + y = \frac{14}{3}$

$-x + 3y = 14$ or (multiply by 3)

$x - 3y = -14$

3.49 $m = \frac{4-1}{\frac{1}{2} - \frac{1}{2}} = \frac{3}{0}$ = no slope

$x = \frac{1}{2}$ (line parallel to the y-axis)

3.50 $m = \frac{5-0}{0-5} = \frac{5}{-5} = -1$

$y - 0 = -1(x - 5)$

$y - 0 = -x + 5$

$x + y = 5$

3.51 $m = \frac{6-6}{5-0} = \frac{0}{5} = 0$

$y - 6 = 0(x - 0)$

$y = 6$

3.52 $y - 5 = 3(x - 5)$

$y - 5 = 3x - 15$

$-3x + y - 5 = -15$

$-3x + y = -15 + 5$

$-3x + y = -10$

$3x - y = 10$

3.53 $y - 2 = -\frac{1}{2}(x - 6)$

$y - 2 = -\frac{1}{2}x + 3$

$\frac{1}{2}x + y - 2 = 3$

$\frac{1}{2}x + y = 3 + 2$

$\frac{1}{2}x + y = 5$

$x + 2y = 10$ (multiply by 2)

3.54 $y - 4 = 0(x - 0)$

$y - 4 = 0$

$y = 4$

3.55 $y + 2 = \frac{2}{5}(x - 5)$

$y + 2 = \frac{2}{5}x - 2$

$-\frac{2}{5}x + y + 2 = -2$

$-\frac{2}{5}x + y = -2 - 2$

$-\frac{2}{5}x + y = -4$

$2x - 5y = 20$ (multiply by -5)

3.56 no slope; $\therefore x = 3$

3.57 $y + 1 = \frac{3}{4}(x - 2)$

$y + 1 = \frac{3}{4}x - \frac{6}{4}$

$-\frac{3}{4}x + y + 1 = -\frac{6}{4}$

$-\frac{3}{4}x + y = -\frac{6}{4} - 1$

$-\frac{3}{4}x + y = -\frac{10}{4}$

$3x - 4y = 10$ (multiply by -4)

3.58 $y - 4 = -\frac{5}{2}(x + 3)$

$y - 4 = -\frac{5}{2}x - \frac{15}{2}$

$\frac{5}{2}x + y - 4 = -\frac{15}{2}$

$\frac{5}{2}x + y = -\frac{15}{2} + 4$

$\frac{5}{2}x + y = -\frac{7}{2}$

$5x + 2y = -7$ (multiply by 2)

3.59 $M = (\frac{-6+2}{2}, \frac{5-3}{2}) = (\frac{-4}{2}, \frac{2}{2}) = (-2, 1)$

$y - 1 = \frac{9}{7}(x + 2)$

$y - 1 = \frac{9}{7}x + \frac{18}{7}$

$-\frac{9}{7}x + y - 1 = \frac{18}{7}$

$-\frac{9}{7}x + y = \frac{18}{7} + 1$

$-\frac{9}{7}x + y = \frac{25}{7}$

$9x - 7y = -25$ (multiply by -7)

3.60 $M = (\frac{5+1}{2}, \frac{-2+0}{2}) = (\frac{6}{2}, \frac{-2}{2}) = (3, -1)$

$m = \frac{-2-0}{5-1} = \frac{-2}{4} = -\frac{1}{2}$

$y + 1 = 2(x - 3)$

$y + 1 = 2x - 6$

$y = 2x - 7$

$-2x + y = -7$

$2x - y = 7$ (multiply by -1)

3.61 $m_{AB} = \frac{1-5}{1-(-5)} = \frac{1-5}{1+5} = \frac{-4}{6} = -\frac{2}{3}$

$m_{BC} = \frac{4-1}{3-1} = \frac{3}{2}$

$m_{AC} = \frac{4-5}{3-(-5)} = \frac{4-5}{3+5} = -\frac{1}{8}$

$\overline{AB} \perp \overline{BC}$, ∴ AB and BC are legs.

$M_{AB} = (\frac{1-5}{2}, \frac{1+5}{2}) = (\frac{-4}{2}, \frac{6}{2}) = (-2, 3)$

$M_{BC} = (\frac{3+1}{2}, \frac{4+1}{2}) = (\frac{4}{2}, \frac{5}{2}) = (2, \frac{5}{2})$

$m = \frac{\frac{5}{2} - 3}{2-(-2)} = \frac{\frac{5}{2} - 3}{2+2} = \frac{-\frac{1}{2}}{4} = -\frac{1}{8}$

$y - 3 = -\frac{1}{8}(x + 2)$

$y - 3 = -\frac{1}{8}x - \frac{1}{4}$

$\frac{1}{8}x + y - 3 = -\frac{1}{4}$

$\frac{1}{8}x + y = -\frac{1}{4} + 3$

$\frac{1}{8}x + y = \frac{11}{4}$

$x + 8y = 22$ (multiply by 8)

3.62 $m_{AB} = \frac{1-5}{1-(-5)} = \frac{1-5}{1+5} = \frac{-4}{6} = -\frac{2}{3}$

$m_{BC} = \frac{4-1}{3-1} = \frac{3}{2}$

$m_{AC} = \frac{4-5}{3-(-5)} = \frac{4-5}{3+5} = -\frac{1}{8}$

$\overline{AB} \perp \overline{BC}$, ∴ AC is hypotenuse.

$y - 4 = \frac{1}{8}(x - 3)$

$y - 4 = -\frac{1}{8}x + \frac{3}{8}$

$\frac{1}{8}x + y - 4 = \frac{3}{8}$

$\frac{1}{8}x + y = \frac{3}{8} + 4$

$\frac{1}{8}x + y = \frac{35}{8}$

$x + 8y = 35$ (multiply by 8)

3.63 $d_{AC} = \sqrt{(2-1)^2 + [2-(-1)]^2}$

$= \sqrt{1^2 + 3^2}$

$= \sqrt{1+9} = \sqrt{10}$

$d_{BD} = \sqrt{(-2-6)^2 + (-2-4)^2}$

$= \sqrt{(-8)^2 + (-6)^2}$

$= \sqrt{64+36} = \sqrt{100} = 10$

∴ BD is longer diagonal.

$m_{BD} = \frac{4-(-2)}{6-(-2)} = \frac{4+2}{6+2} = \frac{6}{8} = \frac{3}{4}$

$y + 2 = \frac{3}{4}(x + 2)$

$y + 2 = \frac{3}{4}x + \frac{6}{4}$

$-\frac{3}{4}x + y + 2 = \frac{6}{4}$

$-\frac{3}{4}x + y = \frac{6}{4} - 2$

$-\frac{3}{4}x + y = -\frac{2}{4}$

$3x - 4y = 2$ (multiply by -4)

3.64 $m_{RS} = \frac{8-5}{1-(-1)} = \frac{8-5}{1+1} = \frac{3}{2}$

$m_{ST} = \frac{-2-8}{7-1} = \frac{-10}{6} = -\frac{5}{3}$

$m_{TU} = \frac{0-(-2)}{2-7} = \frac{0+2}{2-7} = -\frac{2}{5}$

$m_{RU} = \frac{0-5}{2-(-1)} = \frac{0-5}{2+1} = -\frac{5}{3}$

$\overline{ST} \parallel \overline{RU}$; ∴ median goes from $\overline{RS}$ to $\overline{TU}$.

$M_{RS} = (\frac{1-1}{2}, \frac{8+5}{2}) = (\frac{0}{2}, \frac{13}{2}) = (0, \frac{13}{2})$

$M_{TU} = (\frac{2+7}{2}, \frac{0-2}{2}) = (\frac{9}{2}, \frac{-2}{2}) = (\frac{9}{2}, -1)$

$m = \frac{-1 - \frac{13}{2}}{\frac{9}{2} - 0} = \frac{-\frac{15}{2}}{\frac{9}{2}} = -\frac{15}{9} = -\frac{5}{3}$

$y + 1 = -\frac{5}{3}(x - \frac{9}{2})$

$y + 1 = -\frac{5}{3}x + \frac{15}{2}$

$\frac{5}{3}x + y + 1 = \frac{15}{2}$

$\frac{5}{3}x + y = \frac{15}{2} - 1$

$\frac{5}{3}x + y = \frac{13}{2}$

$10x + 6y = 39$ (multiply by 6)

3.65 $m_{PQ} = \frac{5-1}{3-(-1)} = \frac{5-1}{3+1} = \frac{4}{4} = 1$

$m_{QR} = \frac{-5-5}{5-3} = \frac{-10}{2} = -5$

$m_{PR} = \frac{-5-1}{5-(-1)} = \frac{-5-1}{5+1} = \frac{-6}{6} = -1$

$m_{alt} = \frac{1}{5}$

$y - 1 = \frac{1}{5}(x + 1)$

$y - 1 = \frac{1}{5}x + \frac{1}{5}$

$-\frac{1}{5}x + y - 1 = \frac{1}{5}$

$-\frac{1}{5}x + y = \frac{1}{5} + 1$

$-\frac{1}{5}x + y = \frac{6}{5}$

$x - 5y = -6$ (multiply by -5)

3.66 $m_{AC} = \frac{-3-3}{3-(-3)} = \frac{-3-3}{3+3} = \frac{-6}{6} = -1$

$y - 3 = -1(x - 3)$

$y - 3 = -x - 3$

$x + y - 3 = -3$

$x + y = -3 + 3$

$x + y = 0$

$m_{BD} = \frac{-3-3}{-3-3} = \frac{-6}{-6} = 1$

$y - 3 = 1(x - 3)$

$y - 3 = x - 3$

$-x + y - 3 = -3$

$-x + y = -3 + 3$

$-x + y = 0$

$x - y = 0$ (multiply by -1)

SELF TEST 3

3.01 $m = \frac{8-6}{10-5} = \frac{2}{5}$

3.02 $m = \frac{-2-5}{3-(-3)} = \frac{-2-5}{3+3} = -\frac{7}{6}$

3.03 $m = \frac{4-6}{-2-0} = \frac{-2}{-2} = 1$

3.04 $m = \frac{6-3}{4-0} = \frac{3}{4}$

3.05 $m = \frac{-2-5}{6-5} = \frac{-7}{1} = -7$

3.06 $m = \frac{-2-4}{6-(-2)} = \frac{-2-4}{6+2} = \frac{-6}{8} = -\frac{3}{4}$

3.07 $m = \frac{1-7}{3-5} = \frac{-6}{-2} = 3$

$m\perp = -\frac{1}{3}$

3.08 $m = \frac{0-(-2)}{8-4} = \frac{0+2}{8-4} = \frac{2}{4} = \frac{1}{2}$

$m\perp = -2$

3.09 $m = \frac{4-6}{4-6} = \frac{-2}{-2} = 1$

$m\perp = -1$

3.010 $m = \frac{1-(-4)}{5-0} = \frac{1+4}{5-0} = \frac{5}{5} = 1$

$y + 4 = 1(x - 0)$

$y + 4 = x$

$-x + y + 4 = 0$

$-x + y = -4$

$x - y = 4$ (multiply by -1)

3.011 $m = \frac{0-2}{5-(-3)} = \frac{0-2}{5+3} = \frac{-2}{8} = -\frac{1}{4}$

$y - 2 = -\frac{1}{4}(x + 3)$

$y - 2 = -\frac{1}{4}x - \frac{3}{4}$

$\frac{1}{4}x + y - 2 = -\frac{3}{4}$

$\frac{1}{4}x + y = -\frac{3}{4} + 2$

$\frac{1}{4}x + y = \frac{5}{4}$

$x + 4y = 5$ (multiply by 4)

3.012 $m = \frac{4-4}{-6-6} = \frac{0}{-12} = 0$

$y = 4$

3.013 $y - 0 = 5(x - 4)$

$y - 0 = 5x - 20$

$-5x + y = -20$

$5x - y = 20$ (multiply by -1)

3.014 $y - 1 = \frac{1}{2}(x + 6)$

$y - 1 = \frac{1}{2}x + 3$

$-\frac{1}{2}x + y - 1 = 3$

$-\frac{1}{2}x + y = 3 + 1$

$-\frac{1}{2}x + y = 4$

$x - 2y = -8$ (multiply by -2)

3.015 $y - 5 = \frac{3}{2}(x - 2)$

$y - 5 = \frac{3}{2}x - 3$

$-\frac{3}{2}x + y - 5 = -3$

$-\frac{3}{2}x + y = -3 + 5$

$-\frac{3}{2}x + y = 2$

$3x - 2y = -4$ (multiply by -2)

3.016 $d_{AB} = \sqrt{(2-8)^2 + (1-4)^2}$

$= \sqrt{(-6)^2 + (-3)^2}$

$= \sqrt{36 + 9} = \sqrt{45} = 3\sqrt{5}$

$d_{BC} = \sqrt{(8-5)^2 + (4-7)^2}$

$= \sqrt{3^2 + (-3)^2}$

$= \sqrt{9 + 9} = \sqrt{18} = 3\sqrt{2}$

$d_{AC} = \sqrt{(2-5)^2 + (1-7)^2}$

$= \sqrt{(-3)^2 + (-6)^2}$

$= \sqrt{9 + 36} = \sqrt{45} = 3\sqrt{5}$

$\therefore \overline{BC}$ is base.

$M_{BC} = (\frac{8+5}{2}, \frac{4+7}{2}) = (\frac{13}{2}, \frac{11}{2})$

[to (2, 1)]

$m = \dfrac{1 - \frac{11}{2}}{2 - \frac{13}{2}} = \dfrac{-\frac{9}{2}}{-\frac{9}{2}} = 1$

$y - 1 = 1(x - 2)$

$y - 1 = x - 2$

$-x + y - 1 = -2$

$-x + y = -2 + 1$

$-x + y = -1$

$x - y = 1$ (multiply by -1)

3.017 $M_{RS} = (\frac{-1+5}{2}, \frac{6+5}{2}) = (\frac{4}{2}, \frac{11}{2}) = (2, \frac{11}{2})$

$m_{RS} = \frac{5-6}{5-(-1)} = \frac{5-6}{5+1} = -\frac{1}{6}$; $\therefore m\perp = 6$

$y - \frac{11}{2} = 6(x - 2)$

$y - \frac{11}{2} = 6x - 12$

$-6x + y - \frac{11}{2} = -12$

$-6x + y = -12 + \frac{11}{2}$

$-6x + y = -\frac{13}{2}$

$12x - 2y = 13$ (multiply by -2)

3.018 $m \,||\, = \frac{2}{3}$

$y + 2 = \frac{2}{3}(x - 1)$

$y + 2 = \frac{2}{3}x - \frac{2}{3}$

$-\frac{2}{3}x + y + 2 = -\frac{2}{3}$

$-\frac{2}{3}x + y = -\frac{2}{3} - 2$

$-\frac{2}{3}x + y = -\frac{8}{3}$

$2x - 3y = 8$ (multiply by -3)

3.019 $m_{PS} = \frac{-4-(-2)}{7-2} = \frac{-4+2}{7-2} = -\frac{2}{5}$

$m_{QR} = \frac{-2-(-4)}{7-2} = \frac{-2+4}{7-2} = \frac{2}{5}$

$\overline{PS}$ has negative slope.

$y + 2 = -\frac{2}{5}(x - 2)$

$y + 2 = -\frac{2}{5}x + \frac{4}{5}$

$\frac{2}{5}x + y + 2 = \frac{4}{5}$

$\frac{2}{5}x + y = \frac{4}{5} - 2$

$\frac{2}{5}x + y = -\frac{6}{5}$

$2x + 5y = -6$ (multiply by 5)

3.020 positive
3.021 negative
3.022 zero
3.023 no slope
3.024 positive
3.025 $x = 0$: $0 + y = 5$
$y = 5$
$(0, 5)$
$y = 0$: $x + 0 = 5$
$x = 5$
$(5, 0)$

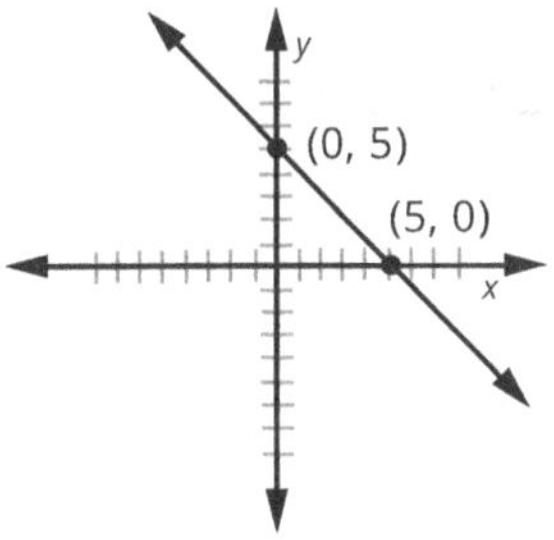

3.026 $x = 0$: $0 + 2y = 6$
$\frac{2y}{2} = \frac{6}{2}$
$y = 3$
$(0, 3)$
$y = 0$: $x + 0 = 6$
$x = 6$
$(6, 0)$

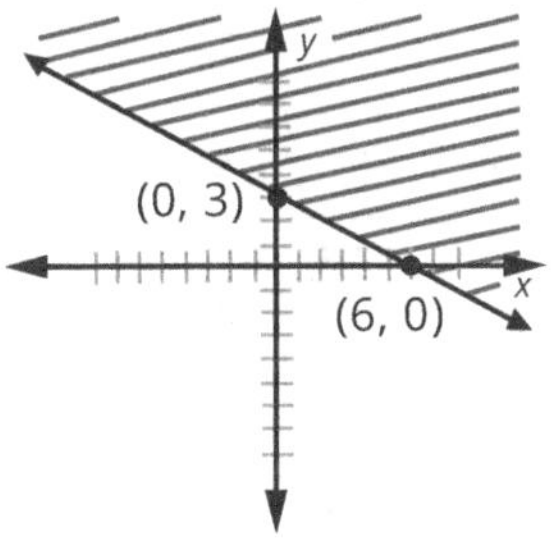

3.027

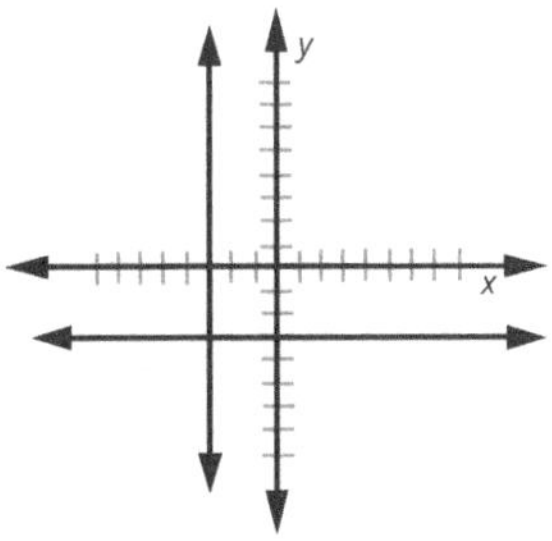

Solution graph:

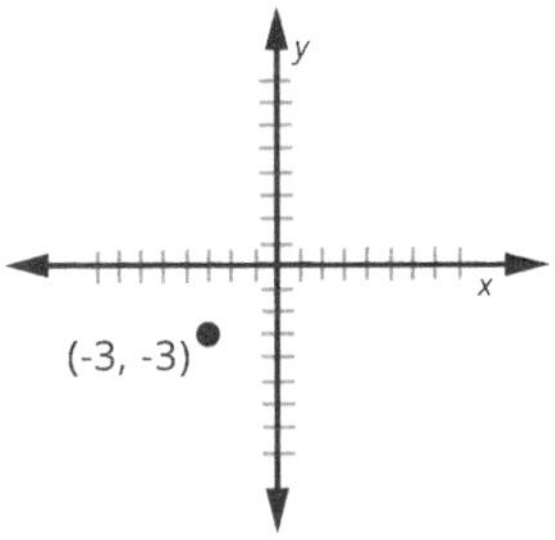

3.028

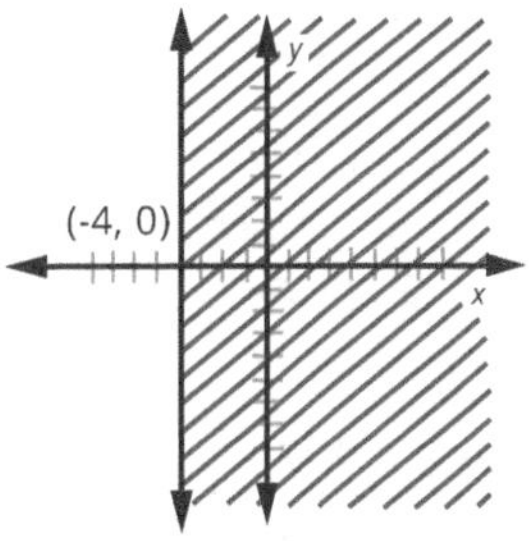

3.029 a. (3, 7)
b. $r = \sqrt{49} = 7$
3.030 a. (-2, 0)
b. $r = \sqrt{10}$
3.031 a. (-3, 6)
b. $r = \sqrt{24} = \sqrt{4 \cdot 6} = \sqrt{4}\sqrt{6} = 2\sqrt{6}$

3.032 $M = (\frac{3 - 2}{2}, \frac{5 + 0}{2}) = (\frac{1}{2}, \frac{5}{2})$

3.033 $M = (\frac{10 - 4}{2}, \frac{6 + 8}{2}) = (\frac{6}{2}, \frac{14}{2}) = (3, 7)$

3.034 $M = (\frac{3 - 7}{2}, \frac{5 - 5}{2}) = (\frac{-4}{2}, \frac{0}{2}) = (-2, 0)$

SECTION 4

4.1 a

4.2 b

4.3 a

4.4 b

4.5 a

4.6 a. $M = (\frac{0 + 2h}{2}, \frac{0 + 0}{2}) = (\frac{2h}{2}, \frac{0}{2}) = (h, 0)$

b. Since $\triangle RST$ is equilateral, the x-coordinate of R is the same coordinate as the one for the midpoint of ST; x-coordinate = h.

c.

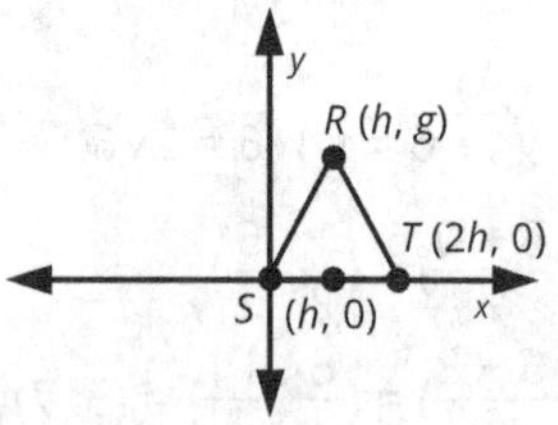

4.7 a. $C(a, 0)$, $D(a, a)$

b. $C(-a, 0)$, $D(-a, a)$

c.

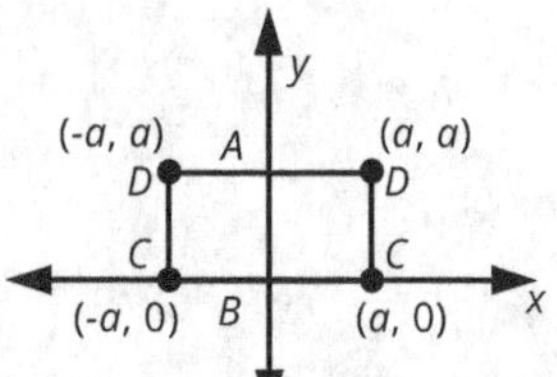

4.8 a. $(a, -b)$, $(-a, -b)$, $(-a, b)$

b.

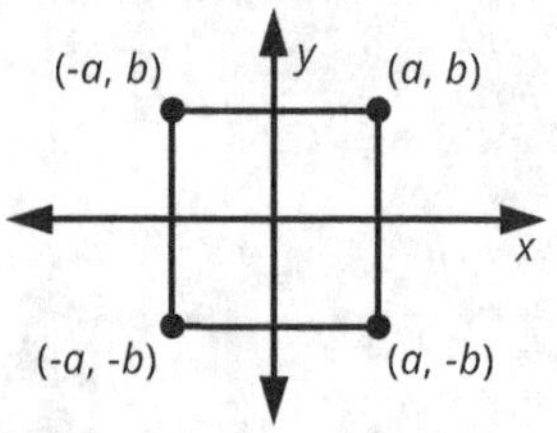

4.9 a. $M = (\frac{0 + j}{2}, \frac{t + t}{2}) = (\frac{j}{2}, \frac{2t}{2}) = (\frac{1}{2}j, t)$

x-coordinate is $\frac{1}{2}j$

b.

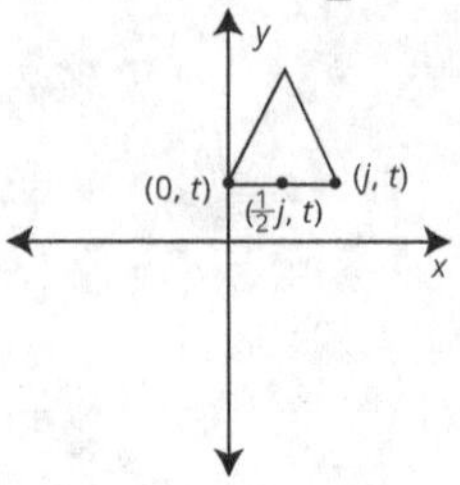

4.10 a. j

b. $d = |h - 0| = |h| = h$

c. h

d. $d = |h + k| = h + k = k + h$

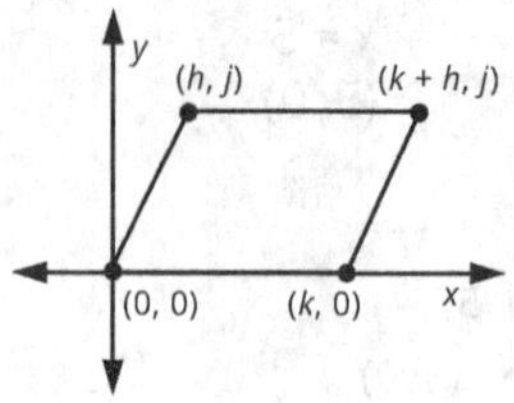

4.11

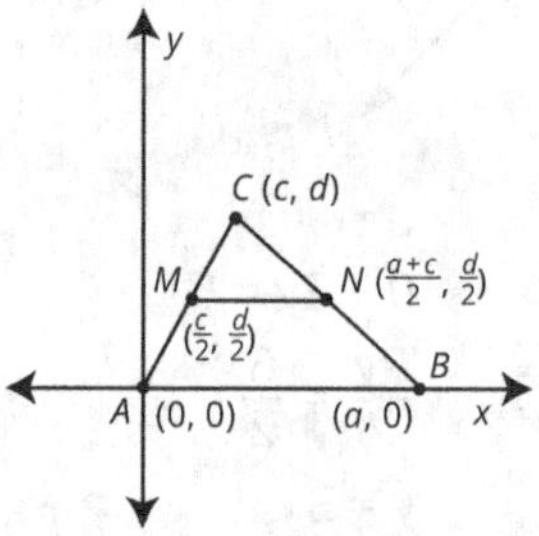

$$M_{AC} = (\frac{0 + c}{2}, \frac{0 + d}{2}) = (\frac{c}{2}, \frac{d}{2})$$

$$M_{BC} = (\frac{a + c}{2}, \frac{0 + d}{2}) = (\frac{a + c}{2}, \frac{d}{2})$$

$$m_{MN} = \frac{\frac{d}{2} - \frac{d}{2}}{\frac{a + c}{2} - \frac{c}{2}} = \frac{0}{\frac{a + c}{2} - \frac{c}{2}} = 0$$

$$m_{AB} = \frac{0 - 0}{a} = \frac{0}{a} = 0$$

Slopes are equal; therefore, $\overline{MN} \parallel \overline{AB}$.

4.12

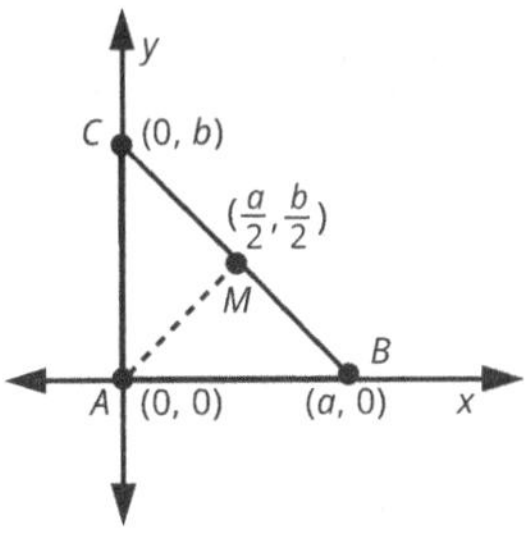

$$M_{BC} = (\frac{0+a}{2}, \frac{b+0}{2}) = (\frac{a}{2}, \frac{b}{2})$$

$$MB = \sqrt{(\frac{a}{2} - a)^2 + (\frac{b}{2} - 0)^2}$$

$$= \sqrt{(\frac{a}{2} - \frac{2a}{2})^2 + (\frac{b}{2})^2}$$

$$= \sqrt{(\frac{a}{2})^2 + (\frac{b}{2})^2} = \sqrt{\frac{a^2}{4} + \frac{b^2}{4}}$$

$$MC = \sqrt{(\frac{a}{2} - 0)^2 + (\frac{b}{2} - b)^2}$$

$$= \sqrt{(\frac{a}{2})^2 + (\frac{b}{2} - \frac{2b}{2})^2}$$

$$= \sqrt{(-\frac{a}{2})^2 + (-\frac{b}{2})^2} = \sqrt{\frac{a^2}{4} + \frac{b^2}{4}}$$

$$MA = \sqrt{(\frac{a}{2} - 0)^2 + (\frac{b}{2} - 0)^2}$$

$$= \sqrt{(\frac{a}{2})^2 + (\frac{b}{2})^2} = \sqrt{\frac{a^2}{4} + \frac{b^2}{4}}$$

7 $\therefore MB = MC = MA$

4.13

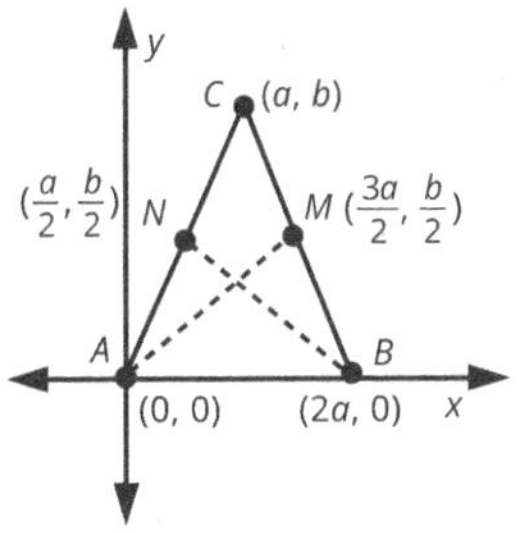

$$M_{AB} = (\frac{0+2a}{2}, \frac{0+0}{2}) = (\frac{2a}{2}, \frac{0}{2}) = (a, 0)$$

x-coordinate of point $C = a$

$$M_{AC} = (\frac{0+a}{2}, \frac{0+b}{2}) = (\frac{a}{2}, \frac{b}{2})$$

$$M_{BC} = (\frac{2a+a}{2}, \frac{0+b}{2}) = (\frac{3a}{2}, \frac{b}{2})$$

$$MA = \sqrt{(\frac{3a}{2} - 0)^2 + (\frac{b}{2} - 0)^2}$$

$$= \sqrt{(\frac{3a}{2})^2 + (\frac{b}{2})^2} = \sqrt{\frac{9a^2}{4} + \frac{b^2}{4}}$$

$$NB = \sqrt{(\frac{a}{2} - 2a)^2 + (\frac{b}{2} - 0)^2}$$

$$= \sqrt{(\frac{a}{2} - \frac{4a}{2})^2 + (\frac{b}{2} - 0)^2}$$

$$= \sqrt{(\frac{-3a}{2})^2 + (\frac{b}{2})^2} = \sqrt{\frac{9a^2}{4} + \frac{b^2}{4}}$$

$\therefore MA = NB$

4.14

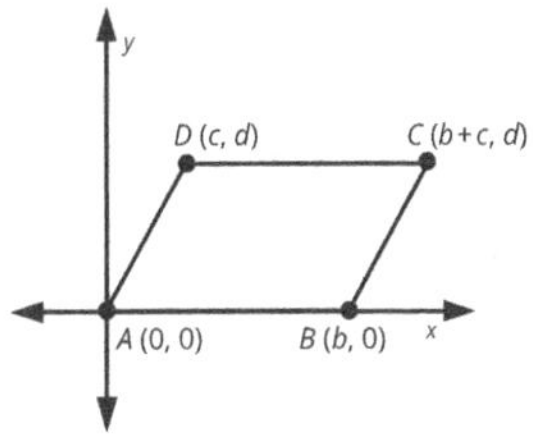

$AD = \sqrt{(c-0)^2 + (d-0)^2} = \sqrt{c^2 + d^2}$

$BC = \sqrt{[(b+c) - b]^2 + (d-0)^2} = \sqrt{c^2 + d^2}$

$AB = \sqrt{(b-0)^2 + (0-0)^2} = \sqrt{b^2 + 0^2} = \sqrt{b^2}$

$CD = \sqrt{[c - (b+c)]^2 + (d-d)^2} = \sqrt{b^2 + 0^2} = \sqrt{b^2}$

$\therefore AD = BC; AB = CD$

4.15

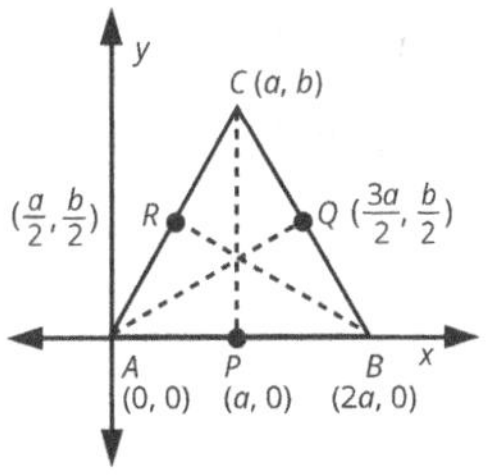

$$M_{AB} = (\frac{0+2a}{2}, \frac{0+0}{2}) = (\frac{2a}{2}, \frac{0}{2}) = (a, 0)$$

$$M_{BC} = (\frac{2a+a}{2}, \frac{0+b}{2}) = (\frac{3a}{2}, \frac{b}{2})$$

$$M_{AC} = (\frac{0+a}{2}, \frac{0+b}{2}) = (\frac{a}{2}, \frac{b}{2})$$

$PC = \sqrt{(a-a)^2 + (0-b)^2}$

$= \sqrt{(-b)^2}$ (Height of equilateral $\triangle = b$

$= a\sqrt{3}$ with side $= 2a$)

$$QA = \sqrt{(0 - \frac{3a}{2})^2 + (0 - \frac{b}{2})^2}$$

$$= \sqrt{(\frac{-3a}{2})^2 + (-\frac{b}{2})^2}$$

$$= \sqrt{\frac{9a^2}{4} + \frac{b^2}{4}}$$

$$= \sqrt{\frac{9a^2}{4} + \frac{(a\sqrt{3})^2}{4}}$$

$$= \sqrt{\frac{9a^2}{4} + \frac{3a^2}{4}}$$

$$= \sqrt{\frac{12a^2}{4}} = \sqrt{3a^2} = a\sqrt{3}$$

$RB = \sqrt{(2a - \frac{a}{2})^2 + (0 - \frac{b}{2})^2}$

$= \sqrt{(\frac{4a}{2} - \frac{a}{2})^2 + (0 - \frac{b}{2})^2}$

$= \sqrt{(\frac{3a}{2})^2 + (-\frac{b}{2})^2} = \sqrt{\frac{9a^2}{4} + \frac{b^2}{4}}$

$= \sqrt{\frac{9a^2}{4} + \frac{(a\sqrt{3})^2}{4}}$

$= \sqrt{\frac{9a^2}{4} + \frac{3a^2}{4}}$

$= \sqrt{\frac{12a^2}{4}} = \sqrt{3a^2} = a\sqrt{3}$

$\therefore PC = QA = RB$

4.16

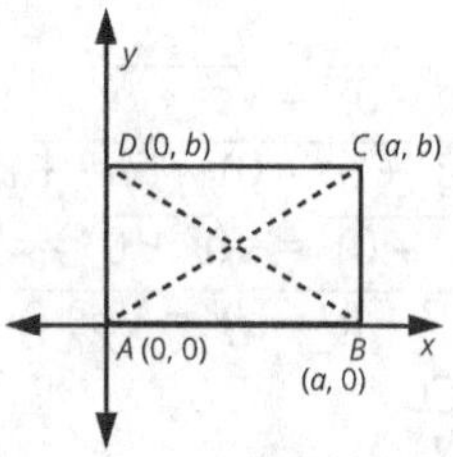

$AC = \sqrt{(a - 0)^2 + (b - 0)^2} = \sqrt{a^2 + b^2}$

$BD = \sqrt{(0 - a)^2 + (b - 0)^2} = \sqrt{(-a)^2 + b^2}$

$= \sqrt{a^2 + b^2}$

$\therefore AC = BD$

4.17

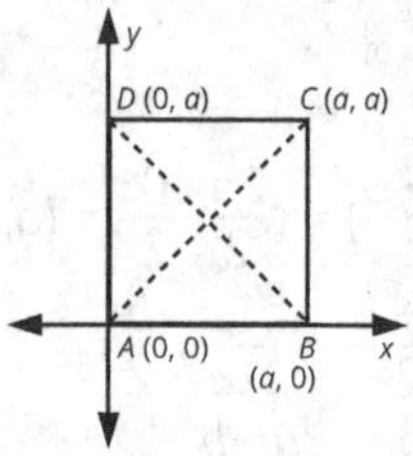

$m_{AC} = \frac{a - 0}{a - 0} = 1$

$m_{BD} = \frac{0 - a}{a - 0} = \frac{-a}{a} = -1$

$m_{AC} \cdot m_{BD} = 1(-1) = -1$

$\therefore \overline{AC} \perp \overline{BD}$

4.18

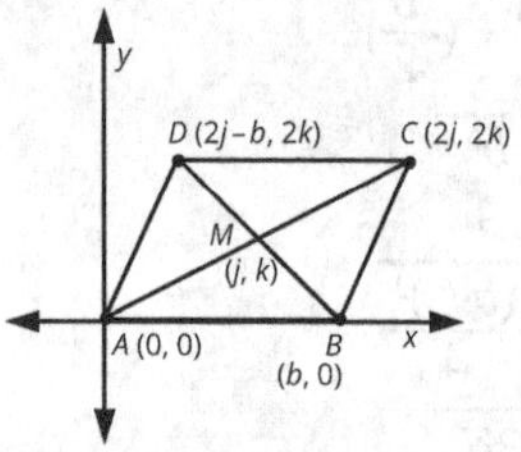

Since M is midpoint of BD, $D\ (2j - b, 2k)$.

Since M is midpoint of AC, $C\ (2j, 2k)$.

$m_{AD} = \frac{2k - 0}{(2j - b) - 0} = \frac{2k}{2j - b}$

$m_{BC} = \frac{2k - 0}{2j - b} = \frac{2k}{2j - b}$

$\overline{AD} \parallel \overline{BC}$

$m_{AB} = \frac{0 - 0}{b - 0} = \frac{0}{b} = 0$

$m_{DC} = \frac{2k - 2k}{2j - (2j - b)} = \frac{0}{-b} = 0$

$\overline{AB} \parallel \overline{DC}$

$\therefore ABCD$ is a parallelogram.

4.19

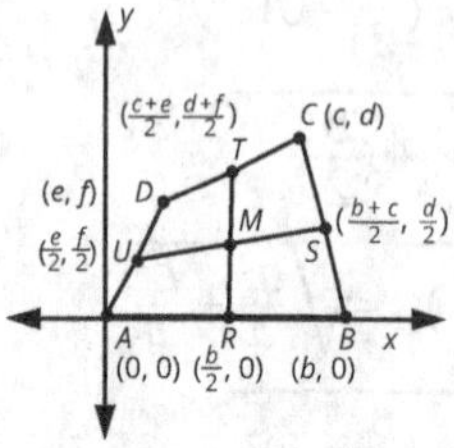

$M_{AB} = (\frac{b + 0}{2}, \frac{0 + 0}{2}) = (\frac{b}{2}, \frac{0}{2}) = (\frac{b}{2}, 0)$

$M_{BC} = (\frac{c + b}{2}, \frac{d + 0}{2}) = (\frac{c + b}{2}, \frac{d}{2})$

$M_{CD} = (\frac{c + e}{2}, \frac{d + f}{2})$

$M_{AD} = (\frac{e + 0}{2}, \frac{f + 0}{2}) = (\frac{e}{2}, \frac{f}{2})$

$M_{SU} = (\frac{\frac{b + c}{2} + \frac{e}{2}}{2}, \frac{\frac{d}{2} + \frac{f}{2}}{2})$

$= (\frac{\frac{b + c + e}{2}}{2}, \frac{\frac{d + f}{2}}{2})$

$= (\frac{b + c + e}{4}, \frac{d + f}{4})$

$M_{RT} = (\frac{\frac{c + e}{2} + \frac{b}{2}}{2}, \frac{\frac{d + f}{2} + 0}{2})$

$= (\frac{\frac{c + e + b}{2}}{2}, \frac{\frac{d + f}{2}}{2})$

$= (\frac{c + e + b}{4}, \frac{d + f}{4})$

Midpoints of both segments are the same point.

$\therefore$ Segments bisect each other.

4.20

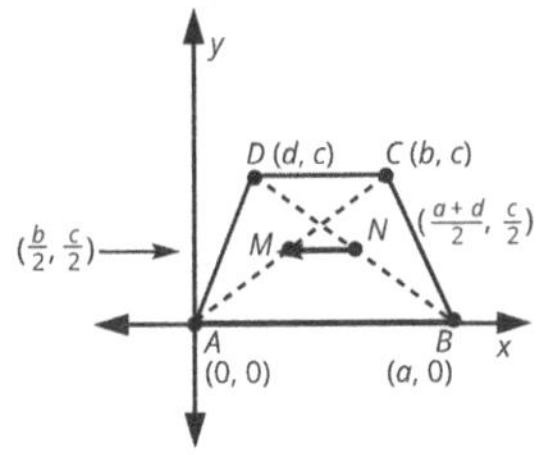

$M_{AC} = (\frac{b+0}{2}, \frac{c+0}{2}) = (\frac{b}{2}, \frac{c}{2})$

$M_{BC} = (\frac{a+d}{2}, \frac{0+c}{2}) = (\frac{a+d}{2}, \frac{c}{2})$

$m_{AB} = \frac{0-0}{a-0} = \frac{0}{a} = 0$

$m_{MN} = \dfrac{\frac{c}{2} - \frac{c}{2}}{\frac{a+d}{2} - \frac{b}{2}} = \dfrac{0}{\frac{a+d}{2} - \frac{b}{2}} = 0$

Slopes are equal;
∴ segments | |.

4.21

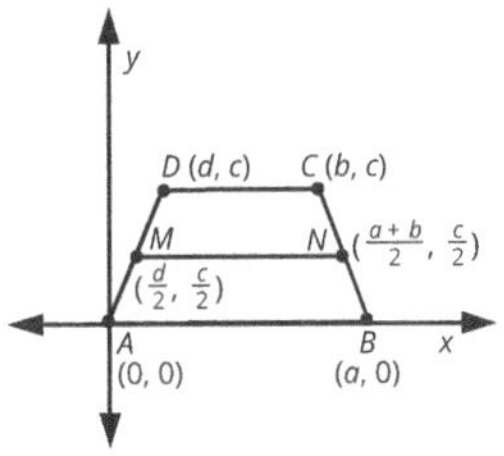

$M_{AD} = (\frac{d+0}{2}, \frac{c+0}{2}) = (\frac{d}{2}, \frac{c}{2})$

$M_{BC} = (\frac{a+b}{2}, \frac{0+c}{2}) = (\frac{a+b}{2}, \frac{c}{2})$

$MN = \sqrt{(\frac{a+b}{2} - \frac{d}{2})^2 + (\frac{c}{2} - \frac{c}{2})^2}$

$= \sqrt{(\frac{a+b-d}{2})^2 + 0^2}$

$= \sqrt{(\frac{a+b-d}{2})^2} = \frac{a+b-d}{2}$

$AB = \sqrt{(a-0)^2 + (0-0)^2} = \sqrt{a^2 + 0^2} = \sqrt{a^2} = a$

$CD = \sqrt{(b-d)^2 + (c-c)^2}$

$= \sqrt{(b-d)^2 + 0^2}$

$= \sqrt{(b-d)^2} = b - d$

$MN = \frac{1}{2}(AB + CD)$

$\frac{1}{2}(a+b-d) = \frac{1}{2}(a+b-d)$

4.22

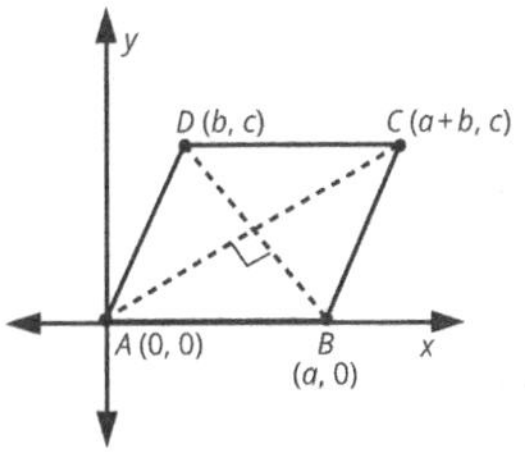

$m_{AC} = \frac{c-0}{a+b-0} = \frac{c}{a+b}$

$m_{BD} = \frac{c-0}{b-a} = \frac{c}{b-a}$

$\frac{c}{a+b} = -\frac{b-a}{c}$

$c(c) = (a+b)(-b+a)$ (cross-multiply)

$c^2 = (a+b)(a-b)$

$c^2 = a^2 - b^2$

$c^2 + b^2 = a^2$

$a^2 = b^2 + c^2$

$\sqrt{a^2} = \sqrt{b^2 + c^2}$

$a = \sqrt{b^2 + c^2}$

$AB = \sqrt{(a-0)^2 + (0-0)^2} = \sqrt{a^2 + 0^2} = \sqrt{a^2} = a$

$AB = \sqrt{b^2 + c^2}$

$BC = \sqrt{(a+b-a)^2 + (c-0)^2} = \sqrt{b^2 + c^2}$

∴ $AB = BC$ and $ABCD$ is a rhombus.

4.23

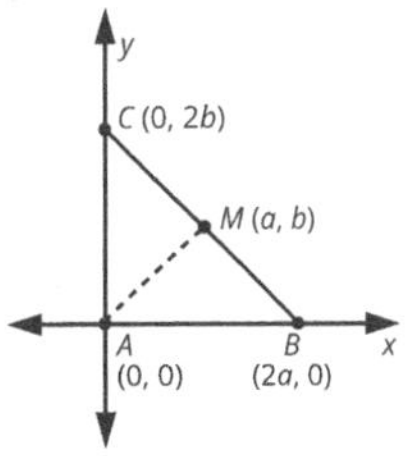

$M_{BC} = (\frac{0+2a}{2}, \frac{2b+0}{2}) = (\frac{2a}{2}, \frac{2b}{2}) = (a, b)$

$AM = \sqrt{(0-a)^2 + (0-b)^2} = \sqrt{(-a)^2 + (-b)^2}$

$= \sqrt{a^2 + b^2}$

$BC = \sqrt{(0-2a)^2 + (2b-0)^2}$

$= \sqrt{(-2a)^2 + (2b)^2} = \sqrt{4a^2 + 4b^2}$

$= \sqrt{4(a^2 + b^2)} = 2\sqrt{a^2 + b^2}$

$= \sqrt{a^2 + b^2} = \frac{1}{2}(2\sqrt{a^2 + b^2})$

$AM = \frac{1}{2}BC$

4.24

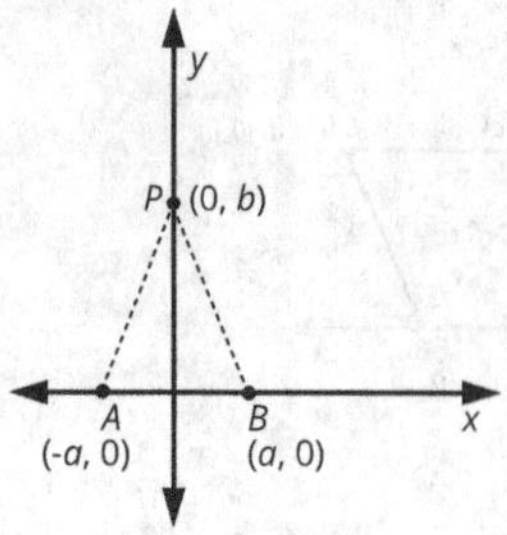

$AP = \sqrt{[0 - (-a)]^2 + (b - 0)^2} = \sqrt{a^2 + b^2}$
$BP = \sqrt{(0 - a)^2 + (b - 0)^2}$
$= \sqrt{(-a)^2 + b^2} = \sqrt{a^2 + b^2}$
$\therefore AP = BP$

4.25

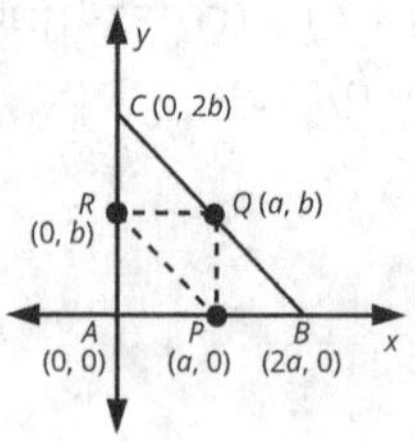

$M_{AB} = (\frac{2a + 0}{2}, \frac{0 + 0}{2}) = (\frac{2a}{2}, \frac{0}{2}) = (a, 0)$

$M_{BC} = (\frac{0 + 2a}{2}, \frac{2b + 0}{2}) = (\frac{2a}{2}, \frac{2b}{2}) = (a, b)$

$M_{AC} = (\frac{0 + 0}{2}, \frac{2b + 0}{2}) = (\frac{0}{2}, \frac{2b}{2}) = (0, b)$

$m_{PQ} = \frac{b - 0}{a - a} = \frac{b}{0}$ = no slope

$m_{RQ} = \frac{b - b}{a - 0} = \frac{0}{a} = 0$

$\therefore \overline{PQ} \perp \overline{RQ}$ and $\triangle PQR$ is a right $\triangle$.

SELF TEST 4

4.01 $B(0, s)$
$D(r, 0)$

4.02 x-coordinate $= \frac{1}{2}RT$

$RT = \sqrt{(2a - 0)^2 + (0 - 0)^2}$
$= \sqrt{(2a)^2 + 0^2}$
$= \sqrt{4a^2} = 2a$
$= \frac{1}{2}(2a) = a$

Let y-coordinate $= c$

$TS = \sqrt{(2a - a)^2 + (0 - c)^2}$
$= \sqrt{a^2 + (-c)^2}$
$= \sqrt{a^2 + c^2}$
$RT = TS$
$\sqrt{a^2 + c^2} = \sqrt{4a^2}$
$a^2 + c^2 = 4a^2$
$c^2 = 4a^2 - a^2$
$c^2 = 3a^2$
$\sqrt{c^2} = \sqrt{3a^2}$
$c = \sqrt{3}\sqrt{a^2}$
$c = a\sqrt{3}$
Point $S = (a, a\sqrt{3})$

4.03 $(a + c, b)$

4.04

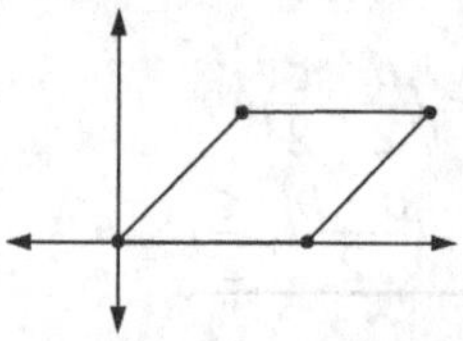

$m_{BD} = \frac{b - 0}{a - c} = \frac{b}{a - c}$

$m_{AC} = \frac{b - 0}{a + c - 0} = \frac{b}{a + c}$

4.05 c

4.06 $(r, 0)$; $(0, r)$

4.07

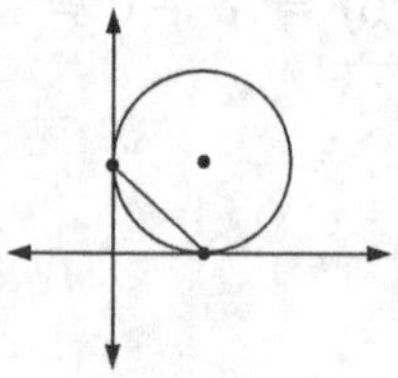

$d = \sqrt{(r - 0)^2 + (0 - r)^2}$
$= \sqrt{r^2 + (-r)^2}$
$= \sqrt{r^2 + r^2}$
$= \sqrt{2r^2} = \sqrt{2}\sqrt{r^2}$
$= r\sqrt{2}$

4.08 $m = \frac{r-0}{0-r} = \frac{r}{-r} = -1$

$y - 0 = -1(x - r)$

$y = -x + r$

$x + y = r$

4.09 Points are (0, 0) and (r, r).

$m_{BD} = \frac{r-0}{r-0} = \frac{r}{r} = 1$

4.010

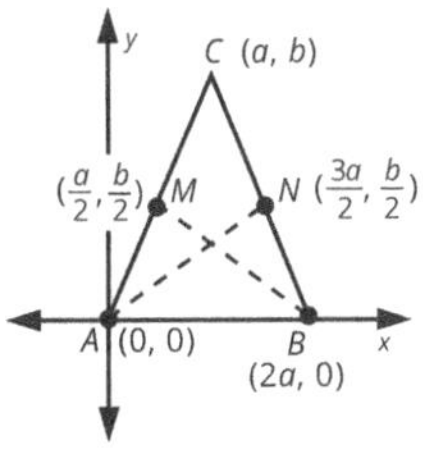

$M_{AC} = (\frac{a+0}{2}, \frac{b+0}{2}) = (\frac{a}{2}, \frac{b}{2})$

$M_{BC} = (\frac{a+2a}{2}, \frac{b+0}{2}) = (\frac{3a}{2}, \frac{b}{2})$

$BM = \sqrt{(\frac{a}{2} - 2a)^2 + (\frac{b}{2} - 0)^2}$

$= \sqrt{(\frac{a}{2} - \frac{4a}{2})^2 + (\frac{b}{2})^2}$

$= \sqrt{(-\frac{3a}{2})^2 + (\frac{b}{2})^2} = \sqrt{\frac{9a^2}{4} + \frac{b^2}{4}}$

$AN = \sqrt{(0 - \frac{3a}{2})^2 + (0 - \frac{b}{2})^2}$

$= \sqrt{(-\frac{3a}{2})^2 + (-\frac{b}{2})^2}$

$= \sqrt{(\frac{9a^2}{4})^2 + \frac{b^2}{4}}$

$\therefore BM = AN$

4.011

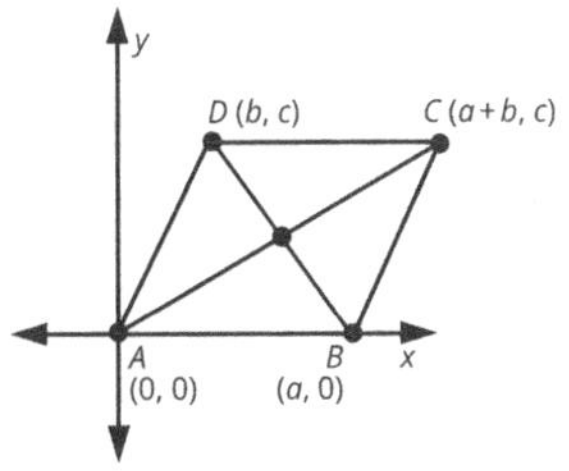

$m_{AC} = \frac{c-0}{a+b-0} = \frac{c}{a+b}$

$m_{BD} = \frac{c-0}{b-a} = \frac{c}{b-a}$

$AB = AD$

$AB = \sqrt{(a-0)^2 + (0-0)^2}$

$= \sqrt{a^2 + 0^2}$

$= \sqrt{a^2} = a$

$AD = \sqrt{(b-0)^2 + (c-0)^2}$

$= \sqrt{b^2 + c^2}$

$a = \sqrt{b^2 + c^2}$

$(a)^2 = (\sqrt{b^2 + c^2})^2$

$a^2 = b^2 + c^2$

$a^2 - b^2 = c^2$

$c^2 = a^2 - b^2$

$\frac{c}{a+b} = \frac{a-b}{c}$

$\frac{c}{a+b} = -\frac{b-a}{c}$

$m_{AC} = -m_{BD}$

$\therefore \overline{AC} \perp \overline{BD}$

4.012

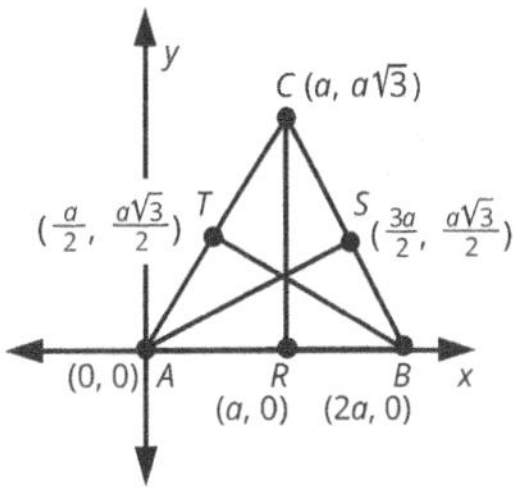

Refer to Problem 4.02 to find coordinates of point *C*.

$M_{AB} = (\frac{2a+0}{2}, \frac{0+0}{2}) = (\frac{2a}{2}, \frac{0}{2}) = (a, 0)$

$M_{BC} = (\frac{a+2a}{2}, \frac{a\sqrt{3}+0}{2}) = (\frac{3a}{2}, \frac{a\sqrt{3}}{2})$

$M_{AC} = (\frac{a+0}{2}, \frac{a\sqrt{3}}{2}) = (\frac{a}{2}, \frac{a\sqrt{3}}{2})$

$AS = \sqrt{(\frac{3a}{2} - 0)^2 + (\frac{a\sqrt{3}}{2} - 0)^2}$

$= \sqrt{(\frac{3a}{2})^2 + (\frac{a\sqrt{3}}{2})^2}$

$= \sqrt{\frac{9a^2}{4} + \frac{3a^2}{4}} = \sqrt{\frac{12a^2}{4}}$

$= \sqrt{3a^2} = \sqrt{3}\sqrt{a^2} = a\sqrt{3}$

$BT = \sqrt{(\frac{a}{2} - 2a)^2 + (\frac{a\sqrt{3}}{2} - 0)^2}$

$= \sqrt{(\frac{a}{2} - \frac{4a}{2})^2 + (\frac{a\sqrt{3}}{2})^2}$

$= \sqrt{(-\frac{3a}{2})^2 + (\frac{a\sqrt{3}}{2})^2}$

$= \sqrt{\frac{9a^2}{4} + \frac{3a^2}{4}} = \sqrt{\frac{12a^2}{4}}$

$= \sqrt{3a^2} = \sqrt{3}\sqrt{a^2} = a\sqrt{3}$

$CR = \sqrt{(a - a)^2 + (0 - a\sqrt{3})^2}$

$= \sqrt{0^2 + (-a\sqrt{3})^2}$

$= \sqrt{3a^2} = \sqrt{3}\sqrt{a^2} = a\sqrt{3}$

$\therefore AS = BT = CR$

4.013

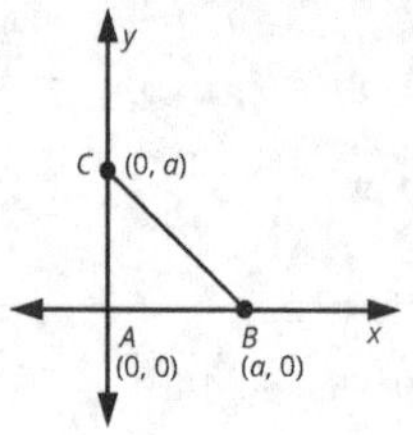

$AB = \sqrt{(0 - a)^2 + (0 - 0)^2}$

$= \sqrt{(-a)^2 + 0^2}$

$= \sqrt{a^2} = a$

$BC = \sqrt{(a - 0)^2 + (0 - a)^2}$

$= \sqrt{a^2 + (-a)^2}$

$= \sqrt{a^2 + a^2}$

$= \sqrt{2a^2} = \sqrt{2}\sqrt{a^2} = a\sqrt{2}$

$BC = AB\sqrt{2}$

4.014

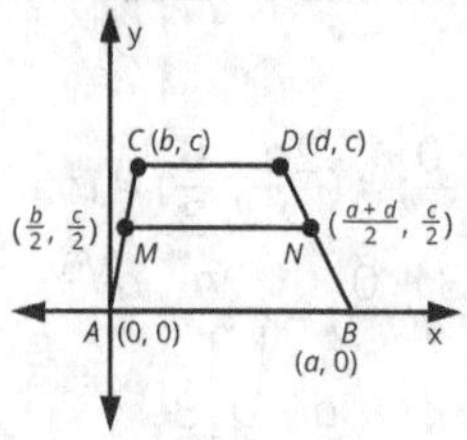

$M_{AC} = (\frac{b+0}{2}, \frac{c+0}{2}) = (\frac{b}{2}, \frac{c}{2})$

$M_{BD} = (\frac{a+d}{2}, \frac{0+c}{2}) = (\frac{a+d}{2}, \frac{c}{2})$

$m_{AB} = \frac{0-0}{a-0} = \frac{0}{a} = 0$

$m_{CD} = \frac{c-c}{d-b} = \frac{0}{d-b} = 0$

$m_{MN} = \dfrac{\frac{c}{2} - \frac{c}{2}}{\frac{a+d}{2} - \frac{b}{2}} = \dfrac{0}{\frac{a+d}{2} - \frac{b}{2}} = 0$

Slopes are equal; ∴ median || to bases.

4.015 line, plane

4.016 line, plane

4.017 line, plane

4.018 point, line, plane

4.019 line, plane

4.020 none

4.021 Some points are (-4, -4), (0, 0), and (2, 2)
$x = y$

4.022 $y \geq -4$

4.023 $y \geq -2 \cup y < 2$
$-2 \leq y < 2$

4.024 Points given are (0, 4) and (4, 0).

$m = \frac{0-4}{4-0} = \frac{-4}{4} = -1$

$y - 4 = -1(x - 0)$

$y - 4 = -x + 0$

$x + y - 4 = 0$

$x + y = 4$

4.025 a. (5, -3)
b. $r = \sqrt{25} = 5$

4.026 a. (0, 0)
b. $r = \sqrt{16} = 4$

4.027 a. (0, 3)
b. $r = \sqrt{8} = 2\sqrt{2}$

4.028
$8 = \frac{1}{2}(x + 5)$
$16 = x + 5$ (multiply by 2)
$16 - 5 = x$
$11 = x$

$2 = \frac{1}{2}(y + 6)$
$4 = y + 6$ (multiply by 2)
$4 - 6 = y$
$-2 = y$
(11, -2)

4.029
$0 = \frac{1}{2}(x - 16)$
$0 = x - 16$ (multiply by 2)
$16 = x$

$-16 = \frac{1}{2}(y + 0)$
$-32 = y + 0$ (multiply by 2)
$-32 = y$
(16, -32)

4.030
$2 = \frac{1}{2}(x + 12)$
$4 = x + 12$ (multiply by 2)
$4 - 12 = x$
$-8 = x$

$6 = \frac{1}{2}(y + 4)$
$12 = y + 4$ (multiply by 2)
$12 - 4 = y$
$8 = y$
(-8, 8)

4.031 $d = \sqrt{(0 - 5)^2 + (6 - 12)^2}$

$= \sqrt{(-5)^2 + (-6)^2}$

$= \sqrt{25 + 36} = \sqrt{61}$

4.032 $d = \sqrt{(4-7)^2 + (1-5)^2}$
$= \sqrt{(-3)^2 + (-4)^2}$
$= \sqrt{9 + 16} = \sqrt{25} = 5$

4.033 $d = \sqrt{(-3-0)^2 + (0-\sqrt{7})^2}$
$= \sqrt{(-3)^2 + (-\sqrt{7})^2}$
$= \sqrt{9 + 7} = \sqrt{16} = 4$

4.034 $m = \dfrac{5-8}{-2-3} = \dfrac{-3}{-5} = \dfrac{3}{5}$

4.035 $m = \dfrac{2-22}{-4-0} = \dfrac{-20}{-4} = 5$

4.036 $m = \dfrac{10-0}{5-0} = \dfrac{10}{5} = 2$

4.037 $m = \dfrac{-5-2}{15-13} = -\dfrac{7}{2}$
$m\perp = \dfrac{2}{7}$

4.038 $m = \dfrac{4-(-1)}{0-2} = -\dfrac{5}{2}$
$m\perp = \dfrac{2}{5}$

4.039 $m = \dfrac{5-2}{8-3} = \dfrac{3}{5}$
$m\perp = -\dfrac{5}{3}$

4.040 $m = \dfrac{-4-0}{4-0} = \dfrac{-4}{4} = -1$
$y - 0 = -1(x - 0)$
$y = -x$
$x + y = 0$

4.041 $m = \dfrac{1-2}{5-(-2)} = -\dfrac{1}{7}$
$y - 2 = -\dfrac{1}{7}(x + 2)$
$y - 2 = -\dfrac{1}{7}x - \dfrac{2}{7}$
$\dfrac{1}{7}x + y - 2 = -\dfrac{2}{7}$
$\dfrac{1}{7}x + y = -\dfrac{2}{7} + 2$
$\dfrac{1}{7}x + y = \dfrac{12}{7}$
$x + 7y = 12$ (multiply by 7)

4.042 $m = \dfrac{6-6}{5-0} = \dfrac{0}{5} = 0$
$y = 6$

4.043 $y - 5 = 3(x - 5)$
$y - 5 = 3x - 15$
$-3x + y - 5 = -15$
$-3x + y = -15 + 5$
$-3x + y = -10$
$3x - y = 10$ (multiply by -1)

4.044 $y - 4 = 0(x - 0)$
$y - 4 = 0$
$y = 4$

4.045 $x = 3$

LIFEPAC TEST

1. $\parallel$

2. y

3. y

4. $5x - y = 8$
$5x - 7 = 8$
$5x = 8 + 7$
$5x = 15$
$\frac{5x}{5} = \frac{15}{5}$
$x = 3$

5. a. (-4, 6)
b. $r = \sqrt{25} = 5$

6. $(x - 2)^2 + (y - 6)^2 = 4$
$(5 - 2)^2 + (6 + 0)^2 \ ? \ 4$
$3^2 + 0^2 \ ? \ 4$
$9 \neq 4$
no

7. $d = \sqrt{(-4 - 4)^2 + (2 - 2)^2}$
$= \sqrt{(-8)^2 + (0)^2}$
$= \sqrt{64} = 8$

8. $M = (\frac{4 - 4}{2}, \frac{2 + 2}{2}) = (\frac{0}{2}, \frac{4}{2}) = (0, 2)$

9. $m = \frac{2 - 2}{4 - (-4)} = \frac{0}{8} = 0$

10. $||$ lines have equal slopes; $\therefore m = 0$.

11. no slope

12. $x = -5$

13. $y + 4 = \frac{3}{5}(x - 2)$
$y + 4 = \frac{3}{5}x - \frac{6}{5}$
$-\frac{3}{5}x + y + 4 = -\frac{6}{5}$
$-\frac{3}{5}x + y = -\frac{6}{5} - 4$
$-\frac{3}{5}x + y = \frac{26}{5}$
$3x - 5y = 26$ (multiply by -5)

14. ctr. $= m = (\frac{6 - 2}{2}, \frac{7 + 1}{2}) = (\frac{4}{2}, \frac{8}{2}) = (2, 4)$
diameter $= d = \sqrt{(-2 - 6)^2 + (1 - 7)^2}$
$= \sqrt{(-8)^2 + (-6)^2}$
$= \sqrt{64 + 36}$
$= \sqrt{100} = 10$
radius $= \frac{1}{2}d = \frac{1}{2}(10) = 5$
$(x - 2)^2 + (y - 4)^2 = 5^2$
$(x - 2)^2 + (y - 4)^2 = 25$

15. $M = (\frac{2 + 4}{2}, \frac{-5 + 1}{2}) = (\frac{6}{2}, \frac{-4}{2}) = (3, -2)$
$m = \frac{-5 - 1}{2 - 4} = \frac{-6}{-2} = 3$
$m = -\frac{1}{3}$
$y + 2 = \frac{1}{3}(x - 3)$
$y + 2 = \frac{1}{3}x + 1$
$\frac{1}{3}x + y + 2 = 1$
$\frac{1}{3}x + y = 1 - 2$
$\frac{1}{3}x + y = -1$
$x + 3y = -3$ (multiply by 3)

16. $M_{RT} = (\frac{2c + 2a}{2}, \frac{2d + 0}{2}) = (a + c, d)$
$M_{ST} = (\frac{2c + 2b}{2}, \frac{2d + 0}{2}) = (b + c, d)$
$MN = \sqrt{[(a + c) - (b + c)]^2 + (d - d)^2}$
$= \sqrt{(a + c - b - c)^2 + 0^2}$
$= \sqrt{(a - b)^2} = a - b$

17. x-intercept:
$4x - 0 = 12$
$4x = 12$
$\frac{4x}{4} = \frac{12}{4}$
$x = 3$
(3, 0)

y-intercept:
$0 - 3y = 12$
$-3y = 12$
$\frac{-3y}{-3} = \frac{12}{-3}$
$y = -4$
(0, -4)

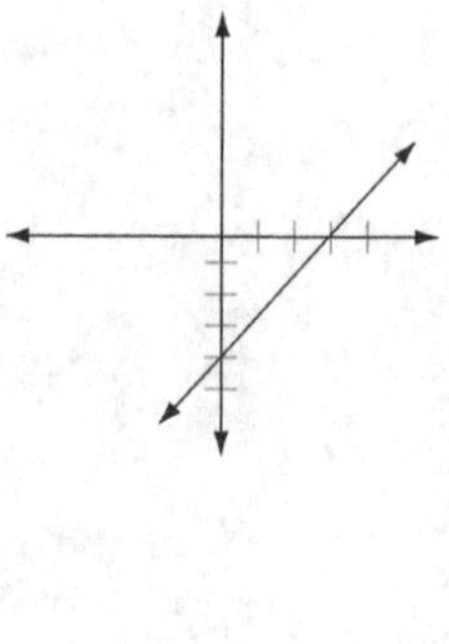

18. $|x| > 2$

$x > 2 \quad x < -2$

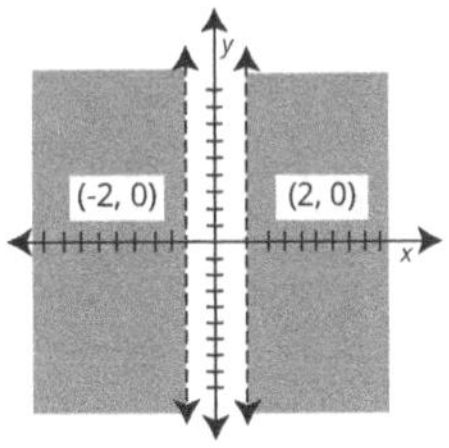

19. $x \geq -1 \cup x \leq 3$

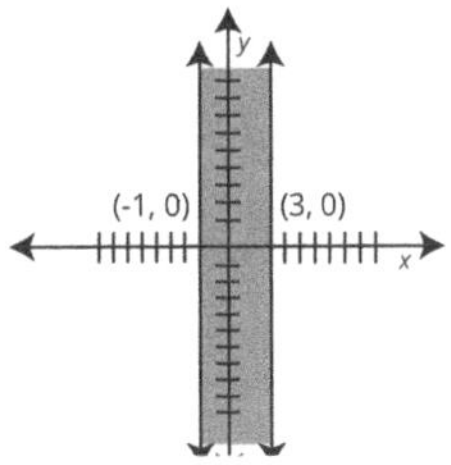

20. false
21. true
22. true
23. true
24. false
25.

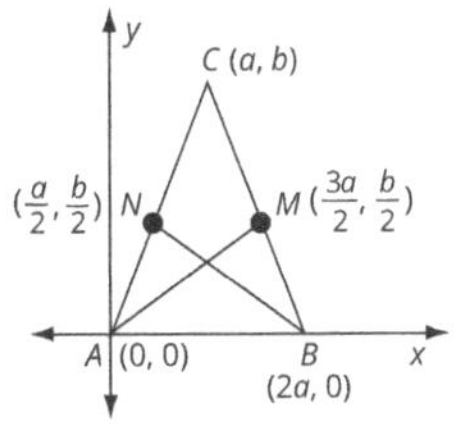

$$M_{AC} = \left(\frac{a+0}{2}, \frac{b+0}{2}\right) = \left(\frac{a}{2}, \frac{b}{2}\right)$$

$$M_{BC} = \left(\frac{a+2a}{2}, \frac{b+0}{2}\right) = \left(\frac{3a}{2}, \frac{b}{2}\right)$$

$$AM = \sqrt{\left(0 - \frac{3a}{2}\right)^2 + \left(0 - \frac{b}{2}\right)^2}$$

$$= \sqrt{\left(-\frac{3a}{2}\right)^2 + \left(-\frac{b}{2}\right)^2}$$

$$= \sqrt{\frac{9a^2}{4} + \frac{b^2}{4}}$$

$$BN = \sqrt{\left(\frac{a}{2} - 2a\right)^2 + \left(\frac{b}{2} - 0\right)^2}$$

$$= \sqrt{\left(\frac{a}{2} - \frac{4a}{2}\right)^2 + \left(\frac{b}{2}\right)^2}$$

$$= \sqrt{\left(-\frac{3a}{2}\right)^2 + \left(\frac{b}{2}\right)^2}$$

$$= \sqrt{\frac{9a^2}{4} + \frac{b^2}{4}}$$

$\therefore AM = BN$

ALTERNATE LIFEPAC TEST

1. through 5.

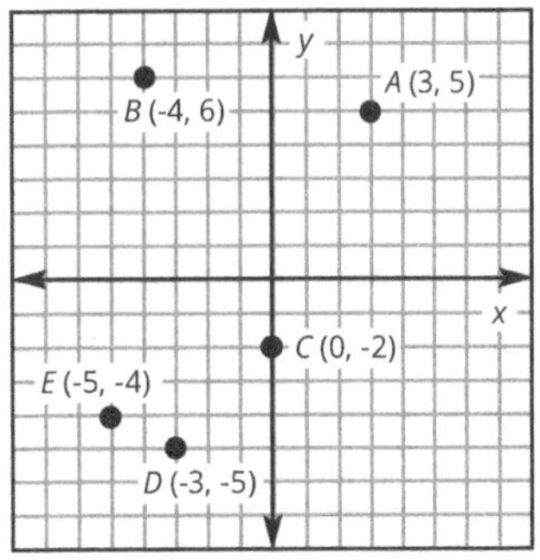

6.
$d = \sqrt{(x_1 - x_2)^2 + (y_1 - y_2)^2}$
$d = \sqrt{(3 - 5)^2 + [4 - (-2)]^2}$
$d = \sqrt{(-2)^2 + (6)^2}$
$d = \sqrt{4 + 36}$
$d = \sqrt{40}$
$d = \sqrt{4 \cdot 10} = \sqrt{4} \cdot \sqrt{10}$
$d = 2\sqrt{10}$

7.
$d = \sqrt{(x_1 - x_2)^2 + (y_1 - y_2)^2}$
$d = \sqrt{(0 - 8)^2 + (0 - 4)^2}$
$d = \sqrt{(-8)^2 + (-4)^2}$
$d = \sqrt{64 + 16}$
$d = \sqrt{80}$
$d = \sqrt{16 \cdot 5} = \sqrt{16} \cdot \sqrt{5}$
$d = 4\sqrt{5}$

8.
$d = \sqrt{(x_1 - x_2)^2 + (y_1 - y_2)^2}$
$d = \sqrt{(1 - 4)^2 + [3 - (-4)]^2}$
$d = \sqrt{(-3)^2 + (7)^2}$
$d = \sqrt{9 + 49}$
$d = \sqrt{58}$

9.
$d = \sqrt{(x_1 - x_2)^2 + (y_1 - y_2)^2}$
$d = \sqrt{(0 - 5)^2 + (-8 - 4)^2}$
$d = \sqrt{(-5)^2 + (-12)^2}$
$d = \sqrt{25 + 144}$
$d = \sqrt{169}$
$d = 13$

10. $d = \sqrt{(x_1 - x_2)^2 + (y_1 - y_2)^2}$
$d = \sqrt{[0 - (-6)]^2 + (6 - 0)^2}$
$d = \sqrt{(6)^2 + (6)^2}$
$d = \sqrt{36 + 36}$
$d = \sqrt{72}$
$d = \sqrt{36 \cdot 2} = \sqrt{36} \cdot \sqrt{2}$
$d = 6\sqrt{2}$

11. $h = 3$, $k = 5$, and $r = 5$
$(x - h)^2 + (y - k)^2 = r^2$
$(x - 3)^2 + (y - 4)^2 = 5^2$
$(x - 3)^2 + (y - 4)^2 = 25$

12. $h = -2$, $k = -6$, and $r = 4$
$(x - h)^2 + (y - k)^2 = r^2$
$[x - (-2)]^2 + [y - (-6)]^2 = 4^2$
$(x + 2)^2 + (y + 6)^2 = 16$

13. $h = 0$, $k = 0$, and $r = 3$
$(x - h)^2 + (y - k)^2 = r^2$
$(x - 0)^2 + (y - 0)^2 = 3^2$
$x^2 + y^2 = 9$

14. $h = 5$, $k = -3$, and $r = 5$
$(x - h)^2 + (y - k)^2 = r^2$
$(x - 5)^2 + [y - (-3)]^2 = 5^2$
$(x - 5)^2 + (y + 3)^2 = 25$

15. $d = \sqrt{(x_1 - x_2)^2 + (y_1 - y_2)^2}$
$d = \sqrt{(2 - 8)^2 + [-3 - (-3)]^2}$
$d = \sqrt{(-6)^2 + (0)^2}$
$d = \sqrt{36}$
$d = 6$
diameter of circle = 6; therefore, radius = 3 and center = (5, -3)

$h = 5$, $k = -3$, and $r = 3$
$(x - h)^2 + (y - k)^2 = r^2$
$(x - 5)^2 + [y - (-3)]^2 = 3^2$
$(x - 5)^2 + (y + 3)^2 = 9$

16. $x = \frac{1}{2}(x_2 + x_1)$
$x = \frac{1}{2}(0 + 0)$
$x = \frac{1}{2}(0)$
$x = 0$

$y = \frac{1}{2}(y_2 + y_1)$
$y = \frac{1}{2}(8 + 0)$
$y = \frac{1}{2}(8)$
$y = 4$
The midpoint is (0, 4).

17. $x = \frac{1}{2}(x_2 + x_1)$
$x = \frac{1}{2}(8 + 0)$
$x = \frac{1}{2}(8)$
$x = 4$

$y = \frac{1}{2}(y_2 + y_1)$
$y = \frac{1}{2}(8 + 0)$
$y = \frac{1}{2}(8)$
$y = 4$
The midpoint is (4, 4).

18. $x = \frac{1}{2}(x_2 + x_1)$
$x = \frac{1}{2}(0 + 8)$
$x = \frac{1}{2}(8)$
$x = 4$

$y = \frac{1}{2}(y_2 + y_1)$
$y = \frac{1}{2}(8 + 0)$
$y = \frac{1}{2}(8)$
$y = 4$
The midpoint is (4, 4).

19. $x = \frac{1}{2}(x_2 + x_1)$

$x = \frac{1}{2}(-8 + 8)$

$x = \frac{1}{2}(0)$

$x = 0$

$y = \frac{1}{2}(y_2 + y_1)$

$y = \frac{1}{2}[8 + (-8)]$

$y = \frac{1}{2}(0)$

$y = 0$

The midpoint is (0, 0).

20. $x = \frac{1}{2}(x_2 + x_1)$

$x = \frac{1}{2}[8 + (-8)]$

$x = \frac{1}{2}(0)$

$x = 0$

$y = \frac{1}{2}(y_2 + y_1)$

$y = \frac{1}{2}[8 + (-8)]$

$y = \frac{1}{2}(0)$

$y = 0$

The midpoint is (0, 0).

21. Both points lie on the *y*-axis; therefore, the line has no slope. The equation is $x = 0$.

22. $y - y_1 = \frac{y_2 - y_1}{x_2 - x_1}(x - x_1)$

$y - 3 = \frac{-4 - 3}{4 - 1}(x - 1)$

$y - 3 = \frac{-7}{3}(x - 1)$

$3y - 9 = -7(x - 1)$

$3y - 9 = -7x + 7$

$3y - \cancel{9} + \cancel{9} + 7x$
$= \cancel{-7x} + \cancel{7x} + 7 + 9$

$7x + 3y = 16$

23. $y - y_1 = \frac{y_2 - y_1}{x_2 - x_1}(x - x_1)$

$y - 3 = \frac{1 - 3}{-2 - 5}(x - 5)$

$y - 3 = \frac{-2}{-7}(x - 5)$

$y - 3 = \frac{2}{7}(x - 5)$

$7y - 21 = 2(x - 5)$

$7y - 21 = 2x - 10$

$7y - \cancel{21} + \cancel{21} - 2x = \cancel{2x} - \cancel{2x} - 10 + 21$

$-2x + 7y = 11$

24. m of the line through (5, 2):

$m_1 = -\frac{1}{m_2}$

$m_1 = \frac{-1}{-2}$

$m_1 = \frac{1}{2}$

$y - y_1 = m(x - x_1)$

$y - 2 = \frac{1}{2}(x - 5)$

$2y - 4 = 1(x - 5)$

$2y - 4 = x - 5$

$\cancel{2y} - \cancel{2y} - 4 + 5$
$= x - 2y - \cancel{5} + \cancel{5}$

$1 = x - 2y$

$x - 2y = 1$

25. Slope of parallel lines are equal.

$y - y_1 = m(x - x_1)$

$y - 1 = \frac{1}{5}(x - 3)$

$5y - 5 = 1(x - 3)$

$5y - 5 = x - 3$

$\cancel{5y} - \cancel{5y} - 5 + 3$
$= x - 5y - \cancel{3} + \cancel{3}$

$-2 = x - 5y$

$x - 5y = -2$

26. midpoint of $\overline{AB}$:

$x = \frac{1}{2}(x_2 + x_1)$

$x = \frac{1}{2}(7 + 3)$

$x = \frac{1}{2}(10)$

$x = 5$

$y = \frac{1}{2}(y_2 + y_1)$

$y = \frac{1}{2}(6 + 2)$

$y = \frac{1}{2}(8)$

$y = 4$

The midpoint is (5, 4).

$\text{slope of } \overline{AB} = \frac{y_2 - y_1}{x_2 - x_1}$

$= \frac{6 - 2}{7 - 3}$

$= \frac{4}{4} = 1$

The slope of l is -1.

Equation of l:

$y - y_1 = m(x - x_1)$

$y - 4 = -1(x - 5)$

$y - 4 = -1(x - 5)$

$y - 4 = -x + 5$

$y + x - 4 + 4$

$= -x + x + 5 + 4$

$y + x = 9$

$x + y = 9$

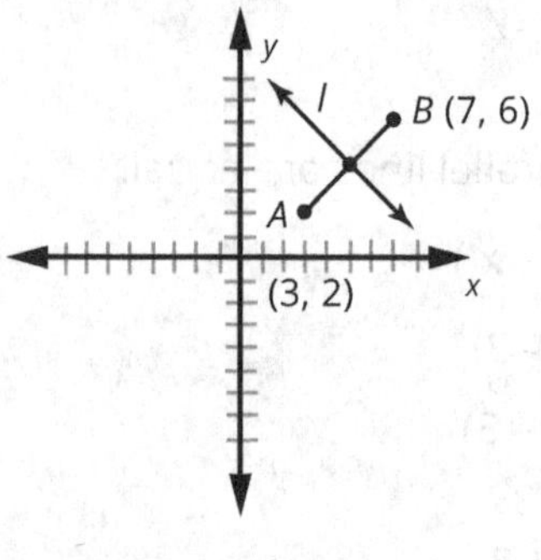

27. $M_{AC} = (\frac{a}{2}, \frac{b}{2})$

$M_{BD} = (\frac{a}{2}, \frac{b}{2})$

$M_{AC} = M_{BD}$

$\therefore$ AC and BD bisect each other.

MATH 1009

ALTERNATE LIFEPAC TEST

NAME ______________________________

DATE ______________________________

SCORE ______________________________

65
81

Graph the given points on one set of axes (each answer, 2 points).

1. *A* (3, 5)
2. *B* (-4, 6)
3. *C* (0, -2)
4. *D* (-3, -5)
5. *E* (-5, -4)

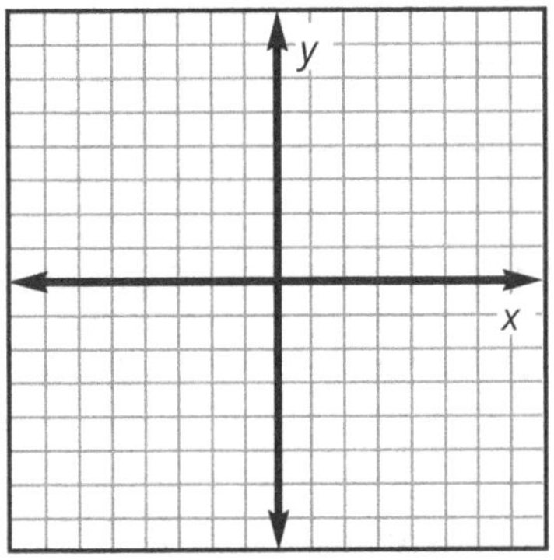

Find the distance between these points (each answer, 3 points).

6. *A* (3, 4), *B* (5, -2) *AB* = ________________
7. *C* (0, 0) , *D* (8, 4) *CD* = ________________
8. *E* (1, 3), *F* (4, -4) *EF* = ________________
9. *H* (0, -8), *I* (5, 4) *HI* = ________________
10. *J* (0, 6), *K* (-6, 0) *JK* = ________________

Write the equation of a circle whose center and other information are given (each answer, 3 points).

11. *A* (3, 4), *r* = 5 ________________
12. *B* (-2, -6) , *r* = 4 ________________
13. *C* (0, 0), *r* = 3 ________________
14. *D* (5, -3), *r* = 5 ________________
15. end points of diameter are *D* (2, -3) and *E* (8, -3) ________________

Find the coordinates of the midpoint of the segment whose end points are given (each answer, 3 points).

16. *M* (0, 0) and *N* (0, 8) ____________________

17. *R* (0, 0) and *S* (8, 8) ____________________

18. *P* (8, 0) and *Q* (0, 8) ____________________

19. *W* (8, -8) and *X* (-8, 8) ____________________

20. *A* (-8, -8) and *B* (8, 8) ____________________

Write the equation of a circle whose center and other information are given (each answer, 3 points).

21. *A* (0, 0), *B* (0, 8) ____________________

22. *C* (1, 3), *D* (4, -4) ____________________

23. *E* (5, 3), F (-2, 1) ____________________

Write the equation of the given line in standard form (each answer, 4 points).

24. The line through *A* (5, 2) and perpendicular to a line with slope of -2

25. The line through B (3, 1) and parallel to a line with slope of $\frac{1}{5}$

26. The line that is the perpendicular bisector of a segment whose end points are *A* (3, 2) and *B* (7, 6)

Sketch and complete the following proof (complete proof, 5 points).

27. Prove: The diagonals of a rectangle bisect each other.

MATH 1010

Unit 10: Review

TEACHER NOTES

MATERIALS NEEDED FOR LIFEPAC	
Required	Suggested
• compass and straightedge	(None)

ADDITIONAL LEARNING ACTIVITIES

Section 1: Geometry, Proof, and Angles

1. Read each of the following statements and have the students tell (without seeing a truth table) whether each statement is true or false. If a student answers with false, have him tell why it is false. Answers are given for the teacher's information.
   a. If two or more points are all on the same line, then the points are collinear. (true)
   b. If *AB* + *BC* = *AC*, then *B* is between points *A* and *C*. (true)
   c. If two planes intersect, then their intersection is a plane. (false; their intersection is a line)
   d. If a line containing two points lies in a plane, then the points lie in the plane. (true)
   e. If a plane contains at least three points, then a line contains at least one point. (false; a plane does contain at least three points, but a line contains at least two points)
   f. If a line contains at least one point, then a plane contains at least three points. (true; since the "If" part of the statement is false and the "then" part of the statement is true, the statement is true)
   g. If a postulate is a statement accepted without proof, then a theorem is a statement that can be proved. (true)
   h. If a postulate is a statement that can be proved, then a theorem is a statement accepted without proof. (true; since both the "If" part and the "then" part of the statement are false, the statement is true)
   i. If the hypothesis is not the "then" clause in a conditional statement, then the conclusion is not the "if" clause in a conditional statement. (true)
   j. If a two-column proof is a formal proof of a theorem composed of two standard parts, then an indirect proof is a proof of a theorem by indirect means. (true; since the "If" part of the statement is false and the "then" part of the statement is true, the statement is true)
   k. If an acute angle equals 45°, then a right angle equals 180°. (false; since the "If" part of the statement is true but the "then" part of the statement is false, the statement is false)
   l. If two complementary angles equal 90°, then two right angles are supplementary. (true)
   m. If a triangle does not contain 180°, then a quadrilateral does not contain 540°. (false; since the "If" part of the statement is false but the "then" part of the statement is true, the statement is false)

n. If two adjacent angles have their exterior sides in perpendicular lines, then the angles are complementary. (false; the angles are supplementary)

o. If all right angles are not equal, then all obtuse angles are equal. (true; since both the "If" part and the "then" part of the statement are false, the statement is true)

p. If the measure of an exterior angle of a triangle equals the sum of the interior angles, then the sum of the measures of the angles of a triangle equals 260°. (true; since both the "If" part and the "then" part of the statement are false, the statement is true)

2. An interior angle of a polygon equals $\frac{(n-2)180°}{n}$, where n is the number of sides of the polygon. Have the students copy the following regular octagon and draw the two lines through the center as shown. Then have the students find the number of degrees in ∠1, ∠2, and ∠3.

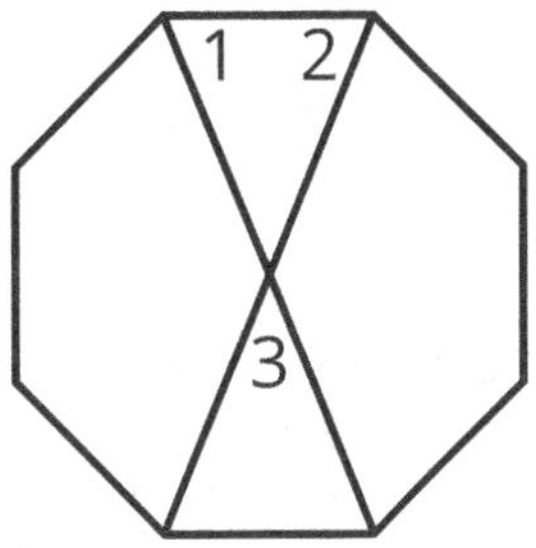

3. Have the student draw and label a figure for each of the following conditions. Then have he or she draw and label a figure such that all of the conditions given are true.
   a. points P, A, and B are collinear
   b. point P is between points A and B
   c. point P is midpoint of $\overline{AB}$
   d. $\overrightarrow{PA}$ and $\overrightarrow{PB}$ are opposite rays

Section 2: Triangles, Quadrilaterals, Polygons, and Circles

1. Draw the following figure on the chalkboard with the stated conditions. Have the students find the lengths of each of the other segments.

Given: $\triangle ABC$ is a 45°-45°-90° △
$\overline{BD}$ is bisector of $\angle ABC$
$\triangle AED$ is a 30°-60°-90° △
$\overline{BC} = 4$

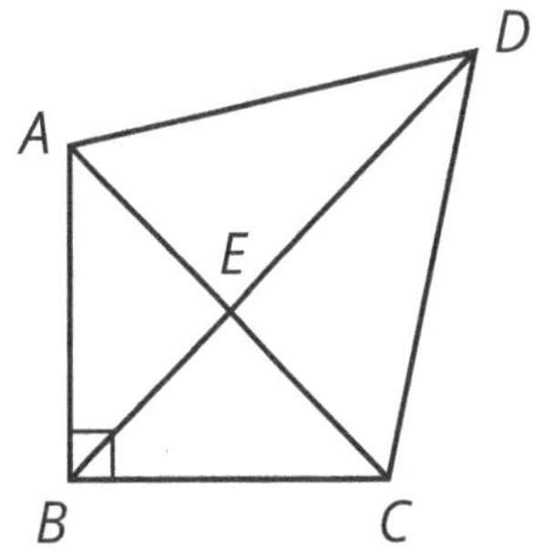

Administer the LIFEPAC Test.

The test is to be administered in one session. Give no help except with directions.
Evaluate the tests and review areas where the students have done poorly.
Review the pages and activities that stress the concepts tested.
If necessary, administer the Alternate LIFEPAC Test.

2. This activity is for two students to do together. Have both students draw and label an example of each of the theorems from Theorem 4-1 through Theorem 4-25 and from Theorem 5-1 through Theorem 5-13 without referring to previous LIFEPACs. They may draw and label five to ten examples at a time. The theorems may or may not be written out. Then have both students trade examples and check each others work. They may check their examples with the ones given in the corresponding LIFEPACs.

   Examples: Theorem 4-1: If two angles and a not included side of one triangle are equal to the corresponding parts of another triangle, then the triangles are congruent. (AAS)

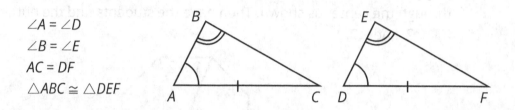

   $\angle A = \angle D$

   $\angle B = \angle E$

   $AC = DF$

   $\triangle ABC \cong \triangle DEF$

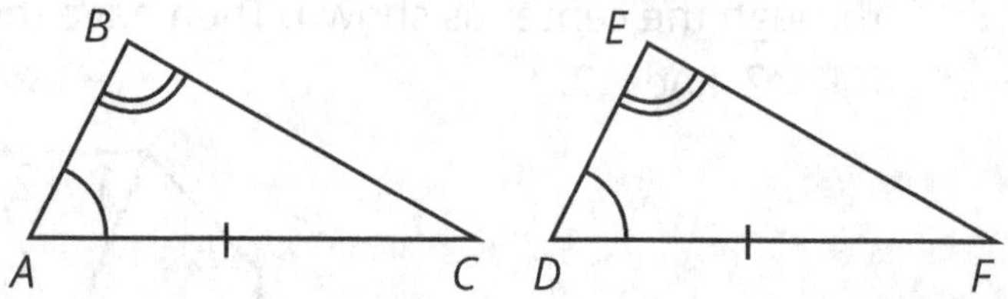

3. This activity is for two students to do together. The first student chooses any theorem from Theorem 6-1 through 6-18 and draws and labels an example of the theorem. Then he gives the figure to the second student to examine; that student tells what the theorem states that corresponds to the figure. If he answers with the correct theorem, he chooses a theorem and proceeds in the same manner as the first student. If he answers with an incorrect theorem, the first student may give him more time to think or he may give him a clue, whichever the second student prefers. The students alternate turns. Each student should be sure he draws the examples accurately and labels any parts necessary for the other student to understand the meaning of the figure. For example, the figure for Theorem 6-1: "A radius drawn to a point of tangency is perpendicular to the tangent" should have the radius and tangent labeled as in the following diagram.

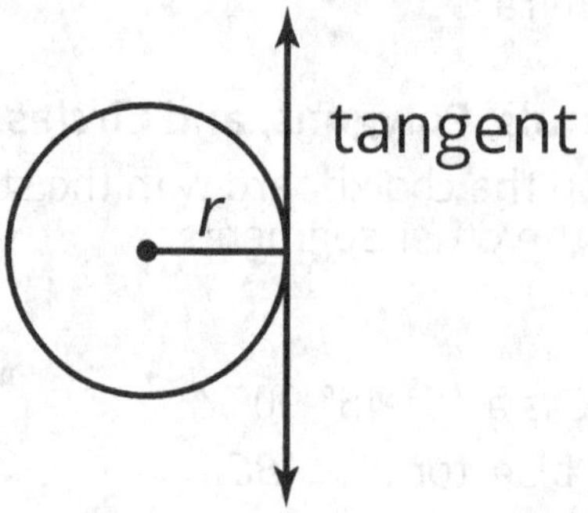

Section 3: Construction, Measurement, and Coordinate Geometry

1. Draw the given figure on the chalkboard. The cube is divided into six square-based pyramids of equal size. If each edge of the cube measures 4 inches, have the class find the altitude, slant height, lateral area, total area, and volume of each pyramid.

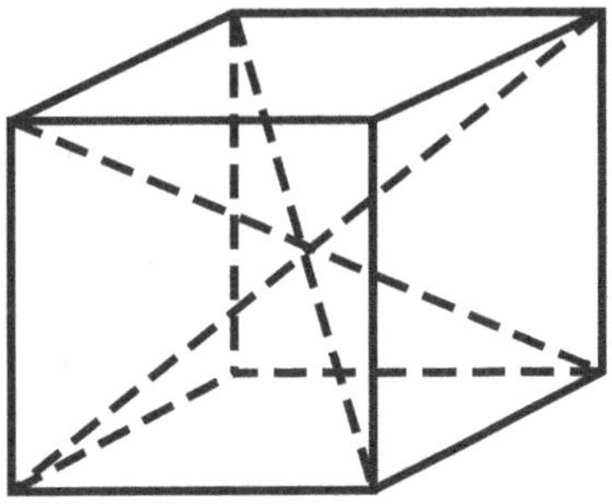

The pyramid that is the base of the cube is shown (with the altitude and slant height) for the teacher's information. The lateral area, total area, and volume may be found by using their formulas after the altitude and slant height are found.

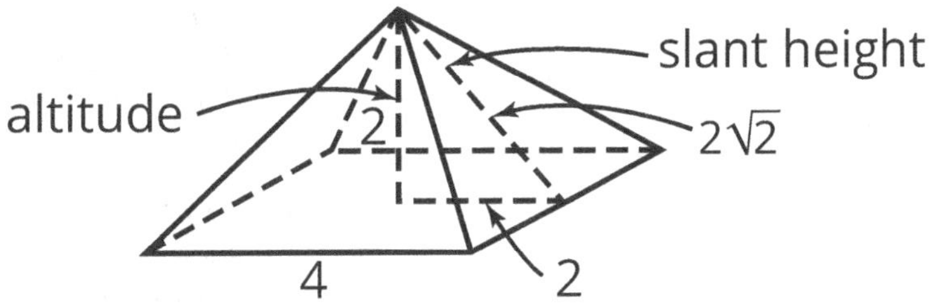

2. Have the class solve this problem. If a cone whose slant height is 6" and radius is 3" is rolled around a cylinder whose altitude is 6" and radius is 3", how much of the cylinder will be covered by one complete turn of the cone? two complete turns of the cone?

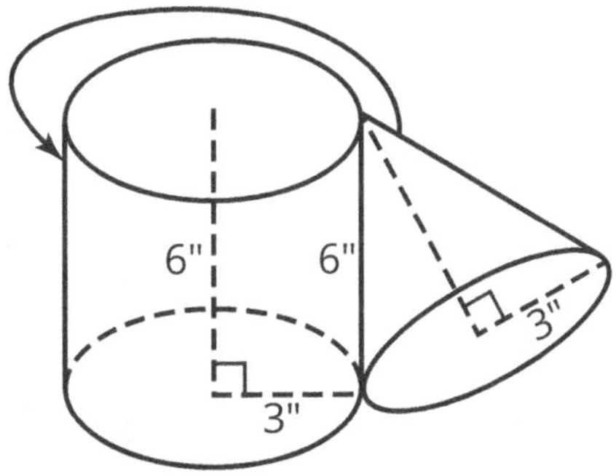

3. Name two points on the coordinate axes. Then have one student find the distance between the two points; one student find the slope of the line containing the given points; one student find the midpoint of the segment with the given points as end points; and one student graph and write the equation of the line containing the given points.

You may want to prepare the answers to several problems beforehand so the students' answers may be checked quickly. Or, you may have each student find the answers to two parts of one problem (such as finding the distance and the slope) and then compare the students' answers.

ANSWER KEYS

SECTION 1

1.1 $\overline{AB}$
1.2 $\overleftrightarrow{AB}$
1.3 $\overrightarrow{AB}$
1.4 plane *M*
1.5 point *p*
1.6 space
1.7 *R*
1.8 *RT*
1.9 three
1.10 two
1.11 proof
1.12 one
1.13 four
1.14 six
1.15 line
1.16
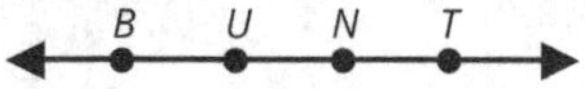

1.17
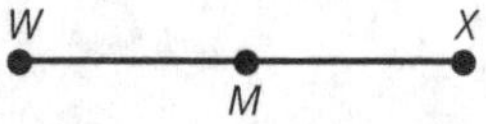

1.18
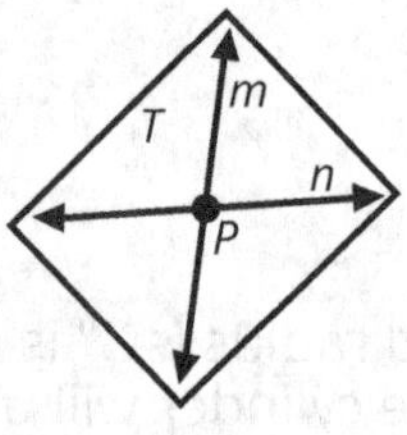

1.19
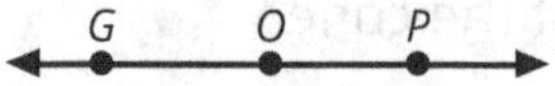

1.20
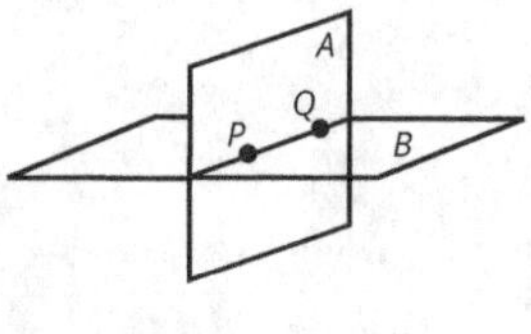

1.21 conditional; true
1.22 conjunction; true
1.23 negation; true
1.24 disjunction; true
1.25 conditional; true
1.26 a. If the alternate interior angles are equal, then the two lines are parallel; true.
b. If the lines are not parallel, then the alternate interior angles are not equal; true.
c. If the alternate interior angles are not equal, then the lines are not parallel; true.
1.27 a. If the vertical angles are equal, then the two lines intersect; true.
b. If two lines do not intersect, then the vertical angles are not equal; true.
c. If the vertical angles are not equal, then the lines do not intersect; true.
1.28 a. If diagonals bisect each other, then the figure is a parallelogram; true.
b. If the figure is not a parallelogram, then the diagonals do not bisect each other; true.
c. If diagonals do not bisect each other, then the figure is not a parallelogram; true.
1.29 a. If base ∠'s are =, then △ is isosceles; true.
b. If △ is not isosceles, then base ∠'s are not =; true.
c. If base ∠'s are not =, then △ is not isosceles; true.
1.30 a. If rights ∠'s are formed, then lines are ⊥; true.
b. If lines are not ⊥, then right ∠'s are not formed; true.
c. If right ∠'s are not formed, then lines are not ⊥; true.
1.31
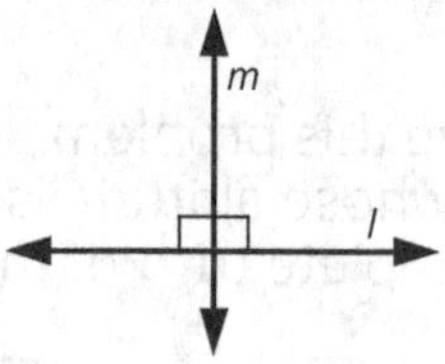

1.32
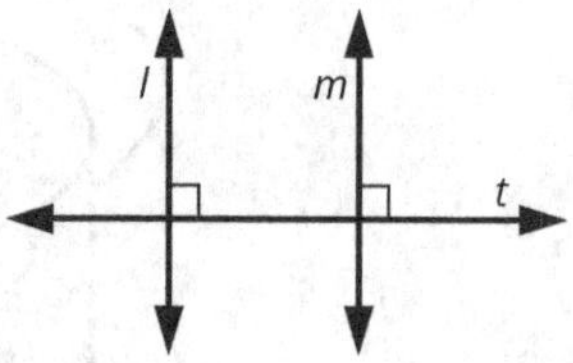

1.33
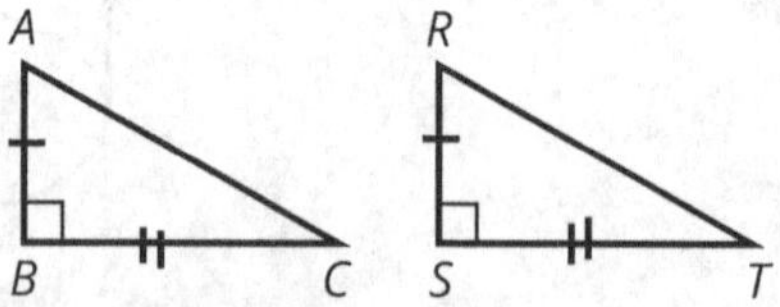

1.34
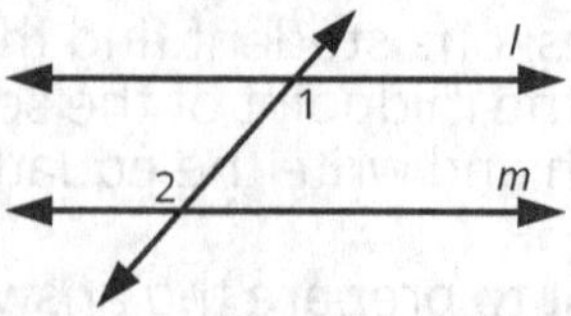

1.35
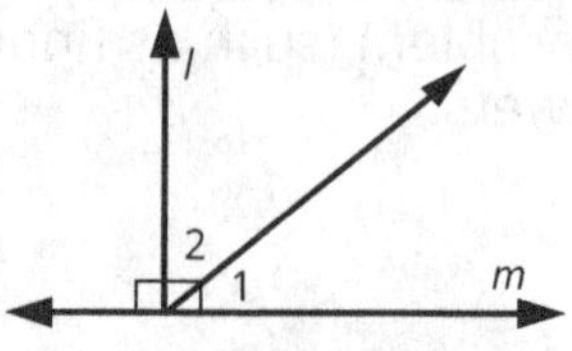

1.36 a. F
b. T

1.37 a. F
b. T
c. T
d. T

1.38 a. T
b. T
c. T
d. F

1.39 a. T
b. T
c. T
d. F

1.40 a. T
b. F
c. F
d. F

1.41 ∠1, ∠7; ∠2, ∠8; ∠3, ∠5; ∠4, ∠6

1.42 ∠4, ∠5; ∠1, ∠8

1.43 ∠2, ∠7; ∠3, ∠6

1.44 ∠1, ∠2; ∠3, ∠4; ∠5, ∠6; ∠7, ∠8

1.45 Any twelve:
∠1, ∠4; ∠1, ∠3; ∠1, ∠5; ∠1, ∠6; ∠2, ∠3; ∠2, ∠4; ∠2, ∠5; ∠2, ∠6; ∠6, ∠8; ∠6, ∠7; ∠5, ∠8; ∠5, ∠7; ∠4, ∠8; ∠3, ∠7; ∠3, ∠8; ∠4, ∠7

1.46 quadrilateral

1.47 pentagon

1.48 hexagon

1.49 octagon

1.50 *n*-gon

1.51 1. **STATEMENT**
r | | *s*
REASON
Given

2. **STATEMENT**
∠2, ∠4 are supplementary
REASON
Exterior sides in opposite rays

3. **STATEMENT**
∠4 = ∠8
REASON
Corresponding ∠'s

4. **STATEMENT**
∠2 + ∠4 = 180°
REASON
Definition of supplementary ∠'s

5. **STATEMENT**
∠2 + ∠8 = 180°
REASON
Substitution

6. **STATEMENT**
∠2, ∠8 are supplementary
REASON
Definition of supplementary ∠'s

1.52 1. **STATEMENT**
l | | *m*, ∠1 = ∠4
REASON
Given

2. **STATEMENT**
∠1 = ∠2
REASON
Alternate interior ∠'s

3. **STATEMENT**
∠3 = ∠4
REASON
Vertical ∠'s

4. **STATEMENT**
∠2 = ∠3
REASON
Substitution

1.53 1. **STATEMENT**
∠1 = ∠3
REASON
Given

2. **STATEMENT**
∠1 = ∠2
REASON
Vertical ∠'s

3. **STATEMENT**
∠2 = ∠3
REASON
Substitution

4. **STATEMENT**
a | | *b*
REASON
If corresponding ∠'s =, then lines | |.

1.54 m $\angle 2$ = 180 – m $\angle 1$
= 180 – 120
= 60°

1.55 m $\angle 4$ = 180 – m $\angle 3$
= 180 – 40
= 140°

1.56 m $\angle 5$ = m $\angle 2$ = 60°

1.57 m $\angle 6$ = 180 – (m $\angle 5$ + m $\angle 7$)
m $\angle 5$ = 60°
m $\angle 7$ = m $\angle 3$ = 40°
m $\angle 6$ = 180 – (60 + 40)
= 180 – 100
= 80°

1.58 m $\angle 7$ = m $\angle 3$ = 40°

1.59 $(n - 2)180 = (3 - 2)180 = (1)180 = 180°$

1.60 $(n - 2)180 = (4 - 2)180 = (2)180 = 360°$

1.61 $(n - 2)180 = (5 - 2)180 = (3)180 = 540°$

1.62 $(n - 2)180 = (6 - 2)180 = (4)180 = 720°$

1.63 $(n - 2)180 = (20 - 2)180 = (18)180 = 3,240°$

1.64 $(n - 2)180 = (50 - 2)180 = (48)180 = 8,640°$

1.65 360°

SELF TEST 1

1.01 e

1.02 f

1.03 b

1.04 d

1.05 a

1.06 a. F
b. T
c. T
d. T

1.07 a. T
b. F
c. F
d. F

1.08 $\angle 3$ = 180 – ($\angle 1$ + $\angle 2$)
= 180 – (30 + 30)
= 180 – 60
= 120°

1.09 $\angle 1$ = 180 – ($\angle 2$ + $\angle 3$)
= 180 – (20 + 130)
= 180 – 150
= 30°

1.010 $\angle 2$ = 180 – ($\angle 1$ + $\angle 3$)
= 180 – (40 + 110)
= 180 – 150
= 30°

1.011 $\angle 3$ = 180 – ($\angle 1$ + $\angle 2$)
= 180 – (45 + 45)
= 180 – 90
= 90°

1.012 $\angle 1$ = 180 – ($\angle 2$ + $\angle 3$)
= 180 – (15 + 118)
= 180 – 133
= 47°

1.013 c
$(n - 2)180 = (3 - 2)180 = (1)180 = 180°$

1.014 c
$(n - 2)180 = (4 - 2)180 = (2)180 = 360°$

1.015 a
$(n - 2)180 = (5 - 2)180 = (3)180 = 540°$

1.016 d
$(n - 2)180 = (20 - 2)180 = (18)180 = 3,240°$

1.017 1. **STATEMENT**
$\overline{JK} \perp \overline{MN}$
REASON
Given

2. **STATEMENT**
$\angle MKJ$ is rt. $\angle$
REASON
$\perp$'s form rt. $\angle$'s

3. **STATEMENT**
$\triangle MKJ$ is rt. $\triangle$
REASON
Definition of rt. $\triangle$

4. **STATEMENT**
$\angle 1$, $\angle 2$ are complementary
REASON
Acute $\angle$'s of rt. $\triangle$ are complementary

1.018 1. **STATEMENT**
m $\angle 5$ = m $\angle 6$
REASON
Given

2. **STATEMENT**
m $\angle 1$ = m $\angle 2$
REASON
Vertical $\angle$'s are =.

3. **STATEMENT**
m $\angle 3$ = m $\angle 4$
REASON
If 2 $\angle$'s of one $\triangle$ = 2 $\angle$'s of another $\triangle$, then third $\angle$'s are =.

1.019 1. **STATEMENT**
$\overline{AC} \perp \overline{CD}$, $\overline{DB} \perp \overline{AB}$
REASON
Given

2. **STATEMENT**
$\angle C$, $\angle B$ are rt. $\angle$'s
REASON
$\perp$'s form rt. $\angle$'s

3. **STATEMENT**
m $\angle C$ = m $\angle B$
REASON
All rt. $\angle$'s are =.

4. **STATEMENT**
m $\angle 1$ = m $\angle 2$
REASON
Vertical $\angle$'s are =.

5. **STATEMENT**
m $\angle A$ = m $\angle D$
REASON
If 2 $\angle$'s of one $\triangle$ = 2 $\angle$'s of another $\triangle$, then third $\angle$'s are =.

SECTION 2

2.1 $\angle T$
2.2 $\angle R$
2.3 $\angle B$
2.4 AC
2.5 AB
2.6 SR

2.7 1. **STATEMENT**
$\overline{AB} \parallel \overline{DE}$, $AC = CE$
REASON
Given

2. **STATEMENT**
$\angle A = \angle E$, $\angle B = \angle D$
REASON
Alternate interior $\angle$'s

3. **STATEMENT**
$\triangle ABC \cong \triangle EDC$
REASON
AAS

2.8 1. **STATEMENT**
$\overline{UT} \parallel \overline{RS}$, $UT = RS$
REASON
Given

2. **STATEMENT**
$\angle 2 = \angle 4$
REASON
Alternate interior $\angle$'s

3. **STATEMENT**
$RT = RT$
REASON
Reflexive

4. **STATEMENT**
$\triangle RST \cong \triangle TUR$
REASON
SAS

5. **STATEMENT**
$\angle S = \angle U$
REASON
CPCTE

2.9 1. **STATEMENT**
$\angle B = \angle C$, $AE = DE$
REASON
Given

2. **STATEMENT**
$\angle BEA = \angle CED$
REASON
Vertical $\angle$'s =.

3. **STATEMENT**
$\triangle ABE \cong \triangle DCE$
REASON
AAS

4. **STATEMENT**
$AB = DC$
REASON
CPCTE

2.10 1. **STATEMENT**
$AC = BC$, $MC = NC$
REASON
Given

2. **STATEMENT**
$\angle C = \angle C$
REASON
Reflexive

3. **STATEMENT**
$\triangle ANC \cong \triangle BMC$
REASON
SAS

4. **STATEMENT**
$\angle ANC = \angle BMC$
REASON
CPCTE

2.11 $AB > BC > AC$

2.12 $6 + 12 = 18$; $18 > 17$
$6 + 17 = 23$; $23 > 17$
$12 + 17 = 29$; $29 > 17$
yes

2.13 $1 + 2 = 3$; $3 \ngtr 3$
$1 + 3 = 4$; $4 > 3$
$2 + 3 = 5$; $5 > 3$
no

2.14 $6 + 8 = 14$; $14 > 10$
$6 + 10 = 16$; $16 > 10$
$8 + 10 = 18$; $18 > 10$
yes

2.15 $\overline{BC}$
2.16 $\overline{AC}$
2.17 $\overline{AB}$
2.18 AB
2.19 AC
2.20 *NO*
2.21 parallelogram

For Problems 2.22 through 2.25, $\angle A$ and $\angle D$ are supplementary.

2.22
$$\begin{aligned} x + 30 + 2x + 60 &= 180 \\ 3x + 90 &= 180 \\ 3x &= 180 - 90 \\ 3x &= 90 \\ \frac{3x}{3} &= \frac{90}{3} \\ x &= 30° \\ \angle A = 30 + 30 &= 60° \end{aligned}$$

2.23 $\angle B = \angle D$
$\angle D = 2x + 60 = 2(30) + 60 = 60 + 60 = 120°$
$\angle B = 120°$

2.24 $\angle C = \angle A$
$\angle C = 60°$

2.25 $\angle D = 2x + 60 = 2(30) + 60 = 60 + 60 = 120°$

2.26
$$\frac{x}{8} = \frac{5}{4}$$
$$x(4) = 8(5)$$
$$4x = 40$$
$$\frac{4x}{4} = \frac{40}{4}$$
$$x = 10$$

2.27
$$\frac{3}{x} = \frac{x}{4}$$
$$3(4) = x(x)$$
$$12 = x^2$$
$$x^2 = 12$$
$$\sqrt{x^2} = \sqrt{12}$$
$$x = \sqrt{4 \cdot 3} = 2\sqrt{3}$$

2.28
$$\frac{x}{3} = \frac{x+2}{2}$$
$$x(2) = 3(x + 2)$$
$$2x = 3x + 6$$
$$2x - 3x = 6$$
$$-x = 6$$
$$x = -6$$

2.29 1. **STATEMENT**
$a \parallel b$
REASON
Given

2. **STATEMENT**
$\angle 1 \cong \angle 2$, $\angle 3 \cong \angle 4$
REASON
Alternate interior $\angle$'s

3. **STATEMENT**
$\triangle MOP \sim \triangle RON$
REASON
AA

2.30

1. **STATEMENT**
$\overline{EC} \perp \overline{AC}$, $\overline{DB} \perp \overline{AC}$, $\angle A = \angle F$
REASON
Given

2. **STATEMENT**
$\overline{EC} \parallel \overline{DB}$
REASON
Two lines $\perp$ to same line are $\parallel$.

3. **STATEMENT**
$\angle 1 = \angle 2$
REASON
Alternate interior $\angle$'s

4. **STATEMENT**
$\angle A = \angle F$
REASON
Given

5. **STATEMENT**
$\triangle MDF \cong \triangle NEF$
REASON
AA

2.31

1. **STATEMENT**
$AB \parallel CD$
REASON
Given

2. **STATEMENT**
$\angle C = \angle B$, $\angle A = \angle D$
REASON
Alternate interior $\angle$'s

3. **STATEMENT**
$\triangle ABM \sim \triangle DCM$
REASON
AA

4. **STATEMENT**
$\frac{MC}{MB} = \frac{CD}{AB}$
REASON
Definition of similar $\triangle$'s

2.32

1. **STATEMENT**
$\overline{RS} \parallel \overline{AB}$, $\angle 1 = \angle 2$
REASON
Given

2. **STATEMENT**
$\frac{CR}{RA} = \frac{CS}{SB}$
REASON
Segment $\parallel$ to sides of $\triangle$ divides other sides proportionally.

3. **STATEMENT**
$\angle 2 = \angle 3$
REASON
Alternate interior $\angle$'s

4. **STATEMENT**
$\angle 1 = \angle 3$
REASON
Substitution

5. **STATEMENT**
$SB = RS$
REASON
Sides opposite = $\angle$'s are =.

6. **STATEMENT**
$\frac{CR}{RA} = \frac{CS}{RS}$
REASON
Substitution

2.33

1. **STATEMENT**
$\triangle ABC$ is rt. $\triangle$, $\overline{BD} \perp \overline{AC}$, $AB = \sqrt{17}$
REASON
Given

2. **STATEMENT**
$\frac{AC}{AB} = \frac{AB}{AD}$
REASON
Leg is geometric mean between hypotenuse and projection of leg on hypotenuse.

3. **STATEMENT**
$(AD)(AC) = (AB)^2$
REASON
POP

4. **STATEMENT**
$(AD)(AC) = 17$
REASON
Substitution

2.34 $AC = \sqrt{6^2 + 8^2}$
$= \sqrt{36 + 64}$
$= \sqrt{100} = 10$

2.35
$$(AB)^2 + (BC)^2 = (AC)^2$$
$$(AB)^2 + 5^2 = 20^2$$
$$(AB)^2 + 25 = 400$$
$$(AB)^2 = 400 - 25$$
$$(AB)^2 = 375$$
$$\sqrt{(AB)^2} = \sqrt{375}$$
$$AB = \sqrt{25 \cdot 15} = 5\sqrt{15}$$

2.36
$$(AB)^2 + (BC)^2 = (AC)^2$$
$$(5\sqrt{2})^2 + (BC)^2 = 10^2$$
$$50 + (BC)^2 = 100$$
$$(BC)^2 = 100 - 50$$
$$(BC)^2 = 50$$
$$\sqrt{(BC)^2} = \sqrt{50}$$
$$BC = \sqrt{25 \cdot 2} = 5\sqrt{2}$$

2.37
$$\text{diagonal} = \sqrt{5^2 + 5^2 + 5^2}$$
$$= \sqrt{25 + 25 + 25}$$
$$= \sqrt{25 \cdot 3}$$
$$= 5\sqrt{3}$$

2.38

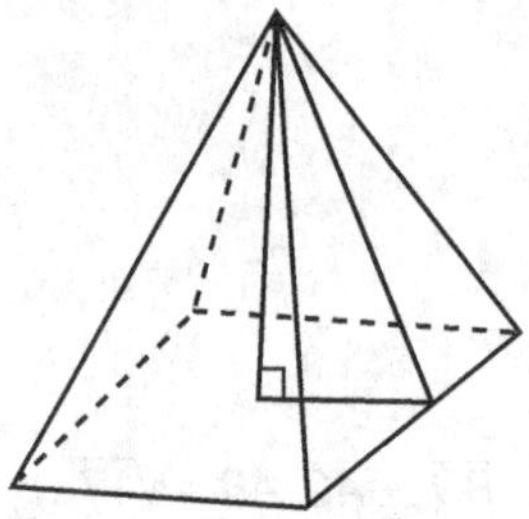

$$3^2 + l^2 = 6^2$$
$$9 + l^2 = 36$$
$$l^2 = 36 - 9$$
$$l^2 = 27$$
$$\sqrt{l^2} = \sqrt{27}$$
$$l = \sqrt{9 \cdot 3} = 3\sqrt{3}$$

2.39 $\tan 20° = \frac{x}{12}$

2.40 $\sin 70° = \frac{x}{8}$

2.41 $\tan 35° = \frac{9}{x}$

2.42 $\sin 80° = \frac{9}{x}$

2.43 $\cos 65° = \frac{x}{12}$

2.44
$$\sin 30° = \frac{x}{8}$$
$$\frac{1}{2} = \frac{x}{8}$$
$$2(x) = 1(8)$$
$$2x = 8$$
$$\frac{2x}{2} = \frac{8}{2}$$
$$x = 4$$

$$\cos 30° = \frac{y}{8}$$
$$\frac{\sqrt{3}}{2} = \frac{y}{8}$$
$$2(y) = \sqrt{3}(8)$$
$$2y = 8\sqrt{3}$$
$$\frac{2y}{2} = \frac{8\sqrt{3}}{2}$$
$$y = 4\sqrt{3}$$

2.45
$$\sin 30° = \frac{5}{x}$$
$$\frac{1}{2} = \frac{5}{x}$$
$$1(x) = 2(5)$$
$$x = 10$$

$$\tan 30° = \frac{5}{y}$$
$$\frac{1}{\sqrt{3}} = \frac{5}{y}$$
$$1(y) = \sqrt{3}(5)$$
$$y = 5\sqrt{3}$$

2.46
$$\tan 30° = \frac{x}{7}$$
$$\frac{1}{\sqrt{3}} = \frac{x}{7}$$
$$\sqrt{3}(x) = 1(7)$$
$$x\sqrt{3} = 7$$
$$\frac{x\sqrt{3}}{\sqrt{3}} = \frac{7}{\sqrt{3}}$$
$$x = \frac{7}{\sqrt{3}} = \frac{7}{\sqrt{3}} \cdot \frac{\sqrt{3}}{\sqrt{3}} = \frac{7\sqrt{3}}{3} \text{ or } \frac{7}{3}\sqrt{3}$$

$$\cos 30° = \frac{7}{y}$$
$$\frac{\sqrt{3}}{2} = \frac{7}{y}$$
$$\sqrt{3}(y) = 2(7)$$
$$y\sqrt{3} = 14$$
$$\frac{y\sqrt{3}}{\sqrt{3}} = \frac{14}{\sqrt{3}}$$
$$x = \frac{14}{\sqrt{3}} = \frac{14}{\sqrt{3}} \cdot \frac{\sqrt{3}}{\sqrt{3}} = \frac{14\sqrt{3}}{3} \text{ or } \frac{14}{3}\sqrt{3}$$

2.47 $x = \frac{8}{\sqrt{2}} = \frac{8}{\sqrt{2}} \cdot \frac{\sqrt{2}}{\sqrt{2}} = \frac{8\sqrt{2}}{2}$ or $4\sqrt{2}$

2.48 $x = 8\sqrt{2}$

2.49 $x = \dfrac{3\sqrt{2}}{\sqrt{2}} = 3$

2.50 $x = \dfrac{6\sqrt{2}}{\sqrt{2}} = 6$

2.51 $\overline{OB}, \overline{OA}, \overline{OD}$

2.52 $\overleftrightarrow{AC}$

2.53 $\overline{AE}, \overline{BE}$

2.54 $\overleftrightarrow{BC}$

2.55 $\overline{BA}$

2.56 $\angle B, \angle E, \angle BAE$

2.57 $\angle BOD, \angle DOA$

2.58 $\widehat{BD}, \widehat{DA}, \widehat{AE}, \widehat{BE}$

2.59 $\widehat{BDA}, \widehat{BEA}$

2.60 $\triangle BEA, \triangle BAC$

2.61 60°

2.62 50°

2.63
$m\widehat{AB} = 180 - m\widehat{BC}$
$m\widehat{BC} = 70°$
$m\widehat{AB} = 180 - 70 = 110°$

2.64
$m\,\widehat{ABD} = 360 - m\widehat{AD}$
$= 360 - 120$
$= 240°$

2.65
$m\widehat{BC} = m\,\angle 1 = 48°$
$m\widehat{CD} = m\ BC = 48°$
$m\,\widehat{BAD} = 360 - (m\widehat{BC} + m\widehat{CD})$
$= 360 - (48 + 48)$
$= 360 - 96$
$= 264°$

2.66
$3 \cdot 4 = 6 \cdot BP$
$12 = 6BP$
$6BP = 12$
$\dfrac{6BP}{6} = \dfrac{12}{6}$
$BP = 2$

2.67
$m\,\angle 1 = \dfrac{1}{2}(m\widehat{AD} + m\widehat{BC})$
$= \dfrac{1}{2}(20 + 30)$
$= \dfrac{1}{2}(50)$
$= 25°$

2.68
$m\,\angle 2 = \dfrac{1}{2}(m\widehat{AB} + m\widehat{DC})$
$115 = \dfrac{1}{2}(m\widehat{AB} + 120)$
$230 = m\widehat{AB} + 120$ (multiply by 2)
$230 - 120 = m\widehat{AB}$
$110° = m\widehat{AB}$

2.69
$AC \cdot BC = EC \cdot DC$
$12 \cdot 6 = EC \cdot 4$
$72 = 4EC$
$\dfrac{72}{4} = \dfrac{4EC}{4}$
$18 = EC$

2.70
$m\,\angle C = \dfrac{1}{2}(m\widehat{AE} - m\widehat{BD})$
$= \dfrac{1}{2}(90 - 30)$
$= \dfrac{1}{2}(60)$
$= 30°$

2.71
$m\,\angle C = \dfrac{1}{2}(m\widehat{AE} - m\widehat{BD})$
$25 = \dfrac{1}{2}(100 - m\widehat{BD})$
$50 = 100 - m\widehat{BD}$ (multiply by 2)
$50 + m\widehat{BD} = 100$
$m\widehat{BD} = 100 - 50$
$m\widehat{BD} = 50°$

2.72
$\dfrac{8+4}{x} = \dfrac{x}{4}$
$\dfrac{12}{x} = \dfrac{x}{4}$
$x(x) = 12(4)$
$x^2 = 48$
$\sqrt{x^2} = \sqrt{48}$
$x = \sqrt{48} = \sqrt{16 \cdot 3} = 4\sqrt{3}$

2.73
$x \cdot x = 2 \cdot 6$
$x^2 = 12$
$\sqrt{x^2} = \sqrt{12}$
$x = \sqrt{12} = \sqrt{4 \cdot 3} = 2\sqrt{3}$

2.74
$99 + x = 180$
$x = 180 - 99$
$x = 81°$

2.75
$(5 + 4)4 = (x + 3)3$
$(9)4 = (x + 3)3$
$36 = 3x + 9$
$36 - 9 = 3x$
$27 = 3x$
$\dfrac{27}{3} = \dfrac{3x}{3}$
$9 = x$

SELF TEST 2

2.01 $\angle P$
2.02 QR
2.03 $\angle Y$
2.04 WZ
2.05 $\angle Z$
2.06 RS
2.07 $\angle Q$
2.08 XW

2.09 $\frac{x}{25} = \frac{2}{5}$
$x(5) = 25(2)$
$5x = 50$
$\frac{5x}{5} = \frac{50}{5}$
$x = 10$

2.010 $\frac{9}{x} = \frac{3}{12}$
$x(3) = 9(12)$
$3x = 108$
$\frac{3x}{3} = \frac{108}{3}$
$x = 36$

2.011 $\frac{3}{2} = \frac{x}{4}$
$2(x) = 3(4)$
$2x = 12$
$\frac{2x}{2} = \frac{12}{2}$
$x = 6$

2.012 $\frac{16}{x} = \frac{x}{4}$
$x(x) = 16(4)$
$x^2 = 64$
$\sqrt{x^2} = \sqrt{64}$
$x = 8$

2.013 $x = \frac{22}{\sqrt{2}} = \frac{22}{\sqrt{2}} \cdot \frac{\sqrt{2}}{\sqrt{2}} = \frac{22\sqrt{2}}{2} = 11\sqrt{2}$

2.014 $x = \frac{12}{\sqrt{2}} = \frac{12}{\sqrt{2}} \cdot \frac{\sqrt{2}}{\sqrt{2}} = \frac{12\sqrt{2}}{2} = 6\sqrt{2}$

2.015 $x = 1.2\sqrt{2}$

2.016 $x = \frac{9\sqrt{2}}{\sqrt{2}} = 9$

2.017 $x = 10\sqrt{2}$

2.018 $x = \frac{24\sqrt{2}}{\sqrt{2}} = 24$

2.019 $m\angle 1 = \frac{1}{2}(m\widehat{VU} - m\widehat{ST})$
$= \frac{1}{2}(80 - 40)$
$= \frac{1}{2}(40)$
$= 20°$

2.020 $m\angle 2 = \frac{1}{2}(m\widehat{UV} + m\widehat{ST})$
$= \frac{1}{2}(70 + 30)$
$= \frac{1}{2}(100)$
$= 50°$

2.021 $m\angle 3 = \frac{1}{2}(m\widehat{VB} - m\widehat{BS})$
$= \frac{1}{2}(60 - 30)$
$= \frac{1}{2}(30)$
$= 15°$

2.022 $m\angle 1 = \frac{1}{2}(m\widehat{UV} - m\widehat{ST})$
$30 = \frac{1}{2}(m\widehat{UV} - 20)$
$60 = m\widehat{UV} - 20$ (multiply by 2)
$60 + 20 = m\widehat{UV}$
$80° = m\widehat{UV}$

2.023 $m\widehat{DB} = m\angle DPB = 60°$

2.024 $m\widehat{DB} = m\widehat{BF}$
$m\widehat{BF} = 180 - m\widehat{AF}$
$= 180 - 110$
$= 70$
$m\widehat{DB} = 70°$

2.025 The center of the circle is P.
Since $AC = CD = DB$, $\triangle CPD$ is equilateral and $\angle CPD = 60°$.

2.026 Since $\overline{AB}$ is also $\perp$ to line t, $\overline{DF} \parallel t$.

2.027 $m\angle DPB = m\widehat{DB} = 60°$
$\triangle DPB$ is equilateral.
$\therefore \overline{DE}$ is $\perp$ bisector of $\overline{PB}$.
$PE = EB = 3$
$PB = PE + EB$
$= 3 + 3$
$= 6$

2.028
1. **GIVEN**
$\overline{AE}$ tangent to $\odot R$ at A and to circle S at E
2. **STATEMENT**
$\overline{RA} \perp \overline{AE}$, $\overline{SE} \perp \overline{AE}$
REASON
Radii $\perp$ to tangent
3. **STATEMENT**
$\overline{RA} \parallel \overline{SE}$
REASON
2 lines $\perp$ to same line are $\parallel$.
4. **STATEMENT**
$\angle R = \angle S$
REASON
Alternate interior $\angle$'s

2.029 1. **STATEMENT**
$\overline{XZ} \mid\mid \overline{BC}$; $\angle 1 = \angle 2$
REASON
Given

2. **STATEMENT**
$YC = ZC$
REASON
Sides opposite = ∠'s are =.

3. **STATEMENT**
$\frac{AX}{XB} = \frac{AY}{YC}$
REASON
Segment | | to side of △ divides other sides proportionally.

4. **STATEMENT**
$\frac{AX}{XB} = \frac{AY}{ZC}$
REASON
Substitution

2.030 1. **STATEMENT**
$\overline{RS} \mid\mid \overline{BC}$; $\angle 1 = \angle 2$
REASON
Given

2. **STATEMENT**
$\angle 2 = \angle 3$
REASON
Alternate interior ∠'s

3. **STATEMENT**
$\angle 1 = \angle 3$
REASON
Substitution

4. **STATEMENT**
$RB = RS$
REASON
Sides opposite = ∠'s are =.

5. **STATEMENT**
$\frac{AR}{RB} = \frac{AS}{SC}$
REASON
Segment | | to side of △ divides other sides proportionally.

6. **STATEMENT**
$\frac{AR}{RS} = \frac{AS}{SC}$
REASON
Substitution

SECTION 3

3.1

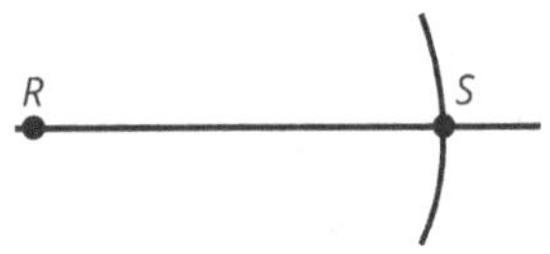

3.2

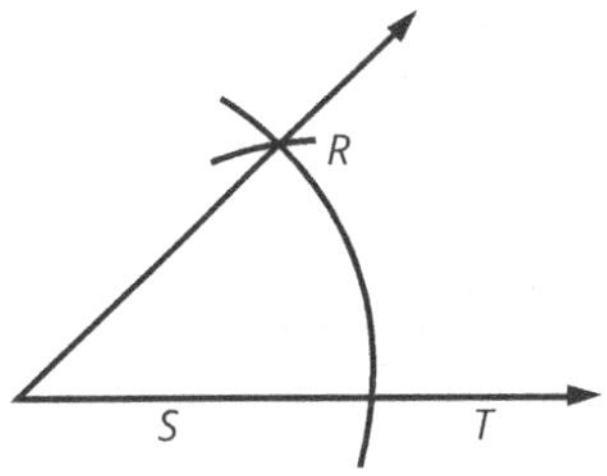

3.3

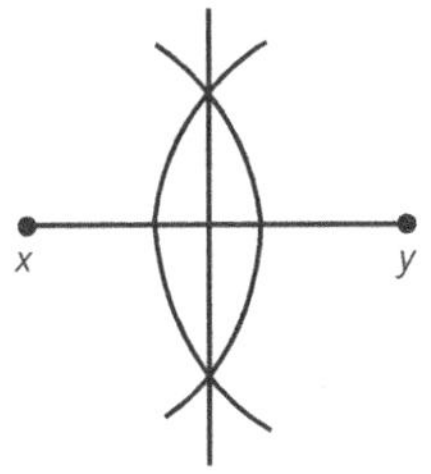

3.4

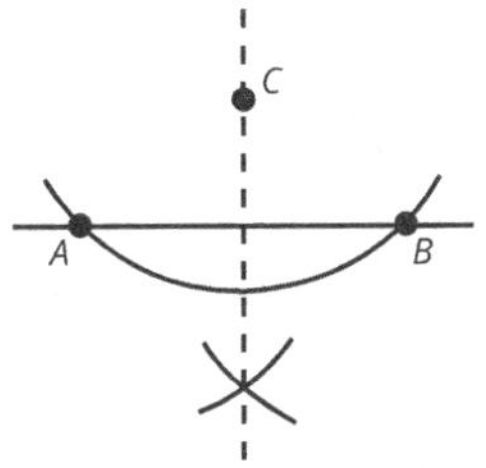

3.5

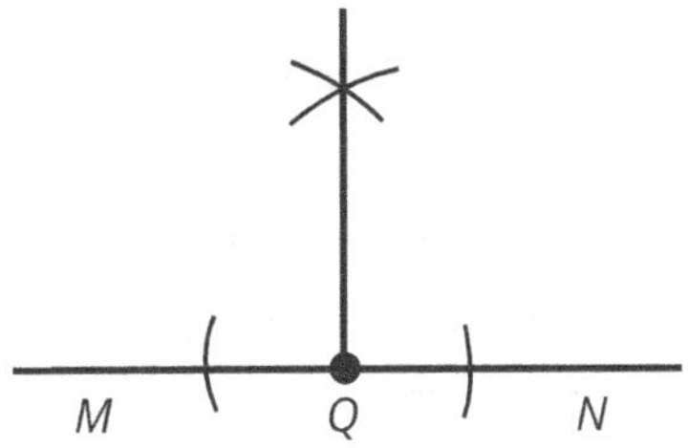

3.6

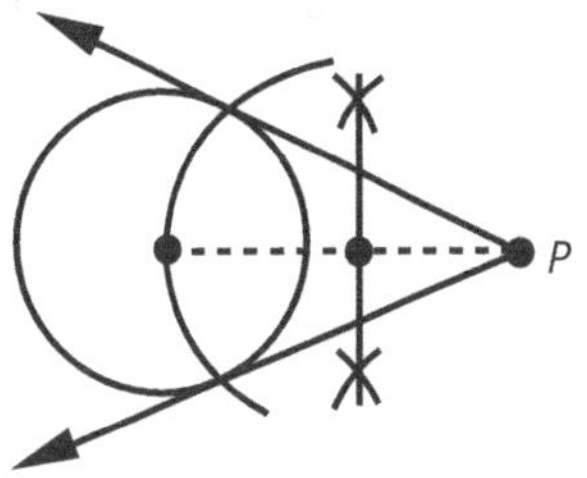

3.7

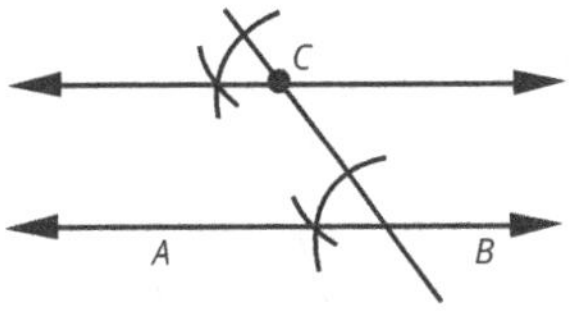

3.8

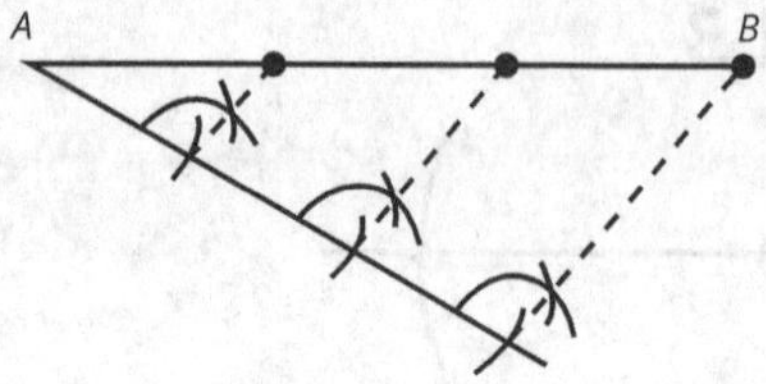

3.9

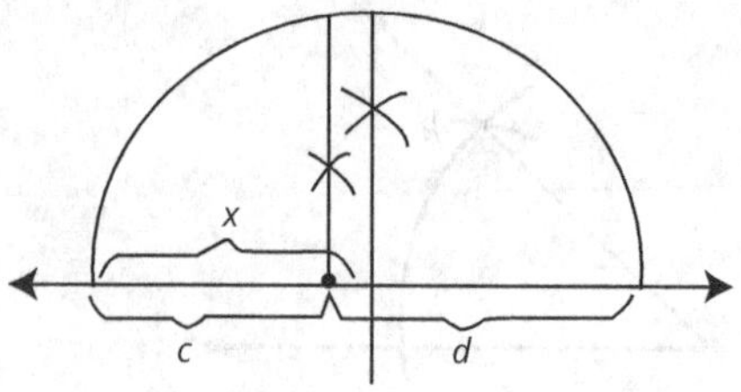

3.10

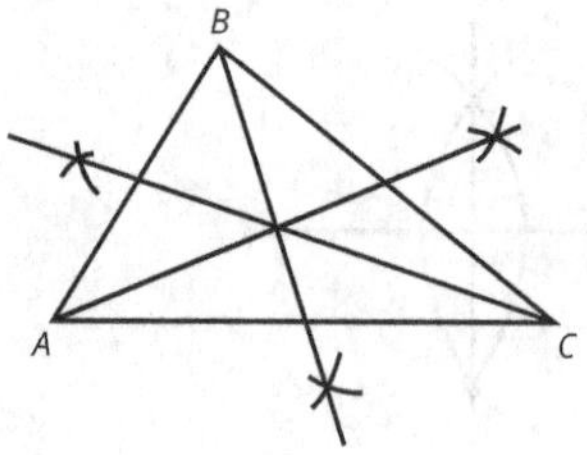

3.11

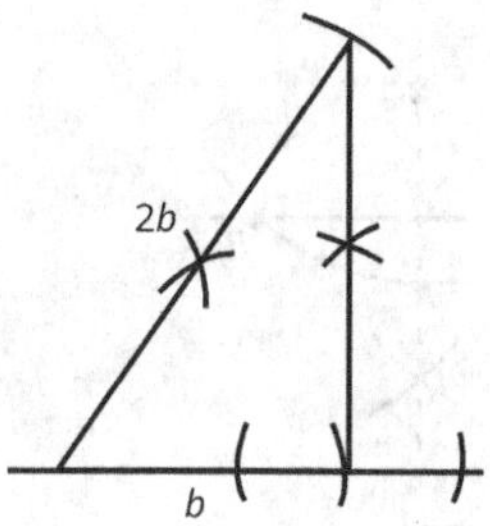

3.12 a line parallel to the given lines and midway between them

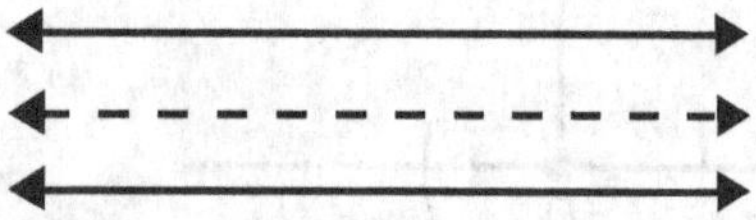

3.13 a line that is the perpendicular bisector of segment *AB*

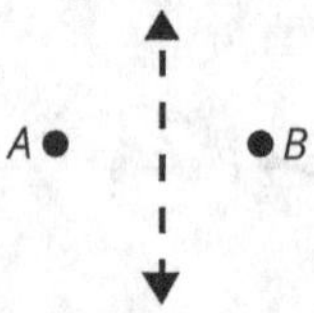

3.14 a sphere

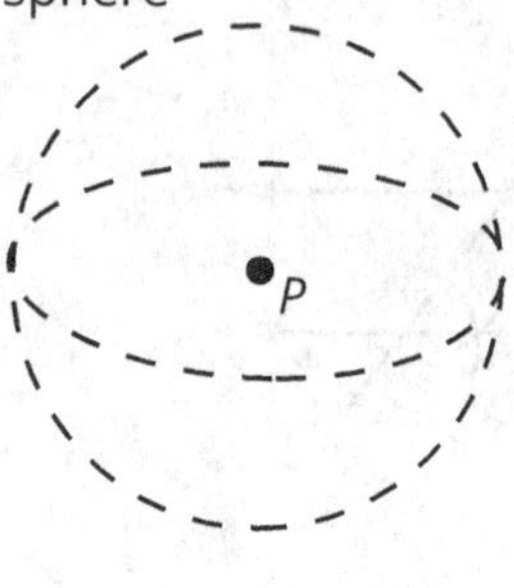

3.15 a cylinder

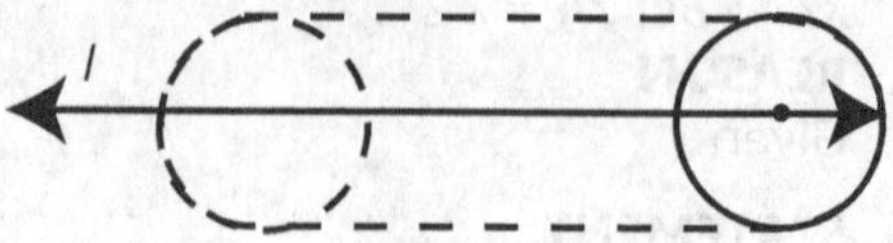

3.16 $A = lw$
$= 5(6)$
$= 30$

3.17 $L.A. = ph$
$= 22(2)$
$= 44$

3.18 $T.A. = L.A. + 2B$
$= 44 + 2(30)$
$= 44 + 60$
$= 104$

3.19 $V = Bh$
$= 30(2)$
$= 60$

3.20 $l = \sqrt{5^2 - 3^2}$
$= \sqrt{25 - 9}$
$= \sqrt{16}$
$= 4$

3.21 $L.A. = \frac{1}{2}pl$
$= \frac{1}{2}(24)(4)$
$= 48$

3.22 $h = \sqrt{4^2 - 3^2}$
$= \sqrt{16 - 9}$
$= \sqrt{7}$

3.23 $T.A. = L.A. + B$
$= 48 + 36$
$= 84$

3.24 $V = \frac{1}{3}Bh$
$= \frac{1}{3}(36)(\sqrt{7})$
$= 12\sqrt{7}$

3.25 $L.A. = 2\pi rh$
$= 2\pi(2)(3)$
$= 12\pi$

3.26 $T.A. = L.A. + 2B$
$= L.A. + 2\pi r^2$
$= 12\pi + 2\pi(2)^2$
$= 12\pi + 8\pi$
$= 20\pi$

3.27 $V = \pi r^2 h$
$= \pi(2)^2(3)$
$= 12\pi$

3.28 $l = \sqrt{3^2 + 4^2}$
$= \sqrt{9 + 16}$
$= \sqrt{25}$
$= 5$

3.29 $L.A. = \pi rl$
$= \pi(3)(5)$
$= 15\pi$

3.30 $T.A. = L.A. + \pi r^2$
$= 15\pi + \pi(3)^2$
$= 15\pi + 9\pi$
$= 24\pi$

3.31 $V = \frac{1}{3}\pi r^2 h$
$= \frac{1}{3}\pi(3)^2(4)$
$= 12\pi$

3.32 $S.A. = 4\pi r^2$
$= 4\pi(4)^2$
$= 4\pi(16)$
$= 64\pi$

3.33 $V = \frac{4}{3}\pi r^3$
$= \frac{4}{3}\pi(4)^3$
$= \frac{4}{3}\pi(64)$
$= \frac{256}{3}\pi$

3.34 $A = \pi r^2$
$= \pi(6)^2$
$= 36\pi$

3.35 $A_{O-AXB} = \frac{90}{360}\pi(6)^2$
$= \frac{1}{4}\pi(36)$
$= 9\pi$

3.36 $A_{AXB} = A_{sector} - A_{\triangle}$
$= 9\pi - \frac{1}{2}bh$
$= 9\pi - \frac{1}{2}(6)(6)$
$= 9\pi - 18$

3.37 $C = 2\pi r$
$= 2\pi(6)$
$= 12\pi$

3.38 apothem $= \frac{4}{2}\sqrt{3} = 2\sqrt{3}$

3.39 4

3.40 central $\angle = \frac{360°}{6} = 60°$

3.41 $A = \frac{1}{2}ap$
$= \frac{1}{2}(2\sqrt{3})24$
$= 24\sqrt{3}$

3.42 $\frac{A_{\triangle ABC}}{A_{\triangle DEF}} = (\frac{s_1}{s_2})^2$
$\frac{12}{A_{\triangle DEF}} = (\frac{4}{1})^2$
$\frac{12}{A_{\triangle DEF}} = 16$
$16A_{\triangle DEF} = 12$ (cross-multiply)
$A_{\triangle DEF} = \frac{12}{16} = \frac{3}{4}$

3.43 $\frac{A_1}{A_2} = (\frac{s_1}{s_2})^2$
$\frac{20}{4} = (\frac{5}{x})^2$
$\frac{20}{4} = \frac{25}{x^2}$
$20x^2 = 100$ (cross-multiply)
$x^2 = 5$ (divide by 20)
$\sqrt{x^2} = \sqrt{5}$
$x = \sqrt{5}$

3.44 through 3.48

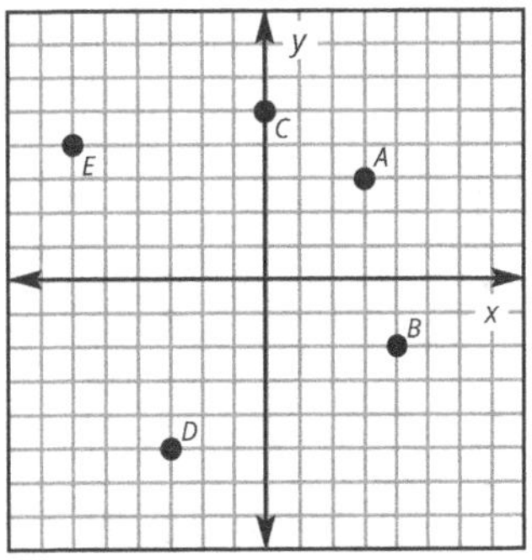

3.49 $d = \sqrt{(5 - 7)^2 + [3 - (-4)]^2}$
$= \sqrt{(-2)^2 + 7^2}$
$= \sqrt{4 + 49}$
$= \sqrt{53}$

3.50 $d = \sqrt{(0 - 6)^2 + (0 - 8)^2}$
$= \sqrt{(-6)^2 + (-8)^2}$
$= \sqrt{36 + 64}$
$= \sqrt{100}$
$= 10$

3.51 $d = \sqrt{(0 - 0)^2 + (8 - 12)^2}$
$= \sqrt{0^2 + (-4)^2}$
$= \sqrt{16}$
$= 4$

3.52 $d = \sqrt{(7 - 4)^2 + [1 - (-6)]^2}$
$= \sqrt{3^2 + 7^2}$
$= \sqrt{9 + 49}$
$= \sqrt{58}$

3.53 $d = \sqrt{[-6-(-12)^2 + (4-4)^2}$
$= \sqrt{6^2 + 0^2}$
$= \sqrt{36}$
$= 6$

3.54 $(x-5)^2 + (y-7)^2 = 4^2$
$(x-5)^2 + (y-7)^2 = 16$

3.55 $(x+3)^2 + (y-5)^2 = 1^2$
$(x+3)^2 + (y-5)^2 = 1$

3.56 $(x-0)^2 + (y-8)^2 = (\sqrt{3})^2$
$x^2 + (y-8)^2 = 3$

3.57 $(x-0)^2 + (y-0)^2 = (\sqrt{5})^2$
$x^2 + y^2 = 5$

3.58 $(x+3)^2 + (y+8)^2 = (2\sqrt{3})^2$
$(x+3)^2 + (y+8)^2 = 12$

3.59 $m = \frac{2-3}{0-1} = \frac{-1}{-1} = 1$
$y - 2 = 1(x-0)$
$y - 2 = x$
$-x + y - 2 = 0$
$-x + y = 2$ or
$x - y = -2$ (multiply by -1)

3.60 $m = \frac{2-3}{-3-3} = \frac{-1}{-6} = \frac{1}{6}$
$y - 3 = \frac{1}{6}(x-3)$
$y - 3 = \frac{1}{6}x - {}_{2}$
$-\frac{1}{6}x + y - 3 = -\frac{1}{2}$
$-\frac{1}{6}x + y = -\frac{1}{2} + 3$
$-\frac{1}{6}x + y = \frac{5}{2}$
$x - 6y = -15$ (multiply by -6)

3.61 $m = \frac{1-3}{6-4} = \frac{-2}{2} = -1$
$y - 3 = -1(x-4)$
$y - 3 = -x + 4$
$x + y - 3 = 4$
$x + y = 4 + 3$
$x + y = 7$

3.62 $m \perp = \frac{1}{2}$
$y - 3 = \frac{1}{2}(x-5)$
$y - 3 = \frac{1}{2}x - \frac{5}{2}$
$-\frac{1}{2}x + y - 3 = -\frac{5}{2}$
$-\frac{1}{2}x + y = -\frac{5}{2} + 3$
$-\frac{1}{2}x + y = \frac{1}{2}$
$x - 2y = -1$ (multiply by -2)

3.63 $m \,||\, = \frac{1}{5}$
$y - 1 = \frac{1}{5}(x-3)$
$y - 1 = \frac{1}{5}x - \frac{3}{5}$
$-\frac{1}{5}x + y - 1 = -\frac{3}{5}$
$-\frac{1}{5}x + y = -\frac{3}{5} + 1$
$-\frac{1}{5}x + y = \frac{2}{5}$
$x - 5y = -2$ (multiply by -5)

3.64

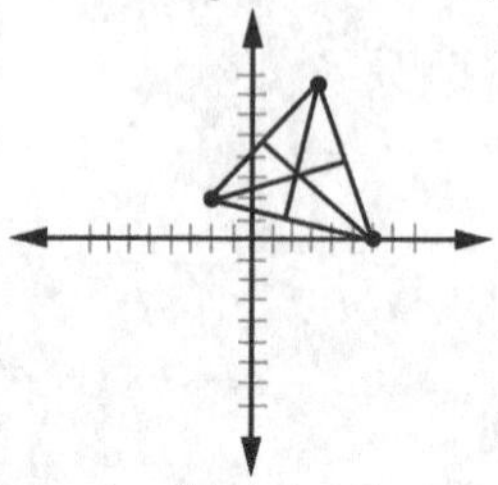

$M_{AB} = (\frac{-2+4}{2}, \frac{2+8}{2}) = (\frac{2}{2}, \frac{10}{2}) = (1, 5)$
$M_{BC} = (\frac{-2+6}{2}, \frac{2+0}{2}) = (\frac{4}{2}, \frac{2}{2}) = (2, 1)$
$M_{AC} = (\frac{6+4}{2}, \frac{0+8}{2}) = (\frac{10}{2}, \frac{8}{2}) = (5, 4)$
$m_{AP} = \frac{1-8}{2-4} = \frac{-7}{-2} = \frac{7}{2}$
$m_{BQ} = \frac{4-2}{5-(-2)} = \frac{2}{7}$
$m_{CR} = \frac{5-0}{1-6} = \frac{5}{-5} = -1$

AP:
$y - 8 = \frac{7}{2}(x-4)$
$y - 8 = \frac{7}{2}x - 14$
$-\frac{7}{2}x + y - 8 = -14$
$-\frac{7}{2}x + y = -14 + 8$
$-\frac{7}{2}x + y = -6$
$7x - 2y = 12$ (multiply by -2)

BQ:
$y - 2 = \frac{2}{7}(x+2)$
$y - 2 = \frac{2}{7}x + \frac{4}{7}$
$-\frac{2}{7}x + y - 2 = \frac{4}{7}$
$-\frac{2}{7}x + y = \frac{4}{7} + 2$
$-\frac{2}{7}x + y = \frac{18}{7}$
$2x - 7y = -18$ (multiply by -7)

CR:
$y - 0 = -1(x-6)$
$y = -x + 6$
$x + y = 6$

3.65 $x = 0$:

$$\begin{aligned} 0 - 3y &= 12 \\ -3y &= 12 \\ \frac{-3y}{-3} &= \frac{12}{-3} \\ y &= -4 \end{aligned}$$

(0, -4)

$y = 0$:

$$\begin{aligned} 4x - 0 &= 12 \\ 4x &= 12 \\ \frac{4x}{4} &= \frac{12}{4} \\ x &= 3 \end{aligned}$$

(3, 0)

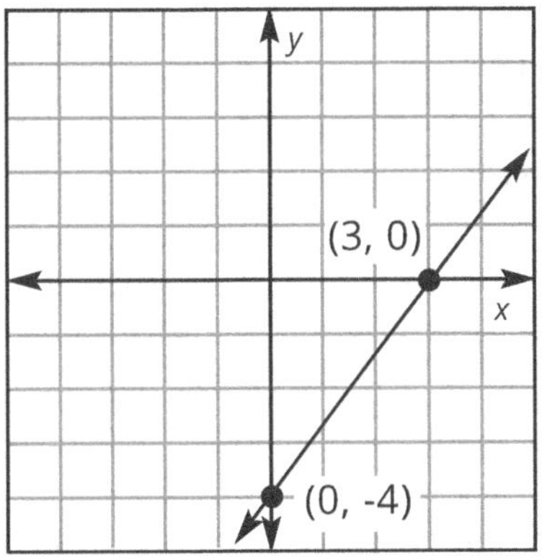

3.66 $|x| \leq 4$

$x \leq 4$ or $x \geq -4$

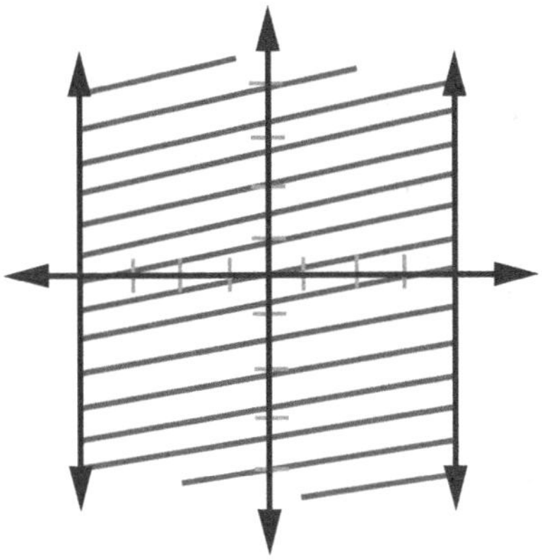

3.67 $4 \geq y > -3$

$y \leq 4$ and $y > -3$

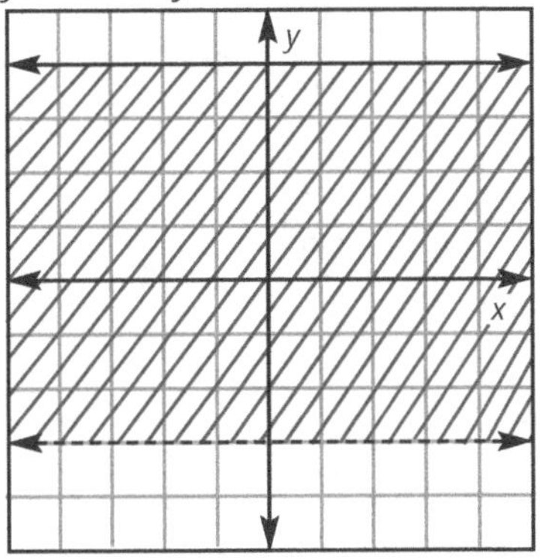

3.68

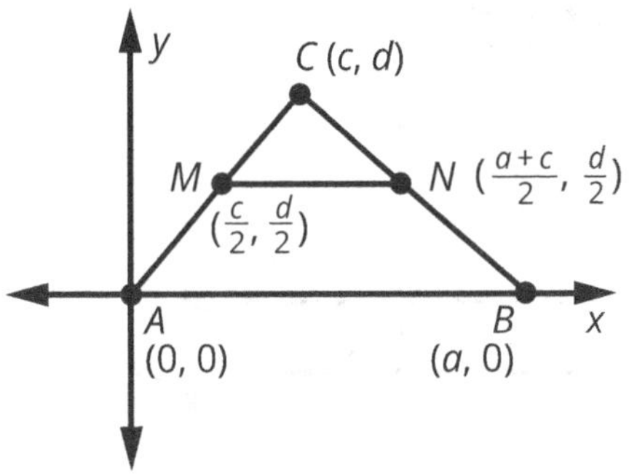

$$M_{AC} = \left(\frac{c+0}{2}, \frac{d+0}{2}\right) = \left(\frac{c}{2}, \frac{d}{2}\right)$$

$$M_{BC} = \left(\frac{a+c}{2}, \frac{0+d}{2}\right) = \left(\frac{a+c}{2}, \frac{d}{2}\right)$$

$$\begin{aligned} MN &= \sqrt{\left(\frac{c}{2} - \frac{a+c}{2}\right)^2 + \left(\frac{d}{2} - \frac{d}{2}\right)^2} \\ &= \sqrt{\left(-\frac{a}{2}\right)^2 + 0^2} \\ &= \frac{a}{2} \end{aligned}$$

$$\begin{aligned} AB &= \sqrt{(0-a)^2 + (0-0)^2} \\ &= \sqrt{(-a)^2 + 0^2} \\ &= \sqrt{a^2} \\ &= a \end{aligned}$$

$$\therefore MN = \frac{1}{2}AB$$

SELF TEST 3

3.01

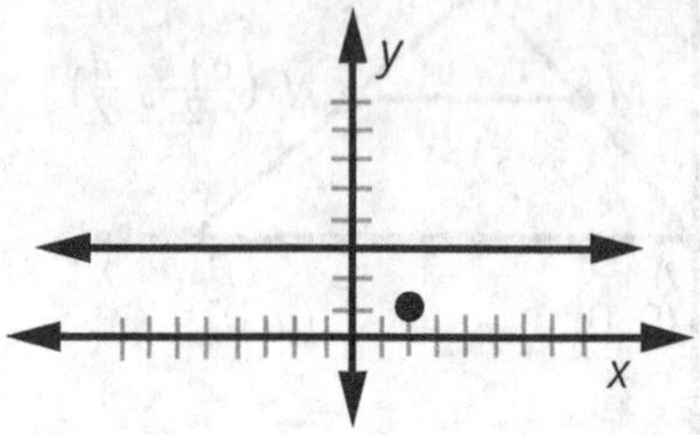

$A' = (2, 1)$

3.02

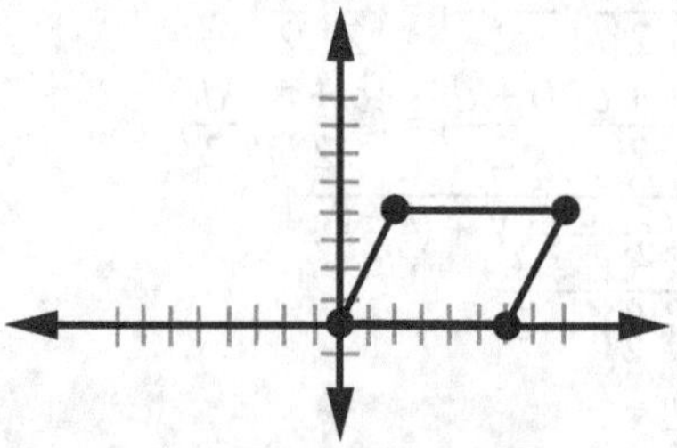

x-coordinate = 6 + 2 = 8
y-coordinate = 4
(8, 4)

3.03 $\frac{2}{5} = \frac{20}{x}$
$2(x) = 5(20)$
$2x = 100$
$\frac{2x}{2} = \frac{100}{2}$
$x = 50$

3.04 $4 \cdot 6 = 3 \cdot x$
$24 = 3x$
$\frac{24}{3} = \frac{3x}{3}$
$8 = x$

3.05 $(x - 3)^2 + (y + 2)^2 = 7^2$
$(x - 3)^2 + (y + 2)^2 = 49$

3.06 $y + 5 = -\frac{2}{3}(x - 2)$
$y + 5 = -\frac{2}{3}x + \frac{4}{3}$
$\frac{2}{3}x + y + 5 = \frac{4}{3}$
$\frac{2}{3}x + y = \frac{4}{3} - 5$
$\frac{2}{3}x + y = -\frac{11}{3}$
$2x + 3y = -11$ (multiply by 3)

3.07 Cylinder:
$V = Bh$
$B = \pi r^2$
$= \pi(4)^2$
$= 16\pi$
$V = 16\pi(10)$
$= 160\pi$

Cone:
$V = \frac{1}{3}Bh$
$B = \pi r^2$
$= \pi(1)^2$
$= \pi$
$V = \frac{1}{3}\pi(2)$
$= \frac{1}{3}\pi$
$= \frac{160\pi}{\frac{2}{3}\pi} = \frac{160}{\frac{2}{3}} = 160(\frac{3}{2}) = 240$ cones

3.08 $m_{AB} = \frac{9 - (-3)}{4 - 0} = \frac{12}{4} = 3$
$m \perp = -\frac{1}{3}$

3.09 $V = \frac{4}{3}\pi r^3$
$= \frac{4}{3}\pi(10)^3$
$= \frac{4}{3}\pi(1{,}000)$
$= \frac{4{,}000}{3}\pi$

3.010 (-3, 4)
3.011 acute
3.012 diameter
3.013 collinear
3.014 disjunction
3.015 deductive

3.016 $3x + 50 + 2x - 20 = 180$
$5x + 30 = 180$
$5x = 180 - 30$
$5x = 150$
$\frac{5x}{5} = \frac{150}{5}$
$x = 30°$

3.017 $\angle B + \angle C = 180 - \angle A$
$= 180 - 80$
$= 100°$

$\angle BPC = 180 - \frac{1}{2}(\angle B + \angle C)$
$= 180 - \frac{1}{2}(100)$
$= 180 - 50$
$= 130°$

3.018 $P_{square} = 4(x + 2) = 4x + 8$
$P_{\triangle} = 3(2x) = 6x$
$4x + 8 = 6x$
$8 = 6x - 4x$
$8 = 2x$
$\frac{8}{2} = \frac{2x}{2}$
$4 = x$

3.019 $\frac{6}{4} = \frac{7}{x}$
$6(x) = 4(7)$
$6x = 28$
$\frac{6x}{6} = \frac{28}{6}$
$x = \frac{28}{6} = \frac{14}{3}$
$\frac{6}{4} = \frac{9}{x}$
$6(x) = 4(9)$
$6x = 36$
$\frac{6x}{6} = \frac{36}{6}$
$x = 6$

3.020 hypotenuse $= \sqrt{8^2 + 10^2}$
$= \sqrt{64 + 100}$
$= \sqrt{164}$
$= \sqrt{4 \cdot 41}$
$= 2\sqrt{41}$

3.021

$m\widehat{BC} = \angle CAB = 70°$
$m\angle CDB = \frac{1}{2} m\ BC$
$= \frac{1}{2}(70)$
$= 35°$

3.022 $A = \frac{1}{2}d_1d_2$
$= \frac{1}{2}(6)(12)$
$= 36$

3.023 1. **STATEMENT**
$\angle 1 = \angle 2$; $AP = BP$
REASON
Given

2. **STATEMENT**
$\angle APD = \angle BPC$
REASON
Vertical ∠'s are =.

3. **STATEMENT**
$\triangle APD \cong \triangle BPC$
REASON
ASA

3.024 1. **STATEMENT**
$\overline{AB} \perp \overline{CD}$
REASON
Given

2. **STATEMENT**
$m\angle 1 = m\angle COB$
REASON
Definition of ⊥

3. **STATEMENT**
$m\angle COB = m\angle 2 + m\angle 3 + m\angle 4$
REASON
Angle addition theorem

4. **STATEMENT**
$m\angle 1 = m\angle 2 + m\angle 3 + m\angle 4$
REASON
Substitution

5. **STATEMENT**
$m\angle 3 = m\angle 7$
REASON
Vertical ∠'s are =.

6. **STATEMENT**
$m\angle 1 = m\angle 2 + m\angle 4 + m\angle 7$
REASON
Substitution

3.025 1. **STATEMENT**
$\overline{XA} \perp \overleftrightarrow{RS}$; $\angle 1 = \angle 2$
REASON
Given

2. **STATEMENT**
∠1, ∠3 are complementary
∠2, ∠4 are complementary
REASON
Adjacent ∠'s with exterior sides in ⊥'s are complementary

3. **STATEMENT**
   $\angle 3 = \angle 4$
   REASON
   Two $\angle$'s complementary to = $\angle$'s are =.
4. **STATEMENT**
   $\frac{BX}{XC} = \frac{AB}{AC}$
   REASON
   $\angle$ bisector proportion theorem

3.026
1. **STATEMENT**
   $\angle 1 = \angle 2$, $\angle 5 = \angle 6$
   REASON
   Given
2. **STATEMENT**
   $AB = AB$
   REASON
   Reflexive
3. **STATEMENT**
   $\triangle ABD \cong \triangle BAC$
   REASON
   AAS
4. **STATEMENT**
   $AD = BC$
   REASON
   CPCTE
5. **STATEMENT**
   $\angle 3 = \angle 4$
   REASON
   Vertical $\angle$'s
6. **STATEMENT**
   $\triangle APD \cong \triangle BPC$
   REASON
   AAS
7. **STATEMENT**
   $DP = CP$
   REASON
   CPCTE
8. **STATEMENT**
   $\triangle DPC$ is an isosceles triangle
   REASON
   definition of isosceles triangle
9. **STATEMENT**
   $\angle 7 = \angle 8$
   REASON
   Base $\angle$'s of isosceles $\triangle$ =.

3.027
1. **STATEMENT**
   $\overline{AB}$ diameter
   $\overline{BC}$ tangent to $\odot O$
   REASON
   Given
2. **STATEMENT**
   $\angle A = \angle A$
   REASON
   Reflexive
3. **STATEMENT**
   $\angle CBA$ is rt. $\angle$
   REASON
   Radius $\perp$ to tangent
4. **STATEMENT**
   $\angle BXA = 90°$
   REASON
   Inscribed in semicircle
5. **STATEMENT**
   $\angle CBA = \angle BXA$
   REASON
   All rt. $\angle$'s are =.
6. **STATEMENT**
   $\triangle AXB \sim \triangle ABC$
   REASON
   AA

3.028
1. **STATEMENT**
   $\overline{AB} \,||\, \overline{CD}$
   REASON
   Given
2. **STATEMENT**
   m $\angle 1$ = m $\angle 2$ + m $\angle 4$
   REASON
   Exterior $\angle$ = sum of remote interior $\angle$'s
3. **STATEMENT**
   m $\angle 3$ = m $\angle 4$
   REASON
   Alternate interior $\angle$'s
4. **STATEMENT**
   m $\angle 1$ = m $\angle 2$ + m $\angle 3$
   REASON
   Substitution

LIFEPAC TEST

1. c
$C = \pi d$
$\frac{C}{d} = \pi$

2. b
$m = \frac{8-3}{3-(-1)} = \frac{8-3}{3+1} = \frac{5}{4}$

3. d

4. b
$7\sqrt{3}(\frac{2}{\sqrt{3}}) = 14$

5. b
$s = \sqrt{36} = 6$
diagonal $= 6\sqrt{2}$

6. b

7. a

8. d

9. b
$m\angle AOC = m\angle AOX + m\angle XOC$
$m\angle AOX = m\angle XOC$
$m\angle AOC = 42 + 42 = 84°$

10. c
$\angle c = 180 - (m\angle A + m\angle B)$
$= 180 - 47 + 62)$
$= 180 - 109$
$= 71°$

11. c

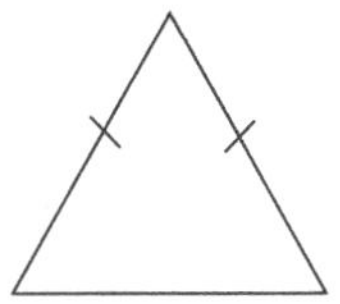

$\angle A = \angle B$
$\angle A = \angle B = 180 - \angle C$
$2\angle A = 180 - \angle C$
$= 180 - 62$
$= 118°$
$A = \frac{118}{2} = 59°$
Longest side = side opposite largest $\angle$ = AB

12. a

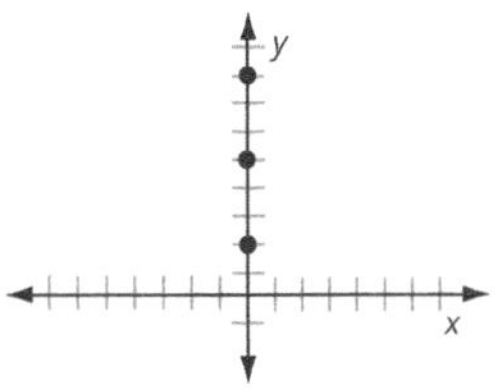

$TJ = |5-2| = 3$
$TH = |y-5| = 3$
$y - 5 = 3$
$y = 3 + 5 = 8$
$H\,(0, 8)$

13. c
$(n-2)180 = 1{,}260$
$180n - 360 = 1{,}260$
$180n = 1{,}260 + 360$
$180n = 1{,}620$
$\frac{180n}{180} = \frac{1{,}620}{180}$
$n = 9$

14. b
$(n-2)180 = (5-2)180 =$
$(3)180 = 540°$
$85 + 90 + 95 + 110 + x = 540$
$380 + x = 540$
$x = 540 - 380 = 160°$
The largest $\angle$ is 160°
The exterior $\angle = 180 - 160 = 20°$

15. a
$x + x + x + 15 + x + 45 = 4x + 60$
$4x + 60 = 360$
$4x = 360 - 60$
$4x = 300$
$\frac{4x}{4} = \frac{300}{4}$
$x = 75°$

16. true

17. true

18. true

19. true

20. true

21. false

22. false

23. false

24. false

25. true

26. true

27. false

28. false
$C = 2\pi r$
$10 = 2\pi r$
$\frac{10}{2\pi} = \frac{2\pi r}{2\pi}$
$\frac{5}{\pi} = r$
$A = \pi r^2$
$= \pi(\frac{5}{\pi})^2$
$= \pi(\frac{25}{\pi^2})$
$= \frac{25}{\pi}$
$100 \neq \frac{25}{\pi}$

29. true

30. true

31. $M_{AB} = \left(\frac{x_2 + x_1}{2}, \frac{y_2 + y_1}{2}\right)$

$(-3, 2) = \left(\frac{0 + x_1}{2}, \frac{2 + y_1}{2}\right)$

$-3 = \frac{0 + x_1}{2}$

$-6 = x_1$ (multiply by 2)

$2 = \frac{2 + y_1}{2}$

$4 = 2 + y_1$ (multiply by 2)

$4 - 2 = y_1$

$2 = y_1$

$B(-6, 2)$

32. $m\angle B + m\angle C = 180 - m\angle A$

$m\angle B = m\angle C$

$2m\angle B = 180 - 38$

$2m\angle B = 142$

$\frac{2m\angle B}{2} = \frac{142}{2}$

$m\angle B = 71°$

33. sum of exterior ∠'s = 360°

$\frac{360}{6} = 60°$

34. When "$p \to q$" is false:

pq
TF

When "*p* or *q*" is true:

pq
TT
TF
FT

∴ *q* must be false.

35. $(n - 2)180 = 900$

$180n - 360 = 900$

$180n = 900 + 360$

$180n = 1{,}260$

$\frac{180n}{180} = \frac{1{,}260}{180}$

$n = 7$

36. $y - 5 = \frac{3}{7}(x - 2)$

$y - 5 = \frac{3}{7}x - \frac{6}{7}$

$-\frac{3}{7}x + y - 5 = -\frac{6}{7}$

$-\frac{3}{7}x + y = -\frac{6}{7} + 5$

$-\frac{3}{7}x + y = \frac{29}{7}$

$3x - 7y = -29$ (multiply by -7)

37. $A = \frac{m\widehat{AB}}{360°}(\pi r^2)$

$m\widehat{AB} = 120°$

$A = \frac{120}{360}(\pi)(6)^2$

$= \frac{1}{3}(\pi)(36)$

$= 12\pi$

38.

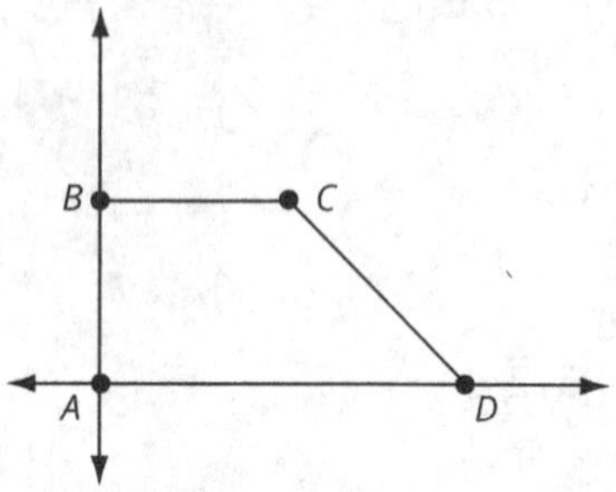

$AD = \sqrt{(b - 0)^2 + (0 - 0)^2}$

$= \sqrt{b^2 + 0^2}$

$= \sqrt{b^2}$

$= b$

$BC = \sqrt{(c - 0)^2 + (a - a)^2}$

$= \sqrt{c^2 + 0^2}$

$= \sqrt{c^2}$

$= c$

$A = \frac{1}{2}h(b_1 + b_2)$

$= \frac{1}{2}a(b + c)$

39. $x^2 < 4$

$\sqrt{x^2} < \sqrt{4}$

$x < 2$ and $x > -2$

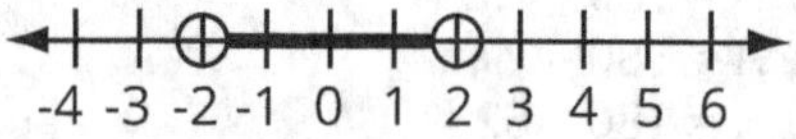

40.

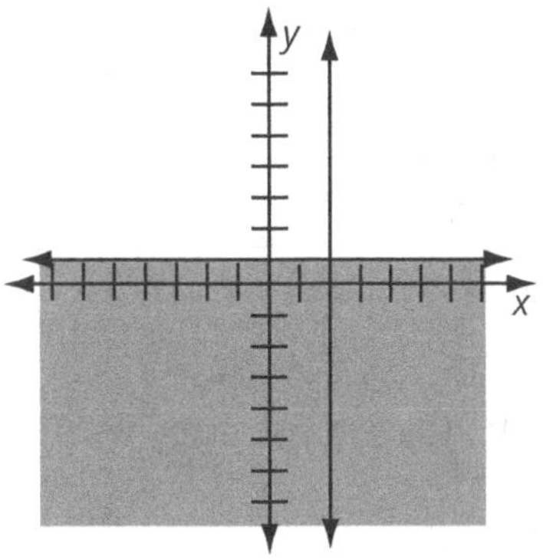

Solution graph:

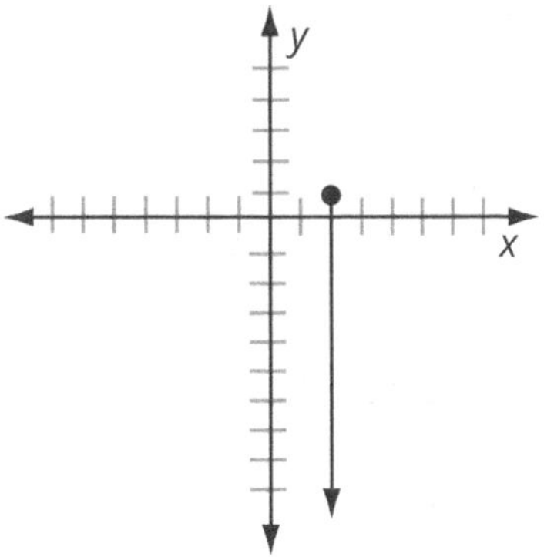

41.

1. **STATEMENT**
   ∠1 = ∠2, ∠5 = ∠6
   REASON
   Given
2. **STATEMENT**
   AB = *AB*
   REASON
   Reflexive
3. **STATEMENT**
   △*ABD* ≅ △*BAC*
   REASON
   AAS
4. **STATEMENT**
   AD = *BC*
   REASON
   CPCTE
5. **STATEMENT**
   ∠3 = ∠4
   REASON
   Vertical ∠'s
6. **STATEMENT**
   △*APD* ≅ △*BPC*
   REASON
   AAS
7. **STATEMENT**
   DP = *CP*
   REASON
   CPCTE
8. **STATEMENT**
   ∠7 = ∠8
   REASON
   Base ∠'s of isosceles △ =.

42.

1. **STATEMENT**
   ∠1 = ∠2, *AP* = *BP*
   REASON
   Given
2. **STATEMENT**
   ∠*APD* = ∠*BPC*
   REASON
   Vertical ∠'s
3. **STATEMENT**
   △*APD* ≅ △*BPC*
   REASON
   ASA

ALTERNATE LIFEPAC TEST

1. c
2. e
3. b
4. a
5. d
6. a. If a quadrilateral is a parallelogram, then two sides of the quadrilateral are equal and parallel.
b. If two sides of a quadrilateral are not equal and parallel, then the quadrilateral is not a parallelogram.
c. If a quadrilateral is not a parallelogram, then two sides of the quadrilateral are not equal and parallel.
7. a. T
b. F
c. T
d. T
8. a. OA or OB or OC
b. $\overleftrightarrow{CE}$
c. $\overleftrightarrow{AD}$
d. $\angle A$ or $\angle D$ or $\angle DCA$
e. $\triangle ADC$ or $\triangle ACE$
9. a. $\angle 1$ and $\angle 2$ are vertical $\angle$'s.
$m\angle 1 = m\angle 2$
$m\angle 1 = 120°$
$m\angle 2 = 120°$
b. $\angle 1$ and $\angle 3$ are corresponding $\angle$'s.
$m\angle 1 = m\angle 3$
$m\angle 1 = 120°$
$m\angle 3 = 120°$
10. a. $m\angle P = m\angle J$
$m\angle J = 30°$
$m\angle P = 30°$
b. $m\angle K = m\angle Q$
$m\angle Q = 70°$
$m\angle K = 70°$
c. $QR = KL$
$KL = 5$
$QR = 5$
11. $T.A. = \frac{1}{2}pl + B$
$p = 4(8) = 32$
$l^2 = \sqrt{8^2 - 4^2}$ (by the Pythagorean Theorem)
$l^2 = \sqrt{64 - 16}$
$l^2 = \sqrt{48}$
$l^2 = \sqrt{16 \cdot 3} = \sqrt{16} \cdot \sqrt{3}$
$l = 4\sqrt{3}$
$B = 8(8) = 64$
$T.A. = \frac{1}{2}(32)(4\sqrt{3}) + 64$
$T.A. = 64\sqrt{3} + 64$
$V = \frac{1}{3}Bh$
$B = 8(8) = 64$
$h^2 = \sqrt{l^2 - 4^2}$ (by the Pythagorean Theorem)
$l = 4\sqrt{3}$
$h^2 = \sqrt{(4\sqrt{3})^2 - 4^2}$
$h^2 = \sqrt{48 - 16}$
$h^2 = \sqrt{32}$
$h^2 = \sqrt{16 \cdot 2} = \sqrt{16} \cdot \sqrt{2}$
$h = 4\sqrt{2}$
$V = \frac{1}{3}(64)(4\sqrt{2})$
$V = \frac{256\sqrt{2}}{3}$
12. a. $\sin\angle A = \frac{\text{opposite}}{\text{hypotenuse}}$
$= \frac{4}{4\sqrt{5}}$
$= \frac{1}{\sqrt{5}}$
$= \frac{1}{\sqrt{5}} \cdot \frac{\sqrt{5}}{\sqrt{5}}$
$= \frac{\sqrt{5}}{\sqrt{25}}$
$= \frac{\sqrt{5}}{5}$
b. $\cos\angle A = \frac{\text{adjacent}}{\text{hypotenuse}}$
$= \frac{8}{4\sqrt{5}}$
$= \frac{2}{\sqrt{5}}$
$= \frac{2}{\sqrt{5}} \cdot \frac{\sqrt{5}}{\sqrt{5}}$
$= \frac{2\sqrt{5}}{\sqrt{25}}$
$= \frac{2\sqrt{5}}{5}$
c. $\tan\angle A = \frac{\text{opposite}}{\text{adjacent}}$
$= \frac{4}{8}$
$= \frac{1}{2}$

13. $d = \sqrt{(x_1 - x_2)^2 + (y_1 - y_2)^2}$
$d = \sqrt{(-3 - 2)^2 + (6 - 8)^2}$
$d = \sqrt{(-5)^2 + (-2)^2}$
$d = \sqrt{25 + 4}$
$d = \sqrt{29}$

14. $m = \frac{y_2 - y_1}{x_2 - x_1}$
$m = \frac{4 - 2}{7 - 3}$
$m = \frac{2}{4}$
$m = \frac{1}{2}$

15. midpoint = $(\frac{x_2 + x_1}{2}, \frac{y_2 + y_1}{2})$
midpoint = $(\frac{2 + (-5)}{2}, \frac{-4 + 6}{2})$
midpoint = $(\frac{2 - 5}{2}, \frac{-4 + 6}{2})$
midpoint = $(\frac{-3}{2}, \frac{2}{2})$
midpoint = $(\frac{-3}{2}, 1)$

16. A point in the center of the triangle

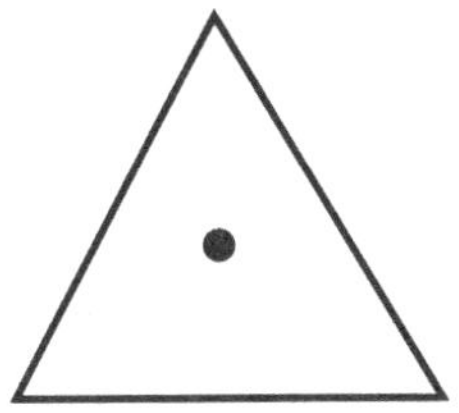

17. Graph $x \geq -3$ and $x < 2$.

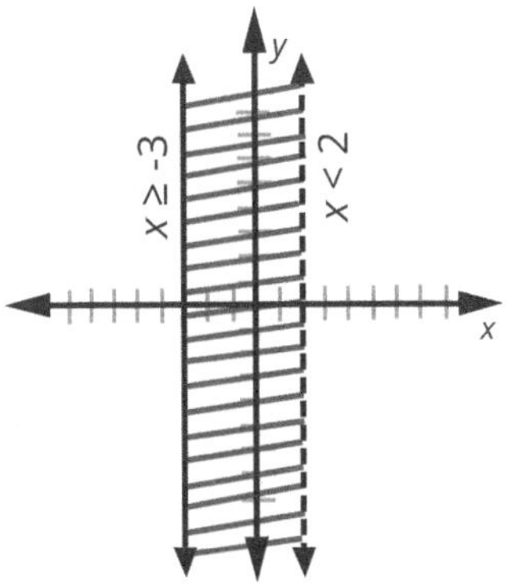

18.
1. **STATEMENT**
$\triangle ABC$ and $\triangle DEF$ are rt. $\triangle$'s.
$AC = DF$
$\angle C = \angle F$
REASON
Given
2. **STATEMENT**
$\angle B = \angle E$
REASON
All rt. $\angle$'s are =.
3. **STATEMENT**
$\triangle ABC \cong \triangle DEF$
REASON
AAS

MATH 1010

ALTERNATE LIFEPAC TEST

NAME ______________________________

DATE ______________________________

SCORE ______________________________

75
94

Match the following items (each answer, 2 points).

1. ______ segment *RS*
2. ______ line *RS*
3. ______ point *S*
4. ______ ray *RS*
5. ______ plane *R*

a. 

b. 

c. 

d. 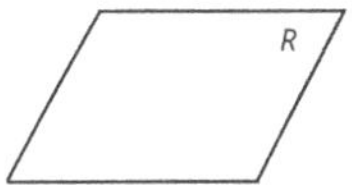

e. 

f.

Write the converse, inverse, and contrapositive of this theorem (each answer, 4 points).

6. If two sides of a quadrilateral are equal and parallel, then the quadrilateral is a parallelogram.

   a. Converse: ____

   ____

   b. Inverse: ____

   ____

   c. Contrapositive: ____

   ____

Complete the following truth table (each answer, 2 points).

7.

p	q	$p \rightarrow q$
T	T	a. ______
T	F	b. ______
F	T	c. ______
F	F	d. ______

Refer to the figure to name the following items (each answer, 2 points).

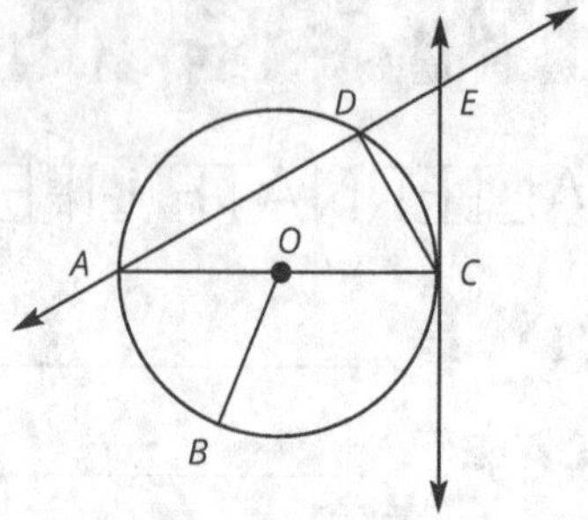

8. a. a radius ______________

b. a tangent ______________

c. a secant ______________

d. an inscribed angle ______________

e. a right triangle ______________

Given the following diagrams, find the required measures (each answer, 3 points).

9. Given: $j \parallel k$

$m\angle 1 = 120°$

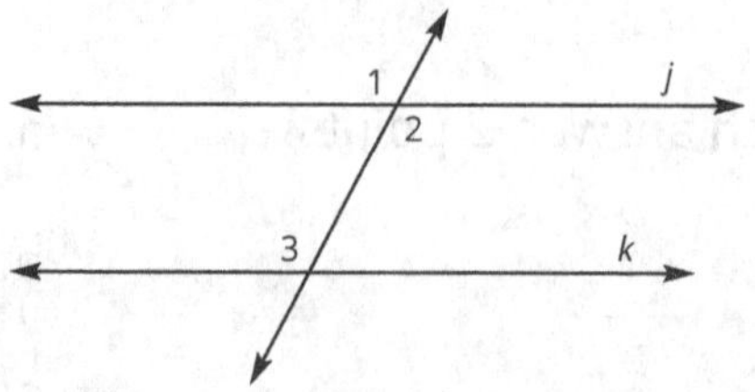

a. $m\angle 2 =$ ________

b. $m\angle 3 =$ ________

10. Given: $\triangle JKL \cong \triangle PQR$

$m\angle J = 30°$

$m\angle Q = 70°$

$KL = 5$

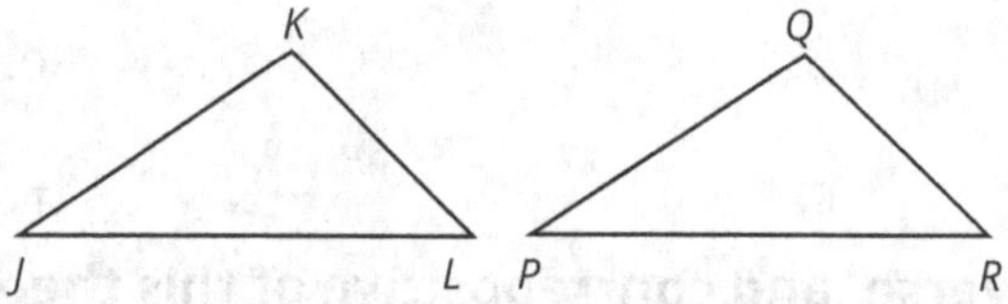

a. $m\angle P =$ ________

b. $m\angle K =$ ________

c. $QR =$ ________

11.

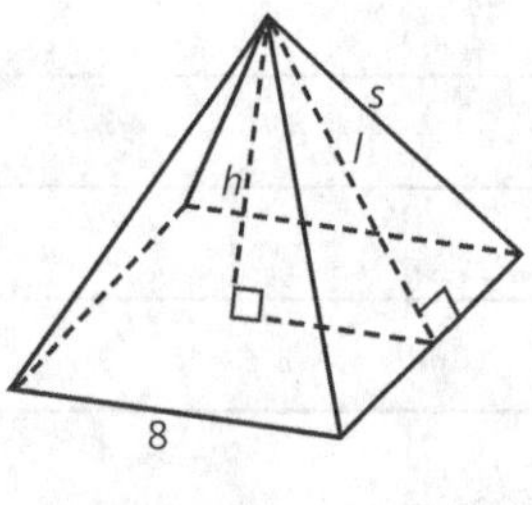

T.A. = ________

V = ________

12. State the required ratio for the labeled angle. Leave your answer in reduced fraction form.

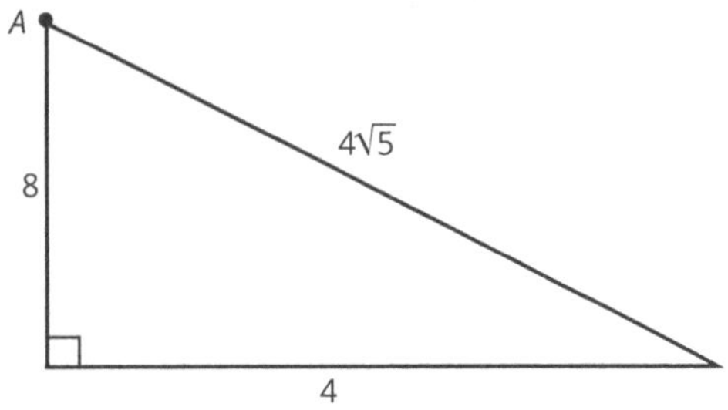

a. $\sin \angle A =$ ________

b. $\cos \angle A =$ ________

c. $\tan \angle A =$ ________

Solve the following problems (each answer, 3 points).

13. Find the distance between point U (-3, 6) and V (2, 8).

14. Find the slope of the line that passes through (3, 2) and (7, 4).

15. Find the midpoint of the segment whose end points are (- 5, 6) and (2, -4).

Sketch and describe the following locus (5 points).

16. What is the locus of points equidistant from all three sides of an equilateral triangle?

Sketch the following graph (4 points).

17. $\{(x, y): -3 \leq x < 2\}$

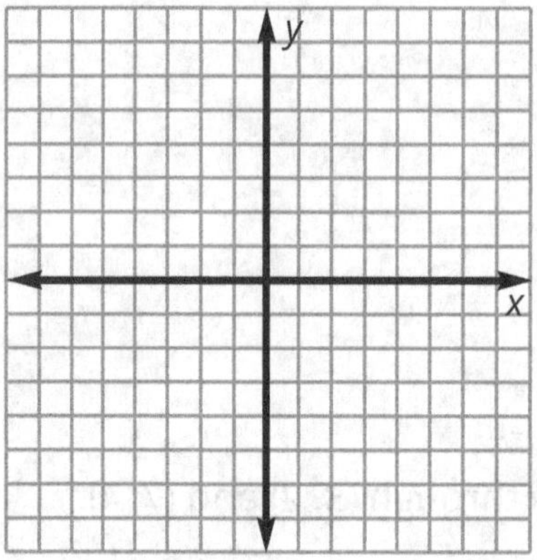

Complete the following proof (6 points).

18. Given: $\triangle ABC$ and $\triangle DEF$ are rt. $\triangle$'s
$AC = DF$
$\angle C = \angle F$

To Prove: $\triangle ABC \cong \triangle DEF$

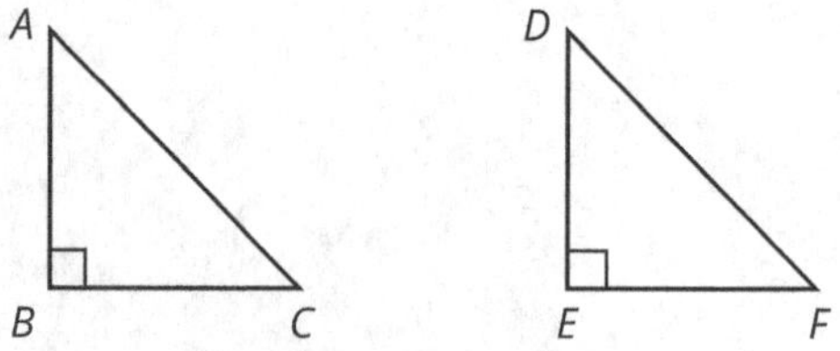

STATEMENT	REASON

A Mathematical System

Introduction

A mathematical system is a logical study of shape, arrangement, and quantity. Algebra, geometry, trigonometry, and calculus are examples of mathematical systems. Geometry is the logical study of the shape and size of things. The word geometry comes from the Greek and means *earth measurement*. Any mathematical system contains four items:

- Basic undefined terms.
- All other terms carefully defined.
- Some basic properties that are accepted without proof. (These are called *postulates*.)
- All other properties that are established by proof. (These are called *theorems*.)

Objectives

Read these objectives. The objectives tell you what you will be able to do when you have successfully completed this LIFEPAC©. When you have finished this LIFEPAC, you should be able to:

1. Identify, draw, and label models of undefined terms and defined terms.
2. Define some basic geometric terms.
3. Define *postulate* and *theorem*, and recognize a model of each.
4. Describe the four items that are involved in a mathematical system.

Survey the LIFEPAC. Ask yourself some questions about this study and write your questions here.

1. UNDEFINED TERMS

In geometry there are three terms that we do not attempt to define. They are point, line, and plane. These three terms are the foundation upon which geometry is built.

Section Objective

When you have completed this section, you should be able to:

1. Identify, draw, and label models of undefined terms and defined terms.

Points

A *point* cannot be seen. It has no size, no shape, no color, no physical properties. It is an imaginary thing. We do, however, represent a point on paper by a dot. A point has position or location.

To be able to talk about a point, we name it with a capital letter and show it on paper as a dot.

Five locations or positions on this page are points and are named *A*, *B*, *C*, *D*, and *E*. More than five points are on the page. In fact, the number of points on this page is infinite.

Complete the following activities.

1.1 We think of a point as a ______________________________ .

1.2 A point is represented by ____________________ .

1.3 Place names on these points.

1.4 How many points are located on this page? ____________________________

1.5 What physical characteristics do points have? __________________

1.6 Have you ever seen a point? ______________

LINES

A *line* can be thought of as a collection of points that are lined up one after the other and extend infinitely far in opposite directions.
A line in geometry is straight, not curved or bent. Since there are an infinite number of points on this page they can be lined up to form an infinite number of lines.

We represent a line on paper like this:

The arrowheads on the ends tell us the line extends indefinitely. Since a line is made up of points, it has no thickness or other physical characteristics. A line is named by naming two of its points and placing a double-pointed arrow above the two letters.

To the right are four lines named $\overleftrightarrow{EB}$, $\overleftrightarrow{LD}$, $\overleftrightarrow{DW}$, and $\overleftrightarrow{MB}$. A line may also be named by using a single lowercase letter as illustrated.

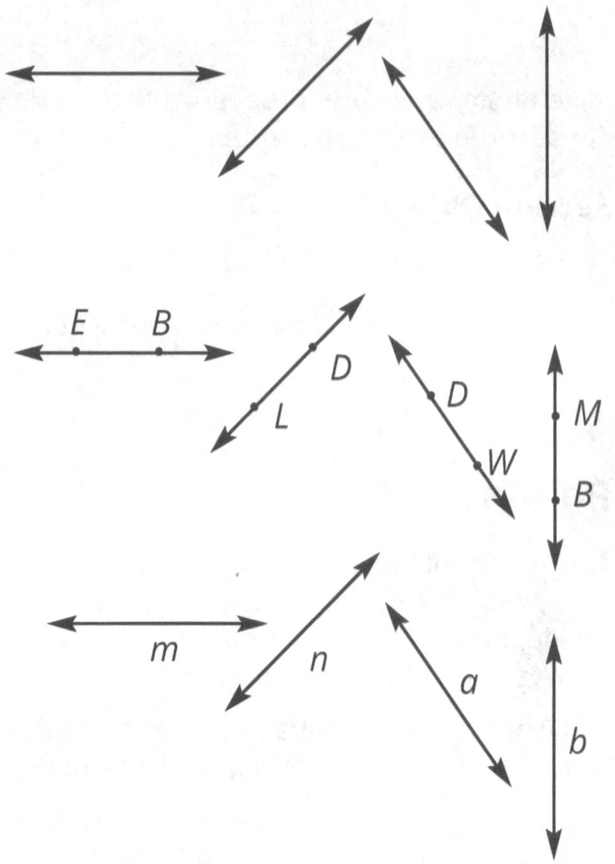

Supply the information required.

1.7 We think of a line as a collection of ______________________.

1.8 Unless otherwise indicated, a line in geometry is understood to be (straight, curved, either)

______________________.

1.9 Name the following lines.

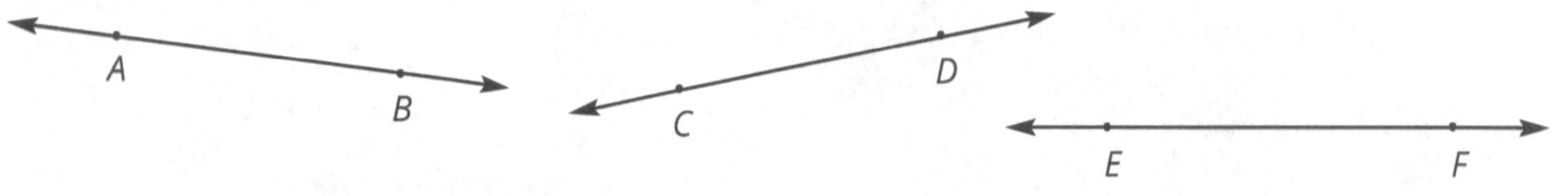

a. ______________________ b. ______________________ c. ______________________

1.10 How many lines are contained on this page? ______________________

1.11 What is indicated by arrowheads on a line? ______________________

____

PLANES

A *plane* can be thought of as a collection of points in a flat surface that extends in all directions without stopping. To represent a plane, a figure is drawn like the ones illustrated. (Remember that the edges are not really there.) A plane is named by using the name of one of its points. Thus we have plane *A*, plane *B*, and plane *C*. As with points and lines, planes do not have any physical properties. A billion planes could be stacked in a pile and still not have enough thickness to be measured. **A plane is defined by at least three points not all on the same line.**

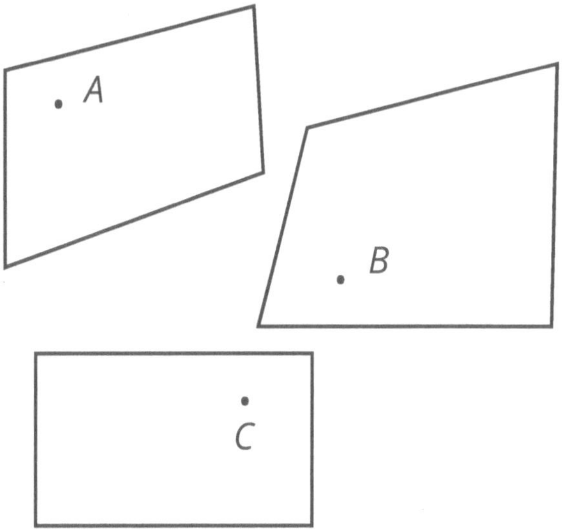

Write the following information.

1.12 A plane can be thought of as a (flat, curved) a. ________________ surface, made up of

b. ________________ .

1.13 Name the following planes.

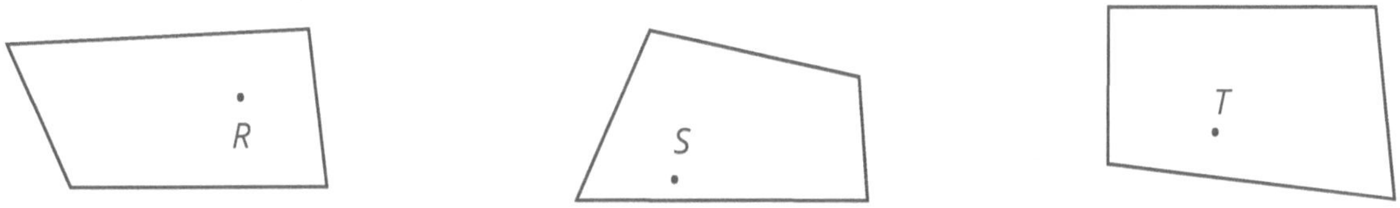

a. ________________ b. ________________ c. ________________

1.14 How long is a plane? ________________

1.15 How thick is a plane? ________________

1.16 Can planes be seen? ________________

We may also use models to represent points, lines, and planes. Representing geometric shapes in some tangible way will help to illustrate some of their mutual relationships.

The sharp end of a pin, tack, or pencil, for example, can be a model for a point. A pencil, meter stick, or soda straw can represent a line. A table top, sheet of cardboard, or wall in a room can be a model for a plane.

Here are some ways points, lines, and planes are related. Note the terms used in talking about points, lines, and planes.

Points *A* and *B* are on line *l*. Line *l* contains points *A*, *B*, and *C*. *C* is a point of $\overleftrightarrow{AB}$.

Lines *a* and *b* intersect at point *P*. *Q* is not a point of line *b*.

Plane *M* and plane *N* intersect at $\overleftrightarrow{AB}$. Their intersection is $\overleftrightarrow{AB}$. Point *C* is in plane *M* but not in plane *N*. Line *t* intersects plane *N* at point *D*. Plane *M* contains line *r*. Every point of line *r* is in plane *M*.

Points *A* and *B* are in both planes *M* and *N*.

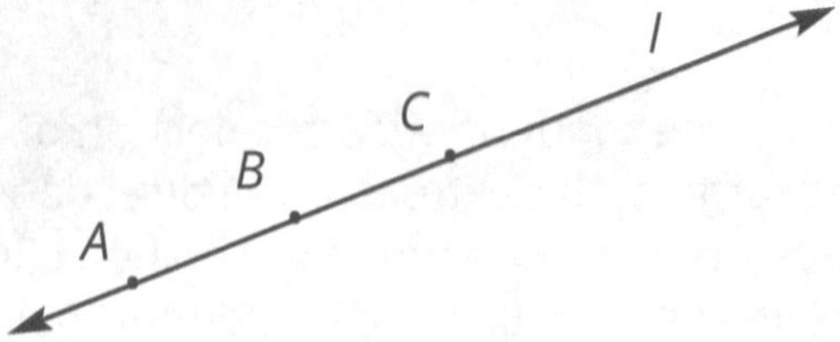

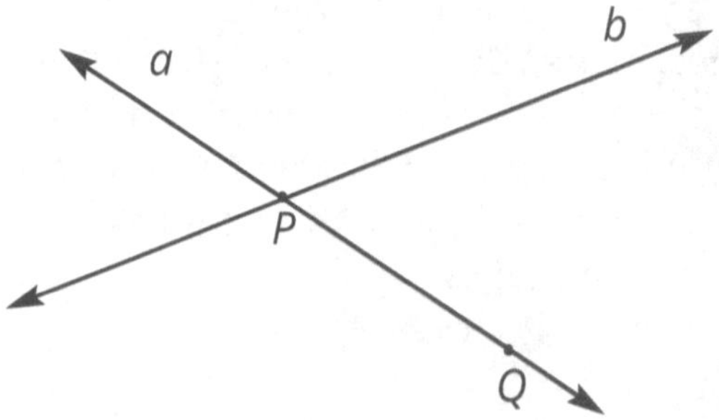

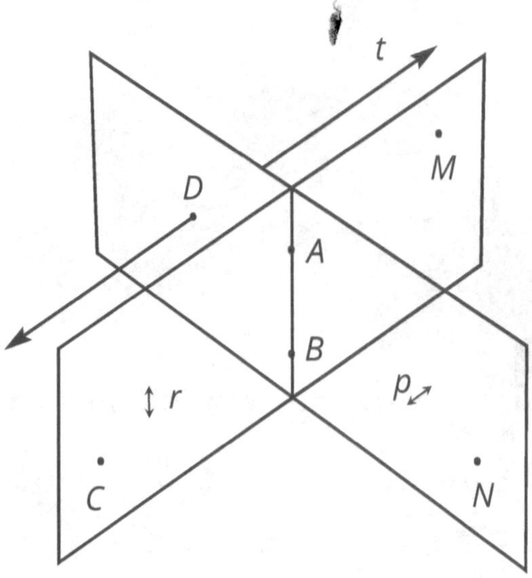

TEACHER CHECK ____________ initials ____________ date

Review the material in this section in preparation for the Self Test. The Self Test will check your mastery of this particular section. The items missed on this Self Test will indicate specific areas where restudy is needed for mastery.

SELF TEST 1

Name the undefined terms for which each is a model (each answer, 3 points).

Figure 1	Figure 2	Figure 3
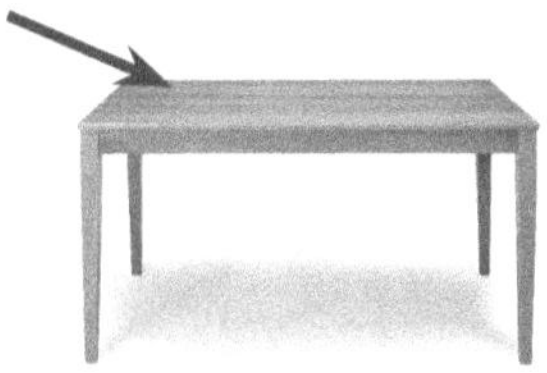	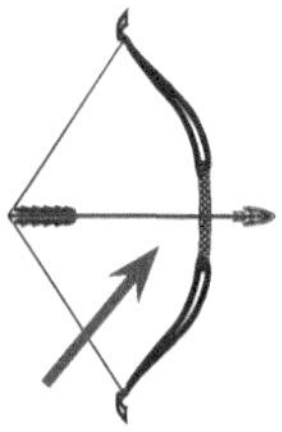	

1.01 ________________________

1.02 ________________________

1.03 ________________________

Figure 4	Figure 5	Figure 6
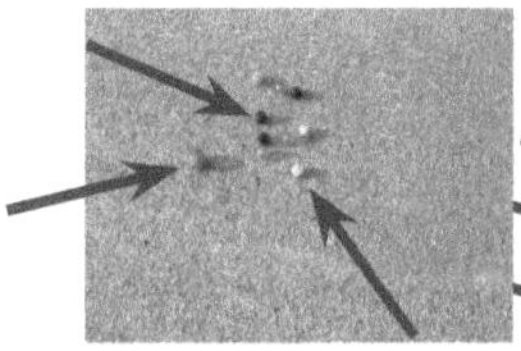		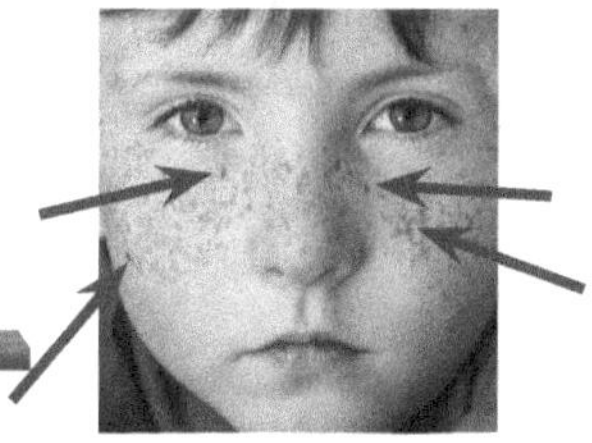

1.04 ________________________

1.05 ________________________

1.06 ________________________

Match the description in Column II with its model in Column I (each answer, 2 points).

	Column I		Column II
1.07		________	a. $\overleftrightarrow{MN}$
1.08	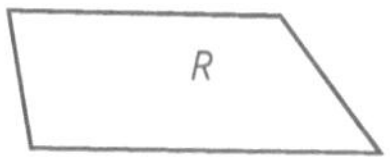	________	b. Point T
1.09		________	c. Plane R
1.010		________	d. Plane S
1.011	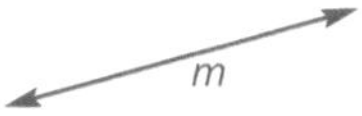	________	e. Point B
1.012		________	f. Line m

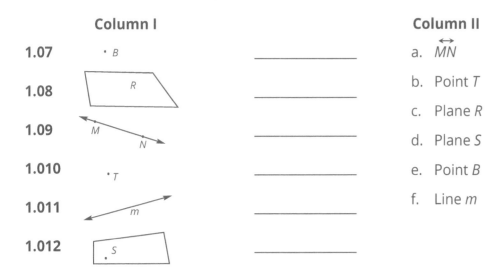

Refer to the model and complete the statements (each answer, 2 points).

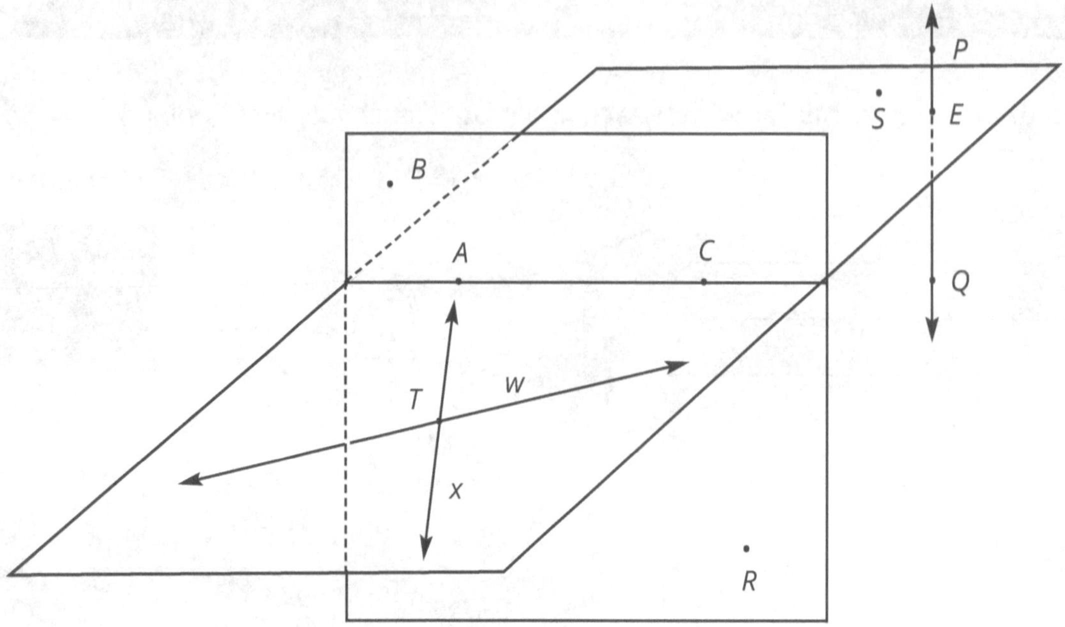

1.013 The intersection of plane *S* and plane *R* is ______________ .

1.014 Line *PQ* a. ______________ plane *S* at point b. ______________ .

1.015 Line *w* and line *x* intersect at ______________ .

1.016 Points *B* and *R* are in plane ______________ .

1.017 Name three lines shown to be in plane *S*.

a. ______________ b. ______________ c. ______________

1.018 Line *w* lies in plane ______________ .

1.019 Name all the points shown to be in plane *S*. ______________

1.020 Name all the points shown to be in plane *R*. ______________

42/52 **SCORE** ______________ **TEACHER** ______________ ______________
initials date

2. BASIC DEFINITIONS

We must define carefully the terms we use in geometry. Arguments and misunderstandings sometimes result because of our failure to define carefully the things we talk about.

Although you probably know in a general way what such geometric figures as circles, triangles, squares, and so on, are in the study of geometry, you will need to know a precise definition for such terms.

Section Objective

When you have completed this section, you should be able to:

2. Define some basic geometric terms.

A DEFINITION OF DEFINITIONS

A definition should contain words whose meanings are already known. The only geometric terms to be used in defining another geometric term should be ones *previously defined* or *accepted as undefined*. A good definition should place the term being defined in its nearest class with a minimum number of restrictions.

It should not be a listing of all the properties of the term. Also, a good definition must be reversible. Thus, "A car is a four-wheel vehicle" is not a good definition because a "four-wheel vehicle" may be a wagon.

Which definitions would be acceptable (a) and which unacceptable (u)?

2.1 *Apple:* a fruit that can be eaten. __________

2.2 *Baseball:* a game played with a ball. __________

2.3 *Triangle:* a geometric figure that has 3 sides, 3 angles, 3 medians, 3 altitudes, and a perimeter. __________

2.4 *Week:* a period of time consisting of seven consecutive days. __________

GEOMETRIC TERMS

During your study of geometry, you will be learning the definition of many terms. Learn each new term *as it is presented* because later terms will be defined by using earlier terms. New terms will be defined as we need them in our study of geometry.

Many of the definitions, theorems, and postulates in this unit will be needed in later units. Lists of these kept and maintained will be very helpful for future reference.

Start a notebook now!

DEFINITIONS:

A. **Space**: the set of all possible points.

B. **Collinear points**: a set of two or more points all on the same line.

C. **Coplanar points**: a set of two or more points all on the same plane.

D. **Betweenness of points**: point *B* is between *A* and *C* if *A*, *B*, and *C* are collinear and the equation, $AB + BC = AC$ is true, where *AB*, *BC*, and *AC* are the distances between points *A* and *B*, *B* and *C*, and *A* and *C*, respectively.

A. Model: Think of all the locations or positions in this room, the outdoors, underground, and in the sky. That set of points is our geometric space.

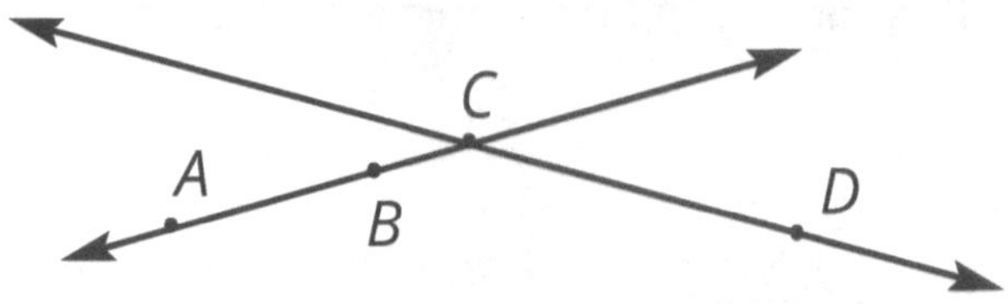

B. Models: Points *A*, *B*, and *C* are collinear. Points *C* and *D* are collinear. Points *A*, *B*, *C*, *D* are not collinear.

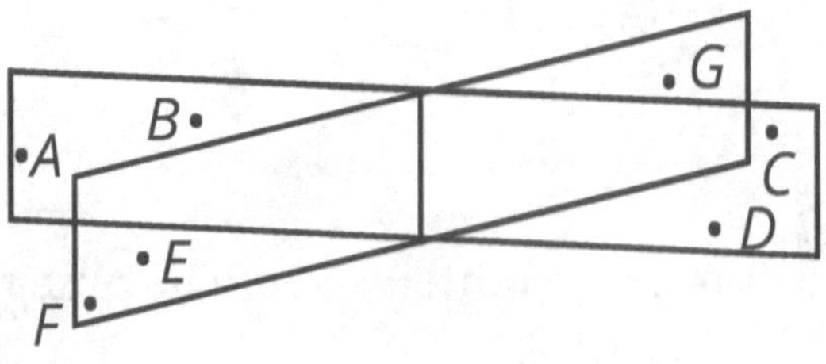

C. Models: Points *A*, *B*, *C*, *D* are coplanar. Points *E*, *F*, *G* are coplanar. Points *A*, *B*, *C*, *F* are not coplanar.

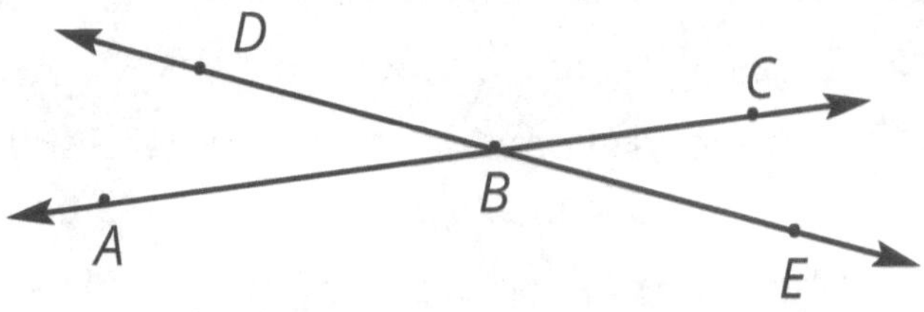

D. Models: Point *B* is between *A* and *C*. Point *B* is between *D* and *E*. But *B* is not between *D* and *C* because *D*, *B*, and *C* are not collinear.

Complete the following activities.

2.5 The set of all points is called ______________________ .

2.6 Is every set of three points collinear? ______________

2.7 Is every set of three points coplanar? ______________

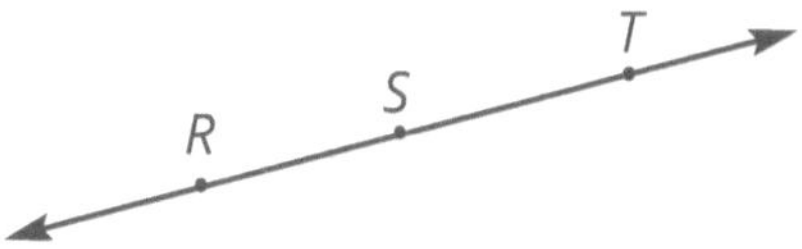

2.8 Point a. ___________ is between point b. ___________ and point c. ___________ .

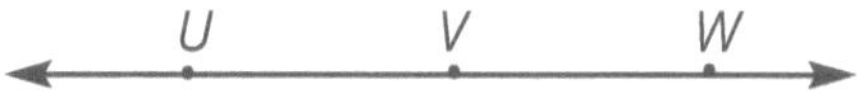

2.9 Write an equation to show that V is between U and W. ____________________________

Answer true or false.

2.10 _____________ *A*, *B*, and *C* are collinear.

2.11 _____________ *A*, *B*, and *C* are coplanar.

2.12 _____________ *S* is between *B* and *C*.

2.13 _____________ *S*, *E*, and *C* are collinear.

2.14 _____________ *A*, *C*, *D*, and *E* are coplanar.

2.15 _____________ *U* is between *C* and *D*.

2.16 _____________ *A*, *R*, *S*, and *C* are coplanar.

2.17 _____________ *C* is between *A* and *D*.

2.18 _____________ *R*, *S*, and *T* are coplanar.
(Hint: Review the definition of a plane.)

2.19 _____________ *B* is shown to be in 4 planes.

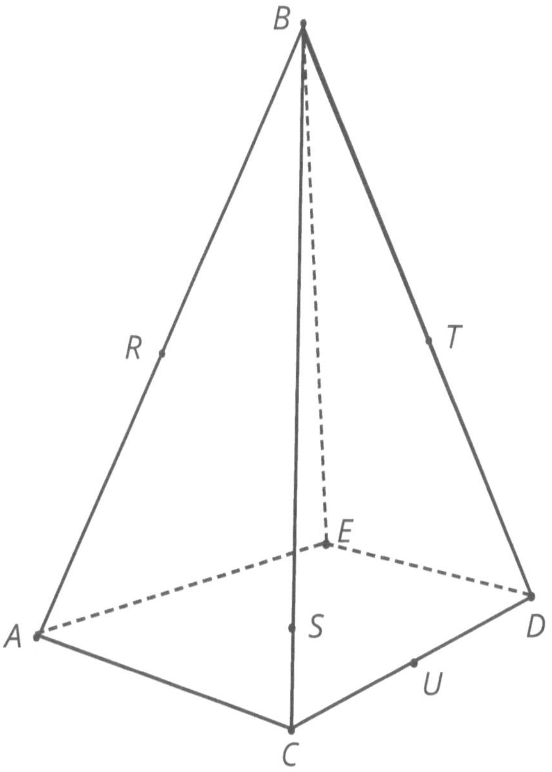

DEFINITIONS:

E. **Line segment**: the set of two different points and all points between them.

F. **Length of a segment**: the distance between the endpoints of a segment.

G. **Midpoint of a segment**: the point on a segment that divides the segment into two equal segments.

H. **Bisector of a segment**: a line or segment that intersects the segment at its midpoint.

I. **Ray**: a ray, $\overrightarrow{AC}$, with endpoint A and containing a second point C, is the set of points on $\overline{AC}$ and all points such that C is between them and A.

J. **Opposite rays**: $\overrightarrow{BA}$ and $\overrightarrow{BC}$ are opposite rays if A, B, and C are collinear and B (the endpoint of both rays) is between A and C.

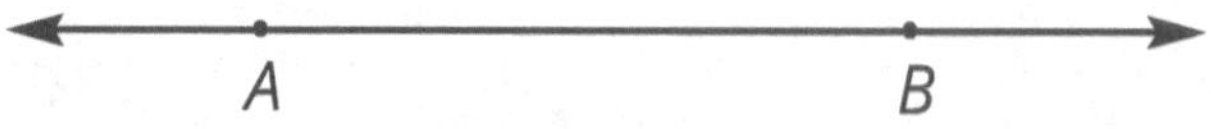

A line segment is usually referred to simply as a *segment*. A and B are the endpoints of segment AB. We name a segment by naming its endpoints and placing a bar, —, above them. The endpoints can be named in either order, so $\overline{AB}$ and $\overline{BA}$ are the same segment.

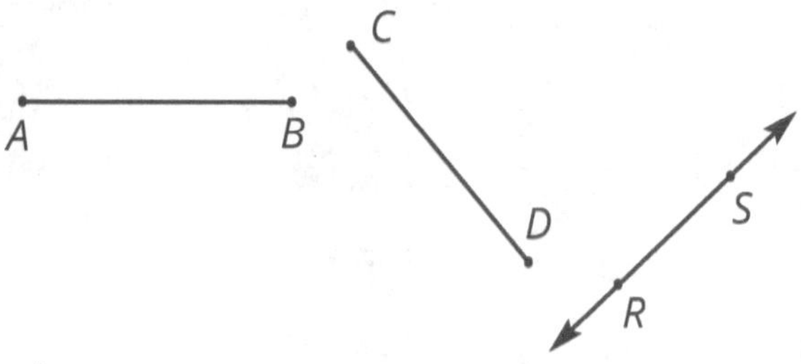

E. Models: $\overline{AB}$, $\overline{CD}$, and $\overline{RS}$ are the names of these segments illustrated. A segment can be thought of as a specific part of a line.

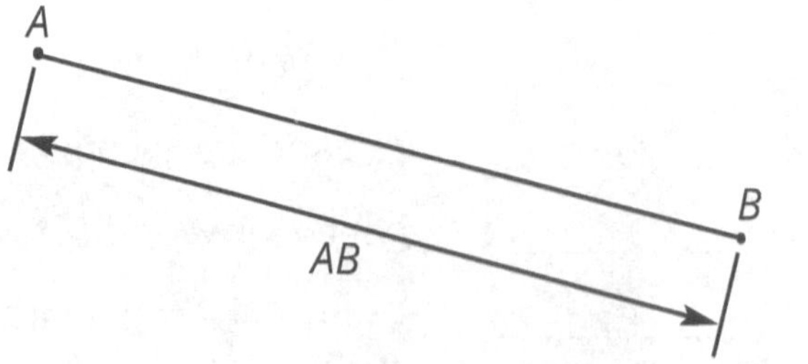

Unlike a line, a segment does have finite length. This *length* is a positive real number and is designated by writing AB. No arrow or bar is written above the letters that designate the length of the segment.

F. Model: AB is the length of $\overline{AB}$.

G. Model: M is the midpoint of $\overline{AB}$ if $AM = MB$.

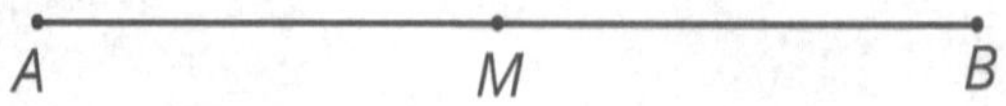

H. Model: If M is the midpoint of $\overline{AB}$, then l and $\overline{RS}$ are bisectors of $\overline{AB}$.

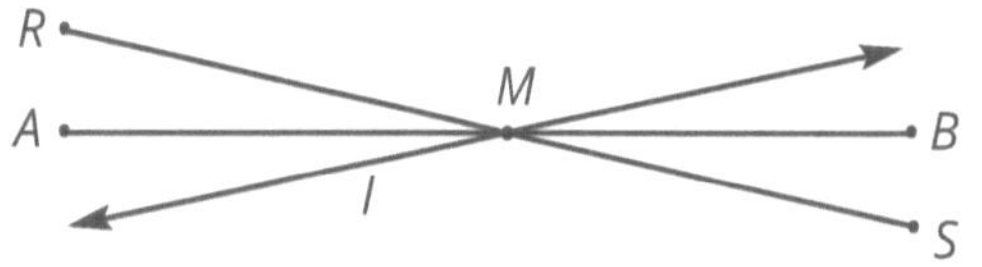

Notice the symbol used to name the ray in definition I: $\overrightarrow{AC}$. The endpoint A of a ray is always named first, followed by the name of any other point on it. A singly-pointed arrow, →, is placed over the two letters.

I. Model: The rays illustrated are named $\overrightarrow{AC}$, $\overrightarrow{RS}$, and $\overrightarrow{XY}$. A ray can be thought of as part of a line going in one direction only.

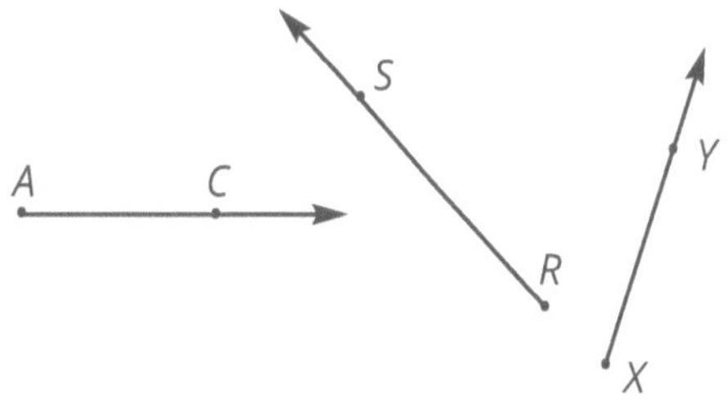

J. Models: $\overrightarrow{BA}$ and $\overrightarrow{BC}$ are opposite rays, but $\overrightarrow{BA}$ and $\overrightarrow{BD}$ are not because D, A, and B are not collinear.

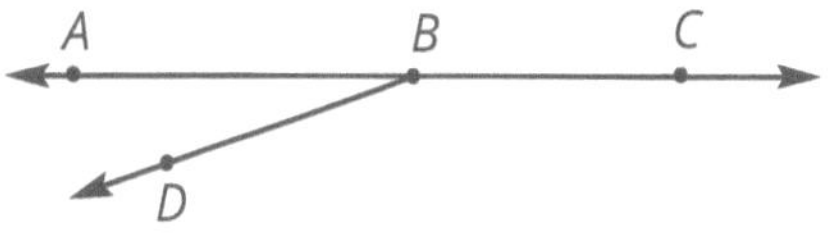

$\overrightarrow{TR}$ and $\overrightarrow{SU}$ are not opposite rays because they do not have a common endpoint. We can think of opposite rays as forming a line.

Complete the following activities.

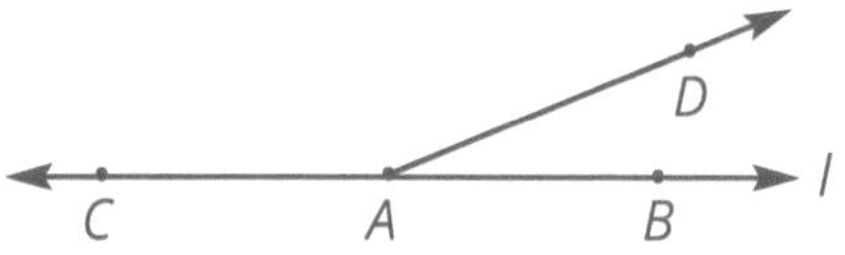

2.20 Do $\overrightarrow{AB}$ and $\overrightarrow{BA}$ name the same ray? ______________

2.21 Do $\overrightarrow{CA}$ and $\overrightarrow{CB}$ name the same ray? ______________

2.22 Name two opposite rays shown. a. ________________ and b. ________________

2.23 Name four segments shown. a. __________, b. __________, c. __________, d. __________.

2.24 Does $CA + AB = CB$? ______________

2.25 What is the endpoint of $\overrightarrow{BC}$? ______________

2.26 With respect to each other, what are AC and AB called? ____________________________

2.27 If AC = AB, what is A with respect to CB ? ____________________________

2.28 Are AD and AC opposite rays? _______________

2.29 Is A between C and D? _______________

SUMMARY

Model	Name	Description
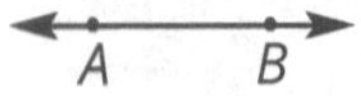	$\overleftrightarrow{AB}$	the line through A and B
	$\overline{AB}$	the segment with endpoints A and B
(a positive number)	AB	the length of segment AB
	$\overrightarrow{AB}$	the ray starting at A and passing through B
	$\overrightarrow{BA}$	the ray starting at B and passing through A

TEACHER CHECK __________ initials __________ date

Review the material in this section in preparation for the Self Test. This Self Test will check your mastery of this particular section as well as your knowledge of the previous section.

SELF TEST 2

Complete the following activities (each answer, 3 points).

2.01 If U is between R and N, what relationship must the three points have?

____

2.02 In the figure shown, A is the midpoint of $\overline{SM}$. Write two equations that follow from this fact.

a. ______________________

b. ______________________

2.03 Point O is between G and D. Write an equation that follows from this fact.

____

2.04 In Activity 2.03, can you conclude that $GO = OD$? ______________________

____

2.05 Write the symbol for the set of points $\overrightarrow{SA}$ and all points T such that A is between S and T.

____

2.06 What is point O on $\overline{MN}$ called if $MO = ON$?

____

2.07 Points S, U, and N are collinear. Which point satisfies the definition of betweenness if $NU + US = NS$?

____

2.08 In Question 2.07, what point is between the other two if $NU = 1$, $SU = 2$, and $SN = 3$?

____

2.09 If points S, O, and N are collinear, how many lines do they determine?

____

2.010 If points N, U, and T are collinear, name all the segments they determine.

____

2.011 The set of all points is called ________________ .

2.012 Opposite rays form a ________________________________ .

2.013 Collinear points are all on the same ________________________ .

Based on the diagram, fill in each space with the correct answer (each answer, 3 points).

2.014 Points *A*, *S*, and *R* are _______________ .

2.015 Points *R*, *T*, and *B* are _______________ .

2.016 Points *A*, *Q*, and *C* are _______________ .

2.017 Points *A*, *B*, and *Q* are _______________ .

2.018 Points *R*, *S*, and *T* are _______________ .

2.019 Points *Q*, *B*, and *C* are _______________ .

2.020 Points *A*, *S*, *Q*, and *R* are _______________ .

2.021 Points *R*, *T*, *B*, and *C* are _______________ .

2.022 Points *A*, *B*, *C*, and *Q* are _______________ .

2.023 Points *R*, *T*, *S*, and *Q* are _______________ .

2.024 Points *S*, *T*, *Q*, and *U* are _______________ .

a. collinear

b. coplanar

c. both collinear and coplanar

d. neither collinear nor coplanar

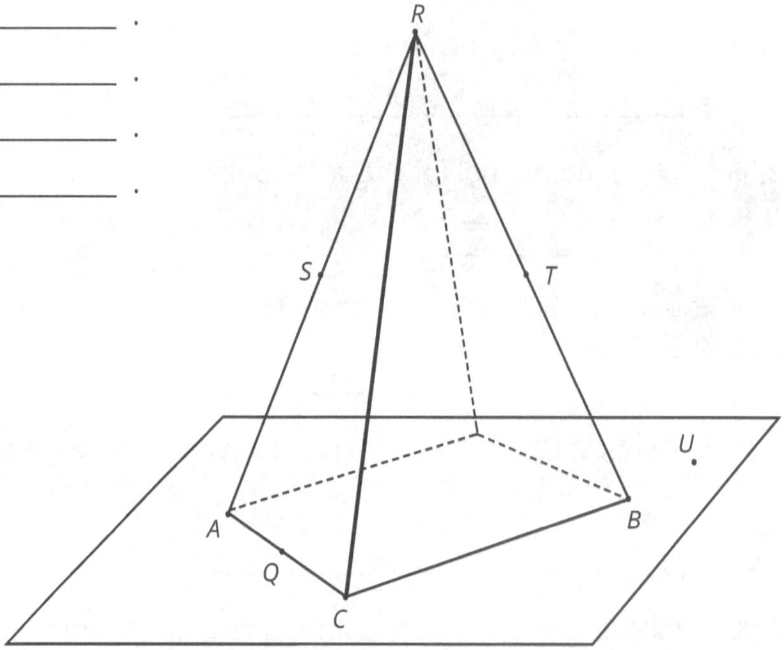

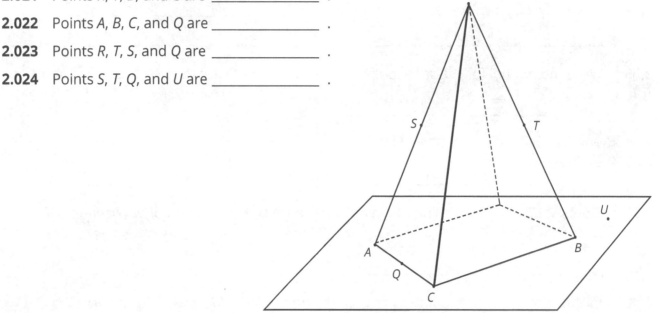

60/72 **SCORE** ____________ **TEACHER** ____________ ____________
initials date

MATH 1001

LIFEPAC TEST

NAME ______________________

DATE ______________________

SCORE ______________________

MATH 1001: LIFEPAC TEST

After each model in Column I, write the matching term from Column II (each answer, 2 points).

Column I

1.  ____________________
2.  ____________________
3.  ____________________
4. • P ____________________
5.  ____________________

Column II

a. $\overleftrightarrow{PQ}$

b. $\overrightarrow{PQ}$

c. $\overline{PQ}$

d. $PQ + QR = PR$

e. point P

f. $\overleftrightarrow{PR}$

Write your answer on the line (each answer, 4 points).

6. The set of all points is called ____________ .
7. The endpoint of $\overrightarrow{AB}$ is point ________ .
8. If point A is between B and C, then $BA + AC =$ ________ .
9. If $RS = ST$ on $\overline{RT}$, point S is called the ____________________ of $\overline{RT}$.
10. A postulate is a statement we accept without ____________ .
11. A theorem is a statement we must ____________ .
12. A line contains at least ____________ points.
13. Space contains at least ____________ points.
14. How many lines are determined by three noncollinear points? ____________
15. $a +$ ________ $= 0$.

Sketch and label the following conditions (each answer, 5 points).

16. Two lines $\overleftrightarrow{AB}$ and $\overleftrightarrow{CD}$ intersecting in point P.

17. A line l and a point Q not on l that are both in plane T.

18. A segment with endpoints U and V and midpoint M.

19. Collinear and coplanar points A, B, C, D.

20. Opposite rays $\overrightarrow{AC}$ and $\overrightarrow{AB}$.

3. GEOMETRIC STATEMENTS

In geometry we shall investigate geometric facts about shape and size. In most cases, we will do this by putting an idea into statement form and then proving the statement true or not true. Nearly all the statements that we make in geometry will be proved. These provable statements are called *theorems*. Some statements, however, are so simple and fundamental that they will be given without proof. These unproven statements are called *postulates*.

You already know a great many geometric facts. For example, you know how to find the area of a rectangle, the area of a triangle, and perhaps the area of a circle. You may also know the Pythagorean relation for right triangles.

Some of the facts you know are so simple you may not think they are important at all. Here is a statement of this type: Two lines cannot cross each other in more than one point. This statement is a *postulate*. Other statements are more complicated: If two sides and the included angle of one triangle are congruent to the corresponding parts of another triangle, then the triangles are congruent. This statement requires proof.

We will organize our geometric knowledge in such a way that the more complicated statements can be proved true or false by using definitions, postulates, and logical reasoning.

Section Objectives

When you have completed this section, you should be able to:

3. Define *postulate* and *theorem*, and recognize a model of each.
4. Describe the four items that are involved in a mathematical system.

POSTULATES

The postulates in geometry are similar to the rules of a game. The rules determine how the game is to be played and what makes it different from other games.

DEFINITION:

Postulate:
a statement accepted without proof.

Different postulates make different geometries. In this course we will spend our time studying Euclidean geometry, named for Euclid, a Greek mathematician of 300 B.C. who set down the postulates or rules of the game that we use.

For almost twenty centuries, this geometry was the only one known, because man took such a long time to realize that more than one set of rules were possible.

Five postulates about points, lines, and planes are listed in the box. More postulates will be introduced from time to time as we need them to develop our geometry as a mathematical system.

POSTULATES:

Postulate 1: A line contains at least two points; a plane contains at least three points not all on one line; space contains at least four points not all in one plane.

Postulate 2: Through any two different points, exactly one line exists.

Postulate 3: Through any three points that are not on one line, exactly one plane exists.

Postulate 4: If two points lie in a plane, the line containing them lies in that plane.

Postulate 5: If two planes intersect, then their intersection is a line.

Postulate 1 gives us more information about lines, planes, and space. It tells the minimum number of points that each of them has. This postulate states that a line cannot have just one point, a plane cannot have just two points, and space cannot have less than four points.

Postulate 2 tells us that for any two points, only one line can be drawn containing them. We also can say that two points determine a line. *Exactly one* means *at least one but no more than one.*

yes

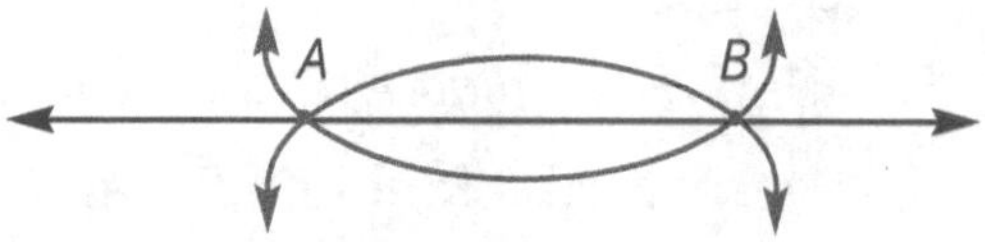

no

Figure 1

Postulate 2 reminds us that a line is straight. See Figure 1.

Postulate 3 tells us that if we have three non-collinear points, then only one plane contains them. We also can say that three points determine a plane. See Figure 2.

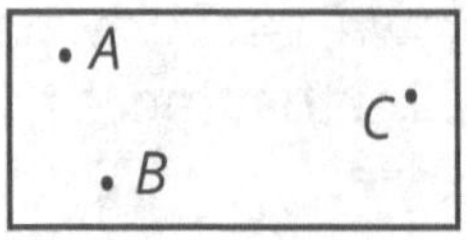

yes

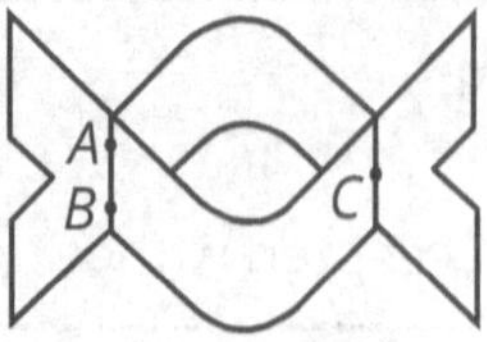

no

Figure 2

Postulate 3 reminds us that the plane in question contains $\overline{AC}$, $\overline{AB}$, and $\overline{BC}$, and that the plane is flat.

Postulate 4 tells us that if we take two points of the plane and determine a line with them, then the line is entirely in that plane. See Figure 3.

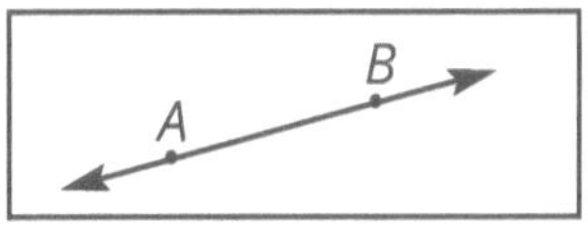

yes

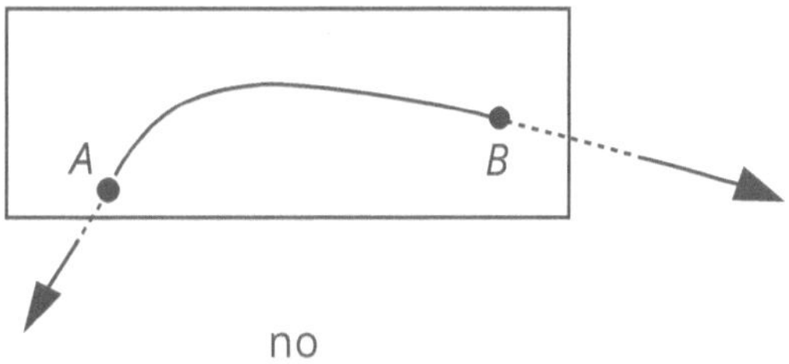

no

Figure 3

Postulate 5 tells us that two planes cannot intersect in a point, but in a line.

Complete the following activities.

3.1 State a postulate about the intersection of two planes.

____

____

____

3.2 How many lines are determined by two points? ____________________

3.3 State the postulate from your answer in 3.2.

____

____

____

3.4 Can two points be noncollinear? a. __________
Why?

b. ____

____

3.5 Does Postulate 3 state that exactly one plane exists through any three points? a. __________
Explain your answer.

b. ____

____

3.6 State the part of the postulate that specifies the minimum number of points in space.

____

____

____

3.7 Write the postulate that states that points *A* and *B* lie in only one line.

____

____

____

3.8 A table with four legs will sometimes wobble if one leg is shorter than the other three, but a table with three legs will not wobble. What postulate explains this fact?

____

____

____

3.9 State the postulate that states $\overleftrightarrow{AB}$ is in plane X when points A and B are in plane X.

____

____

____

3.10 If points A and B are different points in plane X, then a third point exists in X not on $\overleftrightarrow{AB}$. What postulate proves this fact?

____

____

____

Answer true or false.

3.11 ____________ An undefined term cannot be used to state a postulate.

3.12 ____________ A postulate is a statement requiring proof.

3.13 ____________ Two planes can intersect in exactly one point.

3.14 ____________ If two points of a ray lie in a plane, then all of the ray lies in the plane.

3.15 ____________ A plane can have only two points.

3.16 ____________ The intersection of the floor and a wall of a room is a point.

In your study of algebra you assumed some basic properties of equality, of inequality, and of real numbers. These were called axioms. An axiom in algebra is the same as a postulate in geometry — a statement to be accepted without proof.

Because we will be using algebra frequently in our study of geometry, we will now review some of the postulates of algebra. The symbols a, b, c, and so on, represent members of the set of real numbers.

POSTULATES OF ADDITION:

Closure:	The sum, $a + b$, is a real number	
Commutative:	$a + b = b + a$	
Associative:	$(a + b) + c = a + (b + c)$	REMEMBER?
Addition of zero:	$a + 0 = 0 + a = a$	
Additive inverse:	$a + (-a) = (-a) + a = 0$	

POSTULATES OF MULTIPLICATION:

Closure:	The product, ab, is a real number	
Commutative:	$ab = ba$	
Associative:	$(ab)c = a(bc)$	REMEMBER?
Multiplication by one:	$a \cdot 1 = 1 \cdot a = a$	
Multiplicative inverse:	$a \cdot \frac{1}{a} = \frac{1}{a} \cdot a = 1$	
Distributive:	$a(b + c) = ab + ac$ and $(b + c)a = ba + ca$	

Name the postulate for real numbers that is illustrated.

3.17 $5 \cdot 1 = 5$ ______________________

3.18 $3 + 2 = 2 + 3$ ______________________

3.19 $2(x + 3) = 2x + 6$ ______________________

3.20 $25 + 0 = 25$ ______________________

3.21 $5 + (-5) = 0$ ______________________

3.22 $\frac{2}{3} \cdot \frac{3}{3} = \frac{3}{3} \cdot \frac{2}{3} = \frac{2}{3}$ ______________________

3.23 $6 + 0 = 6$ ______________________

3.24 $6 \cdot 12 = 12 \cdot 6$ ______________________

3.25 $3x + 3 = 3(x + 1)$ ______________________

3.26 $\left(\frac{1}{3}\right) 3x = x$ ______________________

POSTULATES OF EQUALITY:

Reflexive:	$a = a$	
Symmetric:	If $a = b$, then $b = a$	REMEMBER?
Transitive:	If $a = b$ and $b = c$, then $a = c$	

POSTULATES OF INEQUALITY:

Comparison:	One and only one of the following statements is true: $a = b$, $a > b$, $a < b$	
Transitive:	If $a < b$ and $b < c$, then $a < c$; If $a > b$ and $b > c$, then $a > c$	REMEMBER?
Addition:	If $a > b$, then $a + c > b + c$; and If $a < b$, then $a + c < b + c$	
Multiplication:	If $a > b$ and $c > 0$, then $ac > bc$; If $a > b$ and $c < 0$, then $ac < bc$	

Name the postulate of equality or inequality that is illustrated.

3.27 If $x + 5 > 8$, then $x > 3$ ______

3.28 If $2x > 10$, then $x > 5$ ______

3.29 If $-3x > 12$, then $x < -4$ ______

3.30 If $\frac{1}{4} + \frac{1}{4} = \frac{2}{4}$ and $\frac{1}{4} = \frac{1}{2}$, then $\frac{1}{4} + \frac{1}{4} = \frac{1}{2}$ ______

3.31 If $5 = x + 2$, then $x + 2 = 5$ ______

3.32 $3 + 2 > 5$ and $3 + 2 = 5$ are not both true. ______

3.33 If $\frac{1}{2}x > -12$, then $x > -24$ ______

3.34 If $-6 < -2$ and $-2 < 2$, then $-6 < 2$ ______

3.35 If $-2x > 24$, then $x < -12$ ______

3.36 $5 = 5$ ______

THEOREMS

On the basis of the first five postulates, it is now possible to *prove* some statements about points, lines, and planes. Statements are of two types: general and specific. A *general* statement is one that covers a large group.

Models: All triangles have three angles.
God loves all His children.
If the product of any two numbers is zero, then one of the numbers is zero.

A *specific* statement applies to a single quantity or object.

Models: A right triangle has one right angle.
God loves you.
If $3x = 0$, then $x = 0$.

In geometry, we will be proving general statements called *theorems*.

DEFINITION:

Theorem:
a general statement that can be proved.

Undefined terms, definitions, postulates, and previously proved theorems are used to prove theorems. Once a theorem has been proved, it can be used in proving subsequent theorems.

The first theorems in a mathematical system often state obvious conclusions that follow from combining definitions and postulates.

THEOREM 1-1:
If two lines intersect, then their intersection is exactly one point.

Planning the proof: Let *a* and *b* be the two given lines and *P*, their given point of intersection. Suppose they also intersect in some point *Q*. But for *two* lines to intersect in *P and Q* is impossible because Postulate 2 tells us that only *one* line contains two given points.

In other words, if lines *a* and *b* intersect in points *P and Q* (see diagram), then line *PQ* is *one* line not two. However, we were given *two* distinct lines (*a* and *b*). So the statement that the two given lines intersect *also* in point *Q* is an impossible condition, and is therefore false. This form of proof is not the more common one; in most cases, a statement is proved *true*, instead of false; this latter is called an indirect proof.

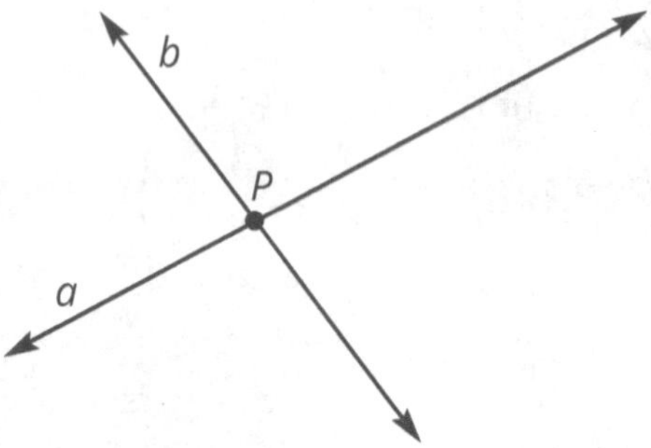

THEOREM 1-2:
Exactly one plane contains a given line and a given point not on the line.

Planning the proof: Postulate 1 tells us that at least two points are on *a*. Since *P* is not on *a*, we have three noncollinear points. Postulate 3 tells us that exactly one plane contains the three points. And finally, Postulate 4 justifies *a* being in the plane since two points of *a* are in the plane.

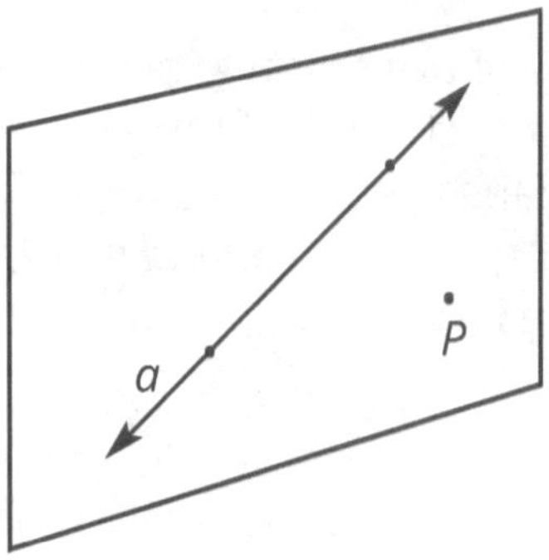

> **THEOREM 1-3:**
> If two lines intersect, then exactly one plane contains both lines.

Planning the proof: Theorem 1-1 tells us the intersection of a and b is one point. Call it P. Postulate 1 tells us each line has at least two points, so another point must be on a and another point on b. Call them R and S. Postulate 3 tells us that exactly one plane contains those three points. Lines a and b will have to lie in this plane because Postulate 4 says so.

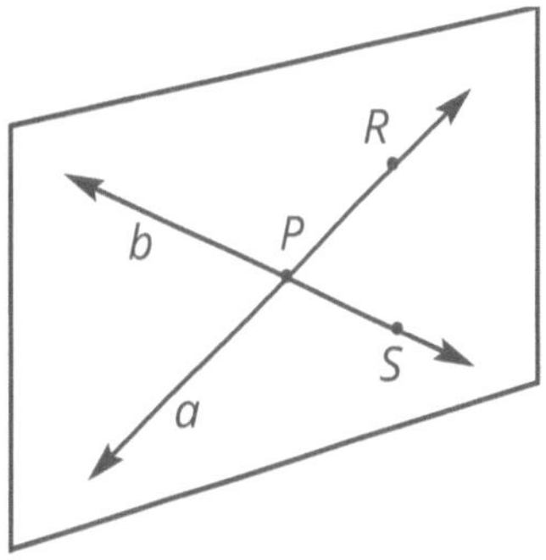

Draw a figure representing the following conditions.

3.37 three collinear points

3.38 three noncollinear points

3.39 two intersecting lines

3.40 two nonintersecting lines

3.41 two intersecting planes

3.42 two nonintersecting planes

Answer true or false.

3.43 ____________ Any two lines lie in exactly one plane.

3.44 ____________ Two intersecting lines have just one point in common.

3.45 ____________ Two intersecting lines lie in two planes.

3.46 ____________ Two points determine a plane.

3.47 ____________ If two planes intersect, their intersection is a line.

Answer questions based on the given information.

Given: *r* and *s* are intersecting lines. Point *P* lies on *r* and *s*. Point *Q* lies on *r* and *s*.

3.48 What can you conclude about *P* and *Q*?

____

____

____

3.49 State the theorem that supports your conclusion.

____

____

Given: The vertices (corners) of triangle *ABC* lie in plane *N*.

3.50 What can you conclude about the sides of triangle *ABC*?

____

____

____

3.51 State the postulate that supports your conclusion.

____

____

Write your answers on the lines.

3.52 How many planes can contain one given point? ____________

3.53 How many planes can contain two given points? ____________

3.54 How many planes can contain three noncollinear points? ____________

3.55 How many planes can contain a line and a point not on the line? ____________

3.56 How many different planes (determined by three of the labeled points) are in the figure shown? Make a complete list.

____

____

____

____

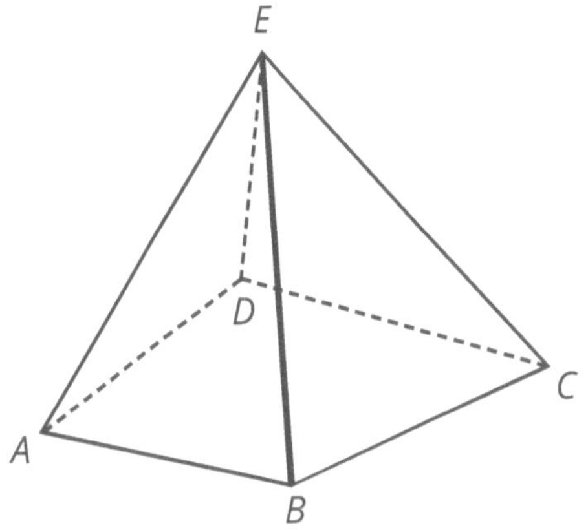

Some theorems from algebra that we will be using in our geometric proofs are listed. You may use in geometry any theorem that you learned in algebra.

PROPERTIES FROM ALGEBRA

PROPERTIES OF EQUALITY:

Addition:	If $a = b$, then $a + c = b + c$ and $c + a = c + b$	
Subtraction:	If $a = b$, then $a - c = b - c$ and $c - a = c - b$	REMEMBER?
Multiplication:	If $a = b$, then $ac = bc$	
Division:	If $a = b$ and $c \neq 0$, then $\frac{a}{c} = \frac{b}{c}$	

PROPERTIES OF INEQUALITY:

Subtraction:	If $a < b$, then $a - c < b - c$	
Division:	If $a < b$ and $c > 0$, then $\frac{a}{c} < \frac{b}{c}$ If $a < b$ and $c < 0$, then $\frac{a}{c} > \frac{b}{c}$	
Substitution:	If $a = b$, a may be replaced by b, and b by a, in any equation or inequality.	REMEMBER?
Zero product:	If $ab = 0$, then $a = 0$ or $b = 0$, or *a and* $b = 0$	

State the property of equality used to arrive at the conclusion.

3.57 If $5x = 20$, then $x = 4$. ______________________

3.58 If $x = 4$, then $5x = 20$. ______________________

3.59 If $x + 8 = 10$, then $x = 2$. ______________________

3.60 If $x = 2$ then $x + 8 = 10$. ______________________

3.61 If $\frac{1}{3}x = 5$, then $x = 15$. ______________________

3.62 If $x - 3 = 7$, then $x = 10$. ______________________

3.63 If $x = 3$, then $x^2 = 3x$. ______________________

Answer true or false; assume a and b are real numbers.

3.64 __________ If $a + 1 = b$, then $b > a$.

3.65 __________ If $a + 2 < b + 3$, then $a < b$.

3.66 __________ If $-2a > 6$, then $a < -3$.

3.67 __________ If $2 > -a$, then $a < -2$.

State the property of equality used to arrive at the conclusion.

Solve $4x + 2 = 14$.

3.68 $4x = 12$ ______________________

3.69 $x = 3$ ______________________

Solve $12 - x = 20 - 5x$.

3.70 $12 + 4x = 20$ ______________________

3.71 $4x = 8$ ______________________

3.72 $x = 2$ ______________________

Solve $2(x + 3) = 8$.

3.73 $2x + 6 =$ ______________________

3.74 $2x = 2$ ______________________

3.75 $x = 1$ ______________________

Solve $x(x + 4) = x(x + 2) + 1$.

3.76 $x^2 + 4x = x^2 + 2x + 1$ ____________________

3.77 $4x = 2x + 1$ ____________________

3.78 $2x = 1$ ____________________

3.79 $x = {}_{2}$ ____________________

Solve $x^2 + 6x + 2x + 12 = 0$.

3.80 $x(x + 6) + 2(x + 6) = 0$ ____________________

3.81 $(x + 2)(x + 6) = 0$ ____________________

3.82 $x + 2 = 0$ or $x + 6 = 0$ ____________________

3.83 $x = -2$ or $x = -6$ ____________________

In this LIFEPAC you have studied the four items that are found in any mathematical system. We shall study geometry as a mathematical system. We have *undefined terms*—points, lines, and planes. We have carefully *defined* some terms and will define others when needed. We have learned what *postulates* are and how they are used to support a statement. We have learned what *theorems* are and how they fit into our system.

TEACHER CHECK ____________ initials ____________ date

Before you take this last Self Test, you may want to do one or more of the following self checks.

1. ________ Read the objectives. Determine if you can do them.
2. ________ Restudy the material related to any objectives that you cannot do.
3. ________ Use the **SQ3R** study procedure to review the material:
   a. **S**can the sections.
   b. **Q**uestion yourself again (review the questions you wrote initially).
   c. **R**ead to answer your questions.
   d. **R**ecite the answers to yourself.
   e. **R**eview areas you did not understand.
4. ________ Review all activities and Self Tests, writing a correct answer for every wrong answer.

SELF TEST 3

Sketch and label a model for each of the following theorems (each answer, 5 points).

3.01 If two lines intersect, then their intersection is exactly one point.

3.02 Exactly one plane contains a given line and a given point not on the line.

3.03 If two lines intersect, then exactly one plane contains both lines.

3.04 Draw a figure showing four points *P*, *Q*, *R*, and *S* in such a position that $\overleftrightarrow{PQ}$, $\overleftrightarrow{PR}$, $\overleftrightarrow{PS}$, $\overleftrightarrow{QR}$, $\overleftrightarrow{QS}$, and $\overleftrightarrow{RS}$ are six different lines.

3.05 Draw a figure showing four points *A*, *B*, *C*, and *D* not all in one plane.

Answer true or false (each answer, 1 point).

3.06 __________ An undefined term cannot be used in a theorem.

3.07 __________ Two lines can intersect in one point.

3.08 __________ Two intersecting lines lie in two planes.

3.09 ________ A line and a point not on the line lie in exactly one plane.

3.010 ________ A segment has exactly one end point.

Complete the following sentences (each answer, 3 points).

3.011 In a mathematical system a proven statement is called a ______________ .

3.012 In a mathematical system some terms are undefined but most terms are ______________ .

3.013 A statement we accept without proof is called a ______________ .

3.014 $\overleftrightarrow{AB}$ is the symbol for ______________ .

3.015 If two planes intersect, their intersection is a ______________ .

After each statement in Column I, write the matching term from Column II (each answer, 2 points).

	Column I		Column II
3.016	segment *AB*	________	a. AB
3.017	ray *AB*	________	b. $\overline{AB}$
3.018	line *AB*	________	c. $\overleftrightarrow{AB}$
3.019	length of $\overline{AB}$	________	d. $\overrightarrow{AB}$
			e. $\overleftrightarrow{BA}$

State the postulate, theorem, or property that justifies the following conclusions (each answer, 5 points).

3.020 Line l and line m intersect at point P.

____

____

3.021 Points A and B determine $\overleftrightarrow{AB}$.

____

____

3.022 If points R and S are in plane N, then $\overleftrightarrow{RS}$ is in plane N.

____

____

3.023 Plane *W* and plane *U* intersect in $\overleftrightarrow{RT}$.

____

____

3.024 If x + 4 = 12, then x = 8.

____

____

3.025 RS = RS.

____

____

66/83 **SCORE** ________ **TEACHER** ________ ________
initials date

Before taking the LIFEPAC Test, you may want to do one or more of the following self checks.

1. ________ Read the objectives. Check to see if you can do them.
2. ________ Restudy the material related to any objectives that you cannot do.
3. ________ Use the **SQ3R** study procedure to review the material.
4. ________ Review activities, Self Tests, and LIFEPAC Glossary.
5. ________ Restudy areas of weakness indicated by the last Self Test.

GLOSSARY

betweenness .... A condition of one point being between two other points on a line.

bisector .... A line or segment that intersects a segment at its midpoint.

collinear .... Occurring on the same line.

coplanar .... Occurring on the same plane.

geometry .... From the Greek for "earth measure."

line segment .... The set of two points and all points between.

midpoint .... A point that divides a segment into two equal segments.

postulate .... A statement accepted without proof.

ray .... A ray, $\overrightarrow{AB}$, is the set of all points AB, and all points P such that B is between A and P.
A is the endpoint of ray $\overrightarrow{AB}$.

space .... The set of all possible points.

Proof

Introduction

One of the main categories of items of our geometric system is the properties we call theorems. Theorems are general statements that can be proved. This LIFEPAC® presents methods of proving theorems by using logical thinking and deductive reasoning.

Objectives

Read these objectives. The objectives tell you what you will be able to do when you have successfully completed this LIFEPAC. When you have finished this LIFEPAC, you should be able to:

1. Identify the various compound sentences.
2. Use truth tables for compound sentences.
3. Explain the difference between inductive and deductive reasoning.
4. Use deductive reasoning in proofs.
5. Describe the six parts of a two-column proof.
6. Write an indirect proof.

Survey the LIFEPAC. Ask yourself some questions about this study and write your questions here.

1. LOGIC

Section Objectives

Review these objectives. When you have completed this section, you should be able to:

1. Identify various compound sentences.
2. Use truth for compound sentences.

A statement in mathematics has a narrow technical meaning. In LIFEPAC 1001 we learned that we must carefully define our terms in mathematics to avoid any misunderstandings. Accordingly, we make the following definition of a statement.

> **DEFINITION**
> **Statement:** A sentence that is either true or false, but not both.

Some of the following sentences are statements:

1. 3 times 5 equals 15.
2. $x + 8 = 20$.
3. A ray is a segment.
4. He is the president.
5. The lights are on.
6. Points *A* and *B* determine a line.

We can determine if they are true or if they are false.

Sentence 1 is a statement. From arithmetic facts we know the statement is true.

Sentence 3 is a statement. We can compare the definition of a ray and a segment and determine that sentence 3 is false.

Sentence 5 is a statement. We can see the light is on or touch the bulb to see if it is hot and then determine if sentence 5 is true or false. Sentence 6 is a true statement. One of our postulates supports its truth.

We cannot determine whether if sentences 2 and 4 are true or not until we have more information: what number does *x* represent, and who is he. So sentences 2 and 4 are not statements.

Write *statement* before each sentence that fits the definition of a statement.

1.1 ____________ The sun comes up in the east.

1.2 ____________ $5 \times 6 = 35$.

1.3 ____________ The moon is made of green cheese.

1.4 ____________ Water boils at 212° F.

1.5 ____________ A line has two end points.

1.6 ____________ Open the door.

1.7 ____________ $x^2 + 3x + 12 = 0$.

1.8 ____________ He is five years old.

1.9 ____________ Genesis is the last book of the Bible.

1.10 ____________ *AB* is the name of a line.

CONJUNCTION

Besides the simple statements you have just looked at, we can have more complicated ones, like these. Note that each statement is either true or false.

a) I cannot go with you because I have nothing to wear, my feet hurt, and I broke my glasses.
b) Gloria is a seamstress and Diane is a singer, while Gladys is neither.
c) Either I'll go to the game Friday or I'll go to the party.
d) Two lines intersect, are parallel, or are skew.
e) If two lines intersect, then the vertical angles formed are equal.

In some of these examples the full statement is made up of simpler statements. We can combine two simple statements to give a more complicated statement. For example:

Mr. Dale lives on a hill.

Mr. Hill lives in the dale.

We can combine these two statements with the word *and*:

Mr. Dale lives on a hill *and* Mr. Hill lives in the dale.

Here are some more examples of combining two statements with and:

a) The sun is shining and today is Monday.
b) I'm going to the game and to the party.
c) $5 + 3 = 8$ and $6 \cdot 3 = 20$.
d) A triangle has three sides and water is wet.
e) A theorem is a proved statement and a postulate is accepted without proof.

All of these statements can be put into the pattern, *p* and *q*, where *p* represents the first statement and *q* represents the second statement. The new statement *p* and *q* is called the conjunction of *p* and *q*.

DEFINITION

Conjunction: A statement formed by combining two statements with the word *and*.

Since a conjunction is a statement, we want to be able to tell whether it is true or false. The following statements are all conjunctions. See if you can decide which ones are true and which ones are false. Then try to find a general rule for finding the truth of a conjunction.

a) $2 \cdot 2 = 4$ and $2 + 2 = 4$
b) $3 + 2 = 5$ and $3 \cdot 2 = 7$
c) $5 + 1 = 7$ and $5 \cdot 1 = 5$
d) $6 - 2 = 8$ and $12 \div 6 = 72$

You probably had no trouble coming to the same conclusion that mathematicians have agreed upon for finding the truth of conjunctions. That is, *p and q* is true only when both *p and q* are true. If one of the parts is false, then the whole statement is false. We can put this rule into a truth table:

CONJUNCTION

p	*q*	*p & q*
T	T	T
T	F	F
F	T	F
F	F	F

Note: A truth table is a list of all possible combinations of T and F for the statements involved in the statement.

The truth table tells us that *p and q* is true (T) only when both *p and q* are true, (top row in table). It is false (F) in all other cases.

Write true or false to tell whether the following conjunctions are true or false. Use the truth table if you need it.

1.11 __________ $6 + 3 = 9$ and $4 \cdot 4 = 20$.

1.12 __________ Dogs have four legs and cats have ten lives.

1.13 __________ January has 31 days and May has 31 days.

1.14 __________ Sugar is sour and lemons are sweet.

1.15 __________ A triangle has four sides and a rectangle has three sides.

1.16 __________ A plane has at least three noncollinear points and a line has at least two points.

1.17 __________ A square root of 16 is 4 and a square root of 9 is -3.

1.18 __________ The intersection of two planes is a point and two lines intersect in a point.

1.19 __________ The alphabet has 28 letters and a week has seven days.

1.20 __________ $6 + 3 = 9$ and $4 \cdot 4 = 16$.

DISJUNCTION

We can combine two statements in another way by using the word *or*. For example:

a) $3 + 2 = 5$ *or* $7 \cdot 7 = 49$

b) $12 - 5 = 7$ *or* $5 - 5 = 10$

c) $5 \cdot 3 = 20$ *or* $7 > -2$

d) $16 \cdot 3 = 163$ *or* $-6 < -10$

These statements are of the form *p or q* where *p* represents the first statement and *q* the second statement. The new statement *p or q* is called the *disjunction of p and q*.

DEFINITION

Disjunction: A statement formed by combining two statements with the word *or*.

The following truth table illustrates disjunction.

DISJUNCTION

p	*q*	*p* or *q*
T	T	T
T	F	T
F	T	T
F	F	F

Notice that a disjunction is true when either *one* or *both* of its parts are true. It is false only when both parts are false.

Write true or false to tell whether the following disjunctions are true or false. Use the truth table if you need it.

1.21 ____________ January is the first month of the year or December is the last month.

1.22 ____________ $5 \cdot 3 = 15$ or $7 + 5 = 20$.

1.23 ____________ A line has only one point or a plane has at least 3 points.

1.24 ____________ George Washington was President of Mexico or Abe Lincoln was President of Spain.

1.25 ____________ 5 is less than 7 or 7 is less than 12.

1.26 ____________ A segment has a midpoint or $\overrightarrow{AB}$ is the name of a ray.

1.27 ____________ A line and a point outside the line are in exactly one plane or two planes intersect in a plane.

1.28 ____________ Some roses are red or some violets are blue.

1.29 ____________ *Collinear* means points on the same plane or coplanar means points on the same line.

1.30 ____________ In this diagram, RS + ST = SR or ST + RS = RT.

NEGATION

Where *p* represents a statement, a new statement, *p is false* can be formed. This statement is usually shortened to *not p* and is written ~*p*. The new statement formed is called the *negation of p* or the negative of *p*.

> **DEFINITION**
>
> **Negation:** If *p* is a statement, the new statement, *not p* or *p is false*, is called the negation of *p*

Some examples of negations are:

a) *p:* It is raining.
not *p:* It is not raining.

b) *p:* $6 + 3 = 12$
~*p:* $6 + 3 \neq 12$

c) *p:* The lights are on.
not *p:* The lights are not on; or the lights are off.

d) *p:* A triangle has six sides.
~*p:* A triangle does not have six sides.

e) *p:* It is false that spinach is good for you.
~*p:* Spinach is good for you.

When we form the negation of a statement in words, we do not usually place not in front of the original statement. Logically, to do so would be correct; but the resulting statement might sound strange. Instead we place the not in the sentence where it sounds better.

The truth table for negation is quite simple:

NEGATION	
p	~*p*
T	F
F	T

If a statement is true, its negation is false.
If a statement is false, its negation is true.

Write the negation of the following statements.

1.31 ______________________ The grass is green.

1.32 ______________________ This rose is white.

1.33 ______________________ $5 + 4 = 90$

1.34 ______________________ $5 > -5$

1.35 ______________________ Geometry is interesting.

1.36 ______________________ A line has no length.

1.37 ______________________ All pigs are fat.

1.38 ______________________ My dog has fleas.

1.39 ______________________ Two points determine a line.

1.40 ______________________ A line does not have a midpoint.

CONDITIONAL

Where *p* and *q* represent statements, the compound statement written *if p, then q* is called a conditional or implication and is expressed in symbols by $p \rightarrow q$.

DEFINITION

Conditional or Implication: A statement formed from two given statements by connecting them in the form of *if* ________, *then* ________.

Hypothesis: the *if* clause in a statement.

Conclusion: the *then* clause in a statement.

Statement p is called the *hypothesis*.
Statement q is called the *conclusion*.

The truth table for a conditional shows the conditions under which this new statement is true.

CONDITIONAL		
p	q	$p \rightarrow q$
T	T	T
T	F	F
F	T	T
F	F	T

Notice that $p \rightarrow q$ is always true except when p, the hypothesis, is true and q, the conclusion, is false.

The example that follows will help you to understand the rationale of the truth in the table.

Model: Roger makes this promise.
"If I get a job, then I'll buy a motorcycle."

Four possibilities are:

1) Roger gets a job. (p is true)
He buys a motorcycle. (q is true)
He keeps his promise. ($p \rightarrow q$ is true)

2) Roger gets a job. (p is true)
He does not buy the motorcycle. (q is false)
He broke his promise. ($p \rightarrow q$ is false)

3) Roger does not get a job. (p is false)
He still buys the motorcycle. (q is true)
He has not broken his promise. ($p \rightarrow q$ is true)

4) Roger does not get a job. (p is false)
He does not buy the motorcycle. (q is false)
He has not broken his promise. ($p \rightarrow q$ is true)

Write true or false to tell whether the conditional $p \rightarrow q$ is true or false. Use the truth table if you need it.

1.41 __________ If 3 + 2 = 5, then 5 + 5 = 10.

1.42 __________ If 6 • 3 = 18, then 4 + 8 = 20.

1.43 __________ If 6 > 10, then 8 • 3 = 24.

1.44 __________ If 3 • 2 = 5, then 6 < 0.

1.45 __________ If dogs have five legs, then cats have three tails.

1.46 __________ If ice is hot, then rain is wet.

1.47 __________ If a week has seven days, then a year has twenty months.

1.48 __________ If water is wet, then 5 + 3 = 15.

1.49 __________ If A and B are the names of two points, then $\overrightarrow{AB}$ is the name of a line through A and B.

1.50 __________ If 5 = 3 + 2, then 3 + 2 = 5.

CONVERSE, INVERSE, CONTRAPOSITIVE

We can do three things to a conditional statement to get new statements. We can interchange the p with the q and get a new conditional, *if* q, *then* p. The hypothesis becomes the conclusion and the conclusion becomes the hypothesis. This new conditional is called the *converse* of the original conditional.

> **DEFINITION**
> **Converse of a conditional:** A statement formed by interchanging the hypothesis and the conclusion in a conditional statement.

Some examples of conditionals and their converses are:

a) **Conditional:** If today is Monday, then tomorrow is Tuesday. (True)

   Converse: If tomorrow is Tuesday, then today is Monday. (True)

b) **Conditional:** If $5 + 5 = 20$, then $3 + 2 = 5$. (True)

   Converse: If $3 + 2 = 5$, then $5 + 5 = 20$. (False)

c) **Conditional:** If a point lies on a line, then the line contains the point. (True)

   Converse: If a line contains a point, then the point lies on the line. (True)

d) **Conditional:** If $3 > 5$, then $3 \neq 4$. (True)

   Converse: If $3 \neq 4$, then $3 > 5$. (False)

A conditional and its converse are different statements. The examples given show that the converse of a true conditional may be true or it may be false.

When the conditional, $p \rightarrow q$, is true and the converse, $q \rightarrow p$, is also true, then the statements, p and q, are said to be *equivalent* statements and can be written $p \leftrightarrow q$. Equivalent statements have the same truth value. Either both are true statements or both are false statements.

In example a), saying "today is Monday," is equivalent to saying "tomorrow is Tuesday."

In example c), "a point lies on the line," is equivalent to "the line contains the point."

Where $p \rightarrow q$ is a conditional, a new conditional can be formed by negating both the hypothesis and the conclusion: $\sim p \rightarrow \sim q$. The new conditional is called the *inverse* of the conditional.

> **DEFINITION**
> **Inverse of a conditional:** A new statement formed by negating both the hypothesis and the conclusion.

Some examples of conditionals and their inverses are:

a) **Conditional:** If $5 + 5 = 20$, then $3 + 2 = 5$. (True)

   Inverse: If $5 + 5 \neq 20$, then $3 + 2 \neq 5$. (False)

b) **Conditional:** If today is Friday, then yesterday was Thursday. (True)

   Inverse: If today is not Friday, then yesterday was not Thursday. (True)

c) **Conditional:** If a point lies in a plane, then the plane contains the point. (True)

   Inverse: If a point does not lie in a plane, then the plane does not contain the point. (True)

A conditional and its inverse are different statements. The examples show that the inverse of a true conditional may be true but it may also be false. The conditional and its inverse are not equivalent statements.

When $p \rightarrow q$ is a conditional, a new conditional can be formed by interchanging the hypothesis and conclusion and negating both of them. $\sim q \rightarrow \sim p$ is the new conditional formed. It is called the *contrapositive* of the conditional.

> **DEFINITION**
>
> **Contrapositive of a conditional:** A new statement formed by exchanging the hypothesis and the conclusion and negating both of them.

Some examples of conditionals and their contrapositives are:

a) **Conditional:** If today is Sunday, then tomorrow is Monday. (True)

Contrapositive: If tomorrow is not Monday, then today is not Sunday. (True)

b) **Conditional:** If a triangle has a right angle, then it is a right triangle. (True)

Contrapositive: If a triangle is not a right triangle, then it does not have a right angle. (True)

c) **Conditional:** If $5 + 8 \neq 13$, then $3 \cdot 2 = 6$. (True)

Contrapositive: If $3 \cdot 2 \neq 6$, then $5 + 8 = 13$. (True)

d) **Conditional:** If $6 > 3$, then $2 > 5$. (False)

Contrapositive: If $2 \not> 5$, then $6 \not< 3$. (False)

Notice in the examples that when the conditional is true, its contrapositive is true. When the conditional is false, its contrapositive is also false. Thus a conditional and its contrapositive are equivalent statements and we can write:

$$(p \rightarrow q) \leftrightarrow (\sim q \rightarrow \sim p)$$

COMPILED TRUTH TABLE

STATEMENTS		NEGATION		CONDITIONAL	CONTRAPOSITIVE	CONVERSE	INVERSE
p	q	$\sim p$	$\sim q$	$p \rightarrow q$	$\sim q \rightarrow \sim p$	$q \rightarrow p$	$\sim p \rightarrow \sim q$
T	T	F	F	T	T	T	T
T	F	F	T	F	F	T	T
F	T	T	F	T	T	F	F
F	F	T	T	T	T	T	T

Notice the arrangement of the T's and F's in the *conditional* and the *contrapositive* columns. They are the same. Also notice the T's and F's in the *converse* and *inverse* columns. They are the same. This arrangement reveals that a conditional and its contrapositive are equivalent statements. Also, the converse and inverse of a conditional are equivalent statements.

Perform these two-step problems.

If "p" denotes the statement "$x > 7$" and "q" the statement "$x > 5$",
a. translate the given conditional into an if_, then_, statement about x (choose one value for "x" that satisfies both "p" and "q", use that number to work all these problems), and
b. tell whether your statement is true or false.

			True or False
1.51	$p \to q$	a. ______	b. ______
1.52	$p \to \sim q$	a. ______	b. ______
1.53	$\sim p \to q$	a. ______	b. ______
1.54	$\sim p \to \sim q$	a. ______	b. ______
1.55	$q \to p$	a. ______	b. ______
1.56	$q \to \sim p$	a. ______	b. ______
1.57	$\sim q \to p$	a. ______	b. ______
1.58	$\sim q \to \sim p$	a. ______	b. ______

Write the converse, inverse, and contrapositive of each of the following statements.

1.59 If two angles are adjacent, then the two angles have the same vertex.

Converse: ______

Inverse: ______

Contrapositive: ______

1.60 If today is Thursday, then tomorrow is Wednesday.

Converse: ______

Inverse: ______

Contrapositive: ______

1.61 If a polygon is a square, then it is a rectangle.

Converse: ______

Inverse: ______

Contrapositive: ______

1.62 If two lines intersect, then their intersection is one point.

Converse: ______________________________

____

Inverse: ______________________________

____

Contrapositive: ______________________________

____

1.63 Write a conditional statement and its converse such that the conditional is true but the converse is false.

Conditional: ______________________________

____

Converse: ______________________________

____

1.64 Write a conditional statement and its converse such that the conditional is true and the converse is true.

Conditional: ______________________________

____

Converse: ______________________________

____

1.65 Write a conditional statement and its contrapositive such that the conditional is true but the contrapositive is false.

Conditional: ______________________________

____

Converse: ______________________________

____

TEACHER CHECK ____________ initials ____________ date

Review the material in this section in preparation for the Self Test. The Self Test will check your mastery of this particular section. The items missed on this Self Test will indicate specific areas where restudy is needed for mastery.

SELF TEST 1

Write the answer in the blank to make true statements (each answer, 3 points).

1.01 When two statements are connected with the word *and*, the new statement is called a(n) ________________________ .

1.02 When two statements are connected with the word *or*, the new statement is called a(n) ________________________ .

1.03 Two statements connected with the words *if-then* form a new statement called a(n) a. ________________________ or b. ________________________ .

1.04 If a statement is true, its negation is ________________________ .

1.05 The converse of $p \rightarrow q$ is ________________________ .

1.06 The inverse of $r \rightarrow s$ is ________________________ .

1.07 The contrapositive of $s \rightarrow t$ is ________________________ .

1.08 If $p \rightarrow q$ is true and p is true, then we can conclude that q is ________________________ .

Answer true or false (each answer, 1 point),

1.09 __________ Snow is white or grass is red.

1.010 __________ Snow is white and grass is red.

1.011 __________ If snow is white then grass is red.

1.012 __________ If grass is red, then snow is white.

1.013 __________ If snow is not white, then grass is not red.

1.014 __________ If grass is not red, then snow is not white.

1.015 __________ The negation of the negation of the statement: snow is not white.

Write the letter for the equivalent statements (each answer, 2 points).

a. inverse b. contrapositive c. converse d. obtuse

1.016 Conditional and ______________________________ are equivalent.

1.017 a. ______________________________ and b. ______________________________ are equivalent.

Given: If 3 < 2, then -6 < 5. Write the converse, inverse, and contrapositive; *and* indicate which statements are *true* and which are *false* (each answer, 4 points for a., 2 points for b.)

True or False

1.018 The converse is a. ______________________________ b. ____________________

1.019 The inverse is a. ______________________________ b. ____________________

1.020 The contrapositive is a. ______________________________ b. ____________________

46/58 **SCORE** ____________ **TEACHER** ____________ ____________
initials date

2. REASONING

The goal of a geometric proof is to arrive at valid *conclusions* by using proper *reasoning* methods. Two types of reasoning methods will be discussed.

Section Objectives

Review these objectives. When you have completed this section, you should be able to:

3. Explain the difference between *inductive* and *deductive* reasoning.
4. Use deductive reasoning in proofs.

INDUCTION

The first type is called *inductive reasoning*. By looking at a number of examples that have something in common, we can discover a possible conclusion.

Model 1: Beverly looks in several robins' nests and comes to the conclusion that all robins' eggs are blue.

Model 2: The boys present at a meeting of their club give their ages as 11, 12, 11, 11, 13, 12, 12, 12, 11, and 12. Wesley comes to the conclusion that all boys in this club are at least eleven years old.

Model 3: Stanley looks at twenty pennies and sees Lincoln's head on them. He concludes that all pennies are Lincoln-head pennies.

Model 4: A scientist mixes two chemicals and the mixture turns green. He does this mixture fifty more times and each time the mixture turns green. He comes to the conclusion that when those two chemicals are mixed, they will always turn green.

Model 5: Stephen measured the three angles of several triangles and found that when he added the three measures, the sum was always 180 degrees. He concludes that the sum of the three angles of every triangle is 180 degrees.

In each of these models, the person looked at several *specific* situations and then arrived at a *general* conclusion. When someone arrives at a general conclusion based on specific examples, he has used inductive reasoning.

> **DEFINITION**
>
> **Inductive reasoning:** The process of making a general conclusion based on specific examples.

You have used inductive thinking all your life. As a small child you thought inductively when you decided that touching a hot stove would burn you. Now you think inductively when you decide, after many trials, which of two restaurants makes the best hamburgers and fries. Inductive thinking occurs when you observe individual events and then guess at a general principle.

We cannot always be sure that a conclusion reached by inductive reasoning is correct. Sometimes we can check every example and then we know the conclusion is correct. However, if we cannot check *every* example (which is usually the case), we cannot be *sure* the conclusion is correct.

If we can find one example that does not agree with the conclusion (called a counter-example), we know the conclusion is not correct.

Pictures may also suggest inductive conclusions; but again, the conclusion is not necessarily correct.

Look at these optical illusions. Does your conclusion agree with the facts?

2.1 Which segment is longer?

____

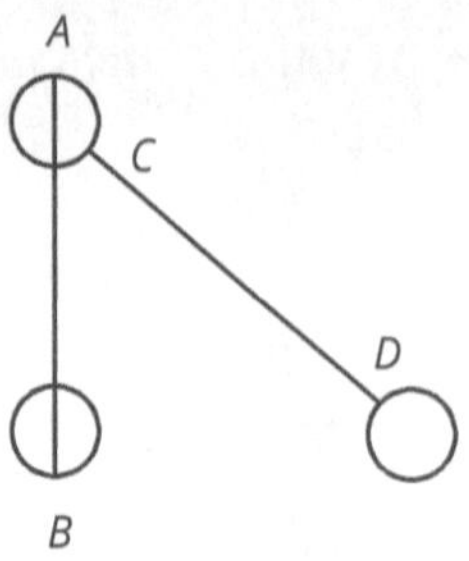

2.2 Which segment is longer?

____

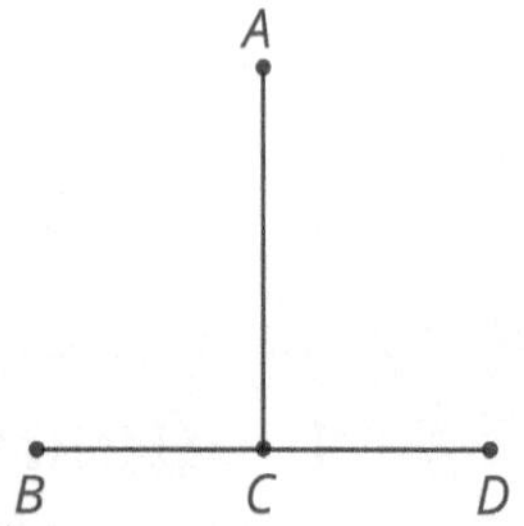

2.3 Which center circle is larger?

____

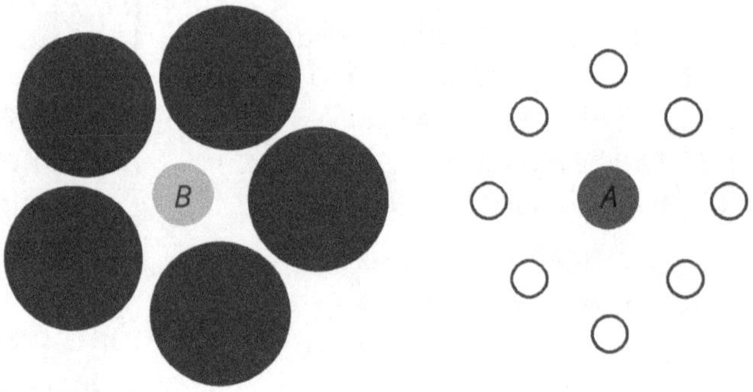

2.4 What does the sign say?

____

2.5 Are all these segments parallel?

____

2.6 What do you see?

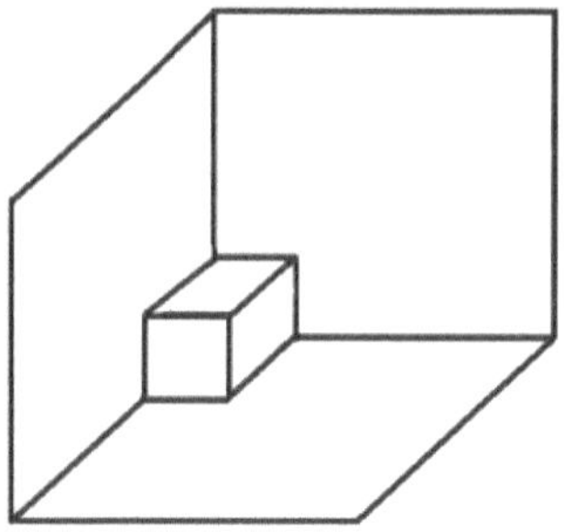

Write a statement of a fact or event to make each conclusion false.

2.7 The first thirty-nine Presidents of the United States were men.

Conclusion: A woman cannot be President of the United States.

Counter-example: ______________________________

2.8 Every map that has ever been drawn can be colored with four colors so that no two regions colored alike touch at more than one point.

Conclusion: Every map can be colored with four colors.

Counter-example: ______________________________

2.9 5 > 0, 6 > 0, 12 > 0, 16 > 0, 20 > 0, 100 > 0.

Conclusion: All numbers are greater than 0.

Counter-example: ______________________________

2.10 On every test Allen has taken this year he has gotten 90% or better.

Conclusion: Allen always gets 90% or better on tests.

Counter-example: ______________________________

State a conclusion that seems reasonable.

2.11 You eat a new kind of fruit and suffer from hives for the first time in your life. A week later, you try the fruit again and the hives recur. A month later you have a similar experience.

Conclusion: ______________________________

2.12 You find a nest with 12 eggs in it. The first 5 hatch out to be snakes.

Conclusion: ______________________________

2.13 A teacher gave all her classes a true-false test on seven consecutive Mondays. Today is Monday.

Conclusion: ______________________________

2.14 $6 + 0 = 6$, $8 + 0 = 8$, $9 + 0 = 9$, $100 + 0 = 100$.

Conclusion: ______________________________

2.15 Donald is older than Jeanette; Donald is older than Elisa. Donald is older than Allen.

Conclusion: ______________________________

DEDUCTION

If appearance and reasoning from examples do not always lead to correct conclusions, what does? In geometry, conclusions are accepted as true if they can be reached by *deductive* reasoning.

> **DEFINITION**
> **Deductive reasoning:** The process of making a conclusion by fitting a specific example into a general statement.

In using deductive reasoning, we start with a general statement that all agree to be true (postulates, definitions). We then look at specific examples to see if they fit the conditions (hypotheses). If they do fit the conditions, then we must logically accept the results (conclusion).

Model 1:

1) If a bug has six legs and a three-part body, then it is an insect.

2) My pet, "Skamper", has six legs and a three-part body.

Conclusion: "Skamper" is an insect.

Model 2:

1) If a girl is a cheerleader at Wooten High, then she must be a junior.
2) Mary is a cheerleader at Wooten High.

Conclusion: Mary is a junior.

Model 3:

1) If $a = b$, then $ac = bc$.

2) $b = 5$ and $c = 2$.

Conclusion: $2b = 10$

Model 4:

1) A rectangle has four right angles.
2) A square is a rectangle.

Conclusion: A square has four right angles.

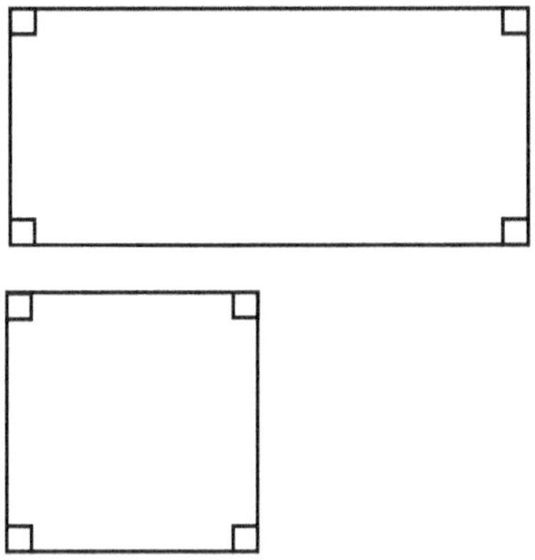

Model 5:

1) All geometry students have studied algebra.
2) You are a geometry student.

Conclusion: You have studied algebra.

Although you may not know anything about bugs or cheerleaders or rectangles, deduction, with no guessing involved, tells you that if statements 1 and 2 are correct, then the conclusions shown are also correct. This process is using deductive reasoning.

p	q	$p \rightarrow q$
T	T	T
T	F	F
F	T	T
F	F	T

We know from the truth table for conditionals, that when $p \rightarrow q$ is true and p is true, then q must be true.

In each of the following exercises, the first two statements are accepted as true. State a true conclusion.

2.16 1) If the mill is on strike, then no one works.

2) The mill is on strike.

Conclusion: ______________________________

2.17 1) If it's Saturday, then Cathy's dad goes fishing.

2) Today is Saturday.

Conclusion: ______________________________

2.18 1) If a figure has four equal sides, then it is a square or a rhombus.

2) This figure has four equal sides.

Conclusion: ______________________________

2.19 1) If $a \cdot b = 0$, then $a = 0$ or $b = 0$

2) $3x = 0$

Conclusion: ______________________________

2.20 1) If two planes intersect, then their intersection is a line.

2) Plane *R* and plane *S* intersect.

Conclusion: ______________________________

2.21 1) If people live in Zook, then they live in Zee.

2) Zela lives in Zook.

Conclusion: ______________________________

2.22 1) All rabbits like lettuce.

2) My pet is a rabbit.

Conclusion: ______________________________

2.23 1) If *B* is between *A* and *C*, then $AB + BC = AC$.

2) *R* is between *S* and *T*

Conclusion: ______________________________

2.24 1) If a triangle has a right angle, then the triangle is a right triangle.

2) Triangle *ABC* is not a right triangle.

Conclusion: ______________________________

(Hint: conditional) contrapositive)

2.25 1) If you accept the hypothesis, then you accept the conclusion.

2) You accept the conclusion.

Conclusion: ______________________________

We use deductive reasoning to prove statements are true. When you solve an equation in algebra, you are using deductive reasoning.

General Principle	**Specific Example**
	$2x + 2 = 6$
If $x = y$, then $x - a = y - a$	$2x + 2 - 2 = 6 - 2$
$a + (-a) = 0$, additive inverse	$2x + 0 = 6 - 2$
$a + 0 = a$, addition of zero	$2x = 6 - 2$
Substitution, 4 for $6 - 2$	$2x = 4$
If $x = b$ then $ax = ab$	$(\frac{1}{2})\, 2x = (\frac{1}{2})\, 4$
$\frac{1}{a} \cdot a = 1$, reciprocal product	$1x = (\frac{1}{2})\, 4$
Substitution, 2 for $(\frac{1}{2})\, 4$	$1x = 2$
	$x = 2$

You might not go through all of these steps to solve the equation, or you might combine steps to make your work easier. The point is that you are using deductive reasoning whenever you solve an equation. You are taking the axioms and theorems of algebra (general statement) and testing your specific equation by them to arrive at the next step in your solution.
When you arrive at the last step $x = 2$, you have proved the statement *if* $2x + 2 = 6$, *then* $x = 2$, to be true.

In the model below, I know that B is between A and C. I want to prove that $AC - AB = BC$. Use the definition of *betweenness* to deduce that $AB + BC = AC$. Since this statement is an equation, use the subtraction property of equality and deduce that $BC = AC - AB$ (subtract AB from both sides of the equation). Finally, use the symmetric property of equality and deduce that $AC - AB = BC$, which is the statement I wanted to prove.

State the general principle (theorem, postulate, or definition) that justifies the conclusion.

2.26 Conclusion: l_1 and l_2 intersect only at point P.

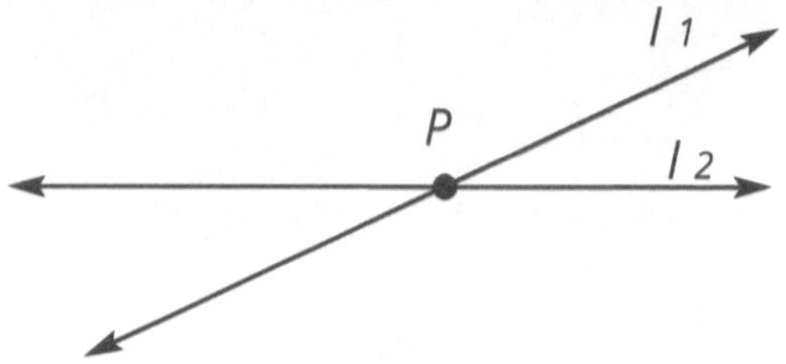

____

____

____

2.27 M is midpoint of $\overline{RS}$

Conclusion: l is a bisector of $\overline{RS}$.

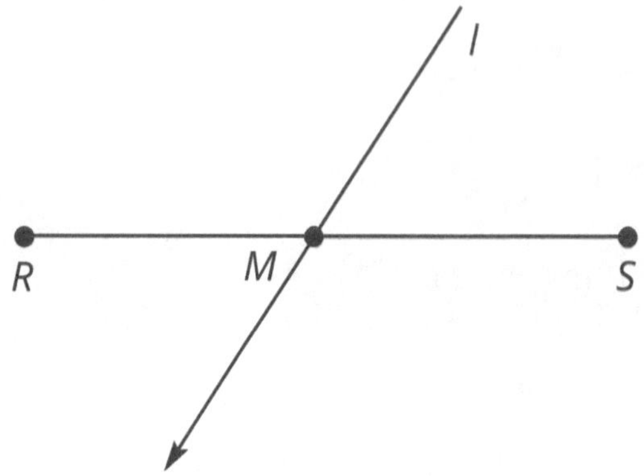

____

____

____

2.28 $\overline{WX} = \overline{XY}$

Conclusion: X is midpoint of $\overline{WY}$.

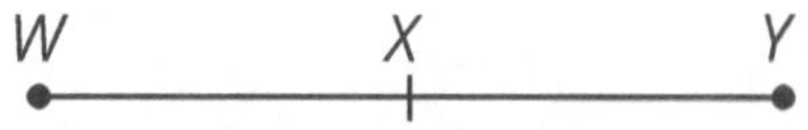

____

____

____

2.29 B is between A and C

Conclusion: A, B and C are collinear.

____

____

____

2.30 *l* is in plane *M*, *x* is on line *l*

Conclusion: *x* is in plane *M*.

____

____

____

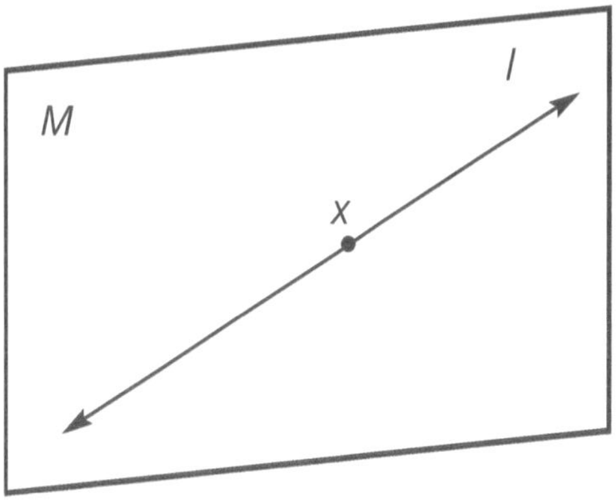

TEACHER CHECK ______________ ______________
initials date

Review the material in this section in preparation for the Self Test. This Self Test will check your mastery of this particular section as well as your knowledge of the previous section.

SELF TEST 2

Write *inductive, deductive*, or *neither* to indicate which type of reasoning is used in each of the following statements (each answer, 2 points).

2.01 ____________ If Sue is older than John and John is older than Bill, then Sue is older than Bill.

2.02 ____________ You watch an ant taste a liquid and die. Several more ants sample the liquid and they die. You conclude the liquid is ant poison.

2.03 ____________ The ceiling and wall of a room meet in a line segment.

2.04 ____________ If $5x + 7 = 12$, then $x = 1$.

2.05 ____________ A courtroom spectator merely looks at the defendant and says, "He's guilty, I tell you."

State a conclusion based on the given statement (each answer, 4 points).

2.06 x is a number such that $5x = 10$. ____________

2.07 g is a number such that $7g = 7h$. ____________

2.08 t is a whole number between 22.3 and 23.1. ____________

2.09 $p \rightarrow q$ is false and p is true. ____________

2.010 p and q is true, and p is true. ____________

Write the answer in the blank (each answer, 3 points).

2.011 You (can, cannot) ____________ always prove a conclusion by inductive reasoning.

2.012 Where p and q are statements, p and q is called the ____________ of p and q.

2.013 Where r and s are statements, r or s is called the ____________ of r and s.

2.014 Reaching a conclusion by looking at several examples is called ____________ reasoning.

2.015 Reaching a conclusion by fitting a specific example into a general statement is called ____________ reasoning.

2.016 If $p \rightarrow q$ is true and p is true, then we know ____________ is true.

Name the property that justifies each step in this solution (each answer, 4 points).

$2x + 2 = 11 - x$

2.017 $3x + 2 = 11$ ________________________________

2.018 $3x = 9$ ________________________________

2.019 $x = 3$ ________________________________

Write the contrapositive of the statement (5 points).

2.020 If dogs have fleas, they scratch all night.

____

____

52/65 **SCORE** __________ **TEACHER** __________ __________

initials date

3. PROOF FORMATS

To prove a statement in geometry means to demonstrate that the statement follows logically from other accepted statements. Thus only definitions, postulates, or previously proven theorems can be used as general statements to support conclusions made in proving statements by deductive reasoning. Two forms of proofs are commonly used.

Section Objectives

Review these objectives. When you have completed this section, you should be able to:

5. Describe the six parts of a two-column proof.
6. Write an indirect proof.

THE TWO-COLUMN PROOF

The two-column form of proof is used extensively in geometry. It enables a student to show each conclusion arrived at and the reason that supports it. The format of a two-column proof consists of six essential parts arranged in order.

They are ...

Statement of the theorem:
Figure:
Given information:
Conclusion to prove:
Plan of proof:
Proof:

DEFINITION
Statement: At the beginning of each proof should be a full written statement of the theorem. If the theorem is not in "*if-then*" form, rephrase it in that form. The form will help you to recognize the *given* and the *to prove.*

Here are our first three theorems from Chapter 1 written in *if-then* form.

Theorem 1-1 *If* two lines intersect, *then* they intersect in exactly one point.

Theorem 1-2 *If* a point lies outside a line, *then* exactly one plane contains the line and the point.

Theorem 1-3 *If* two lines intersect, *then* exactly one plane contains both lines.

The following models are statements written two ways: first, not in *if-then* form; second, in *if-then* form. The statements are equivalent.

Model 1: Two circles that have equal radii have equal areas.

If two circles have equal radii, *then* they have equal areas.

Model 2: When $3x - 1 = 2x$, it follows that $x = 1$.

If $3x - 1 = 2x$, *then* $x = 1$.

Model 3: When I read without my glasses, my eyes get tired.

If I read without my glasses, *then* my eyes get tired.

Model 4: Two planes intersect provided they are not parallel.

If two planes are not parallel, *then* they intersect.

Model 5: The game will be cancelled in the event of rain.

If it rains, *then* the game will be cancelled.

Write the following statements in "*if - then*" form.

3.1 Two opposite rays form a straight line.

____

____

3.2 Joe will sing provided Sam plays the piano.

____

____

3.3 A man that lives in Chicago lives in Illinois.

____

____

3.4 An angle has exactly one bisector.

____

____

3.5 The sum of the measures of the angles of a triangle is 180 degrees.

____

____

Figure: Each proof should have a lettered figure drawn to illustrate the given conditions (hypotheses) of the statement. Although a diagram is not essential to the logical reasoning of a proof, it helps to see the deductions being made. You may be able to make some inductive conclusions and then justify them deductively.

Be sure your figure accurately depicts the given conditions. Do not add any special features that are not given. Do not draw a right triangle or an isosceles triangle when a *triangle* is specified. Make the figure as *general* as possible.

Model 1: The sum of the measures of the angles of a triangle is 180 degrees

The given condition for this statement is a triangle, so draw and label a scalene triangle, not a special one.

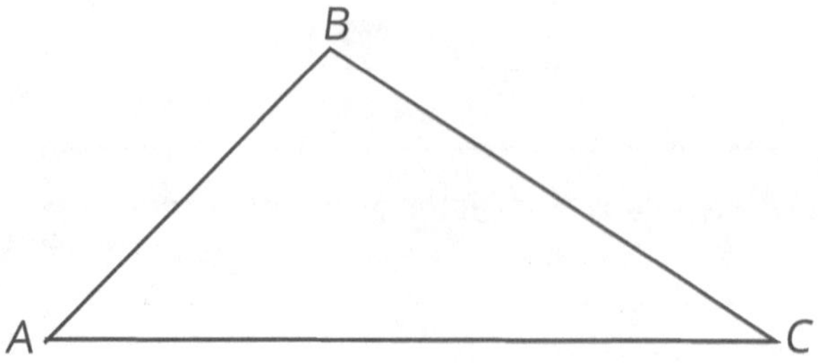

Model 2: If two parallel lines are cut by a third line, the alternate interior angles are equal.

Here parallel lines *l* and *m* are cut by the third line *t*. The numbers 1 and 2 are placed in the angle position to name them.

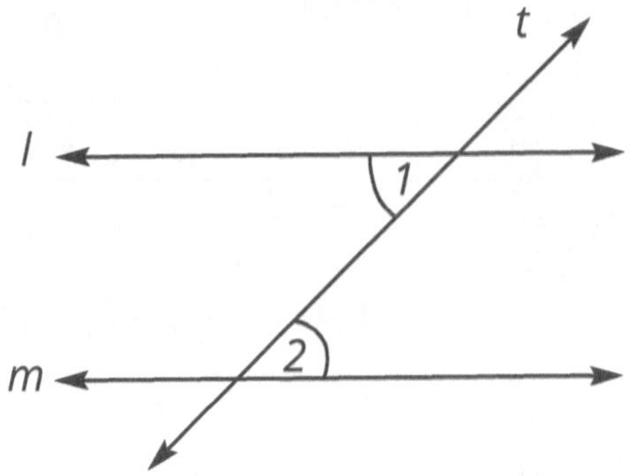

Model 3: Through a point outside a line, exactly one line can be drawn perpendicular to the given line.

l is the given line with *P* the outside point. *m* is the line we want to prove is perpendicular to *l*.

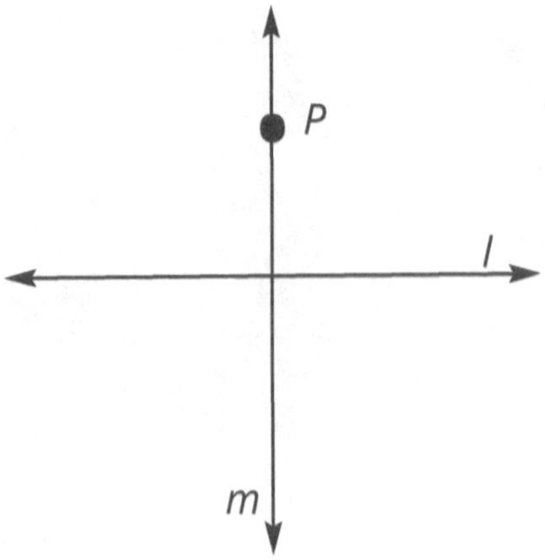

Use a straightedge to make a figure that represents each of these statements.

3.6 Through a point outside a line one line can be drawn parallel to the line.

3.7 If two parallel planes are cut by a third plane, the lines of intersection are parallel.

3.8 If two angles of a triangle are equal, the sides opposite those angles are equal.

3.9 If a segment joins the midpoints of two sides of a triangle, its length is one-half the length of the third side.

3.10 If B is between A and C, then $AB + BC = AC$.

Given: The given conditions of the statement are expressed in terms of the letters or numerals that are used in the figure. Remember that the given information is the hypothesis of the statement, the part that follows the "if." Whenever any information is "given," we know that information is true.

In the previous Model 1, the given information is a triangle and we named it ABC, so we would write:

Given: ΔABC

In Model 2, we are given two parallel lines that are cut by a third line. We would write:

Given: $l \parallel m$
t cuts *l* and *m*

In Model 3, we are given a line and a point outside the line.

Given: line *l*
point P not on l

Use the figures and statements of Exercise 3.6 through 3.10 and write the *Given*.

3.11 (3.6) Given: ______________________________

____

3.12 (3.7) Given: ______________________________

____

3.13 (3.8) Given: ______________________________

____

3.14 (3.9) Given: ______________________________

____

3.15 (3.10) Given: ______________________________

____

To Prove: The part of the statement that requires proof is expressed in terms of the letters or numerals that are used in the figure. Remember, the conclusion—the part that follows the word *then*—is what we want to prove.

In the previous Model 1, the part of the statement we want to prove is, "the sum of its angles is 180 degrees," So we would write:

TO PROVE: $\angle A + \angle B + \angle C = 180^\circ$

In Model 2, we want to prove that the alternate interior angles are equal. In our figure we named the angles 1 and 2, so we would write:

TO PROVE: $\angle 1 = \angle 2$

In Model 3, we want to prove that *m* is perpendicular to *l*. This statement would be written:

TO PROVE: $m \perp l$

Use the figures and statements of Exercise 3.6 through 3.10 and write the *TO PROVE.*

3.16 (3.6) TO PROVE: ______________________

3.17 (3.7) TO PROVE: ______________________

3.18 (3.8) TO PROVE: ______________________

3.19 (3.9) TO PROVE: ______________________

3.20 (3.10) TO PROVE: ______________________

Plan of Proof: This section gives a brief description of the plan you are going to use in the proof. When you are trying to think of a way to do the proof, you can often help yourself by reasoning backwards from the conclusion. Think, "The conclusion is true if some fact *A* is true. Fact *A* in turn will be true if fact *B* is true." Keep this line of thinking until you have your plan in mind. You can also look back at previously proven theorems for possible methods of proof.

Proof: The actual proof will be a series of numbered statements in one column with a like numbered column next to it for the reasons. The only things that can be used as reasons are given data, definitions, postulates, previously proven theorems, and algebraic properties.

Here is a model of the statement-reason two-column proof:

STATEMENT	REASON
1. $4x - 6 = 2(x + 3)$	1. Given
2. $4x - 6 = 2x + 6$	2. Distributive property
3. $4x = 2x + 12$	3. Addition property of equality
4. $2x = 12$	4. Subtraction property of equality
5. $x = 6$	5. Division property of equality

We know each step in the Statement column is true because we are using deductive reasoning and listing the general principle in the Reason column.

In this two-column model, Step 1 is true because it was the given equation. Step 2 is true because we used the distributive property on the equation in Step 1.

Step 3 is true since we added 6 to both sides of the equation in Step 2. Step 4 is correct because we subtracted $2x$ from both sides of the equation. Finally, Step 5, the statement we want to prove, is true because we used the division property on Step 4.

Supply the reasons in the following proofs.

		STATEMENT	REASON
	1.	$12 - x = 20 - 5x$	1. Given
3.21	2.	$12 + 4x = 20$	2. ______
3.22	3.	$4x = 8$	3. ______
3.23	4.	$x = 2$	4. ______

		STATEMENT	REASON
	1.	$2(x + 3) = 8$	1. Given
3.24	2.	$2x + 6 = 8$	2. ______
3.25	3.	$2x = 2$	3. ______
3.26	4.	$x = 1$	4. ______

		STATEMENT	REASON
	1.	$x(x + 4) = x(x + 2) + 1$	1. Given
3.27	2.	$x^2 + 4x = x^2 + 2x + 1$	2. ______
3.28	3.	$2x = 1$	3. ______
3.29	4.	$x = \frac{1}{2}$	4. ______

GIVEN: $x^2 + 6x + 2x + 12 = 0$

TO PROVE: $x = -6$ or $x = -2$

		STATEMENT	REASON
3.30	1.	$x^2 + 6x + 2x + 12 = 0$	1. ______
3.31	2.	$x^2 + 8x + 12 = 0$	2. ______
3.32	3.	$(x + 6)(x + 2) = 0$	3. ______
3.33	4.	$x + 6 = 0$ or $x + 2 = 0$	4. ______
3.34	5.	$x = -6$ or $x = -2$	5. ______

THE PARAGRAPH PROOF

The type of proof discussed in the previous section is known as a *direct* proof. Each step follows directly from the one before it until the desired conclusion is reached. Another type of proof is often used to prove theorems. This type of proof is called an *indirect proof*.

Most indirect proofs are presented in a paragraph form. Mathematicians often use the paragraph form for direct as well as for indirect proofs. A paragraph form of indirect reasoning often seems more natural than a two-column proof.

In an indirect proof we tentatively assume that the *negative* of the conclusion is true. We then reason logically, step by step, until we reach a conclusion that *contradicts* an established fact. When the *reasoning* is correct, the weakness must lie in the assumed statement. The assumed statement is therefore false, and the desired conclusion must be correct. Remember the truth table for negation:

NEGATION	
P	***~P***
T	F
F	T

If a statement is true, its negative is false; if the statement is false, its negation is true.

By an *established fact* is meant a property that is *given*, a *postulate*, a *definition*, or a *theorem* that has already been proved. Algebraic properties are included in this category.

Model 1: Given: $a = b$

$a \neq c$

To Prove: $b \neq c$

Proof: Suppose $b = c$ (negative of $b \neq c$). Then $a = c$ by the transitive property. But it is given that $a \neq c$. This statement is a contradiction. (Both $a = c$ and $a \neq c$ cannot be true at the same time.) Therefore, our supposed relationship is false and its negative (the *To Prove*) is true.

Model 2: Prove: If n is a number such that $n^2 = 3n$, then $n \neq 5$.

Given: n is a number $n^2 = 3n$

To Prove: $n \neq 5$

Proof: Suppose $n = 5$. Then, if we substitute 5 in $n^2 = 3n$ we get $5^2 = 3(5)$ or $25 = 15$, but this condition cannot be. We have reached a contradiction.
So $n = 5$ is false and $n \neq 5$ is true.

Model 3: If two lines intersect, then they intersect in exactly one point.

Given: l intersects m

To Prove: P is the only point of intersection

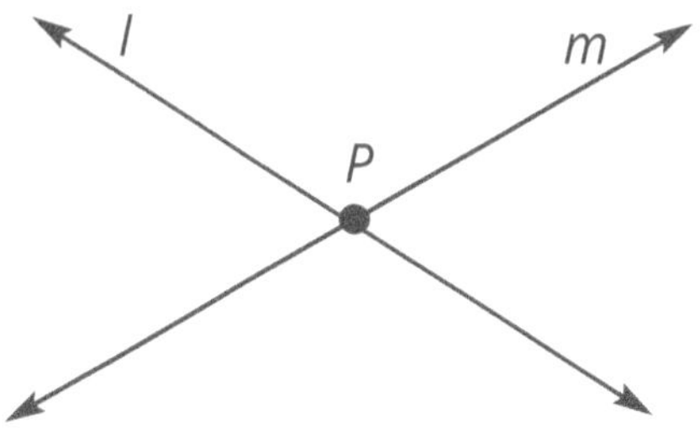

Proof: Suppose l and m had a second point of intersection, S. Then, l and m would have to be the same line since Postulate 2 tells us that only one line exists through two different points. This postulate contradicts the given condition that l and m are different lines. So l and m having a second point of intersection is false, and P being the only point must be true.

TO WRITE AN INDIRECT PROOF

1) Assume the negative of the conclusion is true.
2) Reason from your assumed statement until you reach a contradiction of a known fact.
3) Point out how the assumed statement must be false and that the conclusion of the theorem must be true.

Write the negative of the following statements.

3.35 Apple makes good pies.

3.36 The sun is hot today.

3.37 $3 + 2 = 7$.

3.38 A right angle measures less than 90°.

3.39 Seven is a prime number.

3.40 A line contains at least two points.

Write the negative of the conclusion for the following theorems.

3.41 If a number is odd, its square is odd.

3.42 If two lines intersect, they intersect in no more than one point.

3.43 If that plant is poison ivy, its leaves are in groups of three.

3.44 If $x^2 + 5x - 6 = 0$, then $x \neq 4$.

3.45 If two angles of a triangle are unequal, then the sides opposite them are unequal.

Write an indirect proof of the following statement.

3.46 If $2x < 50$, then $x < 25$.

____

____

____

____

Prove this theorem indirectly.

3.47 Assume you know that the sum of the angles of a triangle equals 180˚ and a right angle = 90˚. Prove that a triangle cannot have two right angles.

____

____

____

____

____

____

TEACHER CHECK ____________ ____________
initials date

Before you take this last Self Test, you may want to do one or more of these self checks.

1. _______ Read the objectives. See if you can do them.
2. _______ Restudy the material related to any objectives that you cannot do.
3. _______ Use the **SQ3R** study procedure to review the material:
   a. **S**can the sections.
   b. **Q**uestion yourself.
   c. **R**ead to answer your questions.
   d. **R**ecite the answers to yourself.
   e. **R**eview areas you did not understand.
4. _______ Review all vocabulary, activities, and Self Tests, writing a correct answer for every wrong answer.

SELF TEST 3

Write the answers in the blank. (each answer, 3 points)

3.01 A two-column proof has ______________ essential parts.

3.02 The statement part of a two-column proof should be written in ____________________ form.

3.03 The given part of a theorem is preceded by the word __________________________ .

3.04 The to prove part of a theorem is preceded by the word ________________________ .

3.05 A brief description telling how you are going to prove the statement is called the ____ .

Tell whether the following statements are always true, sometimes true, or never true (each answer, 2 points).

3.06 ______________________ The hypothesis of a statement is the *if* part.

3.07 ______________________ The conclusion of a statement is the *then* part.

3.08 ______________________ In a proof the figure should fit the hypothesis.

3.09 ______________________ A proof should have more steps in the reason column than steps in the statement column.

3.010 ______________________ In the plan of a proof, you should use the plan that was used on previous theorems.

Sketch a figure for each statement (each figure, 5 points).

3.011 A ray has one point at a given distance from the end point of the ray.

3.012 A segment has one midpoint.

3.013 There is exactly one plane through any three noncollinear points.

Make a deduction from the two given statements (each answer, 4 points).

3.014 1) All cows have tails.

2) Jersey is a cow.

Conclusion: ______________________________

3.015 1) All right angles are equal.

2) $\angle 1$ and $\angle 2$ are right angles.

Conclusion: ______________________________

3.016 1) Three noncollinear points determine a plane.

2) Points *S*, *O*, *N* are noncollinear.

Conclusion: ______________________________

3.017 1) Bruce has beans for supper only on Friday.

2) Today is Thursday.

Conclusion: ______________________________

Supply the reason for each statement in this proof (each answer, 5 points).

	STATEMENT	REASON
	1. $2x + x + 4) = -17$	1. Given
3.018	2. $3x + 4 = -17$	2. ______________
3.019	3. $3x = -21$	3. ______________
3.020	4. $x = -7$	4. ______________

57/71 **SCORE** __________ **TEACHER** __________ __________
initials date

Before taking the LIFEPAC Test, you may want to do one or more of these self checks.

1. _______ Read the objectives. See if you can do them.
2. _______ Restudy the material related to any objectives that you cannot do.
3. _______ Use the **SQ3R** study procedure to review the material.
4. _______ Review activities, Self Tests, and LIFEPAC vocabulary words.
5. _______ Restudy areas of weakness indicated by the last Self Test.

GLOSSARY

conjunction .... A statement formed by combining two statements with the word and.

contrapositive of a conditional .... A statement formed by interchanging the hypothesis and the conclusion in a conditional statement, and negating both.

converse of a conditional .... A statement formed by interchanging the hypothesis and the conclusion in a conditional statement.

deductive reasoning .... The process of making a conclusion by fitting a specific example into a general statement.

disjunction .... A statement formed by combining two statements with the word or.

inductive reasoning .... The process of making a general conclusion based on specific examples.

inverse of a conditional .... A statement formed by negating both the hypothesis and the conclusion in a conditional statement.

negation .... If *p* is a statement, the new statement, *not p* or *p is false* is the negation of *p*.

statement .... A sentence that is true or false, but not both.

NOTES

MATH 1002

LIFEPAC TEST

NAME ______________________

DATE ______________________

SCORE ______________________

MATH 1002: LIFEPAC TEST

Write the letter and the term that describes each statement (each answer, 2 points).

a. conjunction   b. disjunction   c. negation   d. conditional

1. ________________ All angles are right angles or a triangle has four sides.
2. ________________ If a polygon has six sides, then it is a hexagon.
3. ________________ The lights are off and the radio is on.
4. ________________ A triangle is acute provided all the angles have a measure of less than 90 degrees.
5. ________________ Geometry is fun or ducks do not like water.

Write the converse, inverse, and contrapositive of these statements (each answer, 4 points).
If two angles add to 90°, then they are complementary.

6. Converse: ______________________________

____

7. Inverse: ______________________________

____

8. Contrapositive: ______________________________

____

If it rains, then the flowers will bloom.

9. Converse: ______________________________

____

10. Inverse: ______________________________

____

11. Contrapositive: ______________________________

____

Write inductive or deductive to state which type of reasoning is used (each answer, 2 points).

12. ____________________ You eat at several Mexican restaurants and decide that Mexican food is hot.

13. ____________________ All professional athletes earn a lot of money. Wes plays professional football so he makes a lot of money.

14. ____________________ If 60 seconds are in a minute, 60 minutes in an hour, and 24 hours in a day, then 86,400 seconds are in a day.

15. ____________________ You visit a farm and notice that white chickens lay white eggs and speckled chickens lay brown eggs, so you decide that only white chickens lay white eggs.

Answer with *always*, *sometimes*, or *never* (each answer, 4 points).

16. If p is true and q is false, then $p \rightarrow q$ is ____________________ true.

17. When p is false and q is true, then p *or* q is ____________________ true.

18. If p is true and $\sim q$ is false, then $p \rightarrow \sim q$ is ____________________ false.

19. If p is true and q is true, then $\sim p \rightarrow \sim q$ is ____________________ true.

20. If $p \rightarrow q$ is true and q is true, then p is ____________________ true.

Write the given and the to prove in the following proofs (each answer, 4 points).
If one angle of a triangle is 90°, then the other two add to 90°.

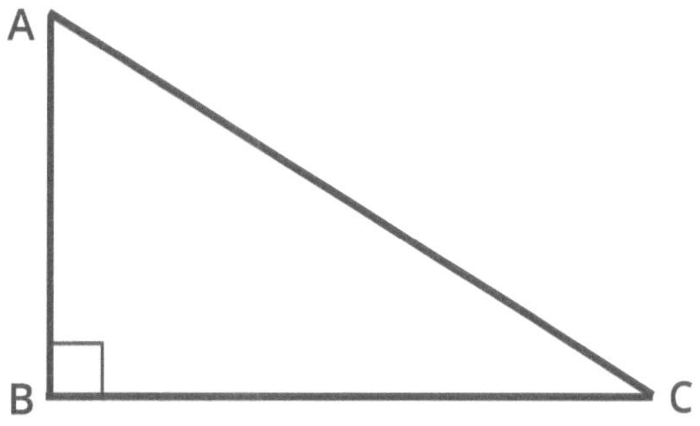

21. Given: ____________________

22. To Prove: ____________________

If Paul is older than Bill and Fred is younger than Bill, then Bill's age is between Paul's and Fred's.

23. Given: ____________________

24. To Prove: ____________________

Give an indirect proof of the following statement (10 points).

25. If $x^2 + x = 4$, then $x \neq 2$.

MATH 1003
ANGLES AND PARALLELS

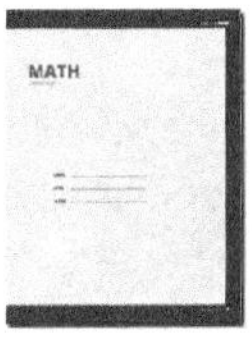

LIFEPAC Test is located at the back of the booklet. Please remove before starting the unit.

Author:
Milton R. Christen, M.A.

Editor-in-Chief:
Richard W. Wheeler, M.A.Ed.

Consulting Editor:
Robert L. Zenor, M.A., M.S.

Revision Editor:
Alan Christopherson, M.S.

Page 39: © Comstock, Stockbyte, Thinkstock

AOP

804 N. 2nd Ave. E.
Rock Rapids, IA 51246-1759

Angles and Parallels

Introduction

In this LIFEPAC®, we shall study another basic geometric idea. Lines, segments, and rays can be placed in such a way as to form angles. Angles are present everywhere and are very important in the study of geometry. Many angle relationships will be presented, along with methods for measuring angles. We shall also learn about parallels and how special angles are formed using parallels. Many theorems will be presented in connection with angles and parallels.

Objectives

Read these objectives. The objectives tell you what you will be able to do when you have successfully completed this LIFEPAC. When you have finished this LIFEPAC, you should be able to:

1. Identify angles as acute, right, or obtuse.
2. Find the measure of angles with a protractor.
3. Add and subtract measures of angles.
4. Find the measure of angles by their relationship with other angles.
5. Prove theorems about angles.
6. Define terms related to parallels.
7. Prove theorems about parallel and related angles.
8. Classify triangles by their sides and by their angles.
9. Prove theorems about triangles and their related angles.

Survey the LIFEPAC. Ask yourself some questions about this study and write your questions here.

1. ANGLE DEFINITIONS AND MEASUREMENT

To continue our study of geometry, we must learn basic angle definitions and measurement methods. Definitions will help in identifying and classifying angles; measurement will allow us to add and subtract angles.

Section Objectives

Review these objectives. When you have completed this section, you should be able to:

1. Identify angles as acute, right, or obtuse.
2. Find the measure of angles with a protractor.
3. Add and subtract measures of angles.

ANGLE DEFINITIONS

These definitions relate to angles. Make sure you know them, because you will be using them many times in this LIFEPAC.

> **DEFINITION**
>
> **Angle** ($\angle$): the union of two noncollinear rays that have a common end point.

The two rays that form the angle are called its *sides*, and the common end point is called the *vertex* of the angle. The symbol for angle is $\angle$.

Models:

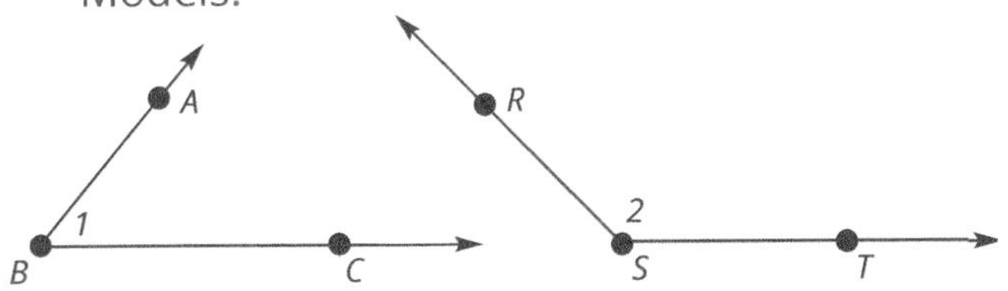

The angle to the left is formed by the union of $\overrightarrow{BA}$ and $\overrightarrow{BC}$. Its sides are $\overrightarrow{BA}$ and $\overrightarrow{BC}$. Its vertex is *B*. We can name the angle $\angle ABC$, $\angle CBA$, $\angle B$, or $\angle 1$. The angle to the right is the union of $\overrightarrow{SR}$ and $\overrightarrow{ST}$. The vertex is point *S*. This angle can be called $\angle RST$, $\angle TSR$, $\angle S$, or $\angle 2$.

Notice that when three letters are used to name an angle, the vertex letter is always placed between the other two.

If no confusion will result, the vertex letter can be used alone; or a numeral can be used. You should never use a single letter when several angles have the same vertex.

Model:

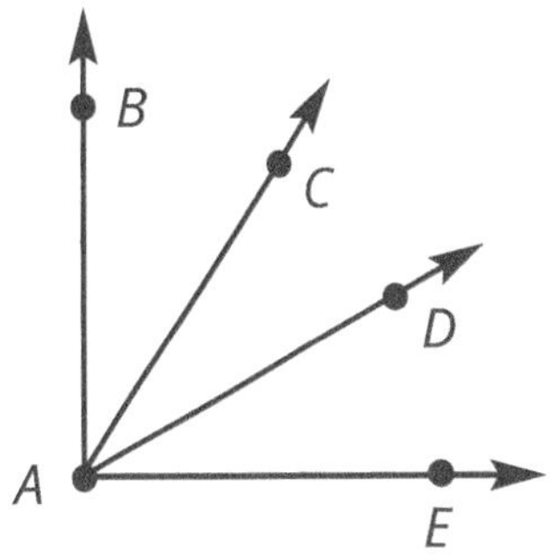

$\angle A$ could mean:

$\angle BAC$, the angle formed by $\overrightarrow{AB}$ and $\overrightarrow{AC}$; or

$\angle CAD$, the angle formed by $\overrightarrow{AC}$ and $\overrightarrow{AD}$; or

$\angle DAE$, the angle formed by $\overrightarrow{AD}$ and $\overrightarrow{AE}$; or

$\angle BAD$, the angle formed by $\overrightarrow{AB}$ and $\overrightarrow{AD}$; or

$\angle CAE$, the angle formed by $\overrightarrow{AC}$ and $\overrightarrow{AE}$; or

$\angle BAE$, the angle formed by $\overrightarrow{AB}$ and $\overrightarrow{AE}$.

DEFINITION

Acute angle: an angle whose measure is less than 90°.

Models:

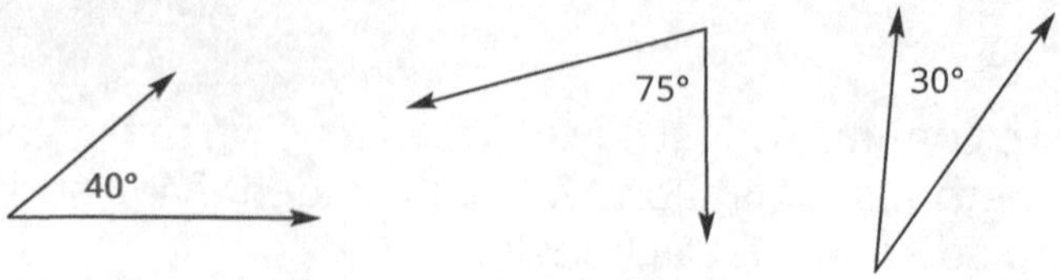

These angles are all acute angles.

DEFINITION

Right angle (rt. ∠): an angle whose measure equals 90°.

Models:

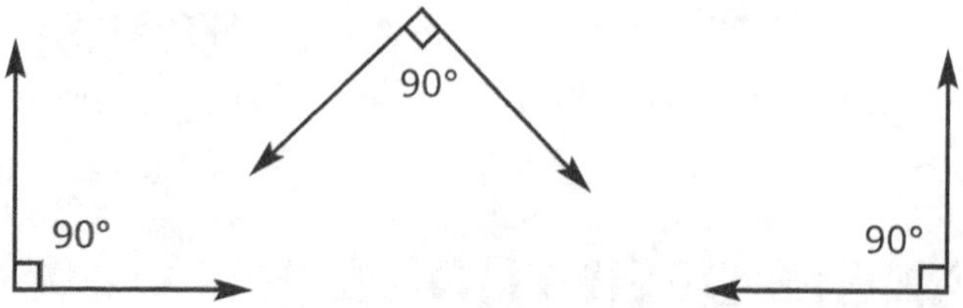

These angles are all right angles. A little box at the vertex indicates a right angle.

DEFINITION

Obtuse angle: an angle with a measure greater than 90° but less than 180°.

Models:

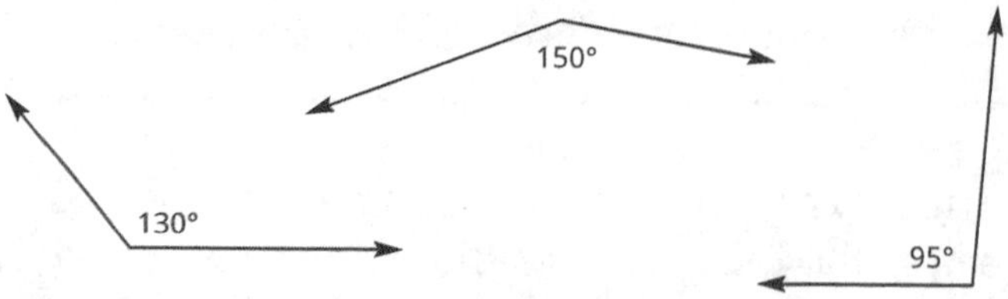

These angles are all obtuse angles.

DEFINITION

Bisector of an angle: a ray that is in the interior of the angle and divides the angle into two angles of equal measure.

Model:

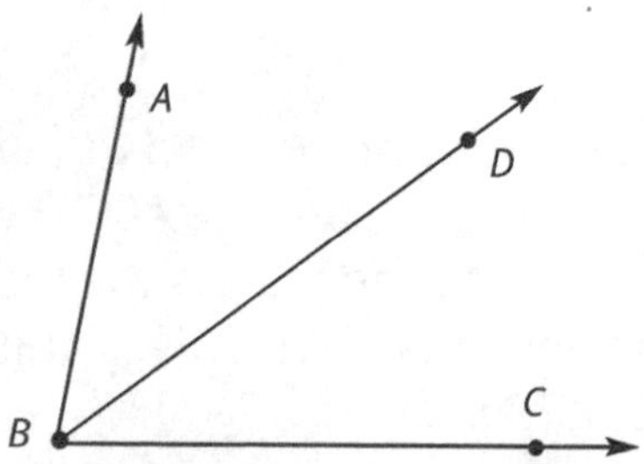

If the measure of $\angle ABD$ (m $\angle ABD$) equals the measure of $\angle DBC$ (m $\angle DBC$), then $\overrightarrow{BD}$ bisects $\angle ABC$.

Given the following angle, complete the following items.

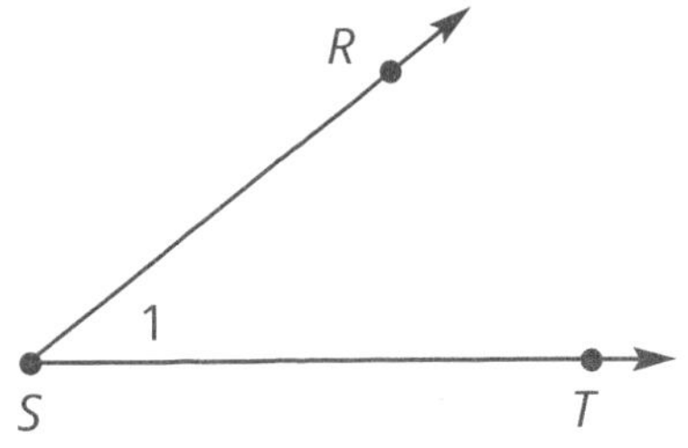

1.1 State four ways of naming this angle. ____________________

1.2 What point is the vertex of this angle? __________

1.3 Name the sides of this angle. ____________________

Write your answers on the lines.

1.4 Name the sides of $\angle ABC$. ____________________

1.5 Name the vertex of $\angle ABC$. __________

Given the following angles, complete the following items.

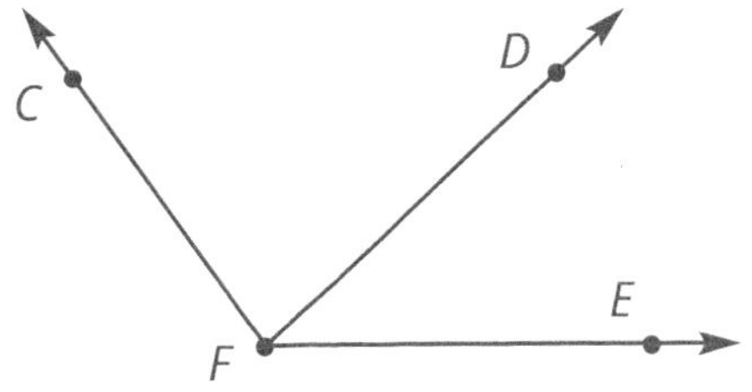

1.6 Name three angles with vertex F. ____________________

1.7 $\overrightarrow{FC}$ and $\overrightarrow{FE}$ are the sides of what angle? __________

1.8 What ray is the common side of $\angle CFD$ and $\angle DFE$? __________

1.9 If m $\angle DFE$ = m $\angle CFD$, name the bisector of $\angle CFE$. __________

Given the following angles, complete the following items.

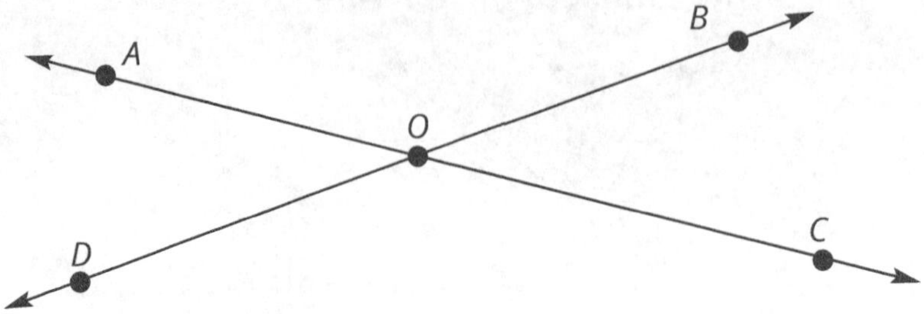

1.10 Name the acute angles. ______________________________

1.11 Name the obtuse angles. ______________________________

Complete the following activity.

1.12 In the space provided:

a. Draw a right angle.

b. Draw a bisector of the right angle. Label all parts.

c. What kind of angles are formed by the bisector?

____

> **DEFINITION**
>
> **Perpendicular lines**: two lines that intersect such that the four angles formed are equal to each other.

Model:

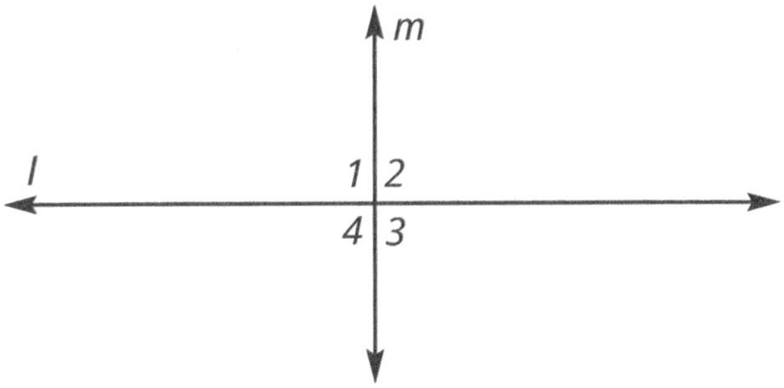

When m $\angle 1$ = m $\angle 2$ = m $\angle 3$ = m $\angle 4$, we say that line *l* is perpendicular ($\perp$) to line *m*.

Segments and rays that are parts of lines can also be called perpendicular if the lines of which they are part are perpendicular.

Models:

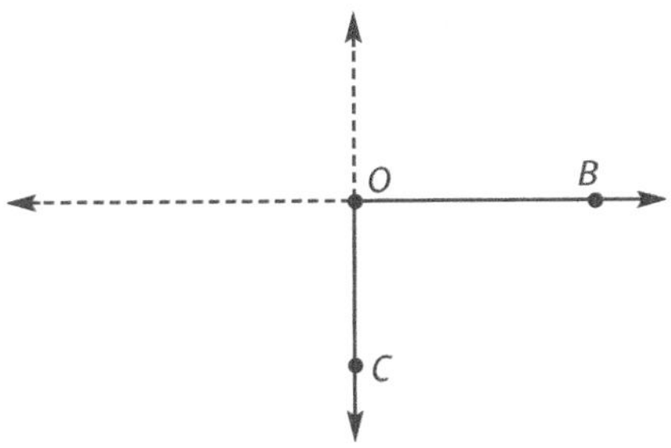

$\overrightarrow{OB} \perp \overrightarrow{OC}$

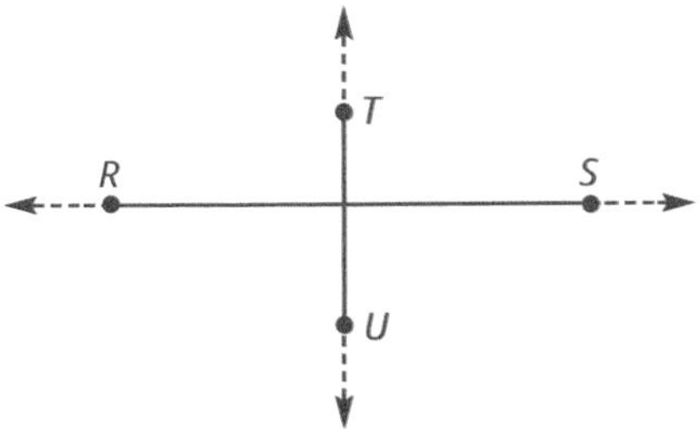

$\overline{RS} \perp \overline{TU}$

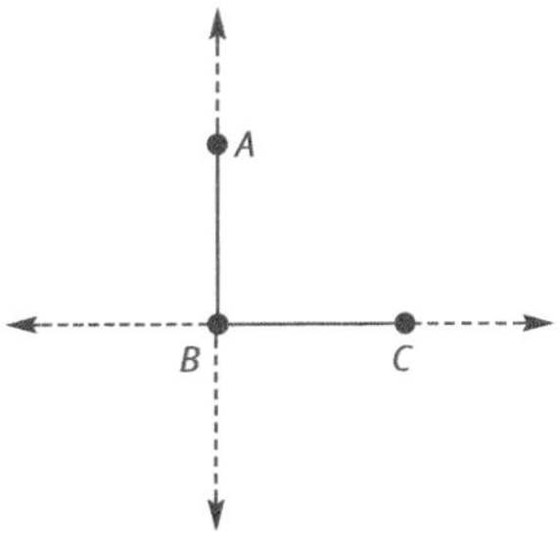

$\overline{AB} \perp \overline{BC}$

Betweenness of rays means that for any $\angle AOC$, $\overrightarrow{OB}$ is between $\overrightarrow{OA}$ and $\overrightarrow{OC}$ when all three rays have the same end point *and* when *OB* lies in the interior of $\angle AOC$. Both of these conditions must be true for $\overrightarrow{OB}$ to be between $\overrightarrow{OA}$ and $\overrightarrow{OC}$.

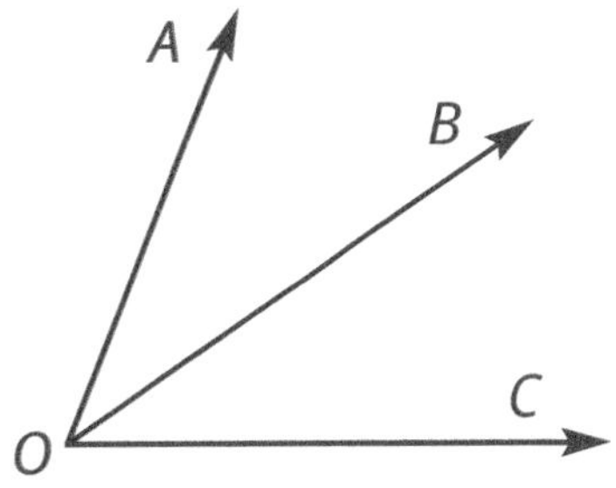

Models:

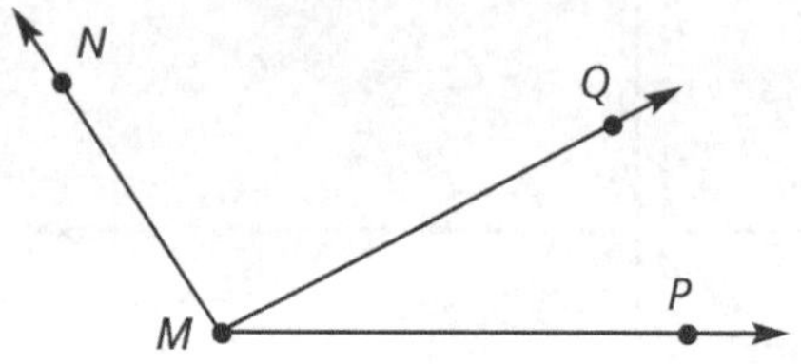

$\overrightarrow{MQ}$ is between $\overrightarrow{MN}$ and $\overrightarrow{MP}$.

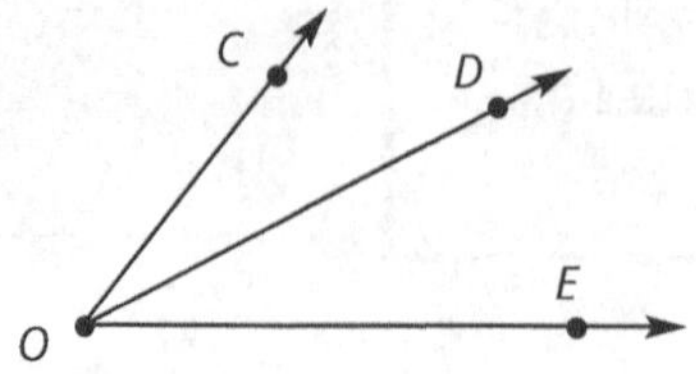

$\overrightarrow{OD}$ is between $\overrightarrow{OC}$ and $\overrightarrow{OE}$.

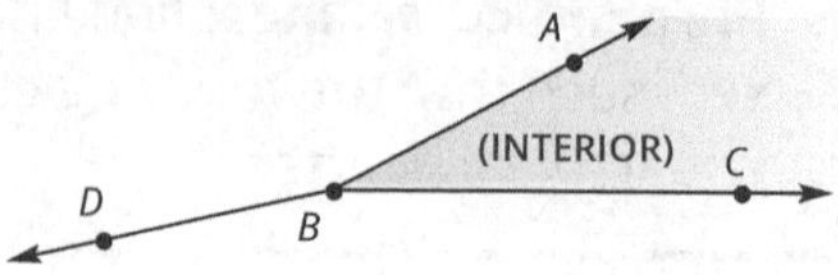

$\overrightarrow{BD}$ is not between $\overrightarrow{BA}$ and $\overrightarrow{BC}$.
It is not in the interior of $\angle ABC$.

Complete the following activities.

1.13 a. Draw lines $\perp$ to l through points A, B, C, and D.

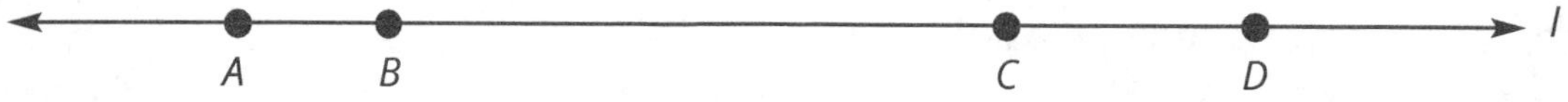

b. What does inductive reasoning tell you about these lines?

____

1.14 a. Draw ray $\overrightarrow{OB}$ between ray $\overrightarrow{OA}$ and $\overrightarrow{OC}$.

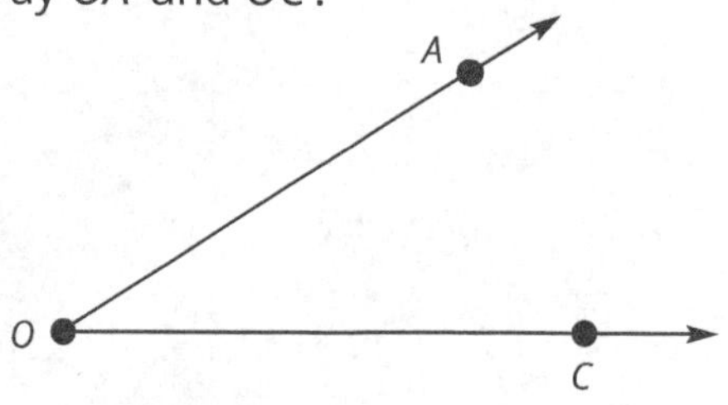

b. What does inductive reasoning tell you about the sum of the measures of $\angle AOB$ and $\angle BOC$?

____

____

1.15 a. Draw $\overleftrightarrow{RS} \perp \overleftrightarrow{TU}$ at O. Draw $\overrightarrow{OA}$ between $\overrightarrow{OT}$ and $\overrightarrow{OS}$. Draw $\overrightarrow{OB}$ opposite $\overrightarrow{OA}$.

b. What does inductive reasoning tell you about m $\angle AOS$ and m $\angle BOR$?

____

c. About m $\angle AOT$ and m $\angle BOU$?

____

1.16 a. Draw several $\perp$ lines.

b. What kinds of angles are formed? (acute, obtuse, or right) ________________

1.17 a. Using $\overrightarrow{OA}$, $\overrightarrow{OB}$, $\overrightarrow{OC}$, and $\overrightarrow{OD}$, make a diagram so that $\angle AOB$ is an acute $\angle$, $\angle BOC$ is an obtuse $\angle$, and $\angle COD$ is a right $\angle$.

b. What kind of angle is $\angle AOD$? ____________________________

1.18 What is the measure of a rt. $\angle$? ________________

1.19 What is the measure of an obtuse $\angle$? __________________________

1.20 What is the measure of an acute $\angle$? ______________________

ANGLE MEASUREMENT

We now need to work with angle measurement. The following postulates will help us to establish a method for measuring angles.

> **POSTULATE 6**
>
> P6: Every angle corresponds with a unique real number greater than 0° and less than 180°.
>
> **(angle measurement postulate)**

P6 tells us that every angle has a measure that is a real number between 0° and 180°. No angle has a measure of 0°; no angle has a measure of 180°.

The next postulate tells us how to find the measurement number.

> **POSTULATE 7**
>
> P7: The set of rays on the same side of a line with a common end point in the line can be put in one-to-one correspondence with the real numbers from 0° to 180° inclusive in such a way:
>
> 1. that one of the two opposite rays lying in the line is paired with zero and the other is paired with 180°.
> 2. that the measure of any angle whose sides are rays of that given set is equal to the absolute value of the difference between the numbers corresponding to its sides.
>
> **(protractor postulate)**

P7 tells us how to build and use a protractor to measure an angle.

Take a line and a point O on that line.

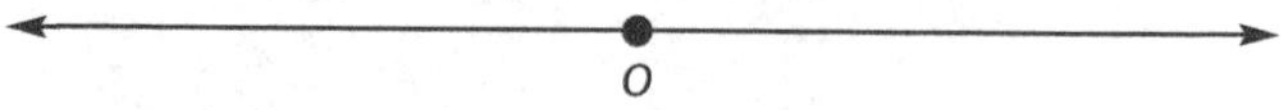

Place a set of rays all on the same side of the line with common end point O.

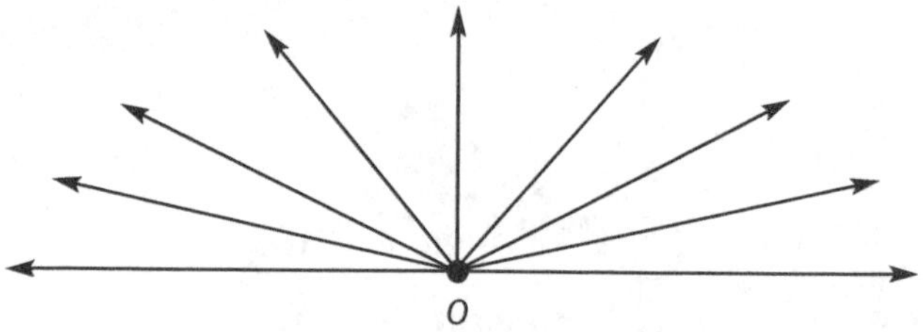

Then match the numbers from 0° to 180° inclusive with the rays in such a way that one of the two opposite rays is paired with zero and the other is paired with 180°.

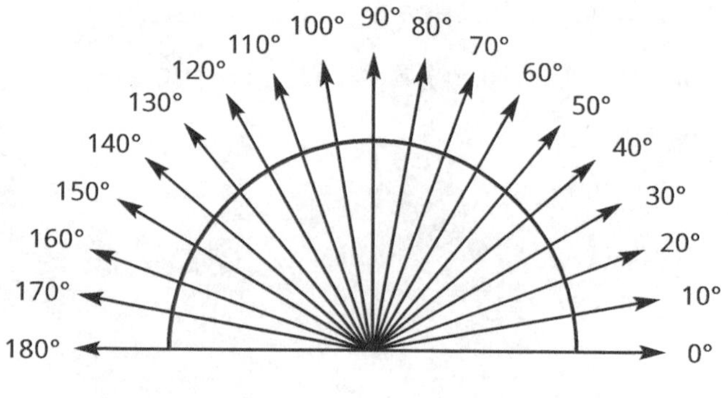

You have built a protractor. Now, to find the measure of an angle, place the sides of the angle along the rays of the protractor, lining up the vertex of the angle with point *O*. Noting the numbers associated with the rays, subtract one ray number from another and take the absolute value of the difference to make the answer a positive number. This number is the measure of the angle. You can line up one ray of the angle with the zero ray, but this step is not necessary. You only need to have the vertex matching the *O* mark on the protractor.

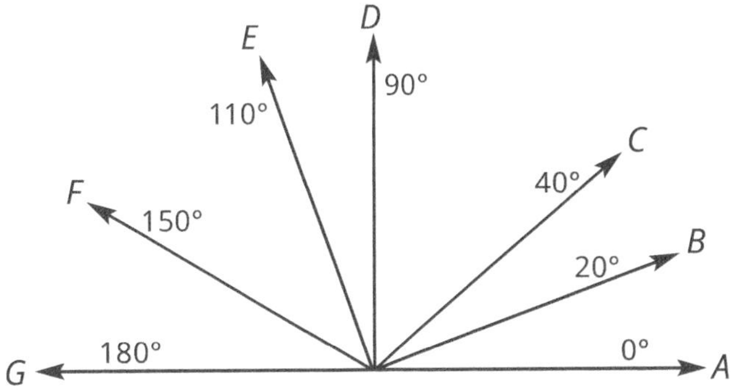

$m\angle AOB = |20° - 0°| = |20°| = 20°$

$m\angle BOC = |40° - 20°| = |20°| = 20°$

$m\angle COD = |90° - 40°| = |50°| = 50°$

The order in which you subtract does not affect the measure.

$m\angle COP = |40° - 90°| = |-50°| = 50°$

$m\angle FOC = |40° - 150°| = |-110°| = 110°$

$m\angle DOG = |90° - 180°| = |-90°| = 90°$

Refer to this diagram to complete the following items.

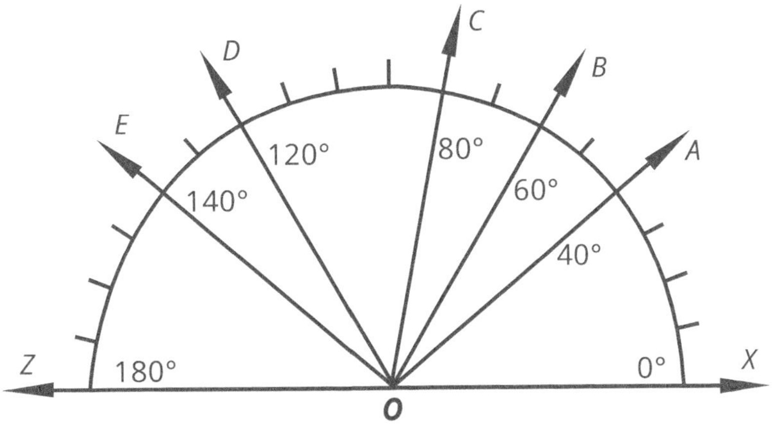

1.21 Write the measure of the following ∠'s.

a. $m\angle AOX$ = ______________

b. $m\angle BOX$ = ______________

c. $m\angle BOA$ = ______________

d. $m\angle COB$ = ______________

e. $m\angle DOX$ = ______________

f. $m\angle BOE$ = ______________

g. $m\angle EOD$ = ______________

h. $m\angle AOD$ = ______________

i. $m\angle AOC$ = ______________

1.22 Name three angles with a measure of 20°. ______________________________

1.23 Name two angles with a measure of 40°. ______________________________

1.24 Does $\angle EOZ$ have the same measure as $\angle AOX$? ______________________

1.25 What ray is a common side of $\angle EOB$ and $\angle BOA$? ________________

1.26 a. What ray is between $\overrightarrow{OC}$ and $\overrightarrow{OA}$? ________________

b. Does this ray divide $\angle COA$ into two angles of equal measure? ______________

1.27 Name six angles that have $\overrightarrow{OA}$ as a side. ______________________________

1.28 Does m $\angle COX$ = m$\angle AOX$ + m$\angle COA$? __________

1.29 Are m $\angle COB$ and m $\angle BOA$ equal? __________

1.30 What is $\overrightarrow{OB}$ called with respect to $\angle COA$? ______________________________

THEOREM 3-1

If OA lies between $\overrightarrow{OB}$ and $\overrightarrow{OC}$, then m $\angle BOA$ + m$\angle AOC$ = m$\angle BOC$.

(angle addition theorem)

The proof of Theorem 3-1 follows.

Given: $\overrightarrow{OA}$ is between $\overrightarrow{OB}$ and $\overrightarrow{OC}$

To Prove: m$\angle BOA$ + m$\angle AOC$ = m$\angle BOC$

Plan: Use the protractor postulate and the addition property of equality.

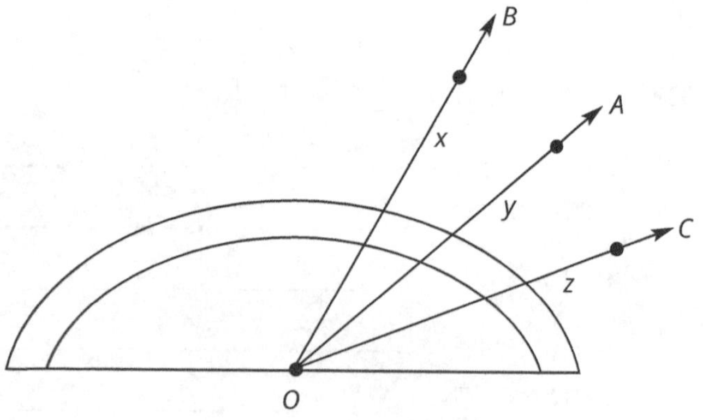

STATEMENT	REASON
1. $\overrightarrow{OA}$ is between $\overrightarrow{OB}$ and $\overrightarrow{OC}$	1. Given
2. m $\angle BOA = \lvert x - y \rvert = x - y$ m $\angle AOC = \lvert y - z \rvert = y - z$ m $\angle BOC = \lvert x - z \rvert = x - z$	2. Protractor Postulate
3. m $\angle BOA$ + m $\angle AOC$ = $(x - y) + (y - z) = x - z$	3. Addition property of equality (add the first two equations in Step 2)
4. m $\angle BOA$ + m $\angle AOC$ = m $\angle BOC$	4. Substitution

In practical problems, angle measures that are not integers are sometimes expressed in degrees (°), minutes (′), and seconds (″).

REMEMBER?

$1° = 60'$ $\qquad 1' = \frac{1°}{60}$

$1' = 60''$ $\qquad 1'' = \frac{1'}{60}$

$1'' = \frac{1°}{3600}$

To find the decimal numeral that is equivalent to a degree, minute, and second measure, you must express minutes and seconds in degree equivalents, divide, and combine terms.

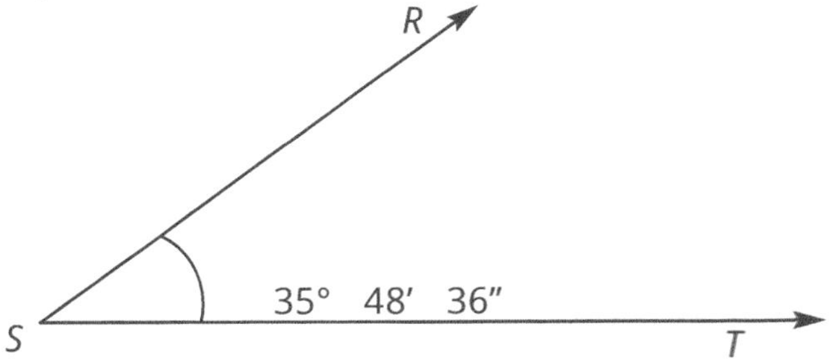

Model:

$$35°\,48'\,36'' = 35° + 48' + 36''$$
$$= 35° + \frac{48}{60}° + \frac{36}{3600}°$$
$$= 35° + .8° + .01°$$
$$= 35.81°$$
$$\therefore \angle RST = 35.81°$$

(∴) means "therefore"

When you add several measures of angles, combine them by like units of measure.

Model:

25°	10′	40″	
16°	45′	30″	
8°	12′	3″	
49°	67′	73″ = 1′ + 13″	60″ = 1′
	+ 1′		
	68′ = 1° + 8′		60′ = 1°
+ 1°			
50°			

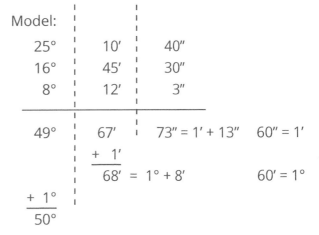

The sum of the three measures is 50° 8′ 13″.

When subtraction involves borrowing, remember that the 1° you borrow is changed into 60′, or the 1′ into 60″, and then proceed to subtract the like units of measure.

Model:

48°	12′	15″
- 17°	20′	30″

Borrow 1′, change to 60″, and add to 15″, giving 75″:

48°	11′	75″
- 17°	20′	30″

Borrow 1°, change to 60′, and add to 11′, giving 71′:

47°	71′	75″
- 17°	20′	30″
30°	51′	45″

The difference of the measures is 30° 51′ 45″.

Complete the following activities.

1.31 Using a straightedge, draw a triangle and a quadrilateral (4 sides) in the space provided. Using a protractor, find the approximate measures of each angle in each figure. Find the sum of the angle measures in each figure.

Sum of ∠'s ______________________ Sum of ∠'s ______________________

1.32 Express $\frac{2}{3}^{\circ}$ in minutes. ______________________

1.33 What fractional part of a degree is 45′? ______________________

1.34 Express $\frac{3}{4}'$ in seconds. ______________________

1.35 Is 24° 59′ 60″ equivalent to 25°? ______________________

Use this diagram to write the required information.

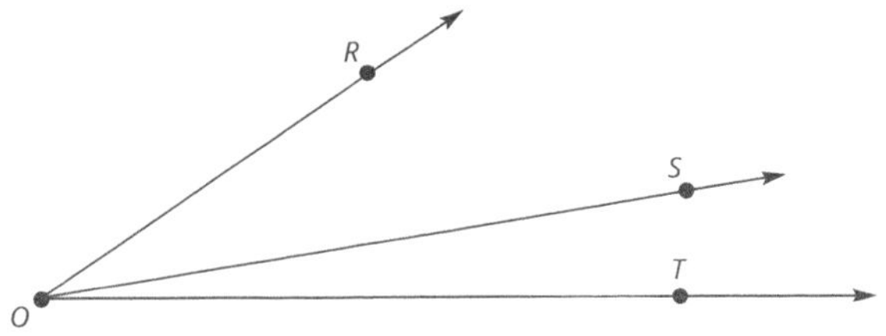

1.36 m $\angle ROS$ = 20° 15′ 40″ m $\angle SOT$ = 10° 12′ 30″ m $\angle ROT$ = ____________

1.37 m $\angle ROS$ = 41° 12′ m $\angle ROT$ = 62° 8′ 12″ m $\angle SOT$ = ____________

1.38 m $\angle SOT$ = 7° 5′ 8″ m $\angle ROT$ = 48° 12′ 16″ m $\angle ROS$ = ____________

1.39 m $\angle ROS$ = 28° 4′ 16″ m $\angle SOT$ = 31° 48′ 50″ m $\angle ROT$ = ____________

1.40 m $\angle ROS$ = 15° 22′ 40″ m $\angle ROT$ = 52° 52′ 52″ m $\angle SOT$ = ____________

Review the material in this section in preparation for the Self Test. This Self Test will check your mastery of this particular section. The items missed on this Self Test will indicate specific areas where restudy is needed for mastery.

SELF TEST 1

Complete the following items (each answer, 3 points).

1.01 Draw an acute angle and label it so its name is $\angle WON$.

1.02 Name the vertex of $\angle WON$. ____________

1.03 Name the sides of $\angle WON$. ____________________________

1.04 Draw $\overrightarrow{OS}$ the bisector of $\angle BOT$.

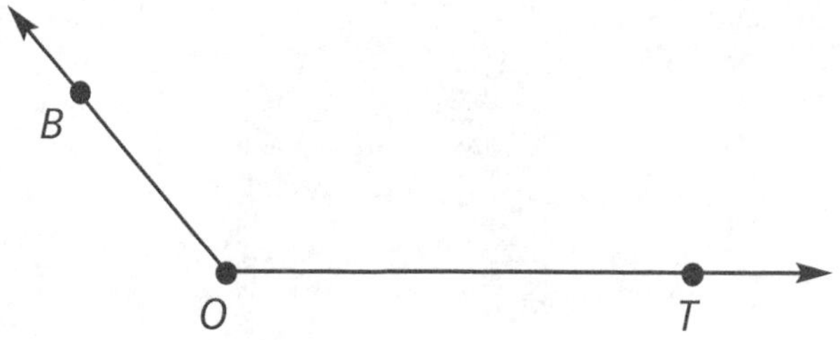

1.05 Draw $\overleftrightarrow{RA} \perp \overleftrightarrow{TU}$ at point Q.

1.06 What is the measure of an obtuse angle? ____

1.07 What is the measure of an acute angle? ____

Given the following diagram, write the required information (each answer, 3 points).

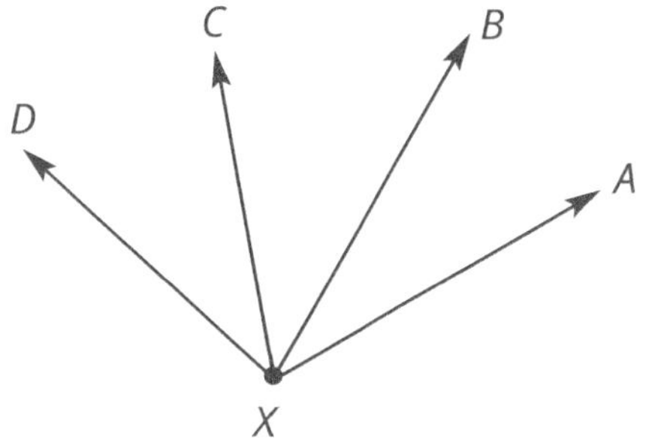

1.08 m $\angle BXA$ = 30° 20′ m $\angle CXB$ = 40° 35′ m $\angle CXA$ = ____________

1.09 m $\angle DXB$ = 70° 15′ 12″ m $\angle DXC$ = 30° 30′ 20″ m $\angle CXB$ = ____________

1.010 Name the largest angle in the figure. ____________

1.011 m $\angle DXB$ + m $\angle BXA$ = ____________

Write the required information (each answer, 3 points).

1.012 Can we have an angle with a measure of 0 degrees? ____________

1.013 Can we have an angle with a measure of 180 degrees? ____________

1.014 Find the sum.

	20°	15′	18″
	30°	41′	32″
+	2°	30′	15″

1.015 Find the difference.

	60°	50′	40″
–	30°	40′	50″

Supply the reasons in the following proof (each answer, 4 points).

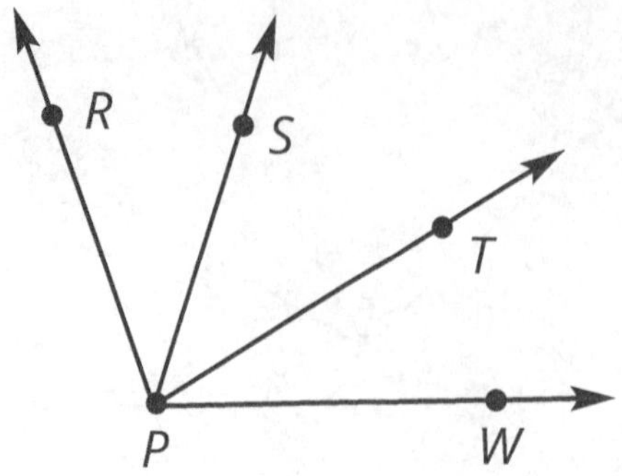

Given: m $\angle RPS$ = m $\angle TPW$
To Prove: m $\angle RPT$ = m $\angle SPW$

STATEMENT	REASON
1. m $\angle RPS$ = m $\angle TPW$	1.016 ________________
2. m $\angle RPS$ + m $\angle SPT$ = m $\angle TPW$ + m $\angle SPT$	1.017 ________________
3. m $\angle RPS$ + m $\angle SPT$ = m $\angle RPT$	1.018 ________________
4. m $\angle TPW$ + m $\angle SPT$ = m $\angle SPW$	1.019 ________________
5. m $\angle RPT$ = m $\angle SPW$	1.020 ________________

52/65 **SCORE** ________ **TEACHER** ________ ________
initials date

2. ANGLE RELATIONSHIPS AND THEOREMS

Angles are related to each other in many ways. They can be related by position or by measure. In this next section angle relationships and several theorems dealing with angle relationships will be presented.

Section Objectives

Review these objectives. When you have completed this section, you should be able to:

4. Find the measure of angles by their relationship with other angles.
5. Prove theorems about angles.

RELATIONSHIP DEFINITIONS

The definitions in this section explain many common angle relationships. Be sure to understand whether the angles are related by position or by measure.

> **DEFINITION**
>
> **Adjacent angles**: two angles in the same plane that have a common vertex and a common side, but no interior points in common.

The rays not common to both angles are called *exterior* sides of the angles.

Adjacent angles must meet four requirements, according to our definition.

First, they must be in the same plane.

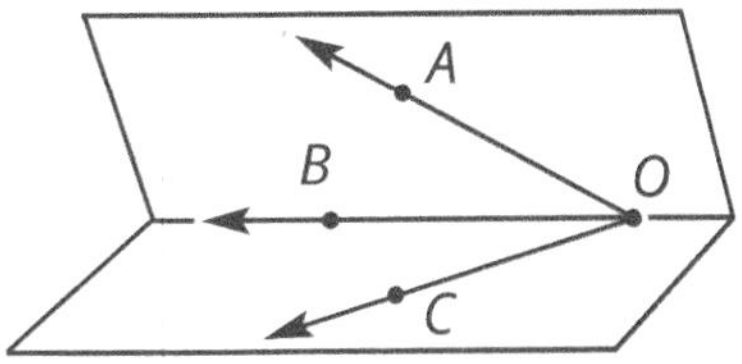

$\angle AOB$ and $\angle BOC$ are NOT in the same plane. They are NOT adjacent angles.

Second, they must have a common vertex.

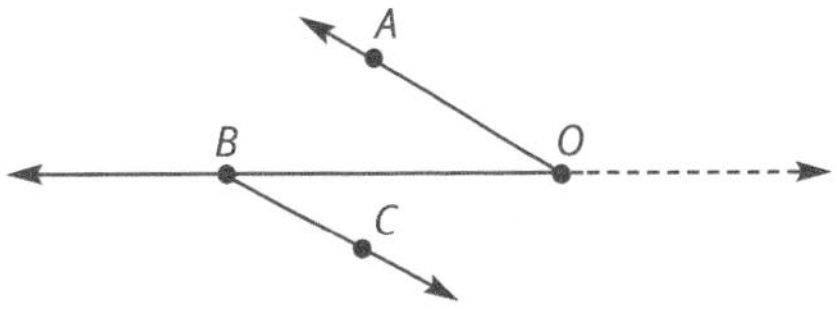

$\angle AOB$ and $\angle OBC$ do NOT have a common vertex. They are NOT adjacent angles.

Third, they must have a common side.

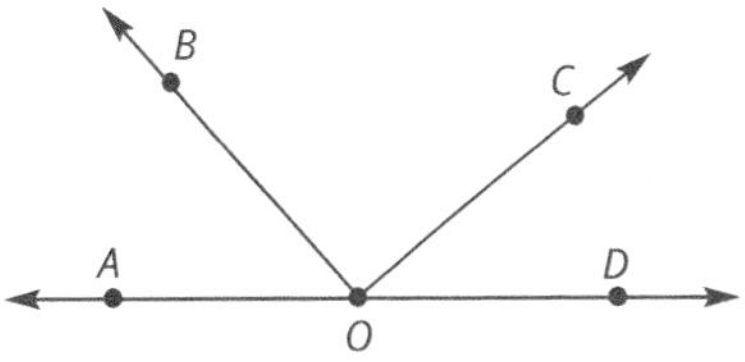

$\angle BOA$ and $\angle COD$ do NOT have a common side. They are NOT adjacent angles.

Fourth, they must have no interior points in common.

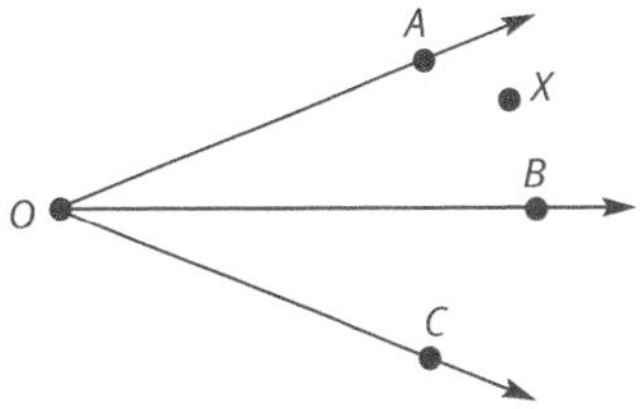

Point X is in the interior of $\angle AOB$ and is in the interior of $\angle AOC$, so $\angle AOB$ and $\angle AOC$ are NOT adjacent angles.

Even though $\angle AOB$ and $\angle AOC$ are not adjacent angles, two angles in the figure do meet all four requirements. The angles are $\angle AOB$ and $\angle BOC$. They are in the same plane; they have a common vertex, O; they have a common side, $\overrightarrow{OB}$; and no point in the interior of $\angle AOB$ is in the interior of $\angle BOC$.

The model below shows some other examples of adjacent angles.

Model:

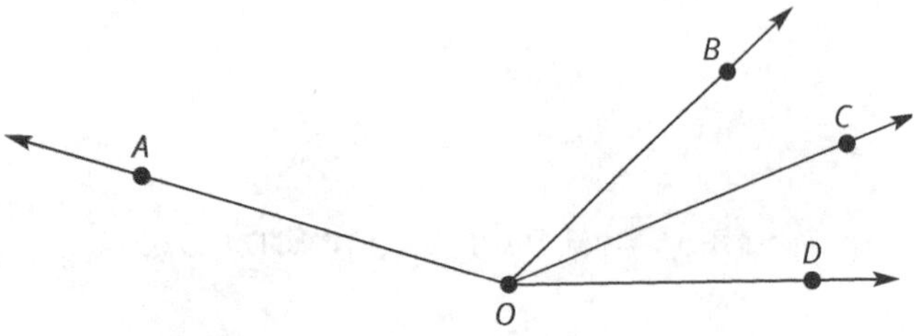

$\angle AOB$ and $\angle BOC$ are adjacent.
$\angle BOC$ and $\angle COD$ are adjacent.
$\angle AOC$ and $\angle COD$ are adjacent.
$\angle AOB$ and $\angle BOD$ are adjacent.

> **DEFINITION**
> **Complementary angles**: two angles with measures that, when added together, equal 90°. Each angle is called the *complement* of the other.

Models:

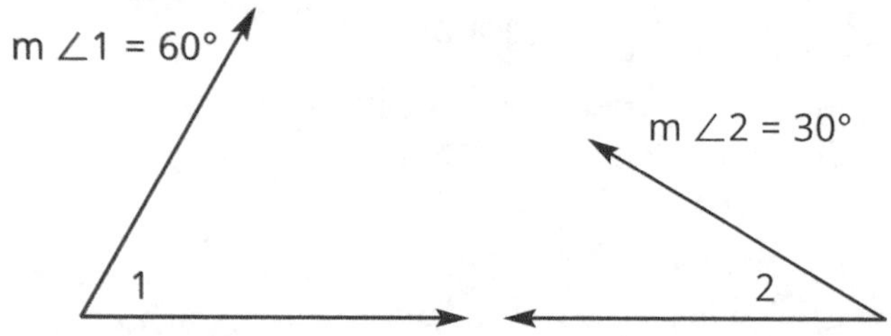

$\angle 1$ and $\angle 2$ are complementary.

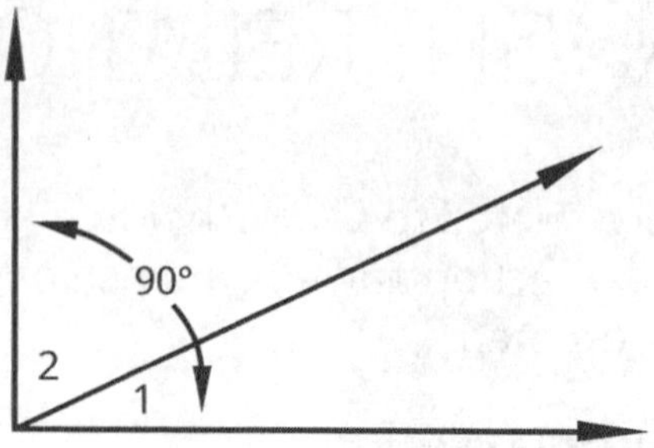

$\angle 1$ and $\angle 2$ are complementary.

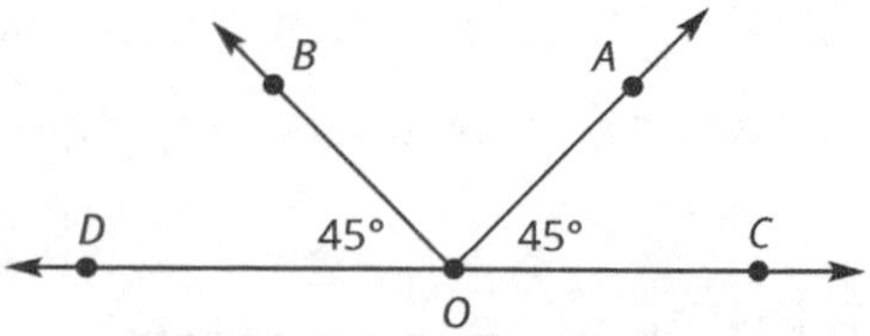

$\angle BOD$ and $\angle AOC$ are complementary.

> **DEFINITION**
> **Supplementary angles**: two angles with measures that, when added together, equal 180°. Each angle is called the *supplement* of the other.

Models:

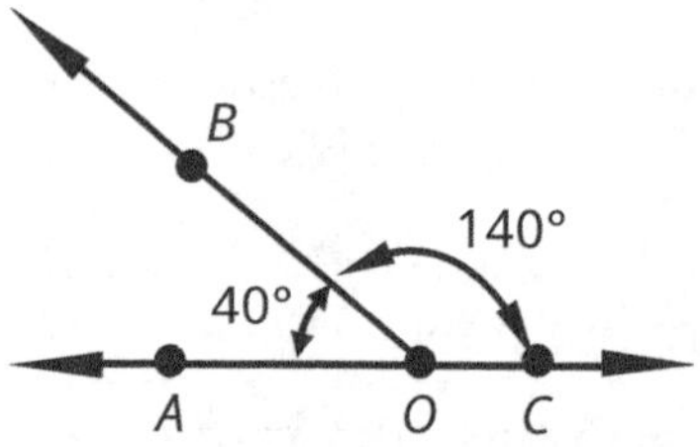

$\angle AOB$ and $\angle BOC$ are supplementary.

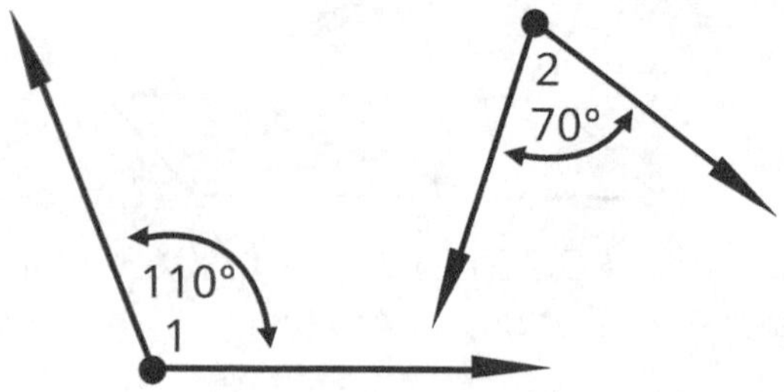

$\angle 1$ and $\angle 2$ are supplementary.

Vertical angles are angles with sides that form two pairs of opposite rays.

REMEMBER?

Opposite rays form a straight line.

Models:

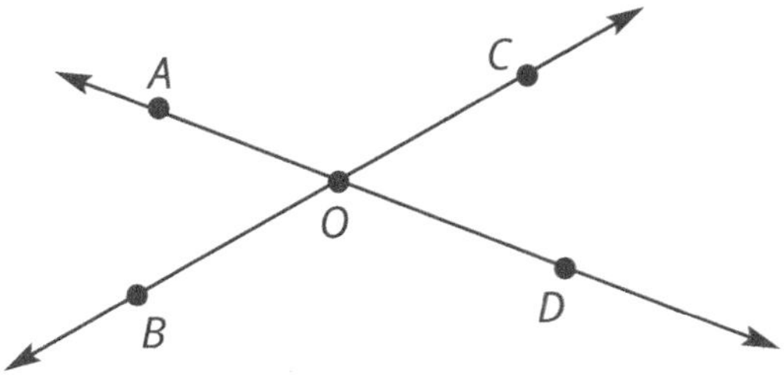

$\angle AOB$ and $\angle COD$ are vertical angles.

$\angle AOC$ and $\angle BOD$ are vertical angles.

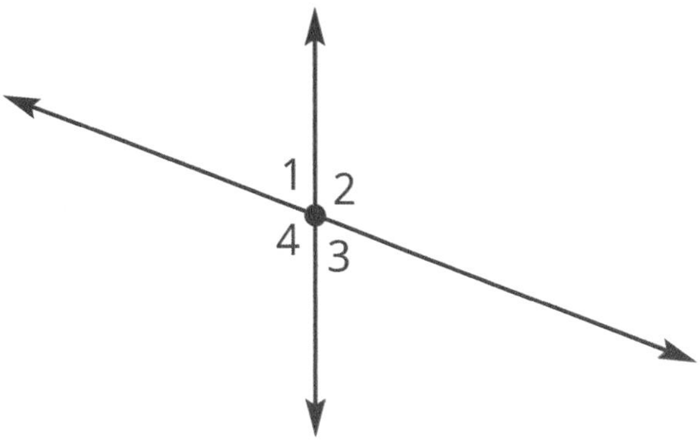

$\angle 1$ and $\angle 3$ are vertical angles.

$\angle 2$ and $\angle 4$ are vertical angles.

Write the correct letter for the answer on each blank.

2.1 _______ Angles with measures that add to 90°.

2.2 _______ Angles with sides that form two pairs of opposite rays.

2.3 _______ Angles in the same plane with a common vertex and a common side but no common interior points.

2.4 _______ Angles with measures that add to 180°.

a. adjacent angles

b. complementary angles

c. supplementary angles

d. right angles

e. vertical angles

THEOREMS

These theorems about angle relationships will help you to work with related angles. Each theorem will be followed by an illustrating diagram and by the proof of the theorem. Read the theorems and their proofs carefully. Notice that in the proofs of the theorems other theorems are stated rather than being referred to by number. You should follow the same procedure when you are asked to complete a proof, because learning the theorems is more important than learning their numbers.

> **THEOREM 3-2**
> If the exterior sides of two adjacent angles are opposite rays, then the angles are supplementary.

Given: $\angle ADC$, $\angle CDB$ are adjacent angles.
DA, DB are opposite rays.

To Prove: $\angle ADC$, $\angle CDB$ are supplementary angles.

Plan: Use the protractor postulate and the definition of supplementary angles.

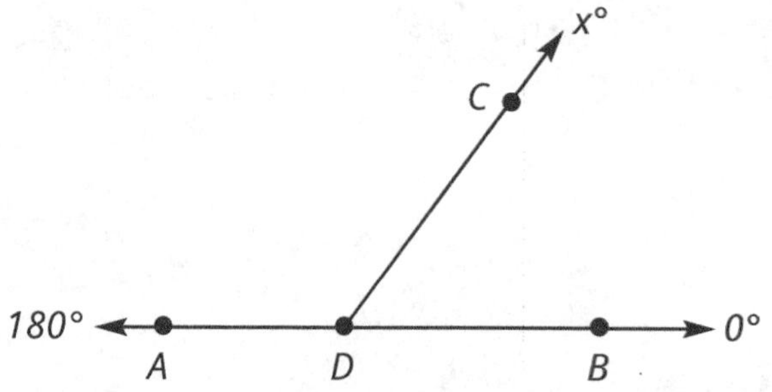

STATEMENT	REASON
1. $\angle ADC$, $\angle CDB$ are adjacent angles. $\overrightarrow{DA}$ is opposite $\overrightarrow{DB}$.	1. Given
2. Pair $\overrightarrow{DB}$ with 0. Pair $\overrightarrow{DA}$ with 180.	2. Protractor Postulate
3. $m\angle ADC = \lvert 180 - x \rvert = 180 - x$ $m\angle CDB = \lvert x - 0 \rvert = x$	3. Protractor Postulate
4. $m\angle ADC + m\angle CDB = (180 - x) + x = 180$	4. Addition property of equality
5. $\angle ADC$, $\angle CDB$ are supplementary.	5. Definition of supplementary angles

THEOREM 3-3
If two lines are perpendicular, then they form right angles.

Given: $l \perp m$

To Prove: $\angle 1$ is rt. $\angle$, $\angle 2$ is rt. $\angle$, $\angle 3$ is rt. $\angle$, $\angle 4$ is rt. $\angle$.

Plan: Show that m $\angle 1 = 90°$ m $\angle 2 = 90°$ by using Theorem 3-2 and properties of algebra.

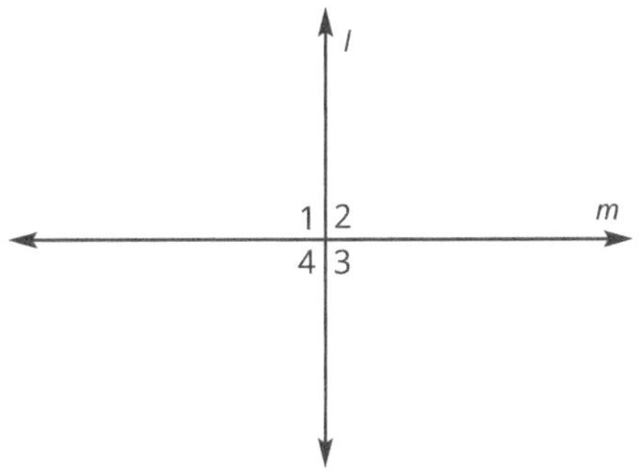

STATEMENT	REASON
1. $l \perp m$	1. Given
2. $\angle 1$, $\angle 2$ are adjacent	2. Definition of adjacent $\angle$'s
3. $\angle 1$, $\angle 2$ are supplementary	3. Exterior sides in opposite rays
4. m $\angle 1$ + m $\angle 2 = 180°$	4. Definition of supplementary $\angle$'s
5. m $\angle 1$ = m $\angle 2$	5. Definition of $\perp$
6. m $\angle 1$ + m $\angle 1 = 180°$	6. Substitution
7. 2m $\angle 1 = 180°$	7. Addition
8. m $\angle 1 = 90°$	8. Division property of equality
9. $\angle 1$ is rt. $\angle$	9. Definition of rt. $\angle$

By a similar method, we can show ∠2, ∠3, and ∠4 are also rt. ∠'s.

THEOREM 3-4

If two adjacent angles have their exterior sides in perpendicular lines, then the angles are complementary.

Given: *l* ⊥ *m*, ∠1, ∠2 are adjacent angles

To Prove: ∠1, ∠2 are complementary

Plan: Use angle addition theorem and Theorem 3-3 to show m ∠1 + m ∠2 = 90°.

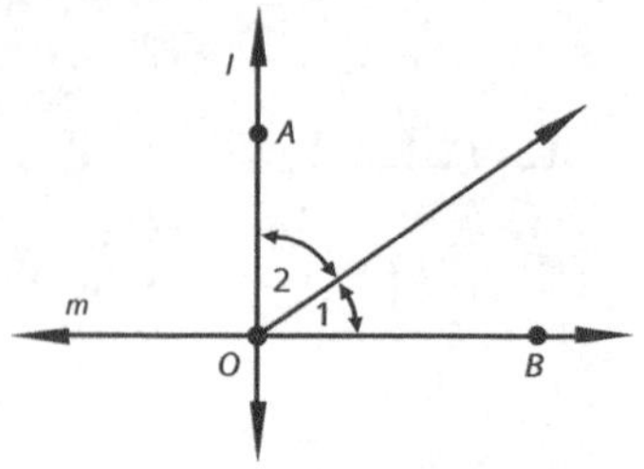

STATEMENT	REASON
1. *l* ⊥ *m*; ∠1, ∠2 adj. ∠'s	1. Given
2. m ∠AOB = 90°	2. ⊥'s form rt. ∠'s
3. m ∠1 + m ∠2 = m ∠AOB	3. Angle addition theorem
4. m ∠1 + m ∠2 = 90°	4. Substitution
5. ∠1, ∠2 are complementary	5. Definition of complementary ∠'s

THEOREM 3-5

If two angles are supplementary to the same angle or to equal angles, then they are equal to each other.

Given: ∠2, ∠3 are supplementary
∠1, ∠3 are supplementary

To Prove: m ∠1 = m ∠2

Plan: Use equation form to express supplementary angles. Then use properties of algebra.

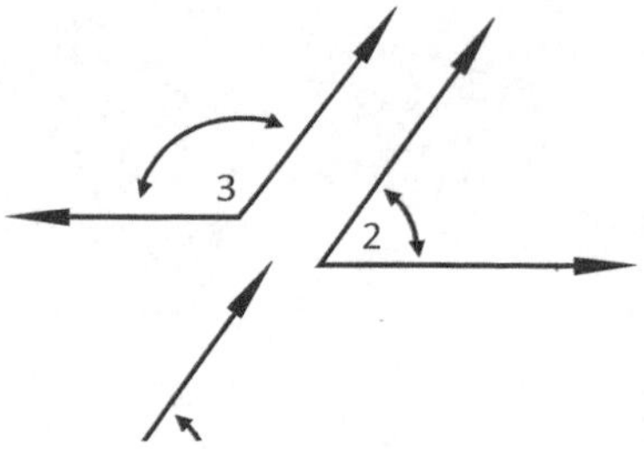

STATEMENT	REASON
1. ∠2 supplement of ∠3 ∠1 supplement of ∠3	1. Given
2. m ∠2 + m ∠3 = 180° m ∠1 + m ∠3 = 180°	2. Definition of supplementary + 's
3. m ∠1 + m ∠3 = m ∠2 + m ∠3	3. Substitution
4. m ∠1 = m ∠2	4. Subtraction property of equality

THEOREM 3-6
If two angles are complementary to the same angle or to equal angles, then they are equal to each other.

Given: $\angle 2$, $\angle 3$ are complementary;
$\angle 1$, $\angle 3$ are complementary

To Prove: $m\angle 1 = m\angle 2$

Plan: Use equation form to express complementary angles.
Then use properties of algebra.

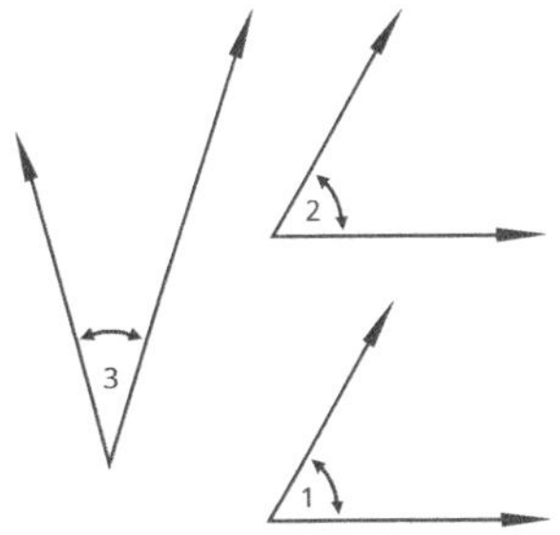

The remainder of the proof is left for you to do. Refer to the proof of Theorem 3-5 if you have trouble.

Complete the proof for Theorem 3-6.

2.5 STATEMENT	REASON
1. ______________________	1. ______________________
2. ______________________	2. ______________________
3. ______________________	3. ______________________
4. ______________________	4. ______________________

THEOREM 3-7

If two lines intersect, the vertical angles formed are equal.

Given: $\overleftrightarrow{AD}$ and $\overleftrightarrow{BC}$ intersect at *O*.

To Prove: m ∠1 = m ∠2
m ∠3 = m ∠4

Plan: Use the fact that several pairs of supplementary angles are formed, and use Theorem 3-5.

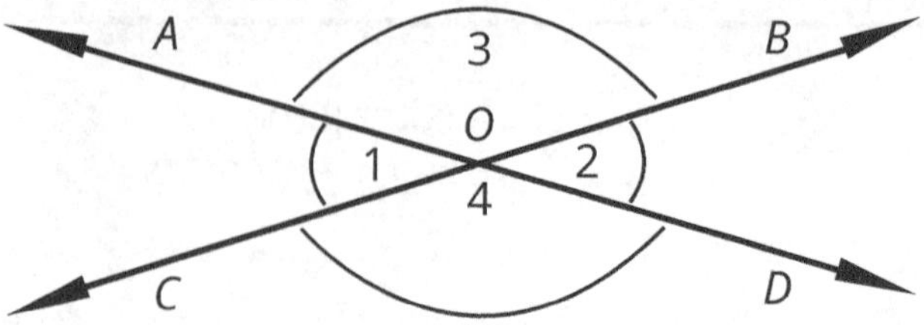

STATEMENT	REASON
1. $\overleftrightarrow{AD}$ and $\overleftrightarrow{BC}$ intersect at *O*	1. Given
2. ∠1, ∠3 are supplementary ∠2, ∠3 are supplementary	2. Exterior sides in opposite rays
3. m ∠1 = m ∠2	3. Two ∠'s supplementary to same ∠ =.
4. ∠1, ∠4 are supplementary	4. Same as Step 2
5. m ∠3 = m ∠4	5. Same as Step 3

Given the following diagram, name these angles.

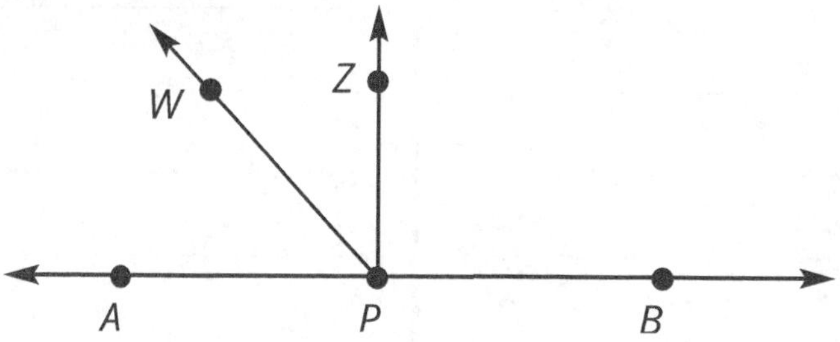

2.6 Two right angles ____________________

2.7 An obtuse angle ____________________

2.8 Two complementary angles ____________________

2.9 A pair of opposite rays ____________________

2.10 Two ∠'s adjacent to ∠*ZPW* ____________________

2.11 Two nonequal supplementary ∠'s ____________________

2.12 Two nonadjacent ∠'s ____________________

2.13 Two equal supplementary ∠'s ____________________

2.14 If m ∠*APW* = 20°, find m ∠*WPZ*. ____________________

Given the following diagram, name these angles.

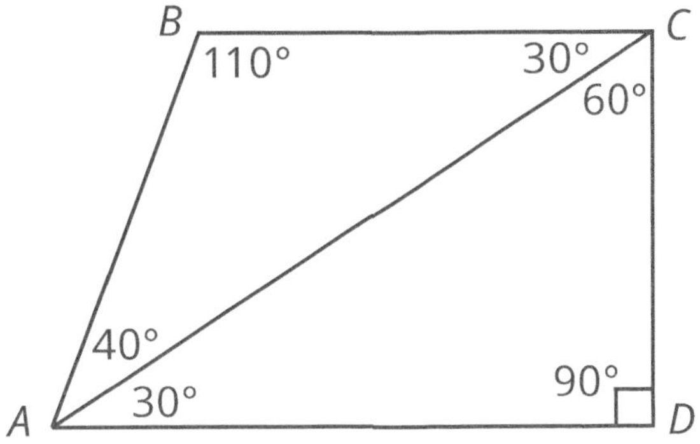

2.15 Two right ∠'s ______________________________

2.16 An obtuse ∠ ______________________________

2.17 Two adjacent complementary ∠'s ______________________________

2.18 An ∠ supplementary to ∠*DAB* ______________________________

2.19 Two segments perpendicular to $\overline{DC}$ ______________________________

2.20 Two nonadjacent complementary ∠'s ______________________________

2.21 An ∠ equal to ∠*DAC* ______________________________

2.22 A supplement to ∠*ABC* ______________________________

2.23 A complement to ∠*CAB* ______________________________

2.24 Are ∠*D* and ∠*B* vertical ∠'s? ______________________________

Find these angle measures.

2.25 If two angles with the same measure are complementary, find the measure of each.

2.26 If two angles are both vertical and supplementary, find the measure of each.

2.27 One angle is three times another. The two angles are complementary. Find the measure of each.

2.28 An angle has a measure of $3x$. How can you express the measure of its complement?

2.29 An angle has a measure of $3x - 10°$ and its complement has measure $2x + 20°$.
Find the measure of each.

2.30 An angle has a measure of $2x + 20°$ and its vertical angle a measure of $5x - 34°$.
Find the measure of each.

Write the reasons for the following proof.

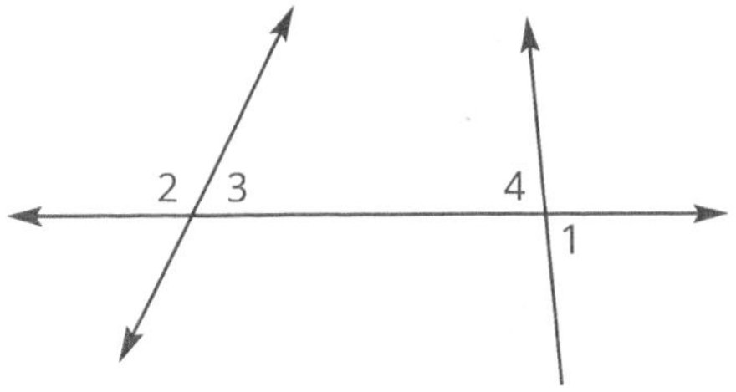

Given: m ∠3 = m ∠4

To Prove: ∠1, ∠2 are supplementary

STATEMENT	REASON
1. m ∠3 = m ∠4	**2.31** ______________
2. ∠2, ∠3 are supplementary	**2.32** ______________
3. m ∠2 + m ∠3 = 180°	**2.33** ______________
4. m ∠2 + m ∠4 = 180°	**2.34** ______________
5. m ∠1 = m ∠4	**2.35** ______________
6. m ∠2 + m ∠1 = 180°	**2.36** ______________
7. ∠1, ∠2 are supplementary	**2.37** ______________

THEOREM 3-8

All right angles are equal.

Given: ∠1, ∠2 are rt. ∠'s

To Prove: m ∠1 = m ∠2

Plan: Use definition of rt. ∠ and substitution

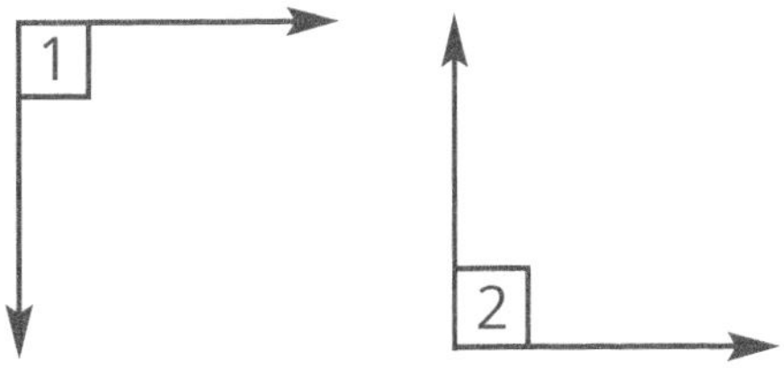

Complete the proof for Theorem 3-8.

2.38

STATEMENT	REASON
1. ______________	1. ______________
2. ______________	2. ______________
3. ______________	3. ______________

Theorem 3-9 is the converse of Theorem 3-3. In a converse, the hypothesis and the conclusion are switched. We must prove the converse since a conditional and its converse are not equivalent statements.

THEOREM 3-9

If two lines meet and form right angles, then the lines are perpendicular.

Given: $\angle 1, \angle 2, \angle 3, \angle 4$ are right $\angle$'s.

To Prove: $l \perp m$

Plan: Show m $\angle 1$ = m $\angle 2$ = m $\angle 3$ = m $\angle 4$ and then use definition of $\perp$ lines.

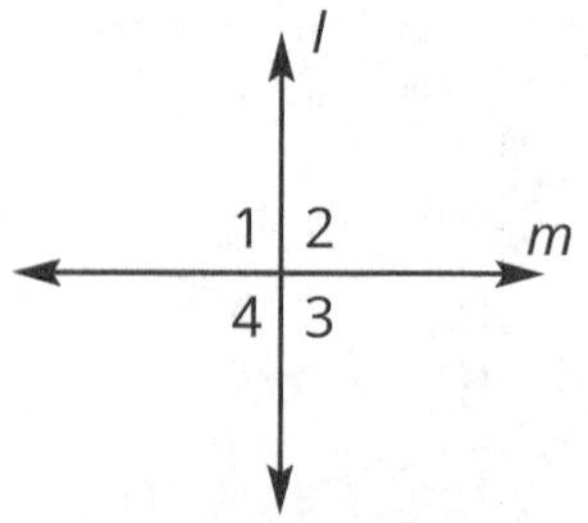

STATEMENT	REASON
1. $\angle 1, \angle 2, \angle 3, \angle 4$ are rt. $\angle$'s	1. Given
2. m $\angle 1$ = m $\angle 2$ = m $\angle 3$ = m $\angle 4$	2. All right angles are equal
3. $l \perp m$	3. Definition of $\perp$ lines

Given the following diagram, complete these items.

$\overleftrightarrow{AD} \perp \overleftrightarrow{BF}$

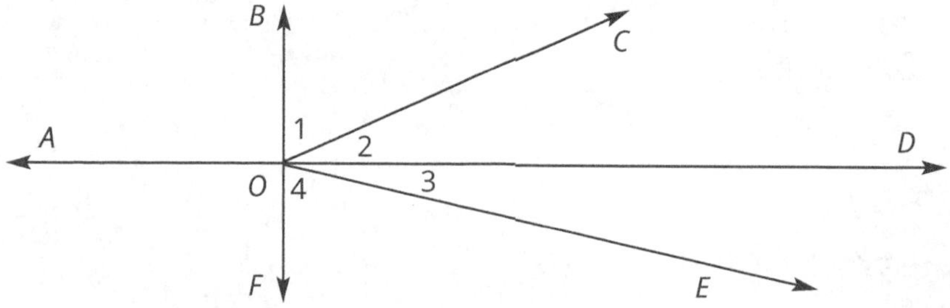

2.39 m $\angle 1$ + m $\angle 2$ = ______________

2.40 If m $\angle 1$ = 60°, then m $\angle 2$ = ______________

2.41 If m $\angle 3$ = 50°, then m $\angle 4$ = ______________

2.42 Are $\overleftrightarrow{OC}$ and $\overleftrightarrow{OE}$ opposite rays? ______________

2.43 Is ∠1 a supplement of ∠*COF*? ______________

2.44 If m ∠*COF* = 150°, then m ∠*BOC* = ______________

2.45 m ∠*AOB* = ______________

2.46 m ∠3 + m ∠4 = ______________

2.47 m ∠1 + m ∠2 + m ∠3 + m ∠4 = ______________

2.48 Name two pairs of complementary angles.

a. ____________________________ b. ____________________________

2.49 If m ∠4 = 20° 15′, then m ∠3 = ____________________________

Write the theorem that supports each conclusion from the diagram.

$\overleftrightarrow{RU} \perp \overleftrightarrow{SW}$

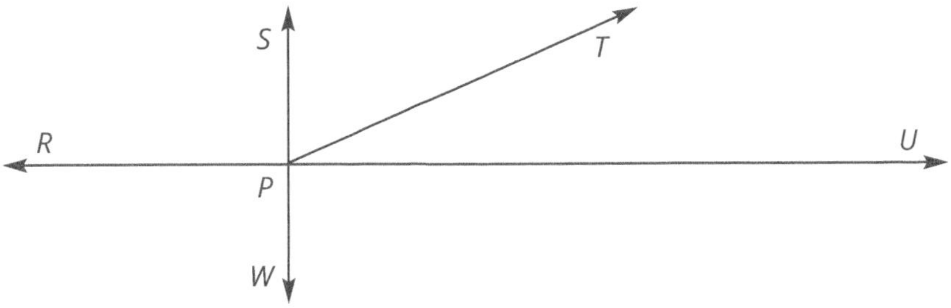

2.50 m ∠*SPU* = m ∠*SPT* + m ∠*TPU*. ____

____

2.51 ∠*RPS* is a right angle. ____

____

2.52 ∠*SPT* and ∠*TPU* are complementary. ____

____

2.53 ∠*RPT* and ∠*TPU* are supplementary. ____

____

Write a reason to support each statement in the following proof.

Given: $\overrightarrow{ST} \perp \overrightarrow{SR}$

To Prove: m $\angle 1 = 90° -$ m $\angle 2$

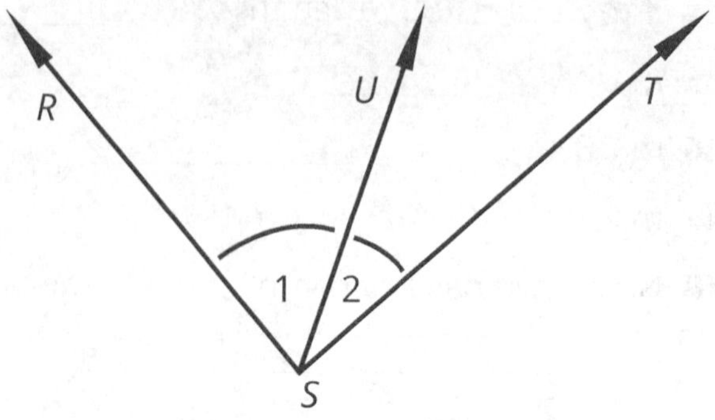

STATEMENT	REASON
1. $\overrightarrow{ST} \perp \overrightarrow{SR}$	**2.54** ________________
2. $\angle RST$ is a rt. $\angle$	**2.55** ________________
3. m $\angle RST = 90°$	**2.56** ________________
4. m $\angle 1$ + m $\angle 2$ = m $\angle RST$	**2.57** ________________
5. m $\angle 1$ + m $\angle 2 = 90°$	**2.58** ________________
6. m $\angle 1 = 90° -$ m $\angle 2$	**2.59** ________________

Review the material in this section in preparation for the Self Test. This Self Test will check your mastery of this particular section as well as your knowledge of the previous section. The items missed on this Self Test will indicate specific areas where restudy is needed for mastery.

SELF TEST 2

Draw the following figures (each figure, 2 points).

2.01 Draw two adjacent angles and label them $\angle AOB$, $\angle BOC$.

2.02 Draw two lines so that the vertical angles formed are supplementary.

Complete the following statements (each answer, 3 points).

2.03 If the exterior sides of adjacent angles are opposite rays, then

____

2.04 If two adjacent angles have their exterior sides in perpendicular lines, then

____

2.05 If two angles are supplementary to the same angles, then

____

2.06 If two lines are perpendicular, then they form

____

2.07 If two lines intersect, then the vertical $\angle$'s formed are

____

2.08 All right angles are ______________________________ .

2.09 If two lines meet and form right angles, then ____ .

2.010 Complementary $\angle$'s have a sum of ________________ .

2.011 Supplementary $\angle$'s have a sum of ________________ .

Find the following angle measures (each answer, 3 points).

2.012 $\angle A$ and $\angle B$ are supplementary. m $\angle A = 37° \, 15'$. Find m $\angle B$.

2.013 $\angle C$ and $\angle D$ are vertical $\angle$'s. m $\angle C = 63° \, 15' \, 47''$. Find m $\angle D$.

2.014 $\angle ABC$, $\angle CBD$ are adjacent $\angle$'s. $\overrightarrow{BA} \perp \overrightarrow{BD}$. m $\angle ABC = 45°$. Find m $\angle CBD$.

2.015 $\angle ABC$, $\angle CBD$ are adjacent $\angle$'s. $\overrightarrow{BA}$ is opposite $\overrightarrow{BD}$. m $\angle ABC = 45°$. Find m $\angle CBD$

2.016 $\angle BOA$, $\angle COD$ are vertical angles. If m $\angle BOA = 30°$, find m $\angle BOC$.

Complete the following proof (each answer, 4 points).

Given: m $\angle CBD$ = m $\angle DBE$

To Prove: m $\angle ABC$ + m $\angle DBE$ = 180°

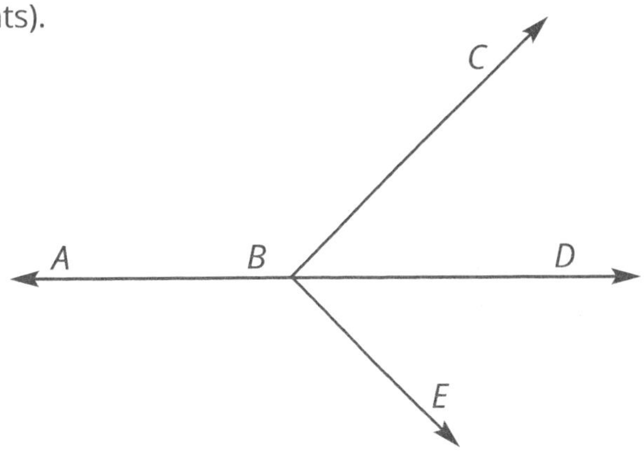

STATEMENT	REASON
1. m $\angle CBD$ = m $\angle DBE$	**2.017** ______________________
2. $\angle ABC$, $\angle CBD$ are supplementary	**2.018** ______________________
3. m $\angle ABC$ + m $\angle CBD$ = 180°	**2.019** ______________________
4. m $\angle ABC$ + m $\angle DBE$ = 180°	**2.020** ______________________

50/62 **SCORE** ____________ **TEACHER** ____________ ____________
initials date

3. PARALLELS

You need only to look around you in any room to see the many examples of parallel lines and planes. When parallel lines are crossed with another line, special angles are formed. Basic properties of parallels, the special angles they form, and several theorems and postulates will be studied in this section.

Section Objectives

Review these objectives. When you have completed this section, you should be able to:

6. Define terms related to parallels.
7. Prove theorems about parallels and related angles.

BASIC PROPERTIES

The figure, a rectangular solid, shows line segments in three possible positions:

1. $\overline{AB}$ and $\overline{AD}$ intersect in point A.
2. $\overline{AB}$ and $\overline{DC}$ are in the same plane but do not intersect.
3. $\overline{AB}$ and $\overline{EF}$ are in different planes and do not intersect.

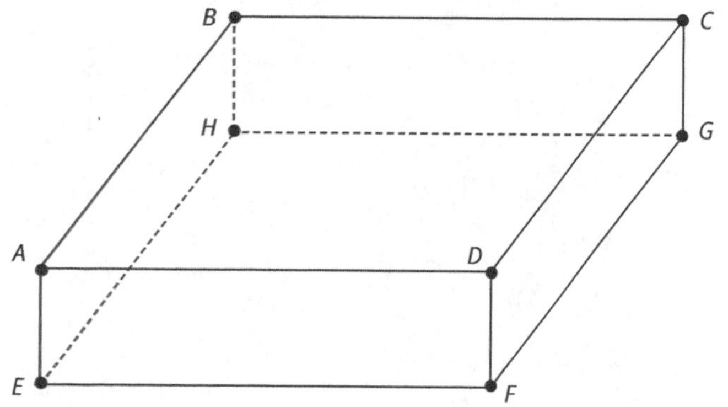

> **DEFINITION**
> **Parallel lines** ($\parallel$ lines): lines that are in the same plane and have no points in common.

Many pairs of parallel segments are in this figure. $\overline{AB} \parallel \overline{DC}$, $\overline{DC} \parallel \overline{FG}$, $\overline{FG} \parallel \overline{EH}$, $\overline{EH} \parallel \overline{AB}$, $\overline{EF} \parallel \overline{AD}$, $\overline{AD} \parallel \overline{BC}$, $\overline{BC} \parallel \overline{HG}$, $\overline{HG} \parallel \overline{EF}$, $\overline{AE} \parallel \overline{DF}$, $\overline{DF} \parallel \overline{CG}$, $\overline{CG} \parallel \overline{BH}$, and $\overline{BH} \parallel \overline{AE}$.

Do you think you can name more? The figure has eighteen pairs altogether. We have listed twelve. See if you can find the other six pairs of parallel segments.

> **DEFINITION**
> **Skew lines:** two lines that do not lie in the same plane.

Many pairs of skew segments are in the figure. $\overline{AB}$ and $\overline{DF}$, $\overline{AB}$ and $\overline{CG}$, $\overline{AB}$ and $\overline{EF}$, $\overline{AB}$ and $\overline{HG}$, $\overline{CD}$ and $\overline{BH}$, $\overline{CD}$ and $\overline{AE}$, $\overline{CD}$ and $\overline{HG}$, and $\overline{CD}$ and $\overline{EF}$ are a few of them. See if you can name some more skew segments. Remember that they are not in the same plane.

A line and a plane are parallel if they have no point in common.

Models:

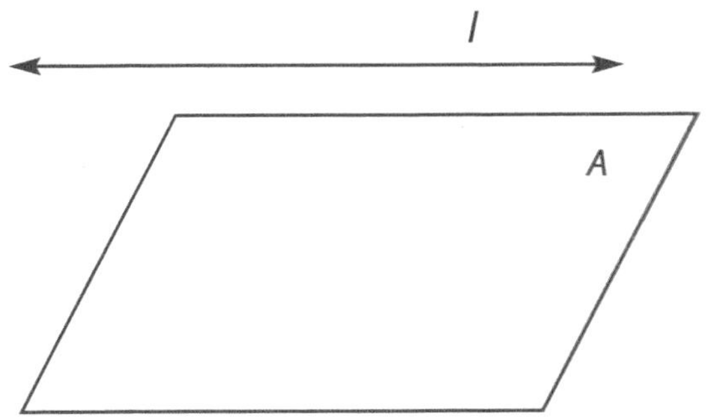

l || *A*

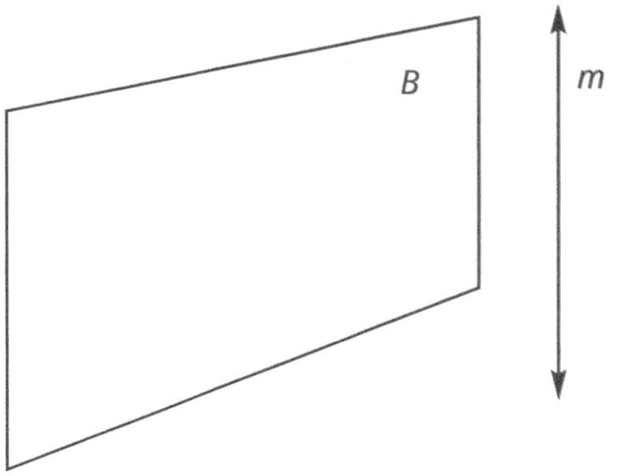

m || *B*

DEFINITION

Parallel planes: planes that have no point in common.

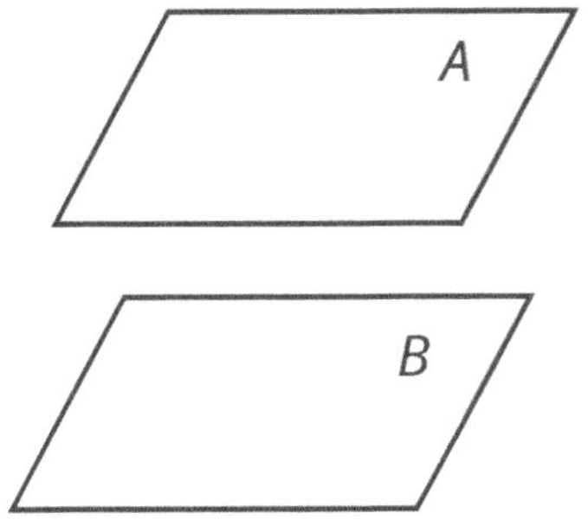

Plane *A* || Plane *B*

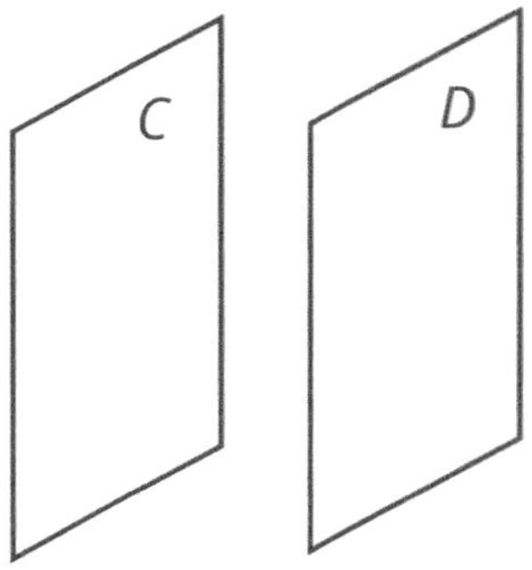

Plane *C* || Plane *D*

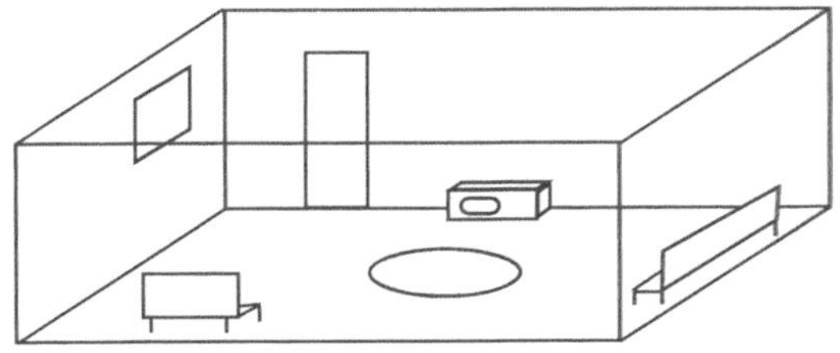

The ceiling and floor of some rooms are a model of parallel planes. So are opposite walls of a room.

The front and back cover of a book represent parallel planes.

THEOREM 3-10
If two parallel planes are cut by a third plane, then the lines of intersection are parallel.

Given: plane *A* | | plane *B*;
plane *A* and *B* cut by plane *C*
in *l* and *m*

To Prove: *l* | | *m*

Plan: Use definition of | | lines.

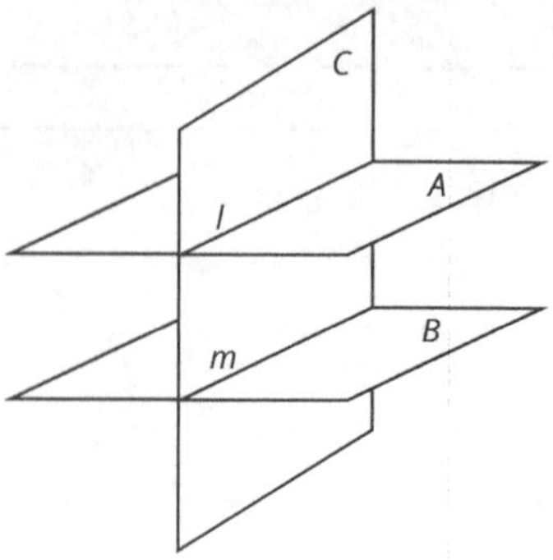

STATEMENT	REASON
1. *l* and *m* are in same plane	1. Given in plane *C*
2. *l* lies in plane *A* *m* lies in plane *B*	2. Intersection of two planes is a line.
3. Plane *A*, plane *B* have no point in common	3. Definition of		planes
4. *l*, *m* have no point in common	4. *l*, *m* are part of planes *A* and *B*.
5. *l*		*m*	5. Definition of		lines: in same plane and no point in common.

For each statement, write *always, sometimes* or *never* true.

3.1 ____________ Skew lines are parallel.

3.2 ____________ A line on the wall and a line on the floor are skew.

3.3 ____________ Two lines that do not intersect are skew.

3.4 ____________ Two planes each parallel to a third plane are parallel to each other.

3.5 ____________ Two lines parallel to a third line are parallel to each other.

3.6 ____________ Two lines parallel to the same plane are parallel to each other.

3.7 ____________ If two planes are parallel, a line in one plane is parallel to a line in the other plane.

3.8 ____________ Two lines skew to the same line are skew to each other.

3.9 ____________ A line that intersects one of two parallel lines intersects the other also.

3.10 ____________ Through a point not in a plane are an infinite number of lines parallel to the plane.

TRANSVERSAL AND SPECIAL ANGLES

This section will present the special angles that are formed when parallel lines are crossed by another line.

DEFINITION

Transversal: A line that intersects two or more coplanar lines in different points.

Models:

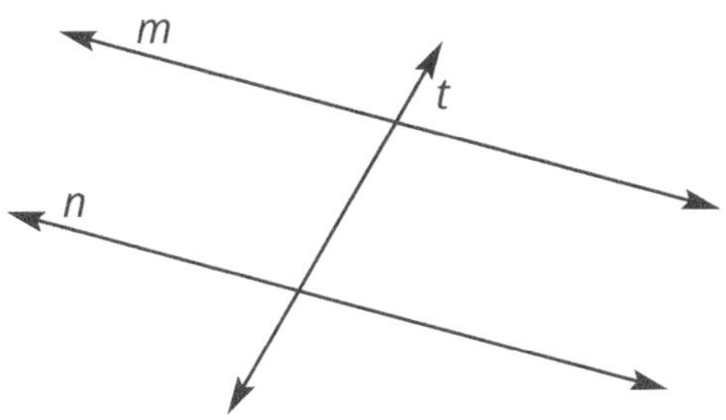

t is the transversal of *m* and *n*.

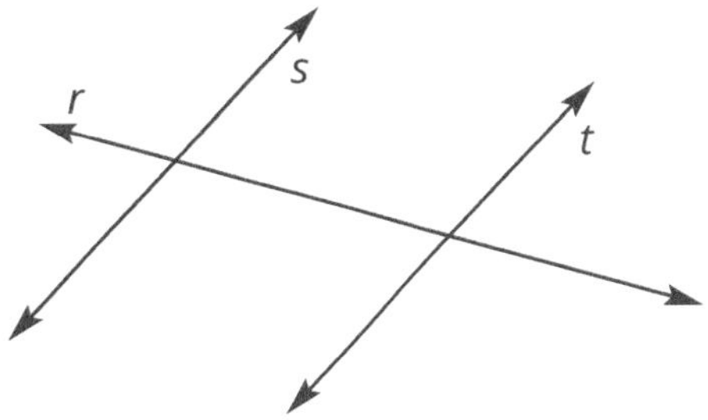

r is the transversal of *s* and *t*.

When two lines are cut by a transversal, eight angles are formed.

These angles have some special names:

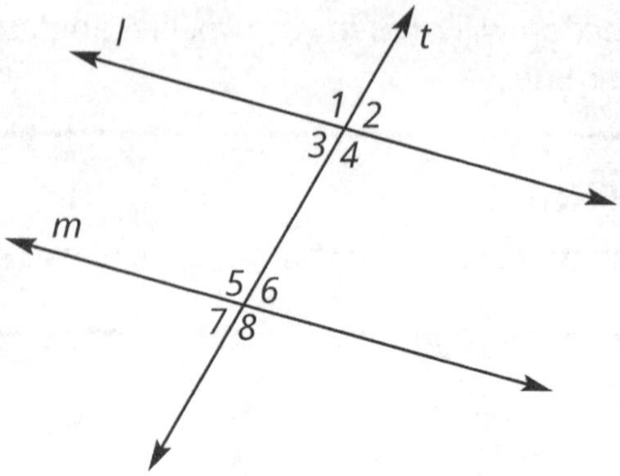

∠1, ∠2, ∠7, ∠8 are called *exterior* ∠'s. They are on the outside of the two lines.

∠3, ∠4, ∠5, ∠6 are called *interior* ∠'s. They are on the inside of the two lines.

∠3 and ∠6, ∠4 and ∠5 are pairs of alternate interior ∠'s. They are interior ∠'s on opposite sides of the transversal with different vertices.

∠1 and ∠8, ∠2 and ∠7 are pairs of alternate exterior ∠'s. They are exterior angles on opposite sides of the transversal with different vertices.

∠1 and ∠5, ∠2 and ∠6, ∠3 and ∠7, and ∠4 and ∠8 are called *corresponding* ∠'s. They are in corresponding positions. ∠1 and ∠5 are to the left of the transversal and above the | | lines. ∠4 and ∠8 are to the right of the transversal and below the | | lines. The other pairs of corresponding ∠'s have similar positions.

When the two lines that are cut by a transversal are parallel, certain pairs of angles appear to be the same size. The following postulates and theorems deal with this idea.

POSTULATE 8

P8: If two parallel lines are cut by a transversal, then the corresponding angles have equal measure.

Model:

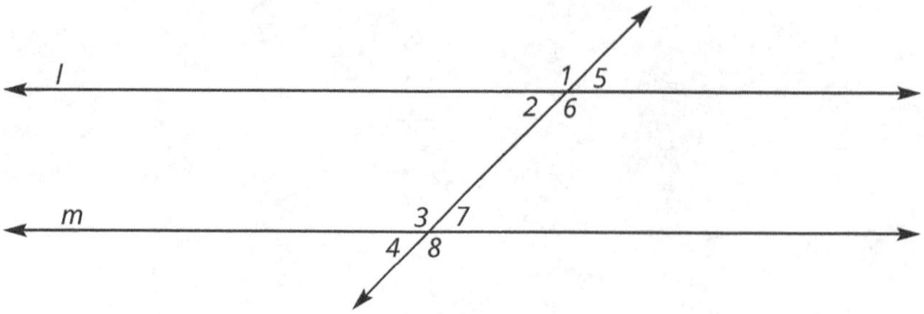

l | | *m*

P8 tells us that the following pairs of angles have the same measure:

m ∠1 = m ∠3; m ∠5 = m ∠7; m ∠2 = m ∠4; m ∠6 = m ∠8

THEOREM 3-11

If a transversal is perpendicular to one of two parallel lines, then it is perpendicular to the other one also.

Given: $l \parallel m$
$t \perp l$

To Prove: $t \perp m$

Plan: Use P8 and theorem about right ∠'s forming perpendiculars.

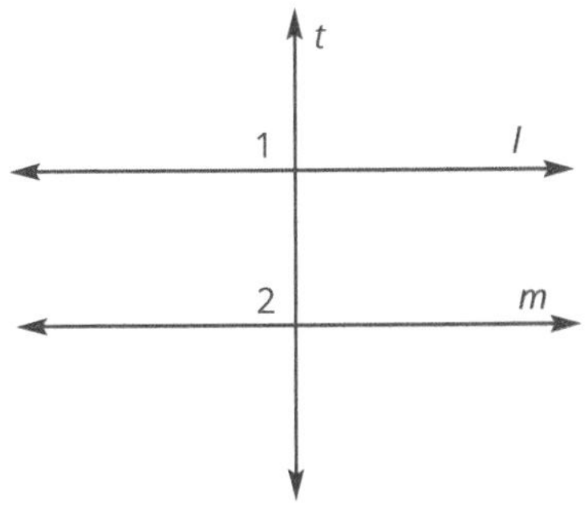

STATEMENT	REASON
1. $l \parallel m$, $t \perp l$	1. Given
2. ∠1 is a rt. ∠	2. ⊥'s form rt. ∠'s.
3. m ∠1 = 90°	3. Definition of rt. ∠
4. m ∠1 = m ∠2	4. Corresponding ∠'s are =.
5. m ∠2 = 90°	5. Substitution
6. ∠2 is a rt. ∠	6. Definition of rt. ∠
7. $t \perp m$	7. If ∠'s formed are rt. ∠'s, then lines are ⊥.

THEOREM 3-12
If two parallel lines are cut by a transversal, then the alternate interior angles are equal.

Given: $l \parallel m$

To Prove: m ∠1 = m ∠2

Plan: m ∠1 = m ∠3, m ∠2 = m ∠3

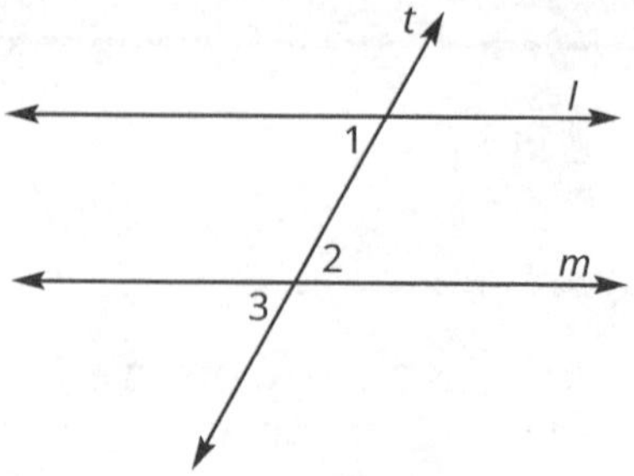

STATEMENT	REASON
1. $l \parallel m$	1. Given
2. m ∠1 = m ∠3	2. If lines ||, then corresponding ∠'s =.
3. m ∠2 = m ∠3	3. Vertical ∠'s are equal.
4. m ∠1 = m ∠2	4. Substitution

THEOREM 3-13
If two parallel lines are cut by a transversal, then the alternate exterior angles are equal.

Given: $l \parallel m$

To Prove: m ∠1 = m ∠2

Plan: Same plan as Theorem 3-12

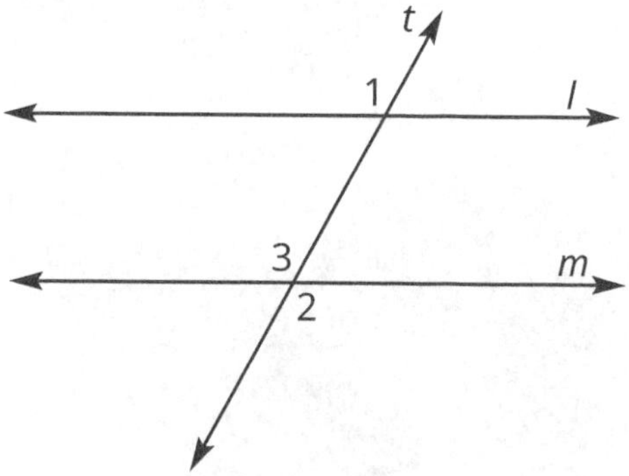

Complete the proof for Theorem 3-13.

3.11

STATEMENT	REASON
1. ______________	1. ______________
2. ______________	2. ______________
3. ______________	3. ______________
4. ______________	4. ______________

Given *l* || *m* and m ∠1 = 60°, find the measures of the other angles.

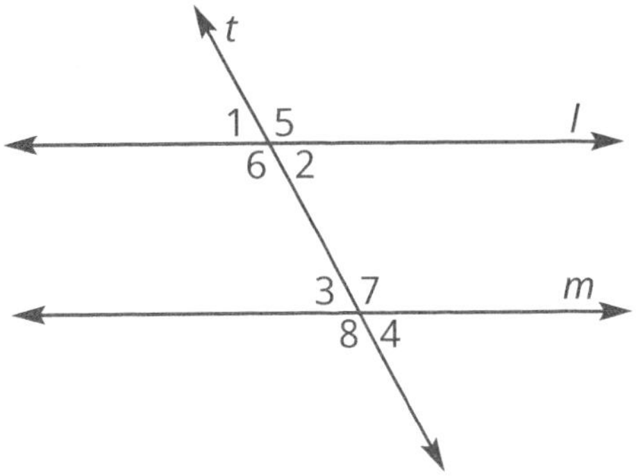

3.12 m ∠2 = ________________

3.13 m ∠3 = ________________

3.14 m ∠4 = ________________

3.15 m ∠5 = ________________

3.16 m ∠6 = ________________

3.17 m ∠7 = ________________

3.18 m ∠8 = ________________

3.19 Name two pairs of alternate interior angles.

a. ________________ b. ________________

3.20 Name two pairs of alternate exterior angles.

a. ________________ b. ________________

Complete the following proofs.

3.21

Given: *a* || *b*, m ∠2 = m ∠3

To Prove: m ∠1 = m∠3

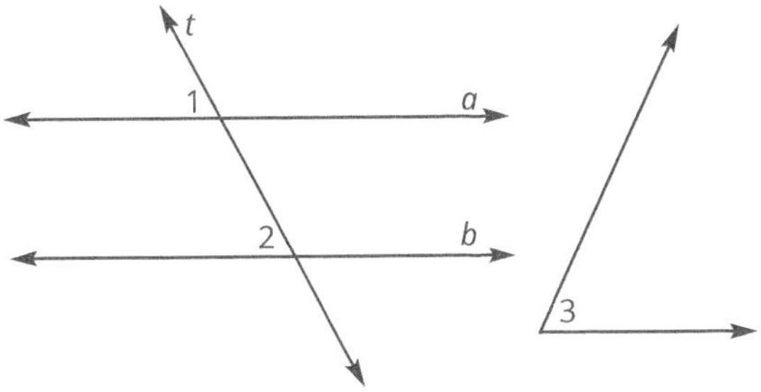

STATEMENT	REASON
1. ________________	1. ________________
2. ________________	2. ________________
3. ________________	3. ________________

3.22

Given: $c \parallel d$, $m\angle 4 = m\angle 5$

To Prove: $m\angle 7 = m\angle 8$

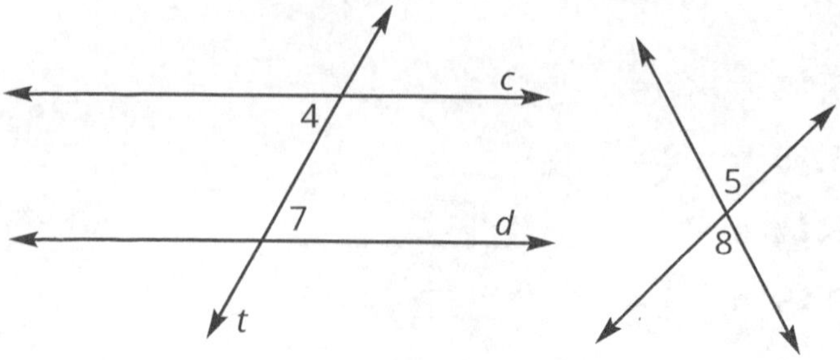

STATEMENT	REASON
1. ______	1. ______
2. ______	2. ______
3. ______	3. ______
4. ______	4. ______

3.23

Given: $a \parallel b$, $c \parallel d$

To Prove: $m\angle 1 = m\angle 16$

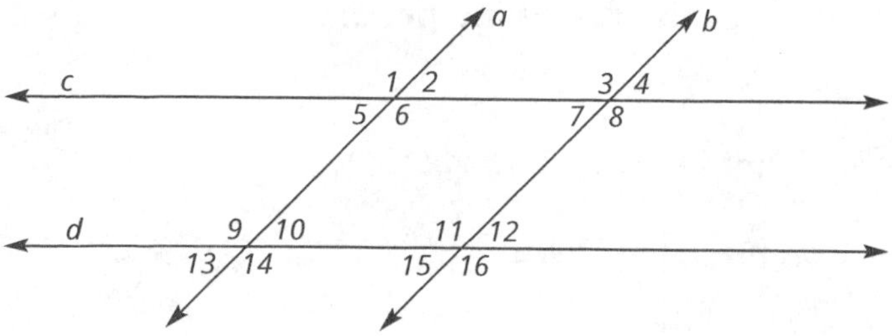

STATEMENT	REASON
1. ______	1. ______
2. ______	2. ______
3. ______	3. ______
4. ______	4. ______
5. ______	5. ______

3.24

Given: *s* || *t*

To Prove: ∠1, ∠7 are supplementary

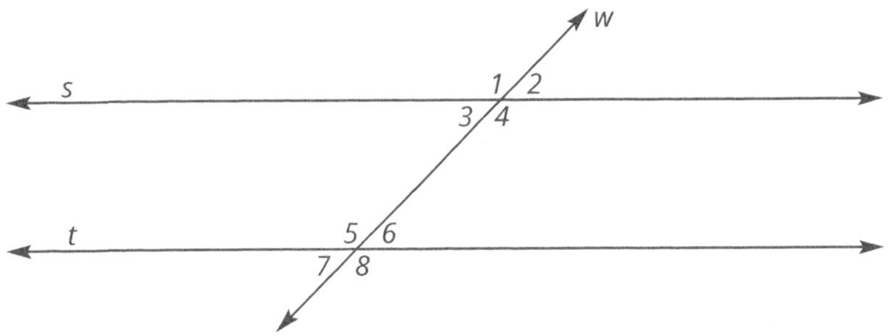

STATEMENT	REASON
1. ______	1. ______
2. ______	2. ______
3. ______	3. ______
4. ______	4. ______
5. ______	5. ______
6. ______	6. ______

3.25

Given: *s* || *t*

To Prove: ∠3, ∠5 are supplementary

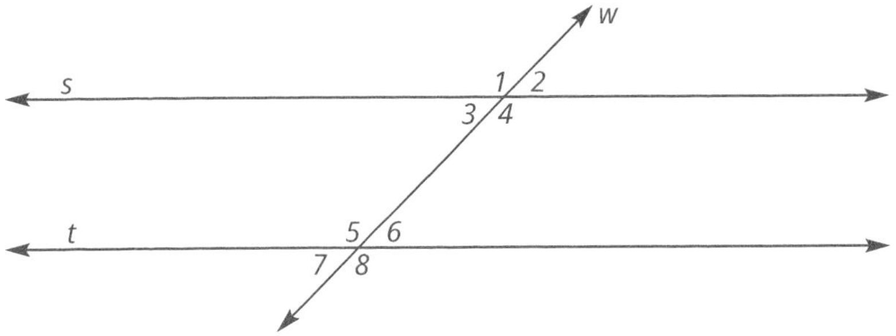

STATEMENT	REASON
1. ______	1. ______
2. ______	2. ______
3. ______	3. ______
4. ______	4. ______
5. ______	5. ______
6. ______	6. ______

In the geometry we are learning, Euclidean geometry, exactly one parallel to a line exists through an outside point. Some geometries, called non-Euclidian, have postulates that lead to no parallels or more than one parallel to the line.

P10 is the converse of P8. Using it is another way to prove lines parallel. The following theorems are converses of earlier theorems about parallel lines.

POSTULATE 9

Through a point not on the line, one and only one line can be drawn parallel to the line.

POSTULATE 10

If two lines are cut by a transversal so that corresponding angles are equal, then the lines are parallel.

THEOREM 3-14

In a plane, if two lines are perpendicular to a third line, then they are parallel to each other.

Given: $l \perp t, m \perp t$

To Prove: $l \parallel m$

Plan: Use P10

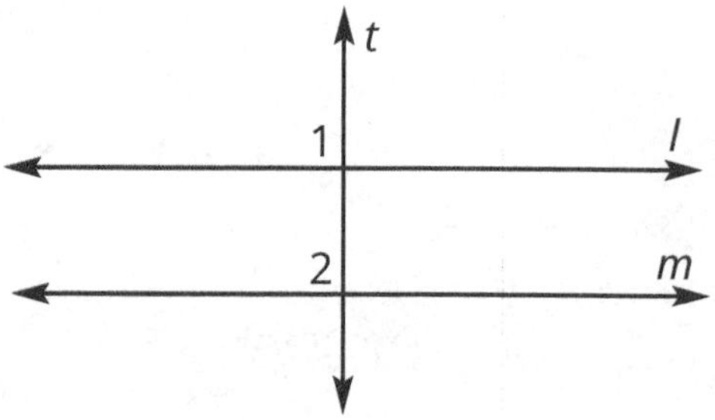

STATEMENT	REASON
1. $l \perp t, m \perp t$	1. Given
2. $\angle 1$ is rt. $\angle$, $\angle 2$ is rt. $\angle$	2. $\perp$'s form rt. $\angle$'s.
3. m $\angle 1$ = m $\angle 2$	3. All rt. $\angle$'s are =.
4. $l \parallel m$	4. If corresponding $\angle$'s =, then lines are $\parallel$.

THEOREM 3-15

If two lines are cut by a transversal so that alternate interior angles are equal, then the lines are parallel.

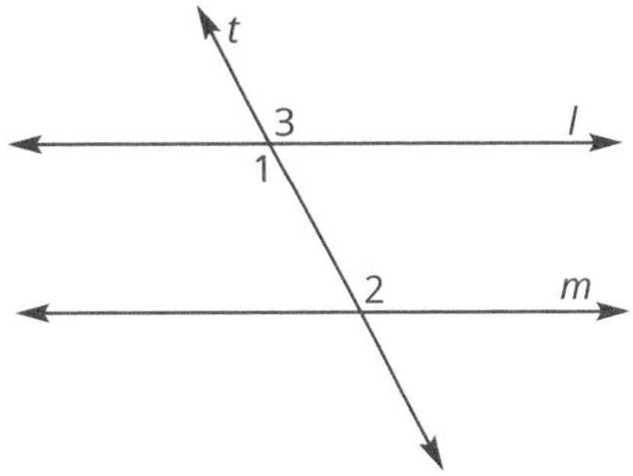

Given: m ∠1 = m ∠2

To Prove: *l* || *m*

Plan: Use P10 by showing m ∠2 = m ∠3

STATEMENT	REASON
1. m ∠1 = m ∠2	1. Given
2. m ∠1 = m ∠3	2. Vertical ∠'s are =.
3. m ∠2 = m ∠3	3 Substitution
4. *l* || *m*	4. If corresponding ∠'s =, then lines are ||.

THEOREM 3-16

If two lines are cut by a transversal so that alternate exterior angles are equal, then the lines are parallel.

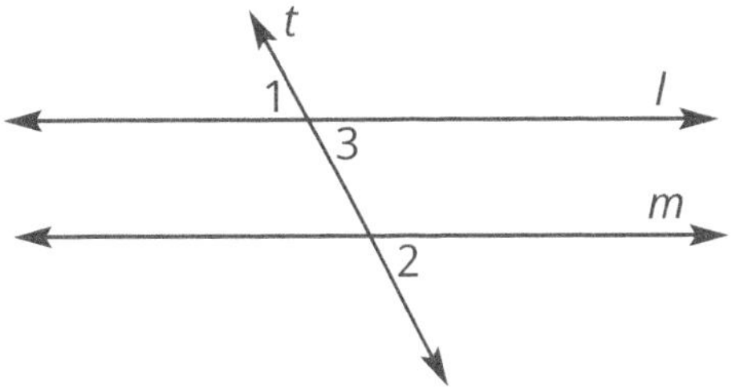

Given: m ∠1 = m ∠2

To Prove: *l* || *m*

Plan: Same as Theorem 3-15

3.26

STATEMENT	REASON
1. ______________________	1. ______________________
2. ______________________	2. ______________________
3. ______________________	3. ______________________
4. ______________________	4. ______________________

Write the converse of these statements. Is the original statement true or false? Is the converse true or false? Write true or false for each statement and its converse.

3.27 ____________ If each of two angles has a measure of 28°, then the two angles have equal measure.

Converse: ____

____

3.28 ____________ If two angles are both obtuse, then the two angles are equal.

Converse: ____

____

3.29 ____________ If $3 - 2x = 13$, then $x = -5$.

Converse:____

____

3.30 ____________ If $x^2 = 25$, then $x = 5$.

Converse:____

____

3.31 ____________ If two $\angle$'s are supplementary, they are not equal.

Converse:____

____

Name the segments, if any, that can be deduced to be parallel in the figures shown.

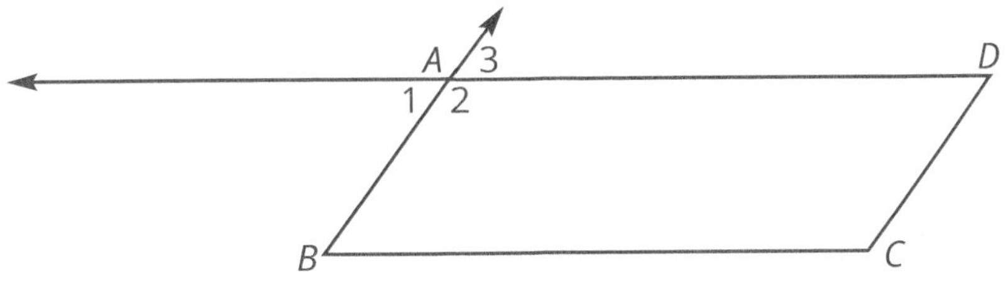

3.32 When m ∠3 = m ∠B ____________________

3.33 When m ∠1 = m ∠B ____________________

3.34 When m ∠1 = m ∠D ____________________

3.35 When m ∠2 = m ∠C ____________________

3.36 When m ∠2 = m ∠6 ____________________

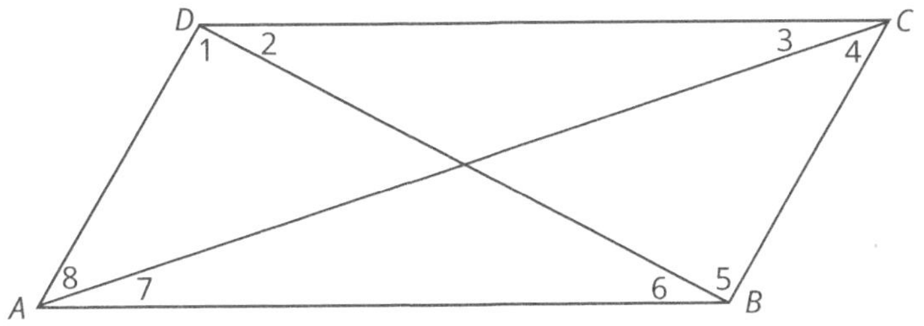

3.37 When m ∠1 = m ∠6 ____________________

3.38 When m ∠1 = m ∠5 ____________________

3.39 When m ∠8 = m ∠4 ____________________

3.40 When m ∠7 = m ∠8 ____________________

3.41 When m ∠7 = m ∠4 ____________________

3.42 When m ∠7 = m ∠1 ____________________

3.43 When m ∠7 = m ∠3 ____________________

3.44 When m ∠2 = m ∠3 ____________________

Complete the following proofs.

3.45

Given: m ∠2 = 122°
m ∠3 = 58°

To Prove: *l* || *m*

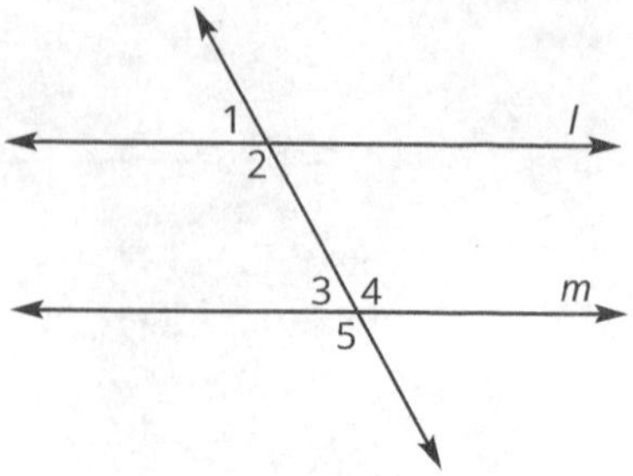

STATEMENT	REASON
1. ______	1. ______
2. ______	2. ______
3. ______	3. ______
4. ______	4. ______
5. ______	5. ______
6. ______	6. ______
7. ______	7. ______

3.46

Given: m ∠6 = m ∠8
b || *c*

To Prove: *a* || *b*

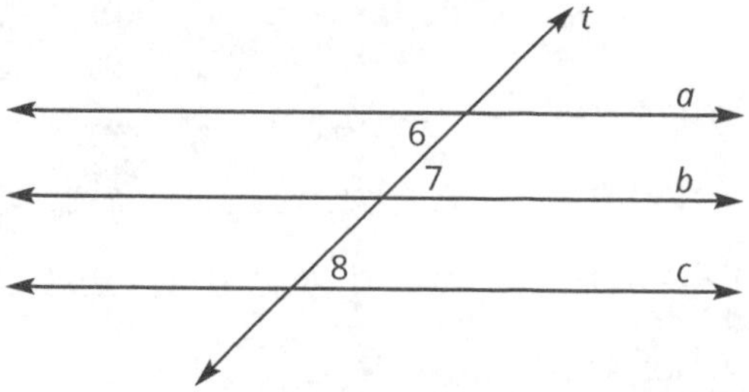

STATEMENT	REASON
1. ______	1. ______
2. ______	2. ______
3. ______	3. ______
4. ______	4. ______

3.47

Given: $j \parallel k$
$m\angle 1 = m\angle 3$

To Prove: $l \parallel m$

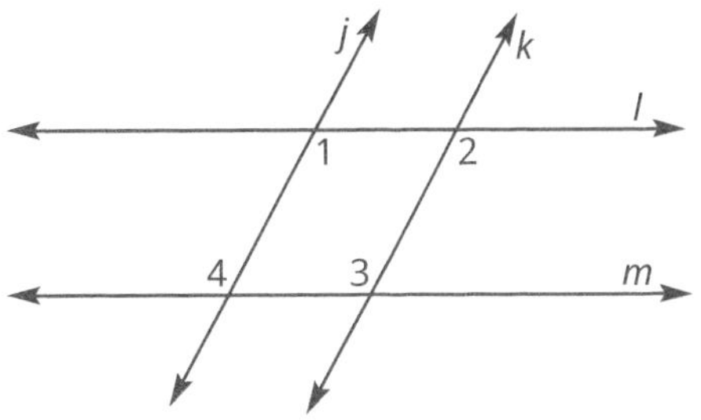

STATEMENT	REASON
1. ________	1. ________
2. ________	2. ________
3. ________	3. ________
4. ________	4. ________

3.48

Given: $\angle A$, $\angle B$, $\angle C$, $\angle D$ are rt. $\angle$'s

To Prove: $\overline{AD} \parallel \overline{BC}$ $\quad \overline{AB} \parallel \overline{DC}$

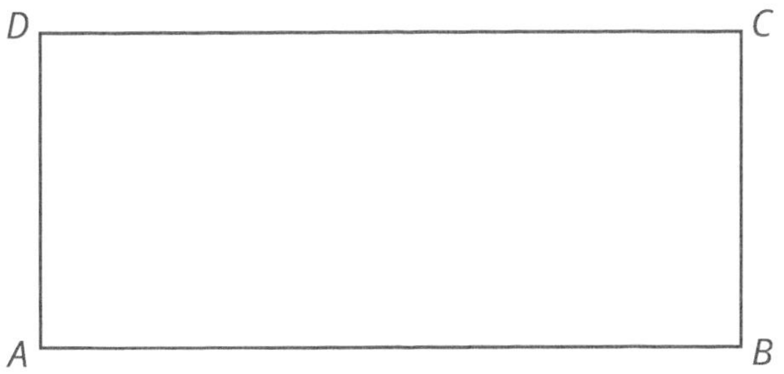

STATEMENT	REASON
1. ________	1. ________
2. ________	2. ________
3. ________	3. ________

3.49

Given: m ∠1 + m ∠5 = 180°
m ∠1 + m ∠4 = 180°

To Prove: $\overrightarrow{YZ} \parallel \overrightarrow{UV}$

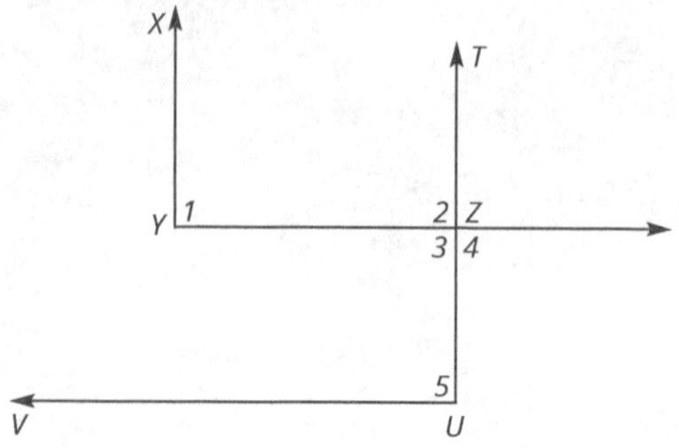

STATEMENT	REASON
1. ______	1. ______
2. ______	2. ______
3. ______	3. ______
4. ______	4. ______

3.50 Prove: If two lines are cut by a transversal so that interior angles on the same side of the transversal are supplementary, the lines are parallel.

Given: ∠1, ∠2 are supplementary ∠'s

To Prove: $l \parallel m$

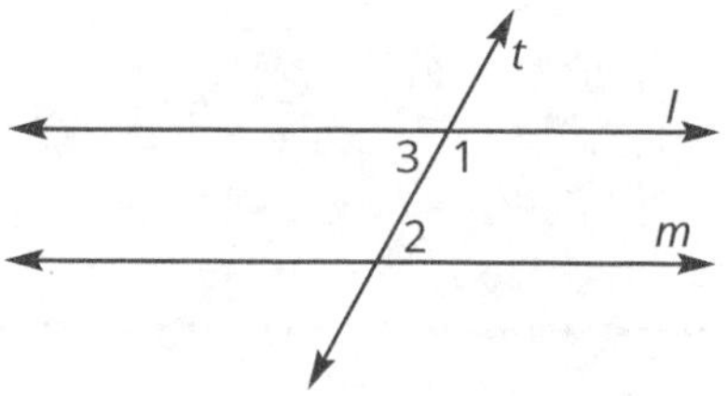

STATEMENT	REASON
1. ______	1. ______
2. ______	2. ______
3. ______	3. ______
4. ______	4. ______
5. ______	5. ______
6. ______	6. ______
7. ______	7. ______

Review the material in this section in preparation for the Self Test. This Self Test will check your mastery of this particular section as well as your knowledge of the previous sections.

SELF TEST 3

Write the correct answers on the lines (each answer, 3 points).

3.01 Parallel lines lie in the same plane and have ______________________ .

3.02 Skew lines do not lie in the same ______________ .

3.03 If two parallel planes are cut by a third plane, the lines of intersection are

______________________ .

3.04 If two parallel lines are cut by a transversal, the corresponding angles are

______________________ .

3.05 Through a point not on the line, exactly one line can be drawn parallel to the

______________________ .

3.06 If corresponding angles are equal, the lines are ______________________ .

3.07 In a plane, if two lines are perpendicular to the same line, the two lines are

______________________ .

3.08 If two adjacent angles have their exterior sides in perpendicular lines, the two angles are

______________________ .

3.09 If two adjacent angles have their exterior sides in opposite rays, then the two angles are ______________________ .

3.010 If an angle has a measure of 45° 12′ 10″, the measure of its complement is

______________________ .

For each figure in 3.011 through 3.015, can you conclude that l | | m?
Write *yes* **or** *no* (each answer, 2 points).

3.011 __________

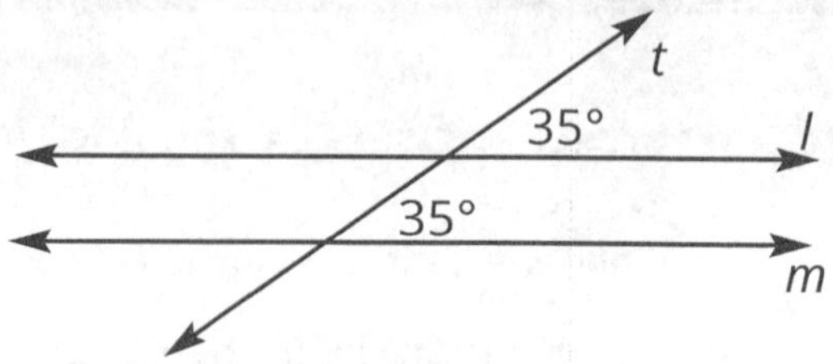

3.012 __________

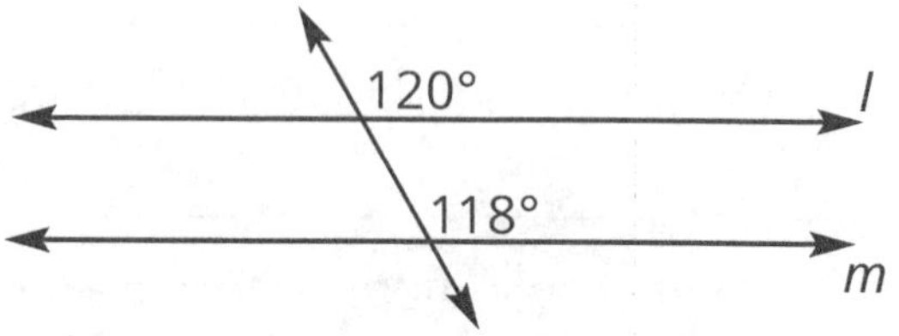

3.013 __________

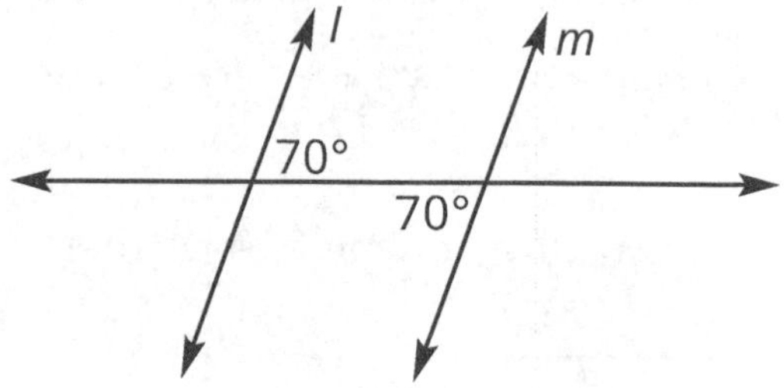

3.014 __________

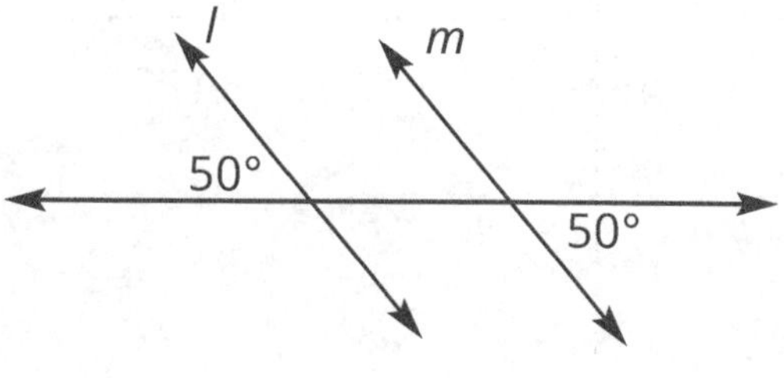

3.015 __________

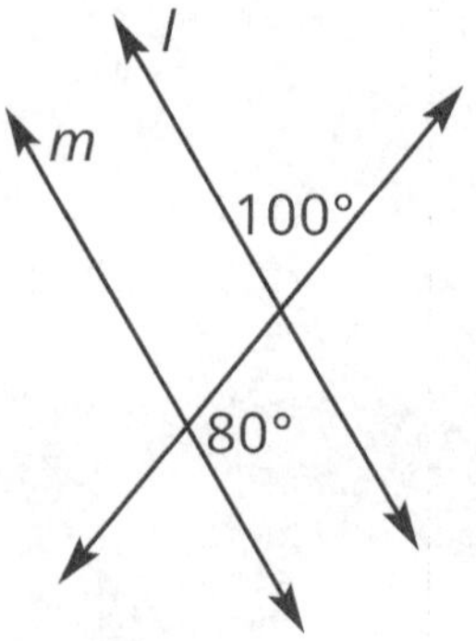

Complete the following proofs (each answer, 4 points).

Given: $l \parallel m$

To Prove: ∠1, ∠2 are supplementary

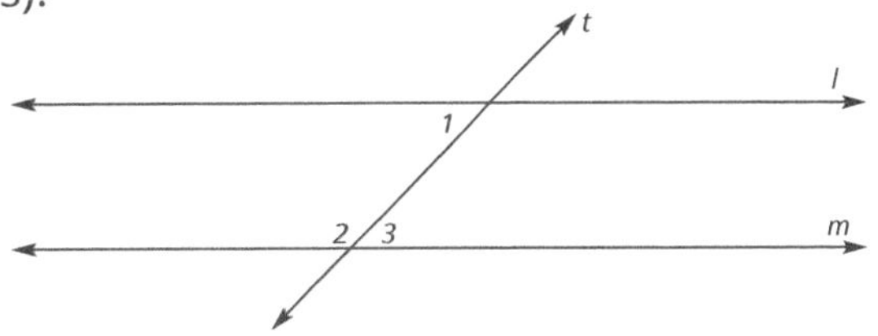

STATEMENT	REASON
3.016 ______________________	Given
m ∠1 = m ∠3	**3.017** ______________________
3.018 ______________________	If adjacent ∠'s have exterior sides in opposite rays, ∠'s are supplementary.
m ∠2 + m ∠3 = 180°	**3.019** ______________________
3.020 ______________________	Substitution
∠1, ∠2 are supplementary	**3.021** ______________________

Given: m ∠1 = m ∠3
m ∠2 = m ∠3

To Prove: $l \parallel m$

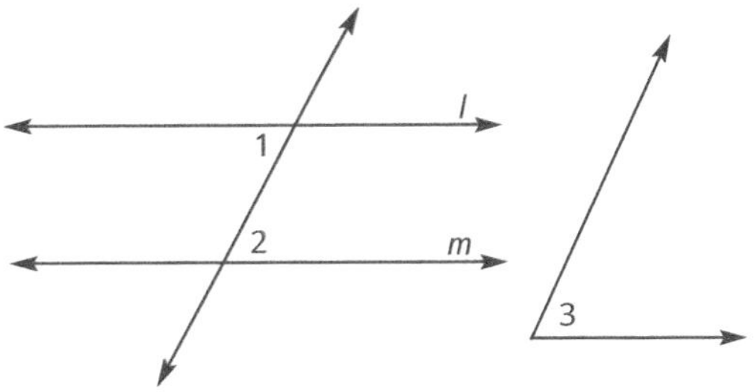

STATEMENT	REASON
m ∠1 = m ∠3; m ∠2 = m ∠3	**3.022** ______________________
m ∠1 = m ∠2	**3.023** ______________________
∠1, ∠2 are alternate interior angles	**3.024** ______________________
3.025 ______________________	If alternate interior ∠'s =, then lines ||.

64/80 **SCORE** __________ **TEACHER** __________ __________
initials date

4. APPLYING PARALLELS TO POLYGONS

We shall now use some of the statements about parallels to prove some useful theorems concerning triangles and other polygons.

Section Objectives

Review these objectives. When you have completed this section, you should be able to:

8. Classify triangles by their sides and by their angles.
9. Prove theorems about triangles and their related angles.

TRIANGLES

Triangles are some of the simplest geometric figures. Understanding and being able to prove theorems about triangles will help you to work with more complex polygons.

The three points that are used are called the *vertices* of the triangle. *A*, *B*, and *C* are the vertices of the model triangle.

The three segments that are used are called the *sides* of the triangle. $\overline{AB}$, $\overline{BC}$, and $\overline{AC}$ are the sides of $\triangle ABC$. A triangle also has three angles formed by the sides. $\angle A$, $\angle B$, and $\angle C$ are the three angles of the model triangle. We name a triangle by using its three vertices. The model triangle is called $\triangle ABC$.

DEFINITION

Triangle ($\triangle$): the union of three segments determined by three noncollinear points.

Model:

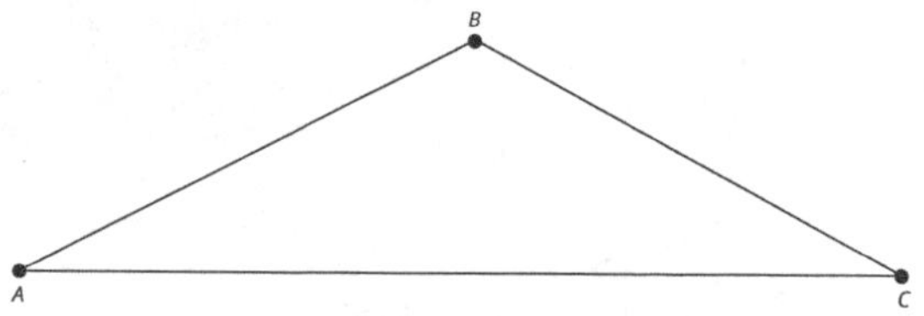

Triangles can be given special names according to the number of equal sides they have.

DEFINITIONS

A. **Scalene** △: a triangle in which no two sides have the same length.

B. **Isosceles** △: a triangle in which at least two sides have the same length.

C. **Equilateral** △: a triangle in which all three sides have the same length.

A. Model:

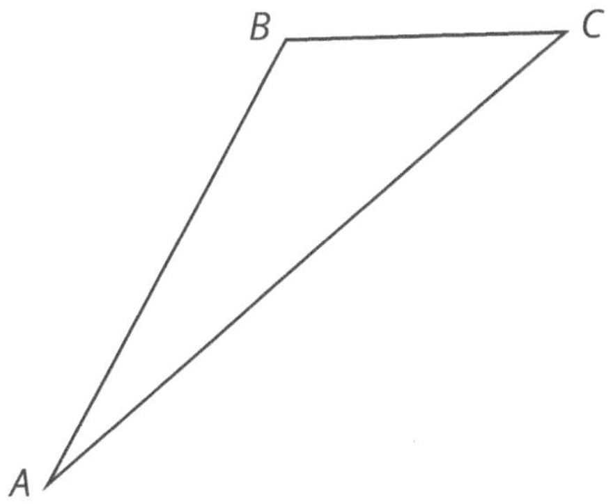

Scalene

B. Model:

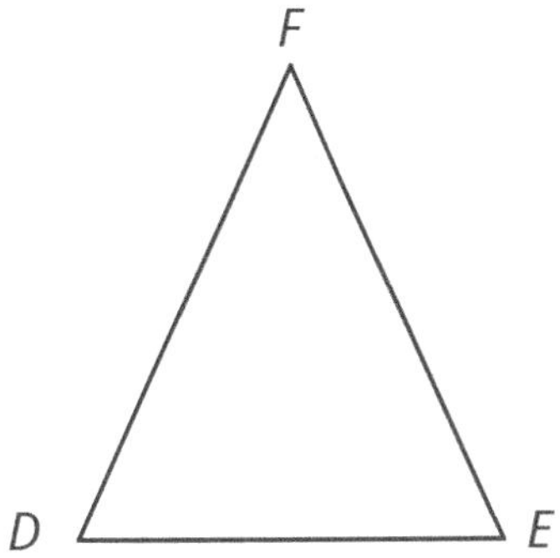

Isosceles

C. Model:

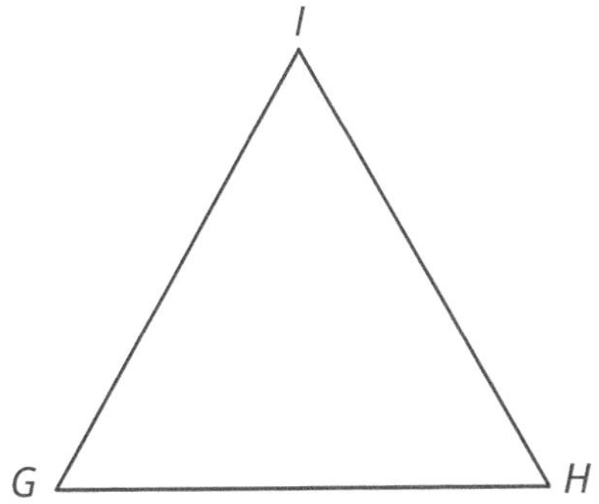

Equilateral *and* Isosceles

Triangles can also be classified by the measures of their angles.

> **DEFINITIONS**
>
> D. **Acute** △: a triangle in which all three angles are acute.
>
> E. **Obtuse** △: a triangle in which one angle is obtuse.
>
> F. **Right** △: a triangle in which one angle is a right angle.
>
> G. **Equiangular** △: a triangle in which all angles are equal.

D. Model:

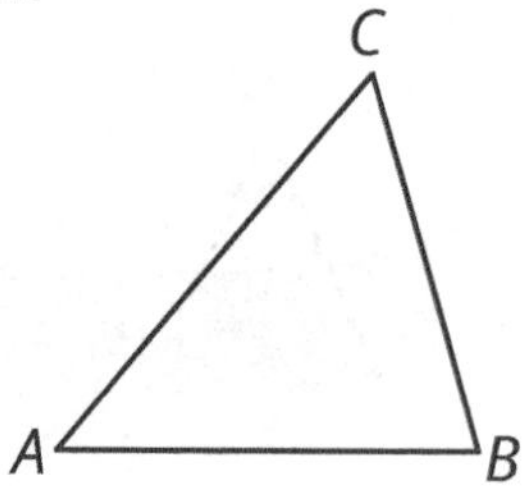

Acute

F. Model:

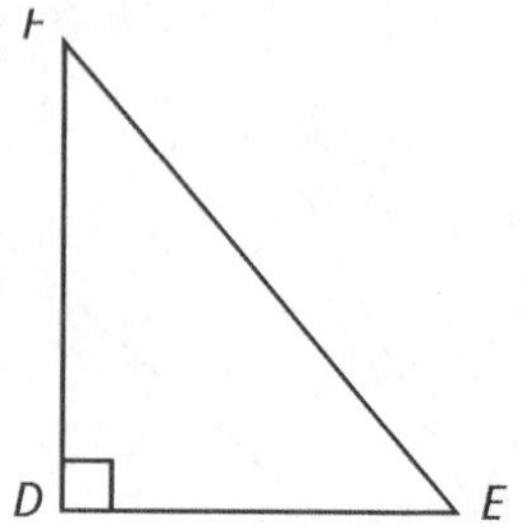

Right

E. Model:

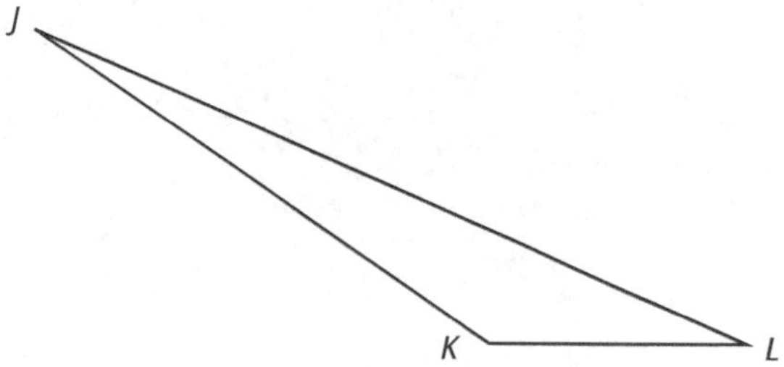

Obtuse

G. Model:

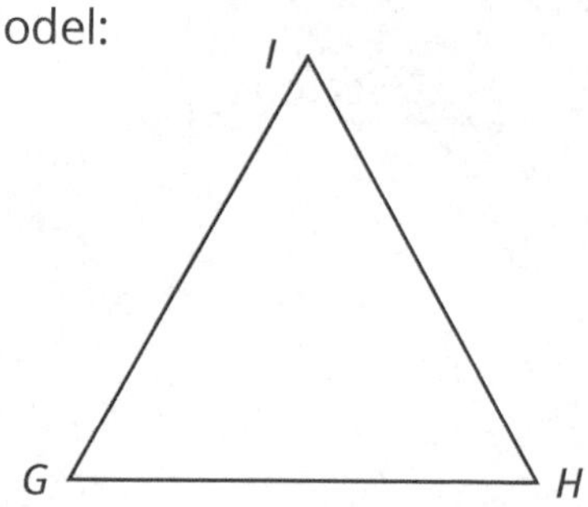

Equiangular

Notice that we can combine both types of classification for one triangle.

Models:

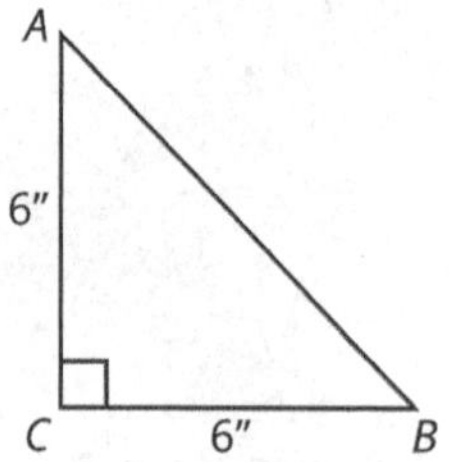

△*ABC* is a right isosceles triangle.

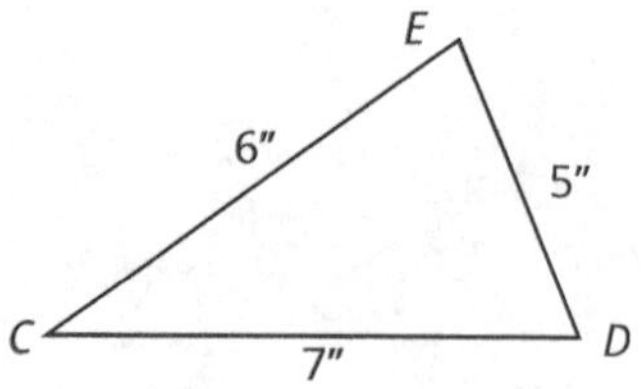

△*CDE* is an acute scalene triangle.

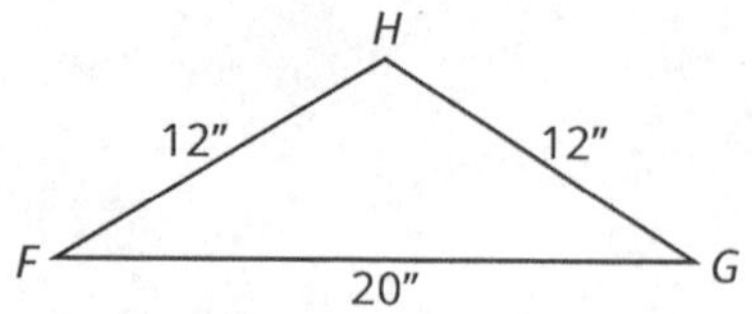

△*FGH* is an obtuse isosceles triangle.

Identify these △'s by writing *scalene, isosceles,* **or** *equilateral.*

4.1 ________________________________

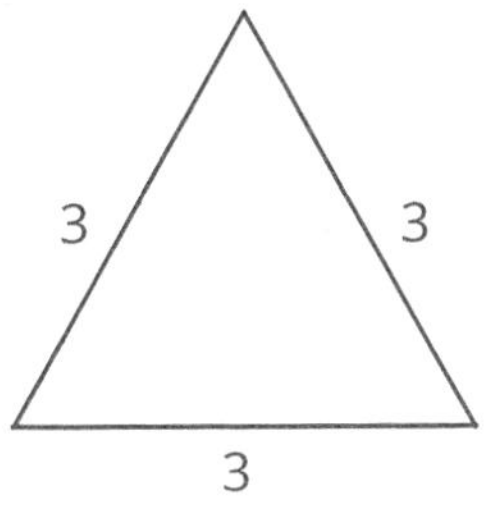

4.2 ________________________________

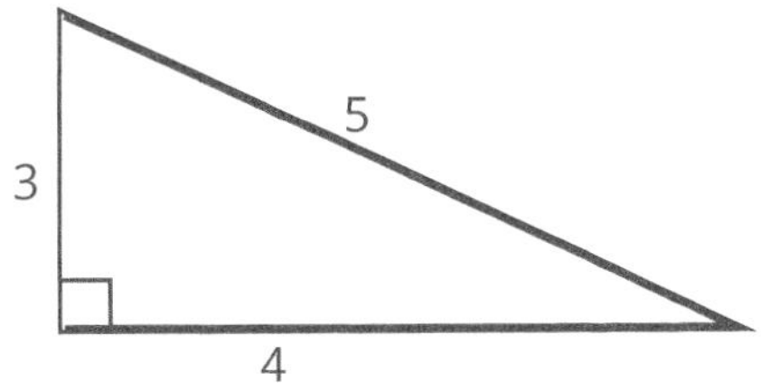

4.3 ________________________________

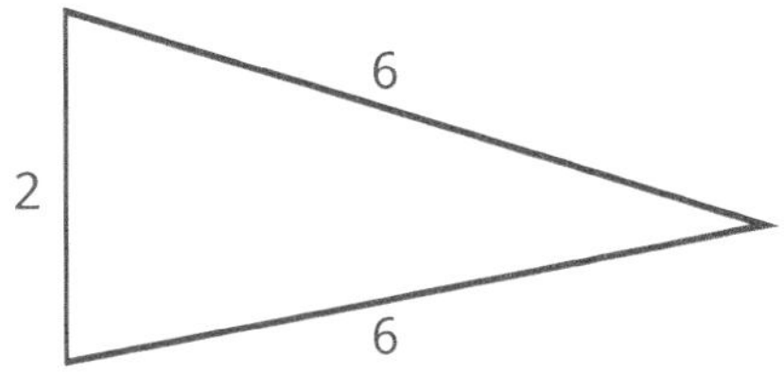

4.4 ________________________________

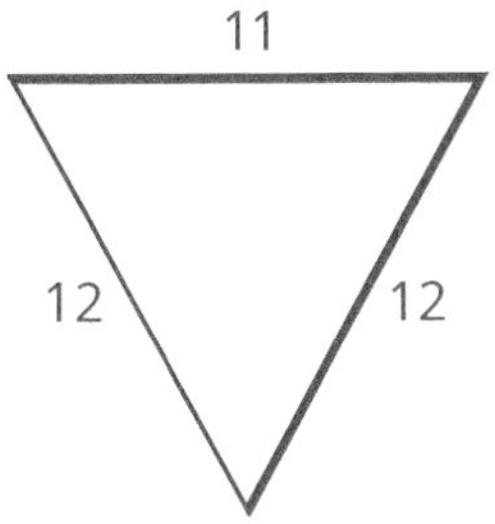

4.5 ________________________________

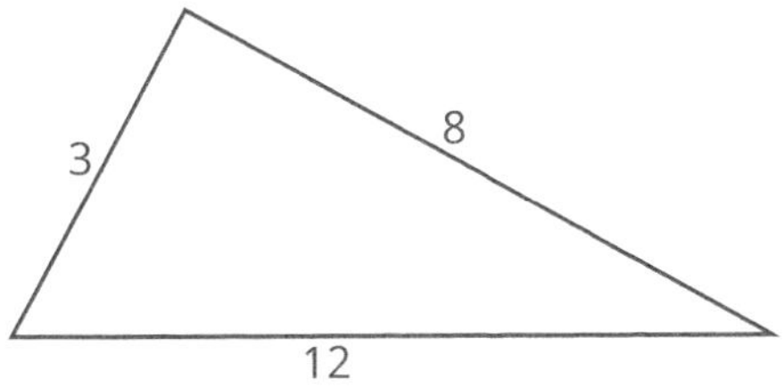

Identify these △'s by writing *acute, obtuse, right,* or *equiangular.*

4.6 ________________________

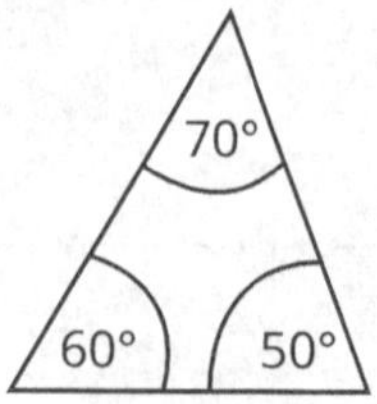

4.7 ________________________

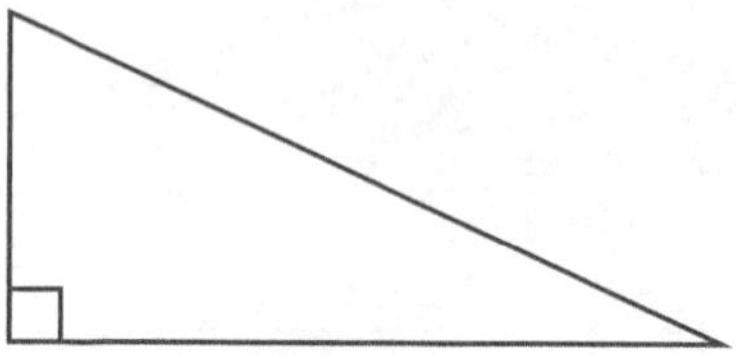

4.8 ________________________

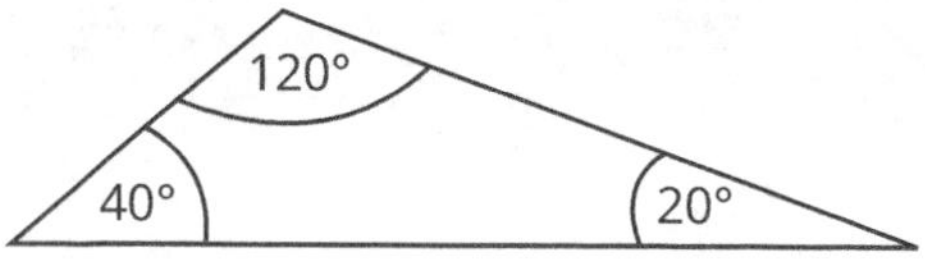

4.9 ________________________

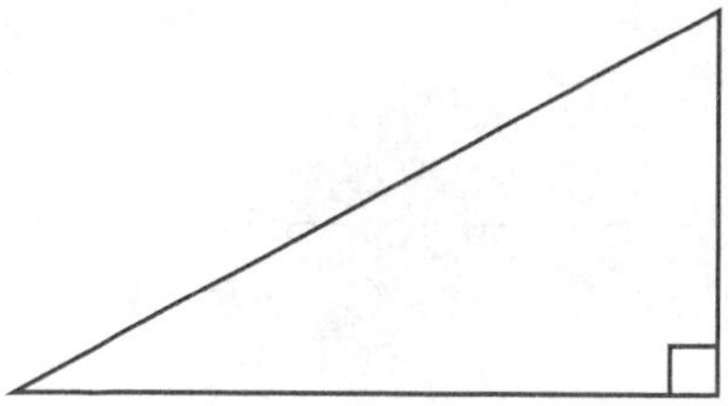

4.10 ________________________

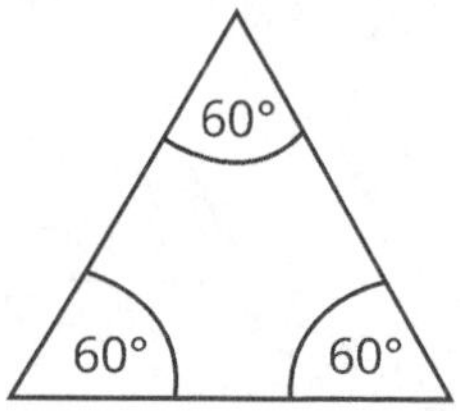

Before we come to the next theorem we need to know the following definitions.

DEFINITION

Exterior angle of a △: an angle formed by one side of a △ and an extension of another side.

Models:

∠*CBD* is an exterior ∠ of △*ABC*.

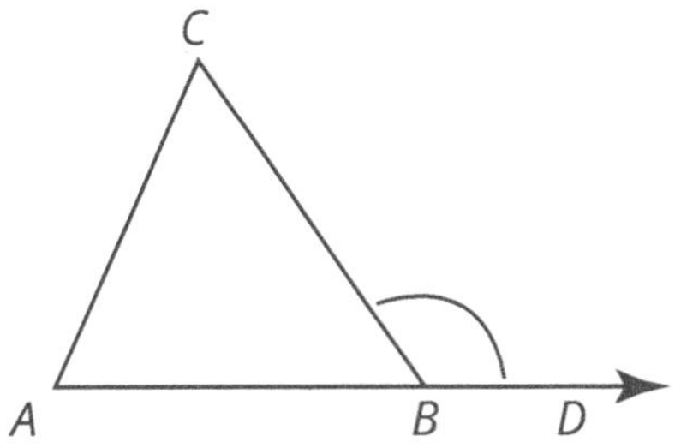

∠*ACD* is an exterior ∠ of △*ABC*.

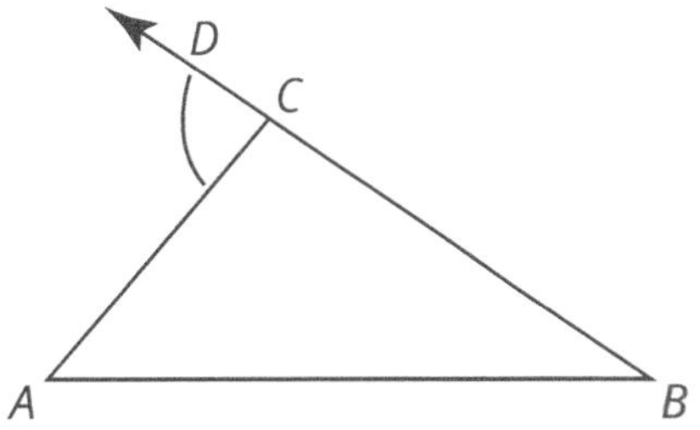

∠*BAF* is an exterior ∠ of △*ABC*.

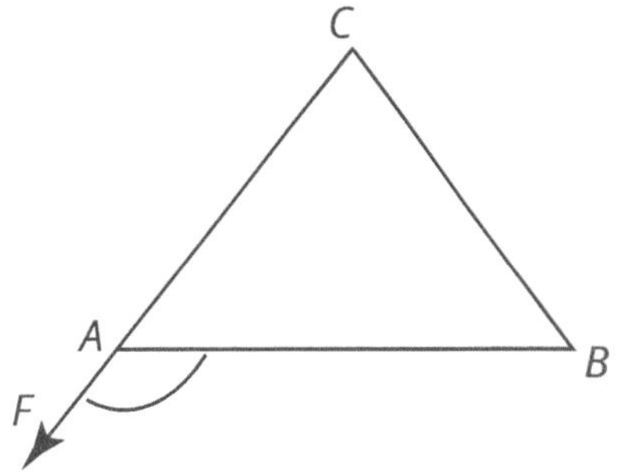

The triangle has a total of six exterior ∠'s, two at each vertex.

Model:

Notice that the pairs are also vertical angles. ∠1 and ∠6, ∠2 and ∠3, and ∠4 and ∠5 are vertical angles.

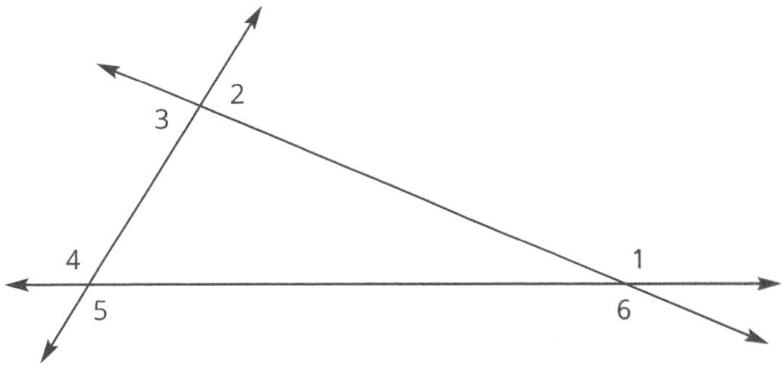

> **DEFINITION**
> **Remote interior angles**: with respect to an exterior angle, the two interior angles of the triangle that are not adjacent to the exterior angle.

Models:

$\angle 1$ and $\angle 2$ are remote interior angles with respect to $\angle 4$.

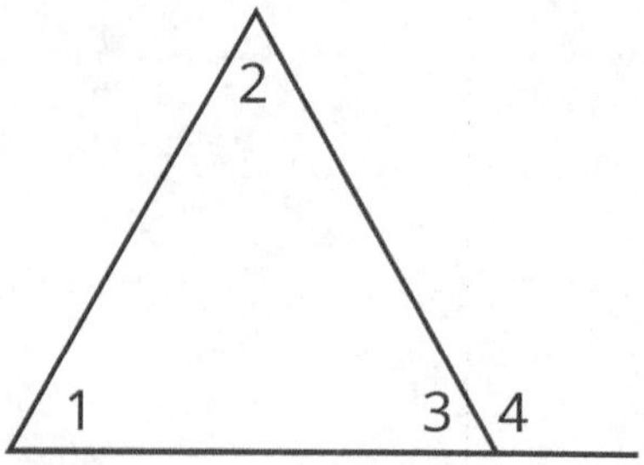

$\angle 2$ and $\angle 3$ are remote interior angles with respect to $\angle 5$.

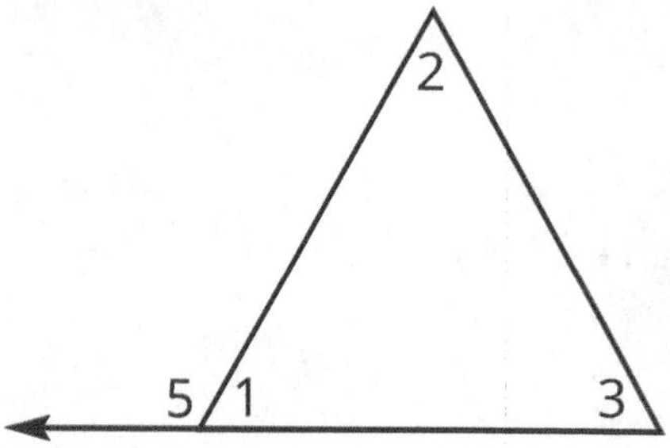

$\angle 1$ and $\angle 3$ are remote interior angles with respect to $\angle 6$.

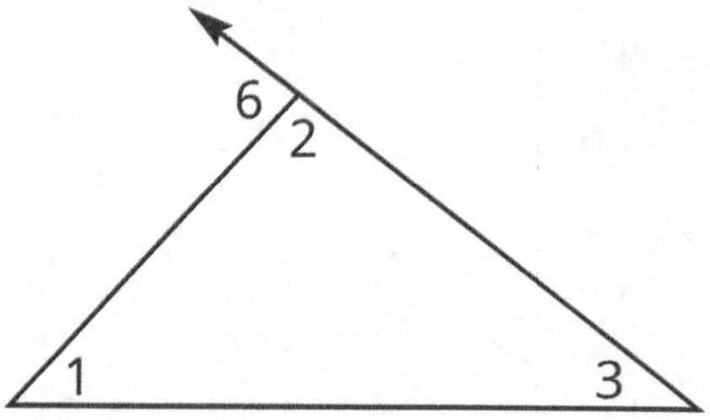

> **DEFINITION**
> **Auxiliary line**: a line introduced in a figure to make a proof possible.

When you use an auxiliary line, you should show it in your figure as a dotted line. Your proof should include a step justifying the fact that the line exists.

THEOREM 3-17

The sum of the measures of the angles of a triangle is 180°.

Given: $\triangle RST$

To Prove: $m\angle 1 + m\angle 2 + m\angle 3 = 180°$

Plan: Use auxiliary line through T and parallel to $\overline{RS}$. The three angles at T total 180°. Use substitution to show the 3 ∠'s of the △ = 180°.

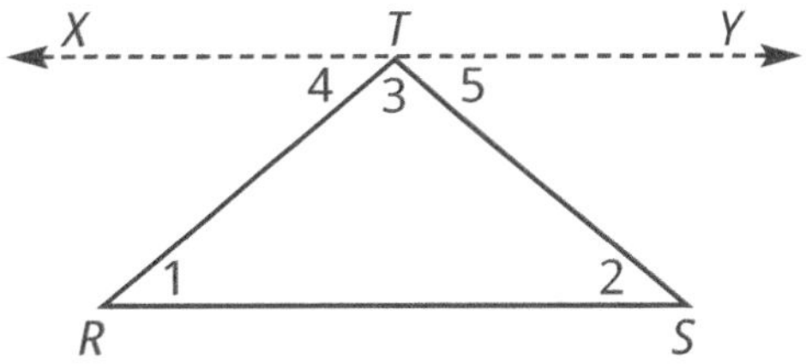

STATEMENT	REASON
1. Through T draw $\overleftrightarrow{XY} \parallel \overline{RS}$	1. Auxiliary line: P9.
2. $m\angle XTS + m\angle 5 = 180°$	2. Exterior sides in opposite rays.
3. $m\angle XTS = m\angle 4 + m\angle 3$	3. Angle addition theorem
4. $m\angle 4 + m\angle 3 + m\angle 5 = 180°$	4. Substitution
5. $m\angle 1 = m\angle 4$; $m\angle 2 = m\angle 5$	5. If lines ||, then alternate interior ∠'s =.
6. $m\angle 1 + m\angle 2 + m\angle 3 = 180°$	6. Substitution

So far, all proved statements have been called theorems. Sometimes, when a statement can be proved in a few easy steps by application of a theorem, the statement is called a *corollary* of the theorem.

A corollary can be used as a reason in a proof just as a theorem is used.

DEFINITION

Corollary: a statement that is easily proved by applying a theorem.

Theorem 3-17 has four corollaries:

Corollary 1: If two angles of one triangle are equal to two angles of a second triangle, then the third angles are also equal.

Corollary 2: Each angle of an equiangular triangle has a measure of 60°.

Corollary 3: A triangle has at most one right angle or one obtuse angle.

Corollary 4: The acute angles of a right triangle are complementary.

THEOREM 3-18

The measure of an exterior angle of a triangle is equal to the sum of the measures of the remote interior angles.

Given: $\triangle ABC$ with exterior $\angle 1$

To Prove: m $\angle 1$ = m $\angle 3$ + m $\angle 4$

Plan: Use Theorem 3-17 and the fact that $\angle 1$ and $\angle 2$ are supplementary.

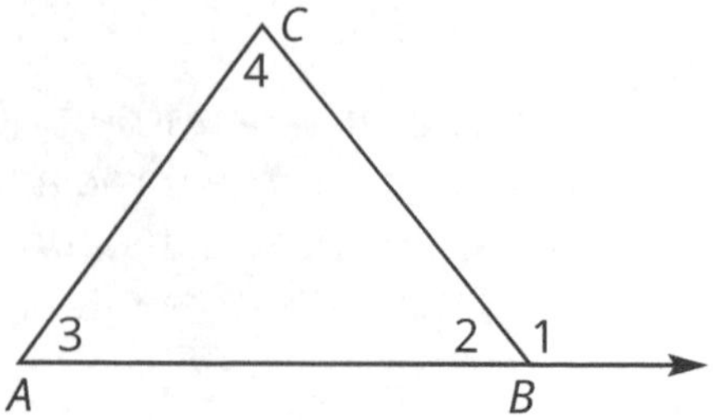

STATEMENT	REASON
1. $\triangle ABC$ with ext. $\angle 1$	1. Given
2. m $\angle 2$ + m $\angle 3$ + m $\angle 4$ = 180°	2. Sum of measures of $\angle$'s of $\triangle$ = 180°
3. m $\angle 1$ + m $\angle 2$ = 180°	3. Exterior sides in opposite rays.
4. m $\angle 2$ + m $\angle 3$ + m $\angle 4$ = m $\angle 1$ + m $\angle 2$	4. Substitution
5. m $\angle 3$ + m $\angle 4$ = m $\angle 1$	5. Subtraction property of equality.

Given the following diagram, find the missing measures.

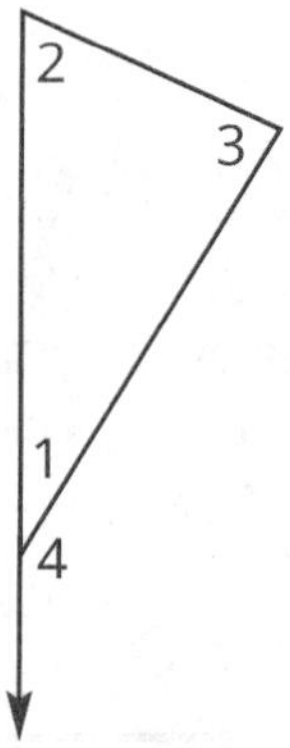

4.11 m $\angle 2$ = 50° m $\angle 3$ = 100° m $\angle 4$ = ________

4.12 m $\angle 1$ = 30° m $\angle 2$ = 45° m $\angle 3$ = ________

4.13 m $\angle 2$ = a° m $\angle 3$ = b° m $\angle 4$ = ________

4.14 m $\angle 2$ = 40° m $\angle 4$ = 150° m $\angle 3$ = ________

4.15 m $\angle 2$ = $2x$° m $\angle 3$ = $5x$° m $\angle 1$ = ________

4.16 m $\angle 1$ = $3x$° m $\angle 2$ = $4x$° m $\angle 3$ = $2x$° find x ________

4.17 m $\angle 4$ = $2x$° m $\angle 2$ = $\frac{4}{3}x$° m $\angle 3$ = 20° find x ________

Given the following diagram, find the missing measures.

Given: $\overline{PM} \perp \overline{MO}$

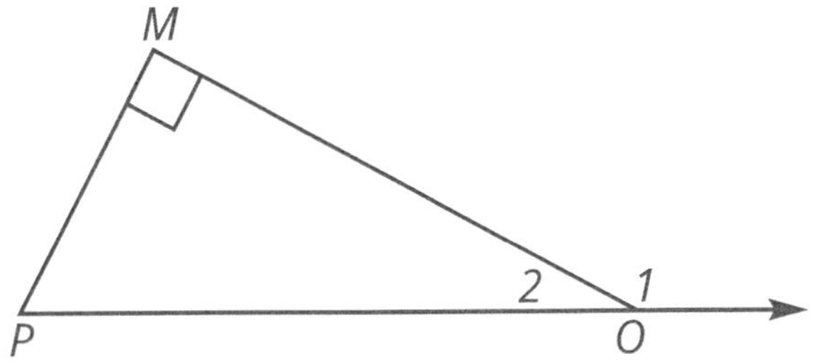

4.18 m ∠2 = 50° m ∠1 = ________________

4.19 m ∠2 = 30° m ∠*P* = ________________

4.20 m ∠*P* = m ∠2 m ∠*P* = ________________

4.21 m ∠*P* = 40° m ∠1 = ________________

Given the following diagram, find the missing measures.

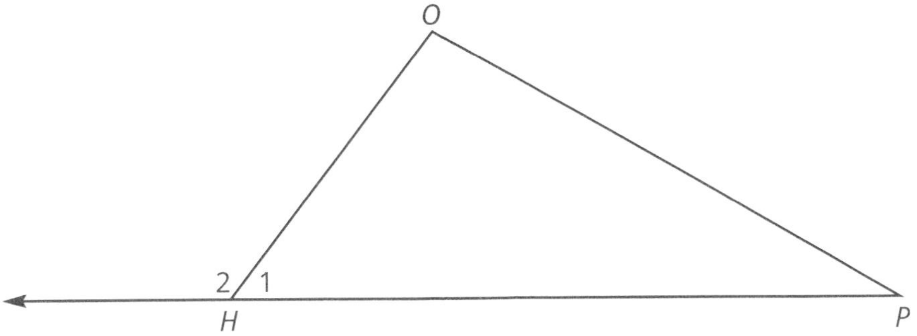

4.22 m ∠*P* = 38° m ∠*O* = 70° a. m ∠1 = ____________ b. m ∠2 = ____________

4.23 m ∠1 = 46° m ∠*P* = 38° a. m ∠2 = ____________ b. m ∠O = ____________

4.24 m ∠*O* = 90° m ∠1 = 35° a. m ∠2 = ____________ b. m ∠P = ____________

4.25 m ∠*O* = 90° m ∠1 = 63° a. m ∠2 = ____________ b. m ∠P = ____________

4.26 m ∠*O* = m ∠*P* m ∠1 = 36° m ∠2 = ____________

Given the following diagram, find the missing measures.

Given: m ∠3 = m ∠7
m ∠2 = 60°
m ∠6 = 115°

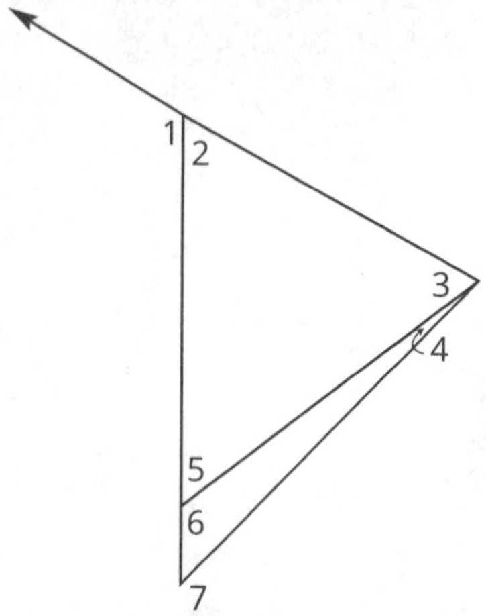

4.27 m ∠1 = ________________

4.28 m ∠3 = ________________

4.29 m ∠4 = ________________

4.30 m ∠5 = ________________

4.31 m ∠7 = ________________

Given the following diagram, find the missing measures.

Given: *l* || *m*
m ∠1 = 140°
m ∠3 = 50°

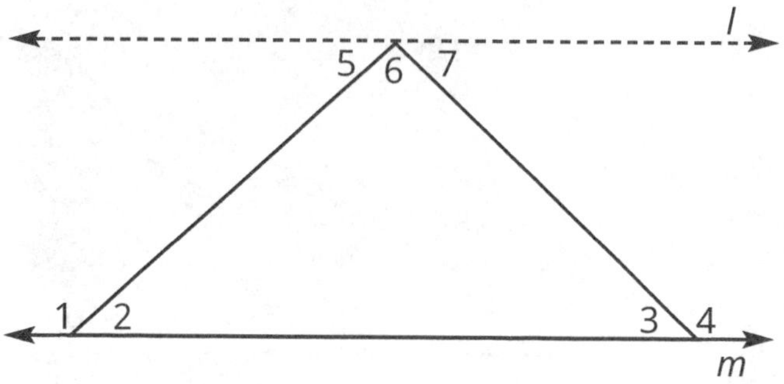

4.32 m ∠2 = ________________

4.33 m ∠4 = ________________

4.34 m ∠5 = ________________

4.35 m ∠6 = ________________

4.36 m ∠7 = ________________

Complete the following proofs.

4.37

Given: $\overline{JK} \perp \overline{MN}$

To Prove: ∠1, ∠2 are complementary

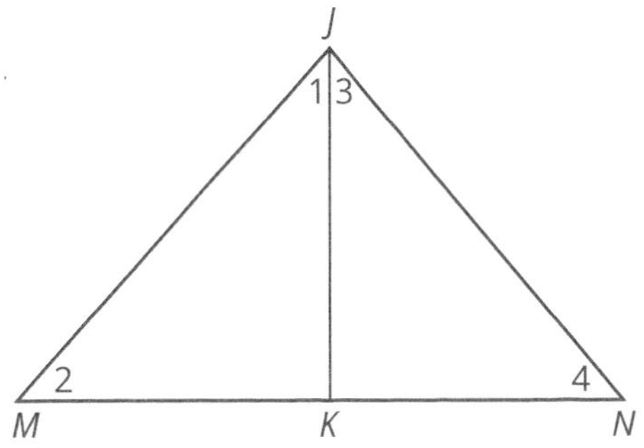

STATEMENT	REASON
1. ______	1. ______
2. ______	2. ______
3. ______	3. ______
4. ______	4. ______

4.38

Given: m ∠5 = m ∠6

To Prove: m ∠3 = m ∠4

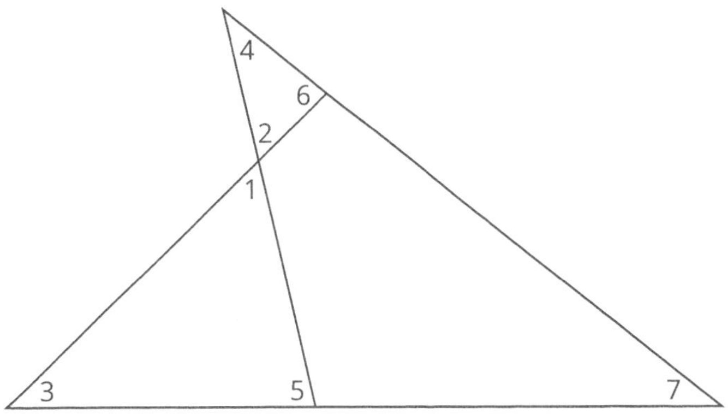

STATEMENT	REASON
1. ______	1. ______
2. ______	2. ______
3. ______	3. ______

4.39

Given: $\overline{AC} \perp \overline{CD}$
$\overline{DB} \perp \overline{AB}$

To Prove: m $\angle A$ = m $\angle D$

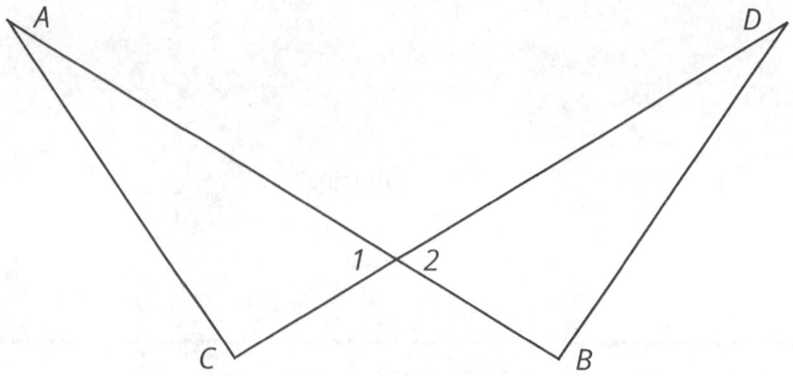

STATEMENT	REASON
1. ______	1. ______
2. ______	2. ______
3. ______	3. ______
4. ______	4. ______
5. ______	5. ______
	______
	______

OTHER POLYGONS

Working with polygons will be easier now that you have studied the properties of triangles and the theorems related to triangles. This section includes properties and a theorem relating to polygons.

> **DEFINITION**
>
> **Polygon:** any closed figure bounded by three or more segments that only intersect at their end points. The segments are called the *sides* and the end points are called the *vertices* of the polygon.

Models:

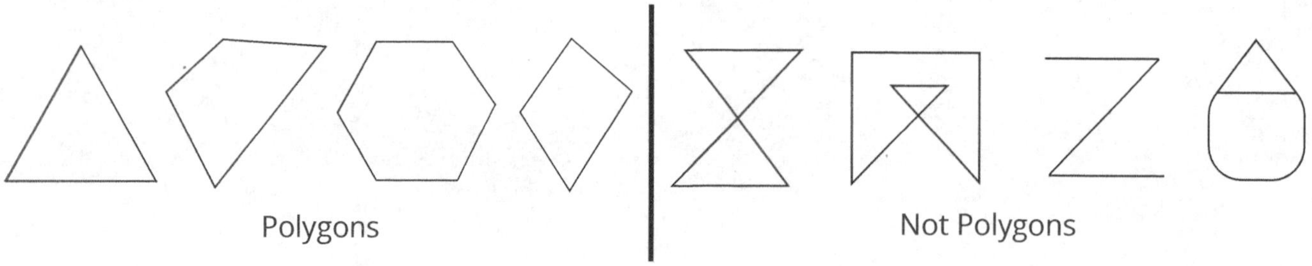

Polygons are given names depending on the number of sides they have.

Models:

three sides

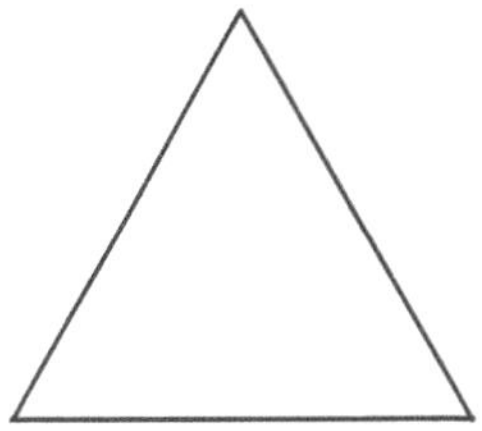

triangle

four sides

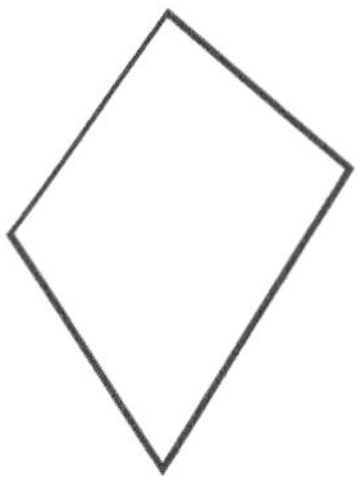

quadrilateral

five sides

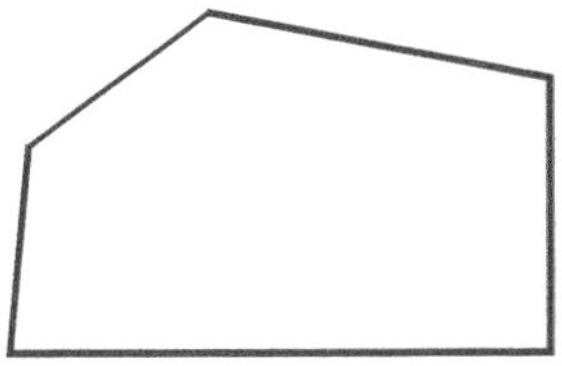

pentagon

six sides

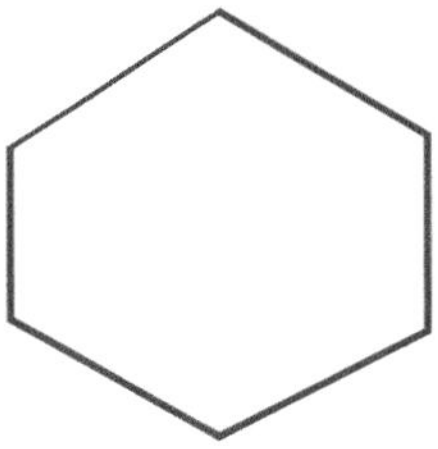

hexagon

eight sides

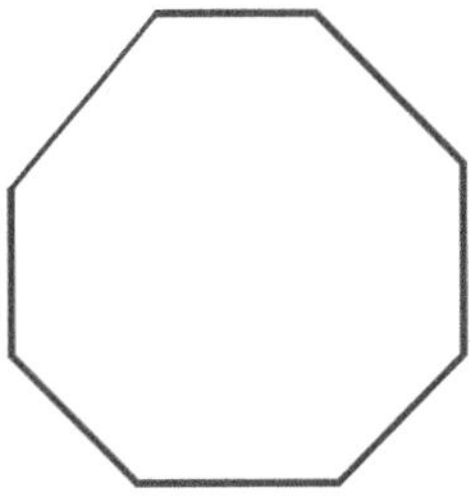

octagon

n sides

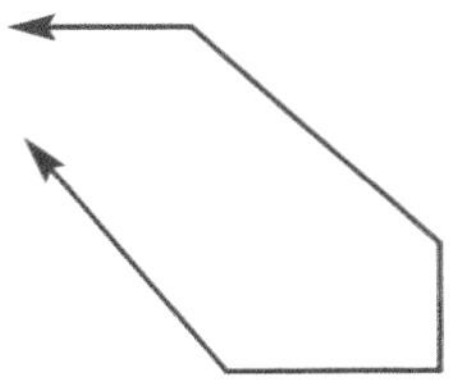

n-gon

The endpoints of one side of a polygon are called *consecutive vertices*; two sides that have a common end point are *consecutive sides*.

> **DEFINITIONS**
>
> **Consecutive vertices**: the end points of one side of a polygon.
>
> **Consecutive sides**: any two sides of a polygon that have a common end point.

We name a polygon by writing the vertices in order.

Model:

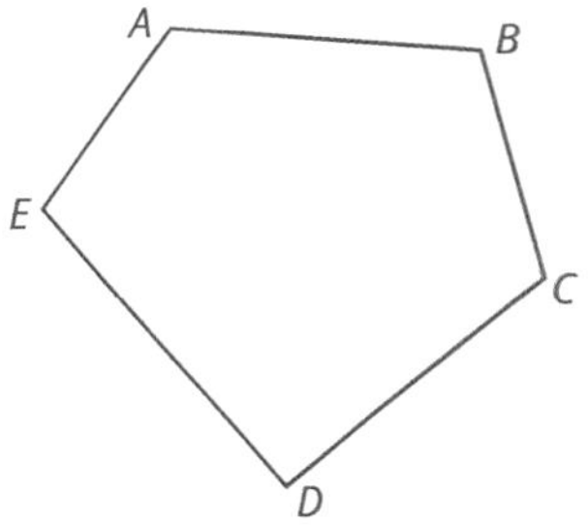

Polygon *ABCDE*

A and *B*, *B* and *C*, *C* and *D*, *D* and *E*, *E* and *A* are consecutive vertices. $\overline{AB}$ and $\overline{BC}$, $\overline{BC}$ and $\overline{CD}$, $\overline{CD}$ and $\overline{DE}$, $\overline{DE}$ and $\overline{EA}$, $\overline{EA}$ and $\overline{AB}$ are consecutive sides.

> **DEFINITIONS**
>
> **Diagonal of a polygon**: a segment joining two nonconsecutive vertices.

Model:

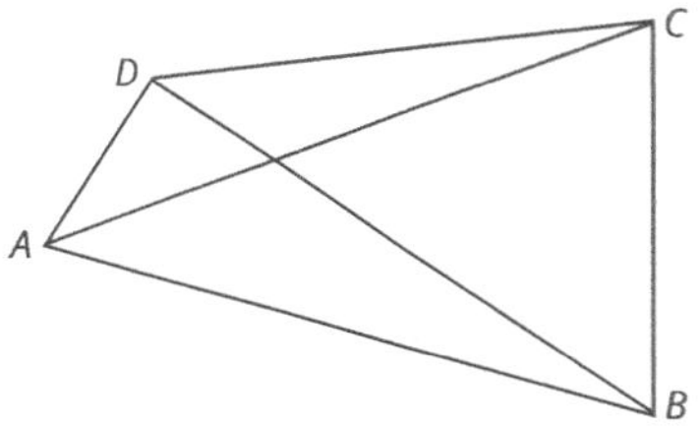

$\overline{AC}$ and $\overline{BD}$ are diagonals of quadrilateral *ABCD*.

DEFINITION

Regular polygon: a polygon with all the angles equal and all the sides equal.

Models:

Regular triangle Regular quadrilateral Regular pentagon Regular hexagon

THEOREM 3-19

The sum of the measures of the angles of a quadrilateral is 360°.

Given: quadrilateral *ABCD*

To Prove: m $\angle A$ + m $\angle B$ + m $\angle C$ + m $\angle D$ = 360°

Plan: Draw diagonal *AC*, making two △'s. The sum of ∠'s in each △ is 180°.

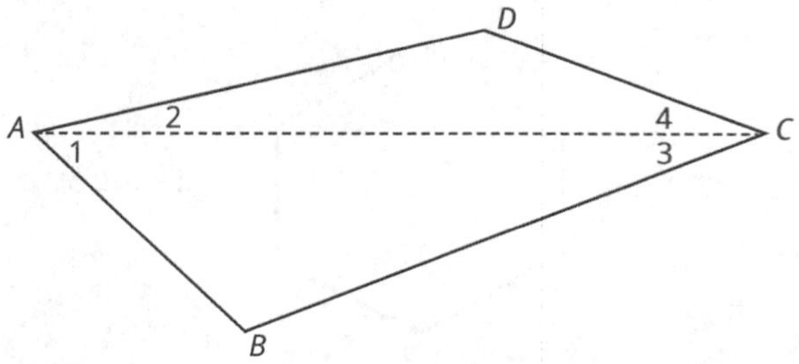

STATEMENT	REASON
1. quadrilateral *ABCD* with diagonal *AC*	1. Given
2. m $\angle 1$ + m $\angle 3$ + m $\angle B$ = 180° m $\angle 2$ + m $\angle 4$ + m $\angle D$ = 180°	2. Sum of ∠'s of △ = 180°
3. m $\angle 1$ + m $\angle 2$ + m $\angle 3$ + m $\angle 4$ + m $\angle B$ + m $\angle D$ = 360°	3. Addition property of equality
4. m $\angle A$ = m $\angle 1$ + m $\angle 2$ m $\angle C$ = m $\angle 3$ + m $\angle 4$	4. Angle addition theorem
5. m $\angle A$ + m $\angle B$ + m $\angle C$ + m $\angle D$ = 360°	5. Substitution

Using Theorem 3-17 and the method of proof in Theorem 3-19, we can arrive at a method to find the sum of the angles of any polygon.

Draw all diagonals from one vertex. The diagonals divide the polygon into triangles. Each triangle's angles have a sum of 180. Multiply the number of triangles by 180° to get the sum of the angles of the polygon.

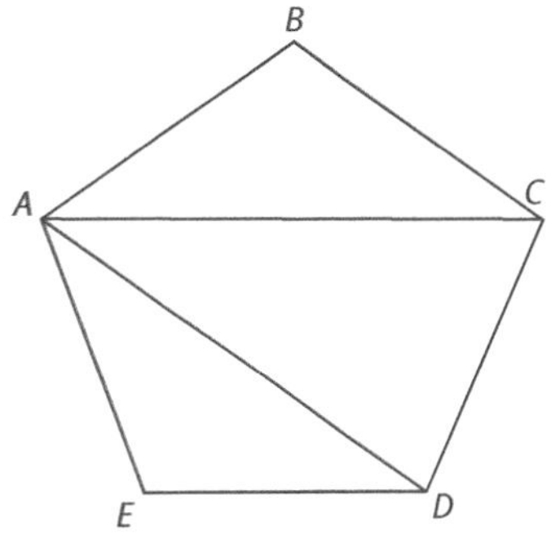

SIDES	NUMBER OF DIAGONALS FROM ONE VERTEX	NUMBER OF △'S	SUM OF ∠'S
4	1	2	2 x 180° = 360°
5	2	3	3 x 180° = 540°
6	3	4	4 x 180° = 720°
8	5	6	6 x 180° = 1,080°
n	$n - 3$	$n - 2$	$(n - 2)180°$

The sum of the measures of the angles of any n-gon is $(n - 2)180°$.

Another interesting conclusion is reached when we find the sum of the exterior angles of a polygon.

At each vertex the sum of an interior angle and an exterior angle equals 180°.

Any figure has n such pairs. Therefore, the sum of the interior angles and the exterior angles is $180°n$.

Now, if we subtract the sum of the interior angles, we get the sum of the exterior angles.

$180°n - (n - 2)180°$
$= 180°n - 180°n + 360°$
$= 360°$

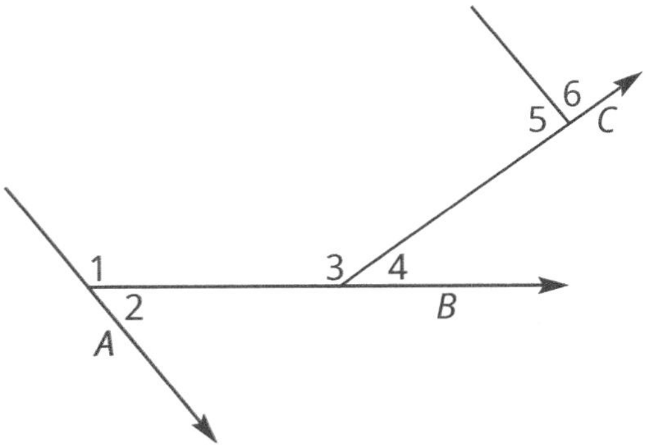

The sum of the exterior angles of an n-gon, one at each vertex, is 360°.

Whatever number of sides the polygon has, the sum of the exterior angles is always 360°.

Draw all possible diagonals from one vertex of the type of polygon named and tell how many triangles are formed.

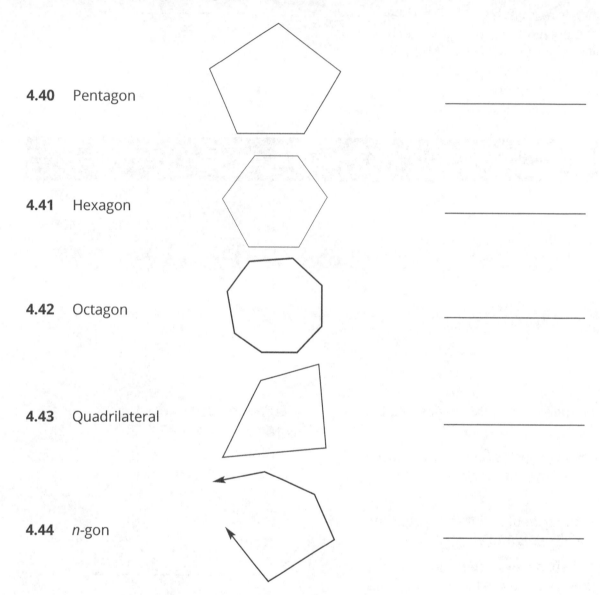

4.40 Pentagon

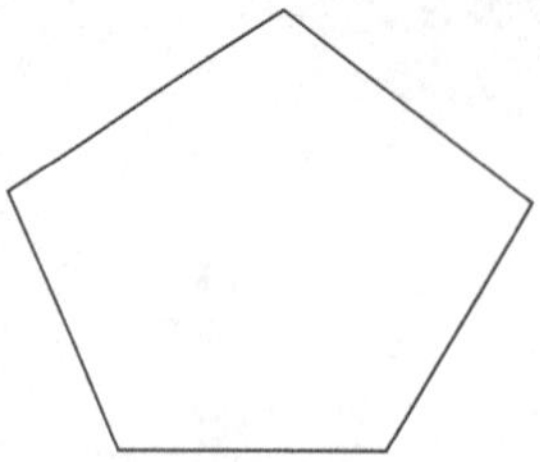

____

4.41 Hexagon

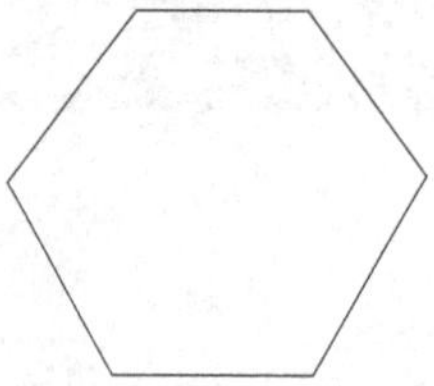

____

4.42 Octagon

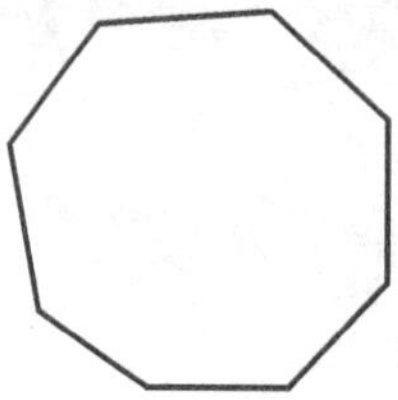

____

4.43 Quadrilateral

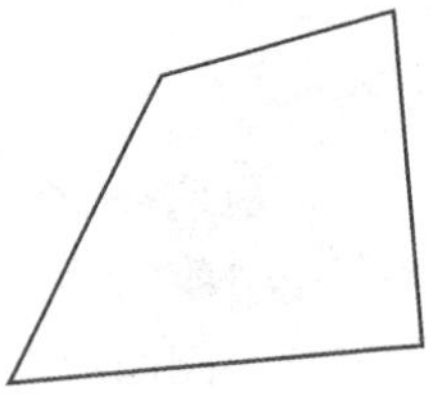

____

4.44 *n*-gon

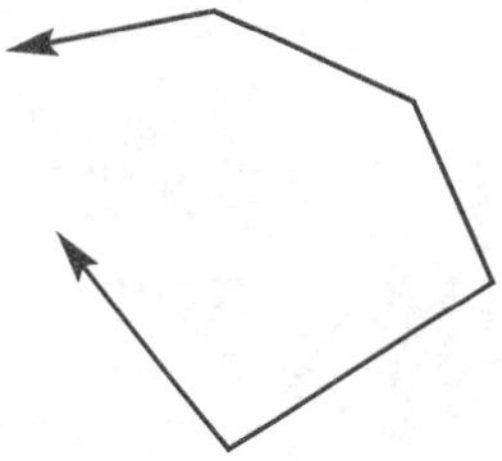

____

Complete the following items.

4.45 A polygon is such that when all diagonals from one vertex are drawn, eleven triangles are formed. How many sides does the polygon have? __________

4.46 The sum of the angles of a 7-gon is __________.

4.47 The sum of the angles of a 12-gon is __________.

4.48 The sum of the angles of a 20-gon is __________.

4.49 The sum of the angles of a 100-gon is __________.

4.50 The measures of three angles of a quadrilateral are 80°, 90°, and 103°. Find the measure of the fourth angle. ______________

4.51 What is the measure of one exterior angle of a regular hexagon? ______________

4.52 One exterior angle of a regular pentagon measures ______________ .

4.53 One exterior angle of a regular 16-gon measures ______________ .

4.54 How many sides does a regular polygon have if one exterior angle is 90°? ______________

4.55 How many sides does a regular polygon have if one exterior angle is 72°? ______________

4.56 How many sides does a regular polygon have if one exterior angle is 1°? ______________

4.57 Find the measure of one interior angle of a regular octagon. ______________

4.58 Find one interior angle of a regular 10-gon. ______________

4.59 Find one interior angle of a regular *n*-gon. ______________

4.60 Find the number of sides of a regular polygon if one interior angle is 60°. ______________

Before you take this last Self Test, you may want to do one or more of the following self checks.

1. ________ Read the objectives. Determine if you can do them.
2. ________ Restudy the material related to any objectives that you cannot do.
3. ________ Use the **SQ3R** study procedure to review the material:
   a. **S**can the sections.
   b. **Q**uestion yourself again (review the questions you wrote initially).
   c. **R**ead to answer your questions.
   d. **R**ecite the answers to yourself.
   e. **R**eview areas you did not understand.
4. ________ Review all activities and Self Tests, writing a correct answer for every wrong answer.

SELF TEST 4

Write the correct answers on the lines (each answer, 3 points).

4.01 A triangle with two equal sides is called a(n) ____________________ triangle.

4.02 A triangle with no sides equal is called ____________________ .

4.03 The sum of the measures of the angles of a triangle is ____________________ .

4.04 An exterior angle of a triangle equals the sum of the ____________________ angles.

4.05 A polygon with five sides is called a ____________________ .

4.06 If all the ∠'s are equal and all the sides are equal, then the polygon is called a ____________________ polygon.

4.07 If alternate interior angles are equal, then lines are ____________________ .

4.08 Supplementary angles total ____________________ .

4.09 An acute angle has a measure of ____________________ 90°.

4.010 If the exterior sides of two adjacent angles are in perpendicular lines, then the angles are ____________________ .

Identify the triangle by writing *acute, obtuse, or right,* **and** *scalene, isosceles* **or** *equilateral* (each answer, 3 points).

4.011 ______________________________

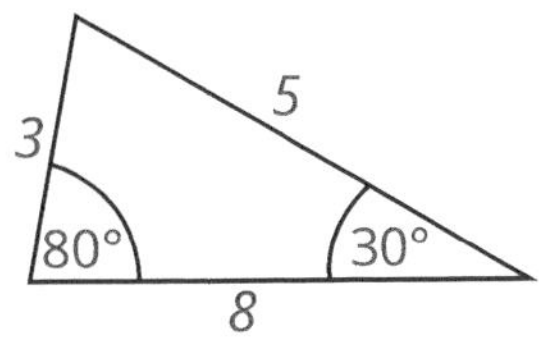

4.012 ______________________________

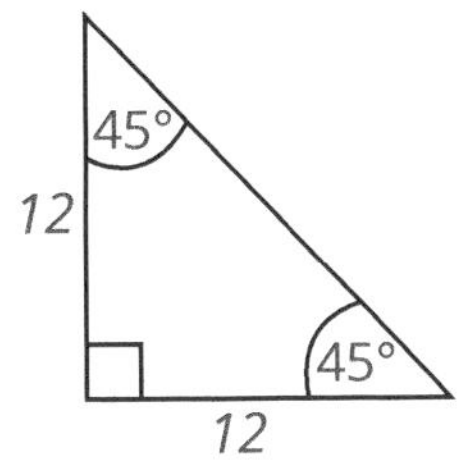

4.013 ______________________________

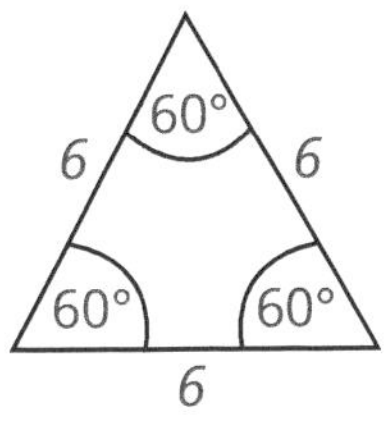

4.014 ______________________________

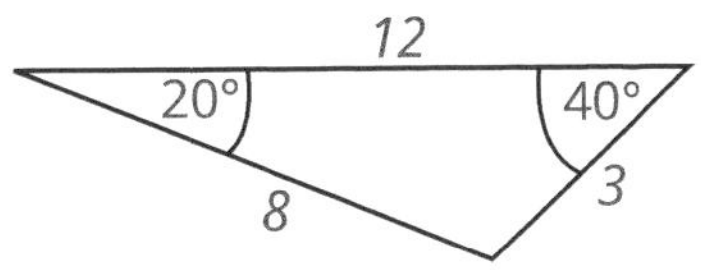

4.015 ______________________________

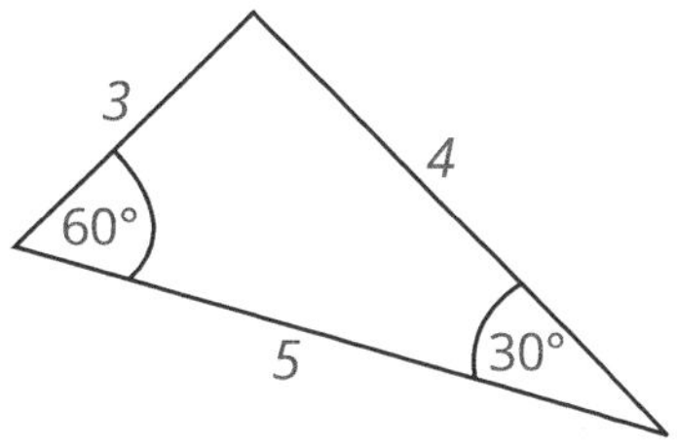

Identify ∠1 and ∠2. Write all that apply of the following terms: ***acute, right, obtuse, adjacent, vertical, complementary, supplementary*** (each answer, 3 points).

4.016 ________________________________

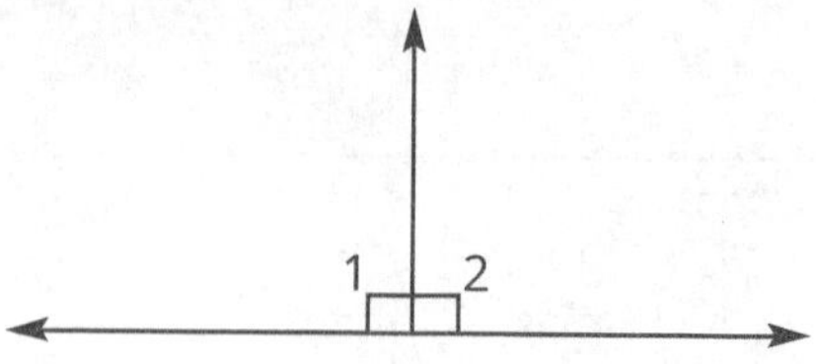

4.017 ________________________________

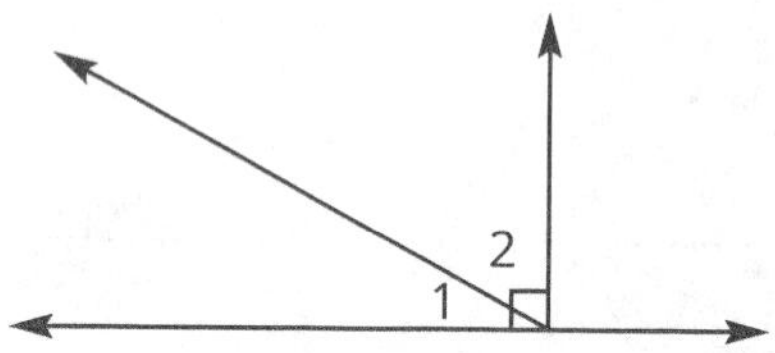

4.018 ________________________________

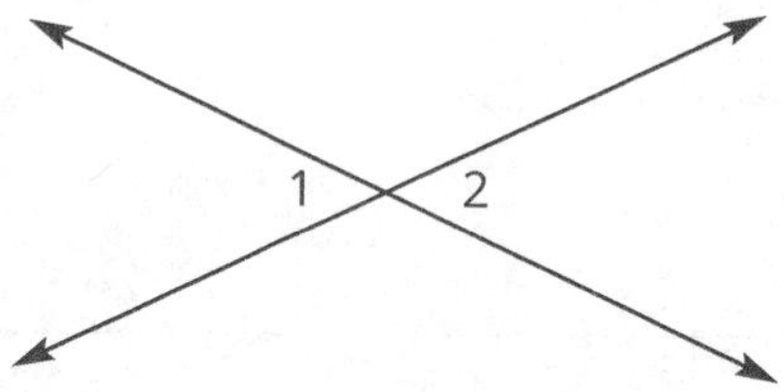

4.019 ________________________________

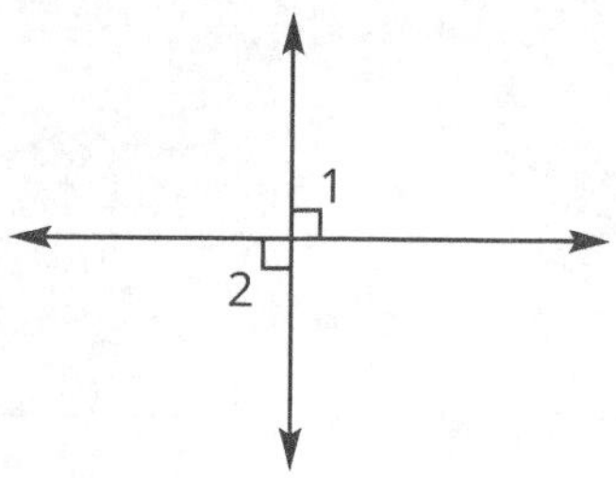

4.020 ________________________________

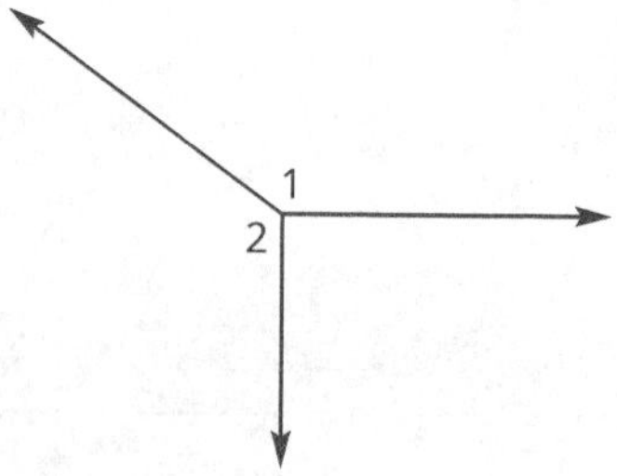

48/60 **SCORE** ____________ **TEACHER** ____________ ____________
initials date

Before taking the LIFEPAC Test, you may want to do one or more of the following self checks.

1. ________ Read the objectives. Check to see if you can do them.
2. ________ Restudy the material related to any objectives that you cannot do.
3. ________ Use the **SQ3R** study procedure to review the material.
4. ________ Review activities, Self Tests, and LIFEPAC Glossary.
5. ________ Restudy areas of weakness indicated by the last Self Test.

GLOSSARY

acute angle .... An angle that measures less than 90°.

acute triangle .... A triangle with all three angles acute.

adjacent angles .... Angles in the same plane that have a common vertex and a common side, but no interior points in common.

alternate exterior angles .... When two coplanar lines are cut by a transversal, the exterior angles on opposite sides of the transversal with different vertices are alternate exterior angles.

alternate interior angles .... When two coplanar lines are cut by a transversal, the interior angles on opposite sides of the transversal with different vertices are alternate interior angles.

angle .... The union of two noncollinear rays that have a common endpoint.

auxiliary line .... A line introduced in a figure to make a proof possible.

betweenness of rays .... For any $\angle XYZ$, $\overrightarrow{YA}$ is between $\overrightarrow{YX}$ and $\overrightarrow{YZ}$ when all three rays have a common endpoint and when $\overrightarrow{YA}$ lies in the interior of $\angle XYZ$.

bisector of an angle .... A ray in the interior of the angle that divides the angle into two angles of equal measure.

complementary angles .... Two angles whose sum of measures is 90°.

consecutive sides .... Any two sides of a polygon that have a common endpoint.

consecutive vertices .... The endpoints of one side of a polygon.

corollary .... A statement that is easily proved by applying a theorem.

corresponding angles .... Angles in corresponding positions in a figure.

diagonal of a polygon .... A segment joining two nonconsecutive vertices.

equiangular triangle .... A triangle with all three angles of the same measure.

exterior angle .... An angle on the outside of a figure.

exterior sides .... The rays not common to a pair of adjacent angles.

hexagon .... A polygon with six sides.

interior angle .... An angle on the inside of a figure.

isosceles triangle .... A triangle with at least two sides of the same length.

***n*-gon** .... A polygon with *n* sides.

obtuse angle .... An angle that measures more than 90° but less than 180°.

octagon .... A polygon with eight sides.

obtuse triangle .... A triangle with one obtuse angle.

parallel lines .... Lines in the same plane with no points in common.

parallel planes .... Planes that have no points in common.

pentagon .... A polygon with five sides.

perpendicular lines .... Lines that intersect to form right angles.

quadrilateral .... A polygon with four sides.

regular polygon .... A polygon with all the angles equal and all the sides equal.

remote interior angles .... Interior angles of a figure that are not adjacent to some particular exterior angle.

right angle .... An angle that measures 90°.

right triangle .... A triangle with one right angle.

scalene triangle .... A triangle with no two sides of the same length.

sides .... The portions of the two rays that form an angle.

skew lines .... Lines that are not in the same plane.

supplementary angles .... Two angles whose sum of measures is 180°.

transversal .... A line that intersects two or more coplanar lines in different points.

triangle .... A polygon with three sides.

vertex .... The common endpoint of the two sides of an angle.

vertical angles .... Angles with sides that form two pairs of opposite rays.

NOTES

MATH 1003

LIFEPAC TEST

NAME ______________________

DATE ______________________

SCORE ______________________

98

122

MATH 1003: LIFEPAC TEST

Complete the following proofs (each answer, 4 points).

1. Given: $\overleftrightarrow{AB} \perp \overleftrightarrow{CD}$

To Prove: m ∠2 + m ∠4 + m ∠7 = m ∠1

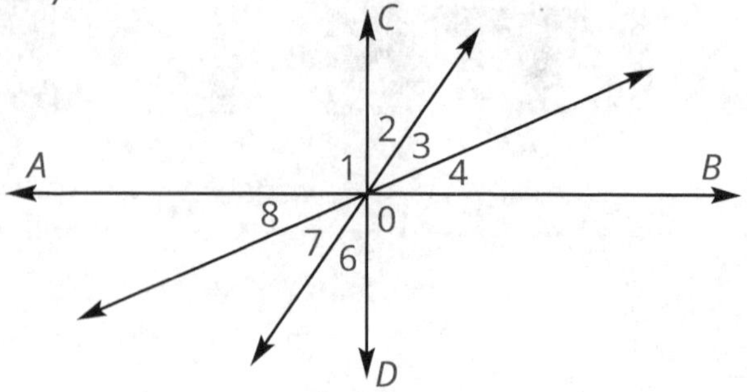

STATEMENT	REASON
1. ____________________	1. ____________________
2. ____________________	2. ____________________
3. ____________________	3. ____________________
4. ____________________	4. ____________________
5. ____________________	5. ____________________
6. ____________________	6. ____________________

2. Given: $\overline{AB} \parallel \overline{CD}$

To Prove: m ∠1 = m ∠2 + m ∠3

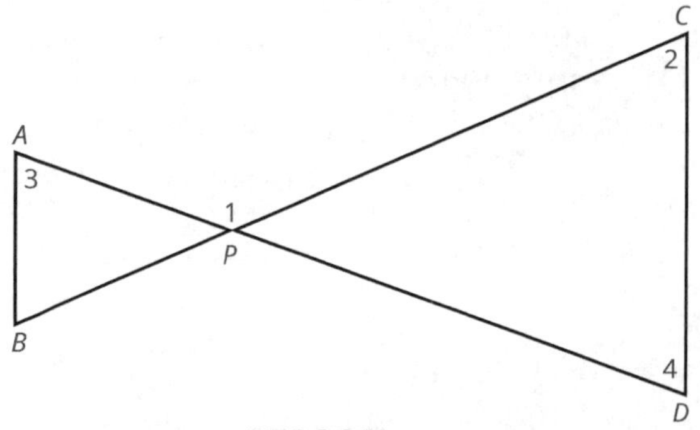

STATEMENT	REASON
1. ____________________	1. ____________________
2. ____________________	2. ____________________
3. ____________________	3. ____________________
4. ____________________	4. ____________________

Answer true or false (each answer, 1 point).

3. __________ The sum of the interior angles of a quadrilateral equals 360°.

4. __________ The sum of the exterior angles of a pentagon equals 360°.

5. __________ The sum of the interior angles of a triangle is 360°.

6. __________ The sum of the interior angles of an *n*-gon is 180° (*n* – 2).

7. __________ An exterior angle of a triangle equals the sum of the interior angles.

8. __________ A triangle can have two right angles.

Write the correct letter and answer on the blank (each answer, 2 points).

9. ________ Scalene △

10. ________ Obtuse △

11. ________ Hexagon

12. ________ Right △

13. ________ Pentagon

14. ________ Quadrilateral

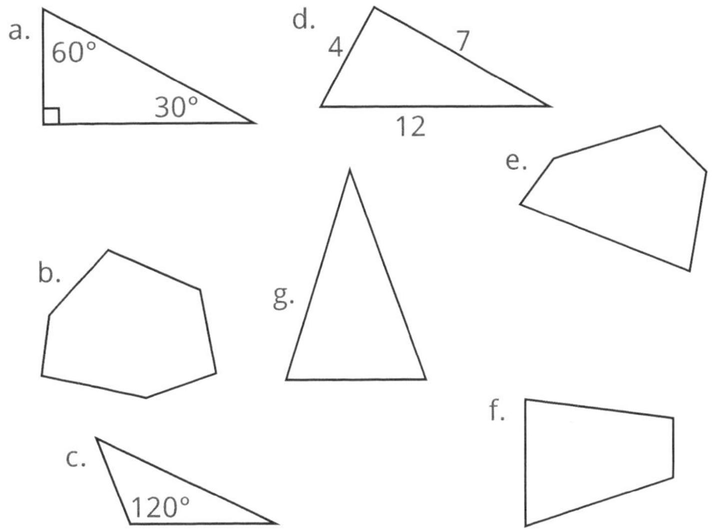

Complete the following items (each answer, 3 points).

15. An isosceles △ has ____________ equal sides.

16. A pentagon has ____________ diagonals from each vertex.

17. If all sides of a polygon are equal and all angles are equal, then it is a ____________________ polygon.

18. If the sum of the interior angles of a polygon is 180°, the polygon has ____________________ sides.

19. If an interior angle of a regular polygon is 120°, what is the measure of one exterior angle? ____________________ .

20. The sum of the measures of the acute angles of a right triangle total ____________________ .

Find the following angle measures (each answer, 3 points).

21. Find m ∠1

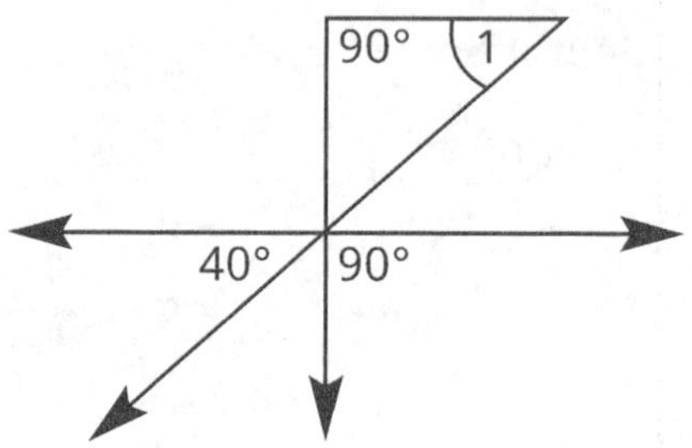

22. Given: *l* || *m*

Find m ∠1

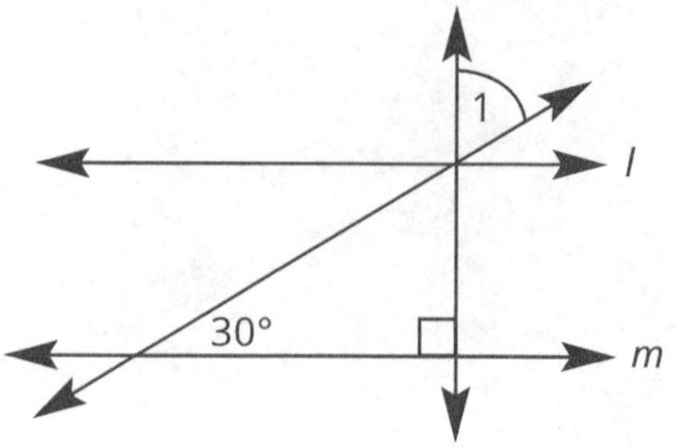

MATH 1004
Congruency

LIFEPAC Test is located at the back of the booklet. Please remove before starting the unit.

Author:
Milton R. Christen, M.A.

Editor-in-Chief:
Richard W. Wheeler, M.A.Ed.

Editor:
Robin Hintze Kruetzberg, M.B.A.

Consulting Editor:
Robert L. Zenor, M.A., M.S.

Revision Editor:
Alan Christopherson, M.S.

AOP

804 N. 2nd Ave. E.
Rock Rapids, IA 51246-1759

Congruency

Introduction

You have learned in previous LIFEPACs about geometry as a system. You have studied points and lines, induction and deduction, and angle relationships. The next step in your study of geometry is to learn about congruent triangles and some quadrilaterals related to congruent triangles. Theorems and properties relating to these figures will be presented in this LIFEPAC®. Completion of this LIFEPAC should prepare you for studying more complex and interesting geometric concepts.

Objectives

Read these objectives. The objectives tell you what you will be able to do when you have successfully completed this LIFEPAC. When you have finished this LIFEPAC, you should be able to:

1. State the definition of congruent triangles.
2. Prove triangles congruent by using SSS, SAS, ASA, and AAS statements.
3. Prove right triangles congruent by using HL, LL, HA, and LA statements.
4. Prove corresponding parts equal when triangles are in normal position.
5. Prove corresponding parts equal when triangles are overlapping.
6. Prove properties of isosceles triangles.
7. Prove inequalities in one triangle.
8. Prove inequalities in two triangles.
9. Identify the properties of parallelograms, rectangles, squares, rhombuses, and trapezoids.

Survey the LIFEPAC. Ask yourself some questions about this study and write your questions here.

1. TRIANGLES

Most of the material goods we use today are mass produced. Every product is produced by the thousands, and all are exactly alike. They are the same size and the same shape. When your car needs a new part, the mechanic can replace the old part with a new one that is exactly the same as the old one. Figures, whether plane or solid, that have the same size and the same shape are called congruent figures.

Section Objectives

Review these objectives. When you have finished this section, you should be able to:

1. State the definition of congruent triangles.
2. Prove triangles congruent by using SSS, SAS, ASA, and AAS statements.
3. Prove right triangles congruent by using HL, LL, HA, and LA statements.

DEFINING CONGRUENT TRIANGLES

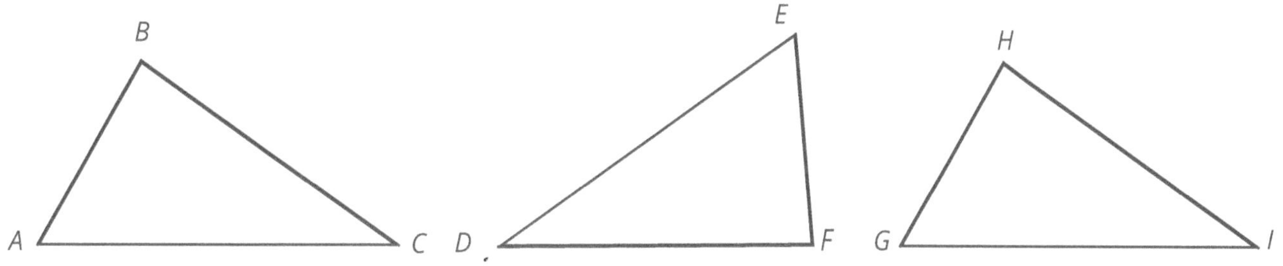

All three triangles shown are congruent. One way of describing the situation is to say any one of these triangles can be moved onto any other one in such a way that it fits exactly. To show this fit we can match the vertices of the triangles. This matching can take place in several ways, but only one way will make one triangle fit exactly over the other.

Model 1: $A \leftrightarrow E$

$B \leftrightarrow F$

$C \leftrightarrow D$

When the vertices are matched as in Model 1, then $\triangle$ ABC will fit over $\triangle$ EFD.

Model 2: $A \leftrightarrow G$

$B \leftrightarrow H$

$C \leftrightarrow I$

When the vertices are matched as in Model 2, then $\triangle ABC$ will fit over $\triangle GHI$.

A matching of vertices in this way is called a *one-to-one correspondence* between the vertices of the two triangles. The angles at the vertices that are matched are called *corresponding angles*. Three *corresponding sides* also match.

Model 3: $AB \leftrightarrow GH \leftrightarrow EF$

$BC \leftrightarrow HI \leftrightarrow FD$

$CA \leftrightarrow IG \leftrightarrow DE$

> **DEFINITION**
>
> **One-to-one correspondence:** the situation when each member of a set, such as angles of a triangle, can be paired with one and only one member of another set.
>
> **Corresponding angles:** angles paired with one another in a one-to-one correspondence.
>
> **Corresponding sides:** sides paired with one another in a one-to-one correspondence.

For each part (angle or side) of one triangle, a corresponding part of the other triangle exists. Therefore, we have a one-to-one correspondence between all six parts of one triangle with all six parts of another triangle.

If the one-to-one correspondence of all six parts leads to one triangle fitting over the other exactly, then the triangles are *congruent*. The symbol for congruent is ≅.

> **DEFINITION**
>
> **Congruent Triangles:** If a one-to-one correspondence between the parts of two triangles is such that the corresponding parts are equal, then the triangles are congruent.

To show which parts correspond to each other, we name the triangles in a special way.

Model 4:

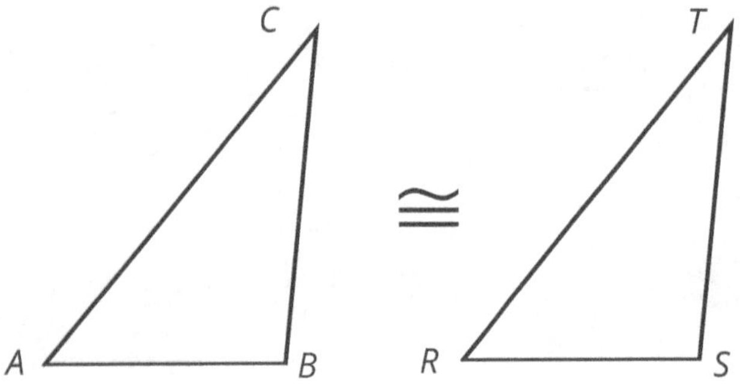

First write the name of one triangle, then write the vertices of the other triangle so that the corresponding vertices are in matching position in the name.

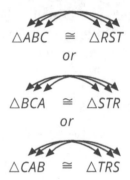

$\triangle ABC \cong \triangle RST$

or

$\triangle BCA \cong \triangle STR$

or

$\triangle CAB \cong \triangle TRS$

When we draw models of congruent triangles, we often mark pairs of corresponding parts in the same way, to show which parts are equal.

Model 5:

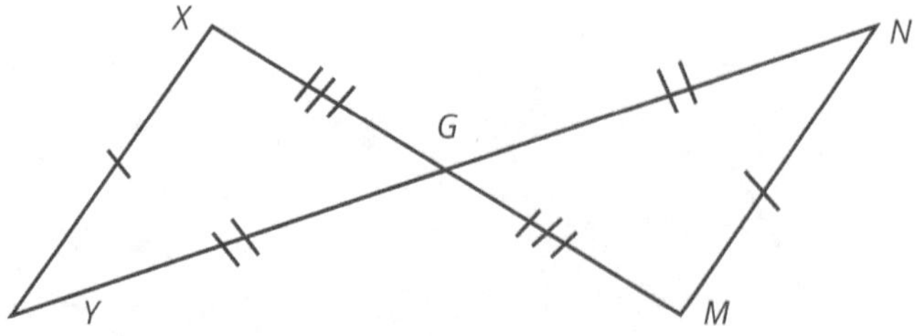

The marks /, //, and /// show that $YX = MN$, $YG = GN$, and $XG = GM$.

Model 6:

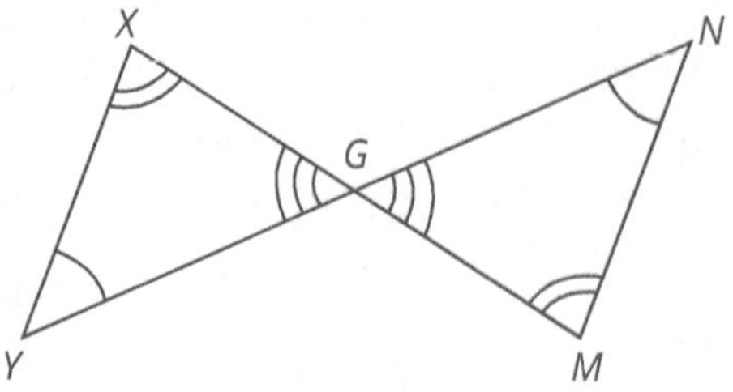

The marks ⌒, ⌒⌒, and ⌒⌒⌒ show that $\angle Y = \angle N$, $\angle X = \angle M$, and $\angle XGY = \angle MGN$.

Two more definitions that we will be using are the definitions for *included angle* and *included side*.

DEFINITION

Included Angle: the angle formed by two sides of a triangle.

Model:

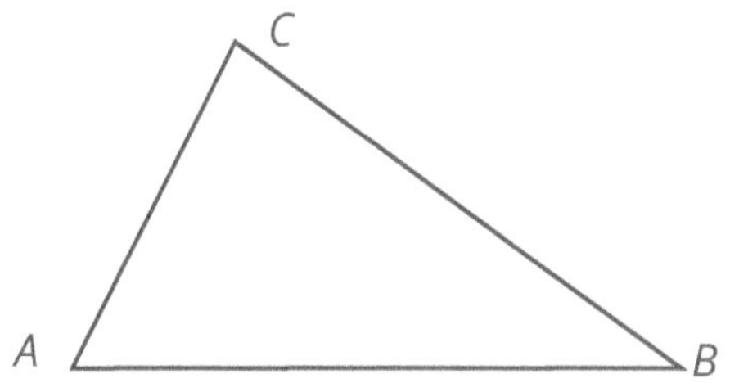

$\angle C$ is the included angle between sides $\overline{AC}$ and $\overline{BC}$. $\angle B$ is the included angle between sides $\overline{AB}$ and $\overline{BC}$. $\angle A$ is the included angle between sides $\overline{AB}$ and $\overline{AC}$.

DEFINITION

Included Side: the side of a triangle that is formed by the common side of two angles.

Model:

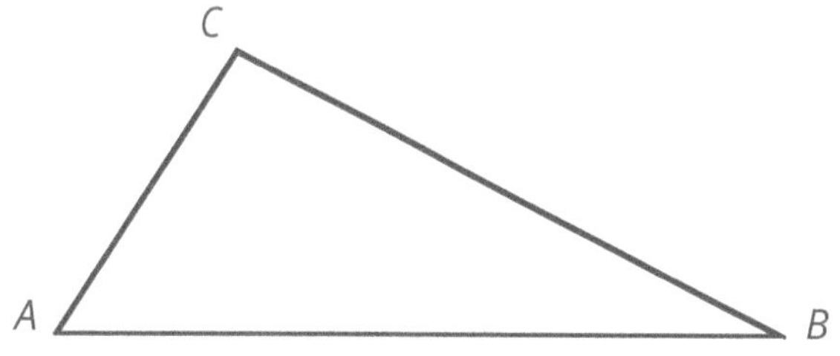

$\overline{AB}$ is the included side between $\angle A$ and $\angle B$. $\overline{BC}$ is the included side between $\angle B$ and $\angle C$. $\overline{AC}$ is included between $\angle A$ and $\angle C$.

Complete the correspondence so a congruence can be established.

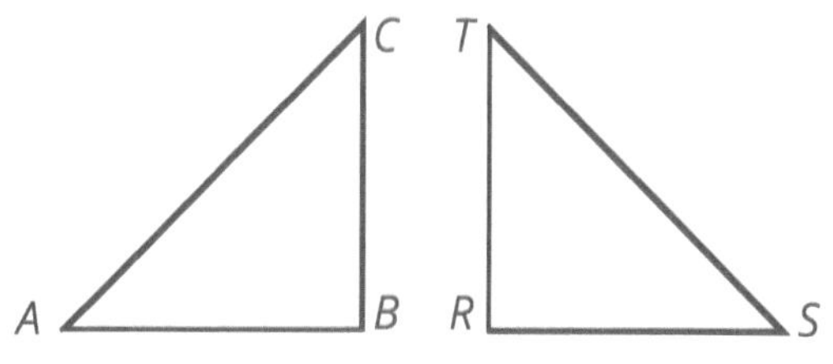

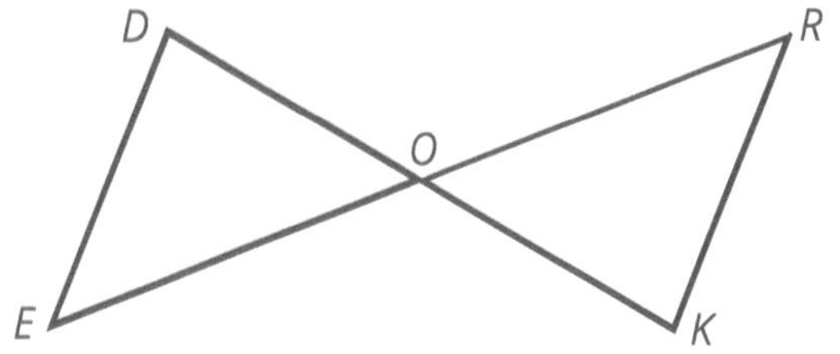

1.1 $A \leftrightarrow$ ____________

1.2 $B \leftrightarrow$ ____________

1.3 $C \leftrightarrow$ ____________

1.4 $E \leftrightarrow$ ____________

1.5 $D \leftrightarrow$ ____________

1.6 $O \leftrightarrow$ ____________

Basing your answer on the appearance of the figures, write true or false.

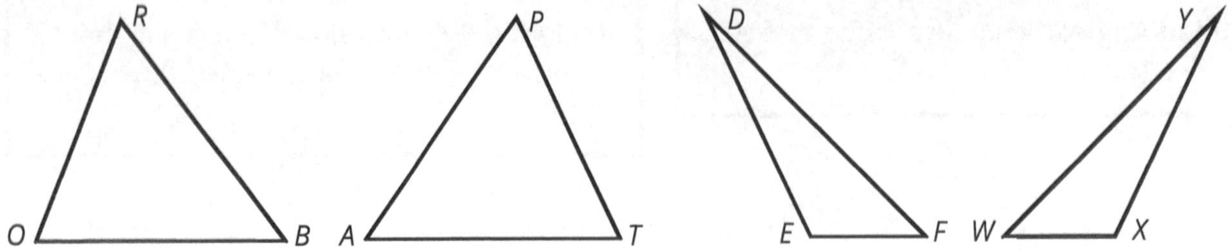

1.7 ____________ $\triangle ROB \cong \triangle PTA$

1.8 ____________ $\triangle ROB \cong \triangle PAT$

1.9 ____________ $\triangle RBO \cong \triangle PTA$

1.10 ____________ $\triangle OBR \cong \triangle APT$

1.11 ____________ $\triangle DEF \cong \triangle WXY$

1.12 ____________ $\triangle DFE \cong \triangle YWX$

1.13 ____________ $\triangle FED \cong \triangle WXY$

1.14 ____________ $\triangle PAT \cong \triangle WXY$

1.15 ____________ $\triangle ROB \cong \triangle DEF$

In the following pairs of congruent triangles, complete the pairs of corresponding parts.

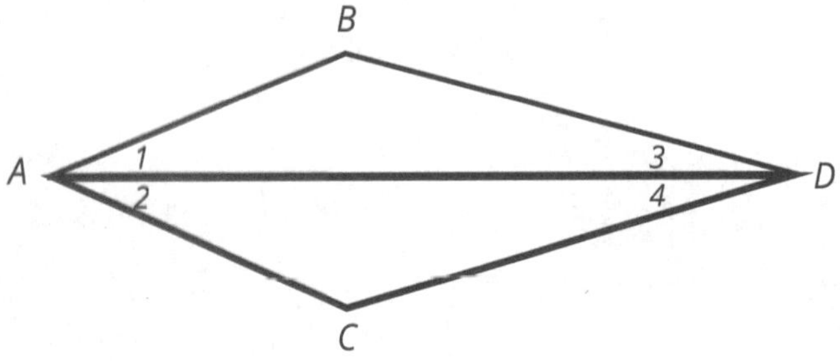

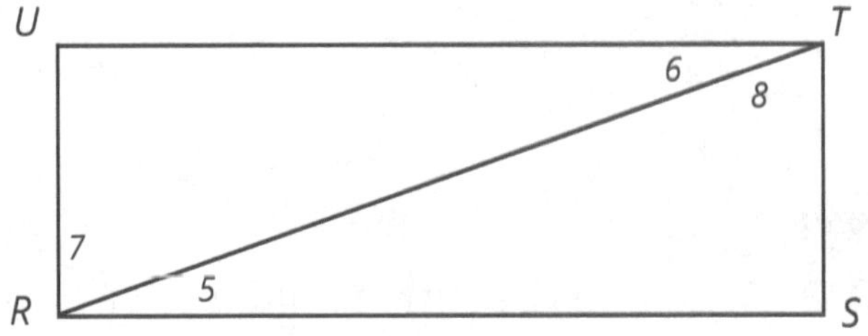

1.16 $\overline{AB} \leftrightarrow$ ____________

1.17 $\overline{CD} \leftrightarrow$ ____________

1.18 $\overline{AD} \leftrightarrow$ ____________

1.19 $\angle 1 \leftrightarrow$ ____________

1.20 $\angle 3 \leftrightarrow$ ____________

1.21 $\angle B \leftrightarrow$ ____________

1.22 $\overline{RS} \leftrightarrow$ ____________

1.23 $\overline{TS} \leftrightarrow$ ____________

1.24 $\overline{RT} \leftrightarrow$ ____________

1.25 $\angle 5 \leftrightarrow$ ____________

1.26 $\angle 7 \leftrightarrow$ ____________

1.27 $\angle U \leftrightarrow$ ____________

Name the included angle or the included side asked for.

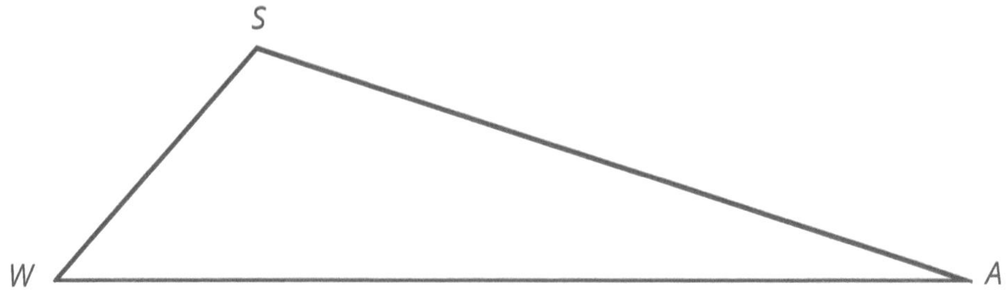

1.28 Included angle between $\overline{WA}$ and $\overline{AS}$: ______________

1.29 Included angle between $\overline{SW}$ and $\overline{WA}$: ______________

1.30 Included side between $\angle S$ and $\angle A$: ______________

1.31 Included side between $\angle S$ and $\angle W$: ______________

1.32 Included angle between $\overline{SW}$ and $\overline{AS}$: ______________

1.33 Included side between $\angle A$ and $\angle W$: ______________

PROVING TRIANGLES CONGRUENT

Suppose you take two identical sets of three sticks with the sticks in one set the same length as the sticks in the other set.

Connect the three sticks in each set at their end points.

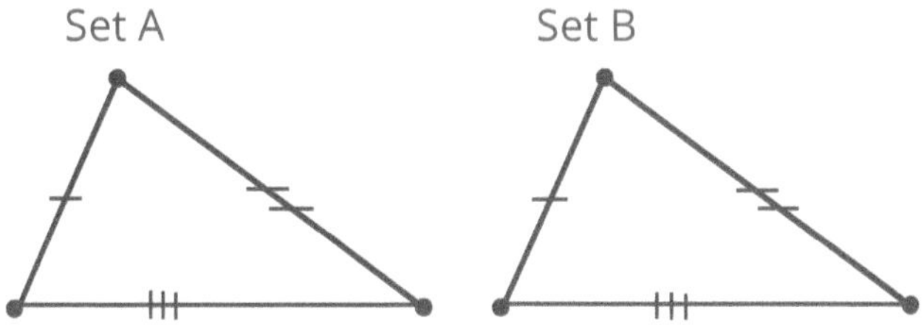

However you put the sticks together, the two △'s formed will be the same size and shape. The two triangles will be congruent. This result suggests the following postulate.

> **POSTULATE 11**
>
> **P11:** If three sides of one triangle are equal to three sides of another triangle, then the triangles are congruent.
>
> **(SSS Postulate)**

Postulate 11 states that we only need to show that three sides of one triangle are equal to three sides of the other triangle for the triangles to be congruent. We do not need to know anything about the angles to use this postulate. The following two postulates can be used to prove triangles congruent in other ways.

> **POSTULATE 12**
>
> **P12:** If two sides and the included angle of one triangle are equal to two sides and the included angle of another triangle, then the triangles are congruent.
>
> **(SAS Postulate)**
>
> **POSTULATE 13**
>
> **P13:** If two angles and the included side of one triangle are equal to two angles and the included side of another triangle, then the triangles are congruent.
>
> **(ASA Postulate)**

With the ASA postulate we can prove the next congruent triangle statement.

> **THEOREM 4-1**
>
> If two angles and a not-included side of one triangle are equal to the corresponding parts of another triangle, then the triangles are congruent.
>
> **(AAS Theorem)**

Note: We will use $\angle A$ for $m\angle A$.

Given: $\angle A = \angle R$
$\angle B = \angle S$
$BC = ST$

Prove: $\triangle ABC \cong \triangle RST$

Plan: Show that $\angle C = \angle T$ and use ASA

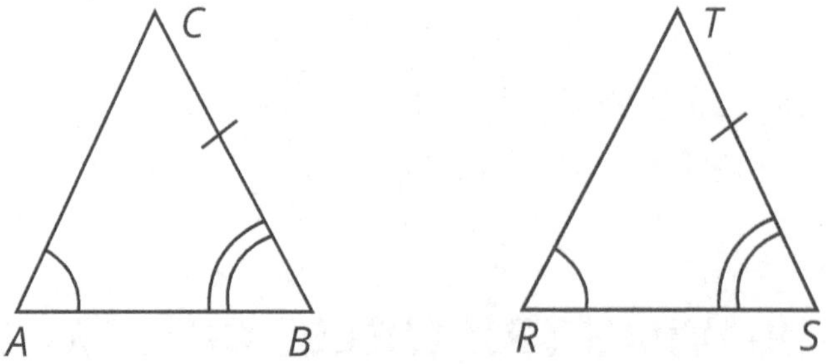

STATEMENT	REASON
1. $\angle A = \angle R$ $\angle B = \angle S$ $BC = ST$	1. Given
2. $\angle C = \angle T$	2. If 2 $\angle$'s of one $\triangle$ are = to 2 $\angle$'s of another, then the third $\angle$'s are also =
3. $\triangle ABC \cong \triangle RST$	3. ASA postulate

We now have four ways that can be used to prove any two triangles congruent: SSS, SAS, ASA, and AAS. When you use these abbreviations, make sure you understand the complete statement.

Two other statements about sides and angles of triangles are correspondence statements only, not congruence statements. They are AAA and SSA.

$\angle A = \angle D$, $\angle B = \angle E$, and $\angle C = \angle F$ but $\triangle ABC$ does not fit exactly over $\triangle DEF$.

AAA

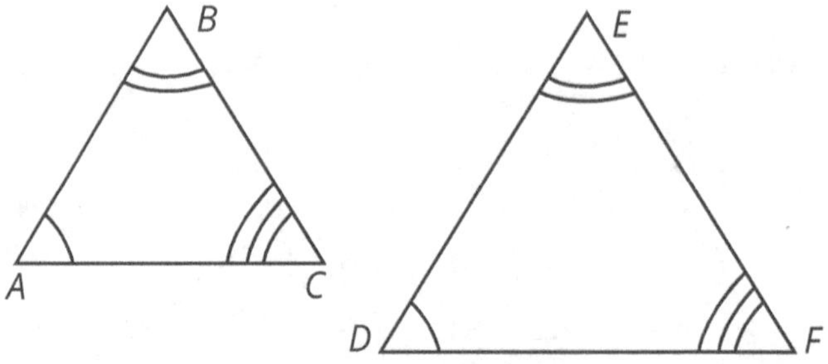

The triangles are the same shape, but different sizes. They are not congruent $\triangle$'s.

The other statement, SSA, is also not a congruence statement.

$AB = DE$, $BC = EF$, and $\angle C = \angle F$; but $\triangle ABC$ will not fit $\triangle DEF$; therefore, the two triangles are not congruent.

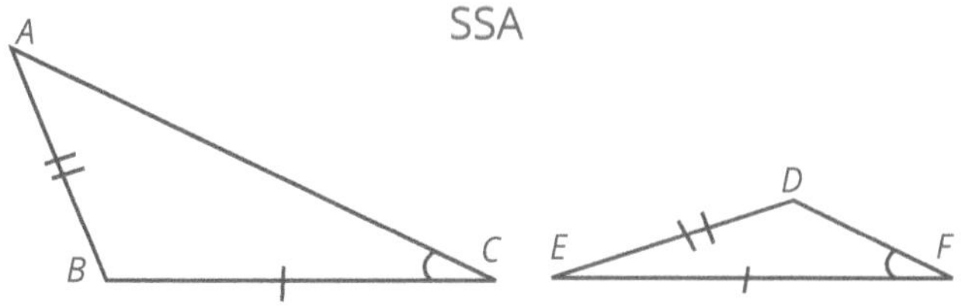

These two triangles are not the same shape.

Remember that when you are asked to write a postulate or theorem, you should write the statement or its abbreviation (such as SSS) rather than writing the number of the theorem or postulate. The statements are easier and more important to learn than are their numbers.

Write the abbreviation of the postulate or theorem that supports the conclusion that $\triangle WAS \cong \triangle NOT$.

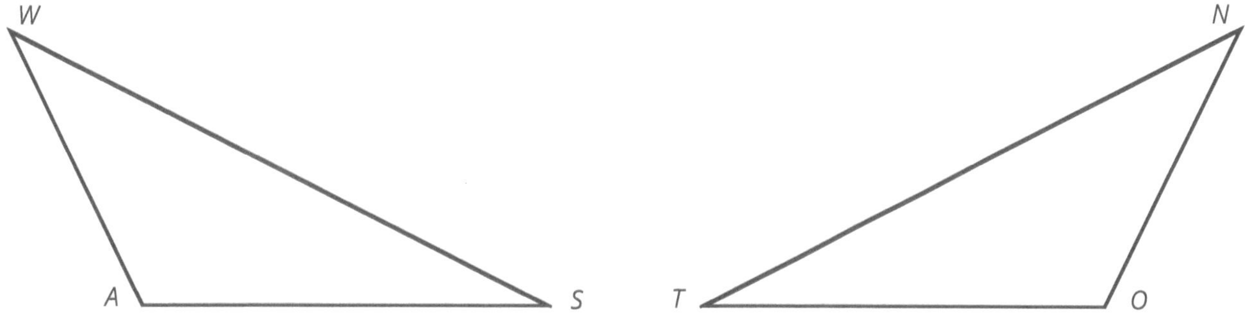

Given:

1.34 $\angle A = \angle O$, $WA = NO$, $AS = OT$ ________

1.35 $WA = NO$, $AS = OT$, $SW = TN$ ________

1.36 $\angle A = \angle O$, $\angle W = \angle N$, $SW = TN$ ________

1.37 $WS = NT$, $AS = OT$, $\angle S = \angle T$ ________

1.38 $WA = NO$, $WS = NT$, $\angle W = \angle N$ ________

1.39 $\angle W = \angle N$, $\angle S = \angle T$, $WS = NT$ ________

1.40 $\angle W = \angle N$, $\angle S = \angle T$, $WA = NO$ ________

Complete the two-column proofs.

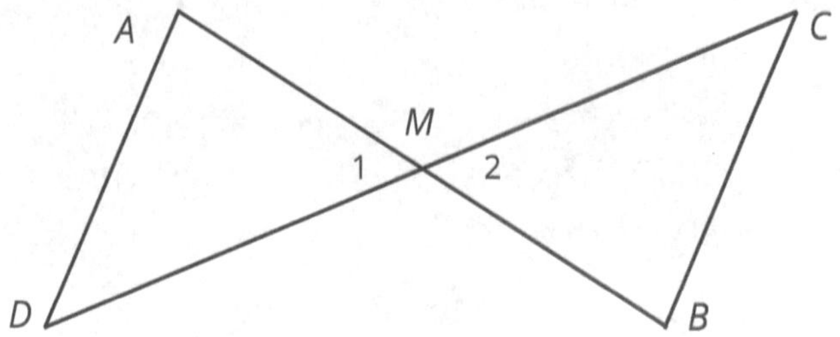

1.41 Given: $AM = BM$

$DM = CM$

Prove: $\triangle AMD \cong \triangle BMC$

STATEMENT	REASON
1. ______	1. ______
2. ______	2. ______
3. ______	3. ______

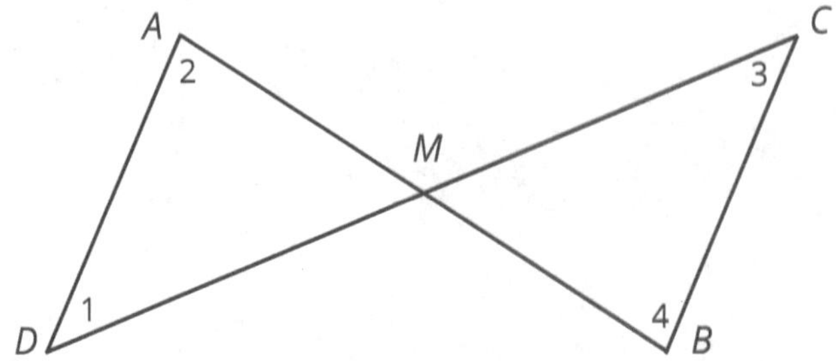

1.42 Given: $\overline{AD} \mid\mid \overline{BC}$

$AD = BC$

Prove: $\triangle ADM \cong \triangle BCM$

STATEMENT	REASON
1. ______	1. ______
2. ______	2. ______
3. ______	3. ______

REVIEW THE POSTULATE OF EQUALITY

Reflexive: a = a

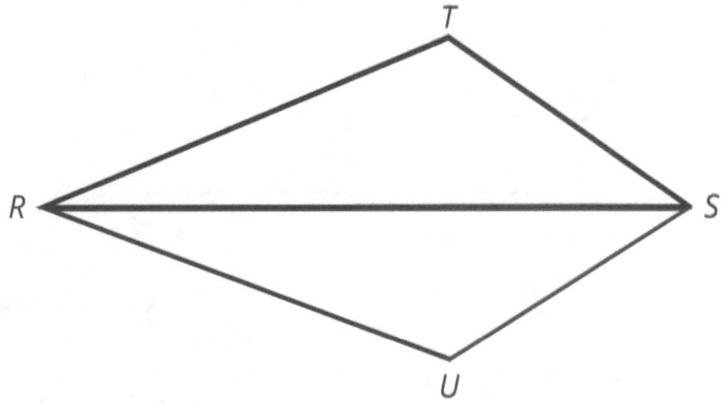

1.43 Given: $RT = RU$

$TS = US$

Prove: $\triangle RST \cong \triangle RSU$

STATEMENT	REASON
1. ______	1. ______
2. ______	2. ______
3. ______	3. ______

1.44 Given: $\overline{CM} \perp \overline{AB}$

$\angle 3 = \angle 4$

Prove: $\triangle AMC \cong \triangle BMC$

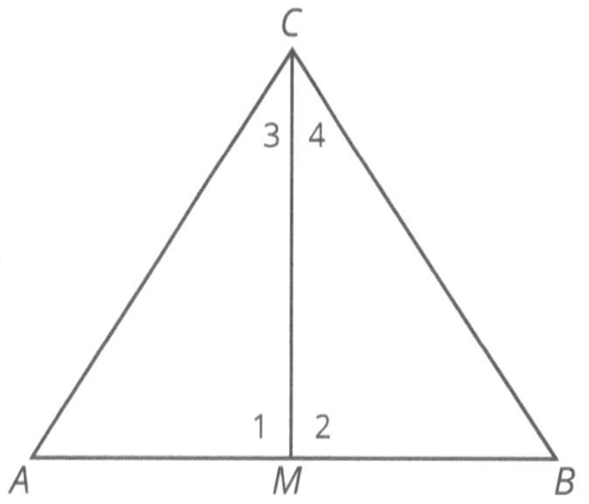

STATEMENT	REASON
1. ______________	1. ______________
2. ______________	2. ______________
3. ______________	3. ______________
4. ______________	4. ______________

1.45 Given: $\overline{DC} \parallel \overline{AB}$

$\overline{AD} \parallel \overline{BC}$

Prove: $\triangle ACD \cong \triangle CAB$

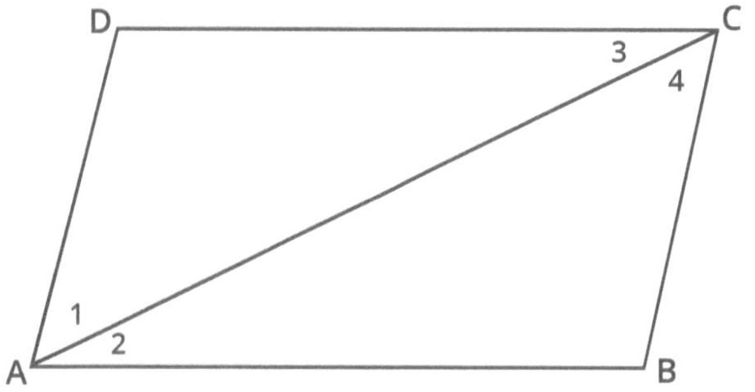

STATEMENT	REASON
1. ______________	1. ______________
2. ______________	2. ______________
3. ______________	3. ______________
4. ______________	4. ______________

Write the required information.

Given: $\triangle ABC \cong \triangle RST$

If $AB = 6$, $ST = 8$, $AC = 12$,

$\angle A = 40°$, $\angle T = 20°$, then

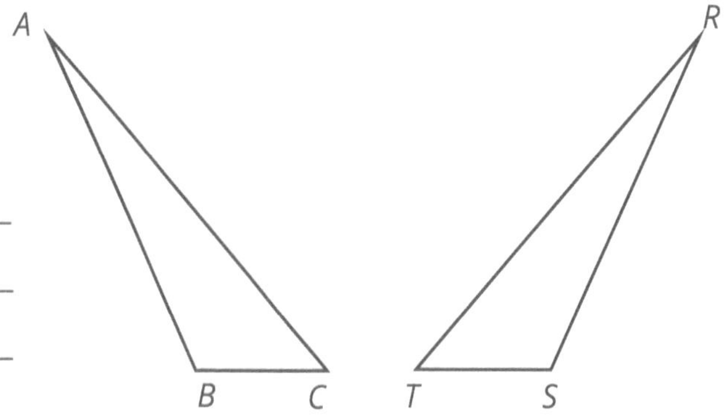

1.46 $BC =$ ______________

1.47 $RT =$ ______________

1.48 $\angle C =$ ______________

1.49 $\angle B =$ ______________

1.50 $\angle S =$ ______________

1.51 $\angle R =$ ______________

1.52 $RS =$ ______________

PROVING RIGHT TRIANGLES CONGRUENT

Right triangles are a special kind of triangle with some special congruence statements all their own. Remember the parts of a right triangle? Make sure you know and understand the full wording of the statements. Remember that the A in HA and LA represents an *acute* angle, not just any angle.

The hypotenuse is the side opposite the right angle. It is the longest side of the triangle. The other two sides are called legs.

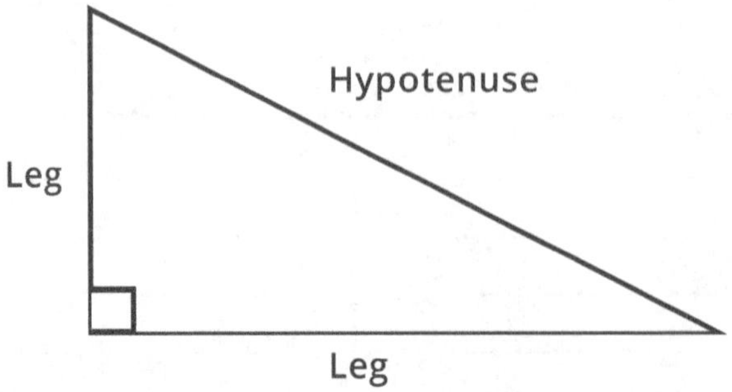

> **THEOREM 4-2**
>
> If two legs of one right triangle are equal to two legs of another right triangle, then the two right triangles are congruent.
>
> **(LL Theorem)**

Given: $XY = MN$

$YZ = NO$

$\triangle XYZ$, $\triangle MNO$ are rt. $\triangle$'s

Prove: $\triangle XYZ \cong \triangle MNO$

Plan: Show $\angle Y = \angle N$ and use SAS

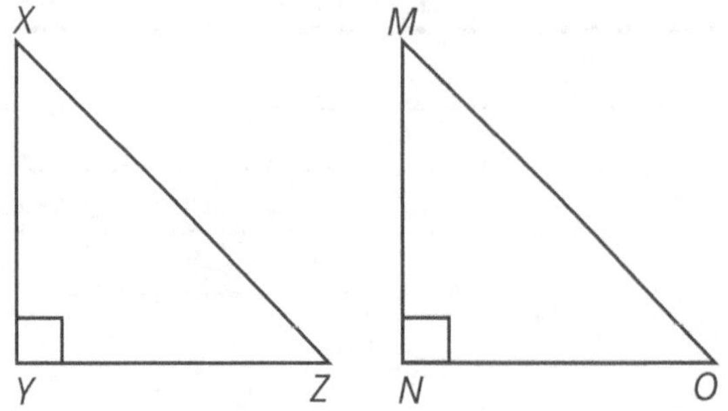

STATEMENT	REASON
1. $XY = MN$, $YZ = NO$ $\triangle XYZ$, $\triangle MNO$ are rt. $\triangle$'s	1. Given
2. $\angle Y = \angle N$	2. All rt. $\angle$'s are =
3. $\triangle XYZ \cong \triangle MNO$	3. SAS

Another congruence statement that can be used for right triangles is given in the next postulate.

POSTULATE 14

P14: If the hypotenuse and a leg of one right triangle are equal to the hypotenuse and leg of another right triangle, then the triangles are congruent.

(HL Postulate)

THEOREM 4-3

If the hypotenuse and an acute angle of one right triangle are equal to the hypotenuse and an acute angle of another right triangle, then the triangles are congruent.

(HA Theorem)

Two more theorems will be proved for congruent right triangles.

Given: $\triangle ABC$, $\triangle RST$ are rt. $\triangle$'s
$AC = RT$
$\angle C = \angle T$

Prove: $\triangle ABC \cong \triangle RST$

Plan: Show $\angle B = \angle S$ and use AAS

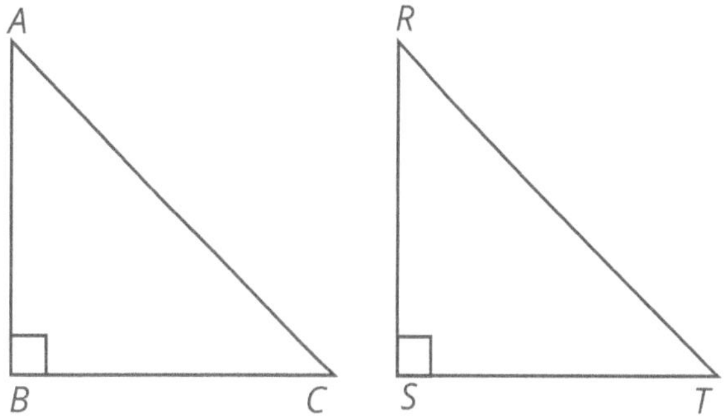

STATEMENT	REASON
1. $\triangle ABC$, $\triangle RST$ are right triangles $AC = RT$ $\angle C = \angle T$	1. Given
2. $\angle B = \angle S$	2. All rt. $\angle$'s are =
3. $\triangle ABC \cong \triangle RST$	3. AAS

THEOREM 4-4

If a leg and an acute angle of one right triangle are equal to the corresponding parts of another right triangle, then the triangles are congruent.

(LA Theorem)

Given: $\triangle ABC$, $\triangle DEF$ are rt. $\triangle$'s
$AB = DE$
$\angle A = \angle D$

Prove: $\triangle ABC \cong \triangle DEF$

Plan: Show $\angle B = \angle E$ and use ASA

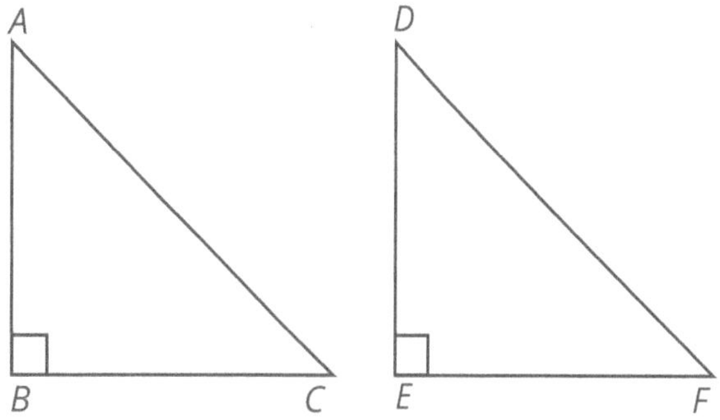

STATEMENT	REASON
1. $\triangle ABC$, $\triangle DEF$ are rt. $\triangle$'s $AB = DE$ $\angle A = \angle D$	1. Given
2. $\angle B = \angle E$	2. All rt. $\angle$'s are =
3. $\triangle ABC \cong \triangle DEF$	3. ASA

These statements are the congruence statements for right triangles: HA, LL, LA, and HL.

Which of the congruence statements for right triangles would you use to prove $\triangle ABC \cong \triangle DEF$?

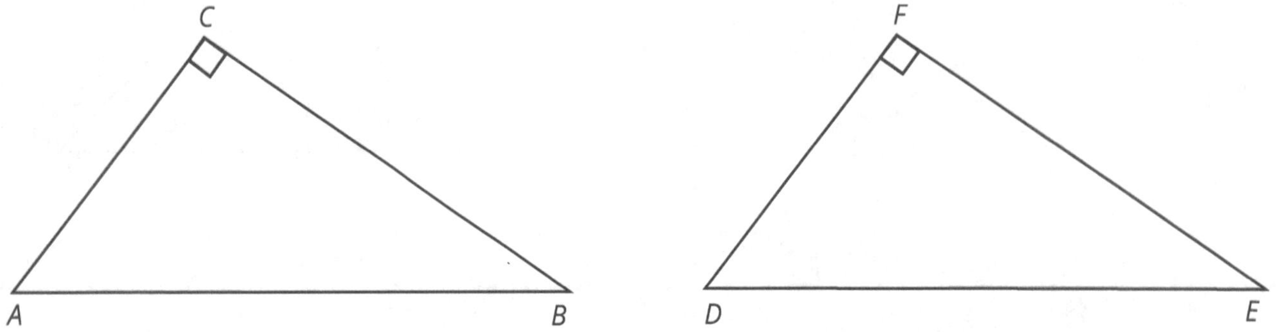

Given:

1.53 $\angle C$, $\angle F$ are rt. $\angle$'s; $AB = DE$; $\angle A = \angle D$ ____________________

1.54 $\angle C$, $\angle F$ are rt. $\angle$'s; $AC = DF$; $\angle B = \angle E$ ____________________

1.55 $\angle C$, $\angle F$ are rt. $\angle$'s; $\angle B = \angle E$; $BC = EF$ ____________________

1.56 $\angle C$, $\angle F$ are rt. $\angle$' s; $AC = DF$; $BC = EF$ ____________________

1.57 $\angle C$, $\angle F$ are rt. $\angle$' s; $AB = DE$; $BC = EF$ ____________________

Complete the two-column proofs.

1.58 Given: $\angle 3$, $\angle 4$ are rt. $\angle$' s
$RS = RT$
Prove: $\triangle RZS \cong \triangle RZT$

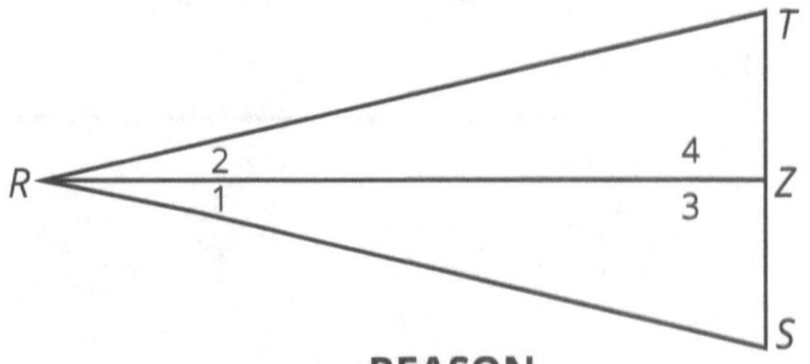

STATEMENT	REASON
1. ________________	1. ________________
2. ________________	2. ________________
3. ________________	3. ________________

1.59 Given: ∠3, ∠4 rt. ∠'s
$AX = BX$
Prove: △ AXC ≅ △ BXC

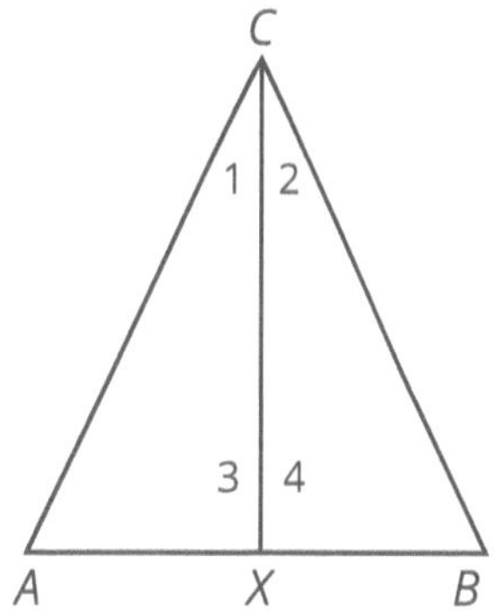

STATEMENT	REASON
1. ______	1. ______
2. ______	2. ______
3. ______	3. ______

1.60 Given: $\overline{AB} \perp \overline{BD}$
$\overline{AB} \perp \overline{BC}$
$AC = AD$
Prove: △ ABC ≅ △ ABD

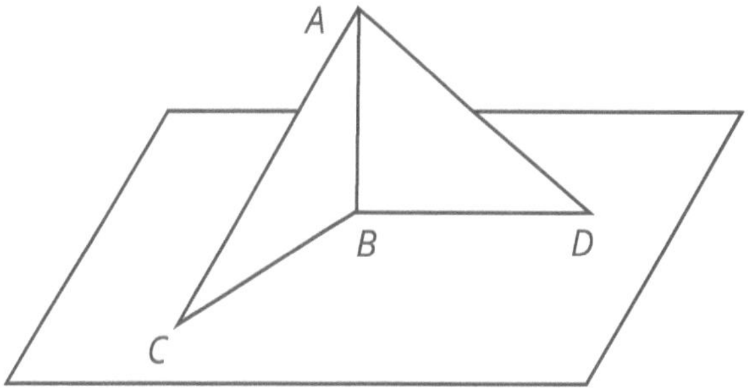

STATEMENT	REASON
1. ______	1. ______
2. ______	2. ______
3. ______	3. ______
4. ______	4. ______

1.61 Given: ∠D, ∠B are rt. ∠'s
$\overline{DC} \parallel \overline{AB}$
Prove: △ ADC ≅ △ CBA

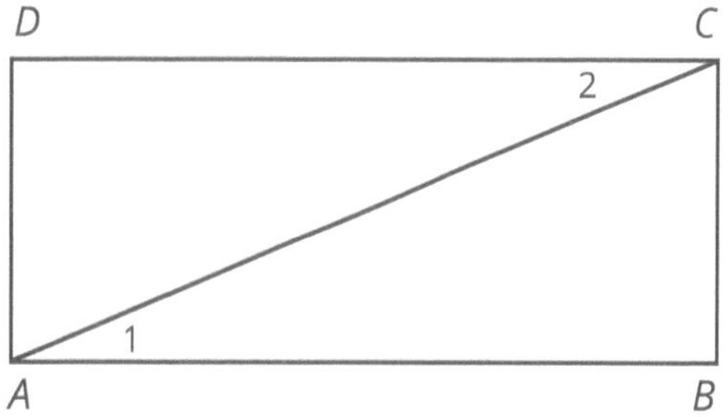

STATEMENT	REASON
1. ______	1. ______
2. ______	2. ______
3. ______	3. ______
4. ______	4. ______

1.62 Given: $\overline{RS} \perp \overline{ST}$

$\overline{RS} \perp \overline{SQ}$

$\angle STR = \angle SQR$

Prove: $\triangle RST \cong \triangle RSQ$

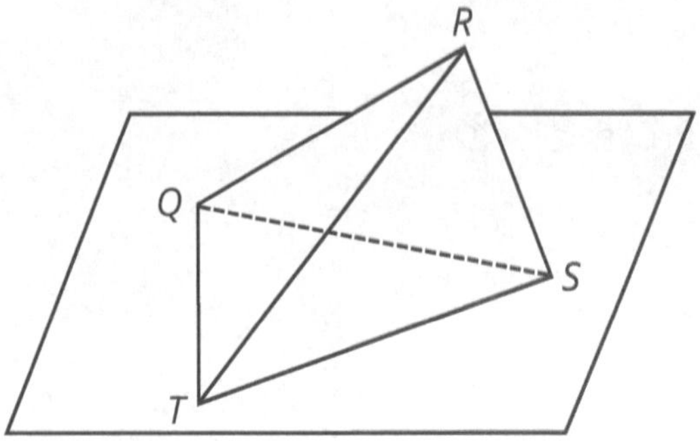

STATEMENT	REASON
1. ______	1. ______
2. ______	2. ______
3. ______	3. ______
4. ______	4. ______

TEACHER CHECK ______ initials ______ date

Review the material in this section in preparation for the Self Test. This Self Test will check your mastery of this particular section. The items missed on this Self Test will indicate specific areas where restudy is needed for mastery.

SELF TEST 1

Name the corresponding parts if $\triangle RST \cong \triangle WXY$ (each answer, 3 points).

1.01 $\angle R$ = ______________________ **1.02** $\angle S$ = ______________________

1.03 $\angle T$ = ______________________ **1.04** RS = ______________________

1.05 ST = ______________________ **1.06** RT = ______________________

Answer the following questions about this triangle (each answer, 3 points).

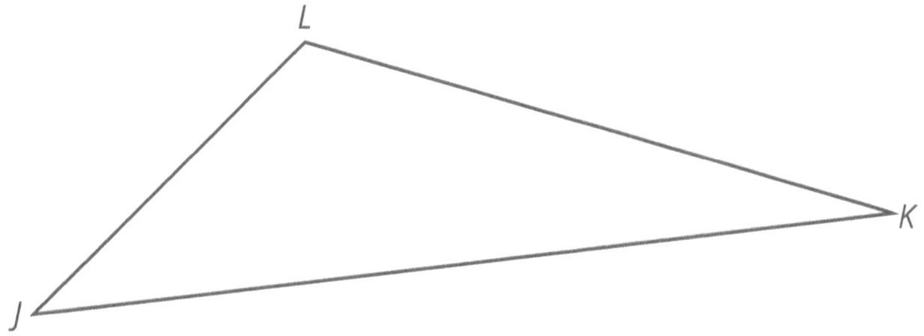

1.07 $\angle J$ is included between a. ______________ and b. ______________ .

1.08 $\overline{JK}$ is included between a. ______________ and b. ______________ .

1.09 $\angle K$ is included between $\overline{LK}$ and ______________________ .

1.010 $\angle L$ is not an included angle for sides ______________ and ______________ .

Write the complete statements (each answer, 4 points).

1.011 ASA ____

____

____

1.012 HL ____

____

____

1.013 SSS ____

____

____

1.014 LA ____

____

____

1.015 SAS ____

____

____

Complete the proof (each answer, 4 points).

Given: $\overline{CA} \parallel \overline{DB}$

E is midpoint of $\overline{AD}$

Prove: $\triangle AEC \cong \triangle DEB$

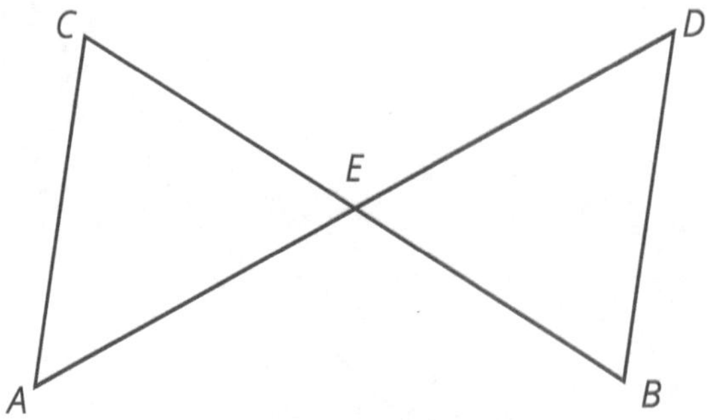

STATEMENT	REASON
1.016 ____________________	____________________
1.017 ____________________	____________________
1.018 ____________________	____________________
1.019 ____________________	____________________

Write the congruence statement that you would use to show the △'s ≅ (each answer, 3 points).

1.020 ____________

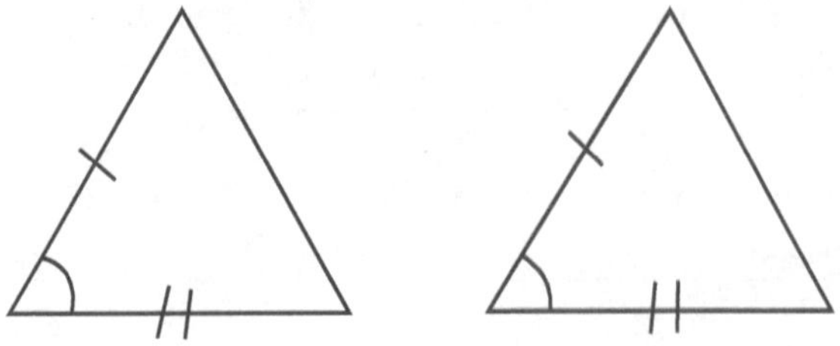

1.021 ____________

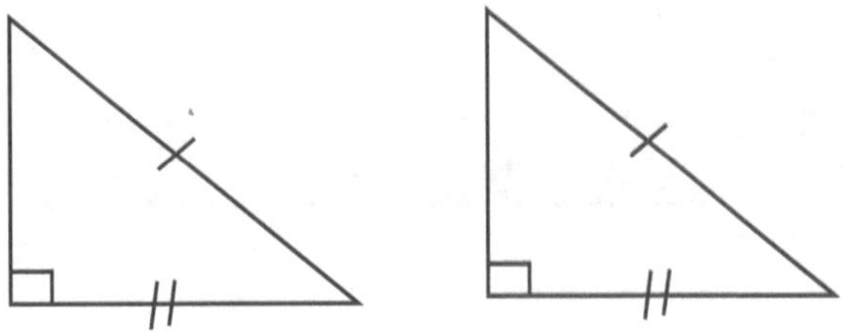

1.022 ____________

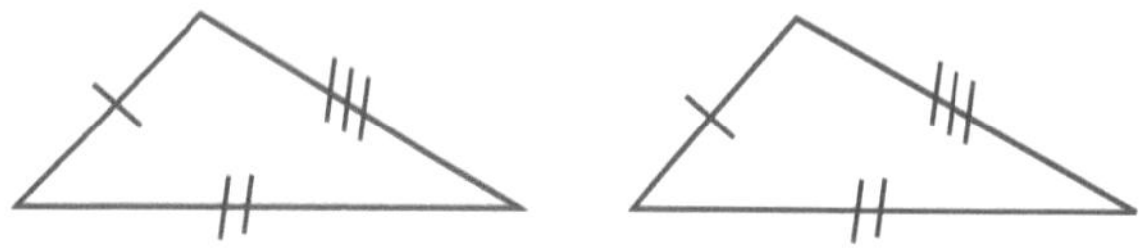

1.023 ____________

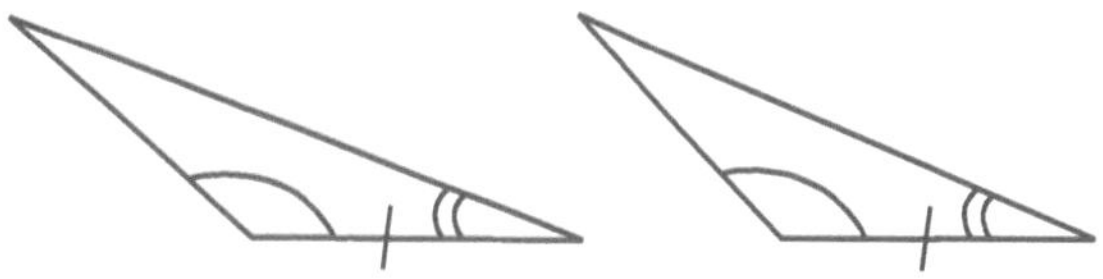

1.024 ____________

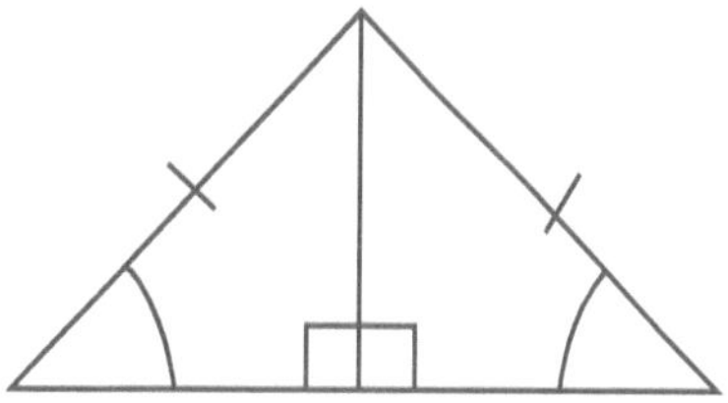

1.025 ____________

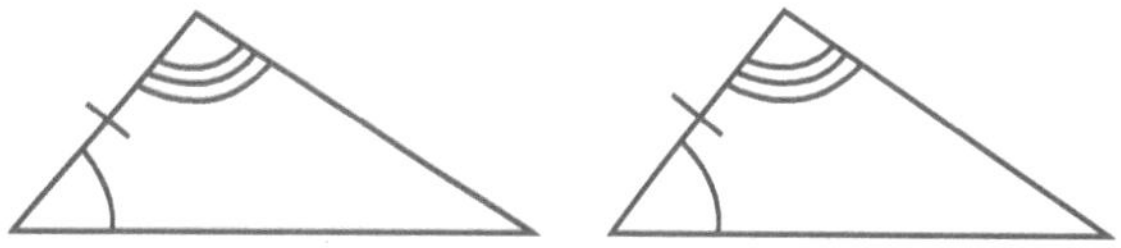

75/93 **SCORE** ____________ **TEACHER** ____________ ____________
initials date

2. CORRESPONDING PARTS

Our definition of congruent triangles states that all six corresponding parts are equal. When we proved that triangles were congruent, we only had to show that three pairs of parts were equal: SAS, SSS, ASA, or AAS.

Once we have established the triangles congruent, then we know by definition that all the corresponding parts are equal. We can write this expression as CPCTE: Corresponding parts of congruent triangles are equal.

To prove that two angles or two segments are equal, try to find congruent triangles of which they are parts.

Section Objectives

Review these objectives. When you have finished this section, you should be able to:

4. Prove corresponding parts equal when triangles are in normal position.
5. Prove corresponding parts equal when triangles are overlapping.
6. Prove properties of isosceles triangles.

INDEPENDENT TRIANGLES

Most of the time the positions of the triangles are such that little doubt arises as to which triangles you are working with.

Model 1:

Given: $AC = BC$

$AX = BX$

Prove: $\angle 1 = \angle 2$

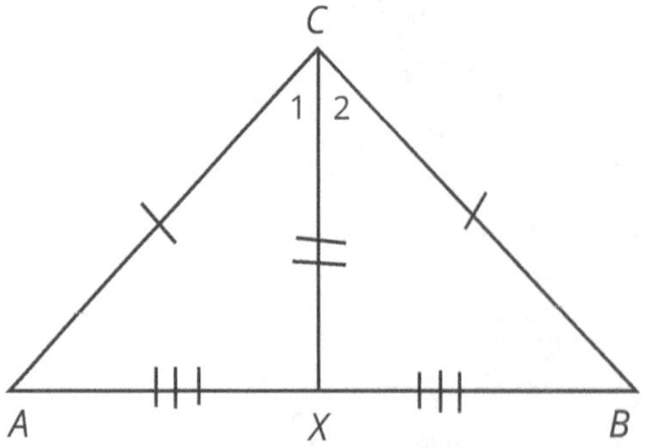

STATEMENT	REASON
1. $AC = BC$, $AX = BX$	1. Given
2. $CX = CX$	2. Reflexive
3. $\triangle AXC \cong \triangle BXC$	3. SSS
4. $\angle 1 = \angle 2$	4. CPCTE

Model 2:

Given: $\angle R = \angle S$

N is midpoint of $\overline{RS}$

Prove: $RU = ST$

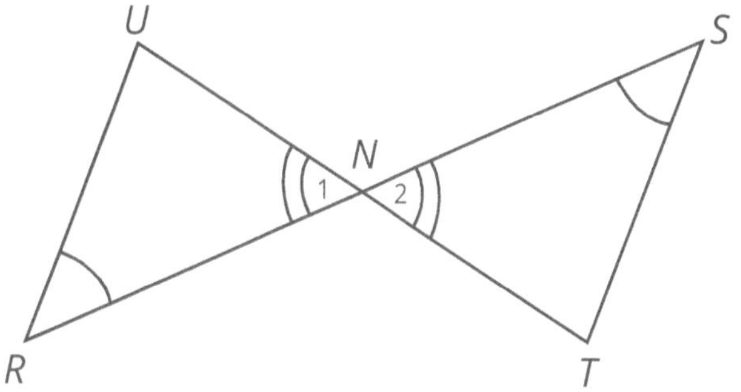

STATEMENT	REASON
1. $\angle R = \angle S$ N is midpoint of $\overline{RS}$	1. Given
2. $RN = NS$	2. Definition of midpoint
3. $\angle 1 = \angle 2$	3. Vertical $\angle$'s are =
4. $\triangle RNU \cong \triangle SNT$	4. *ASA*
5. $RU = ST$	5. CPCTE

Complete the following proofs related to this figure.

2.1 Given: $AB = CD$

$BC = DA$

Prove: $\angle B = \angle D$

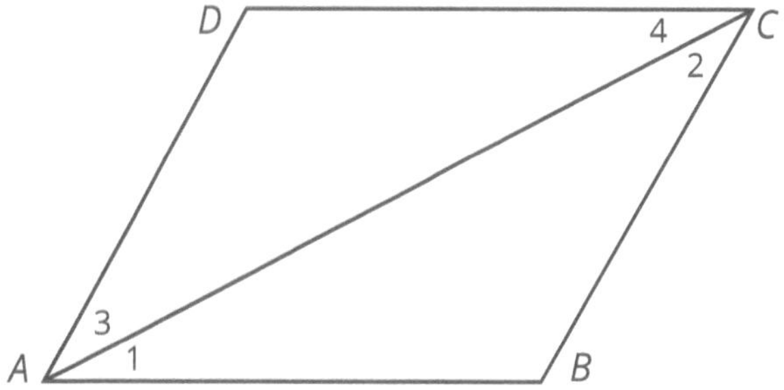

STATEMENT	REASON
1. __________	1. __________
2. __________	2. __________
3. __________	3. __________
4. __________	4. __________

2.2 Given: $AB = CD$

$\angle 1 = \angle 4$

Prove: $AD = CB$

STATEMENT	REASON
1. ____________	1. ____________
2. ____________	2. ____________
3. ____________	3. ____________
4. ____________	4. ____________

2.3 Given: $\angle 1 = \angle 4$

$\angle 2 = \angle 3$

Prove: $AB = CD$

STATEMENT	REASON
1. ____________	1. ____________
2. ____________	2. ____________
3. ____________	3. ____________
4. ____________	4. ____________

2.4 Given: $\angle 1 = \angle 4$

$\angle B = \angle D$

Prove: $AD = CB$

STATEMENT	REASON
1. ____________	1. ____________
2. ____________	2. ____________
3. ____________	3. ____________
4. ____________	4. ____________

2.5 Given: $\overline{AB} \mid\mid \overline{CD}$

$\overline{AD} \mid\mid \overline{CB}$

Prove: $AD = CB$

STATEMENT	REASON
1. ____________	1. ____________
2. ____________	2. ____________
3. ____________	3. ____________
4. ____________	4. ____________
5. ____________	5. ____________

2.6 Given: $\overline{AB} \parallel \overline{CD}$

$AB = CD$

Prove: $\angle 2 = \angle 3$

STATEMENT	REASON
1. ______	1. ______
2. ______	2. ______
3. ______	3. ______
4. ______	4. ______
5. ______	5. ______

2.7 Given: $AB = CD$

$AD = CB$

Prove: $\overline{DC} \parallel \overline{AB}$

STATEMENT	REASON
1. ______	1. ______
2. ______	2. ______
3. ______	3. ______
4. ______	4. ______
5. ______	5. ______

Complete the following proofs related to this figure.

2.8 Given: $\overline{TQ}$ bisects $\angle RTS$

$\angle R = \angle S$

Prove: $\overline{TQ} \perp \overline{RS}$

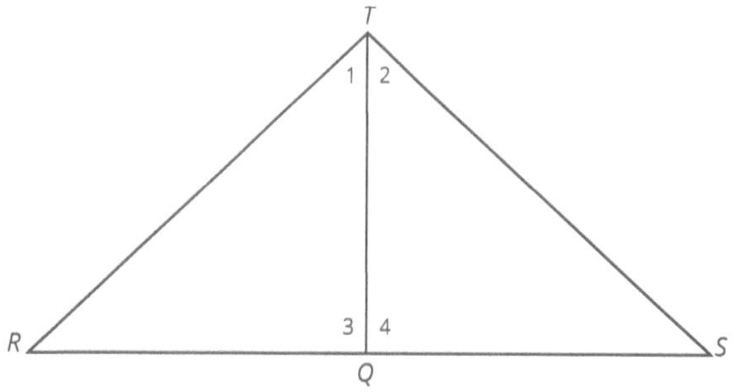

STATEMENT	REASON
1. ______	1. ______
2. ______	2. ______
3. ______	3. ______
4. ______	4. ______
5. ______	5. ______
6. ______	6. ______

2.9 Given: $\overline{TQ}$ bisects $\overline{RS}$

$RT = ST$

Prove: $\overline{TQ} \perp \overline{RS}$

STATEMENT	REASON
1. ______________	1. ______________
2. ______________	2. ______________
3. ______________	3. ______________
4. ______________	4. ______________
5. ______________	5. ______________
6. ______________	6. ______________

2.10 Given: $\overline{TQ}$ is $\perp$ bisector of $\overline{RS}$

Prove: $\angle R = \angle S$

STATEMENT	REASON
1. ______________	1. ______________
2. ______________	2. ______________
3. ______________	3. ______________
4. ______________	4. ______________
5. ______________	5. ______________

Complete the following proofs related to the figures.

2.11 Given: $\angle 2 = \angle 3$

$\angle 4 = \angle 5$

Prove: $RS = RT$

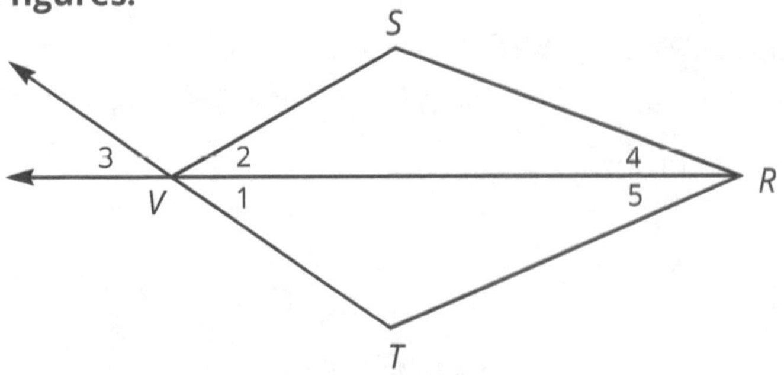

STATEMENT	REASON
1. ______________	1. ______________
2. ______________	2. ______________
3. ______________	3. ______________
4. ______________	4. ______________
5. ______________	5. ______________
6. ______________	6. ______________

2.12 Given: $\triangle ABC$, $\triangle DEF$ are rt. $\triangle$'s
$AB = DE$, $\angle A = \angle D$
Prove: $BC = EF$

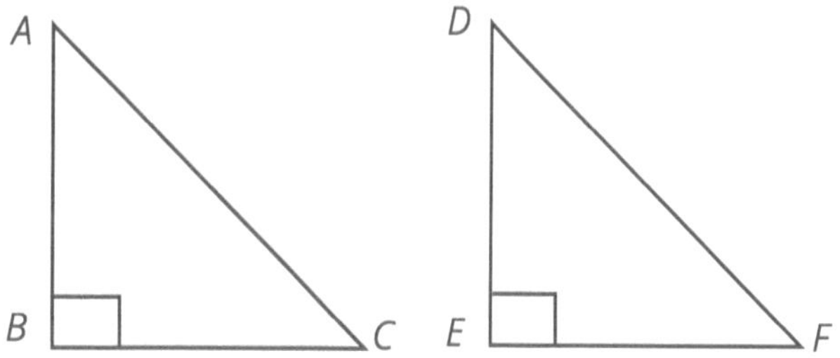

STATEMENT	REASON
1. ____________	1. ____________
2. ____________	2. ____________
3. ____________	3. ____________

2.13 Given: $\angle A$, $\angle B$ are rt. $\angle$'s
$AC = BD$
Prove: $MC = MD$

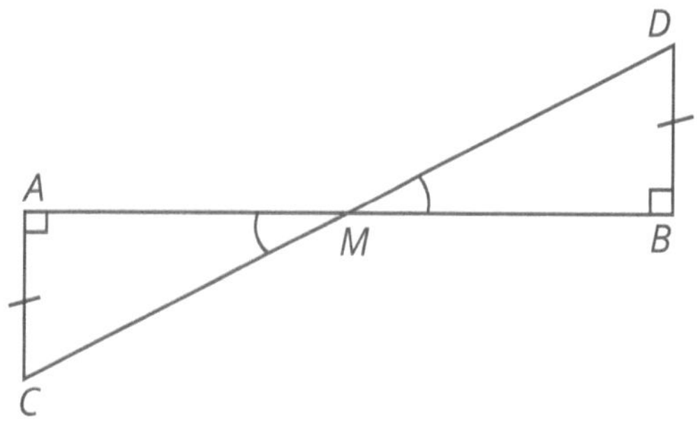

STATEMENT	REASON
1. ____________	1. ____________
2. ____________	2. ____________
3. ____________	3. ____________
4. ____________	4. ____________

2.14 Given: $\angle 1 = \angle 2$
$\angle 3 = \angle 4$
D midpoint of $\overline{BE}$
$BC = DE$
Prove: $\angle A = \angle E$

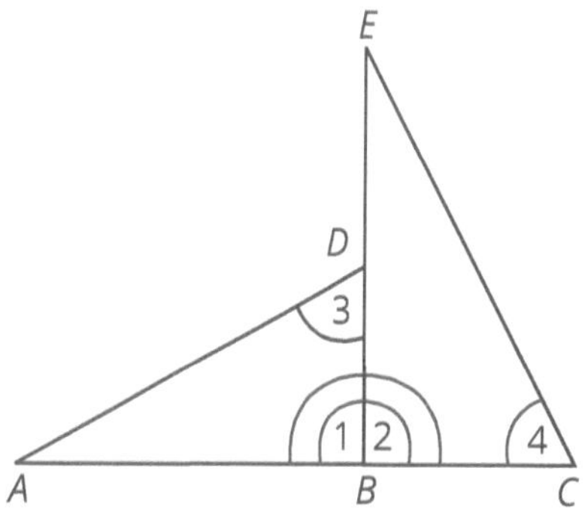

STATEMENT	REASON
1. ____________	1. ____________
2. ____________	2. ____________
3. ____________	3. ____________
4. ____________	4. ____________
5. ____________	5. ____________

2.15 Given: $\angle S = \angle T$

$RV = UV$

Prove: $SR = TU$

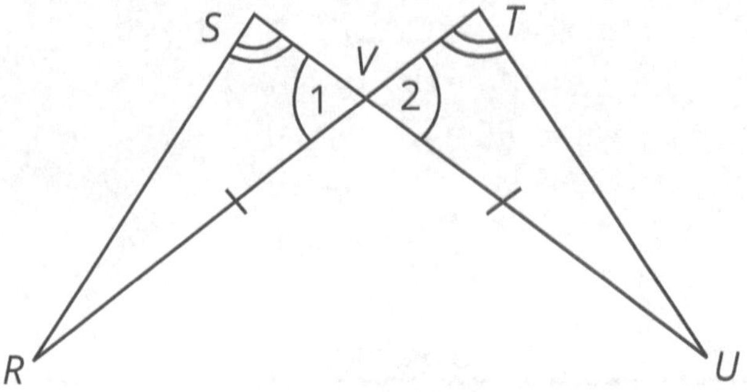

STATEMENT	REASON
1. ______	1. ______
2. ______	2. ______
3. ______	3. ______
4. ______	4. ______

OVERLAPPING TRIANGLES

Many times in geometric figures the triangles with which we need to work are not entirely separate, but overlap each other. Overlapping triangles are triangles with interiors that have points in common.

Model 1:

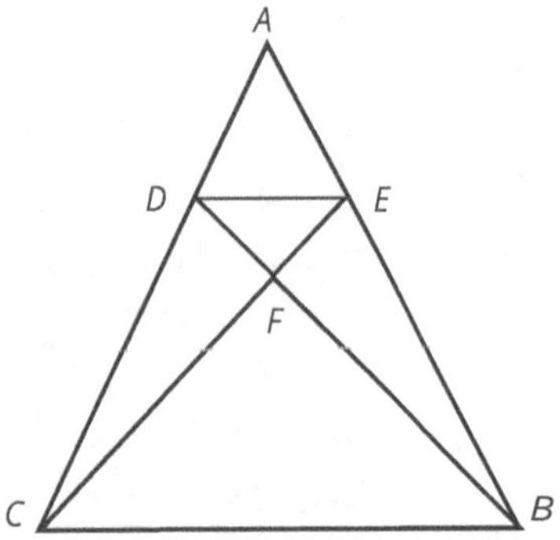

In the figure shown in Model 1, can you see what appear to be congruent triangles?

Does $\triangle DEC$ seem to be congruent to $\triangle EDB$?

What about $\triangle DFC$ and $\triangle EFB$?

Is $\triangle DBC \cong \triangle ECB$? Are there any others?

One way to see the congruent triangles better is to pull the triangles apart.

Model 2:

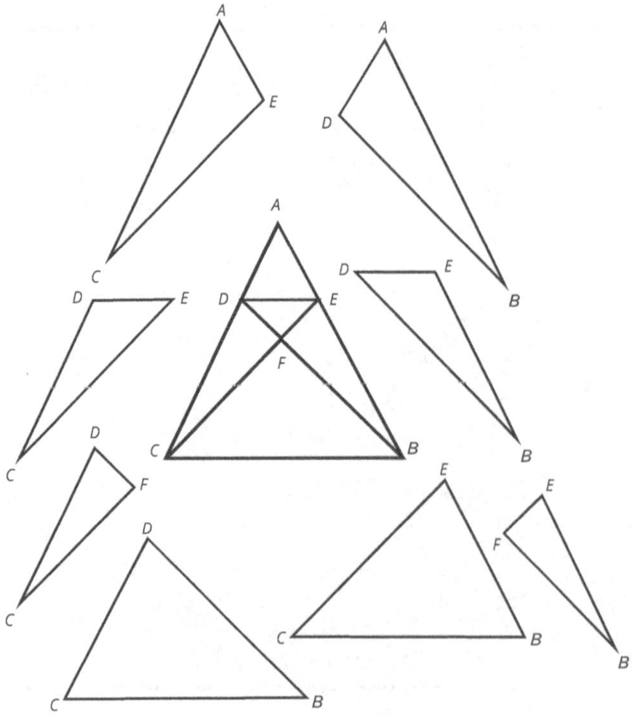

The four pairs of congruent triangles may have been hard to see in the original figure. The relationships became much clearer when the triangles were pulled apart.

Name the △ that seems to be congruent to the given one.

2.16 △ *ADB* ≅ △ ____________________

2.17 △ *BEC* ≅ △ ____________________

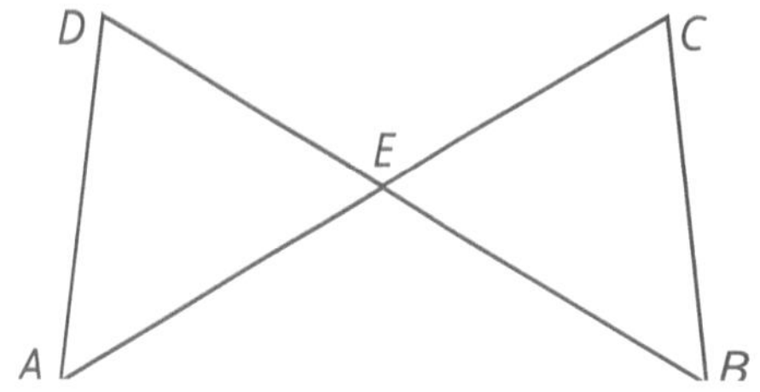

2.18 △ *ACB* ≅ △ ____________________

2.19 △ *ACD* ≅ △ ____________________

2.20 △ *AOD* ≅ △ ____________________

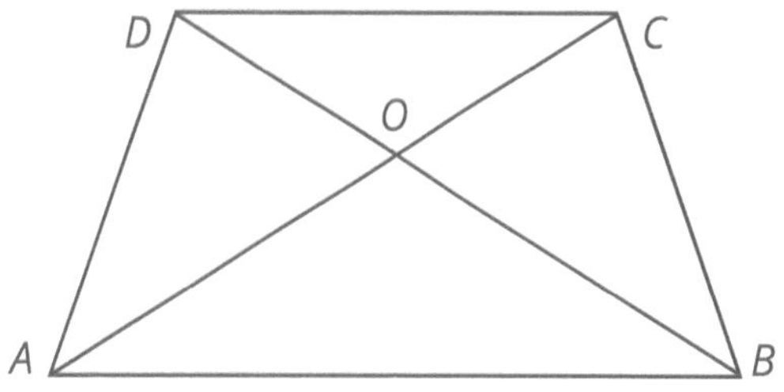

2.21 △ *ABD* ≅ △ ____________________

2.22 △ *AFD* ≅ △ ____________________

2.23 △ *AFE* ≅ △ ____________________

2.24 △ *BCF* ≅ △ ____________________

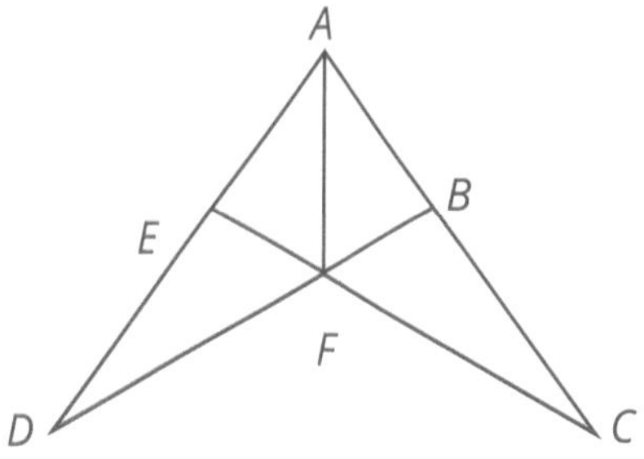

Complete the pairs of △'s.

2.25 △ *EGF* ≅ △ ____________________

2.26 △ *EGA* ≅ △ ____________________

2.27 △ *EBA* ≅ △ ____________________

2.28 △ *FGA* ≅ △ ____________________

2.29 △ *FCA* ≅ △ ____________________

2.30 △ *ECF* ≅ △ ____________________

2.31 △ *AGB* ≅ △ ____________________

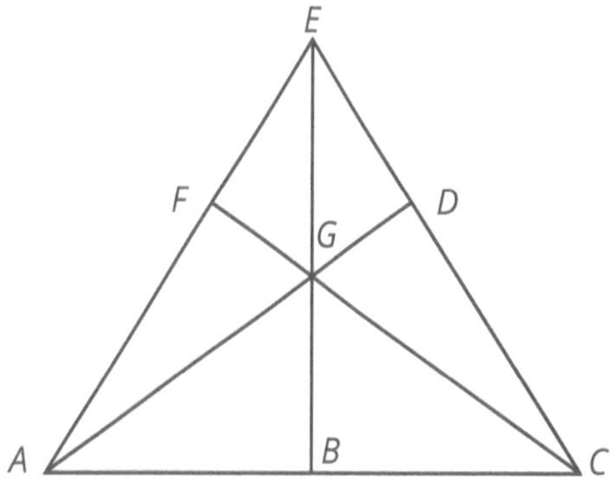

To prove certain segments equal or certain angles equal by using congruent triangles, you must first decide which triangles you are going to prove congruent. This decision takes some practice in seeing to which triangles the two parts belong.

Model 1:

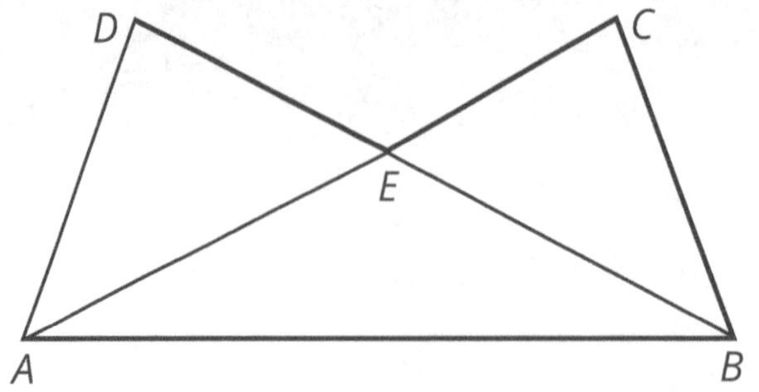

If you want to prove that *DE* = *EC*, use the fact that they are sides of △ *DEA* and △ *CEB*. If you want to prove *AC* = *BD*, you would use △ *ACB* and △ *BDA*. If you want to prove *AD* = *BC*, you have a choice of △ *ADB* ≅ △ *BCA* or △ *ADE* ≅ △ *BCE*. You would use the pair that you can prove congruent from the information given.

Model 2:

Given: *AE* = *BE*

DE = *CE*

Prove: *AD* = *BC*

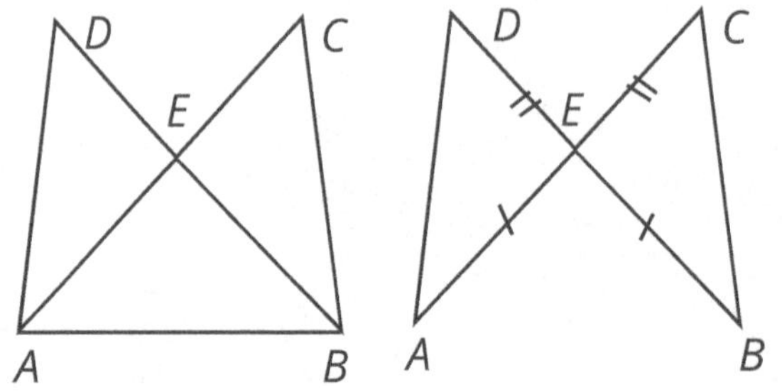

STATEMENT	REASON
1. *AE* = *BE*, *DE* = *CE*	1. Given
2. ∠*DEA* = ∠*CEB*	2. Vertical ∠'s =
3. △ *AED* ≅ △ *BEC*	3. *SAS*
4. *AD* = *BC*	4. CPCTE

Model 3:

Given: *AD* = *BC*

DB = *AC*

Prove: *DB* = *CA*

∠*D* = ∠*C*

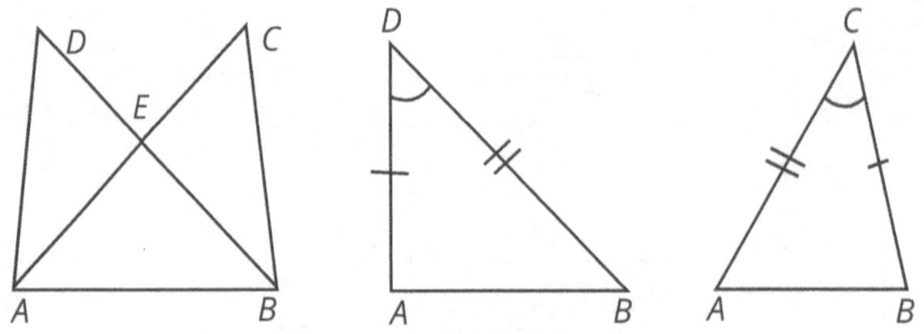

STATEMENT	REASON
1. $AD = BC, DB = AC$	1. Given
2. $AB = AB$	2. Reflexive
3. $\triangle ABD \cong \triangle BAC$	3. *SSS*
4. $DB = CA \quad \angle D = \angle C$	4. CPCTE

Complete the following proofs.

2.32 Given: $RM = SN$

$\angle MRS = \angle NSR$

Prove: $SM = RN$

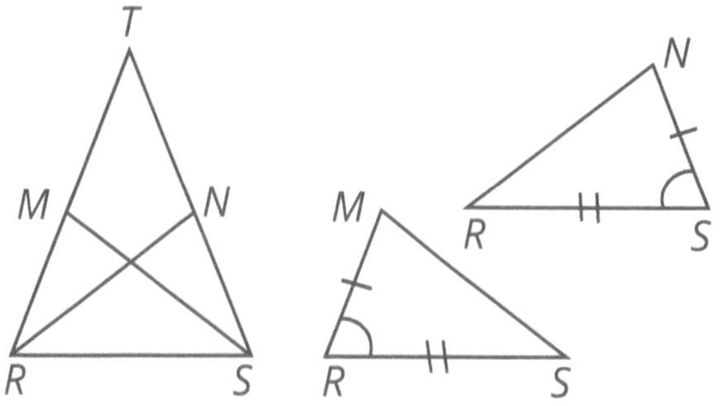

STATEMENT	REASON
1. ______	1. ______
2. ______	2. ______
3. ______	3. ______
4. ______	4. ______

2.33 Given: $RM = SN$

$SM = RN$

Prove: $\angle RMS = \angle SNR$

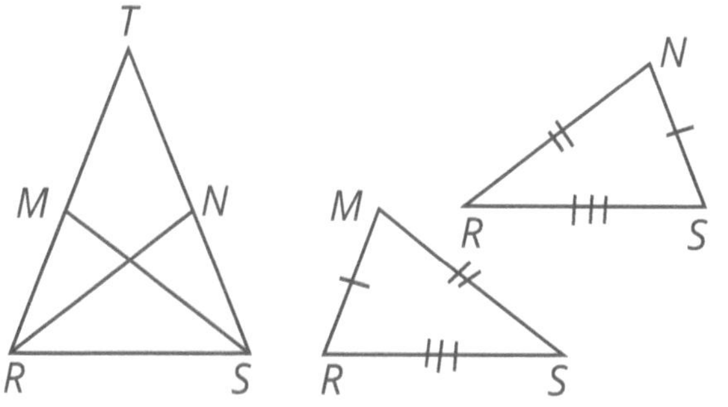

STATEMENT	REASON
1. ______	1. ______
2. ______	2. ______
3. ______	3. ______
4. ______	4. ______

2.34 Given: $RT = ST$
$MT = NT$
Prove: $\angle RNT = \angle SMT$

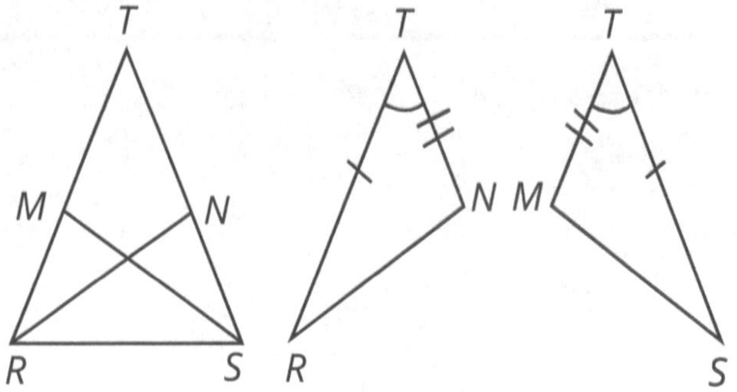

STATEMENT	REASON
1. __________	1. __________
2. __________	2. __________
3. __________	3. __________
4. __________	4. __________

2.35 Given: $RM = SN$
$TM = TN$
Prove: $RN = SM$

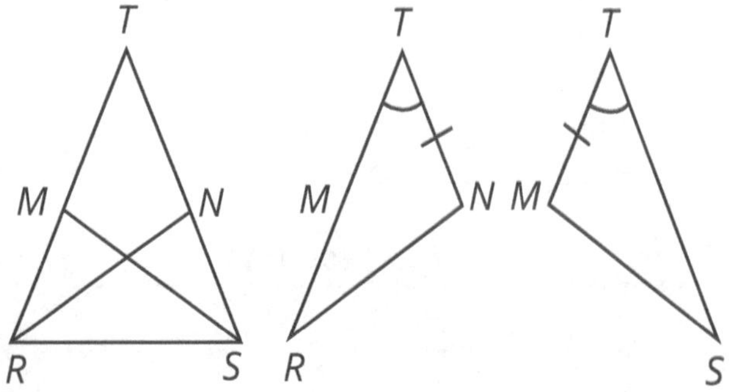

STATEMENT	REASON
1. __________	1. __________
2. __________	2. __________
3. __________	3. __________
4. __________	4. __________
5. __________	5. __________
6. __________	6. __________
7. __________	7. __________

2.36 Given: $AD = BC$
$\overline{BC} \perp \overline{AE}$
$\overline{AD} \perp \overline{BE}$
Prove: $\angle A = \angle B$

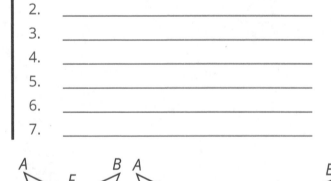

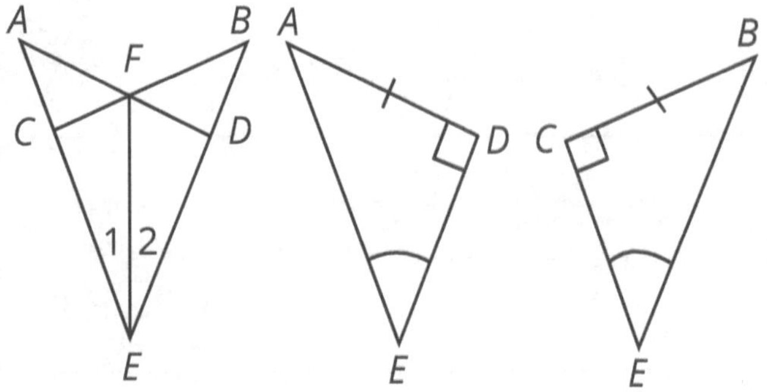

STATEMENT	REASON
1. ______	1. ______
2. ______	2. ______
3. ______	3. ______
4. ______	4. ______
5. ______	5. ______

2.37 Given: $CF = DF$

$\overline{FC} \perp \overline{AE}$

$\overline{FD} \perp \overline{BE}$

Prove: $\angle 1 = \angle 2$

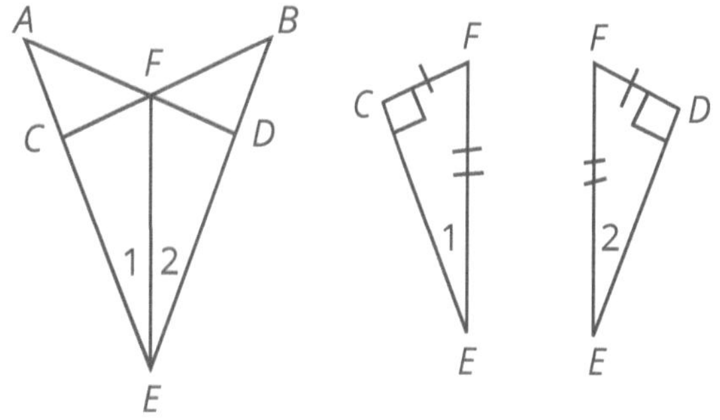

STATEMENT	REASON
1. ______	1. ______
2. ______	2. ______
3. ______	3. ______
4. ______	4. ______
5. ______	5. ______

2.38 Given: $\overline{AD} \perp \overline{BE}$

$\overline{BC} \perp \overline{AE}$

$AF = BF$

Prove: $AC = BD$

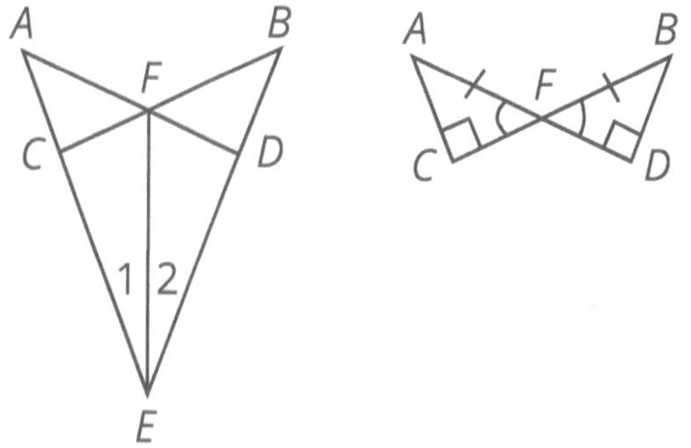

STATEMENT	REASON
1. ______	1. ______
2. ______	2. ______
3. ______	3. ______
4. ______	4. ______
5. ______	5. ______

ISOSCELES TRIANGLES

Recall that a triangle that has at least two sides equal is called an isosceles triangle. The two equal sides are called the legs. The third side is called the *base*. The angle formed by its two equal sides is called the *vertex angle*. The angles that include the base are called *base angles*.

> **DEFINITIONS**
>
> **Base:** the third, unequal side of an isosceles triangle.
>
> **Vertex angle:** the angle formed by the two equal sides of an isosceles triangle.
>
> **Base angles:** the two angles that include the base of an isosceles triangle.

Model:

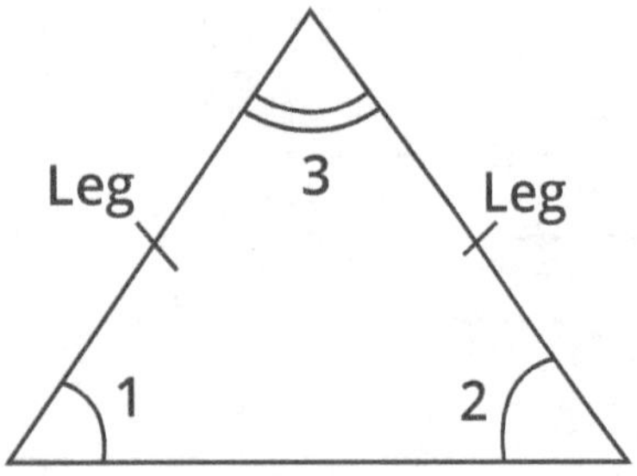

∠1, ∠2 are base angles

∠3 is the vertex angle

Two words often used with isosceles triangles, but applicable to other triangles as well, are the words *altitude* and *median*.

> **DEFINITIONS**
>
> **Altitude of a triangle:** a segment from a vertex perpendicular to the opposite side.
>
> **Median of a triangle:** a segment from a vertex to the midpoint of the opposite side.

Notice that every triangle has three altitudes and three medians, one from each vertex.

Model 1: Medians

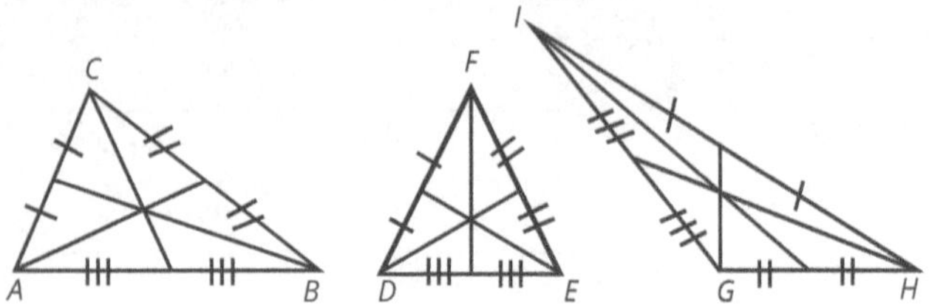

Model 2: Altitudes

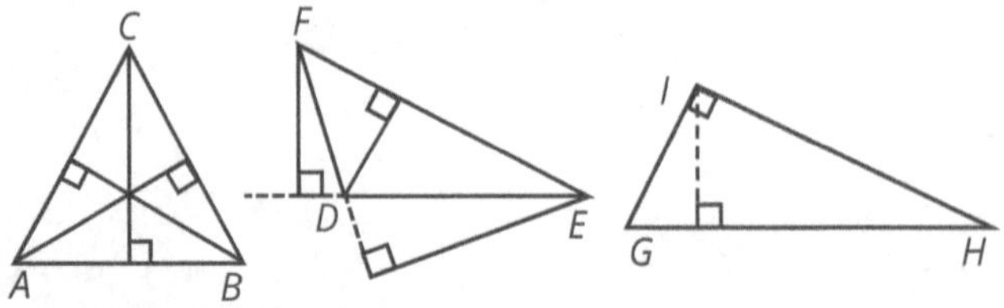

Look at the altitude and the median to the base of an isosceles triangle.

Model 3:

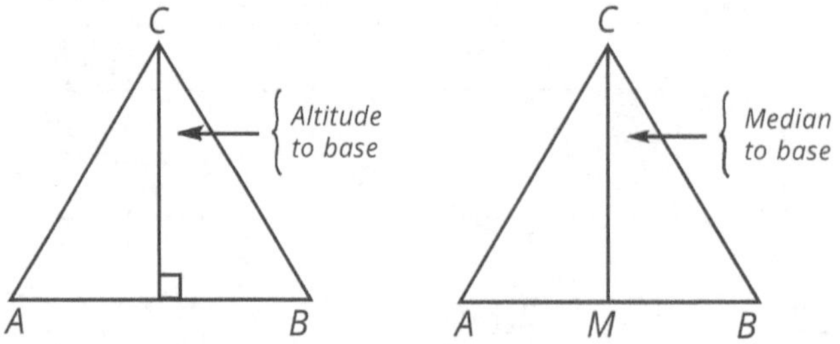

The altitude to the base of an isosceles triangle and the median to the base seem to be the same segment. We can restate this conclusion as a theorem.

> **THEOREM 4-5**
>
> The altitude to the base of an isosceles triangle bisects the base.

Given: △ *ABC* is isosceles

$\overline{BD}$ is altitude to base

Prove: *AD* = *DC*

Plan: Show △'s ≅ , then use CPCTE.

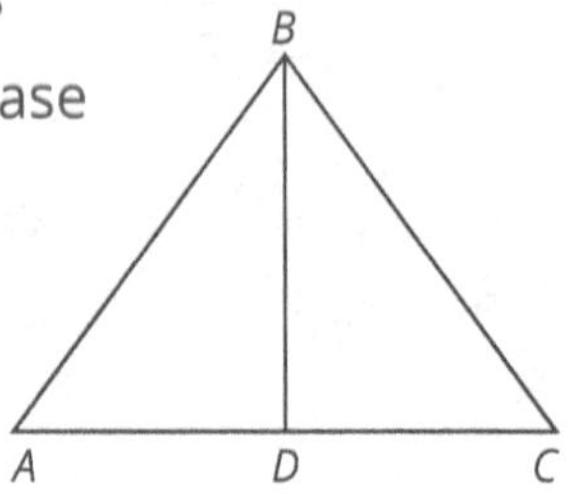

STATEMENT	REASON
1. $\triangle ABC$ is isosceles $\overline{BD}$ is altitude to base	1. Given
2. $AB = BC$	2. Definition of isosceles $\triangle$
3. $\overline{BD} \perp \overline{AC}$	3. Definition of altitude
4. $\angle ADB$, $\angle CDB$ are rt. $\angle$'s	4. $\perp$ form rt. $\angle$'s
5. $BD = BD$	5. Reflexive
6. $\triangle ABD \cong \triangle CDB$	6. HL
7. $AD = DC$	7. CPCTE

The proof of Theorem 4-5 can also be extended to prove two other theorems about isosceles triangles.

From the proof of Theorem 4-5, $\angle A = \angle C$ and $\angle ABD = \angle CBD$ because they are CPCTE also.

THEOREM 4-6

The base angles of an isosceles triangle are equal.

THEOREM 4-7

The altitude to the base of an isosceles triangle bisects the vertex angle of the triangle.

THEOREM 4-8

If two angles of a triangle are equal, then the sides opposite those angles are equal.

Given: $\angle A = \angle C$

Prove: $AB = BC$

Plan: Use auxiliary line (altitude from *B*). Show $\triangle$'s $\cong$, then use CPCTE.

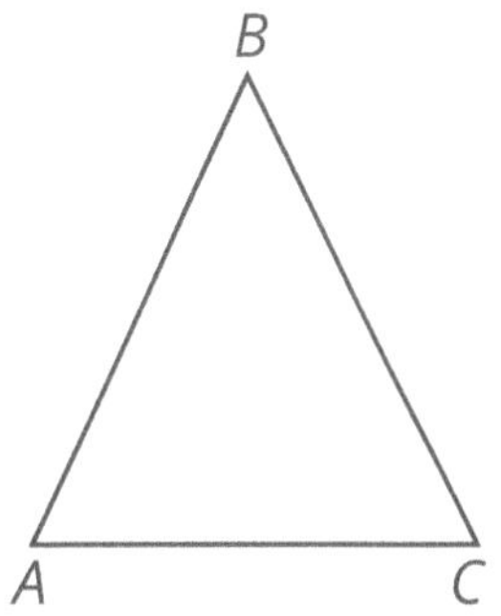

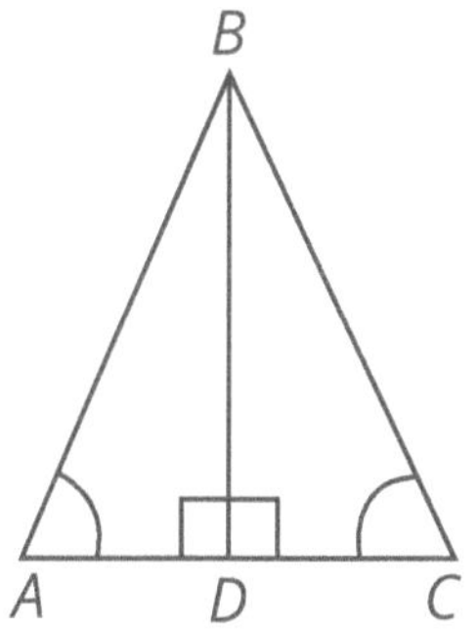

STATEMENT	REASON
1. Draw altitude from *B* to side $\overline{AC}$	1. Auxiliary line
2. $\angle A = \angle C$	2. Given
3. $BD = BD$	3. Reflexive
4. $\angle ADB$, $\angle CDB$ are rt. $\angle$'s	4. $\perp$ form rt. $\angle$'s
5. $\triangle ADB \cong \triangle CDB$	5. *LA*
6. $AB = BC$	6. CPCTE

Write the required information.

Given: *L*, *M*, *N* are midpoints; name the following segments or points.

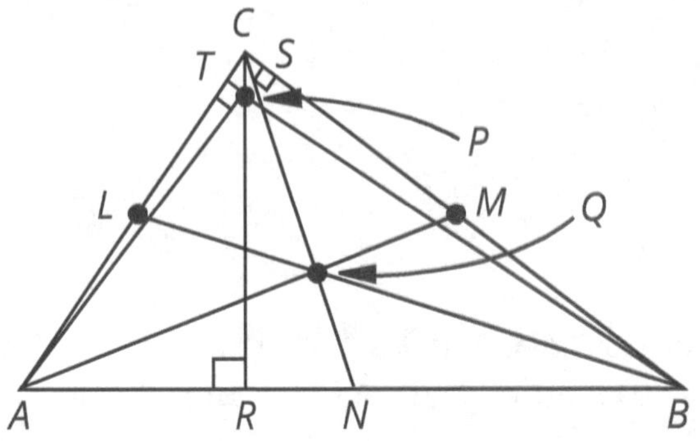

2.39 altitude to $\overline{AB}$ ______________

2.40 median to $\overline{BC}$ ______________

2.41 median to $\overline{AC}$ ______________

2.42 altitude to $\overline{AC}$ ______________

2.43 altitude to $\overline{BC}$ ______________

2.44 median to $\overline{AB}$ ______________

2.45 intersection of medians ______________________

2.46 intersection of altitudes ______________________

Complete the following proofs.

2.47 Given: $\triangle ABC$

$AC = BC$

Prove: $\angle 3 = \angle 1$

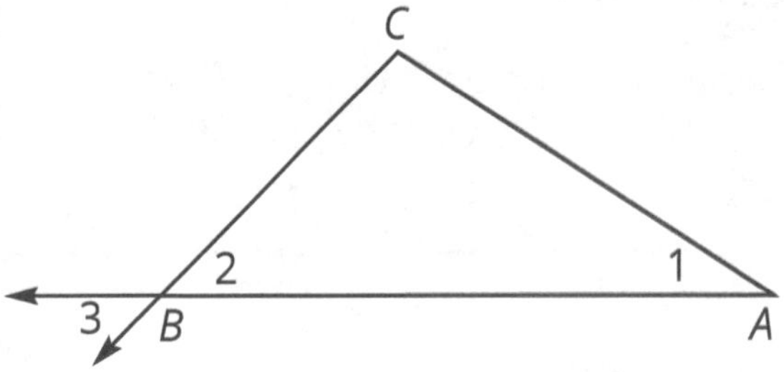

STATEMENT	REASON
1. ______________	1. ______________
2. ______________	2. ______________
3. ______________	3. ______________
4. ______________	4. ______________

2.48 Given: $\triangle ABC$

$\angle 3 = \angle 1$

Prove: $AC = BC$

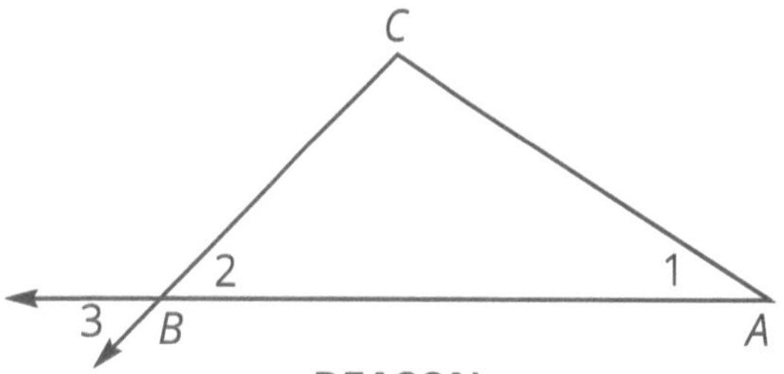

STATEMENT	REASON
1. ______	1. ______
2. ______	2. ______
3. ______	3. ______
4. ______	4. ______

2.49 Given: $\triangle ABR$

$\overline{RA} = \overline{RB}$

$\overrightarrow{RS} \parallel \overline{AB}$

Prove: $\angle 1 = \angle 2$

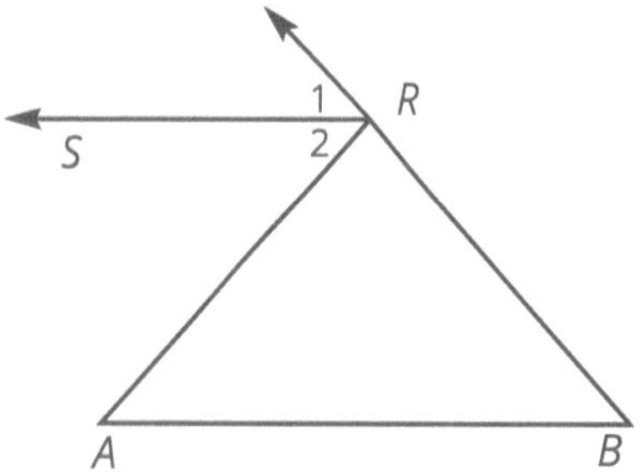

STATEMENT	REASON
1. ______	1. ______
2. ______	2. ______
3. ______	3. ______
4. ______	4. ______
5. ______	5. ______

2.50 Given: $\triangle ABR$

$\overrightarrow{RS} \parallel \overline{AB}$

$\angle 1 = \angle 2$

Prove: $RA = RB$

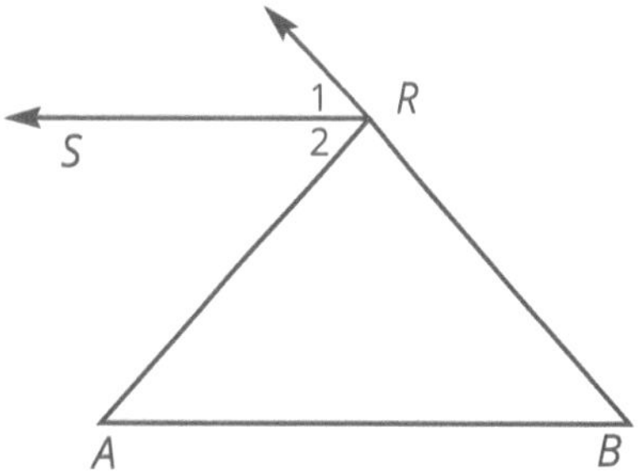

STATEMENT	REASON
1. ______	1. ______
2. ______	2. ______
3. ______	3. ______
4. ______	4. ______
5. ______	5. ______

2.51 Given: $\triangle DEF$
$DF = EF$
Prove: $\angle 3 = \angle 4$

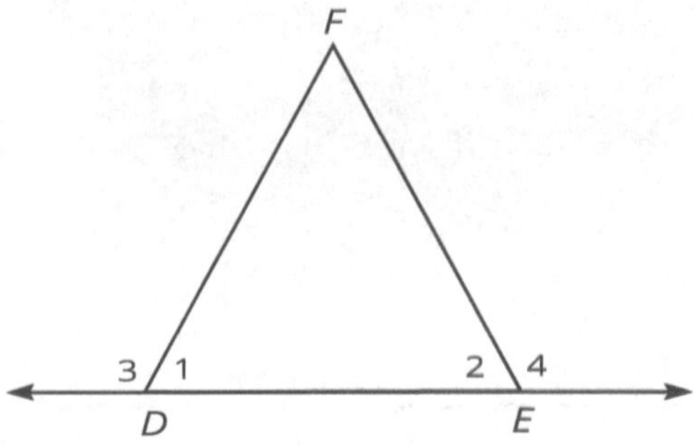

STATEMENT	REASON
1. ______	1. ______
2. ______	2. ______
3. ______	3. ______
4. ______	4. ______

2.52 Given: $\triangle DEF$
$\angle 3 = \angle 4$
Prove: $DF = EF$

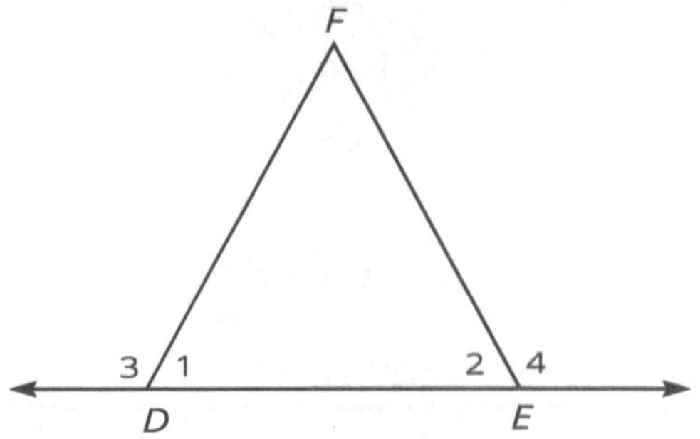

STATEMENT	REASON
1. ______	1. ______
2. ______	2. ______
3. ______	3. ______
4. ______	4. ______

2.53 Given: $AR = AQ$
$RT = QS$
Prove: $\angle RAT = \angle QAS$

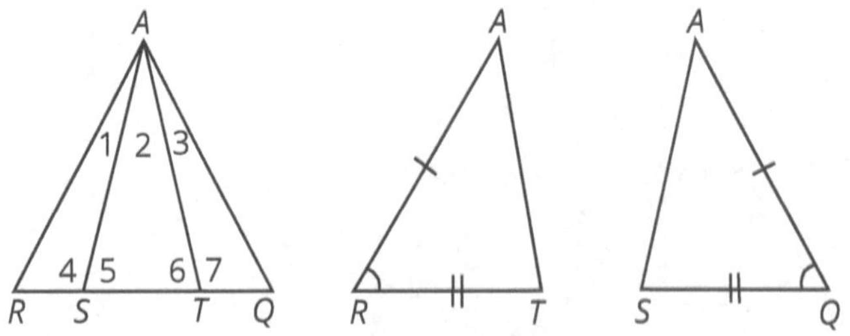

STATEMENT	REASON
1. ______	1. ______
2. ______	2. ______
3. ______	3. ______
4. ______	4. ______

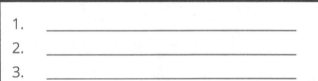

2.54 Given: $AR = AQ$
$\angle 1 = \angle 3$
Prove: $AS = AT$

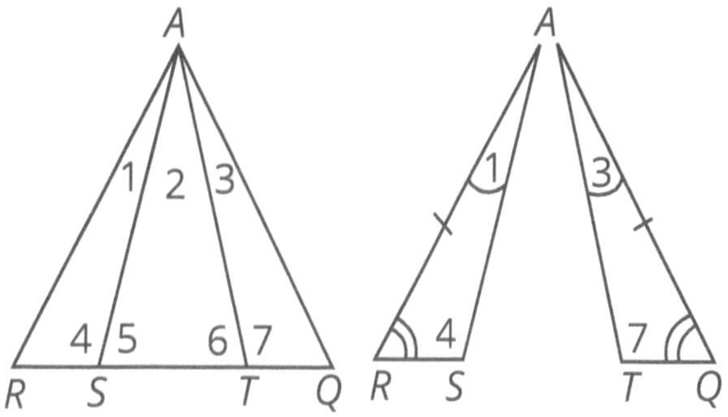

STATEMENT	REASON
1. ____________	1. ____________
2. ____________	2. ____________
3. ____________	3. ____________
4. ____________	4. ____________

2.55 Given: $\angle R = \angle Q$
$AS = AT$
Prove: $RS = QT$

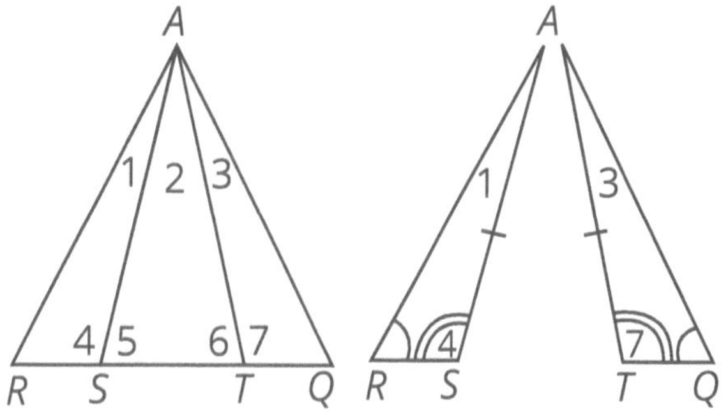

STATEMENT	REASON
1. ____________	1. ____________
2. ____________	2. ____________
3. ____________	3. ____________
4. ____________	4. ____________
5. ____________	5. ____________
6. ____________	6. ____________

TEACHER CHECK ____________ ____________
initials date

Review the material in this section in preparation for the Self Test. This Self Test will check your mastery of this particular section as well as your knowledge of the previous section.

SELF TEST 2

Complete the pairs of corresponding parts if △ *RST* ≅ △ *TXY* (each answer, 3 points).

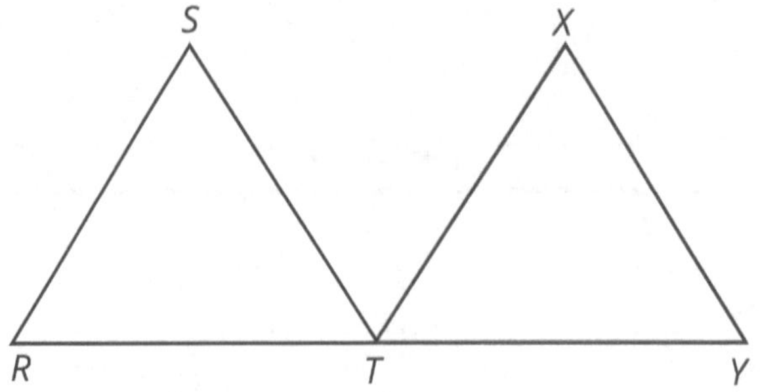

2.01 $\angle R =$ ____________

2.02 $\angle S =$ ____________

2.03 $\angle STR =$ ____________

2.04 $\overline{RS} =$ ____________

2.05 $ST =$ ____________

2.06 $RT =$ ____________

Complete the pairs of corresponding parts if △ *ABD* ≅ △ *EFC* (each answer, 3 points).

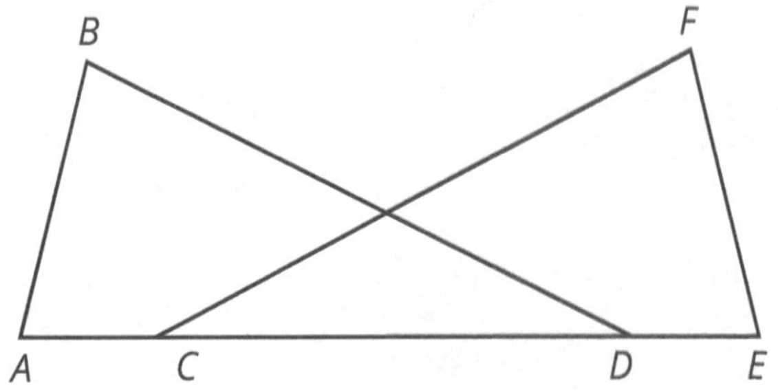

2.07 $\angle A =$ ____________

2.08 $\angle B =$ ____________

2.09 $\angle BDA =$ ____________

2.010 $AB =$ ____________

2.011 $BD =$ ____________

2.012 $AD =$ ____________

Complete the four pairs of triangles that seem to be congruent (each answer, 3 points).

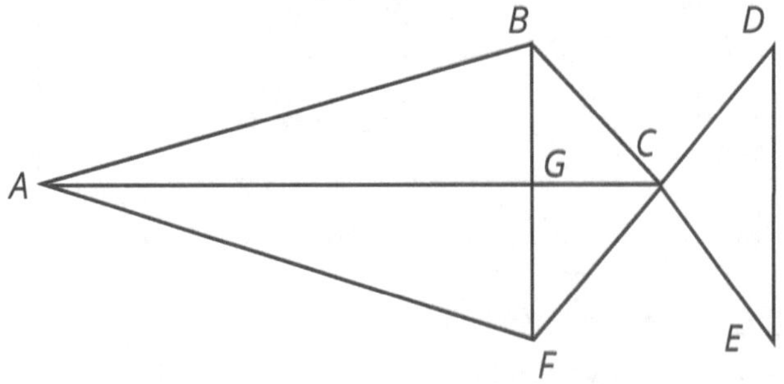

2.013 △ $ABG \cong$ ____________

2.014 △ $BCG \cong$ ____________

2.015 △ $ABC \cong$ ____________

2.016 △ $BCF \cong$ ____________

Complete the following proofs (each answer, 4 points).

Given: $\overline{AD} \parallel \overline{BC}$

$AD = CB$

Prove: $\overline{AB} \parallel \overline{DC}$

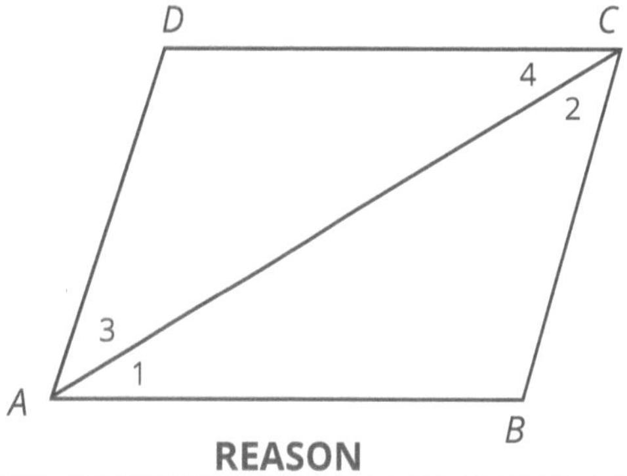

STATEMENT		REASON
2.017	____________________	____________________
2.018	____________________	____________________
2.019	____________________	____________________
2.020	____________________	____________________
2.021	____________________	____________________
2.022	____________________	____________________

Prove: The median from the vertex angle of an isosceles triangle divides the triangle into two congruent triangles.

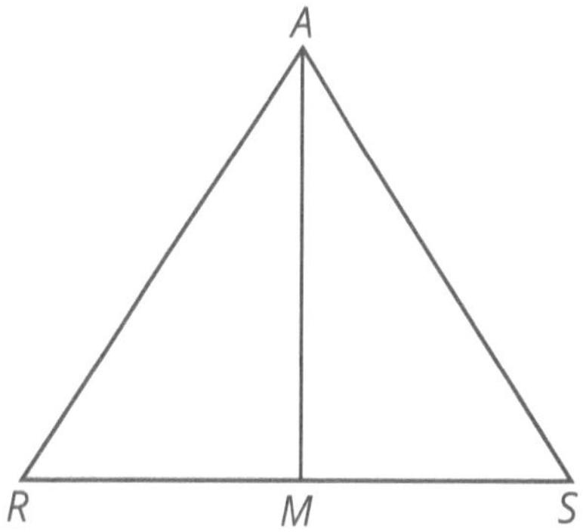

2.023 Given: ____________________

2.024 Prove: ____________________

STATEMENT		REASON
2.025	____________________	____________________
2.026	____________________	____________________
2.027	____________________	____________________
2.028	____________________	____________________
2.029	____________________	____________________

80/100 **SCORE** ____________ **TEACHER** ____________ initials ____________ date

3. INEQUALITIES

In the previous section we discussed equality in congruent triangles. Another possibility is that parts of triangles are not equal. Inequalities exist between the parts.

Section Objectives

Review these objectives. When you have finished this section, you should be able to:

7. Prove inequalities in one triangle.
8. Prove inequalities in two triangles.

INEQUALITIES IN ONE TRIANGLE

Theorem 4-6 states that the base angles of isosceles triangles are equal. Putting this theorem in other words, we could say: if two sides of a triangle are equal, then the angles opposite those sides are equal. The result of applying the contrapositive to this statement is: if two angles of a triangle are not equal, then the sides opposite the angles are not equal. Looking at a figure for this statement suggests a more specific relationship for the angles.

$\triangle ABC$ seems to show that if $\angle C > \angle A$ then $AB > BC$. To prove this statement and others dealing with inequalities we need to use the following theorem from algebra.

Model 1:

$10 = 6 + 4$, 4 is a positive number, therefore, $10 > 6$ (true)

$12 = -10 + 22$	$-12 = -22 + 10$
22 is positive	10 is positive
$\therefore 12 > -10$ (true)	$\therefore -12 > -22$ (true)

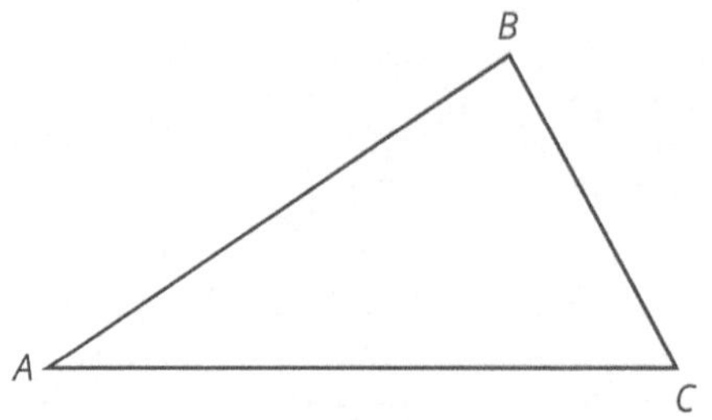

ALGEBRAIC THEOREM

If *a*, *b*, and *c* are real numbers such that $a = b + c$ and *c* is a positive number, then $a > b$.

Model 2:

Prove: $AM > AR$

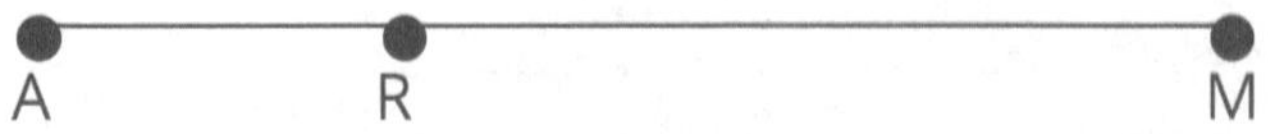

STATEMENT	REASON
1. $AM = AR + RM$	1. Betweeness
2. RM is positive	2. Distance is a positive number
3. $AM > AR$	3. If $a = b + c$ and c is positive, then $a > b$

Model 3:

Prove: $\angle RAT > \angle RAS$

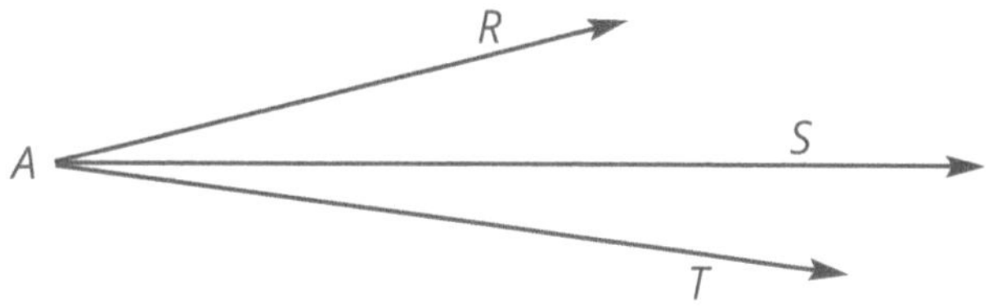

STATEMENT	REASON
1. $\angle RAT = \angle RAS + \angle SAT$	1. $\angle$ addition theorem
2. $\angle SAT$ is a positive number	2. Protractor postulate
3. $\angle RAT > \angle RAS$	3. If $a = b + c$ and $c > 0$, then $a > b$

These models lead to the proof of Theorem 4-9.

> **THEOREM 4-9**
> If two sides of a triangle are not equal, then the angle opposite the longer side is the larger angle.

Given: $AB > BC$

Prove: $\angle C = \angle A$

Plan: Use auxiliary line CX so that $BX = BC$. Show that $\angle 3 > \angle A$, $\angle C > \angle 1$, $\angle 1 = \angle 3$ so that $\angle C > \angle A$.

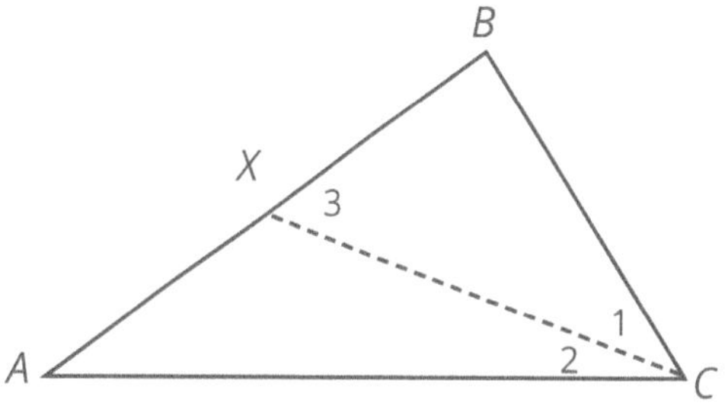

STATEMENT	REASON
1. Draw $\overline{CX}$ so that $BX = BC$	1. Auxiliary line
2. $\angle 1 = \angle 3$	2. Bases $\angle$'s of isosceles $\triangle$'s are =
3. $\angle 3 = \angle A + \angle 2$	3. Exterior $\angle$ of $\triangle$ = sum of remote interior angles
4. $\angle 3 > \angle A$	4. If $a = b + c$ and $c > 0$, then $a > b$
5. $\angle 1 > \angle A$	5. Substitution
6. $\angle C = \angle 1 + \angle 2$	6. Angle addition theorem
7. $\angle C > \angle 1$	7. If $a = b + c$ and $c > 0$, then $a > b$
8. $\angle C > \angle A$	8. Transitive property of inequality

The inverse of Theorem 4-8 can be altered to give us Theorem 4-10.

> **THEOREM 4-10**
> If two angles of a triangle are not equal, then the side opposite the larger angle is the longer side.

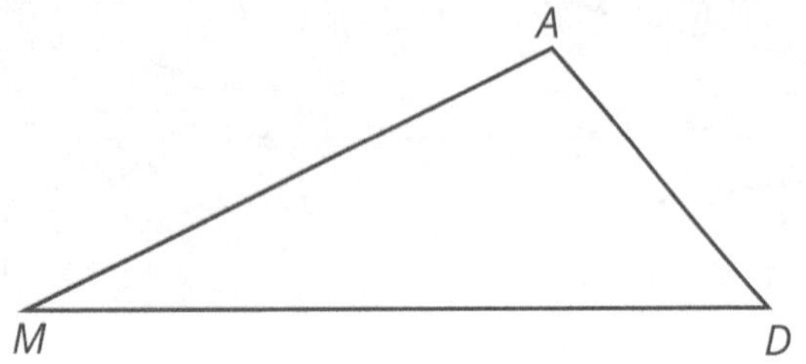

Given: $\angle D > \angle M$

Prove: $MA > DA$

Plan: Use indirect proof and show that $MA = AD$ and $MA < AD$ are both false.

Suppose $MA \not> DA$; then $MA = DA$ or $MA < DA$. If $MA = DA$, then $LM = LD$. This statement contradicts the given information. Also, if $MA < DA$, then by Theorem 4-7, $\angle D < \angle M$. This statement again contradicts the given information. Therefore, the statement $MA \not> DA$ is false and its negation, $MA > DA$, must be true.

See if you can prove this corollary to Theorem 4-10.

Corollary: The perpendicular segment from a point to a line is the shortest distance from the point to the line.

Complete the proof.

3.1 Given: $\overline{PT} \perp \overleftrightarrow{RT}$

Prove: $PT < PR$

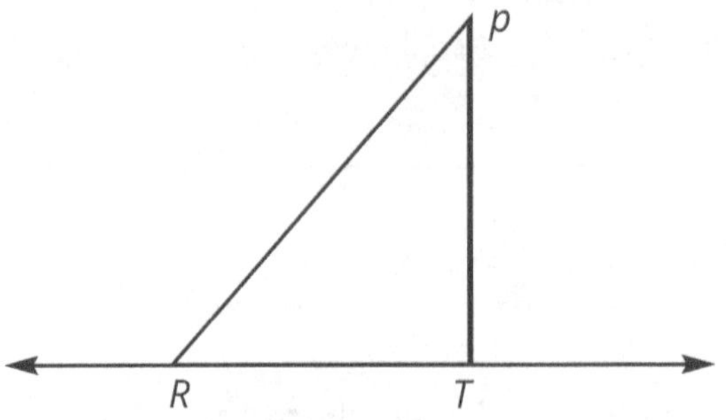

STATEMENT	REASON
1. ______	1. ______
2. ______	2. ______
3. ______	3. ______
4. ______	4. ______

When we first started studying about congruent triangles, we took two sets of three segments and built two triangles that were congruent.

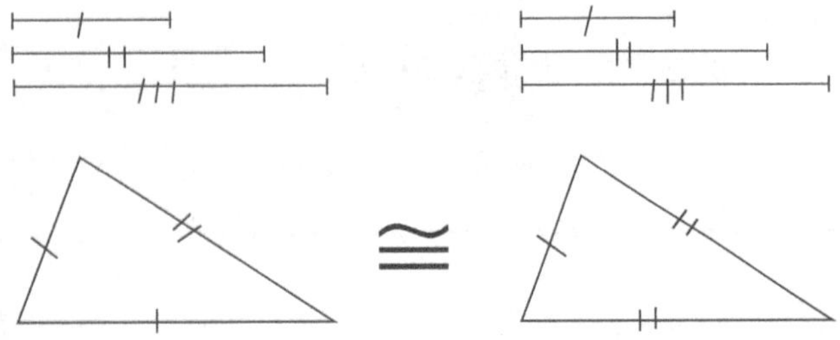

Could we choose any three segments to build our triangles? Or must we be careful about the lengths of the sides? Do you think we could build a triangle with sides 3", 5", and 6"? How about 12 cm, 20 cm, and 16 cm? What about 2 inches, 2 feet, and 2 miles? Or 1 inch, 5 inches, and 7 inches? As you can see, some natural restrictions exist on the lengths of segments that can be used in triangles. Theorem 4-11 explains these restrictions.

THEOREM 4-11

The sum of the length of any two sides of a triangle is greater than the length of the third side (triangle inequality theorem).

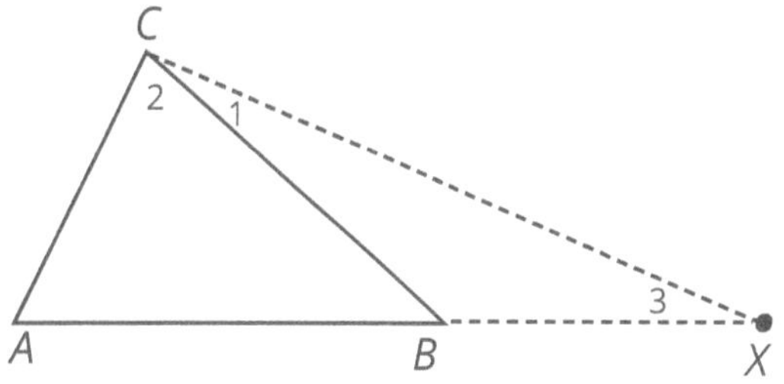

Given: $\triangle ABC$

Prove: $AB + BC > AC$

Plan: Draw an isosceles triangle next to the given triangle and then relate its equal angles to other angles in the figure. Use Theorem 4-8.

STATEMENT	REASON
1. On $\overleftrightarrow{AB}$ draw $BX = BC$; connect C and X	1. Auxiliary line
2. $\angle 1 = \angle 3$	2. Base $\angle$'s of isosceles $\triangle$'s are =
3. $\angle ACX = \angle 1 + \angle 2$	3. $\angle$ addition theorem
4. $\angle ACX > \angle 1$	4. If $a = b + c$ and $c > 0$, then $a > b$
5. $\angle ACX > \angle 3$	5. Substitution
6. In $\triangle ACX$, $AX > AC$	6. Side opposite $\angle$ larger is longer
7. $AX = AB + BX$	7. Betweeness
8. $AB + BX > AC$	8. Substitution
9. $AB + BC > AC$	9. Substitution

Having proved the triangle inequality theorem, we can now tell if we can build a triangle with sides of given length. Remember that the sum of any two sides must be greater than the third side. The triangle inequality theorem also tells us that the shortest path between two points is a straight line.

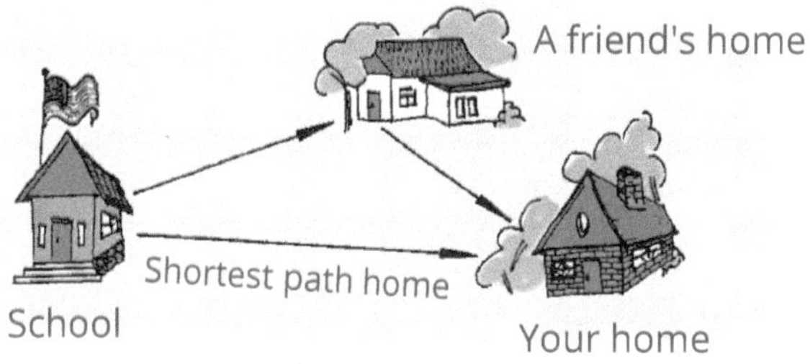

Write the angles according to size from small to large.

3.2 a. ____________ < b. ____________ < c. ____________

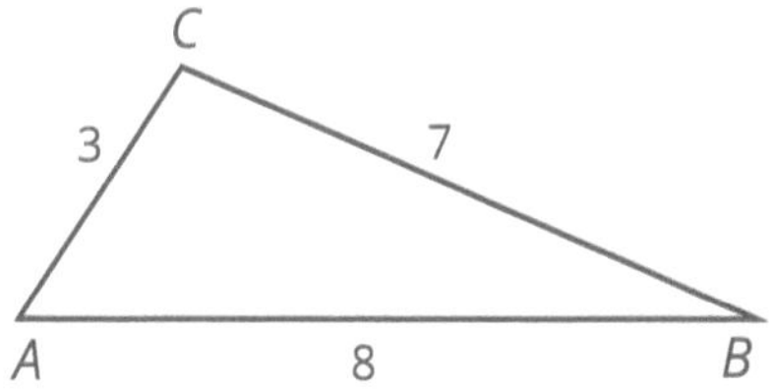

3.3 a. ____________ < b. ____________ < c. ____________

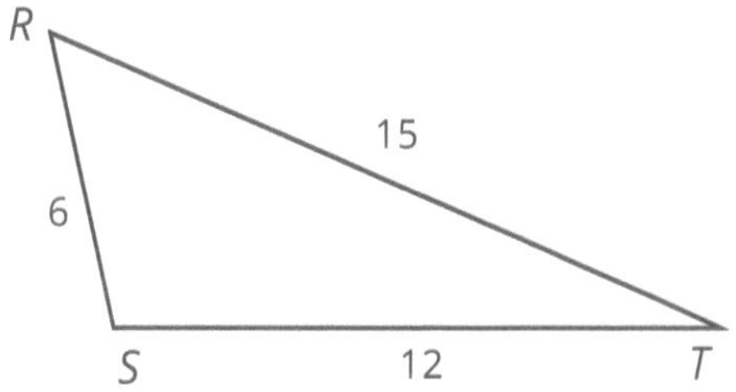

3.4 a. ________________ < b. ________________ < c. ________________

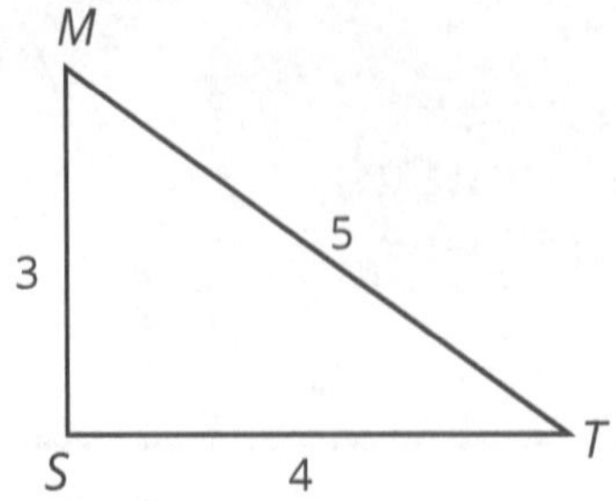

3.5 a. ________________ < b. ________________ < c. ________________

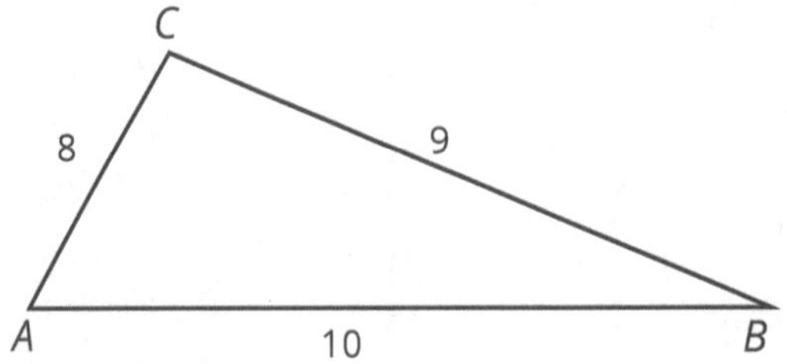

Write the sides according to size from large to small.

3.6 a. ________________ > b. ________________ > c. ________________

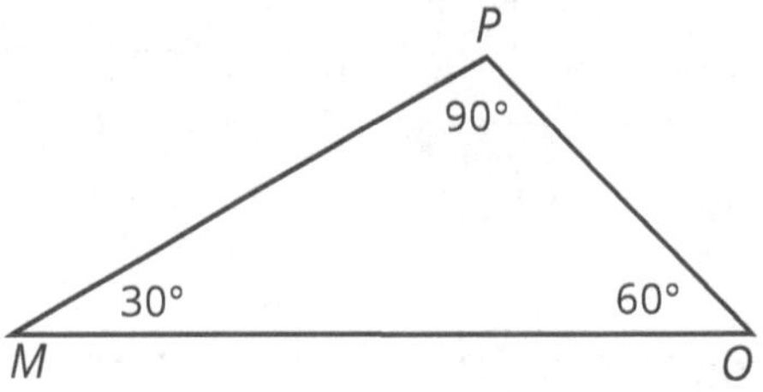

3.7 a. ________________ > b. ________________ > c. ________________

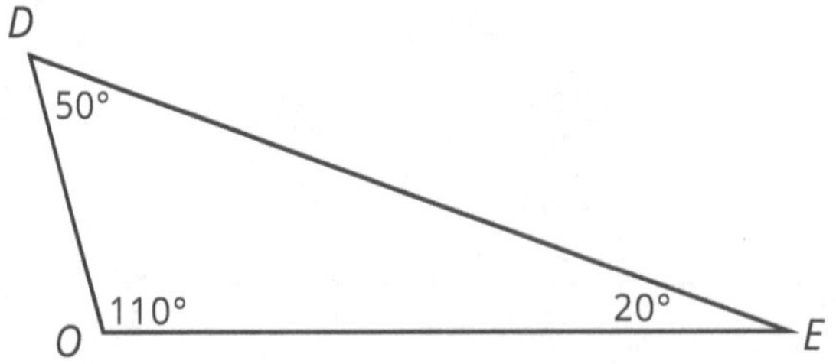

3.8 a. ________________ > b. ________________ > c. ________________

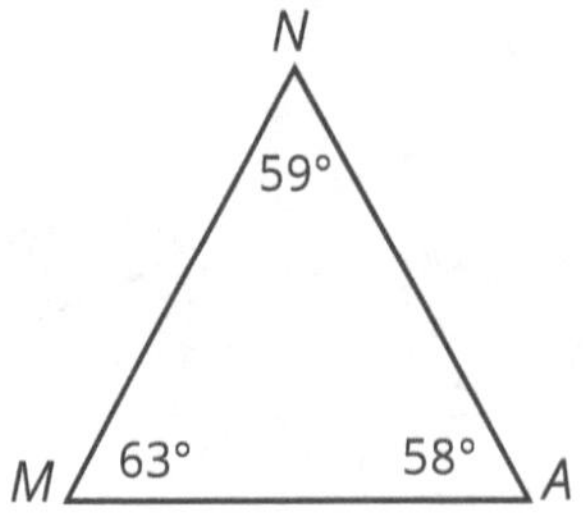

Can a triangle be constructed with sides of the following lengths? Write *yes* or *no*.

3.9 ________ 3", 4", 5"

3.10 ________ 6 ft, 12 ft, 17 ft

3.11 ________ 2 yd, 5 yd, 10 yd

3.12 ________ 12 cm, 12 cm, 13 cm

3.13 ________ 1 mm, 2 mm, 3 mm

3.14 ________ 3.6 cm, 5.7 cm, 9.1 cm

In the following sentences write <, =, or >.

3.15 If $\angle G = 70°$ and $\angle J = 40°$, then GH ________ HJ.

3.16 If $\angle H = 85°$ and $\angle G = 60°$, then HJ ________ JG.

3.17 If $\angle H = 80°$ and $\angle J = 45°$, then HJ ________ HG.

3.18 If $\angle J = 40°$ and $\angle G = 60°$, then HJ ________ GJ.

3.19 If $\angle H = 90°$, then GJ ________ GH.

3.20 If $GH \perp HJ$ then GJ ________ HJ.

3.21 If $GH = 3$ and $HJ = 5$, then $\angle G$ ________ $\angle J$.

3.22 If $GJ = 7$ and $HJ = 6$, then $\angle H$ ________ $\angle G$.

3.23 If $\angle H$ is obtuse, then HG ________ GJ.

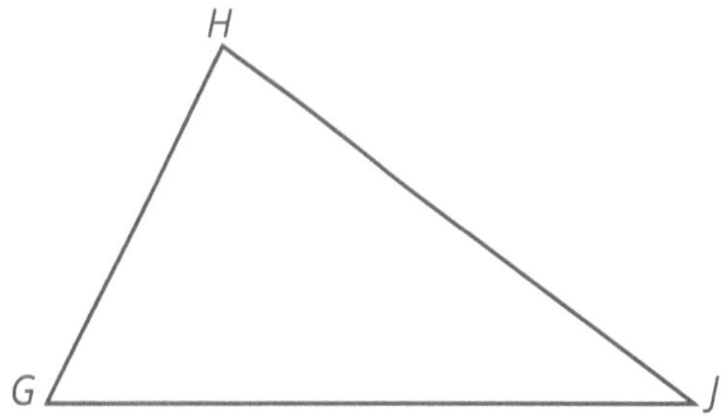

Complete the following proofs.

3.24 Given: $BC = EF$
Prove: $AC > EF$

STATEMENT	REASON
1. ________	1. ________
2. ________	2. ________
3. ________	3. ________
4. ________	4. ________

3.25 Given: $\angle DBC = \angle RST$

Prove: $\angle ABC > \angle RST$

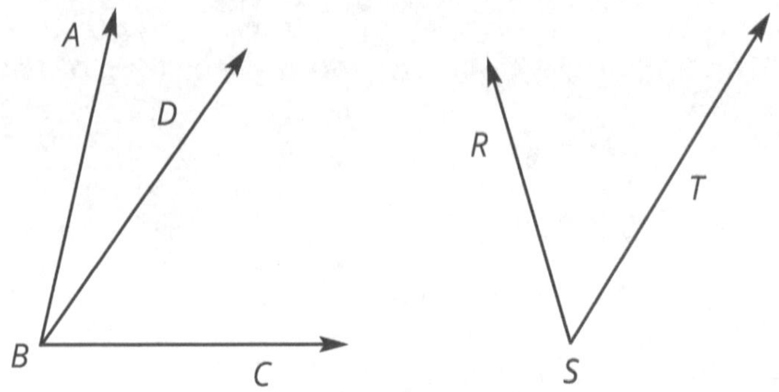

	STATEMENT		REASON
1.	______________	1.	______________
2.	______________	2.	______________
3.	______________	3.	______________
4.	______________	4.	______________

3.26 Given: $\triangle WXY$, $\angle 1$ an exterior $\angle$

Prove: $\angle 1 > \angle 2$

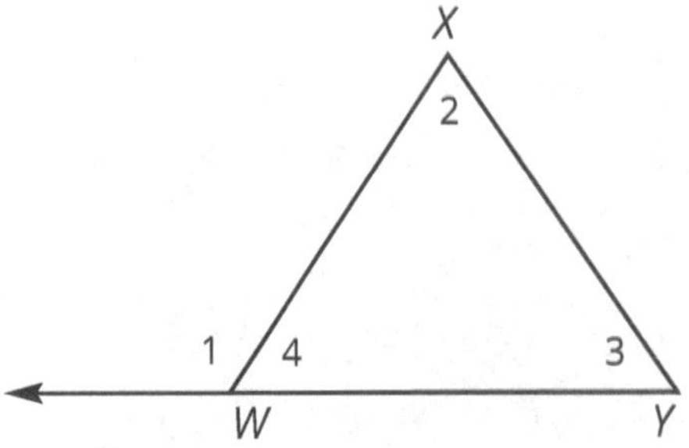

	STATEMENT		REASON
1.	______________	1.	______________
2.	______________	2.	______________
3.	______________	3.	______________

3.27 Given: $WX > XY$

Prove: $\angle 1 > \angle 4$

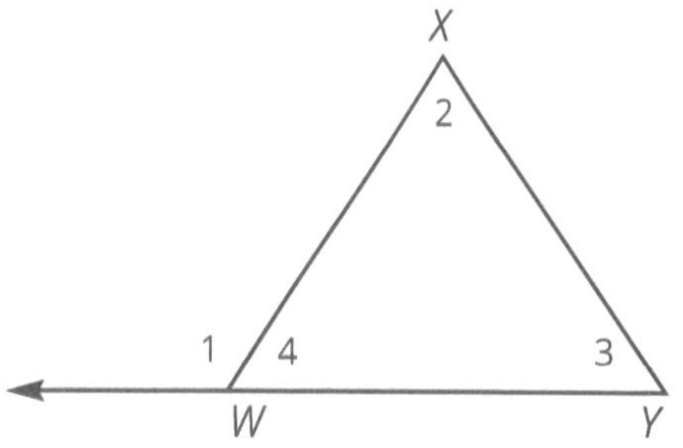

STATEMENT	REASON
1. ______	1. ______
2. ______	2. ______
3. ______	3. ______
4. ______	4. ______
5. ______	5. ______

3.28 Prove: The hypotenuse is the longest side of a right triangle.

Given: ______

Prove: ______

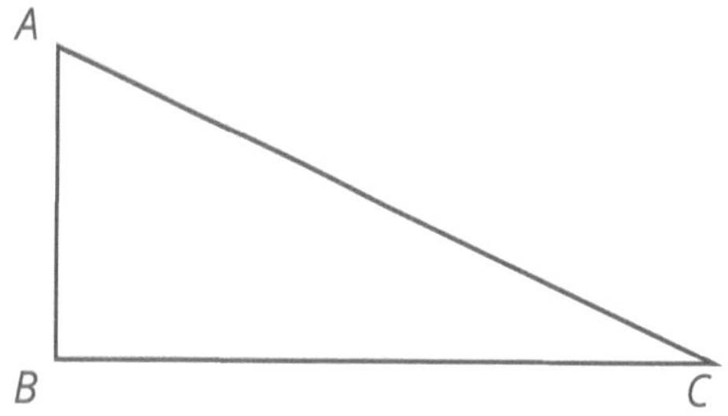

STATEMENT	REASON
1. ______	1. ______
2. ______	2. ______
3. ______	3. ______
4. ______	4. ______
5. ______	5. ______
6. ______	6. ______
7. ______	7. ______
8. ______	8. ______
9. ______	9. ______
10. ______	10. ______
11. ______	11. ______

Complete these items.

3.29 Two sides of a triangle have lengths of 10 and 15. Between what two numbers does the length of the third side lie? ____________________

3.30 Each leg of an isosceles triangle is 12. Between what numbers does the length of the base lie?

____

3.31 a. __________ < *x* < b. __________ (*x* is between...)

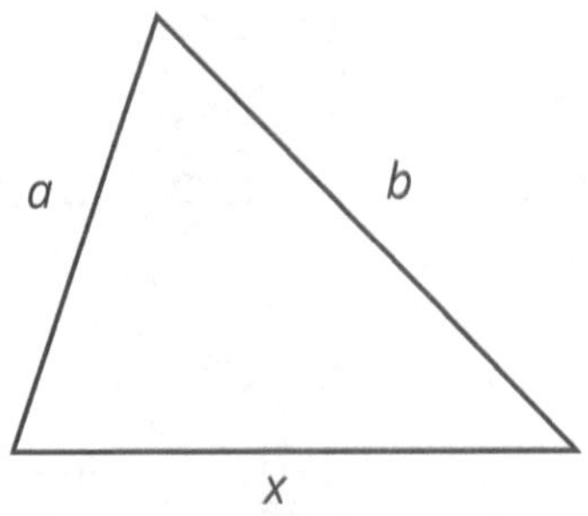

INEQUALITIES IN TWO TRIANGLES

When studying congruent triangles, we use an SAS statement that two sides and the included angle of one triangle are equal to the corresponding parts of another triangle.

Now suppose that the two sides of one triangle were equal to two sides of another, but the included angles were not equal. What can we conclude about the other sides of the triangles?

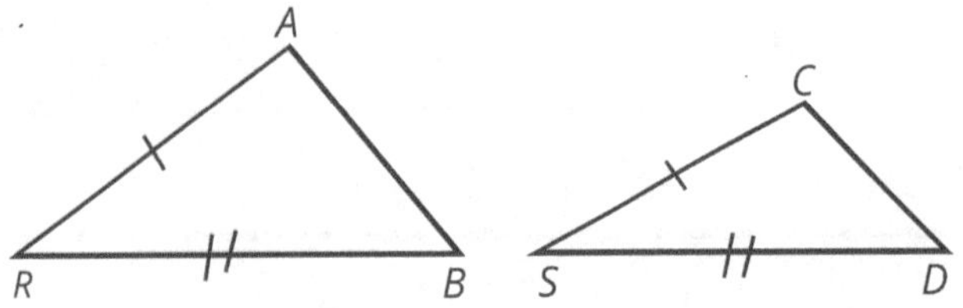

The side opposite the larger angle ($\angle R > \angle S$) appears to be longer ($\overline{AB} > \overline{CD}$).

> **THEOREM 4-12**
> If two sides of one triangle are equal to two sides of another triangle but the included angle of the first is larger than the included angle of the second, then the third side of the first triangle is longer than the third side of the second triangle.

Given: $AB = WX$

$AC = WY$

$\angle A > \angle W$

Prove: $BC > XY$

Plan: An outline of the proof is given in paragraph form.

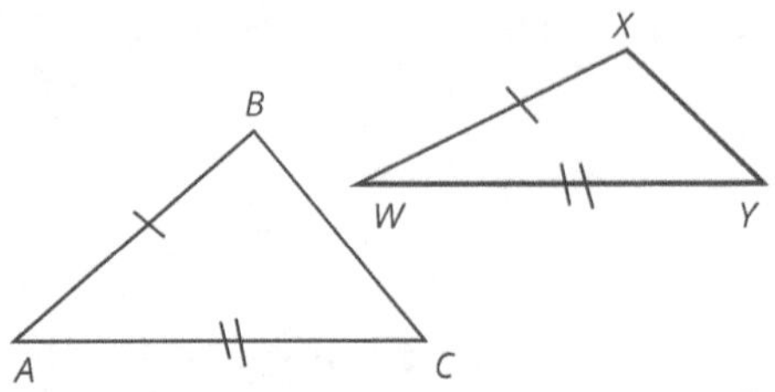

Draw a ray $\overrightarrow{AZ}$ such that $\angle CAZ = \angle YWX$.
On $\overrightarrow{AZ}$ take a point *P* such that $AP = WX$.
Two different cases may be considered.

Case 1: If point *P* lies on $\overline{BC}$, we then have $BC = BP + PC$ and $BC > BP$. $\triangle ACP \cong \triangle WYX$ (SAS); therefore, $XY = PC$. Substituting, we have $BC > XY$.

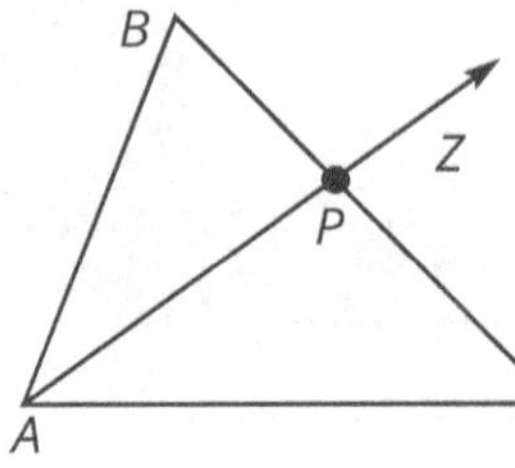

Case 2: If point P does not lie on $\overline{BC}$, make the bisector of $\angle BAZ$. Let Q be the point of intersection with $\overline{BC}$. Since $AB = WX$ and $WX = AP$, then $AB = AP$. Now $\triangle ABQ \cong \triangle APQ$ (SAS); therefore, $BQ = PQ$. $CQ + PQ > CP$, so $CQ + BQ > CP$, and $BC > CP$, but $\triangle PAC \cong \triangle XWY$ (SAS), and $XY = CP$. Substituting in $BC > CP$, we have $BC > XY$.

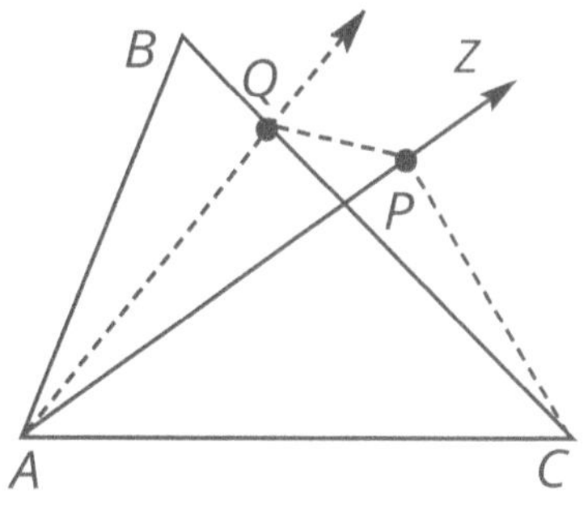

The converse of Theorem 4-12 can be proved by the indirect method.

> **THEOREM 4-13**
>
> If two sides of one triangle are equal to two sides of another triangle but the third side of the first triangle is longer than the third side of the second triangle, then the included angle of the first triangle is larger than the included angle of the second triangle.

Given: $AB = WX$
$AC = WY$
$BC > XY$

Prove: $\angle A > \angle W$

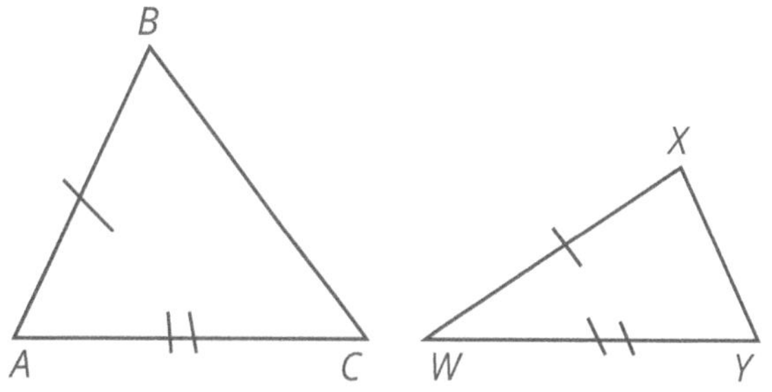

Suppose $\angle A \not> \angle W$; then $\angle A = \angle W$ or $\angle A < \angle W$. If $\angle A = \angle W$, then $\triangle ABC \cong \triangle WXY$ by SAS and $BC = XY$. This conclusion contradicts the given information. If $\angle A < \angle W$, then $BC < XY$ by Theorem 4-12; but this conclusion contradicts the given facts. Since our supposition leads to contradictions, it must be false; and $\angle A > \angle W$ must be true.

Write < or >.

3.32 AD ______ EC

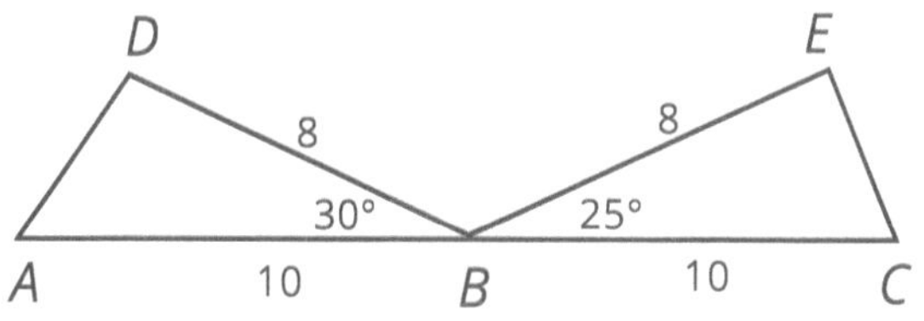

3.33 DB ______ CB

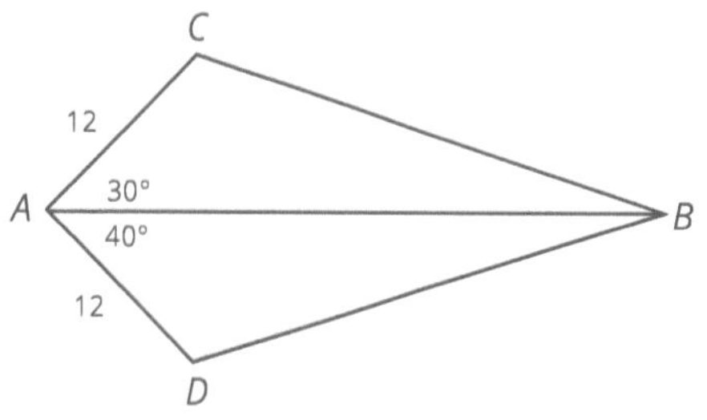

3.34 $\angle 1$ ______ $\angle 2$

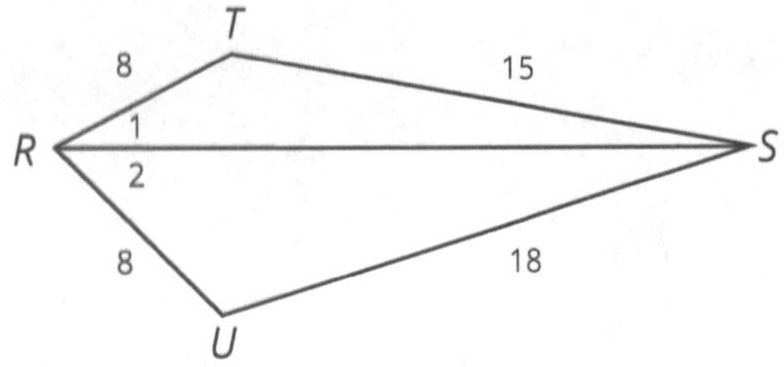

3.35 *LE* ______ *VO*

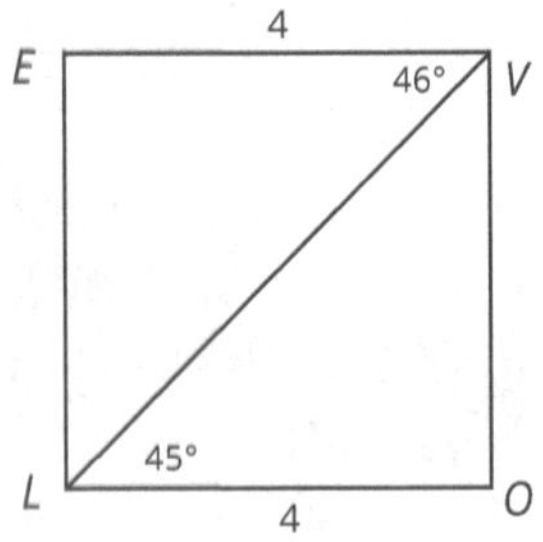

3.36 $\angle 1$ ______ $\angle 2$

AC > *BD*
CE = *EB*
AE = *ED*

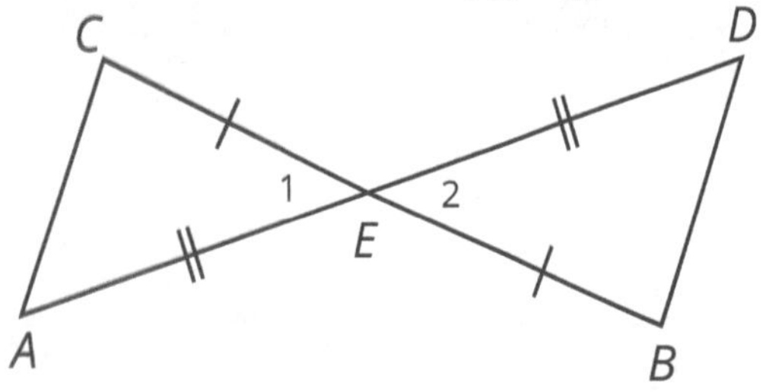

3.37 *BC* ______ *AD*

AB = *BD* = *DC*
$\angle 1 > \angle 4$

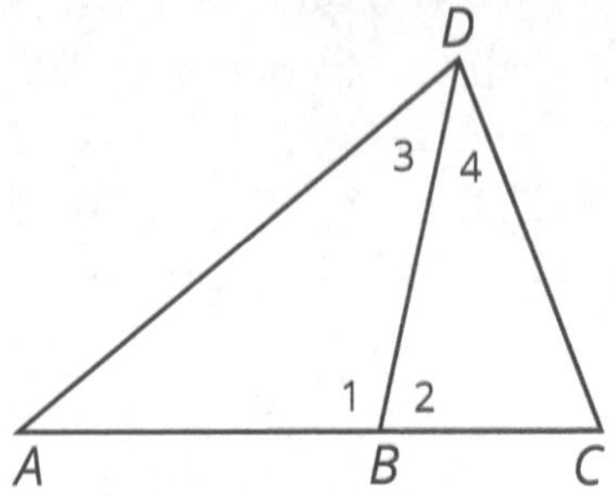

3.38 *RS* ______ *ST*

RQ = *TQ*
$\angle 1 > \angle 2$

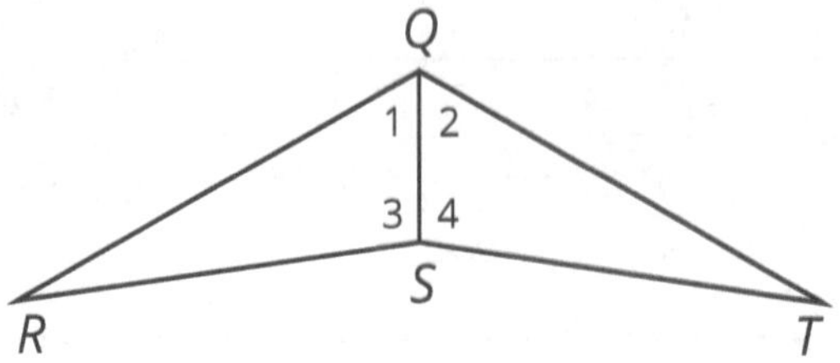

3.39 *BC* ______ *AB*

△ *ABD is equilateral*
AD = *DC*
$\angle 4 = 50°$

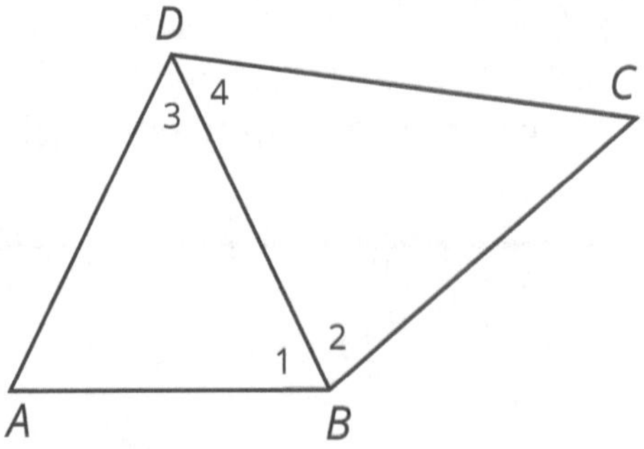

Write <, =, or >.

3.40 *MP* ______ *PK*

3.41 *NP* ______ *ML*

3.42 If *NK* < *MN*, then $\angle 1$ ________ $\angle 2$.

3.43 If $\angle 1 < \angle 2$, then *KN* ________ *MN*.

3.44 If *MN* > *LP*, then $\angle 2$ ________ $\angle 3$.

3.45 If $\angle 3 > \angle 2$, then *PL* ________ *MN*.

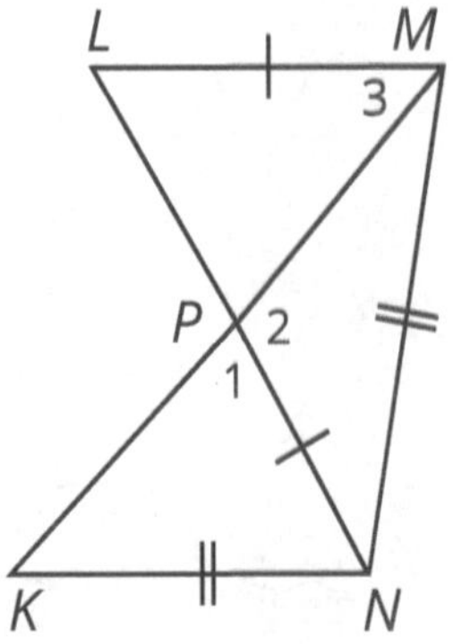

3.46 DB ________ RT

3.47 BC ________ RA

3.48 If $\angle B = 30°$ and $\angle R = 40°$, then DC ________ AT.

3.49 If $\angle B = 30°$ and $\angle R = 20°$, then DC ________ AT.

3.50 If $DC = 12$ and $AT = 10$, then $\angle B$ ________ $\angle R$.

3.51 If $\angle B = \angle R$, then DC ________ AT.

3.52 If $\angle B > \angle R$, then AT ________ DC.

3.53 If $AT < DC$, then $\angle R$ ________ $\angle B$.

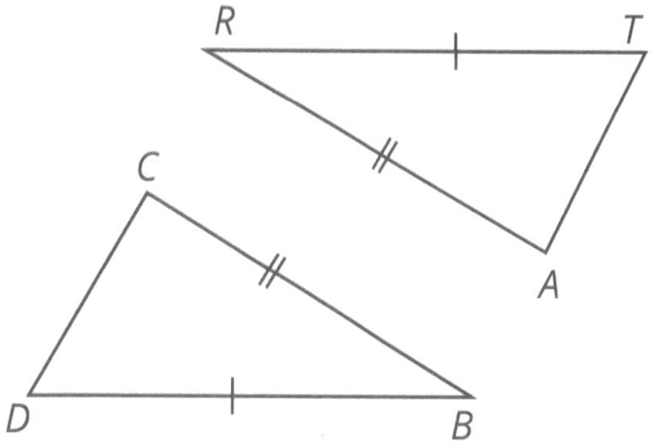

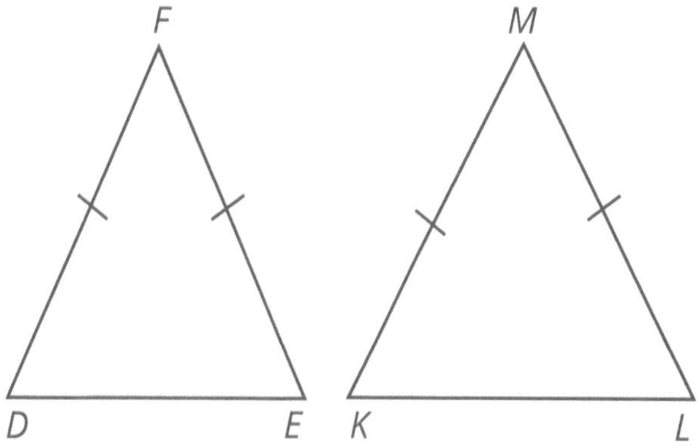

3.54 If $DE < KL$, then $\angle M$ ________ $\angle F$.

3.55 If $\angle M > \angle F$, then DE ________ KL.

3.56 If $\angle F = \angle M$, then DE ________ KL.

TEACHER CHECK ________ ________
initials date

Review the material in this section in preparation for the Self Test. This Self Test will check your mastery of this particular section as well as your knowledge of previous sections.

SELF TEST 3

Write the correct word(s) or symbol(s) in the blank (each answer, 3 points).

3.01 If a = b + c and c ________, then a > b.

3.02 If two sides of a Δ are not =, the angle opposite the ____________________ side is the larger angle.

3.03 In the SSS statement all three a. ____________________ of one triangle are equal to the three b. ____________________ of another triangle.

3.04 If 8 = x + y and y > 0, then x ________ 8.

3.05 a. __________ < x < b. __________

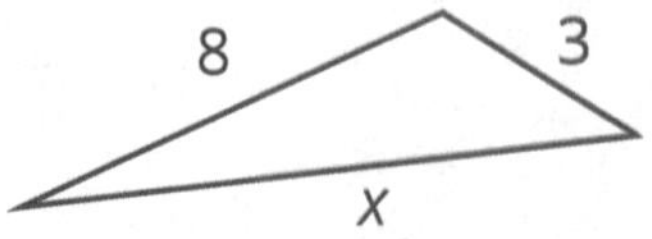

3.06 *AB* ______ *BC*

3.07 *AC* ______ *BC*

3.08 *AB* ______ *AC*

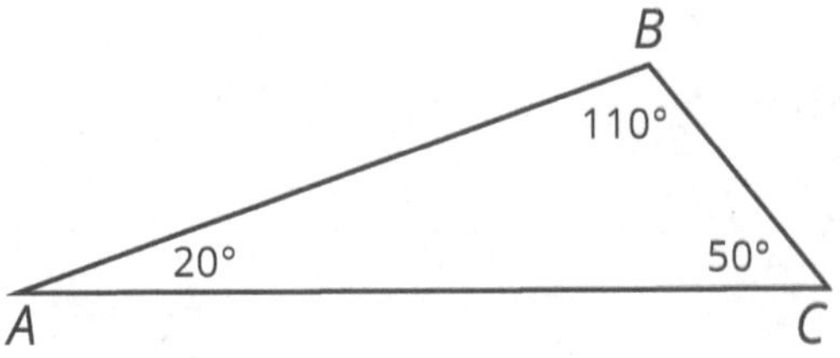

3.09 *AB* ______ *DE*

3.010 If ∠*A* = ∠*D*, then ∠*B* __________ ∠*E*.

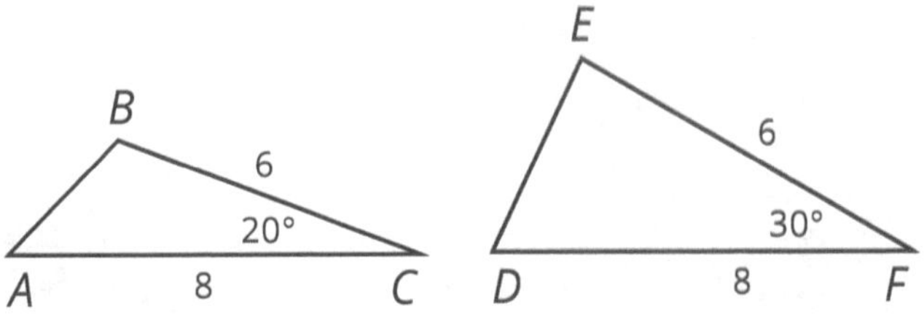

3.011 *BC* ______ *AC*

3.012 ∠*R* ______ ∠*T*

3.013 If *AB* = *RT* and ∠*R* = 70°, then △ *ABC* __________ △ *RTS*.

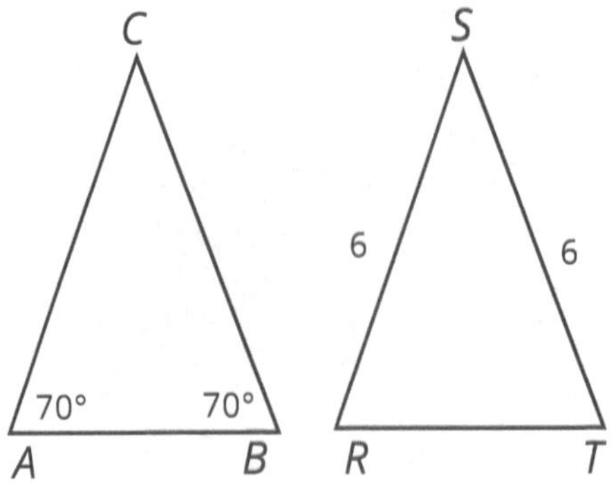

Complete this proof (each answer, 4 points).

Given: $\angle A = \angle B$

M is midpoint of *AB*

Prove: $\triangle AMC \cong \triangle BMC$

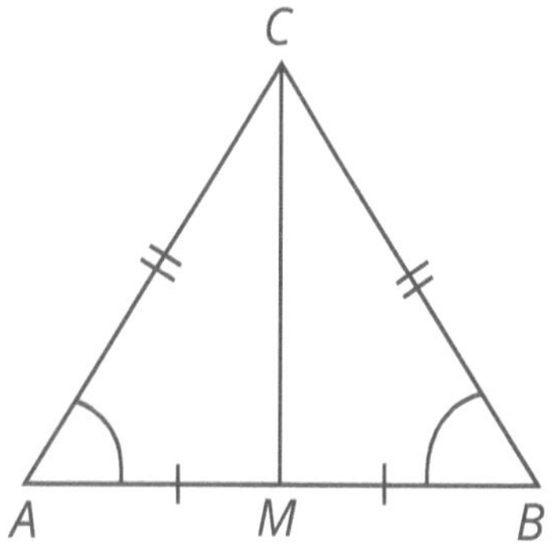

STATEMENT	REASON
3.014 ______________________	______________________
3.015 ______________________	______________________
3.016 ______________________	______________________
3.017 ______________________	______________________

49/61 **SCORE** ____________ **TEACHER** ____________ ____________

initials date

4. QUADRILATERALS

Many familiar objects that we use have four sides and are plane figures: a sheet of notebook paper, a greeting card, a postage stamp, a baseball diamond, a football field, and many more. These shapes are all called *quadrilaterals*.

A quadrilateral is a geometric figure with four sides.	REMEMBER ?

Quadrilaterals have many interesting properties, which you will study in this section. Quadrilaterals are related to triangles because of the congruent triangles that are formed by their diagonals. The main types of quadrilaterals are *parallelograms* and *trapezoids*, *rectangles* and *squares*.

Section Objective

Review this objective. When you have finished this section, you should be able to:

9. Identify the properties of parallelograms, rectangles, squares, rhombuses, and trapezoids.

PARALLELOGRAMS

One of the special quadrilaterals that we study is called a parallelogram. Its name suggests its shape, and its definition will be useful to remember.

DEFINITION

Parallelogram (▱): a quadrilateral with both pairs of opposite sides parallel.

Our definition for parallelogram has two requirements. A parallelogram is a quadrilateral, which means that it has four sides; and the opposite sides of the figure are parallel.

The figures shown are all parallelograms. By the definition of parallelogram, we know that $\overline{RS} \parallel \overline{UT}$ and $\overline{RU} \parallel \overline{ST}$; $\overline{AB} \parallel \overline{DC}$ and $\overline{AD} \parallel \overline{BC}$; and $\overline{WX} \parallel \overline{ZY}$ and $\overline{WZ} \parallel \overline{XY}$.

Theorem 4-14 shows that a diagonal of a parallelogram forms congruent triangles.

THEOREM 4-14

If a diagonal is drawn in a parallelogram, then two congruent triangles are formed.

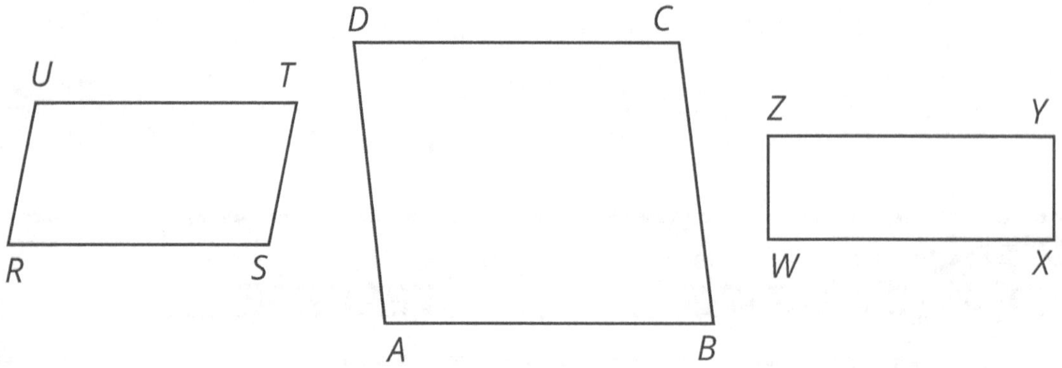

Given: ▱ RSTU
Diagonal $\overline{SU}$

Prove: △ RSU ≅ △ TUS

Plan: Use || lines to show ∠S equal, then use ASA.

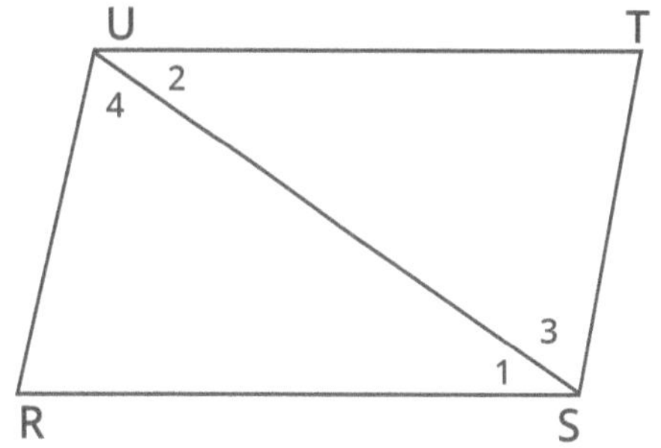

STATEMENT	REASON
1. ▱ *RSTU*; Diagonal $\overline{SU}$	1. Given
2. $\overline{RU} \parallel \overline{ST}, \overline{RS} \parallel \overline{TU}$	2. Definition of ▱
3. ∠1 = ∠2, ∠3 = ∠4	3. If lines || then alternate interior ∠'s are =
4. *SU* = *SU*	4. Reflexive
5. △ *RSU* ≅ △ *TUS*	5. *ASA*

Three corollaries to this theorem will be useful in your study of parallelograms.

Corollary 1: Opposite angles of a parallelogram are equal.

Corollary 2: Opposite sides of a parallelogram are equal.

Corollary 3: Two parallel lines are equidistant throughout.

The following paragraph is a proof of Corollary 3 in outline form.

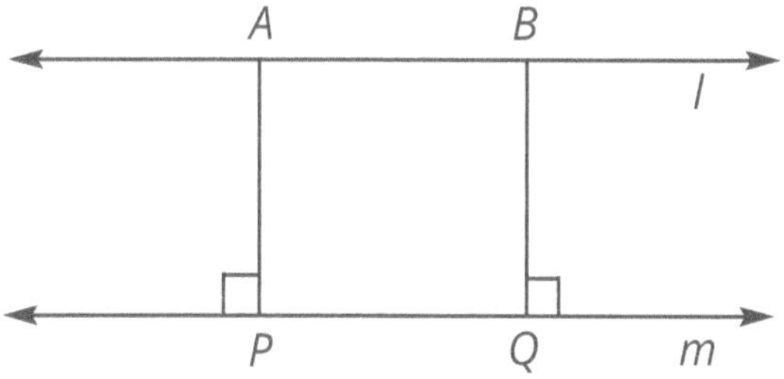

Let *l* and *m* be two parallel lines. Pick two points, *A* and *B*, on *l*. *AP* is the *AB* distance between *l* and *m* at *A*. *BQ* is the distance between *l* and *m* at *B*. $\overline{AP} \perp m$, $\overline{BQ} \perp m$. *APQB* is a parallelogram by definition; and by C-2 the opposite sides (*AP* and *BQ*) are equal *AP* = *BQ*.

THEOREM 4-15
The diagonals of a parallelogram bisect each other.

Given: ▱ *ABCD*
$\overline{AC}$, $\overline{BD}$ are diagonals

Prove: $\overline{AC}$ bisects $\overline{BD}$
(*DM* = *MB*)
$\overline{BD}$ bisects $\overline{AC}$
(*AM* = *MC*)

Plan: Show that *DM* = *MB* and *AM* = *MC* by CPCTE in △ *AMD* and △ *CBM*.

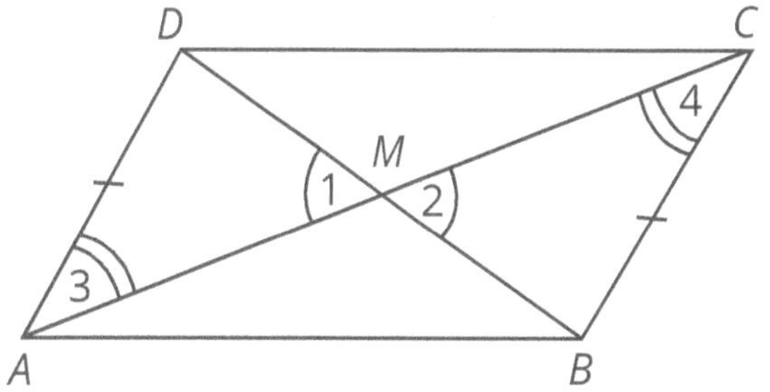

STATEMENT	REASON
1. ▱ *ABCD*; $\overline{AC}$, $\overline{BD}$ are diagonals	1. Given
2. $AD = CB$	2. Opposite sides of ▱ are =
3. 1 = 2	3. Vertical ∠'s are =
4. $\overline{AD} \parallel \overline{BC}$	4. Definition of ▱
5. $\angle 3 = \angle 4$	5. If lines | |, then alternate interior ∠'s are =
6. $\triangle AMD \cong \triangle CMB$	6. AAS
7. $DM = MB$, $AM = MC$	7. CPCTE
8. Diagonal bisect each others	8. Definition of bisector

Complete these items.

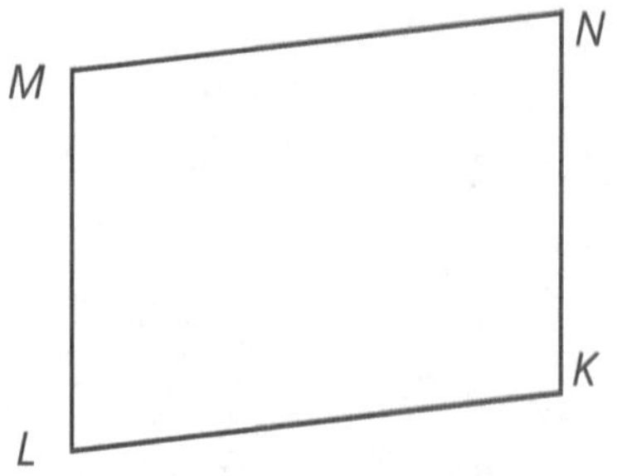

Given: *KLMN* is a parallelogram.

4.1 State the reason why $\overline{ML} \parallel \overline{NK}$. ______________________

4.2 State the reason why $MN = LK$. ______________________

4 3 State the reason why $\angle K = \angle M$. ______________________

4.4 What relationship exists between $\angle N$ and $\angle K$? ______________________

Given: *RSTU* is a parallelogram.

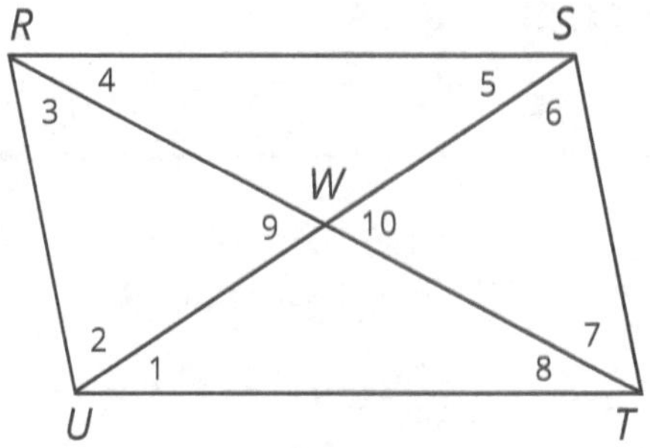

4.5 Name the pairs of equal angles.

____

____

4.6 Name the pairs of equal segments.

____

____

4.7 Name 4 pairs of ≅ △'s. ______________________

4.8 $\angle 1 + \angle 2 + \angle 3 + \angle 4 =$ ______________________

4.9 Which ≅ statement could be used to prove $\triangle RTS \cong \triangle TRU$? ______________________

Complete the following proofs.

4.10 Prove Corollary 1 to Theorem 4-14.

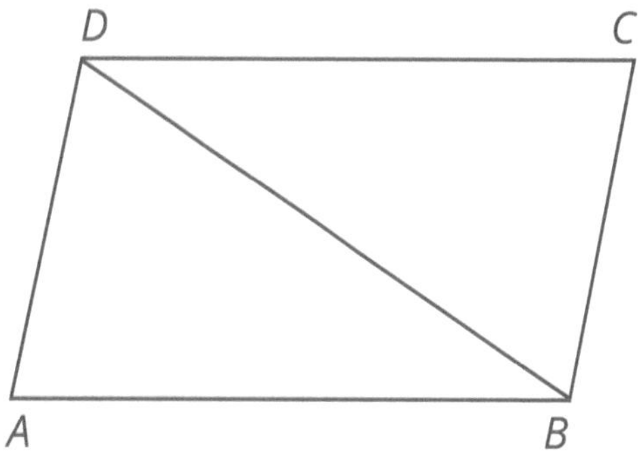

Given: *ABCD* is ▱

Prove: $\angle A = \angle C$

STATEMENT	REASON
1. ______	1. ______
2. ______	2. ______
3. ______	3. ______
4. ______	4. ______

4.11 Prove Corollary 2 to Theorem 4-14.

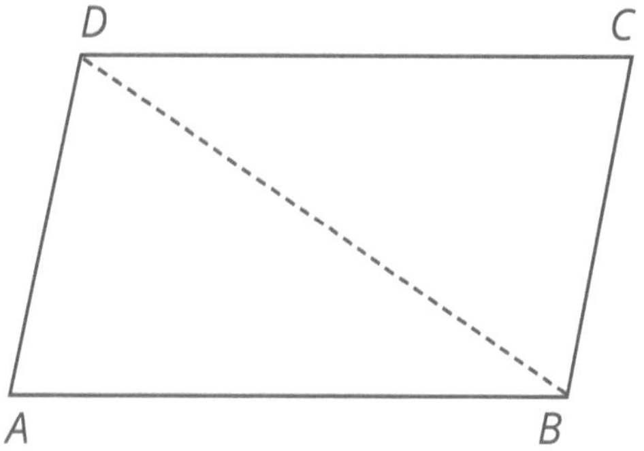

Given: *ABCD* is ▱

Prove: $AB = DC$, $AD = BC$

STATEMENT	REASON
1. ______	1. ______
2. ______	2. ______
3. ______	3. ______
4. ______	4. ______

4.12 Given: ▱ $ABCD$

$\overline{EF}$ contains T

Prove: $ET = FT$

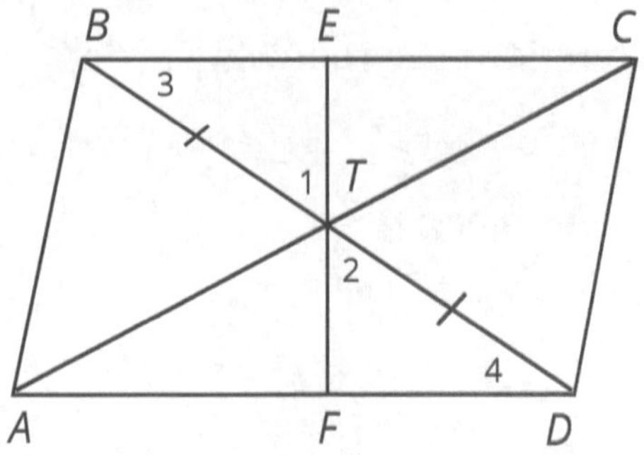

STATEMENT	REASON
1. __________	1. __________
2. __________	2. __________
3. __________	3. __________
4. __________	4. __________
5. __________	5. __________
6. __________	6. __________
7. __________	7. __________

4.13 Given: $\angle A$, $\angle B$, and $\angle C$ are rt. $\angle$'s

Prove: $ABCD$ is ▱

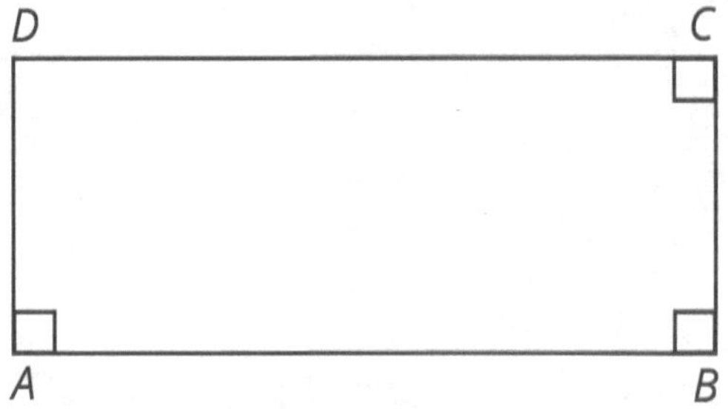

STATEMENT	REASON
1. __________	1. __________
2. __________	2. __________
3. __________	3. __________
4. __________	4. __________
5. __________	5. __________
6. __________	6. __________

4.14 Given: *RSTU* is ▱
RSQP is ▱
Prove: *PQ* = *UT*

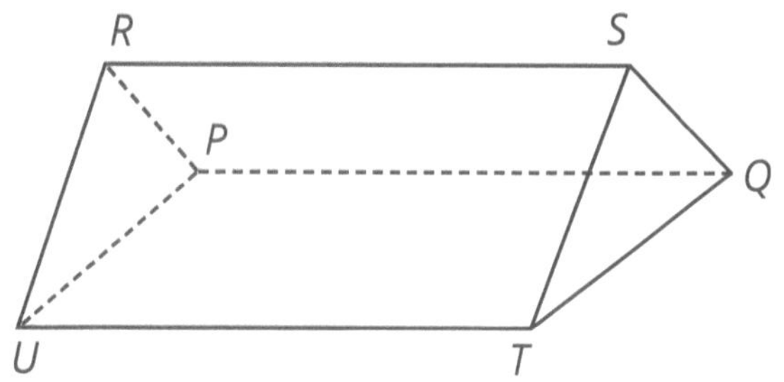

STATEMENT	REASON
1. ______________	1. ______________
2. ______________	2. ______________
3. ______________	3. ______________

The only way we have so far to prove that a quadrilateral is a parallelogram is to show that both pairs of opposite sides are parallel. This method uses the definition of a parallelogram. The following three theorems give us other ways to prove that a quadrilateral is a parallelogram.

THEOREM 4-16
If two sides of a quadrilateral are equal and parallel, then the quadrilateral is a parallelogram.

Given: $\overline{AD} \parallel \overline{BC}$
$AD = BC$
Prove: *ABCD* is ▱
Plan: Draw diagonal *DB* and prove △'s =.
Use CPCTE to show alternate interior ∠'s ≅, which proves $\overline{AB} \parallel \overline{DC}$.
Then use definition of ▱.

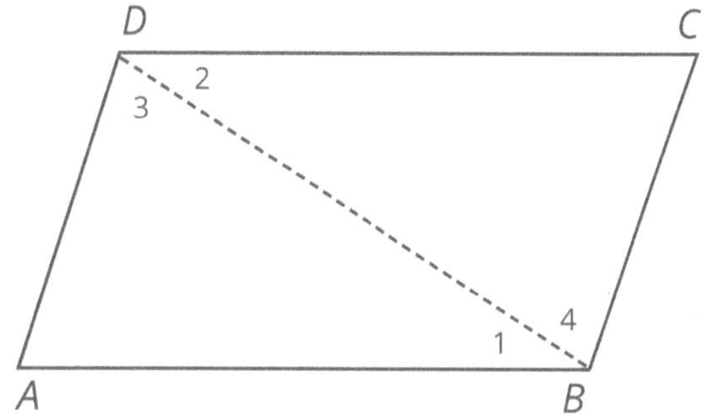

STATEMENT	REASON
1. Draw $\overline{DB}$	1. Auxiliary line
2. $\overline{AD} \parallel \overline{BC}$, $AD = BC$	2. Given
3. $\angle 3 = \angle 4$	3. If lines || alternate interior ∠'s =
4. $DB = DB$	4. Reflexive
5. $\triangle ABD \cong \triangle CDB$	5. SAS
6. $\angle 1 = \angle 2$	6. CPCTE
7. $\overline{AD} \parallel \overline{BC}$,	7. If alternate interior ∠'s =, then lines are ||
8. *ABCD* is ▱	8. Definition of ▱

> **THEOREM 4-17**
> If both pairs of opposite sides of a quadrilateral are equal, then the quadrilateral is a parallelogram.

Given: $AB = CD$, $BC = AD$

Prove: $ABCD$ is ▱

Plan: Draw a diagonal and prove the △'s ≅. Then use Theorem 4-16.

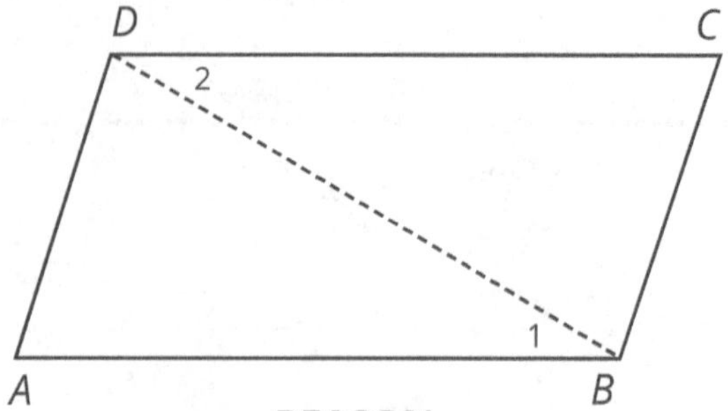

STATEMENT	REASON
1. Draw $\overline{DB}$	1. Auxiliary line
2. $AB = CD$, $BC = AD$	2. Given
3. $DB = DB$	3. Reflexive
4. $\triangle ABD \cong \triangle CDB$	4. SSS
5. $\angle 1 = \angle 2$	5. CPCTE
6. $\overline{AB} \parallel \overline{CD}$,	6. If alternate interior ∠'s =, then lines are ∥
7. $ABCD$ is ▱	7. If two sides = and ∥, then ▱

> **THEOREM 4-18**
> If the diagonals of a quadrilateral bisect each other, then the quadrilateral is a parallelogram.

Given: $ABCD$ is quadrilateral
$DO = OB$
$AO = OC$

Prove: $ABCD$ is ▱

Plan: Show $\triangle AOB \cong \triangle COD$, then use Theorem 4-16.

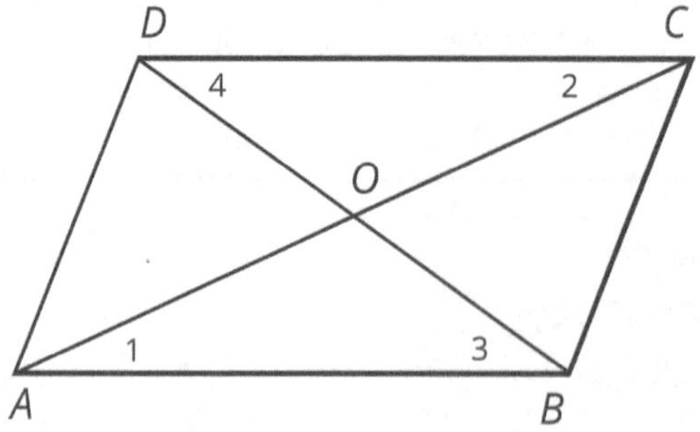

Finish the proof of this theorem.

4.15

STATEMENT	REASON
1. ______________	1. ______________
2. ______________	2. ______________
3. ______________	3. ______________

STATEMENT	REASON
4. ______________________	4. ______________________
5. ______________________	5. ______________________
6. ______________________	6. ______________________

The next theorem is a very useful theorem about triangles that uses parallelograms in its proof.

> **THEOREM 4-19**
> If you connect the midpoints of two sides of a triangle, the resulting segment is parallel to the third side and equals half the length of the third side.

Given: M midpoint of $\overline{AC}$
N midpoint of $\overline{BC}$

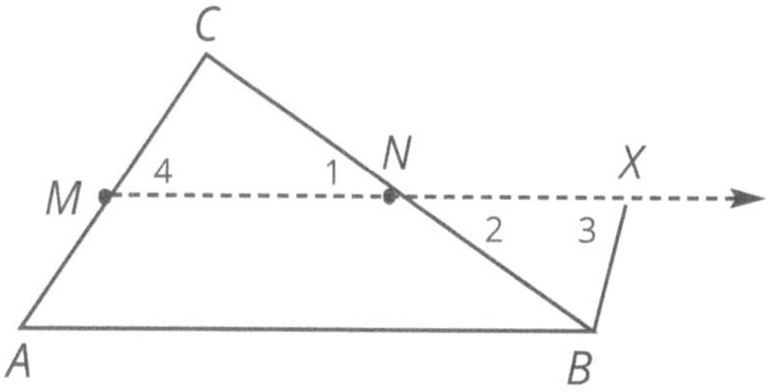

Prove: $\overline{MN} \parallel \overline{AB}$
$\overline{MN} = \frac{1}{2} AB$

Plan: Use auxiliary lines to form ▱ $ABXM$.
Use properties of ▱ to show $\overline{MN} \parallel \overline{AB}$.
Use betweenness and substitution to show $MN = \frac{1}{2} AB$.

STATEMENT	REASON
1. M midpoint of AC N midpoint of BC	1. Given
2. Draw $\overleftrightarrow{MX}$ so $NX = MN$ Draw $\overline{XB}$	2. Auxiliary lines
3. $\angle 1 = \angle 2$	3. Vertical ∠'s are =
4. $AM = MC$, $BN = NC$	4. Definition of midpoint
5. $\triangle MNC \cong \triangle XNB$	5. SAS
6. $\angle 3 = \angle 4$, $BX = MC$	6. CPCTE
7. $AM = BX$	7. Substitution
8. $\overline{AM} \parallel \overline{BX}$,	8. If alternate interior ∠'s = lines ||
9. $AMXB$ is ▱	9. If two sides = and ||, then ▱
10. $\overline{MX} \parallel \overline{AB}$, so $\overline{MN} \parallel \overline{AB}$	10. Opposite sides of ▱ are ||
11. $MN + NX = MX$	11. Betweeness
12. $2MN + MX$	12. Substitution
13. $MN = \frac{1}{2} MX$	13. Division property of equality
14. $MX = AB$	14. Opposite sides of ▱ are =
15. $MN = \frac{1}{2} AB$	15. Substitution

Use the figures to complete the following items.

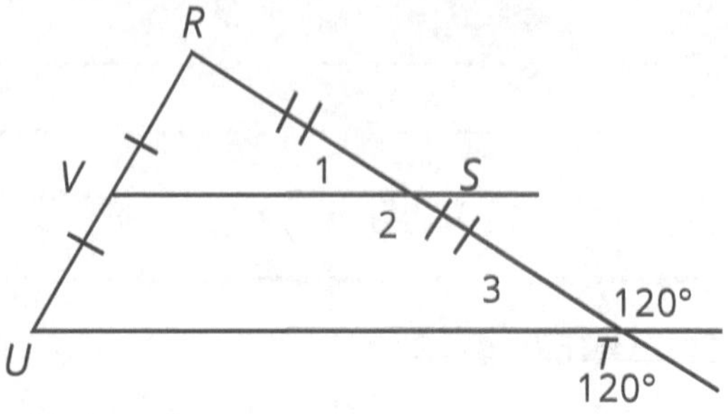

4.16 $\overline{VS}$ || ____________

4.17 If $UT = 20$, then $VS =$ ____________.

4.18 If $VS = 12$, then $UT =$ ____________.

4.19 If $\angle 1 = \angle 60°$, then $\angle 3 =$ ____________.

4.20 $\angle 2 + \angle 3 =$ ____________

4.21 If $\angle 2 = 120°$, then $\angle 3 =$ ____________.

4.22 If M is midpoint of $\overline{UT}$, name a segment parallel to $\overline{RU}$. ____________

4.23 If M is midpoint of $\overline{UT}$, name a segment parallel to $\overline{RT}$. ____________

Given: R, S, T are midpoints of AC, AB, and CB.

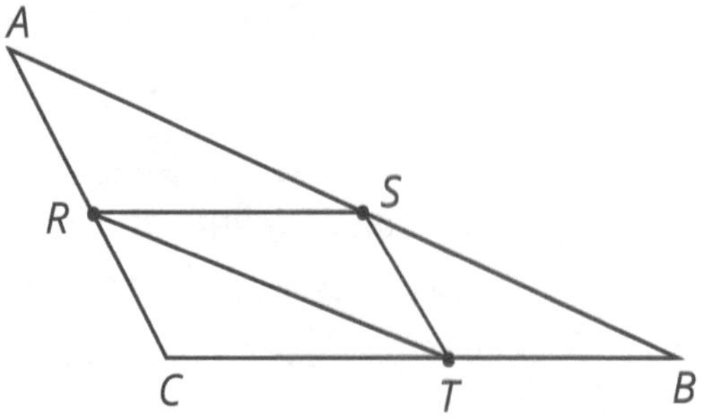

4.24 $\overline{AB}$ || ____________

4.25 $\overline{RT}$ || ____________

4.26 $\overline{AC}$ || ____________

4.27 $RS = \frac{1}{2}$ ____________

4.28 $RT = \frac{1}{2}$ ____________

4.29 $AB = 2$ ____________

4.30 $RCTS$ is a ____________.

Given: $\angle H = 2x + 60°$
$\angle T = x + 30°$
$HALT$ is a ▱

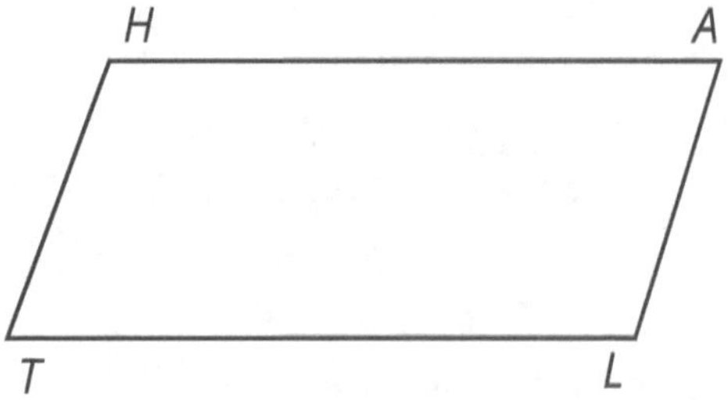

4.31 $\angle H =$ ____________

4.32 $\angle A =$ ____________

4.33 $\angle L =$ ____________

4.34 $\angle T =$ ____________

Given: $FLAG$ is ▱
$GXYZ$ is ▱

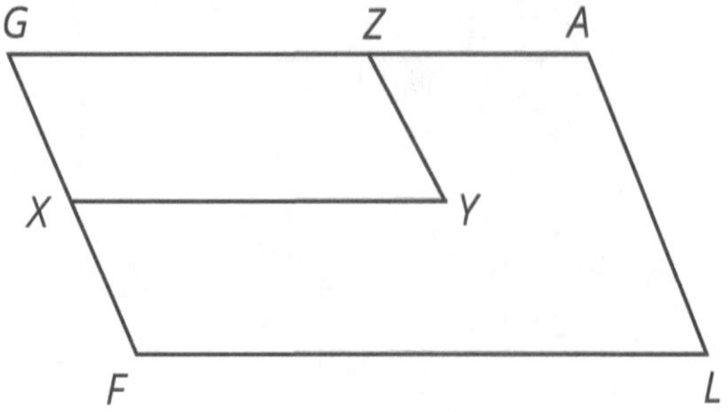

4.35 XY || a. ________ and || b. ________

4.36 ZY || a. ________ and || b. ________

4.37 $\angle Y =$ a. ________ and b. ________

4.38 $\angle F =$ a. ________ and b. ________ and c. ________

4.39 Given: *ABEF* is ▱

$\overline{EB} \parallel \overline{DC}$

Prove: *ACDF* is ▱

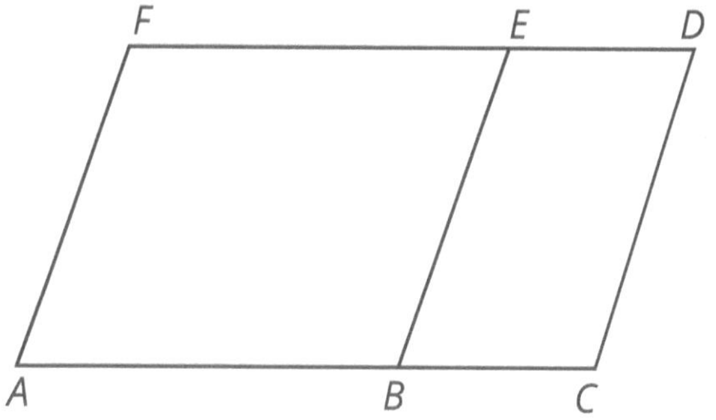

STATEMENT	REASON
1. ______	1. ______
2. ______	2. ______
3. ______	3. ______
4. ______	4. ______
5. ______	5. ______

We shall now study three special parallelograms: the *rectangle*, the *rhombus*, and the *square*.

DEFINITIONS

Rectangle: a parallelogram with four right angles.

Rhombus: a parallelogram with all sides equal.

Square: a rectangle with all sides equal and four right angles.

Since a rectangle, a rhombus, and a square are defined as special parallelograms, they all have properties of a parallelogram, and all the theorems that apply to a parallelogram also apply to them.

You will prove the following three theorems about rectangles and rhombuses as an activity.

THEOREM 4-20
The diagonals of a rectangle are equal.

THEOREM 4-21
The diagonals of a rhombus are perpendicular.

THEOREM 4-22
Each diagonal of a rhombus bisects two angles of the rhombus.

Rectangles, rhombuses, and squares have many more properties in addition to those given in Theorems 4-20, 4-21, and 4-22. We shall consider some of them in the activities that follow.

Complete the following proofs.

4.40 Prove Theorem 4-20.
Hint: Show △ *RST* ≅ △ *SRU.*

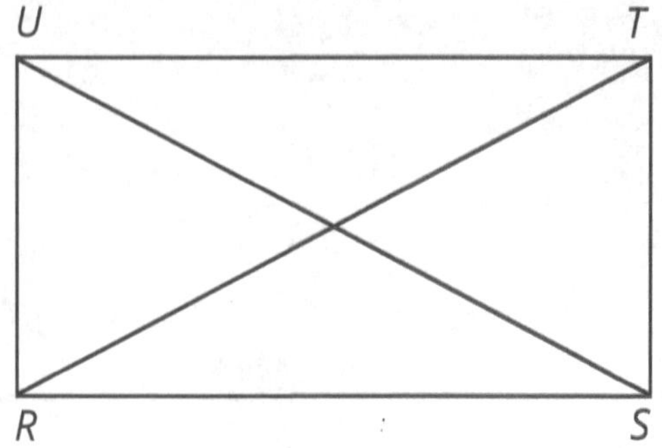

Given: ____________________

Prove: ____________________

STATEMENT	REASON
1. ____________	1. ____________
2. ____________	2. ____________
3. ____________	3. ____________
4. ____________	4. ____________
5. ____________	5. ____________
6. ____________	6. ____________

4.41 Prove Theorem 4-21.
Hint: Show △ *DOA* ≅ △ *BOA*; use equality of ∠1 and ∠2 to establish perpendicular.

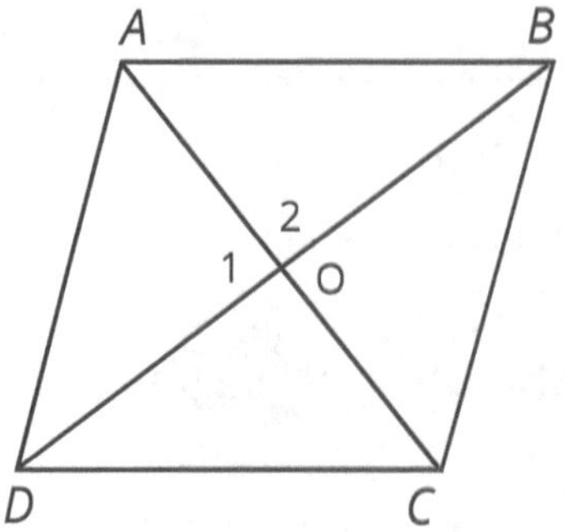

Given: ____________________

Prove: ____________________

STATEMENT	REASON
1. ____________	1. ____________
2. ____________	2. ____________
3. ____________	3. ____________
4. ____________	4. ____________
5. ____________	5. ____________
6. ____________	6. ____________
7. ____________	7. ____________

4.42 Prove Theorem 4-22.
Hint: Prove $\triangle ADB \cong \triangle CDB$.

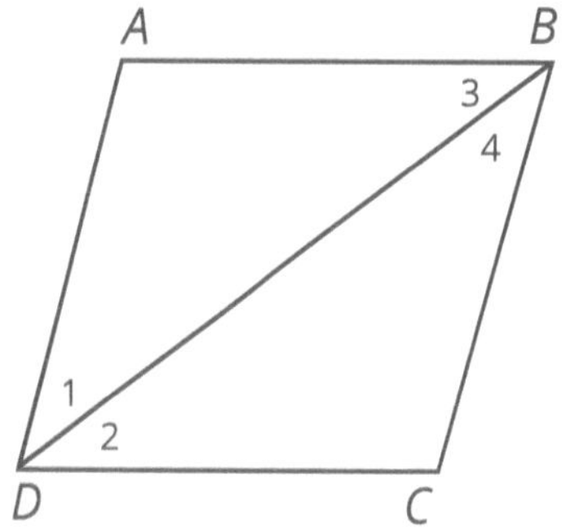

Given: ____________________

Prove: ____________________

STATEMENT	REASON
1. ________	1. ________
2. ________	2. ________
3. ________	3. ________
4. ________	4. ________

4.43 **Prove**: If the diagonals of a parallelogram are equal, then the parallelogram is a rectangle.

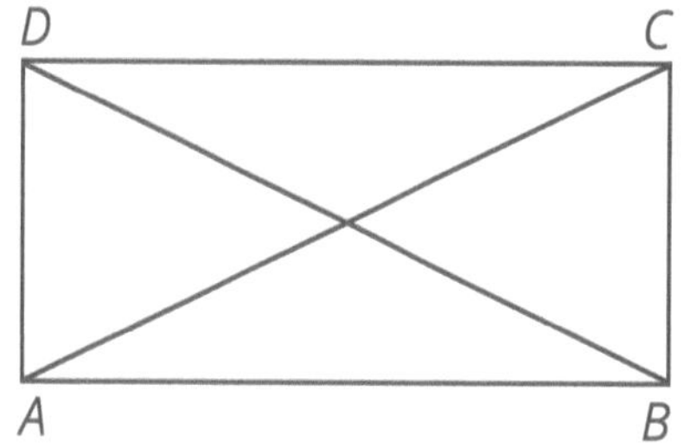

Given: ____________________

Prove: ____________________

STATEMENT	REASON
1. ________	1. ________
2. ________	2. ________
3. ________	3. ________
4. ________	4. ________
5. ________	5. ________
6. ________	6. ________
7. ________	7. ________
8. ________	8. ________
9. ________	9. ________
10. ________	10. ________

4.44 **Prove**: If the four sides of a quadrilateral are equal, the quadrilateral is a rhombus.

Given: ______________________

Prove: ______________________

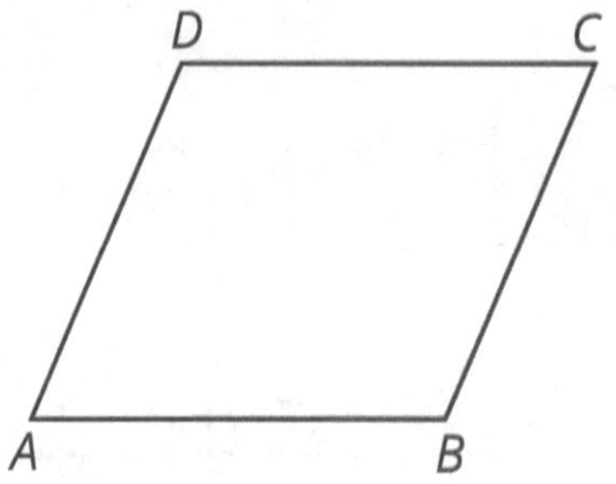

STATEMENT	REASON
1. ______________	1. ______________
2. ______________	2. ______________
3. ______________	3. ______________

4.45 **Prove**: The quadrilateral formed by joining in order the midpoints of the sides of a rectangle is a parallelogram.

Given: ______________________

Prove: ______________________

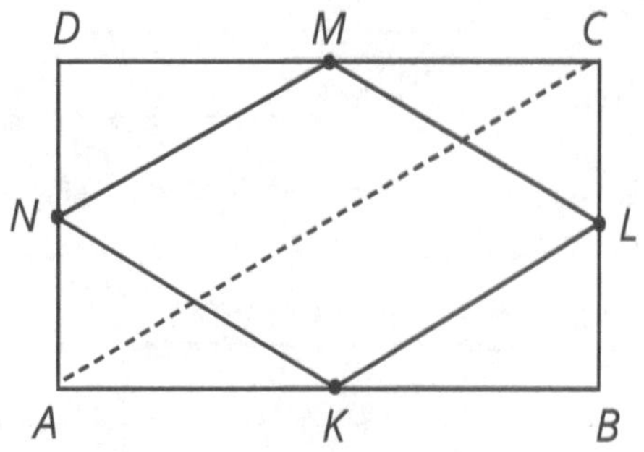

STATEMENT	REASON
1. ______________	1. ______________
2. ______________	2. ______________
3. ______________	3. ______________
4. ______________	4. ______________
5. ______________	5. ______________
6. ______________	6. ______________

This chart shows how special parallelograms are related. Each figure on a lower level has all the properties of those on higher levels preceding it in the chart.

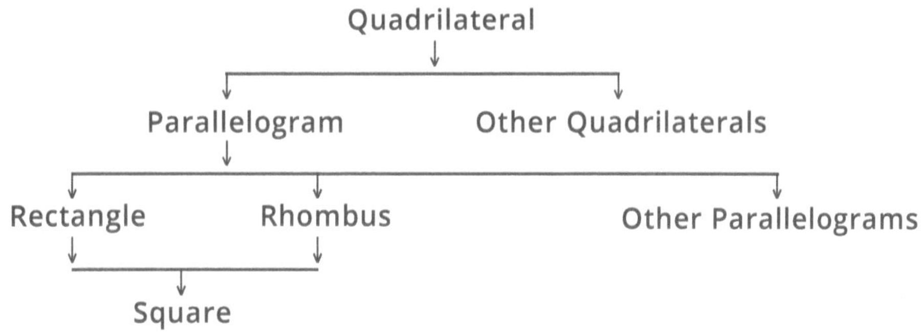

Write true or false.

4.46 ____________ Every quadrilateral is a parallelogram.

4.47 ____________ Every square is a rhombus.

4.48 ____________ No parallelogram is a rhombus.

4.49 ____________ The diagonals of a rhombus are $\perp$.

4.50 ____________ The diagonals of a rectangle are $\perp$.

4.51 ____________ The opposite angles of a rhombus are equal.

4.52 ____________ Every parallelogram is a rhombus.

4.53 ____________ Every square is a rectangle.

4.54 ____________ Every square is a parallelogram.

Refer to these figures to complete the following items.

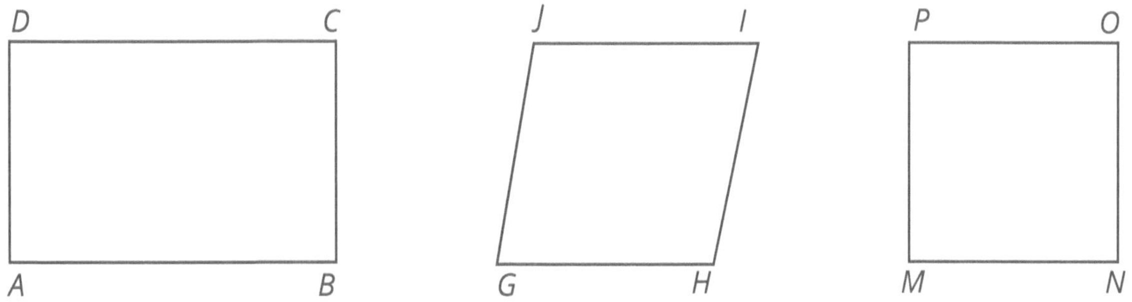

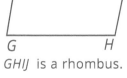

ABCD is a rectangle. *GHIJ* is a rhombus. *MNOP* is a square.

4.55 $\overline{GI} \perp$ ____________

4.56 If $\angle GHI = 120°$, then $\angle GJI =$ ____________ .

4.57 If $DC = 12$, then $AB =$ ____________ .

4.58 $\angle C =$ ____________

4.59 If $PO = 8$, then $ON =$ ____________ .

4.60 If $HI = 16$, then $GH =$ ____________ .

4.61 $\overline{JH}$ bisects a. ∠__________ and b. ∠__________

4.62 If $AC = 20$, then $BD =$ __________ .

4.63 If $MO = 10$, then $NP =$ __________ .

4.64 If $GI = 20$, $\angle H = 100°$, then HJ __________ 20 .

TRAPEZOIDS

In the chart on quadrilaterals the other branch on the level with parallelograms, labeled "Other Quadrilaterals," leads to figures known as *trapezoids*.

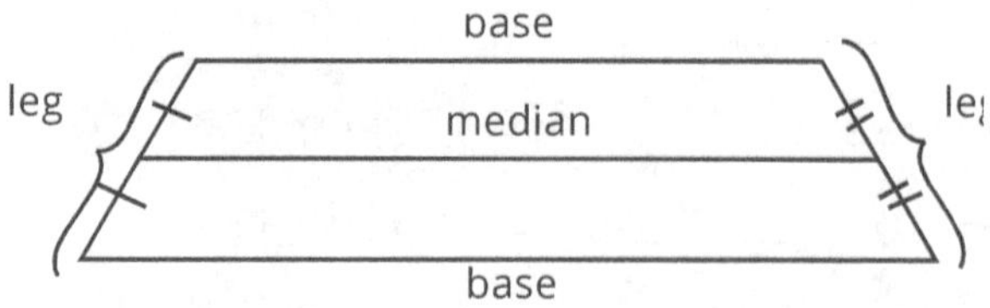

DEFINITION

Trapezoid: a quadrilateral with exactly one pair of parallel sides.

If the two legs are the same length, then the figure is called an isosceles trapezoid.

The four figures shown are all trapezoids. The parallel sides of the trapezoid are called the *bases* and the nonparallel sides are called the *legs*. The *median* of a trapezoid is a segment connecting the midpoints of the legs.

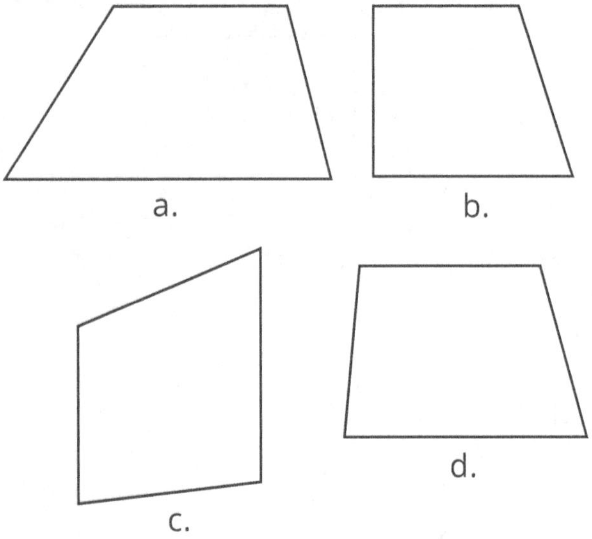

DEFINITIONS

Bases of a trapezoid: the parallel sides.

Legs of a trapezoid: the nonparallel sides.

Median of a trapezoid: the segment connecting the midpoints of the legs.

Isosceles trapezoid: a trapezoid with legs of the same length.

THEOREM 4-23

The median of a trapezoid is parallel to the bases, and its length is half the sum of the lengths of the bases.

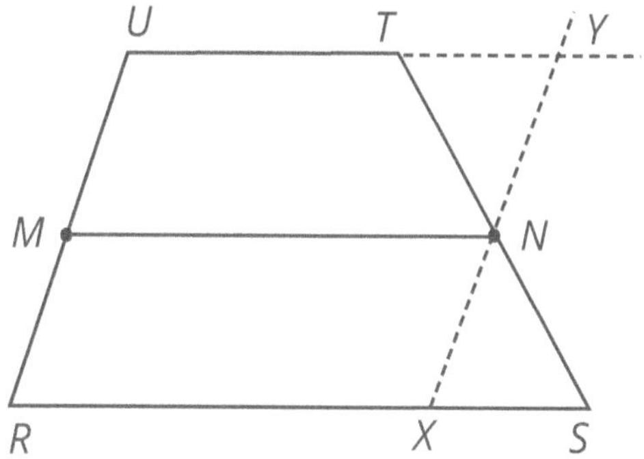

Given: *RSTU* is trapezoid

$\overline{MN}$ is median

Prove: $\overline{MN} \parallel \overline{RS}$

$MN = \frac{1}{2}(RS + UT)$

Outline of proof:

Draw auxiliary line $\overleftrightarrow{XY} \parallel \overline{RU}$. $\triangle SXN \cong \triangle TYN$ by ASA. $XN = YN$ and $XN = \frac{1}{2}XY$. *RXYU* is a parallelogram with $RU = XY$. Substituting *RU* for *XY* we get $XN = \frac{1}{2}RU = RM$

Since $\overline{XN}$ and $\overline{RM}$ are = and $\parallel$. *RXNM* is a parallelogram and $MN \parallel RS$.

$MN = RX = RS - XS$

$MN = UY = UT + TY$

$2MN = RS + UT + (TY - XS)$ but $TY = XS$; therefore,

$2MN = RS + UT$

$MN = \frac{1}{2}(RS + UT)$

THEOREM 4-24
The base angles of an isosceles trapezoid are equal.

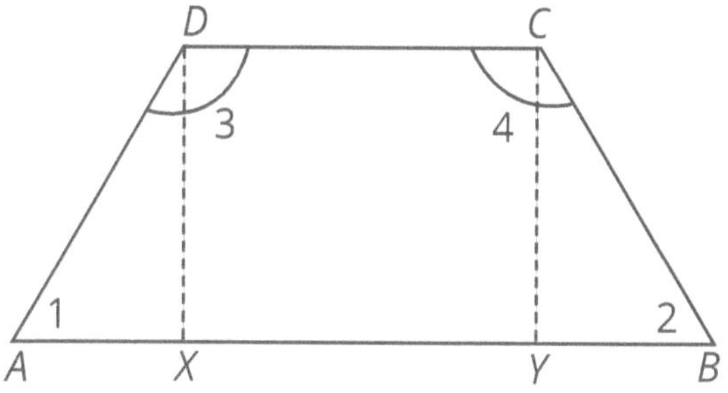

Given: *ABCD* is isosceles trapezoid

Prove: $\angle 1 = \angle 2$

$\angle 3 = \angle 4$

Plan: Show *XYCD* is ▱, then $DX = CY$.

Use CPCTE.

STATEMENT	REASON
1. $\overline{DC} \parallel \overline{AB}$ $AD = BC$	1. Definition of isosceles trapezoid
2. Draw $\overline{DX} \perp \overline{AB}$ $\overline{CY} \perp \overline{AB}$	2. Auxiliary lines
3. $\overline{DX} \parallel \overline{CY}$	3. Two lines $\perp$ to same line $\parallel$
4. *XYCD* is ▱	4. Definition of ▱
5. $DX = CY$	5. Opposite sides of ▱ are =
6. $\triangle AXD \cong \triangle BYC$	6. HL
7. $\angle 1 = \angle 2$	7. CPCTE
8. $\angle 1 = \angle 3$ are supplementary $\angle 2 = \angle 4$ are supplementary	8. Interior $\angle$'s on same side of transversal are supplementary
9. $\angle 3 = \angle 4$	9. $\angle$'s supplementary to equal $\angle$'s are =

THEOREM 4-25
The diagonals of an isosceles trapezoid are equal.

Given: *ABCD* is isosceles trapezoid
Prove: *AC* = *BD*
Plan: Prove $\triangle ABD \cong \triangle BAC$

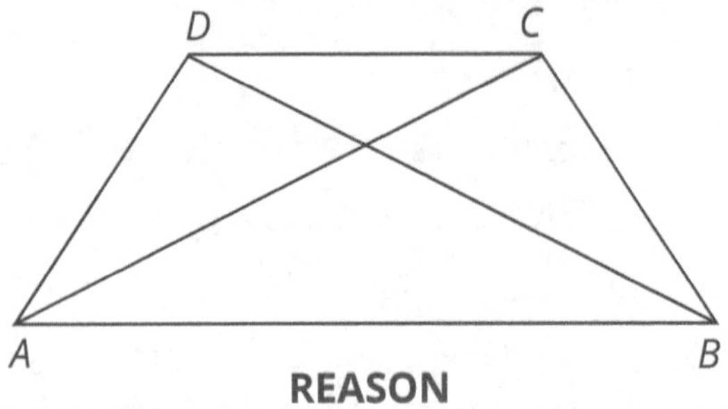

STATEMENT	REASON
1. $AB = AB$	1. Reflexive
2. $AD = BC$	2. Given; isosceles trapezoid
3. $\angle DAB = \angle CBA$	3. Base ∠'s of isosceles trapezoid are =
4. $\triangle ABD \cong \triangle BAC$	4. SAS
5. $AC = BD$	5. CPCTE

Refer to the figures to complete the following items.

Given: Quadrilateral *ROSE* is trapezoid with median $\overline{MN}$

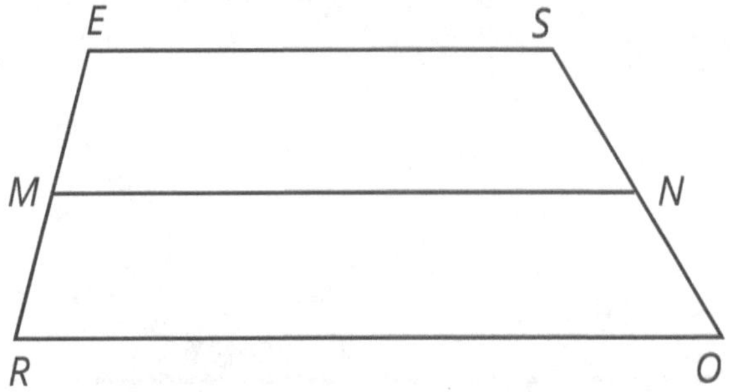

4.65 If *RO* = 10 and *ES* = 6, then *MN* = ____________.

4.66 If *RO* = *x* and *ES* = *y*, then *MN* = ____________.

4.67 If *MN* = 24 and *RO* = 30, then *ES* = ____________.

4.68 If *MN* = 24 and *ES* = 10, then *RO* = ____________.

Given: Quadrilateral *PQRS* is isosceles trapezoid

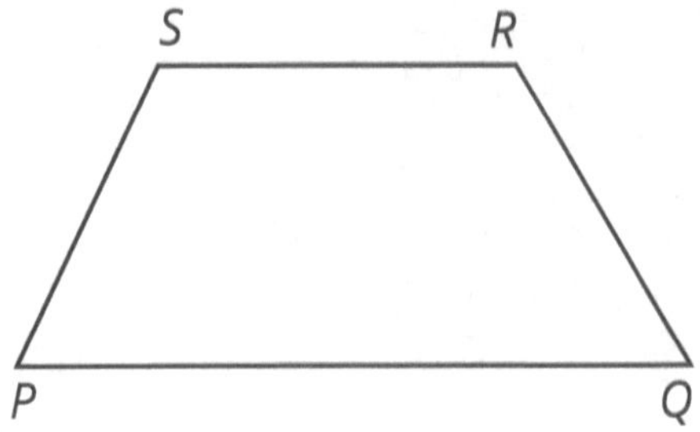

4.69 If ∠*P* = 50°, then ∠*Q* = a. ____________,
∠*R* = b. ____________, ∠*S* = c. ____________.

4.70 If ∠*P* = 60°, then ∠*Q* = a. ____________,
∠*R* = b. ____________, ∠*S* = c. ____________.

4.71 If ∠R = 100°, then ∠*S* = a. ____________, ∠p = b. ____________, ∠Q = c. ____________.

4.72 If ∠S = 120°, then ∠*Q* = a. ____________, ∠R = b. ____________, ∠*P* = c. ____________.

4.73 If *RP* = 12, then *SQ* = ____________.

Complete this proof to challenge your geometric ability.

Given: *ABCD* is a cube (all faces are squares)

Prove: *HB* = *EC*

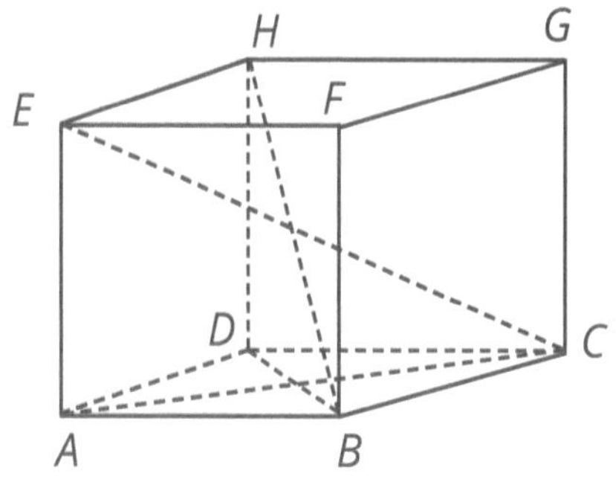

STATEMENT	REASON
1. ______	1. ______
2. ______	2. ______
3. ______	3. ______
4. ______	4. ______
5. ______	5. ______
6. ______	6. ______
7. ______	7. ______

TEACHER CHECK ______ initials ______ date

Before you take this last Self Test, you may want to do one or more of these self checks.

1. ______ Read the objectives. See if you can do them.

2. ______ Restudy the material related to any objectives that you cannot do.

3. ______ Use the **SQ3R** study procedure to review the material:

a. **S**can the sections.

b. **Q**uestion yourself.

c. **R**ead to answer your questions.

d. **R**ecite the answers to yourself.

e. **R**eview areas you did not understand.

4. ______ Review all vocabulary, activities, and Self Tests, writing a correct answer for every wrong answer.

SELF TEST 4

Refer to the figures to complete the following items (each answer, 3 points).

Given: *BOAT* is an isosceles trapezoid

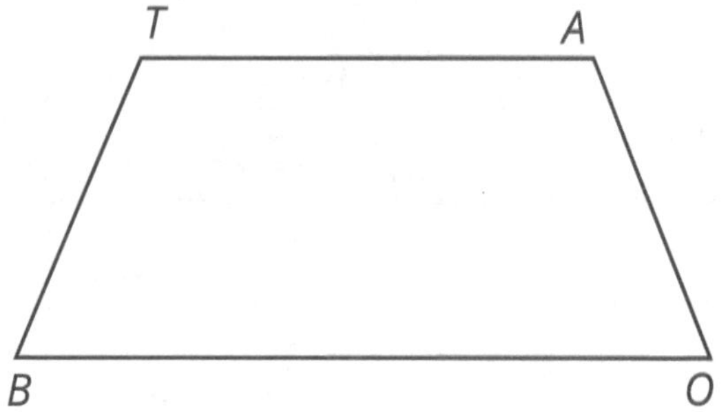

4.01 If *BO* = 12 and *TA* = 6, find the length of the median. ________________

4.02 If ∠T = 130°, find ∠*O*.

____

Given: *R, S, T* are midpoints of $\overline{AB}$, $\overline{BC}$, and $\overline{CA}$

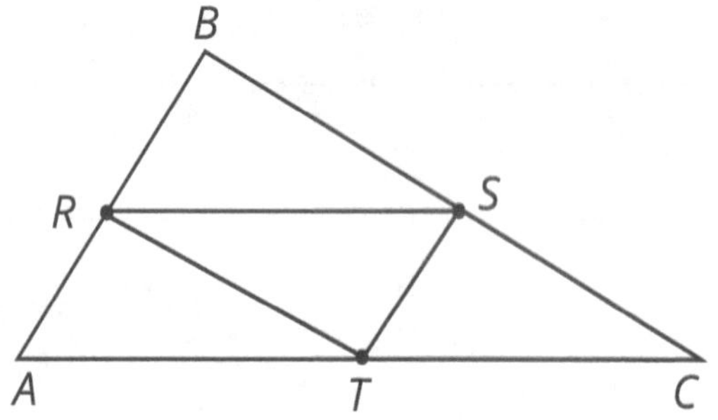

4.03 Name three parallelograms shown:
a. ________, b. ________, and c. ________.

4.04 If *RS* = 5, then *AC* = ________.

4.05 If the perimeter (distance around) of △ ABC is 20, then the perimeter of △ *RST* is ________.

Given: *ABCD* is a rectangle

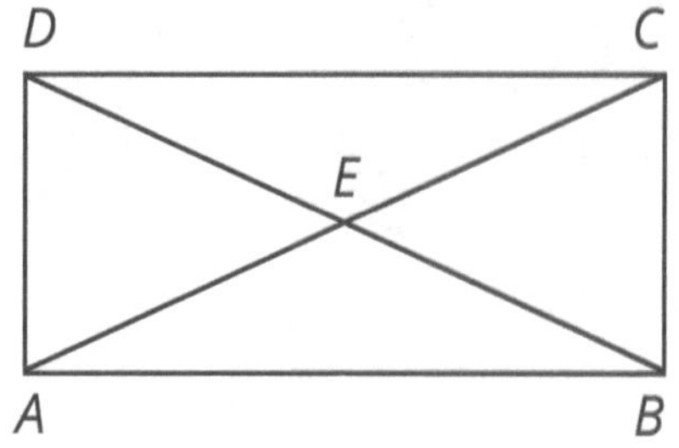

4.06 If *AC* = 10, then *BD* = ________.

4.07 If *AC* = 12, then *BE* = ________.

Given: *WXYZ* is a rhombus

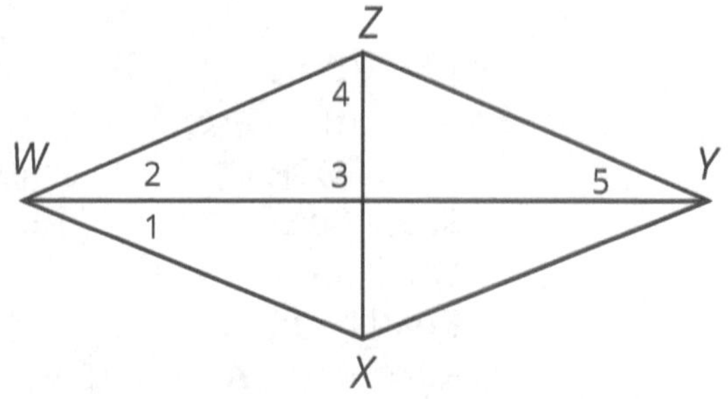

4.08 If ∠1 = 25°, then ∠2 = ________.

4.09 If ∠1 = 35°, then ∠4 = ________.

4.010 If ∠5 = 20°, then ∠1 = ________.

4.011 If *WX* = 5, find the perimeter of *WXYZ*

________________.

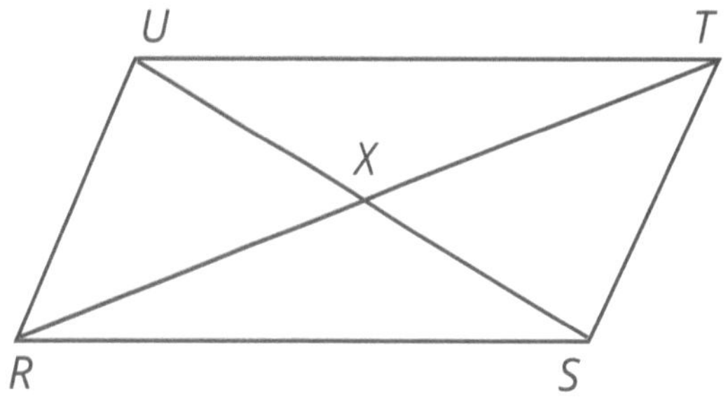

Given: *RSTU* is a parallelogram

4.012 $RS =$ ____________

4.013 $SX =$ ____________

4.014 $\triangle RST \cong$ ____________

4.015 $\triangle SXT \cong$ ____________

4.016 $\angle TRS =$ ____________

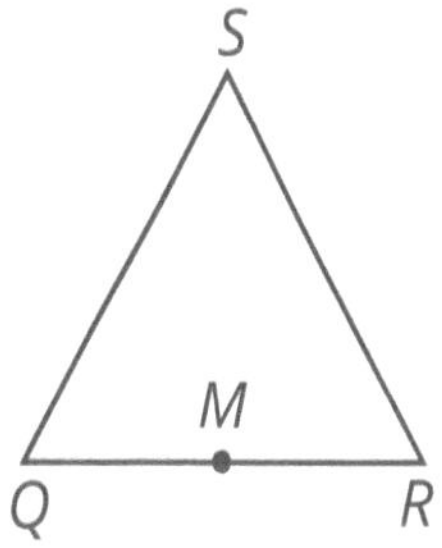

Given: *QRS* is an isosceles $\triangle$

4.017 $\angle Q =$ ____________

4.018 $RS =$ ____________

4.019 If *M* is midpoint of *RQ*, then $\triangle SQM \cong$ ____________ .

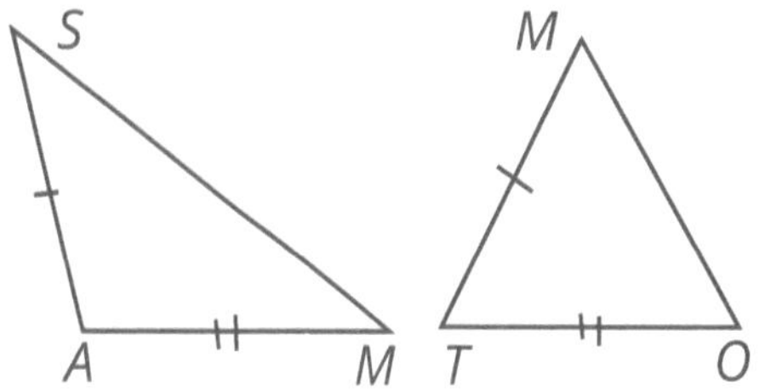

4.020 If $SM > MO$, then $\angle A$ ________ $\angle T$.

4.021 If $\angle A > \angle T$, then $\overline{MO}$ ________ SM.

4.022 If $\angle A = \angle T$, then SM ________ MO.

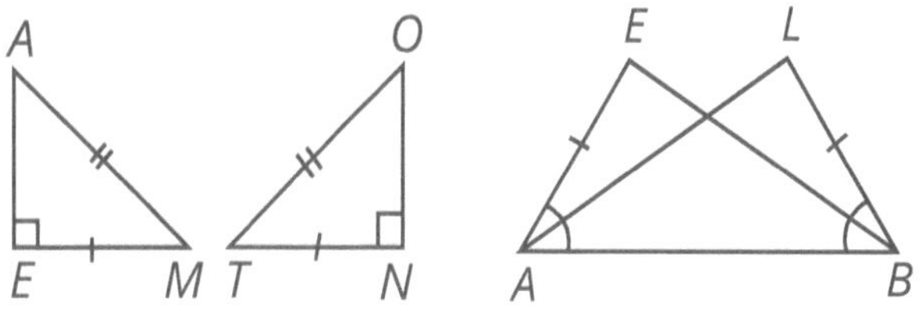

4.023 Why is $\triangle MAE \cong \triangle TON$? ____________

4.024 Why is $\triangle ABL \cong \triangle BAE$?

4.025 What reason justifies saying $AL = BE$?

____

65/81 **SCORE** ____________ **TEACHER** ____________ ____________
initials date

Before taking the LIFEPAC Test, you may want to do one or more of these self checks.

1. ________ Read the objectives. Check to see if you can do them.
2. ________ Restudy the material related to any objectives that you cannot do.
3. ________ Use the **SQ3R** study procedure to review the material.
4. ________ Review activities, Self Tests, and LIFEPAC vocabulary words.
5. ________ Restudy areas of weakness indicated by the last Self Test.

GLOSSARY

base angles .... The two angles that include the base of an isosceles triangle.

base of an isosceles triangle .... The third, unequal side of an isosceles triangle.

bases of a trapezoid .... The parallel sides of a trapezoid.

congruent figures .... If a one-to-one correspondence between the parts of two figures is such that the corresponding parts are equal, then the figures are congruent.

corresponding angles .... Angles paired with one another in a one-to-one correspondence between geometric figures.

corresponding sides .... Sides paired with one another in a one-to-one correspondence between figures.

included angle .... The angle formed by two sides of a triangle.

included side .... The side of a triangle formed by the common side of two angles.

isosceles trapezoid .... A trapezoid with both legs of the same length.

legs of a trapezoid .... The nonparallel sides of a trapezoid.

median of a trapezoid .... The segment connecting the midpoints of the legs.

one-to-one correspondence .... The situation when each member of a set, such as angles of a triangle, can be paired with one and only one member of another set.

parallelogram .... A quadrilateral with both pairs of opposite sides parallel.

rectangle .... A parallelogram with four right angles.

rhombus .... A parallelogram with all sides equal.

square .... A rectangle with all sides equal and four right angles.

trapezoid .... A quadrilateral with exactly one pair of parallel sides.

vertex angle .... The angle formed by the two equal sides of an isosceles triangle.

MATH 1004

LIFEPAC TEST

NAME ______________________________

DATE ______________________________

SCORE ______________________________

MATH 1004: LIFEPAC TEST

Write SSS, SAS, ASA, AAS, HL, LA, LL, or HA, to indicate the method you would use to prove the two ∠'s ≅ . If no method applies, write *none* (each answer, 3 points).

1. ______________________________

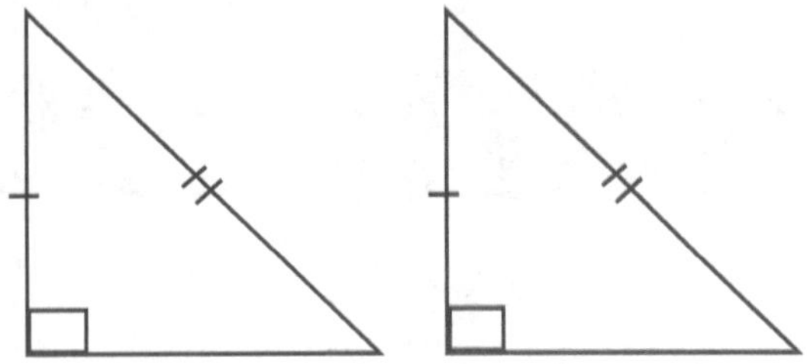

2. ______________________________

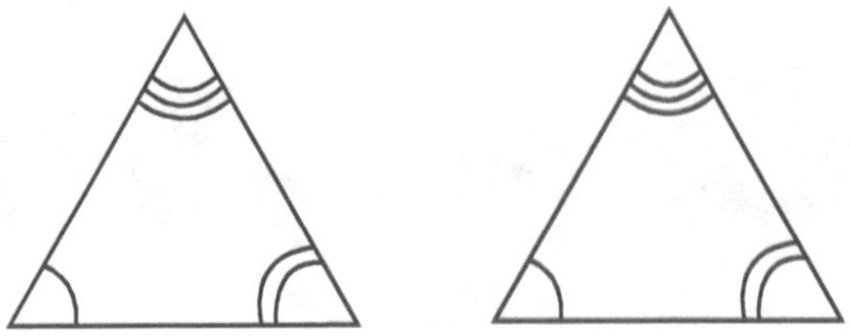

3. ______________________________

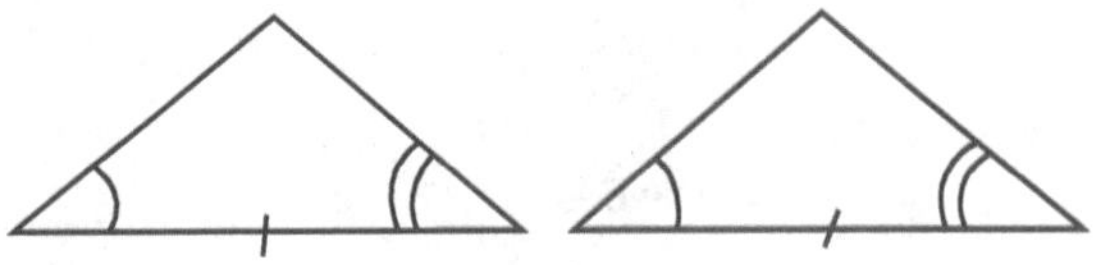

4. ______________________________

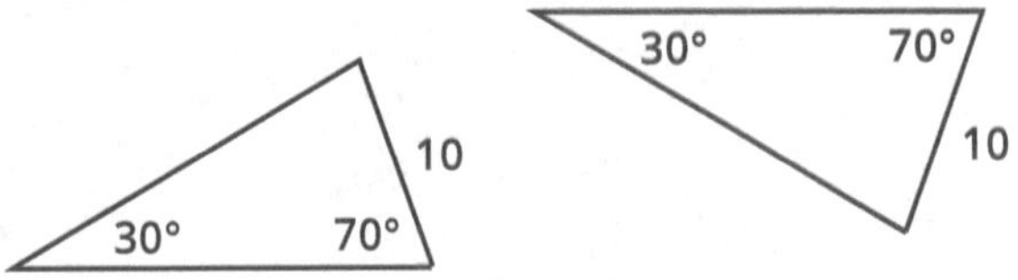

5. ______________________________

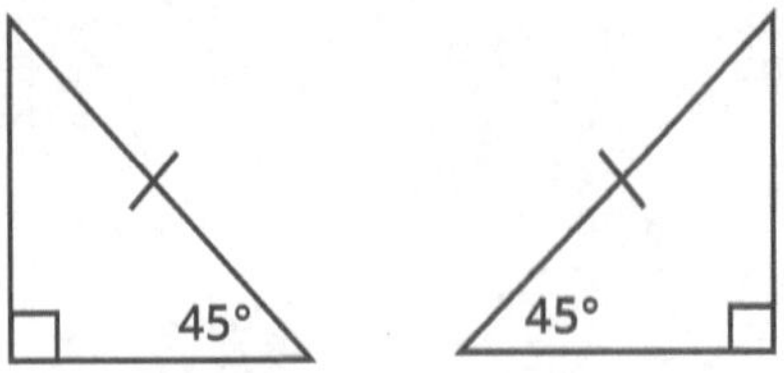

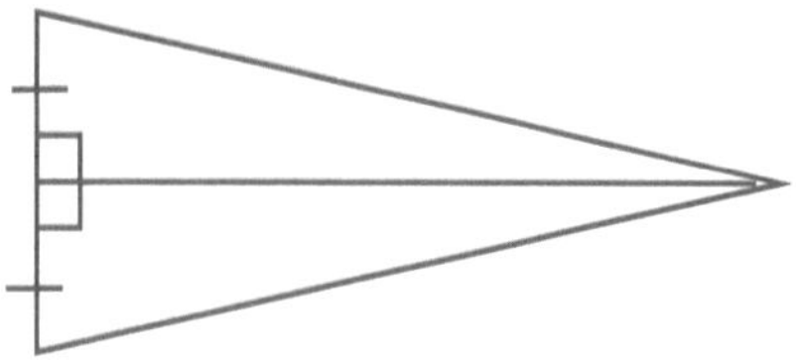

6. ______________________________

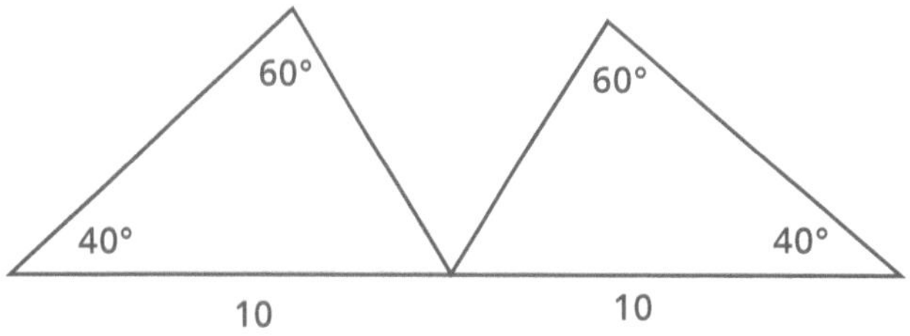

7. ______________________________

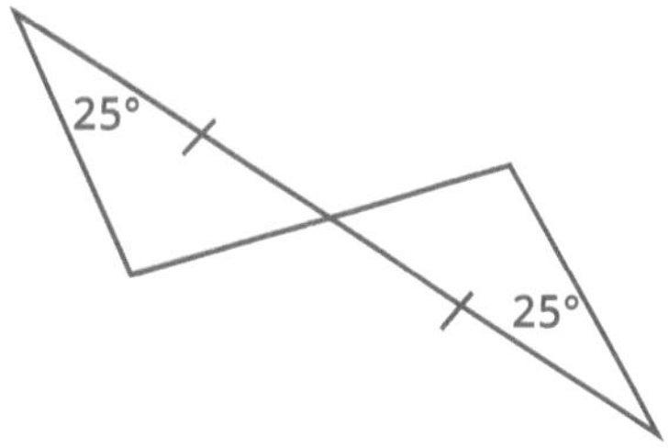

8. ______________________________

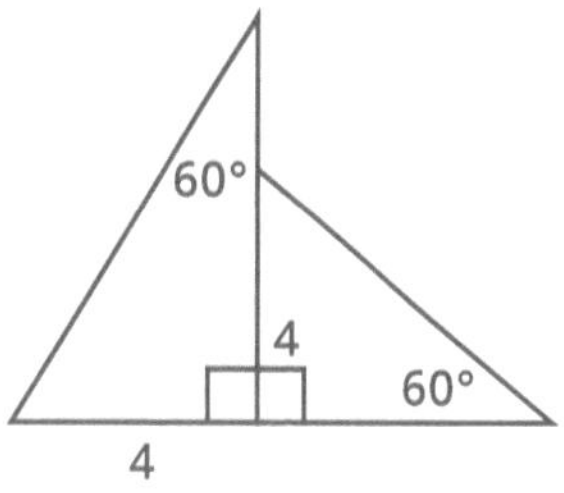

9. ______________________________

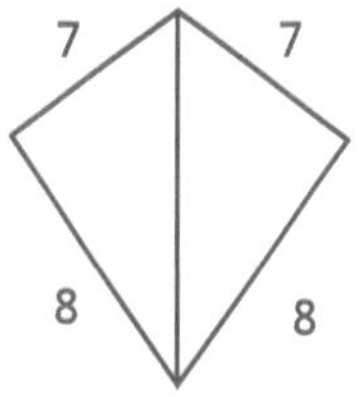

10. ______________________________

Write the reasons for this proof (each answer, 4 points).

Given: $\angle 1 = \angle 2$

$\angle 5 = \angle 6$

Prove: $MQ = MP$

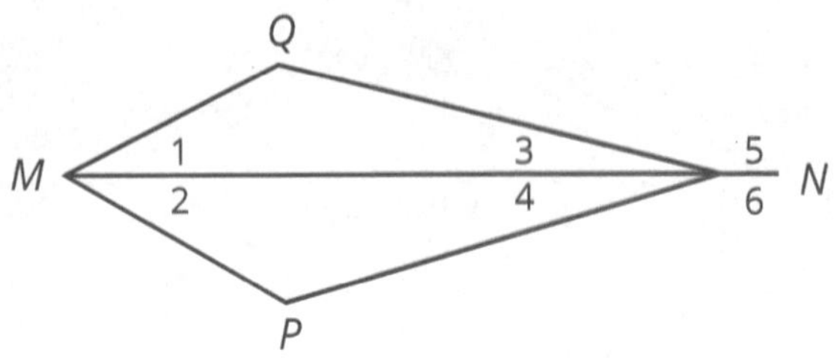

STATEMENT	REASON
11. $\angle 3$, $\angle 5$ are supplementary $\angle 4$, $\angle 6$ are supplementary	**11.** ________________
12. $\angle 5 = \angle 6$	**12.** ________________
13. $\angle 3 = \angle 4$	**13.** ________________
14. $\angle 1 = \angle 2$	**14.** ________________
15. $MN = MN$	**15.** ________________
16. $\triangle MNQ \cong \triangle MNP$	**16.** ________________
17. $MQ = MP$	**17.** ________________

Refer to the figure to complete the following items (each answer, 3 points).

Given: $AB = BC$

18. The longest segment shown is ________________ .

19. $\angle CBD$ = ________________

20. $\angle ADB$ = ________________

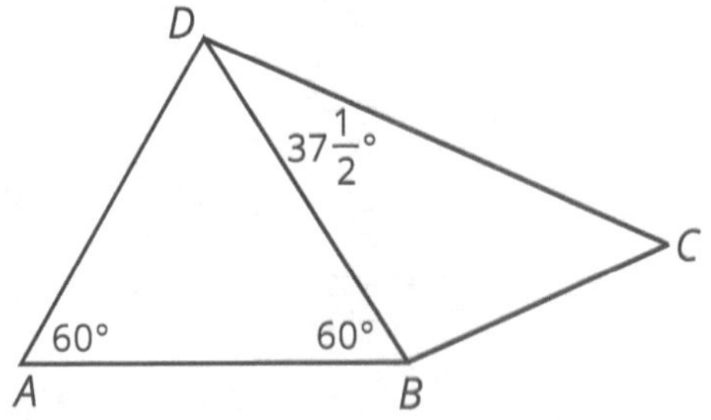

Write *always, sometimes,* or *never* (each answer, 2 points).

21. A square is ________________ a rectangle.

22. The diagonals of a rhombus are ________________ $\perp$.

23. The diagonals of a rectangle are ________________ equal.

24. The diagonals of a trapezoid are ________________ perpendicular.

MATH 1005

Similar Polygons

LIFEPAC Test is located at the back of the booklet. Please remove before starting the unit.

Author:
Milton R. Christen, M.A.

Editor-in-Chief:
Richard W. Wheeler, M.A.Ed.

Editor:
Robin Hintze Kreutzberg, M.B.A.

Consulting Editor:
Robert L. Zenor, M.A., M.S.

Revision Editor:
Alan Christopherson, M.S.

AOP

804 N. 2nd Ave. E.
Rock Rapids, IA 51246-1759

Similar Polygons

Introduction

In our study of congruent triangles, we learned that congruent triangles have the same size and the same shape. We are now going to study objects that have the same shape, but not necessarily the same size.

We have all looked at photographs. The photograph shows a smaller or larger version of the object that was photographed. The picture is the same shape but a different size.

We have all taken trips and used a road map to help get us from here to there. A map is a smaller version of the real thing.

Some of you may have built model airplanes or may have a model train. These models are scaled-down versions of a real item. The model is the same shape as the real thing but the size is different.

These examples are all practical examples of similarly shaped objects. In mathematics we also study similar shapes. In this LIFEPAC® we shall learn and use some principles of algebra in our study of similarity and its application to the right triangle.

Objectives

Read these objectives. The objectives tell you what you will be able to do when you have successfully completed this LIFEPAC. When you have finished this LIFEPAC, you should be able to:

1. Write ratios in simplest form.
2. Name the properties of proportions.
3. Solve proportion problems.
4. Identify similar polygons by using definitions, postulates, and theorems.
5. Use theorems about special segments in similar triangles.
6. Solve problems about similar right triangles.
7. Use the Pythagorean Theorem.
8. Solve triangle problems using trigonometry.
9. Find measurements indirectly.

Survey the LIFEPAC. Ask yourself some questions about this study and write your questions here.

1. PRINCIPLES OF ALGEBRA

Before we learn and use some of the properties of similar polygons, we should review some basic principles from algebra.

Section Objectives

Review these objectives. When you have completed this section, you should be able to:

1. Express ratios in simplest form.
2. Name the properties of proportion.
3. Solve proportion problems.

RATIOS AND PROPORTIONS

Two ideas from algebra that we need to review at this time are ratios and proportions.

> **DEFINITION**
>
> **Ratio:** the comparison of two numbers by division. The quotient is the ratio of the two numbers.

The ratio of 3 to 15 is $\frac{1}{5}$. The ratio of 8 to 2 is $\frac{4}{1}$. The ratio of a to b is $\frac{a}{b}$. Notice the quotients, $\frac{1}{5}$, $\frac{4}{1}$, $\frac{a}{b}$, are written as fractions. We can arrive at the ratio by dividing the "to" number into the "of" number. Keep in mind that you are not finding the ratio of one object to another, but rather the ratio of two numbers that are measures of the object in the same unit.

Rather than go through a division process to find a ratio, we can set up the two numbers as a fraction and reduce the fraction.

The "of" number will be the numerator (top) and the "to" number will be the denominator (bottom).

Ratio is simply a number. No units are connected to a ratio.

Model 1: Find the ratio of 6 to 8.

$\frac{6}{8} = \frac{3}{4}$

Model 2: If AB = 6 inches and CD = 18 inches, find the ratio of AB to CD.

$\frac{AB}{CD} = \frac{6}{18} = \frac{1}{3}$

Model 3: If $\angle A = 35°$, $\angle B = 50°$, find the ratio of $\angle A$ to $\angle B$.

$\frac{A}{B} = \frac{35}{50} = \frac{7}{10}$

Model 4: If the side of one triangle is 2 feet and the side of another triangle is 18 inches, find the ratio of the small side to the large side.

$\frac{18}{24} = \frac{3}{4}$ (2 feet was changed to 24 inches)

$\frac{1\frac{1}{2}}{2} = \frac{\frac{3}{2}}{2} = \frac{3}{4}$ (18 inches was changed to $1\frac{1}{2}$ feet)

The ratio of two numbers can also be written in the form *a*:*b*. This form is useful when we are comparing three or more numbers.

Model 5: The ratio of 3 to 4 to 5 can be written as 3:4:5.

This ratio means that the ratio of the first to the second is $\frac{3}{4}$, the ratio of the second to the third is $\frac{4}{5}$, and the ratio of the first to the third is $\frac{3}{5}$.

The following sets of numbers all have the ratio 3:4:5.

{12, 16, 20}	$\frac{12}{16} = \frac{3}{4}, \frac{16}{20} = \frac{4}{5}, \frac{12}{20} = \frac{3}{5}$
{3*x*, 4*x*, 5*x*}	$\frac{3x}{4x} = \frac{3}{4}, \frac{4x}{5x} = \frac{4}{5}, \frac{3x}{5x} = \frac{3}{5}$
{15x^2, 20x^2, 25x^2}	$\frac{15x^2}{20x^2} = \frac{3}{4}, \frac{20x^2}{25x^2} = \frac{4}{5}, \frac{15x^2}{25x^2} = \frac{3}{5}$

Express each ratio in simplest form.

1.1 $\frac{6}{12}$ = ____________

1.2 $\frac{6}{9}$ = ____________

1.3 $\frac{18}{29}$ = ____________

1.4 $\frac{36}{72}$ = ____________

1.5 21:28 = ____________

1.6 25:45 = ____________

1.7 10:20 = ____________

1.8 15:25:35 = ____________

If *a* = 3 and *b* = 5, find each ratio.

1.9 $\frac{a}{b}$ = ____________

1.10 $\frac{b}{a}$ = ____________

1.11 $\frac{a}{(a+b)}$ = ____________

1.12 $\frac{b}{(a+b)}$ = ____________

If *c* = 4 and *d* = 5, find each ratio.

1.13 *c* to *d* = ____________

1.14 *d* to *c* = ____________

1.15 $\frac{d}{(c+d)}$ = ____________

1.16 $\frac{(d-c)}{(d+c)}$ = ____________

Use the following figures to find each ratio in simplest form.

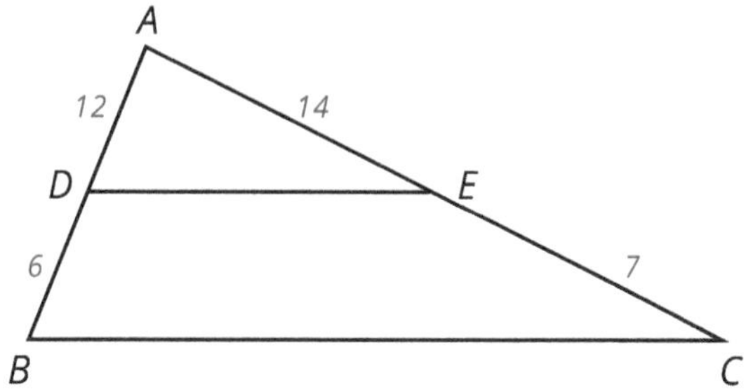

1.17 $\frac{AD}{DB}$ = __________ **1.18** $\frac{AD}{AB}$ = __________

1.19 $\frac{DB}{AB}$ = __________ **1.20** $\frac{AE}{AC}$ = __________

1.21 $\frac{AC}{AE}$ = __________ **1.22** $\frac{EC}{AC}$ = __________

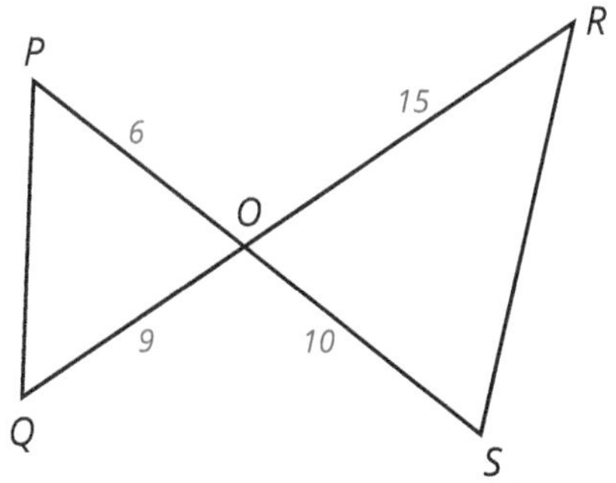

1.23 $\frac{PO}{OS}$ = __________ **1.24** $\frac{PO}{PS}$ = __________

1.25 $\frac{OS}{PS}$ = __________ **1.26** $\frac{OR}{QO}$ = __________

1.27 $\frac{OR}{QR}$ = __________ **1.28** $\frac{QR}{PS}$ = __________

Work the following problems.

1.29 The measures of the angles of a triangle are in the ratio of 1:2:3. Find the measure of each angle. (Hint: The sum of the angles of a triangle = 180°.)

1.30 The distance from *A* to *B* is 60 feet. The distance from *B* to *C* is 10 yards. The distance from *C* to *D* is 20 inches. Find the ratio of *AB*:*BC*:*CD*.

> **DEFINITION**
>
> **Proportion:** an equation that states that two ratios are equal.

The proportion $\frac{a}{b} = \frac{c}{d}$ tells us that the ratio *a* to *b* and the ratio *c* to *d* are equal ratios. The proportion can be read, *a* is to *b* as *c* is to *d*; or, the quotient of *a* and *b* equals the quotient of *c* and *d*. The proportion can also be written $a:b = c:d$.

Each of the four numbers *a*, *b*, *c*, and *d* is called a **term** of the proportion: *a* is the first term, *b* is the second term, *c* is the third term, and *d* is the fourth term.

The first and the fourth terms are known as the **extremes** of the proportion. The second and third terms are called the **means**.

The fact that more than two ratios are equal is often expressed in the form of an **extended proportion**.

$\frac{a}{b} = \frac{c}{d} = \frac{e}{f} = \frac{g}{h}$ is an extended proportion stating that all four ratios are the same number. Another extended proportion is $\frac{1}{2} = \frac{2}{4} = \frac{3}{6} = \frac{4}{8} = \frac{5}{10} = \frac{6}{12} = \frac{7}{14} = \frac{8}{16}$.

We can pick any two of the ratios and form a regular proportion: $\frac{3}{6} = \frac{6}{12}$, $\frac{7}{14} = \frac{2}{4}$.

Since a proportion is an equation, we can use the properties of equality to transform a proportion to another form. For example, $\frac{a}{b} = \frac{c}{d}$ can be written as $ad = bc$ by using the multiplication property of equality (multiply each side of the equation by *bd*).

$$\frac{a}{b} = \frac{c}{d}$$

$$(bd)\frac{a}{b} = (bd)\frac{c}{d}$$

$$ad = bc$$

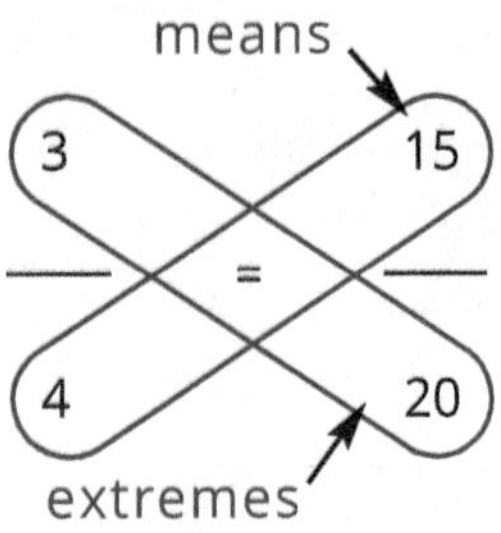

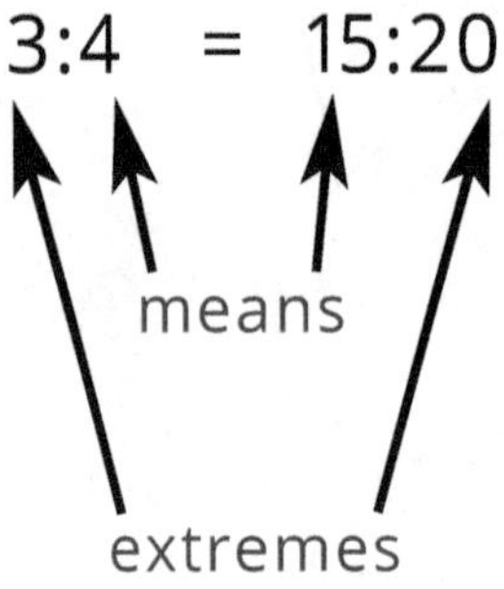

Name the means and the extremes in these proportions.

1.31 $\frac{3}{4} = \frac{15}{20}$ means: ________ extremes: ________

1.32 $\frac{5}{7} = \frac{20}{28}$ means: ________ extremes: ________

1.33 $\frac{6}{11} = \frac{x}{y}$ means: ________ extremes: ________

1.34 3:9 = 2:6 means: ________ extremes: ________

1.35 1:2 = 4:8 means: ________ extremes: ________

1.36 $x:y = 3:7$ means: ________ extremes: ________

Find the value of x in each of these proportions.

1.37 $\frac{x}{25} = \frac{2}{5}$ $x =$ ____________ **1.38** $\frac{x}{6} = \frac{3}{2}$ $x =$ ____________

1.39 $\frac{9}{x} = \frac{3}{12}$ $x =$ ____________ **1.40** $\frac{10}{7} = \frac{x}{5}$ $x =$ ____________

1.41 $9{:}x = x{:}4$ $x =$ ____________ **1.42** $\frac{1}{2}{:}x = \frac{2}{3}{:}\frac{3}{4}$ $x =$ ____________

1.43 $\frac{(x+3)}{6} = \frac{5}{4}$ $x =$ ____________ **1.44** $\frac{(x+1)}{(x+2)} = \frac{2}{3}$ $x =$ ____________

1.45 $\frac{3}{2} = \frac{x}{4}$ $x =$ ____________

Find the ratio of x to y.

1.46 $2x = 3y$ ____________ **1.47** $5x = 7y$ ____________

1.48 $\frac{x}{3} = \frac{y}{2}$ ____________ **1.49** $2x - 3y = 0$ ____________

1.50 $x - 5y = 0$ ____________

Along with our knowledge of complementary and supplementary angles, ratios can help us solve geometry problems.

Model: Two complementary angles have measures in the ratio of 4 to 5. Find the measure of each angle.

Solution: Let $4x$ = measure of the smaller angle.
$5x$ = measure of the larger angle.

Then $4x + 5x = 90°$ (angles are complementary)

$9x = 90°$

$x = 10°$

$4x = 40°$

$5x = 50°$

Solve the following problems. Show your work and circle your answer.

1.51 Two complementary angles have measures in the ratio of 1 to 5. Find the measure of each angle.

1.52 The ratio of the measures of two supplementary angles is 3:7. Find the measure of each angle.

1.53 A 30-inch segment is cut into two parts whose lengths have the ratio 3 to 5. Find the length of each part.

1.54 The perimeter of a triangle is 48 inches and the sides are in the ratio of 3:4:5. Find the length of each side.

1.55 A triangle has a perimeter of 18 inches. If one side has a length of 8 inches, find the other two sides if their lengths are in the ratio of $\frac{2}{3}$.

PROPERTIES OF PROPORTIONS

You will often wish to change a proportion into some equivalent equation. Although we can make this change by using basic properties of algebra, we will save time and steps by using some special properties of proportions. When we use these properties for a reason on a proof, we shall simply write POP (Property of Proportion).

In these statements the variables used represent nonzero numbers.

> **CROSS PRODUCT PROPERTY**
>
> If $\frac{a}{b} = \frac{c}{d}$, then $ad = bc$.

Model 1:

$$\frac{3}{5} = \frac{15}{25}$$
$$3 \cdot 25 = 5 \cdot 15$$
$$75 = 75$$

Model 2:

$$\frac{6}{11} = \frac{12}{22}$$
$$6 \cdot 22 = 11 \cdot 12$$
$$132 = 132$$

Model 3:

$$\frac{x}{10} = \frac{3}{5}$$
$$5x = 30$$
$$x = 6$$

> **EQUIVALENT FORMS PROPERTY**
>
> $\frac{a}{b} = \frac{c}{d}, \frac{a}{c} = \frac{b}{d}, \frac{d}{b} = \frac{c}{a}, \frac{b}{a} = \frac{d}{c}$ are equivalent proportions. The cross product of each proportion gives the same equation, $ad = bc$.

Model 1:

$$\frac{2}{4} = \frac{5}{10}$$
$$20 = 20$$

Model 2:

$$\frac{10}{4} = \frac{5}{2}$$
$$20 = 20$$

Model 3:

$$\frac{2}{5} = \frac{4}{10}$$
$$20 = 20$$

Model 4:

$$\frac{4}{2} = \frac{10}{5}$$
$$20 = 20$$

DENOMINATOR SUM PROPERTY

If $\frac{a}{b} = \frac{c}{d}$, then $\frac{(a+b)}{b} = \frac{(c+d)}{d}$.

We can add 1 to both sides of the equation:

$$\frac{a}{b} = \frac{c}{d}$$

$$\frac{a}{b} + 1 = \frac{c}{d} + 1$$

$$\frac{a}{b} + \frac{b}{b} = \frac{c}{d} + \frac{d}{d}$$

$$\frac{(a+b)}{b} = \frac{(c+d)}{d}$$

Model 1:

$$\frac{2}{4} = \frac{5}{10}$$

$$\frac{(2+4)}{4} = \frac{(5+10)}{10}$$

$$\frac{6}{4} = \frac{15}{10}$$

Model 2:

$$\frac{3}{9} = \frac{1}{3}$$

$$\frac{(3+9)}{9} = \frac{(1+3)}{3}$$

$$\frac{12}{9} = \frac{4}{3}$$

Model 3:

$$\frac{2}{8} = \frac{3}{12}$$

$$\frac{(2+8)}{8} = \frac{(3+12)}{12}$$

$$\frac{10}{8} = \frac{15}{12}$$

DENOMINATOR DIFFERENCE PROPERTY

If $\frac{a}{b} = \frac{c}{d}$, then $\frac{(a-b)}{b} = \frac{(c-d)}{d}$.

We can subtract 1 from both sides of the equation:

$$\frac{a}{b} = \frac{c}{d}$$

$$\frac{a}{b} - 1 = \frac{c}{d} - 1$$

$$\frac{a}{b} - \frac{b}{b} = \frac{c}{d} - \frac{d}{d}$$

$$\frac{(a-b)}{b} = \frac{(c-d)}{d}$$

Model 1:

$$\frac{8}{3} = \frac{16}{6}$$

$$\frac{(8-3)}{3} = \frac{(16-6)}{6}$$

$$\frac{5}{3} = \frac{10}{6}$$

Model 2:

$$\frac{12}{3} = \frac{4}{1}$$

$$\frac{(12-3)}{3} = \frac{(4-1)}{1}$$

$$\frac{9}{3} = \frac{3}{1}$$

Model 3:

$$\frac{6}{8} = \frac{3}{4}$$

$$\frac{(6-8)}{8} = \frac{(3-4)}{4}$$

$$-\frac{2}{8} = -\frac{1}{4}$$

NUMERATOR-DENOMINATOR SUM PROPERTY

If $\frac{a}{b} = \frac{c}{d} = \frac{e}{f} = \frac{g}{h} = \ldots$, then $\frac{(a+c+e+g+\ldots)}{(b+d+f+h+\ldots)} = \frac{a}{b} = \frac{c}{d} = \frac{e}{f} \ldots$

Let $\frac{a}{b} = x, \frac{c}{d} = x, \frac{e}{f} = x, \ldots$

then $a = bx, c = dx, e = fx, \ldots$

so
$$\frac{(a+c+e+\ldots)}{(b+d+f+\ldots)} = \frac{(bx+dx+fx+\ldots)}{(b+d+f+\ldots)}$$
$$= x\frac{(b+d+f+\ldots)}{(b+d+f+\ldots)}$$
$$= x$$
$$= \frac{a}{b} = \frac{c}{d} = \frac{e}{f} \ldots$$

Model 1:
$$\frac{1}{2} = \frac{2}{4} = \frac{3}{6} = \frac{4}{8}$$
$$\frac{(1+2+3+4)}{(2+4+6+8)} = \frac{1}{2}$$
$$\frac{10}{20} = \frac{1}{2}$$

Model 2:
$$\frac{3}{5} = \frac{6}{10} = \frac{9}{15}$$
$$\frac{(3+6+9)}{(5+10+15)} = \frac{6}{10}$$
$$\frac{18}{30} = \frac{6}{10}$$

Name the POP illustrated.

1.56 If $\frac{a}{2} = \frac{b}{5}$, then $\frac{(a+2)}{2} = \frac{(b+5)}{5}$. ____________________

1.57 If $\frac{(a+1)}{3} = \frac{b}{5}$, then $5(a+1) = 3b$. ____________________

1.58 If $\frac{x}{y} = \frac{r}{s} = \frac{t}{u}$, then $\frac{(x+r+t)}{(y+s+u)} = \frac{x}{y}$. ____________________

1.59 If $\frac{x}{4} = \frac{y}{3}$, then $\frac{x}{y} = \frac{4}{3}$. ____________________

1.60 If $\frac{(x+3)}{2} = \frac{(y+6)}{3}$, then $\frac{(x+1)}{2} = \frac{(y+3)}{3}$. ____________________

1.61 If $\frac{r}{x} = \frac{s}{t}$, then $sx = rt$. ____________________

Given $xy = ab$, form a proportion in which:

1.62 x is the first term. ______________________

1.63 x is the second term. ______________________

1.64 a is the second term. ______________________

1.65 b is the first term. ______________________

1.66 y is one of the extremes. ______________________

Find x and y in each proportion.

1.67 $\frac{2}{x} = \frac{5}{y} = \frac{3}{5}$ $x =$ ____________ $y =$ ____________

1.68 $\frac{2}{x} = \frac{y}{4} = \frac{1}{4}$ $x =$ ____________ $y =$ ____________

1.69 $\frac{2}{3} = \frac{x}{6} = \frac{9}{y}$ $x =$ ____________ $y =$ ____________

Find the fourth term of a proportion when the first three terms are:

1.70 2, 3, and 4. ______________________

1.71 6, 2, and 8. ______________________

1.72 $\frac{1}{2}$, $\frac{2}{3}$, and $\frac{3}{4}$. ______________________

Find the value of a in each proportion.

1.73 $\frac{(a + 1)}{4} = \frac{2}{3}$ $a =$ ____________

1.74 $\frac{(a - 2)}{3} = \frac{a}{4}$ $a =$ ____________

1.75 $\frac{a}{4} = \frac{9}{a}$ $a =$ ____________

Given $\frac{BX}{XC} = \frac{AB}{AC}$, complete the following proportions.

1.76 $\frac{BX}{BA}$ = ______________________

1.77 $\frac{BX + XC}{XC}$ = ______________________

1.78 $\frac{AC}{XC}$ = ______________________

1.79 $\frac{AC}{AB}$ = ______________________

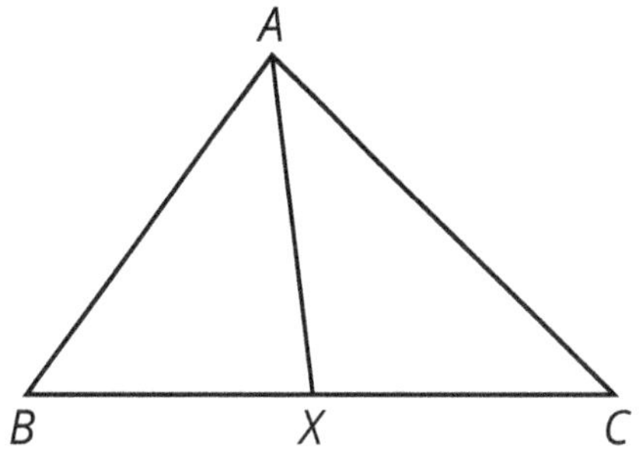

Given $\frac{AX}{XB} = \frac{AY}{YC}$, find the missing lengths.

	AX	XB	AY	YC
1.80	3	4	6	________
1.81	5	4	________	6
1.82	________	4	4	8
1.83	7	________	14	4

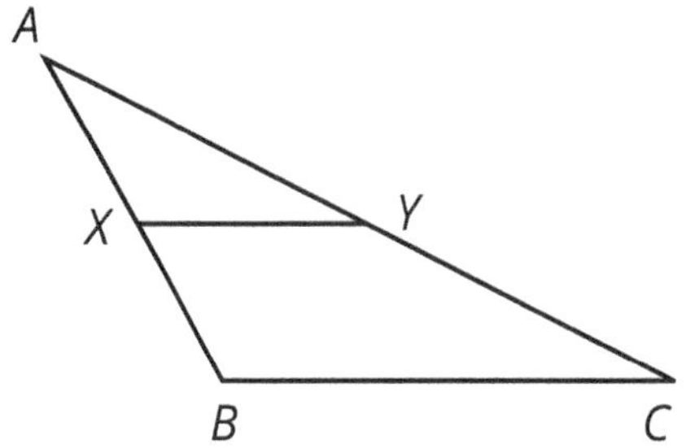

If $\frac{a}{b} = \frac{5}{7}$ and $\frac{c}{d} = \frac{3}{4}$, find each ratio in simplest form.

1.84 $\frac{d}{c}$ = ______________________

1.85 $\frac{(a + b)}{b}$ = ______________________

1.86 $\frac{(a + b)}{a}$ = ______________________

1.87 $\frac{(c + d)}{c}$ = ______________________

1.88 $\frac{2c}{3d}$ = ______________________

1.89 $\frac{d}{c}$ = ______________________

TEACHER CHECK ____________ ____________
initials date

Review the material in this section in preparation for the Self Test. The Self Test will check your mastery of this particular section. The items missed on this Self Test will indicate specific areas where restudy is needed for mastery.

SELF TEST 1

Complete the following statements (each answer, 3 points).

1.01 A ratio compares two numbers by ____________________.

1.02 The ratio of 3 to 4 is written as ____________________.

1.03 Another way of writing the ratio of 3 to 4 is ____________________.

1.04 In writing the ratio of measurement numbers, the units must be the ____________________.

1.05 The ratio of 3 to 4 and the ratio of 4 to 3 (are/are not) ______________ the same number.

1.06 A proportion is an equation that states two ____________________ are equal.

1.07 "If $\frac{2}{3} = \frac{x}{y}$, then $2y = 3x$" is an example of the ____________________ POP.

1.08 "If $\frac{x}{y} = \frac{2}{3} = \frac{a}{b}$, then $\frac{(x + 2 + a)}{(y + 3 + b)} = \frac{2}{3}$" is an example of the ____________________ POP.

1.09 In the proportion $\frac{a}{b} = \frac{p}{q}$, the third term is ____________________.

1.010 In the proportion $\frac{5}{6} = \frac{10}{12}$, the means are a. ______________ and b. ______________.

Express each ratio in simplest form (each answer, 2 points).

1.011 Ratio of 6 feet to 3 feet. ____________________

1.012 Ratio of 7 yards to 6 feet. ____________________

1.013 Ratio of 12 to 100. ____________________

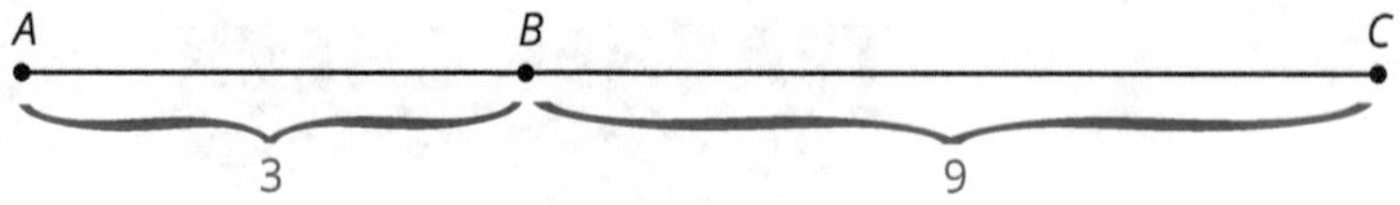

1.014 Ratio of *AB* to *BC*. ____________________

1.015 Ratio of *BC* to *AC*. ____________________

Find x in the following proportions (each answer, 2 points).

1.016 $\frac{x}{7} = \frac{3}{5}$ $x =$ ____________

1.017 $3:8 = x:32$ $x =$ ____________

1.018 $\frac{5}{2x} = \frac{25}{4}$ $x =$ ____________

1.019 $\frac{x}{3} = \frac{x+2}{5}$ $x =$ ____________

1.020 $\frac{16}{x} = \frac{x}{4}$ $x =$ ____________

1.021 $\frac{x+2}{2} = \frac{6+2}{2}$ $x =$ ____________

Find the required numbers (each answer, 2 points).

Given: $\frac{TU}{TR} = \frac{UW}{RS} = \frac{WT}{ST}$

$TU = 3$
$RS = 15$
$TW = 4$
$TR = 9$

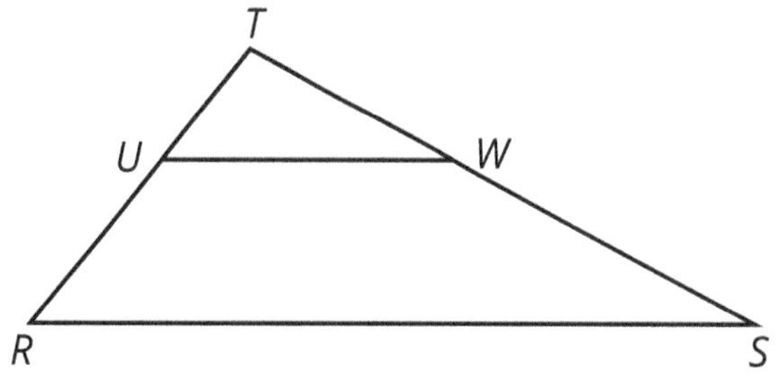

1.022 UW = ____________

1.023 ST = ____________

1.024 WS = ____________

1.025 UR = ____________

54/67 **SCORE** ____________ **TEACHER** ____________ ____________
initials date

2. SIMILARITY

Two figures are **similar** if the larger can be shrunk to fit the smaller or the smaller can be enlarged to fit the larger. When the figures are enlarged or shrunk to fit, all dimensions must be changed in the same ratio.

For the rectangles shown, the ratio of the lengths is $\frac{5}{15}$, or 1 to 3; but the ratio of the widths is $\frac{3}{6}$, or 1 to 2. The rectangles are not similar.

For the cylinders, the ratio of their radii is 4:2, or 2 to 1. The ratio of their heights is 4 to 3. These two cylinders are not similar.

The two crosses are similar. All dimensions are in the same ratio. The ratio is 1 to 2.

The ratio of the dimensions of the square and the rhombus are the same, 1 to 2; but the square could not fit over the rhombus if it were enlarged. Therefore, we need more than the dimensions having the same ratio for figures to be similar.

Section Objectives

Review these objectives. When you have completed this section, you should be able to:

4. Identify similar polygons by using definitions, postulates, and theorems.
5. Use theorems about special segments in similar triangles.
6. Solve problems about similar right triangles.
7. Use the Pythagorean Theorem.

MEANING OF SIMILARITY

We have said that similar figures can be thought of as enlargements or smaller versions of an original object. However, this definition is not very precise. A good definition of similar polygons involves the terms **corresponding sides** and **corresponding angles**.

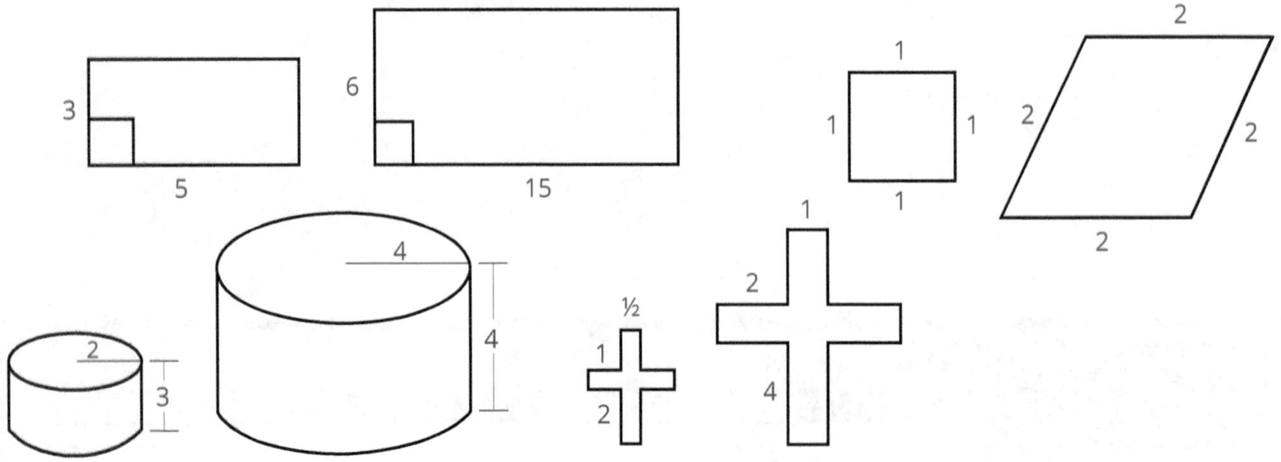

DEFINING SIMILAR POLYGONS

Recall from our study of congruent triangles that we had to set up a one-to-one correspondence between the sides and the angles of the two triangles in such a way that all the corresponding parts were equal. We do the same thing for polygons that we want to show are similar.

The parts of the two polygons can be matched in many ways.

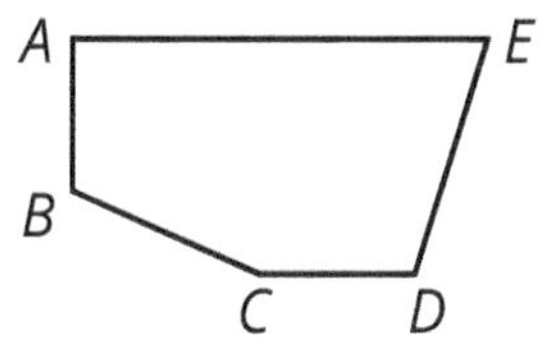

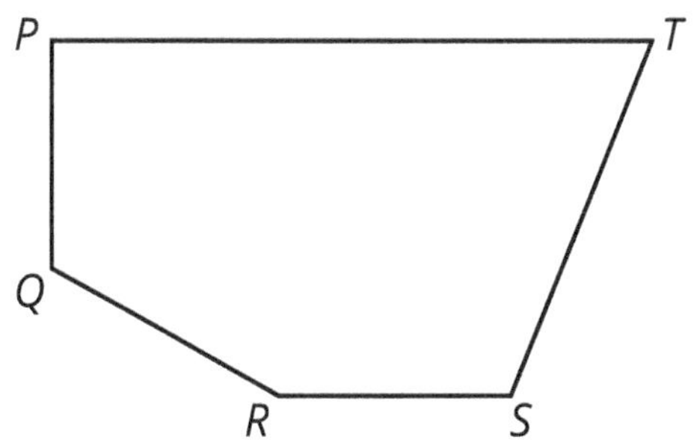

Note to student: These are some sample matchings. Not all of them are correct based on the figures. Read the double arrow in the matchings as "corresponds to."

Models:

$\overline{AB} \leftrightarrow \overline{RS}$ $\quad \angle A \leftrightarrow \angle R$
$\overline{BC} \leftrightarrow \overline{PQ}$ $\quad \angle B \leftrightarrow \angle P$
$\overline{CD} \leftrightarrow \overline{ST}$ $\quad \angle C \leftrightarrow \angle S$
$\overline{DE} \leftrightarrow \overline{PT}$ $\quad \angle D \leftrightarrow \angle P$
$\overline{EA} \leftrightarrow \overline{QR}$ $\quad \angle E \leftrightarrow \angle Q$

$\overline{AB} \leftrightarrow \overline{QR}$ $\quad \angle A \leftrightarrow \angle Q$
$\overline{BC} \leftrightarrow \overline{ST}$ $\quad \angle B \leftrightarrow \angle S$
$\overline{CD} \leftrightarrow \overline{PT}$ $\quad \angle C \leftrightarrow \angle P$
$\overline{DE} \leftrightarrow \overline{PQ}$ $\quad \angle D \leftrightarrow \angle P$
$\overline{EA} \leftrightarrow \overline{RS}$ $\quad \angle E \leftrightarrow \angle R$

$\overline{AB} \leftrightarrow \overline{PQ}$ $\quad \angle A \leftrightarrow \angle P$
$\overline{BC} \leftrightarrow \overline{QR}$ $\quad \angle B \leftrightarrow \angle Q$
$\overline{CD} \leftrightarrow \overline{RS}$ $\quad \angle C \leftrightarrow \angle R$
$\overline{DE} \leftrightarrow \overline{ST}$ $\quad \angle D \leftrightarrow \angle S$
$\overline{EA} \leftrightarrow \overline{TP}$ $\quad \angle E \leftrightarrow \angle T$

If we can match the parts so that the ratios of the matched sides are all the same and the ratios of the angles are all 1:1 (angles are equal), then the matching gives us similar polygons. When the ratios of all the parts are the same, the parts are called corresponding parts.

Now we can give an exact definition for similar polygons.

> **DEFINITION**
>
> **Similar polygons (~):** polygons whose vertices can be matched in 1:1 correspondence so that corresponding angles are equal and corresponding sides are in proportion.

Notice the two parts of our definition: the corresponding angles are all equal and the sides are proportional.

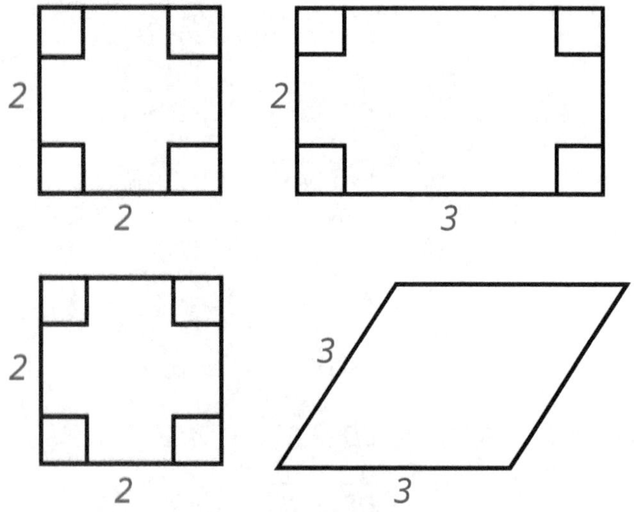

The square and the rectangle have angles equal, but the sides are not in proportion.

The square and the rhombus have sides in proportion, $\frac{2}{3} = \frac{2}{3}$, but the corresponding angles are not equal.

If a particular correspondence is a similarity, we write: polygon *ABCDE* is similar to polygon *PQRST.* The order in which the vertices are named tells you the correspondence and that $\angle A = \angle P$, $\angle B = \angle Q$, $\angle C = \angle R$, $\angle D = \angle S$, $\angle E = \angle T$; and that $\frac{AB}{PQ} = \frac{BC}{QR} = \frac{CD}{RS} = \frac{DE}{ST} = \frac{EA}{TP}$.

PROVING TRIANGLES SIMILAR

Since triangles are polygons, the definition that holds for polygons is also true for triangles. Up to now the only way you have had to *prove* triangles similar was to use the definition. Recall that when we started proving triangles congruent we used the definition. Then we found we could prove triangles congruent by certain congruence postulates and theorems, like the SSS congruence postulate. At least one postulate about similar triangles is needed to provide you with a method other than the definition to prove triangles similar.

> **POSTULATE 15**
>
> P15: If the three angles of one triangle are equal to the three angles of another triangle, then the triangles are similar.
>
> **(AAA for similar triangles)**

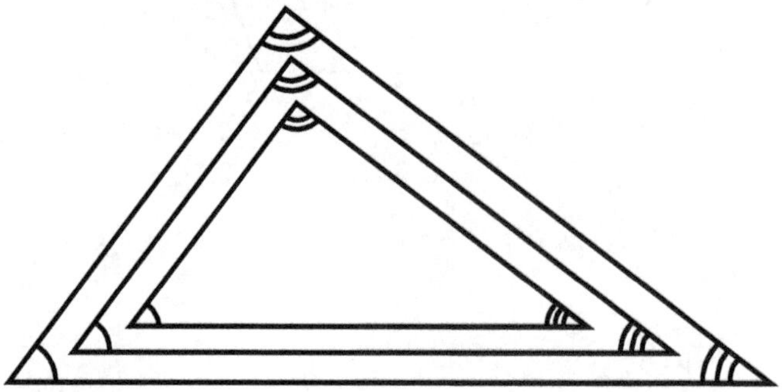

Each of the corresponding angles of one triangle is equal to an angle of the other triangles; all of the triangles are similar to each other.

We have studied a theorem that states that if two angles of a triangle are equal to two angles of another triangle, then the third angles are equal also. One of the pairs of angles in P15 is not needed. We can write this conclusion as a theorem.

THEOREM 5-1

If two angles of one triangle are equal to two angles of another triangle, then the triangles are similar.

(AA for similar triangles)

Given: $\angle A = \angle R$
$\angle B = \angle S$

To Prove: $\triangle ABC \sim \triangle RST$

Plan: Show $\angle C = \angle T$, then use P15

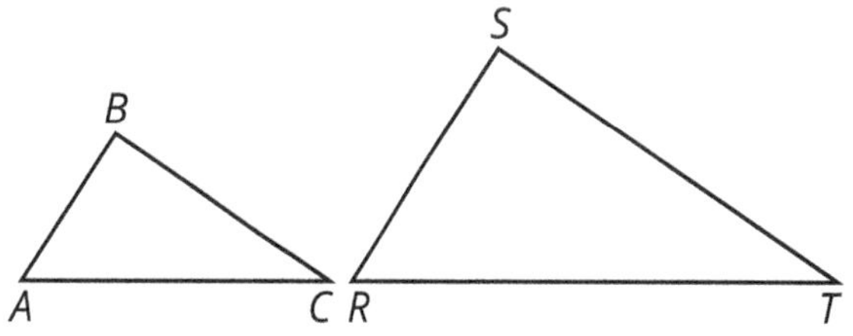

STATEMENT	REASON
1. $\angle A = \angle R$, $\angle B = \angle S$	1. Given
2. $\angle C = \angle T$	2. If two $\angle$'s of one $\triangle$ = two $\angle$'s of another $\triangle$, then the third $\angle$'s are =.
3. $\triangle ABC \sim \triangle RST$	3. AAA similar $\triangle$ postulate

The next two statements are corollaries to Theorem 5-1.

Corollary 1: If a line intersects two sides of a triangle and is parallel to the third side, then a triangle similar to the given triangle is formed.

Corollary 2: Triangles similar to the same triangle are similar to each other.

The proof of C-1 follows:

Given: $l \parallel \overline{AC}$,
intersects $\triangle ABC$ at X and Y

To Prove: $\triangle BXY \sim \triangle BAC$

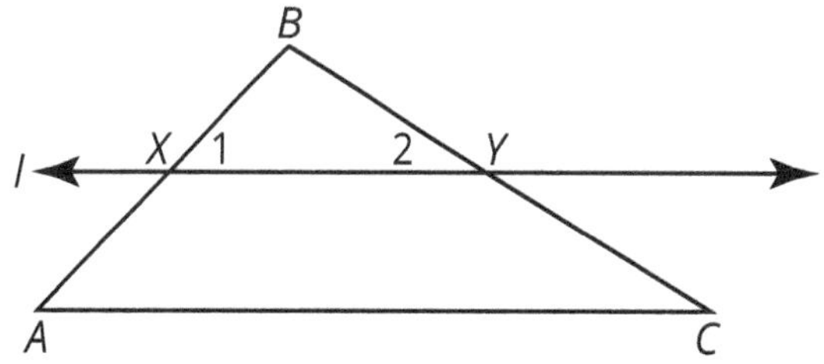

STATEMENT	REASON
1. $l \parallel \overline{AC}$	1. Given
2. $\angle A = \angle 1$, $\angle C = \angle 2$	2. If lines $\parallel$, corresponding $\angle$'s are =.
3. $\triangle BXY \sim \triangle BAC$	3. AA similar $\triangle$ theorem

Prove C-2 as an activity.

2.1 Given: $\triangle ABC \sim \triangle RST$
$\triangle DEF \sim \triangle RST$

To Prove: $\triangle ABC \sim \triangle DEF$

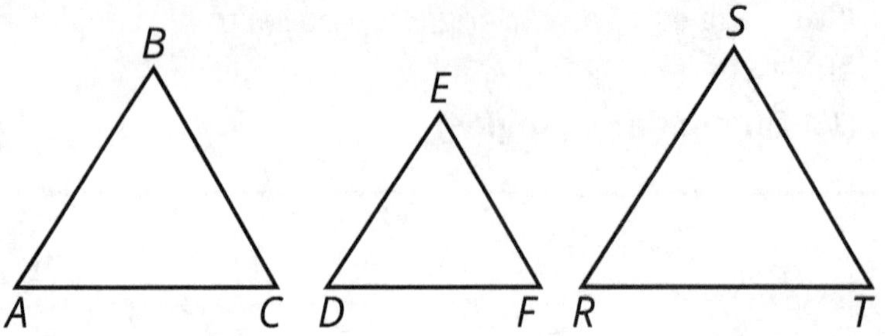

STATEMENT	REASON

The next two theorems are other ways to prove triangles similar.

> **THEOREM 5-2**
>
> If two sides of one triangle are proportional to two sides of another triangle and the included angles are equal, then the triangles are similar.
>
> **(SAS for similar triangles)**

Given: $\frac{AC}{RS} = \frac{AB}{RT}$

$\angle A = \angle R$

To Prove: $\triangle ABC \sim \triangle RTS$

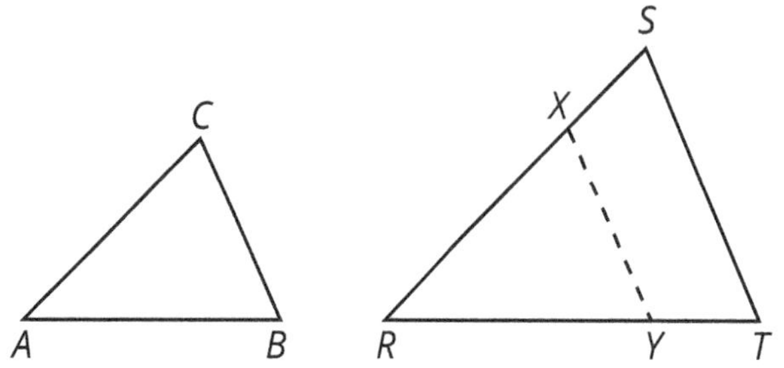

STATEMENT	REASON
1. Draw $\overline{XY} \parallel \overline{ST}$ so that $RX = AC$	1. Auxiliary line
2. $\triangle RYX \sim \triangle RTS$	2. C-1 of AA theorem
3. $\frac{RX}{RS} = \frac{RY}{RT}$	3. Definition of similar polygons
4. $\frac{AC}{RS} = \frac{AB}{RT}$	4. Given
5. $\frac{RX}{RS} = \frac{AB}{RT}$	5. Substitution (Step 1 into 4)
6. $\frac{RY}{RT} = \frac{AB}{RT}$	6. Substitution (Step 3 into 5)
7. $RY = AB$	7. Multiplication property of equality
8. $\angle A = \angle R$	8. Given
9. $\triangle ABC \cong \triangle RYX$	9. SAS
10. $\angle B = \angle RYX$	10. CPCTE
11. $\triangle ABC \sim \triangle RYX$	11. AA theorem
12. $\triangle ABC \sim \triangle RTS$	12. C-2 of AA theorem

THEOREM 5-3

If three sides of one triangle are proportional to three sides of another triangle, then the triangles are similar.

(SSS for similar triangles)

Given: $\frac{AB}{RT} = \frac{BC}{ST} = \frac{CA}{RS}$

To Prove: $\triangle ABC \sim \triangle RTS$

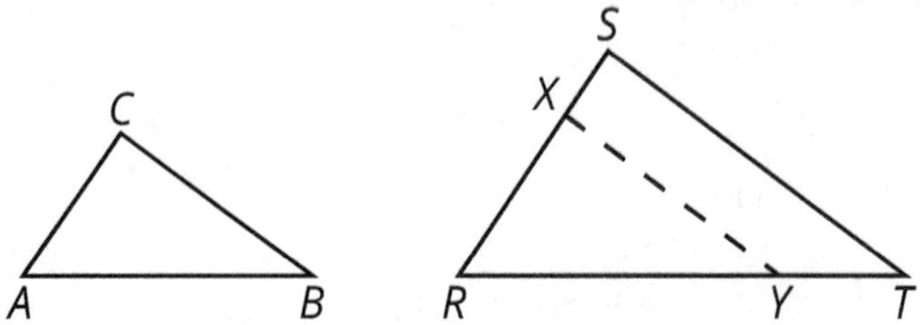

	STATEMENT		REASON
1.	$\frac{AB}{RT} = \frac{BC}{ST} = \frac{CA}{RS}$	1.	Given
2.	Draw $\overline{XY} \parallel \overline{TS}$ so that $CA = XR$	2.	Auxiliary line
3.	$\triangle RYX \sim \triangle RTS$	3.	C-1 of AA theorem
4.	$\frac{RY}{RT} = \frac{YX}{ST} = \frac{XR}{RS}$	4.	Definition of similar polygons
5.	$\frac{RY}{RT} = \frac{YX}{ST} = \frac{CA}{RS}$	5.	Substitution (Step 2 into 4)
6.	$\frac{AB}{RT} = \frac{RY}{RT}, \frac{BC}{ST} = \frac{YX}{ST}$	6.	Substitution (Step 1 into 5)
7.	$AB = RY, BC = YX$	7.	Multiplication property of equality
8.	$\triangle RYX \cong \triangle ABC$	8.	SSS
9.	$\angle A = \angle R, \angle ABC = \angle RYX$	9.	CPCTE
10.	$\triangle RYX \sim \triangle ABC$	10.	AA theorem
11.	$\triangle ABC \sim \triangle RTS$	11.	C-2 of AA theorem

We do not need the ASA or the AAS theorems to prove similar triangles now, because we would already have two angles equal, enough to prove the triangles similar by the AA theorem.

An SSA theorem is not true. We can have a situation where two sides are proportional and a not-included angle are equal, and yet the triangles are not similar:

$\frac{AC}{RT} = \frac{CB}{TS}$ and $\angle A = \angle R$, but $\triangle ABC \nsim \triangle RST$.

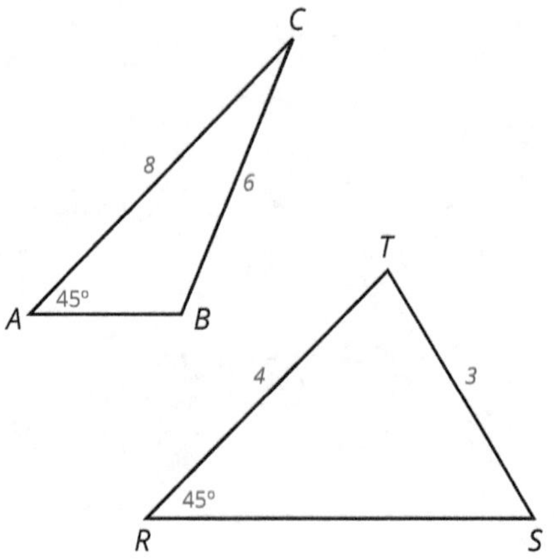

A summary of the ways to prove that triangles are similar is given.

SUMMARY	
Definition	Sides proportional, angles equal
Postulate	AAA
Theorem	AA
Theorem	SSS
Theorem	SAS

Complete the following statements.

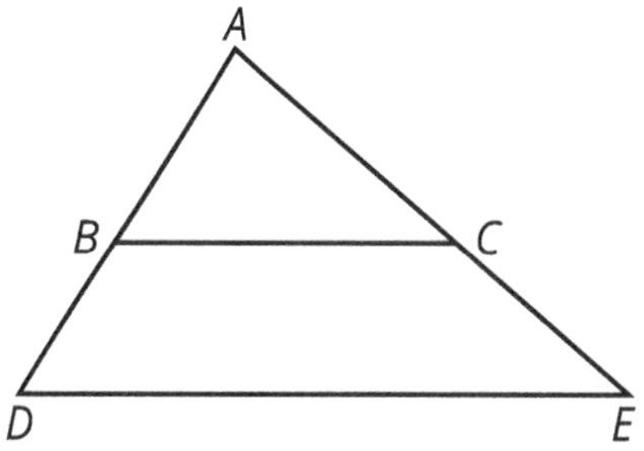

2.2 If $\overline{BC} \parallel \overline{DE}$, then $\triangle DAE \sim$ ____________ .

2.3 If $\triangle ABC \sim \triangle ADE$, then $\frac{AB}{AD} =$ a. ____________

b. ____________ .

2.4 If $\angle BCA =$ ____________ , then $\triangle ABC \sim \triangle ADE$.

2.5 If $\triangle ABC \sim \triangle ADE$, then $\angle D =$ ____________ .

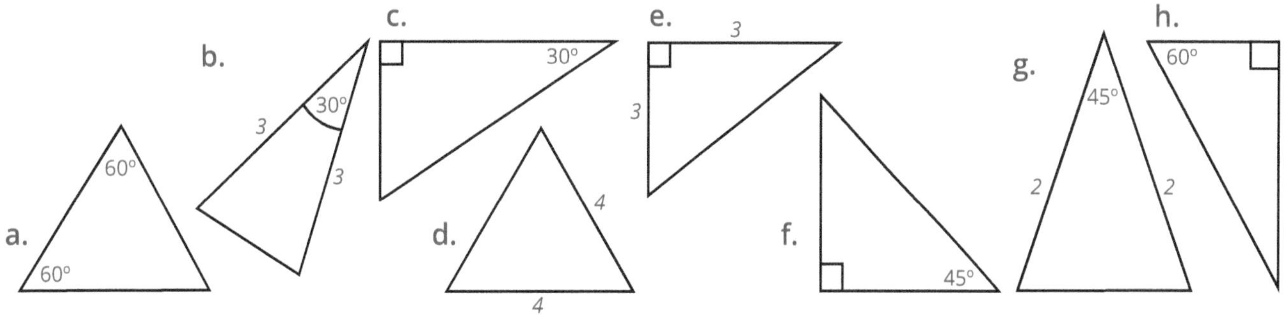

2.6 Which of the triangles shown above are similar?

____

____

Which of these statements can be justified by the AA similarity theorem? Write *yes* or *no*.

2.7 All equilateral triangles are similar. ________

2.8 All isosceles triangles are similar. ________

2.9 All right triangles are similar. ________

2.10 All isosceles right triangles are similar. ________

2.11 All acute triangles are similar. ________

Complete the following proofs.

2.12 **Given:** $k \parallel l$

To Prove: $\triangle ADF \sim \triangle EDB$

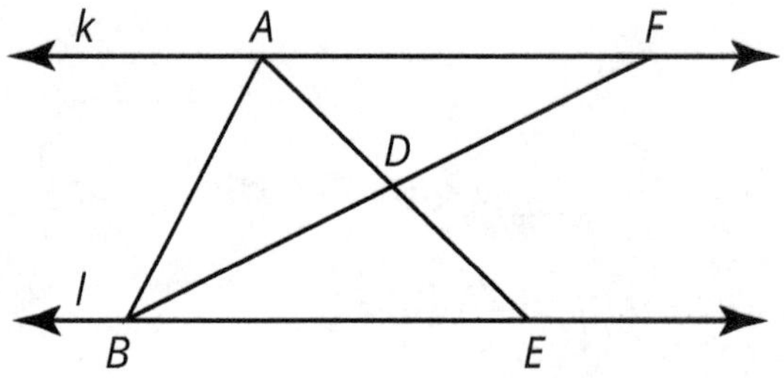

STATEMENT	REASON

2.13 Given: $k \parallel l$

To Prove: $\triangle BCD \sim \triangle ACF$

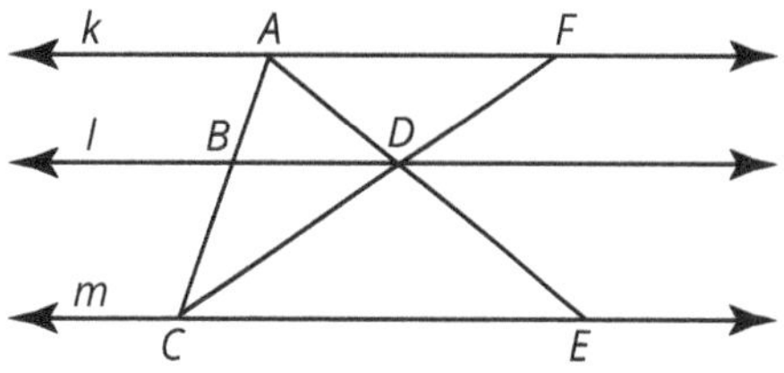

STATEMENT	REASON

2.14 Given: $\overline{DC} \perp \overline{CT}$
$\overline{PB} \perp \overline{CT}$

To Prove: $\triangle SPR \sim \triangle VDR$

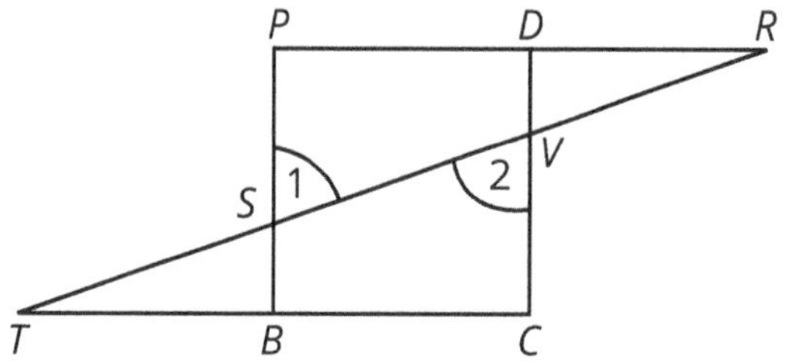

STATEMENT	REASON

Given the figures, can you conclude for each exercise that $\triangle DEF \sim \triangle ABC$? If *yes*, what similarity statement would you use?

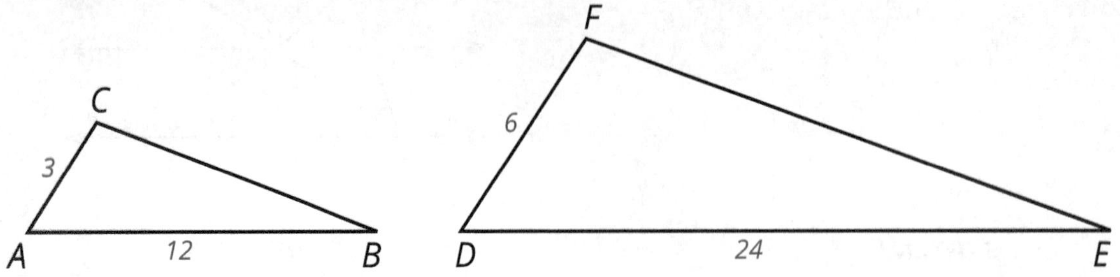

2.15 $\angle A = \angle D$ ____________________________

2.16 $\angle B = \angle E$ ____________________________

2.17 $\angle C = \angle F$ ____________________________

2.18 $\frac{BC}{EF} = \frac{1}{2}$ ____________________________

2.19 $BC = 6$, $EF = 12$ ____________________________

2.20 $BC = 5$, $EF = 15$ ____________________________

Complete the following proofs.

2.21 Given: $\frac{BC}{CD} = \frac{AC}{CE}$

To Prove: $\triangle ACB \sim \triangle ECD$

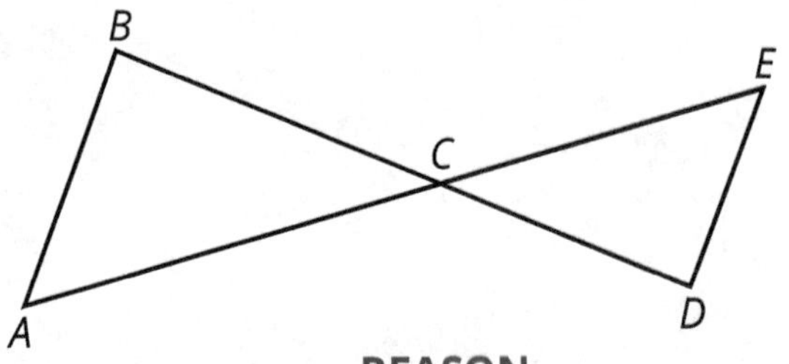

STATEMENT	REASON

2.22 **Given:** $\angle A = \angle D$

To Prove: $\triangle ACB \sim \triangle DCE$

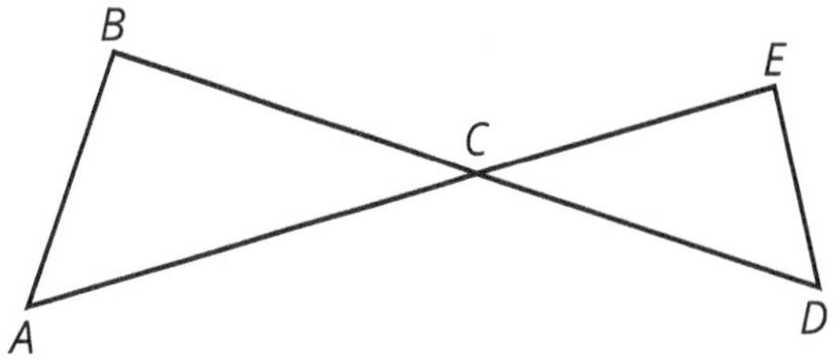

STATEMENT	REASON

2.23 **Given:** $GF = \frac{1}{2}GC$

$GE = \frac{1}{2}GD$

$EF = \frac{1}{2}DC$

To Prove: $\triangle GFE \sim \triangle GCD$

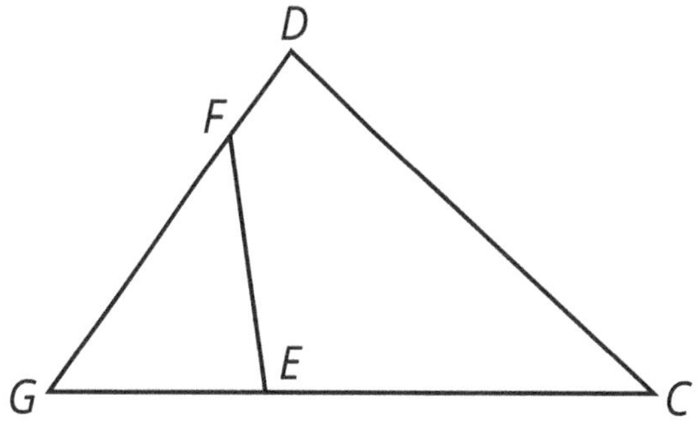

STATEMENT	REASON

2.24 **Given:** $\overline{YZ} \parallel \overline{UV}$

To Prove: $\frac{XY}{XU} = \frac{YZ}{UV}$

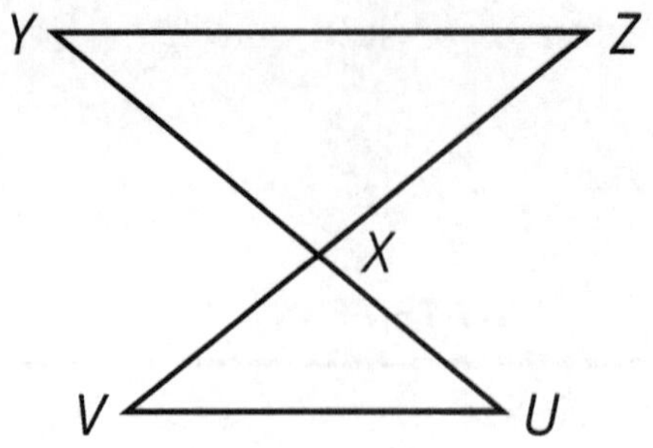

STATEMENT	REASON

THEOREMS ABOUT SIMILAR POLYGONS

Many theorems deal with similar polygons. We shall cover some of them now. Others will be studied in the next section on similar triangles.

> **THEOREM 5-4**
>
> Similarity of polygons is reflexive, symmetric, and transitive.
>
> **(Transitive Part Proof)**

Given: Polygon $ABC\ldots \sim$ Polygon $JKL\ldots$
Polygon $JKL\ldots \sim$ Polygon $RST\ldots$

To Prove: Polygon $ABC\ldots \sim$ Polygon $RST\ldots$

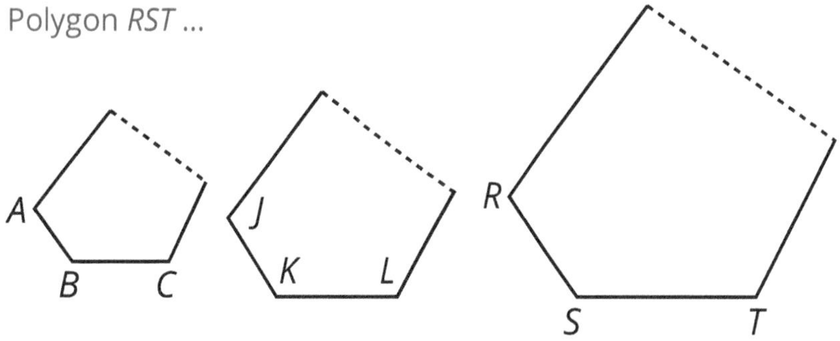

STATEMENT	REASON
1. $\angle A = \angle J$, $\angle B = \angle K$, $\angle C = \angle L$, etc. $\angle J = \angle R$, $\angle K = \angle S$, $\angle L = \angle T$	1. Corresponding $\angle$'s of similar polygons are =
2. $\angle A = \angle R$, $\angle B = \angle S$, $\angle C = \angle T$, etc.	2. Transitive property of equality
3. $\frac{AB}{JK} = \frac{BC}{KL}$, etc. $\frac{JK}{RS} = \frac{KL}{ST}$	3. Sides of similar polygons are proportional
4. $\frac{AB}{BC} = \frac{JK}{KL}$, $\frac{LK}{KL} = \frac{RS}{ST}$	4. POP
5. $\frac{AB}{BC} = \frac{RS}{ST}$, etc.	5. Transitive property of equality
6. $\frac{AB}{RS} = \frac{BC}{ST}$, etc.	6. POP
7. Polygon $ABC\ldots \sim$ Polygon $RST\ldots$	7. Definition of similar polygons

The next theorem is about the **perimeter** of a polygon. Recall that the perimeter is the length around a polygon and can be found by adding all the sides.

THEOREM 5-5

If two polygons are similar, then the ratio of their perimeters equals the ratio of any pair of corresponding sides.

Given: Polygon $ABCDE \sim$ Polygon $QRSTU$

To Prove: $\frac{P_1}{P_2} = \frac{AB}{QR}$

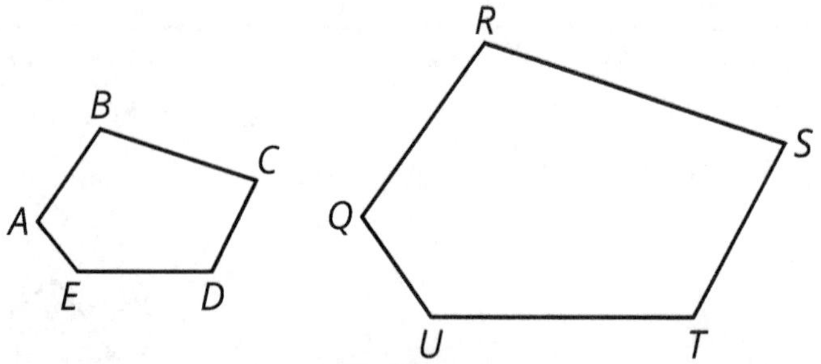

STATEMENT	REASON
1. Polygon $ABCDE \sim$ Polygon $QRSTU$	1. Given
2. $\frac{AB}{QR} = \frac{BC}{RS} = \frac{CD}{ST} = \frac{DE}{TU} = \frac{EA}{UQ}$	2. Definition of similar polygons
3. $\frac{AB + BC + CD + DE + EA}{QR + RS + ST + TU + UQ} = \frac{AB}{QR}$	3. POP
4. $AB + BC + CD + DE + EA = P_1$ $QR + RS + ST + TU + UQ = P_2$	4. Definition of perimeter
5. $\frac{P_1}{P_2} = \frac{AB}{QR}$	5. Substitution

Model: The sides of a polygon are 1, 4, 6, 7, and 9. Find the perimeter of a similar polygon with a longest side of 12.

Solution: Let P_1 = perimeter of first polygon = 27.
Let P_2 = perimeter of second polygon.

By Theorem 5-5, $\frac{27}{P_2} = \frac{9}{12}$

$9P_2 = 324$

$P_2 = 36$

Solve the following problems. Show your work and circle your answer.

2.25 The sides of the smaller of two similar triangles are 3, 4, 5. The shortest side of the larger triangle is 9. Find the other two sides of the larger triangle.

2.26 The smaller of two similar rectangles has dimensions 4 and 6. Find the dimensions of the larger rectangle if the ratio of the perimeters is 2 to 3.

2.27 The perimeters of two similar polygons are 20 and 28. One side of the smaller polygon is 4. Find the corresponding side of the larger polygon.

2.28 One pair of corresponding sides of two similar polygons measures 12 and 15. The perimeter of the smaller polygon is 30. Find the perimeter of the larger.

2.29 If polygon *A* is similar to polygon *B*, must polygon *B* be similar to polygon *A*? How do you know?

2.30 The sides of a polygon are 3, 5, 4, and 6. The shortest side of a similar polygon is 9.

Find the ratio of their perimeters: a. ______________

Find the sides of the larger polygon: b. ______________________

2.31 The sides of a polygon are 3, 5, 6, 8, and 10. The perimeter of a similar polygon is 40. Find the sides of the second polygon.

2.32 A rectangular picture has dimensions $2\frac{1}{2}$ by $1\frac{1}{2}$. It is to be enlarged so the longer dimension will be 10. What is the perimeter of the enlargement?

Given: Rectangle *ABCD* **is similar to rectangle** *ZBXY*.

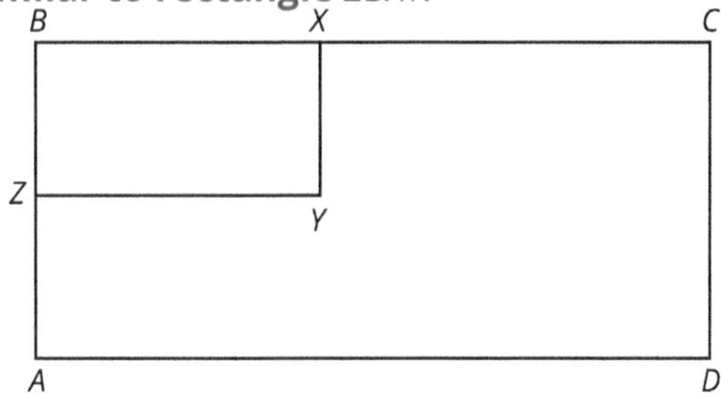

2.33 If $BC = 10$, $BX = 6$, $XY = 4$, then $CD =$ _______________

2.34 If $ZY = 5$, $XC = 3$, $DC = 4$, then $XY =$ _______________

2.35 If $BX = 8$, $BZ = 3$, $DC = 5$, then $XC =$ _______________

2.36 If $BZ = 3$, $BA = 8$, $BC = 12$, then $BX =$ _______________

Given: $\triangle ABC$ **is similar to** $\triangle XYC$.

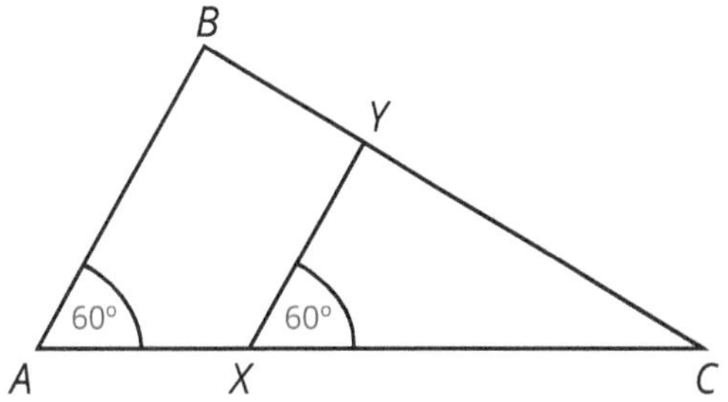

2.37 If $BY = 4$, $YC = 7$, $XC = 10$, then $AC =$ _______________

2.38 If $BY = 6$, $YC = 10$, $AX = 18$, then $XC =$ _______________

2.39 If $BY = 5$, $BC = 20$, $AC = 18$, then $XC =$ _______________

2.40 If $YC = 4$, $BC = 6$, $XY = 5$, then $AB =$ _______________

THEOREMS ABOUT SIMILAR TRIANGLES

Many interesting and useful theorems are about similar triangles and special segments that are found in them. Similar right triangles also give us some special proportions that are practical.

SPECIAL SEGMENTS IN TRIANGLES

The proportions you have been writing thus far have to do with the lengths of the sides of similar triangles. Proportions may also be written that have to do with the lengths of two parts of one segment and the corresponding parts of a second segment.

For example, take segments *AB* and *CD*. Let *X* divide *AB* into two parts and *Y* divide *CD* into two parts. Now segment *AB* and segment *CD* are said to be *divided proportionally* if:

$\frac{AX}{XB} = \frac{CY}{YD}$ or $\frac{AX}{AB} = \frac{CY}{CD}$.

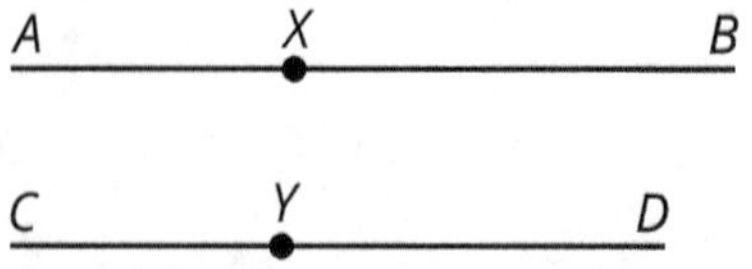

> **THEOREM 5-6**
>
> If a line is parallel to one side of a triangle and intersects the other two sides, it divides them proportionally.

Given: $\overleftrightarrow{XY} \parallel \overline{AC}$

To Prove: $\frac{CY}{YB} = \frac{AX}{XB}$

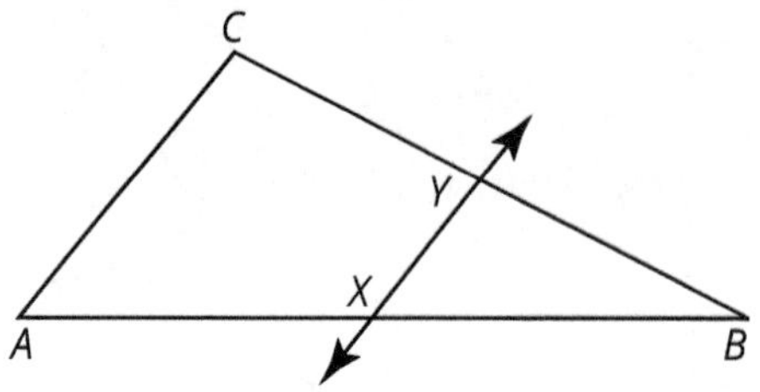

STATEMENT	REASON
1. $\overleftrightarrow{XY} \parallel \overline{AC}$	1. Given
2. $\triangle XYB \sim \triangle ACB$	2. C-1 of Theorem 5-1
3. $\frac{CB}{YB} = \frac{AB}{XB}$	3. Definition of similar triangles
4. $\frac{CB - YB}{YB} = \frac{AB - XB}{XB}$	4. POP
5. $CB - YB = CY$ $AB - XB = AX$	5. Betweenness and subtraction
6. $\frac{CY}{YB} = \frac{AX}{XB}$	6. Substitution

Two other equivalent forms of this type of proportion can be formed. We can use Step 3 of the proof $\frac{CB}{YB} = \frac{AB}{XB}$ and use POP to get $\frac{CB}{CY} = \frac{AB}{AX}$. So we now have three ways of writing the conclusion of Theorem 5-6.

Model 1:

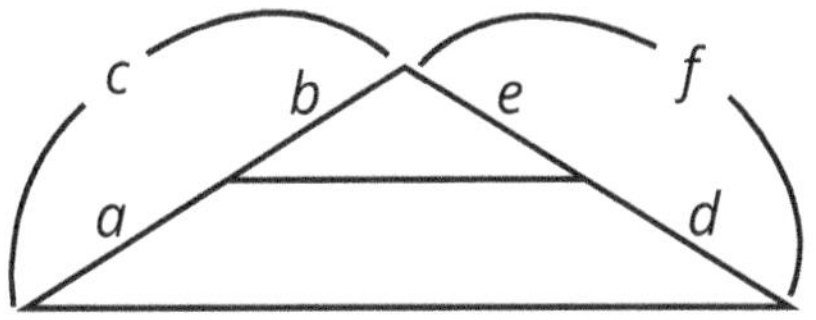

$\frac{a}{b} = \frac{d}{e}$ $\frac{a}{c} = \frac{d}{f}$ $\frac{b}{c} = \frac{e}{f}$

Model 2:

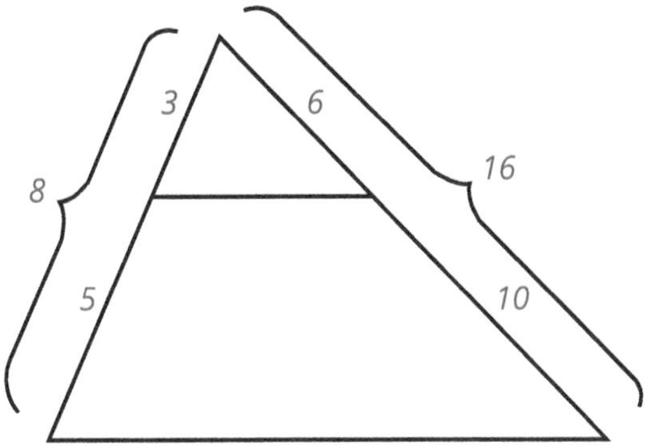

$\frac{5}{3} = \frac{10}{6}$ $\frac{5}{8} = \frac{10}{16}$ $\frac{3}{8} = \frac{6}{16}$

$30 = 30$ $80 = 80$ $48 = 48$

THEOREM 5-7

If a ray bisects an angle of a triangle, it divides the opposite side into segments with lengths proportional to the lengths of the other two sides of the triangle.

Given: $\triangle ABC$, $\angle 1 = \angle 2$

To Prove: $\frac{AD}{DC} = \frac{AB}{BC}$

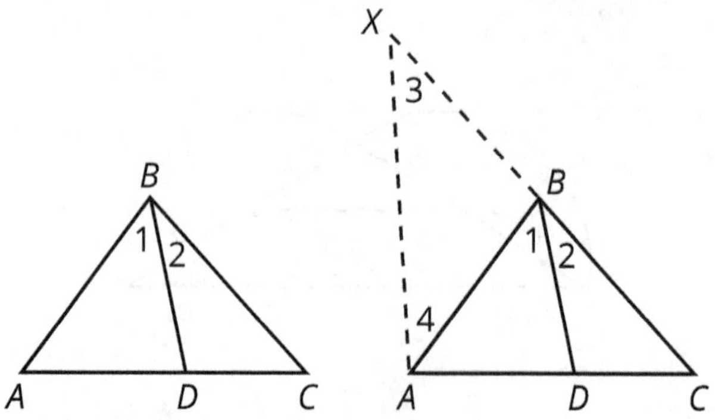

STATEMENT	REASON
1. Draw $\overleftrightarrow{AX} \parallel BD$ through A. Call the point where AX and BC intersect X.	1. Auxiliary line
2. $\frac{AD}{DC} = \frac{XB}{BC}$	2. Theorem 5-6
3. $\angle 3 = \angle 2$	3. If lines parallel, corresponding ∠'s are =
4. $\angle 2 = \angle 1$	4. Given
5. $\angle 1 = \angle 4$	5. If lines parallel, alternate interior ∠'s are =
6. $\angle 3 = \angle 4$	6. Substitution
7. $XB = AB$	7. If two ∠'s of triangle are =, sides opposite them are =
8. $\frac{AD}{DC} = \frac{AB}{BC}$	8. Substitution

> **THEOREM 5-8**
>
> If two triangles are similar, the length of corresponding altitudes have the same ratio as the length of any pair of corresponding sides.

Given: $\triangle ABC \sim \triangle RST$

To Prove: $\frac{BX}{SY} = \frac{AB}{RS} = \frac{BC}{ST} = \frac{CA}{TR}$

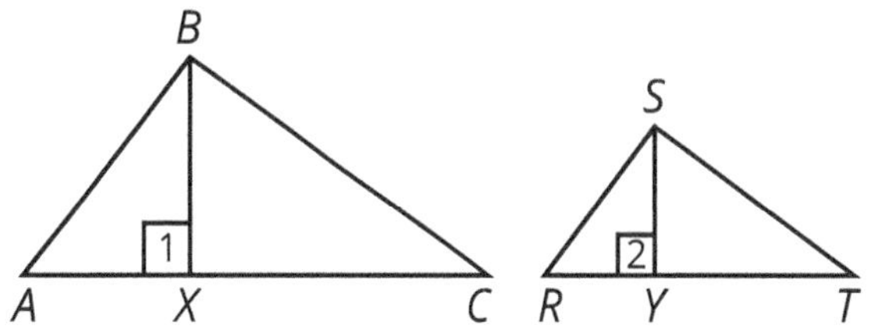

STATEMENT	REASON
1. $\triangle ABC \sim \triangle RST$	1. Given
2. $\frac{AB}{RS} = \frac{BC}{ST} = \frac{AC}{RT}$	2. Definition of similar polygons
3. $\angle A = \angle R$	3. Definition of similar polygons
4. $\angle 1 = \angle 2$	4. Definition of altitude; all right $\angle$'s are =
5. $\triangle AXB \sim \triangle RYS$	5. AA for similar triangles
6. $\frac{BX}{SY} = \frac{AB}{RS}$	6. Definition of similar polygons
7. $\frac{BX}{SY} = \frac{AB}{RS} = \frac{BC}{ST} = \frac{CA}{TR}$	7. Substitution

Model 1: Given the figure with $\overline{RS} \parallel \overline{BC}$, find SC and AC.

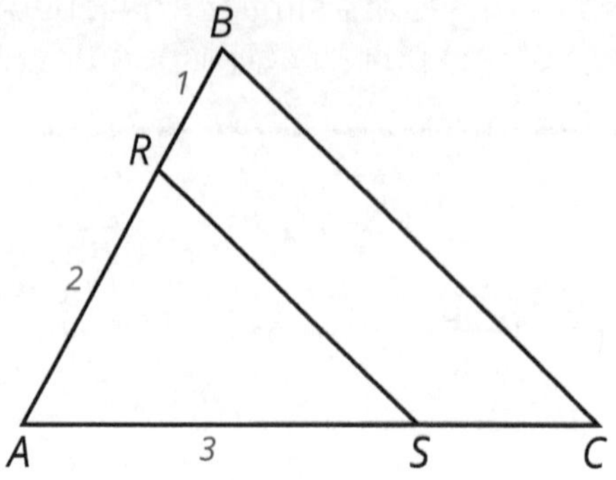

Solution:

$\frac{AS}{SC} = \frac{AR}{RB}$

$\frac{3}{SC} = \frac{2}{1}$

$2SC = 3$

$SC = \frac{3}{2} = 1\frac{1}{2}$

$AC = AS + SC$

$AC = 3 + 1\frac{1}{2}$

$AC = 4\frac{1}{2}$

Model 2: Given the figure with $\angle 1 = \angle 2$, find BX and BC.

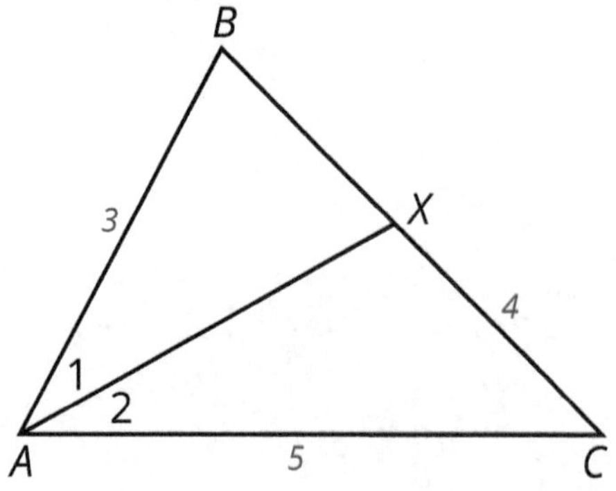

Solution:

$\frac{BX}{XC} = \frac{AB}{AC}$

$\frac{BX}{4} = \frac{3}{5}$

$5BX = 12$

$BX = \frac{12}{5} = 2\frac{2}{5}$

$BC = BX + XC$

$BC = 2\frac{2}{5} + 4$

$BC = 6\frac{2}{5}$

Solve the following problems. Show your work and circle your answer.

2.41 A segment 12" long is divided into two segments having lengths in the ratio of 2:3. Find the length of each segment. (Hint: Let $2x$ and $3x$ represent the length of the parts.)

2.42 A segment is divided into two parts having lengths in the ratio of 5:3. If the difference between the length of the parts is 6", find the length of each part.

Refer to the following figures to find the measures.

Given: $\overline{AB} \parallel \overline{RS}$

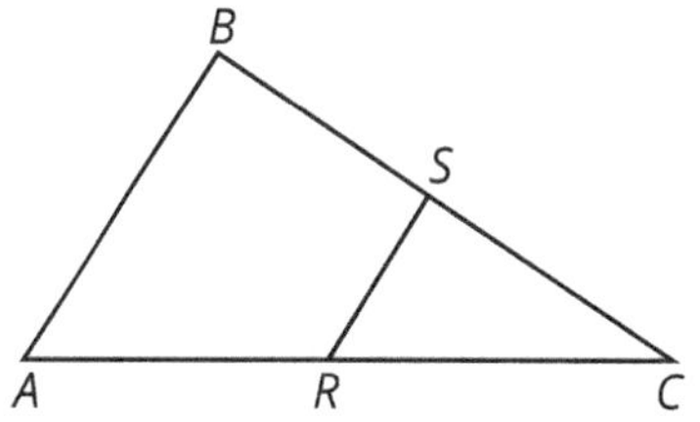

2.43 If $CR = 3$, $RA = 5$, and $CS = 4$, find SB. ____________

2.44 If $CR = 2$, $RA = 3$, and $BC = 10$, find CS. ____________

2.45 If $CR = 4$, $RA = 6$, and $RS = 10$, find AB. ____________

2.46 If $CR = SB$, $RA = 4$, and $CS = 9$, find CR. ____________

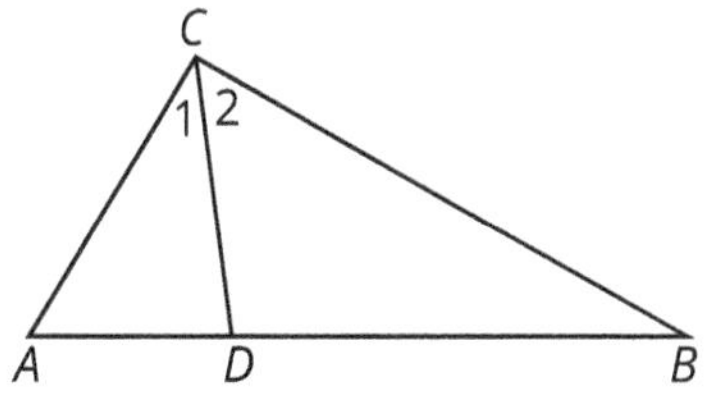

Given: $\angle 1 = \angle 2$

2.47 If $AC = 3$, $BC = 5$, and $AB = 7$, find AD: a. ____________ and DB: b. ____________

2.48 If $AB = 10$, $AC = 6$, and $BC = 6$, find AD: a. ____________ and DB: b. ____________

2.49 If $AB = 10$, $AC = 4$, and $BC = 8$, find AD: a. ____________ and DB: b. ____________

2.50 If $AC:BC = 3:5$ and $AB = 12$, find AD: a. ____________ and DB: b. ____________

In each figure, the segment is parallel to one side of the triangle. Find the values of *x* and *y*.

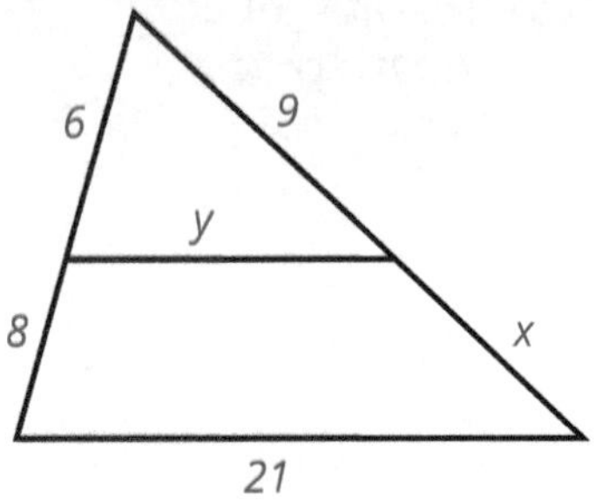

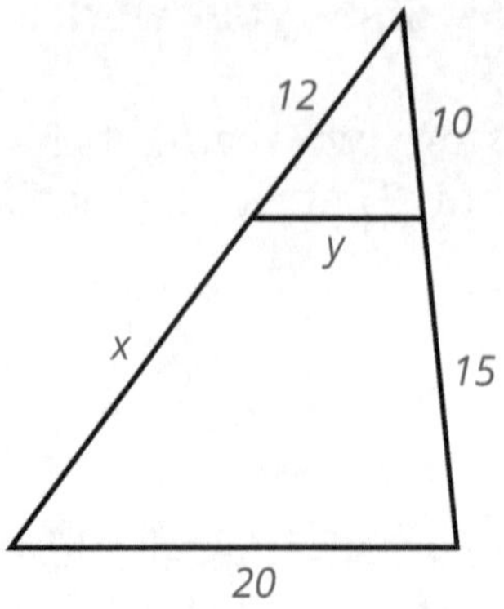

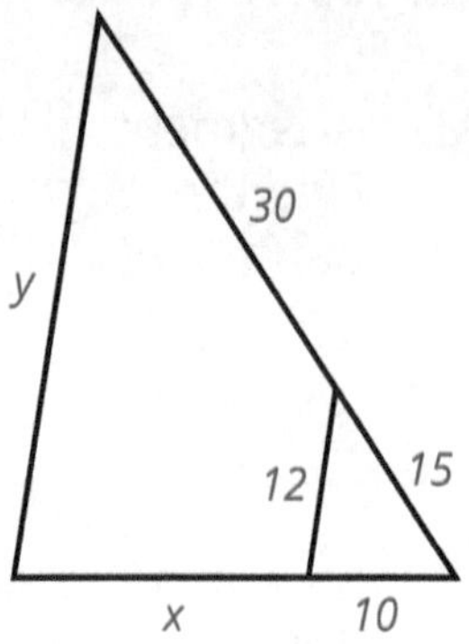

2.51 x = ____________

y = ____________

2.52 x = ____________

y = ____________

2.53 x = ____________

y = ____________

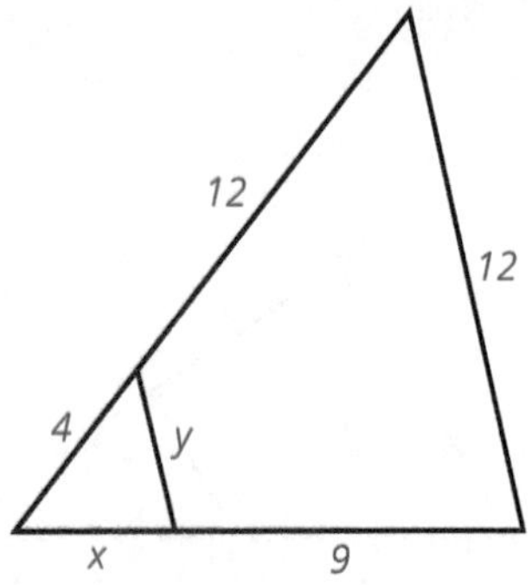

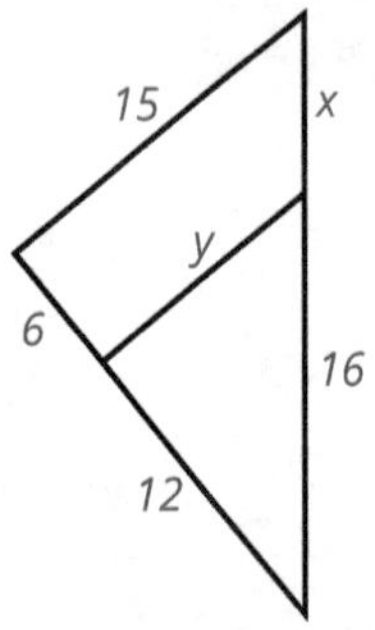

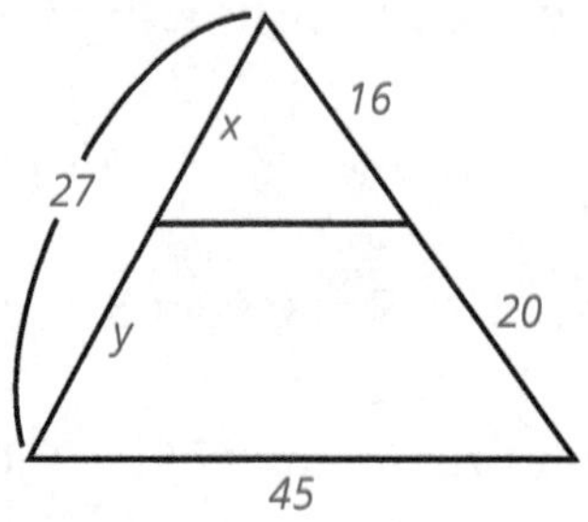

2.54 x = ____________

y = ____________

2.55 x = ____________

y = ____________

2.56 x = ____________

y = ____________

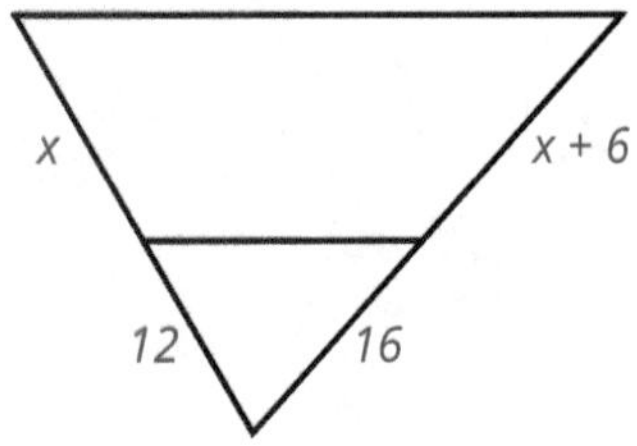

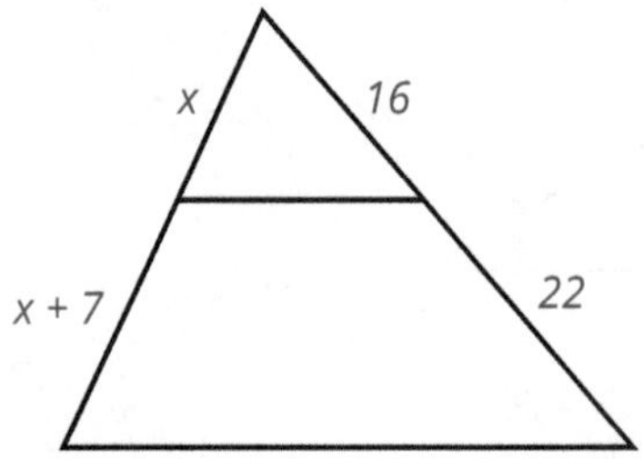

2.57 x = ____________

2.58 x = ____________

Complete the following proofs.

2.59 Given: $\overline{XA} \perp \overleftrightarrow{RS}$

$\angle 1 = \angle 2$

To Prove: $\frac{BX}{XC} = \frac{AB}{AC}$

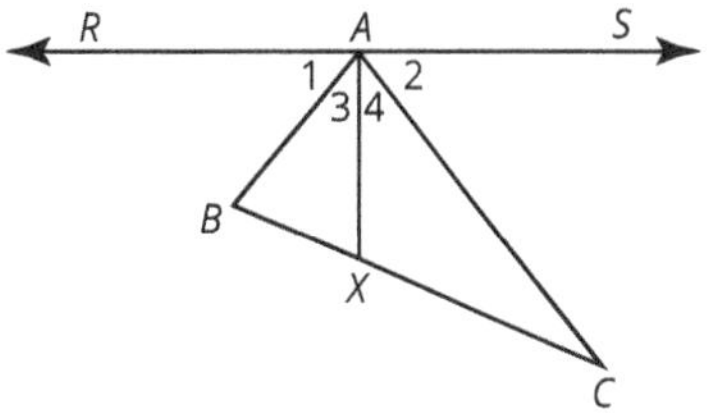

STATEMENT	REASON

2.60 Given: $\overline{XZ} \parallel \overline{BC}$

$\angle 1 = \angle 2$

To Prove: $\frac{AX}{XB} = \frac{AY}{ZC}$

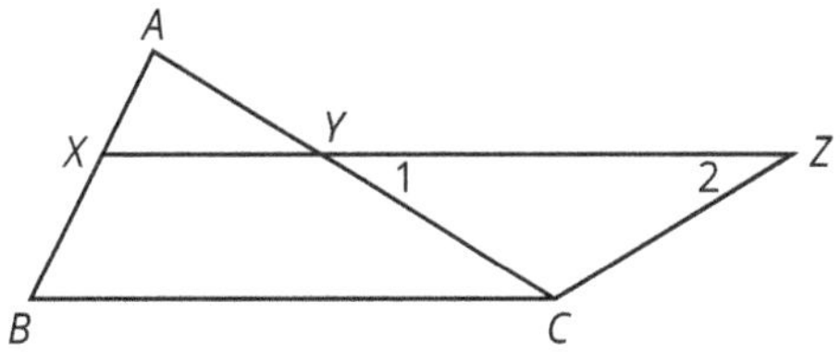

STATEMENT	REASON

2.61 Given: $\overline{RS} \parallel \overline{BC}$
$\angle 1 = \angle 2$

To Prove: $\frac{AS}{SC} = \frac{AR}{RS}$

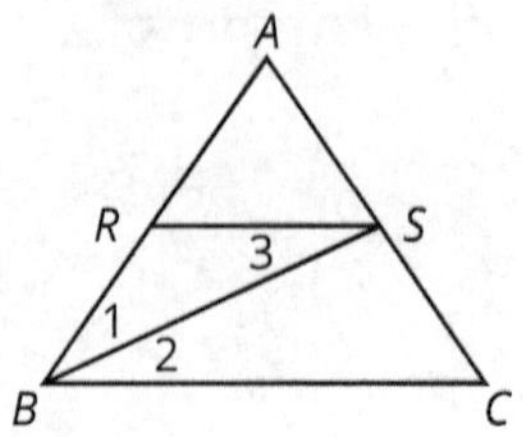

STATEMENT	REASON

SIMILAR RIGHT TRIANGLES

Many special proportions are concerned with right triangles. We need to review some definitions and learn some new ones.

All triangles have three **altitudes**. The segments from a vertex perpendicular to the opposite side are the altitudes. The three altitudes of this right triangle are $\overline{AC}$, $\overline{BC}$, and $\overline{CD}$. Two of them, $\overline{AC}$ and $\overline{BC}$, are also the legs of the right triangle. The third, $\overline{CD}$, is the altitude to the hypotenuse. This altitude to the hypotenuse leads us to some of the interesting proportions we will cover next.

When we have a proportion and both means' positions are occupied with the same number, that number is the **geometric mean** between the other two numbers. The geometric mean can be found by taking the square root of the product of the two numbers.

DEFINITIONS

Altitude: An altitude of a triangle is a perpendicular line from a vertex to the opposite side.

Geometric mean: For any positive real numbers a, b, and x, if $\frac{a}{x} = \frac{x}{b}$, then x is called the geometric mean between a and b. Notice that $x^2 = ab$ or $x = \sqrt{ab}$.

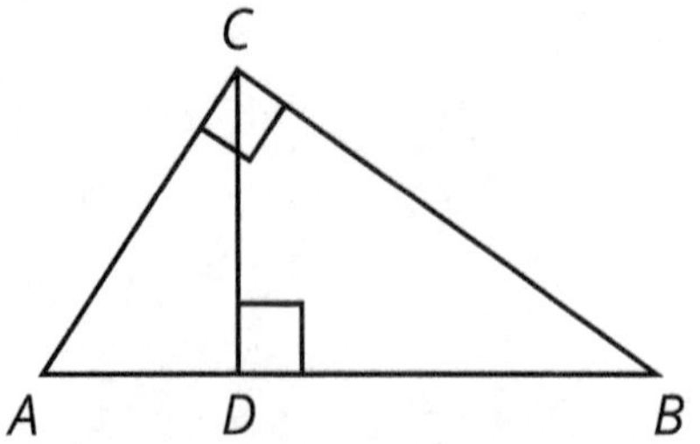

Model 1: Find the geometric mean between 4 and 9.

Solution: $\frac{4}{x} = \frac{x}{9}$ (x in the means' position)

$x^2 = 36$

$x = \sqrt{36} = 6$

Model 2: Five is the geometric mean between 8 and what other number?

Solution: $\frac{8}{5} = \frac{5}{x}$ (5 in the means' position)

$8x = 25$

$x = \frac{25}{8} = 3\frac{1}{8}$

The **projection** of a point on a line is the point where a perpendicular through the given point to the given line intersects the given line. *X* is the projection of *P* on *l*.

If the point is on the line, then the point is its own projection.

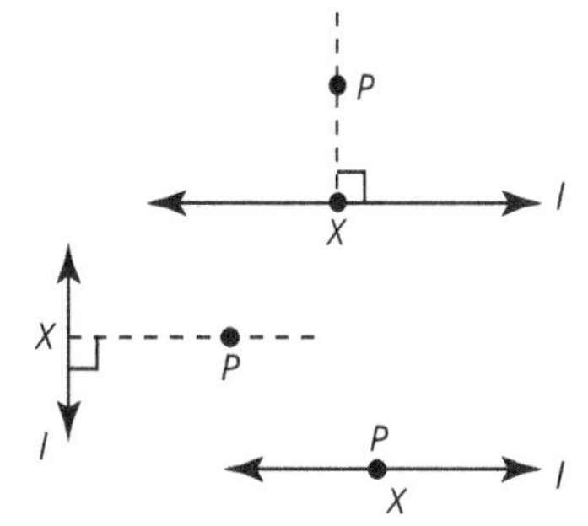

The projection of a segment on a line is the segment whose end points are the projections of the end points of the given segment.

$\overline{XY}$ is the projection of $\overline{RS}$ on line *l*. Notice the length of the projection when the segment is in different positions.

The projection can be equal to or less than the given segment, but it cannot be longer than the given segment.

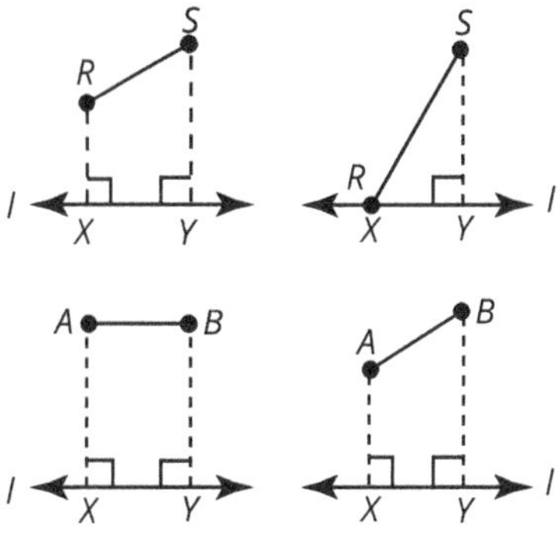

We are now ready to prove some theorems with these ideas.

DEFINITIONS

Projection of a point on a line: the point where a perpendicular through the point to the line intersects the line.

Projection of a segment on a line: the portion of a line with end points that are the projections of the end points of the segment.

THEOREM 5-9

If the altitude to the hypotenuse of a right triangle is drawn, the two triangles formed are similar to each other and similar to the given triangle.

Given: Right $\triangle ABC$
$\overline{CD}$ altitude to hypotenuse

To Prove: $\triangle ADC \sim \triangle CDB$
$\triangle ADC \sim \triangle ACB$
$\triangle CDB \sim \triangle ACB$

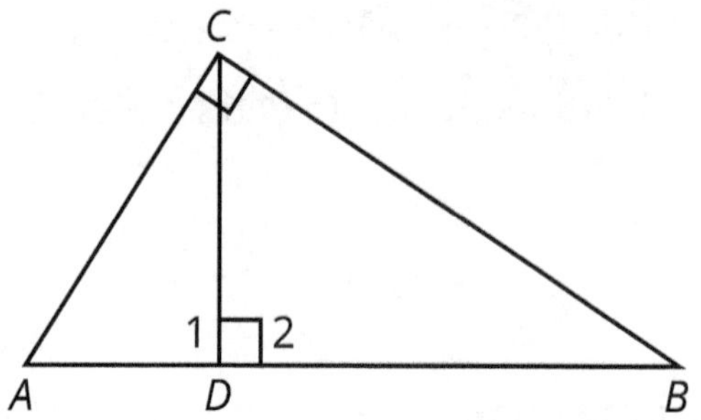

STATEMENT	REASON
1. Right $\triangle ABC$, $\overline{CD} \perp \overline{AB}$	1. Given
2. $\angle 1$, $\angle 2$ are right $\angle$'s	2. $\perp$'s form right $\angle$'s
3. $\angle 1 = \angle ACB = \angle 2$	3. All right $\angle$'s are =
4. $\angle A = \angle A$	4. Reflexive
5. $\triangle ADC \sim \triangle ACB$	5. AA
6. $\angle B = \angle B$	6. Reflexive
7. $\triangle CDB \sim \triangle ACB$	7. AA
8. $\triangle ADC \sim \triangle CDB$	8. Similar polygons are transitive

The next three corollaries to Theorem 5-9 will be very useful in finding the length of segments in right triangles.

Corollary 1: The length of a leg of a right triangle is the geometric mean between the length of the hypotenuse and the length of the projection of that leg on the hypotenuse.

Model:

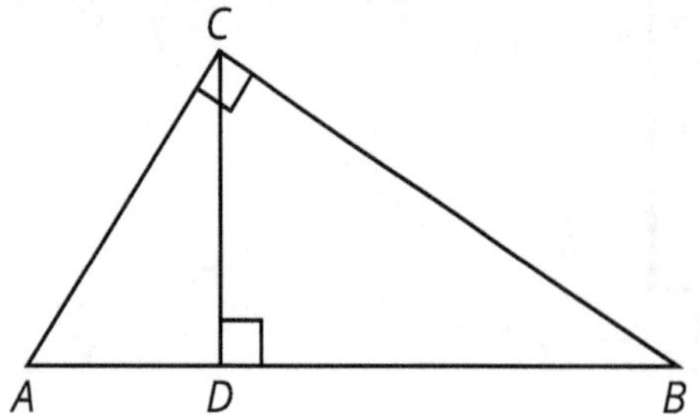

$\frac{AB}{AC} = \frac{AC}{AD}$ and $\frac{AB}{BC} = \frac{BC}{DB}$

Corollary 2: In a right triangle, the length of the altitude to the hypotenuse is the geometric mean between the length of the segments of the hypotenuse.

Model:

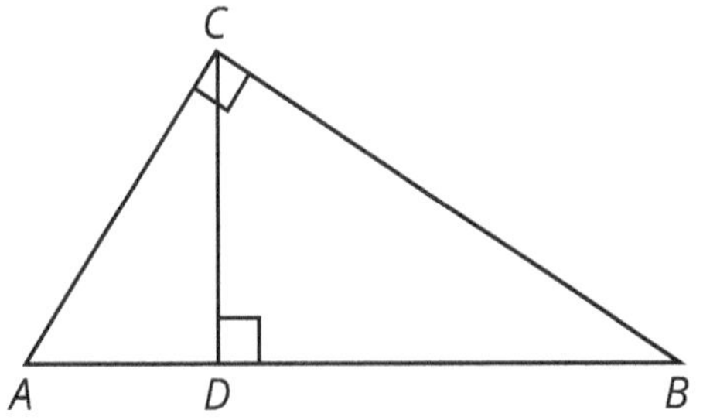

$\frac{AD}{CD} = \frac{CD}{DB}$

Corollary 3: In a right triangle, the product of the hypotenuse and the altitude to the hypotenuse is equal to the product of the lengths of the legs.

Model:

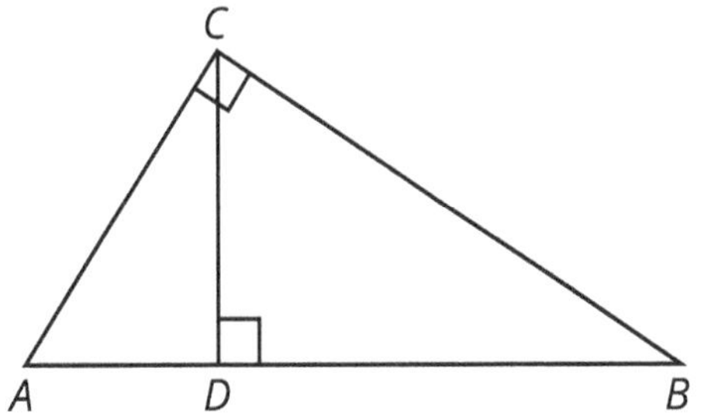

$AB \cdot CD = AC \cdot BC$

The figure below shows all three of these corollaries. The small letters represent the length of the segments.

C-1 $\frac{x}{a} = \frac{a}{c}, \frac{y}{b} = \frac{b}{c}$

C-2 $\frac{x}{h} = \frac{h}{y}$

C-3 $hc = ab$

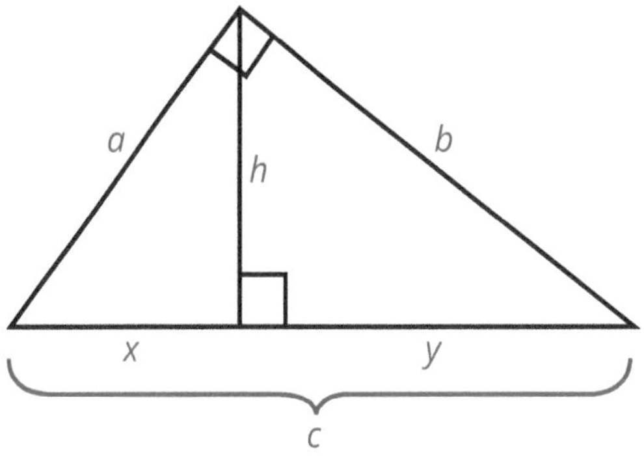

Write the geometric mean between the pairs of numbers.

2.62 2 and 9 ____________

2.63 6 and 3 ____________

2.64 8 and 2 ____________

Find all positive values for *x*.

2.65 $\frac{2}{x} = \frac{x}{6}$ ______________________

2.66 $\frac{x}{4} = \frac{5}{x}$ ______________________

2.67 $\frac{x}{3} = \frac{3}{x}$ ______________________

Write the second number for each pair such that $\sqrt{6}$ is the geometric mean for the pair.

2.68 2 and ______________

2.69 12 and ______________

2.70 6 and ______________

2.71 4 and ______________

Refer to the following figures to find the measures.

2.72 If $AD = 2$ and $DC = 8$, find BD. __________

2.73 If $AD = 3$ and $DC = 6$, find AB. __________

2.74 If $BC = 6$ and $AD = 5$, find DC. __________

2.75 If $DB = 4$ and $DC = 6$, find AD. __________

2.76 If $AC = 12$ and $DC = 8$, find AB. __________

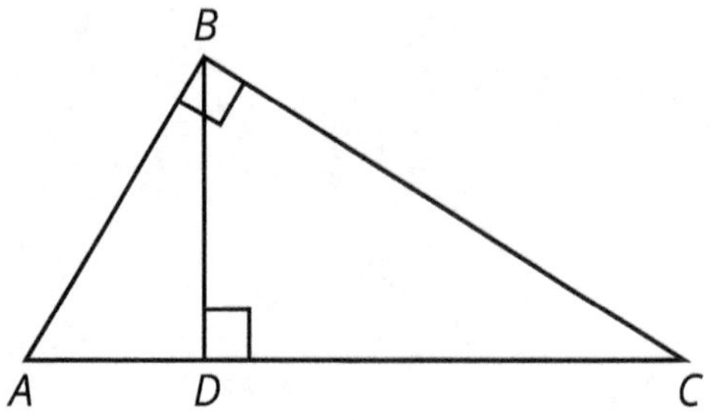

2.77 Find *x*. __________

2.78 Find *y*. __________

2.79 Find *z*. __________

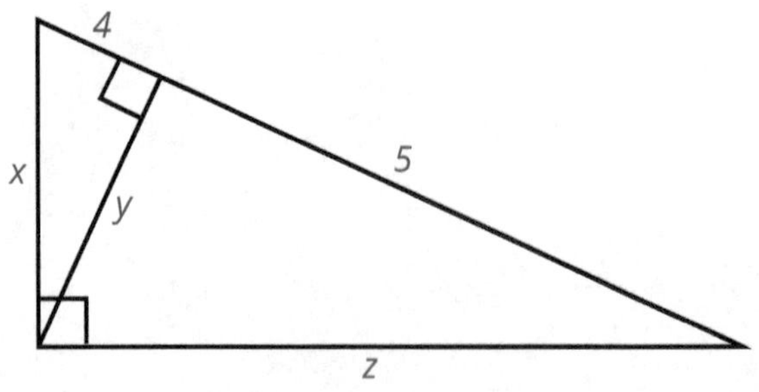

2.80 Find a. ____________

2.81 Find b. ____________

2.82 Find c. ____________

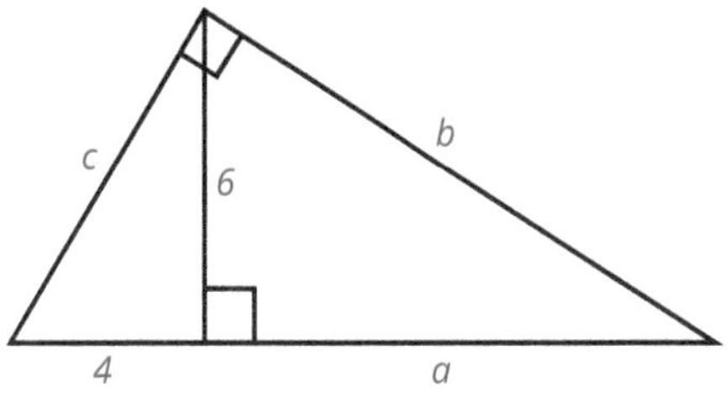

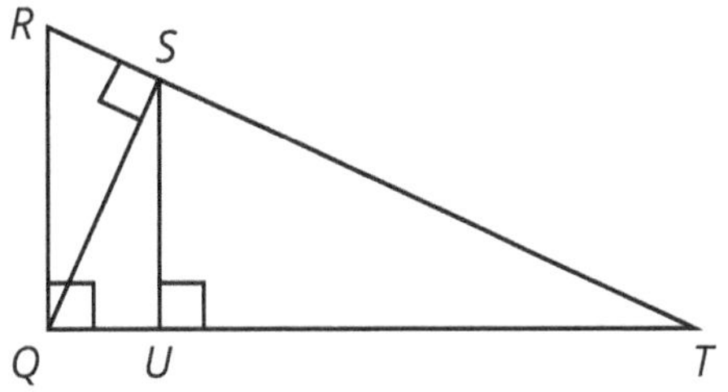

2.83 What segment is the projection of $\overline{QT}$ on $\overline{RT}$? ____________

2.84 What point is the projection of Q on $\overline{RT}$? ____________

2.85 What segment is the projection of $\overline{ST}$ on $\overline{QT}$? ____________

2.86 What segment is the projection of $\overline{QS}$ on $\overline{QT}$? ____________

2.87 What segment is the projection of $\overline{QR}$ on $\overline{RT}$? ____________

Complete the following proofs.

2.88 Given: $\triangle ADC$ is right $\triangle$

$\overline{DB} \perp \overline{AC}$

$DB = n$

To Prove: $AB \cdot BC = n^2$

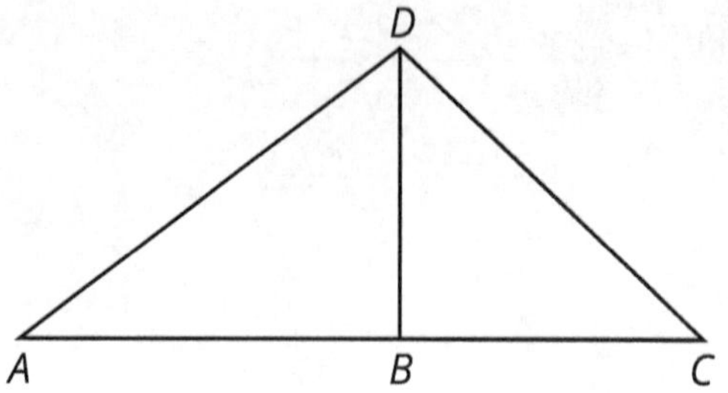

STATEMENT	REASON

2.89 Given: Right $\triangle RST$

$\overline{SU} \perp \overline{RT}$

$RS = \sqrt{15}$

To Prove: $RU \cdot RT = 15$

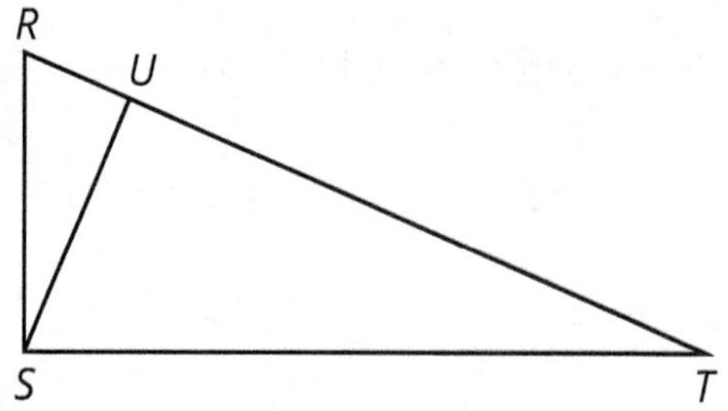

STATEMENT	REASON

PYTHAGOREAN THEOREM

This next theorem is one of the best known and most used theorems in all branches of mathematics. It deals with the relationship between the length of the legs and the length of the hypotenuse of a right triangle.

> **THEOREM 5-10**
>
> In a right triangle, the sum of the squares of the lengths of the legs is equal to the square of the length of the hypotenuse.
>
> **(Pythagorean Theorem)**

Given: Right triangle *ABC*

To Prove: $a^2 + b^2 = c^2$

Plan: Draw the altitude to the hypotenuse and use proportions that involve the legs.

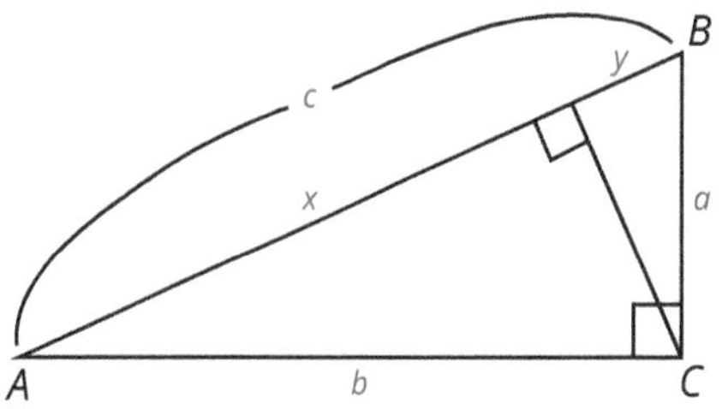

STATEMENT	REASON
1. Draw $\overline{CD}$ the altitude to the hypotenuse	1. Auxiliary line
2. $\frac{c}{b} = \frac{b}{x}, \frac{c}{a} = \frac{a}{y}$	2. Leg is geometric mean between hypotenuse and projection of leg on hypotenuse
3. $b^2 = cx, a^2 = cy$	3. POP
4. $a^2 + b^2 = cx + cy$	4. Addition property of equality
5. $a^2 + b^2 = c(x + y)$	5. Distributive property
6. $x + y = c$	6. Betweenness
7. $a^2 + b^2 = c^2$	7. Substitution

The Pythagorean Theorem is named after a Greek mathematician named Pythagoras (about 584–495 BC). Over two hundred proofs to this theorem have been made over the years. His proof is believed to have been the first formal proof recorded.

The converse of the Pythagorean Theorem is also a very useful statement. It is a way to prove that a triangle is a right triangle.

THEOREM 5-11

If the sum of the squares of two sides of a triangle equals the square of the third side, then the triangle is a right triangle.

Given: $a^2 + b^2 = c^2$

To Prove: $\triangle ABC$ is a right triangle

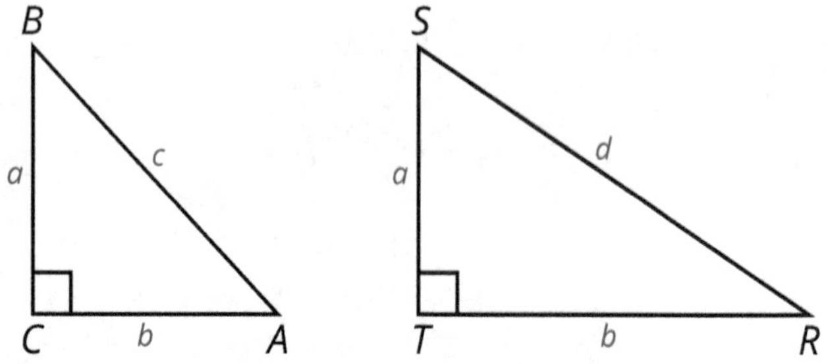

STATEMENT	REASON
1. Draw right $\triangle RST$ with legs a, b and hypotenuse d	1. Auxiliary lines
2. In $\triangle RST$, $a^2 + b^2 = d^2$	2. Pythagorean Theorem
3. $a^2 + b^2 = c^2$	3. Given
4. $c^2 = d^2$	4. Substitution
5. $c = d$	5. Property of algebra
6. $\triangle ABC \cong \triangle RST$	6. SSS
7. $\angle C = \angle T$	7. CPCTE
8. $\angle C$ is right angle	8. Substitution; $\angle T$ is right angle
9. $\triangle ABC$ is right triangle	9. Definition of right triangle

Model 1: Given $\triangle DEF$, a right triangle with $DE = 3$ and $EF = 4$; find DF.

Solution:

$$\begin{aligned} a^2 + b^2 &= c^2 \\ 3^2 + 4^2 &= c^2 \\ 9 + 16 &= c^2 \\ 25 &= c^2 \\ 5 &= c \end{aligned}$$

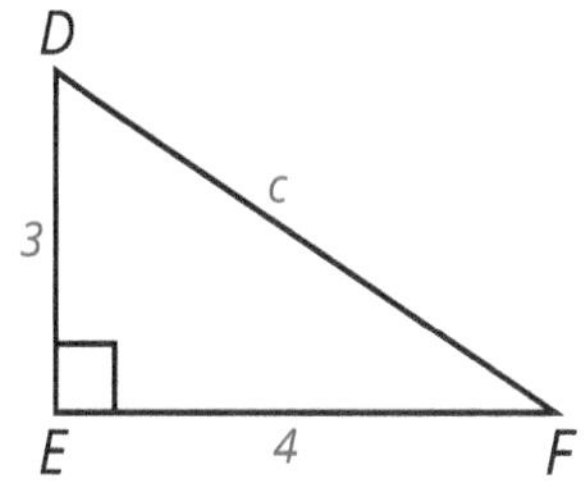

Model 2: The hypotenuse of a right triangle is 10. One leg is 5. Find the other leg.

Solution:

$$\begin{aligned} a^2 + b^2 &= c^2 \\ a^2 + 5^2 &= 10^2 \\ a^2 + 25 &= 100 \\ a^2 &= 75 \\ a = \sqrt{75} &= 5\sqrt{3} \end{aligned}$$

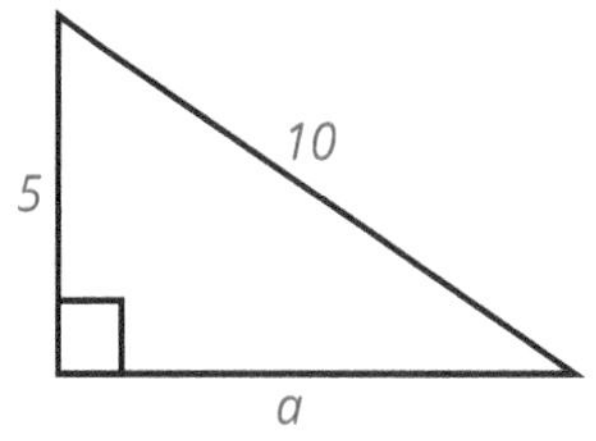

Model 3: Is a triangle with sides 6, 8, and 10 a right triangle?

Solution:

$$\begin{aligned} 6^2 + 8^2 &\ ?\ 10^2 \\ 36 + 64 &\ ?\ 100 \\ 100 &= 100 \end{aligned}$$

Yes, the triangle is a right triangle.

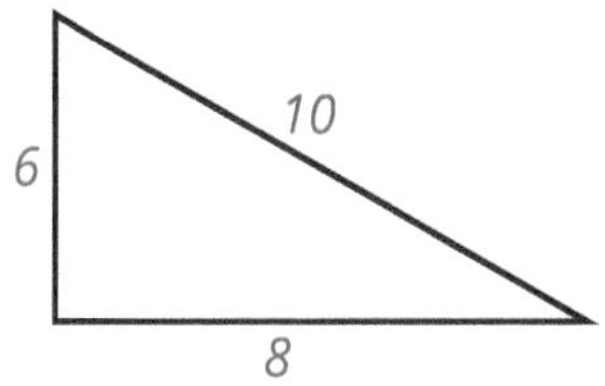

Model 4: Is a triangle with sides 7, 9, and 11 a right triangle?

Solution:

$$\begin{aligned} 7^2 + 9^2 &\ ?\ 11^2 \\ 49 + 81 &\ ?\ 121 \\ 130 &\neq 121 \end{aligned}$$

No, the triangle is not a right triangle.

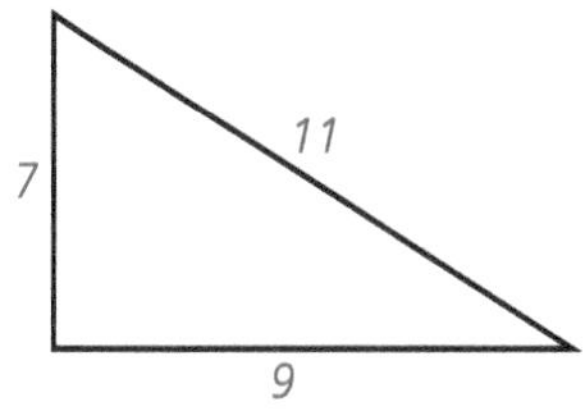

Write the equation to be used to find the missing lengths. Do not solve the equation.

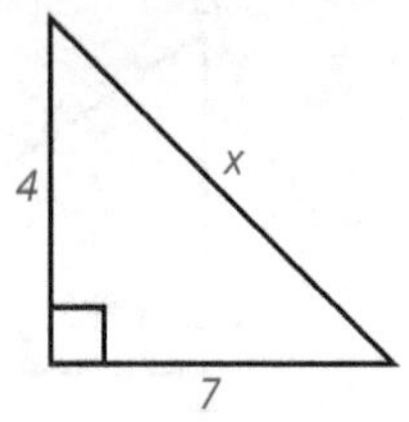

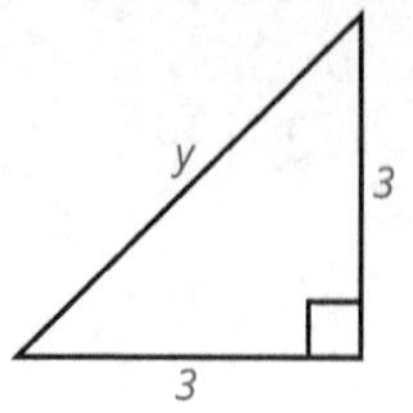

2.90 ______________________ **2.91** ______________________

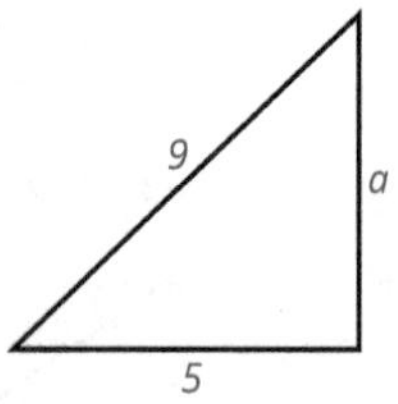

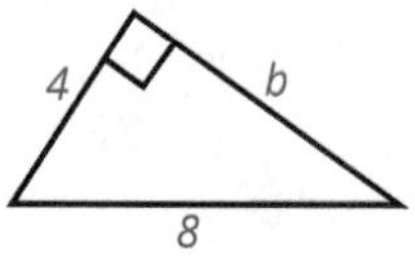

2.92 ______________________ **2.93** ______________________

The lengths of the sides of a triangle are given. Can the triangle be a right triangle? Write *yes* or *no*.

2.94 3, 4, 5 ____________ **2.95** 4, 5, 6 ____________

2.96 6, 8, 10 ____________ **2.97** 3, 3, $3\sqrt{2}$ ____________

For the right triangle shown, the lengths of two sides are given. Find the third side. Leave your answers in simplified, radical form.

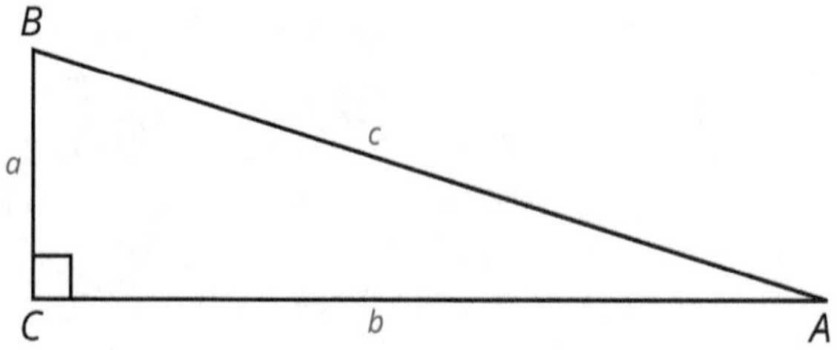

2.98 $a = 5$, $b = 12$, $c =$ ____________

2.99 $a = 4$, $b = 4$, $c =$ ____________

2.100 $a = 40$, $b =$ ____________, $c = 41$

2.101 $a =$ ____________, $b = 9$, $c = 16$

2.102 $a = 8$, $b = 15$, $c =$ ____________

2.103 $a = 5$, $b = 10$, $c =$ ____________

2.104 $a = 16$, $b =$ ____________, $c = 20$

2.105 $a =$ ____________, $b = 8$, $c = 12$

Solve the following problems. Show your work and circle your answer. Leave your answers in simplified, radical form.

2.106 A man walks 7 miles due north, 6 miles due east, and then 4 miles due north. How far is he from his starting point?

2.107 The legs of an isosceles triangle are 6 inches long. If the base is 8 inches long, find the length of the altitude to the base.

2.108 Find the length of the altitude of an equilateral triangle with sides equal to 6 feet.

2.109 An isosceles right triangle has a hypotenuse 6 yards long. Find the length of a leg.

2.110 The diagonals of a rhombus are 12 and 16. Find the perimeter of the rhombus.

30°-60°-90° TRIANGLE

A 30°-60°-90° triangle is a triangle with angle measures of 30°, 60°, and 90°. It is a special case of the right triangle in which you can easily find the lengths of two sides when given the length of one side. The relationship between the sides follows from the Pythagorean Theorem.

> **THEOREM 5-12**
>
> In a 30°-60°-90° triangle, the hypotenuse is twice the short leg, and the longer leg is the short leg times $\sqrt{3}$.

Given: Right $\triangle ABC$
$\angle B = 30°$ $\quad AC = s$
$\angle A = 60°$ $\quad \angle C = 90°$

To Prove: $AB = 2s$
$BC = s\sqrt{3}$

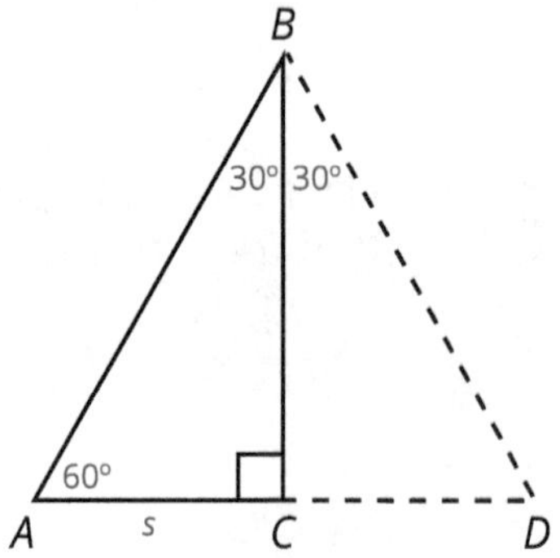

STATEMENT	REASON
1. Draw $\overline{BD}$ so that $\angle CBD = 30°$ Extend $\overline{AC}$ to intersect $\overline{BD}$	1. Auxiliary lines
2. In $\triangle ADB$, D = 60°	2. Sum of $\angle$'s of triangle = 180°
3. $\triangle ADB$ is equilateral	3. Sides opposite equal $\angle$'s are =
4. $CD = s$	4. Altitude of equilateral triangle bisects the side of the triangle
5. $AD = 2s$	5. Betweenness and addition
6. $AB = AD = 2s$	6. Definition of equilateral triangle
7. $(AB)^2 = (AC)^2 + (BC)^2$	7. Pythagorean Theorem
8. $(2s)^2 = (s)^2 + (BC)^2$	8. Substitution
9. $4s^2 = s^2 + (BC)^2$ $3s^2 = (BC)^2$ $s\sqrt{3} = BC$	9. Algebra

The relationship can be remembered in this way:
the side opposite the 30° angle is the short leg;
the side opposite the 60° angle is the long leg;
the hypotenuse is opposite the right angle.

Hypotenuse = 2 • short

Short leg = $\frac{1}{2}$ • hypotenuse

Long leg = short $\sqrt{3}$

Short leg = long ÷ $\sqrt{3}$

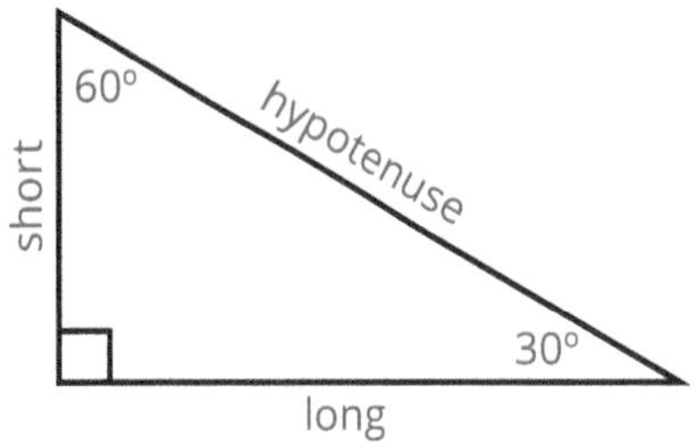

Model: Find the side of an equilateral triangle with an altitude of 6.

Solution: By the 30°-60°-90° theorem,

$AX = 6 \div \sqrt{3}$ (short leg)

$AX = 2\sqrt{3}$

$AC = 2(2\sqrt{3})$ (hypotenuse)

$AC = 4\sqrt{3}$

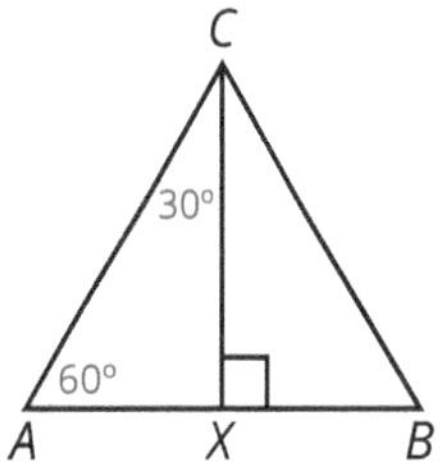

Find the lengths of the missing sides in the following 30°-60°-90° triangles.

	Short	Long	Hypotenuse
2.111	5	a. ________	b. ________
2.112	a. ________	$2\sqrt{3}$	b. ________
2.113	a. ________	b. ________	12
2.114	a. ________	b. ________	10
2.115	7	a. ________	b. ________
2.116	a. ________	3	b. ________

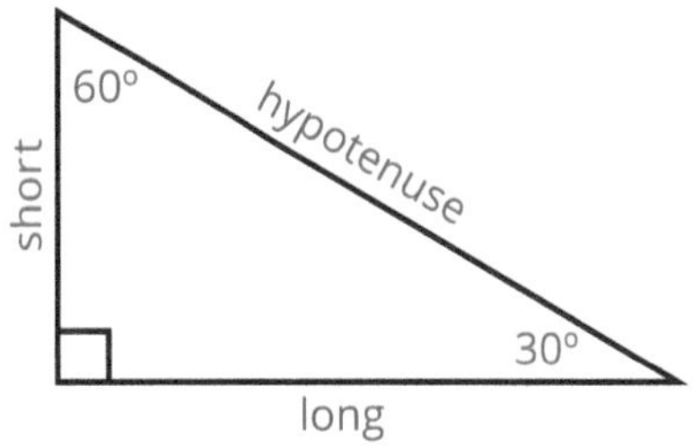

Find the lengths of the missing segments.

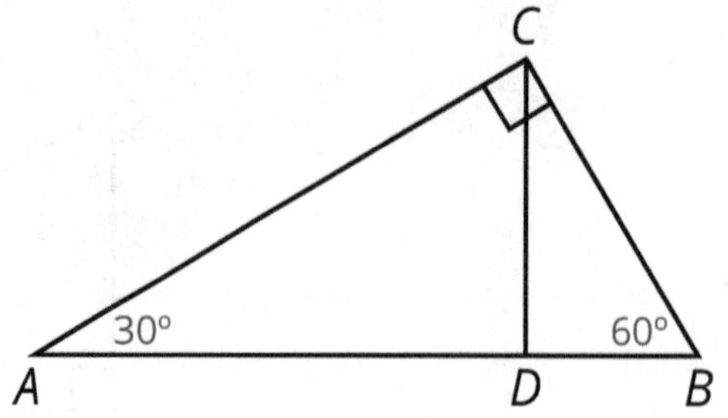

	AB	*BC*	*CD*	*AD*	*DB*	*AC*
2.117	8	a. ________	b. ________	c. ________	d. ________	e. ________
2.118	a. ________	2	b. ________	c. ________	d. ________	e. ________
2.119	a. ________	b. ________	$4\sqrt{3}$	c. ________	d. ________	e. ________
2.120	a. ________	b. ________	c. ________	9	d. ________	e. ________
2.121	a. ________	b. ________	c. ________	d. ________	$10\sqrt{3}$	e. ________
2.122	a. ________	b. ________	c. ________	d. ________	e. ________	$8\sqrt{3}$

> **THEOREM 5-13**
>
> If each acute angle of a right triangle has a measure of 45°, then the measure of the hypotenuse is $\sqrt{2}$ times the length of a leg.
>
> **(45°-45°-90° Theorem)**

Given: $\triangle ABC$
$\angle A = 45°$
$\angle B = 45°$
$AC = s$

To Prove: $AB = s\sqrt{2}$

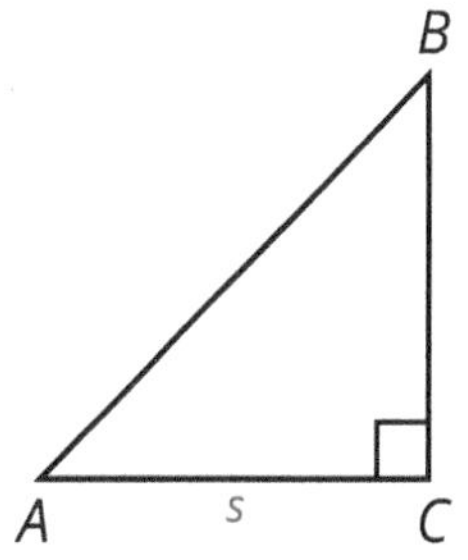

STATEMENT	REASON
1. Right $\triangle ABC$, $\angle A = 45°$, $\angle B = 45°$, $AC = s$	1. Given
2. $BC = s$	2. If two $\angle$'s of triangle are =, the sides opposite them are =
3. $(AB)^2 = (AC)^2 + (BC)^2$	3. Pythagorean Theorem
4. $(AB)^2 = s^2 + s^2$	4. Substitution
5. $(AB)^2 = 2s^2$	5. Addition
6. $AB = s\sqrt{2}$	6. Algebra

This theorem is sometimes the *isosceles right triangle* theorem because the legs of a 45°-45°-90° triangle are equal, making it an isosceles triangle as well.

Model: Find the side of an isosceles right triangle with hypotenuse of 5.

Solution: By the 45°-45°-90° theorem, $AB = AC\sqrt{2}$

$$5 = AC\sqrt{2}$$

$$AC = 5 \div \sqrt{2}$$

$$AC = \frac{5\sqrt{2}}{2}$$

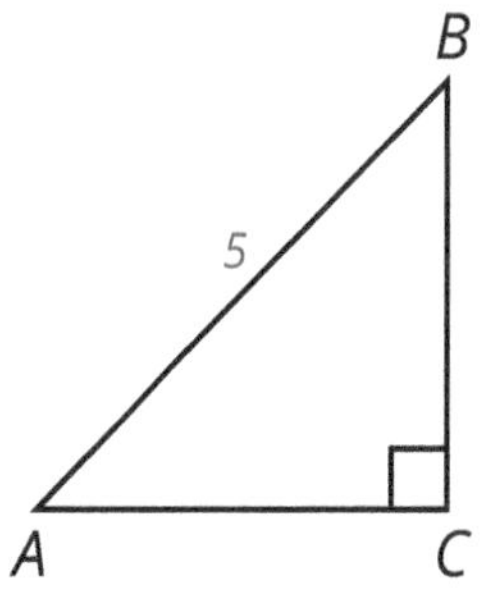

Find the hypotenuse of each isosceles right triangle when the legs are of the given measure.

2.123 6" ____________ **2.124** $3\sqrt{2}$" ____________

2.125 8" ____________ **2.126** $6\sqrt{2}$" ____________

Find the leg of each isosceles right triangle when the hypotenuse is of the given measure.

2.127 12 cm ____________ **2.128** $6\sqrt{2}$ cm ____________

2.129 8 cm ____________ **2.130** $5\sqrt{6}$ cm ____________

Find the diagonal of a square whose sides are of the given measure.

2.131 16" ____________ **2.132** $7\sqrt{3}$ ____________

2.133 5" ____________ **2.134** $3\sqrt{2}$ ____________

Find the side of a square whose diagonal is of the given measure.

2.135 $12\sqrt{10}$ ft. ____________ **2.136** $15\sqrt{2}$ cm ____________

2.137 8 miles ____________ **2.138** $\frac{1}{2}$" ____________

TEACHER CHECK ____________ initials ____________ date

Review the material in this section in preparation for the Self Test. This Self Test will check your mastery of this particular section as well as your knowledge of the previous section.

SELF TEST 2

Complete the following statements (each answer, 3 points).

2.01 The angles of similar triangles are ________________________ .

2.02 The corresponding sides of similar polygons are ________________________ .

2.03 State the SAS similarity theorem. ____

____

____

2.04 State the SSS similarity theorem. ____

____

2.05 If two polygons are similar, the ratio of their perimeters equals

____

2.06 A line parallel to one side of a triangle divides the other two sides ________________

2.07 If two triangles are similar, the ratio of their altitudes equals

____

2.08 The projection of a point onto a line is a ________________________ .

2.09 $a^2 + b^2 = c^2$ is the result of the ________________________ Theorem.

2.010 In a 30°-60°-90° triangle, the hypotenuse equals ________________ the short leg.

2.011 A square with a 4-foot diagonal has ________________________ -foot sides.

2.012 Which of the triangles shown are right triangles? ______________

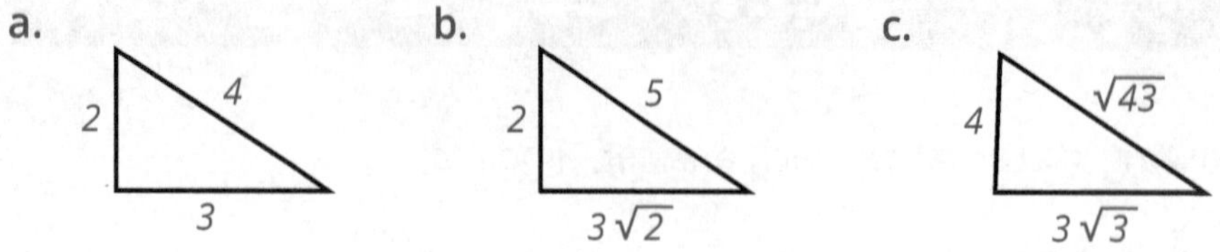

Use the given information to find the measures (each answer, 3 points).

In $\triangle RST$, $\angle RTS = 90°$; $\overline{TX} \perp \overline{RS}$.

2.013 $\triangle RTX \sim$ a. $\triangle$ ______________ and $\sim$ b. $\triangle$ ______________ .

2.014 If $RX = 4$ and $XS = 9$, then $XT =$ ______________ .

2.015 If $RT = 6$ and $RS = 9$, then $RX =$ ______________ .

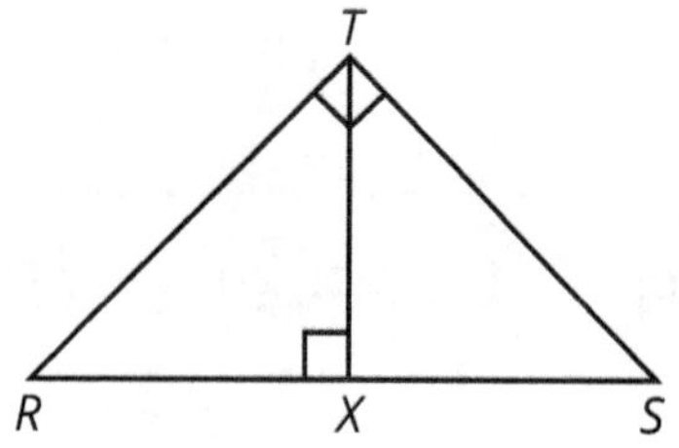

$\triangle ABC$ is a right triangle.

2.016 If $a = 4$ and $b = 6$, then $c =$ ______________ .

2.017 If $a = 3$ and $c = 6$, then $b =$ ______________ .

2.018 If $b = 2$ and $c = 3\sqrt{2}$, then $a =$ ______________ .

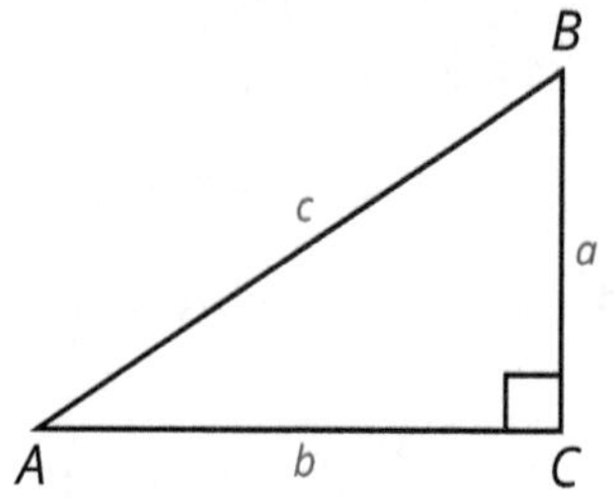

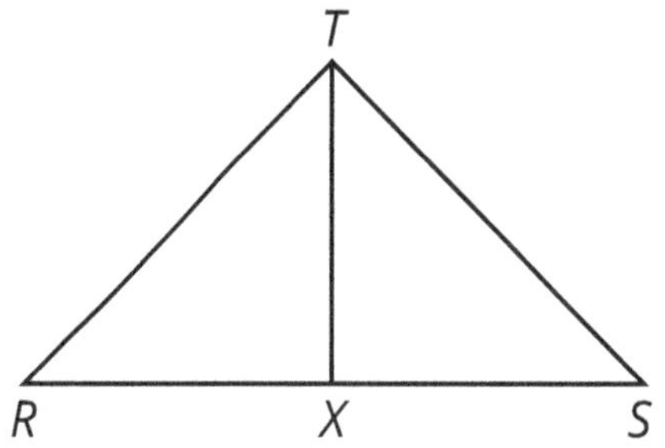

$\triangle RST$ is an equilateral triangle; $\overline{TX} \perp \overline{RS}$.

2.019 If $RX = 3$, then $RT =$ ________________________ .

2.020 If $RT = 8$, then $TX =$ ________________________ .

2.021 If $RX = 2\sqrt{3}$, then $TX =$ ________________________ .

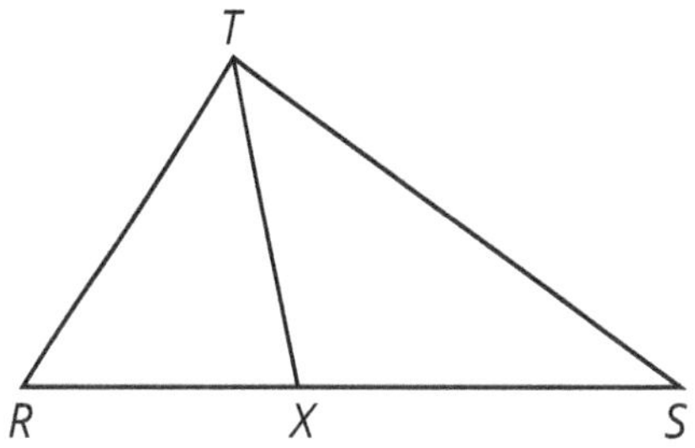

2.022 In $\triangle RST$, $\overline{TX}$ bisects $\angle RTS$.
If $RS = 10$, $RT = 4$, and $ST = 8$, find RX.

____

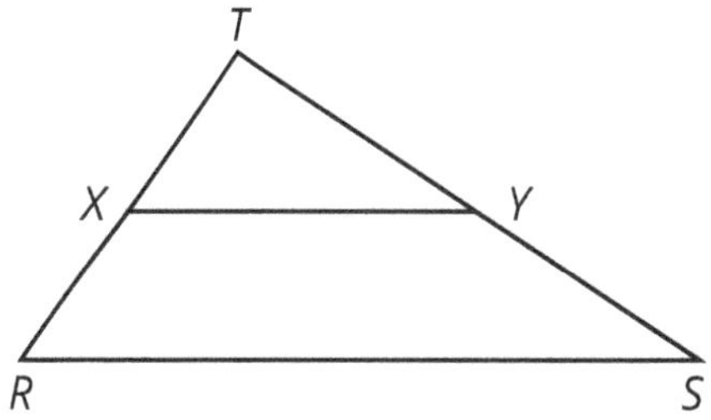

2.023 In triangle RST, $\overline{XY} \,||\, \overline{RS}$.
If $TX = 3$, $XR = TY$, and $YS = 6$, find XR.

____

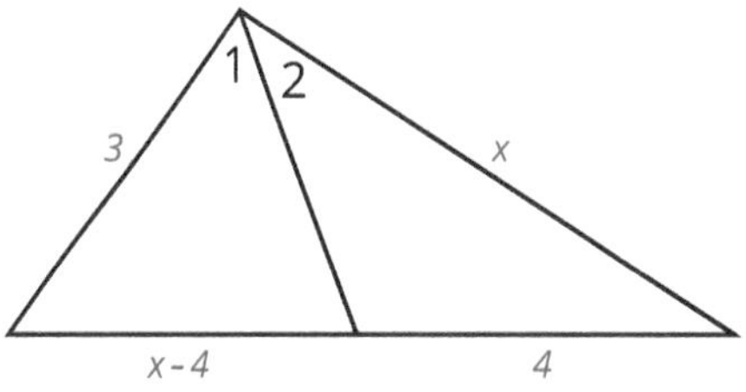

2.024 Given $\angle 1 = \angle 2$, find x. ________________

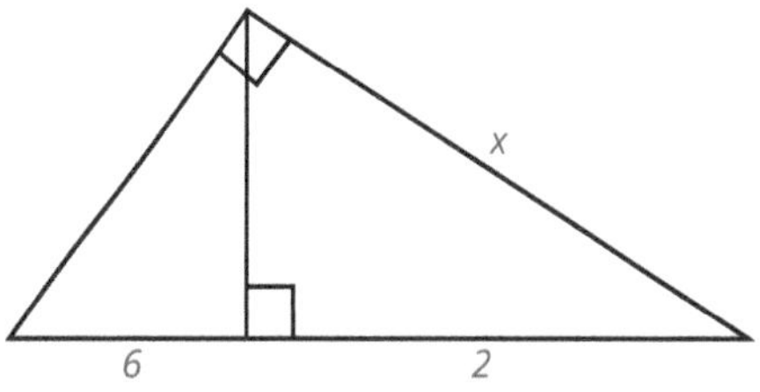

2.025 Find x. ________________

63/78	SCORE ________	TEACHER ________ initials	________ date

3. RIGHT TRIANGLES

As mentioned before, the Pythagorean Theorem is one of the most widely used of all mathematical ideas. It can be found in all branches of mathematics. Whenever a right triangle is formed, the Pythagorean formula can be put into use.

Section Objectives

Review these objectives. When you have completed this section, you should be able to:

7. Use the Pythagorean Theorem.
8. Solve triangle problems using trigonometry.
9. Find measurements indirectly.

GEOMETRY

The Pythagorean Theorem has applications in finding the length of segments in three-dimensional figures. You will need to make sketches of these figures so you can "see" the right triangles that are formed. Two solid figures that we shall study now are called the **rectangular solid** and the regular square **pyramid**.

RECTANGULAR SOLID

A rectangular solid is a figure formed by six rectangles. The six rectangles are called its **faces**. The opposite faces are parallel and the adjacent faces are perpendicular.

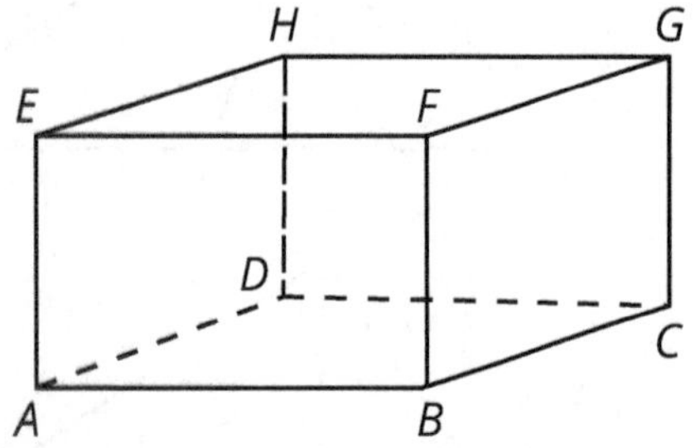

If we take rectangle *ABCD* to be the base, any face that intersects the base is called a **lateral face**. *ABFE*, *BCGF*, *CDHG*, and *ADHE* are lateral faces.

An **edge** is a segment formed by the intersection of two faces. $\overline{AB}$, $\overline{BC}$, $\overline{CD}$, $\overline{AD}$, $\overline{EF}$, $\overline{FG}$, $\overline{GH}$, $\overline{HE}$, $\overline{AE}$, $\overline{BF}$, $\overline{CG}$, and $\overline{DH}$ are all edges.

A **vertex** is any point where two edges intersect. *A*, *B*, *C*, *D*, *E*, *F*, *G*, and *H* are the vertices.

The diagonal of a face is a segment whose end points are nonconsecutive vertices in the same face. $\overline{EB}$, $\overline{BG}$, $\overline{HF}$, $\overline{AC}$, and $\overline{DB}$ are some of the diagonals of a face.

The **diagonal of the rectangular solid** is a segment whose end points are vertices not in the same face. $\overline{AG}$, $\overline{BH}$, $\overline{CE}$, and $\overline{DF}$ are the diagonals of the solid.

Since the faces of the solid are rectangles, many right angles are formed. When we put in the diagonals of the faces, we form many right triangles. Even the diagonal of the solid forms a right triangle. Whenever a right triangle is formed we can use the Pythagorean Theorem to find the missing dimension.

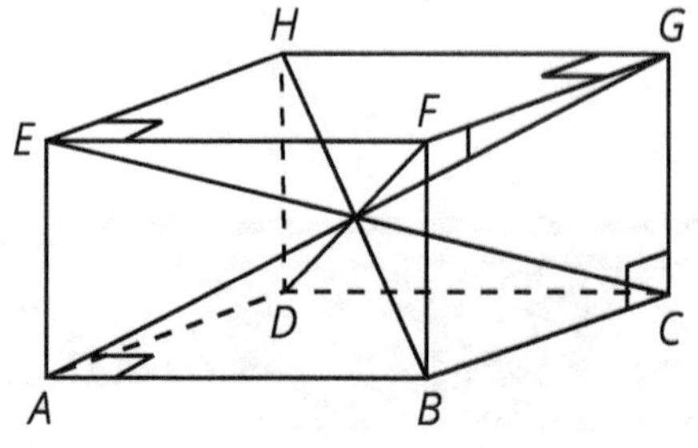

Write the correct answer on the blank.

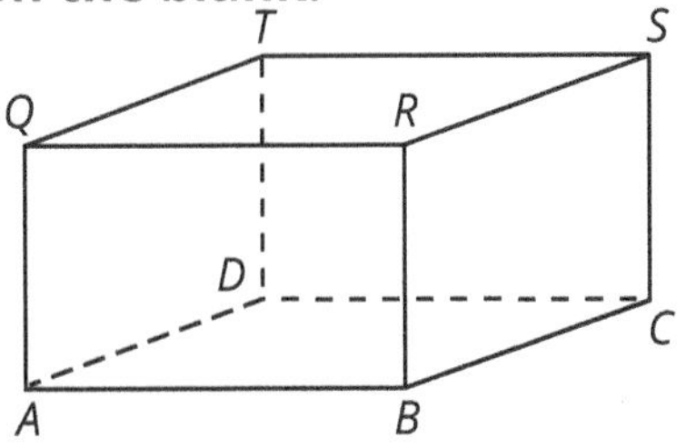

3.1 How many faces does the rectangular solid have? ________________

3.2 Name four segments ⊥ $\overline{RS}$. ________________________________

3.3 Name the four diagonals of the solid. ____________________________________

3.4 If *DB* is drawn, what is the measure of ∠*TDB*? ________________

3.5 Name three edges || $\overline{AB}$. ______________________________

Given *RS* = 6, *ST* = 3, **and** *SL* = 4, **find the required measures.**

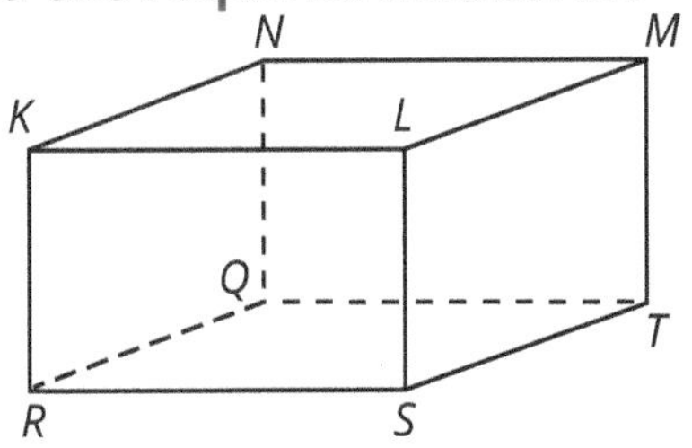

3.6 *QN* = ____________ **3.7** *QT* = ____________ **3.8** *KN* = ____________

3.9 *QS* = ____________ **3.10** *SM* = ____________ **3.11** *RL* = ____________

3.12 *NS* = ____________ **3.13** *KT* = ____________

A rectangular solid has three dimensions: length, width, and height. We can obtain a formula for finding the diagonal of the solid by using the Pythagorean formula twice.

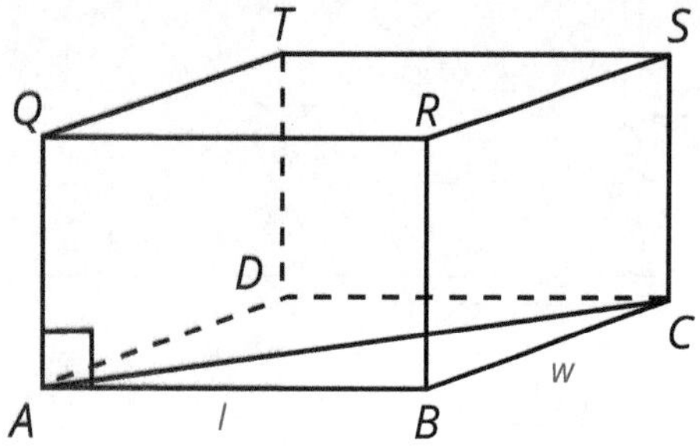

$(AC)^2 = l^2 + w^2$

$AC = \sqrt{l^2 + w^2}$

$(QC)^2 = (AC)^2 + h^2$

$(QC)^2 = l^2 + w^2 + h^2$

$QC = \sqrt{l^2 + w^2 + h^2}$

Therefore, to find the diagonal of a rectangular solid, take the square root of the sum of the squares of the three dimensions.

Model: Find the diagonal of a rectangular solid that measures 3 ft. by 4 ft. by 5 ft.

Solution: Diagonal $= \sqrt{3^2 + 4^2 + 5^2}$

$= \sqrt{9 + 16 + 25}$

$= \sqrt{50} = \sqrt{25 \cdot 2} = \sqrt{25} \cdot \sqrt{2}$

$= 5\sqrt{2}$

A **cube** is a special rectangular solid where all the faces are squares. Since all the faces are squares, all the edges are equal. Using the formula for the diagonal of a rectangular solid where $l = w = h = e$:

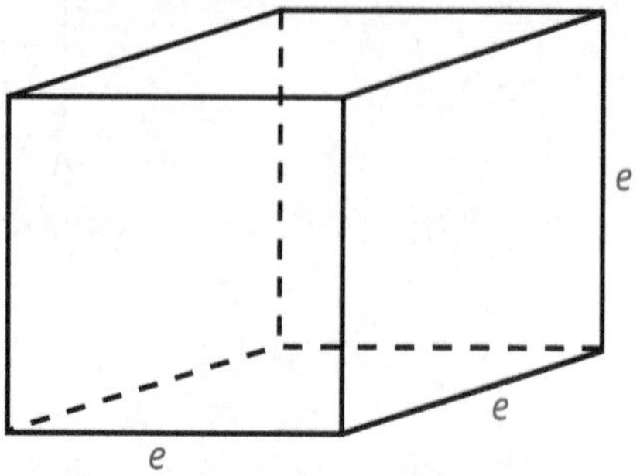

Diagonal $= \sqrt{l^2 + w^2 + h^2}$

$= \sqrt{e^2 + e^2 + e^2}$

$= \sqrt{3e^2}$

$= e\sqrt{3}$

The diagonal of a cube is the length of the edge times $\sqrt{3}$.

Model: Find the diagonal of a cube with edge equal to 4.

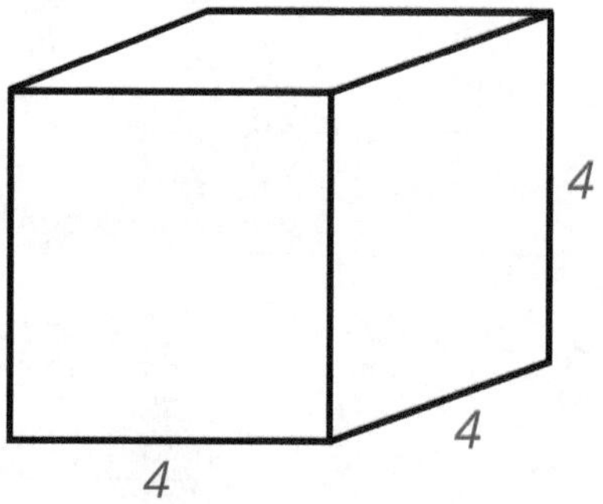

Solution: Diagonal $= e\sqrt{3}$

$= 4\sqrt{3}$

Find the diagonal of the rectangular solid with the given measures.

3.14	$l = 2$	$w = 3$	$h = 6$	________
3.15	$l = 5$	$w = 4$	$h = 2$	________
3.16	$l = 3$	$w = 3$	$h = 2$	________
3.17	$l = 18$	$w = 10$	$h = 2$	________
3.18	$l = 3$	$w = 5$	$h = 5$	________
3.19	$l = 3$	$w = 3$	$h = 3$	________
3.20	$l = 2$	$w = 3$	$h = 5$	________

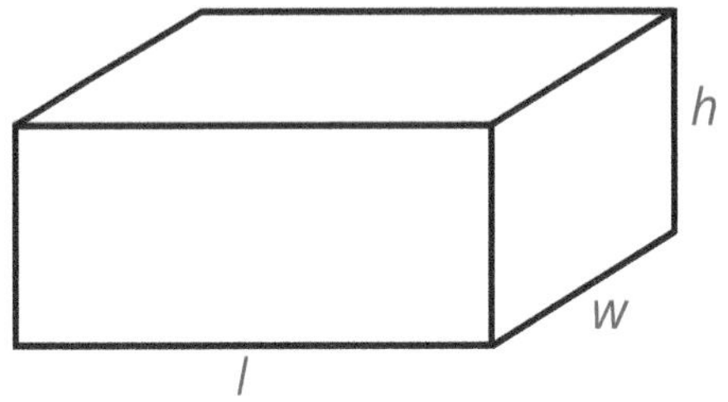

REGULAR SQUARE PYRAMID

A regular square pyramid has a base that is a square, and lateral faces that are congruent isosceles triangles. The altitude of the pyramid is a segment from the vertex perpendicular to the base. *PQ* is the altitude of the pyramid.

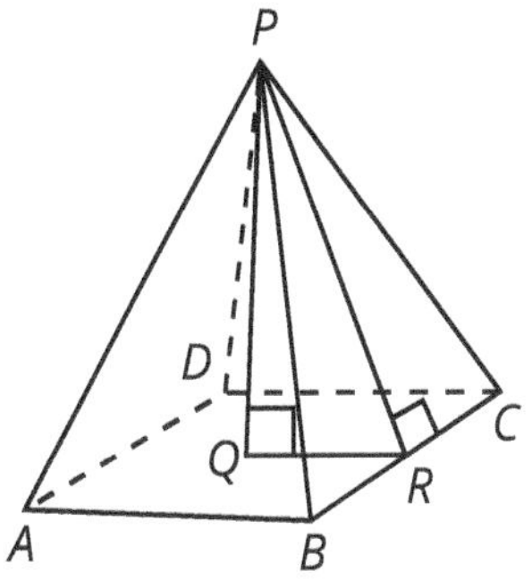

The **slant height** is the altitude of one of the lateral faces. *PR* is the slant height of the pyramid.

Right triangles are formed using the altitude, slant height, and edge. Again we can use the Pythagorean formula to find missing dimensions.

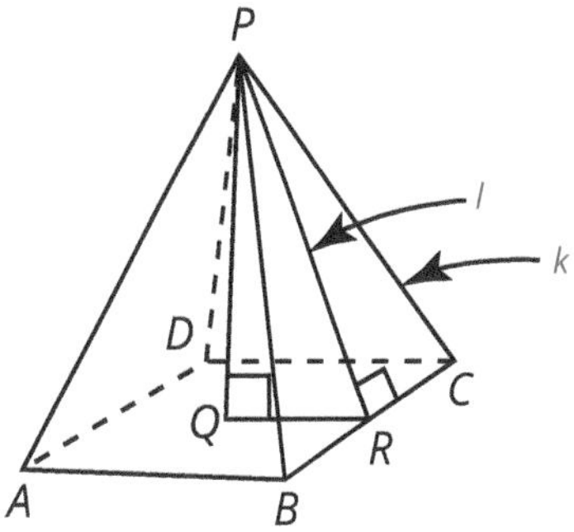

Model: Find *l* and *k* for this pyramid where $AB = 6$, $QR = 3$, and $PQ = 4$.

Solution: In triangle *PQR*:

$l^2 = (PQ)^2 + (QR)^2$

$l^2 = 4^2 + 3^2$

$l^2 = 16 + 9$

$l^2 = 25$

$l = 5$

In triangle *PRC*:

$k^2 = l^2 + (RC)^2$

$k^2 = 5^2 + 3^2$

$k^2 = 25 + 9$

$k^2 = 34$

$k = \sqrt{34}$

Write the correct answer on the blank.

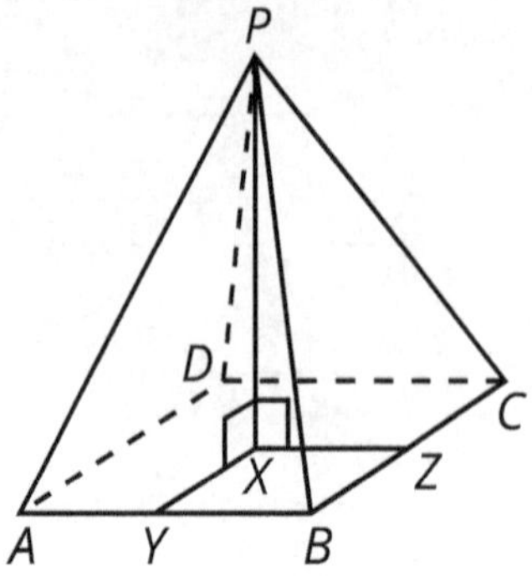

3.21 Name the lateral edges. ______________________________

3.22 Is $\triangle PXY \cong \triangle PXZ$? ____________

3.23 Does $PY = PZ$? ____________

3.24 Is $PB > PY$? ____________

3.25 Must the slant height be greater than the altitude? ____________

3.26 Can all edges have the same length? ____________

Given a regular square pyramid with $RS = 6$ **and** $PX = 4$**, find the following measures.**

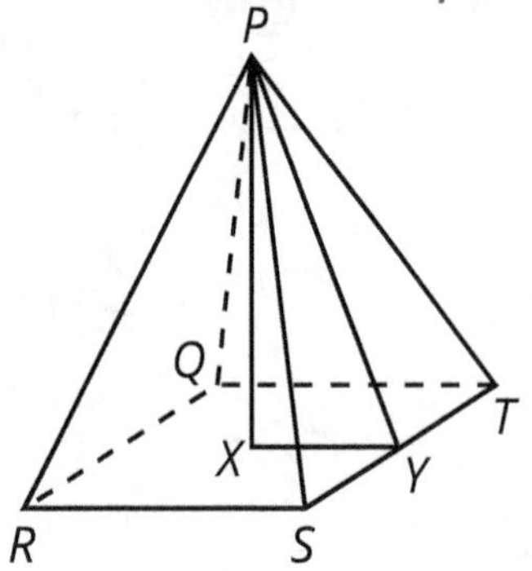

3.27 $XY =$ ____________ **3.28** $PY =$ ____________ **3.29** $SY =$ ____________

3.30 $ST =$ ____________ **3.31** $PS =$ ____________ **3.32** $PT =$ ____________

3.33 $QS =$ ____________ **3.34** $XT =$ ____________

TRIGONOMETRY

The word *trigonometry* comes from the Greek words that mean *triangle measurement*. The study of this branch of mathematics began before the Christian era and is still going strong today. We shall only study the sine, cosine, and tangent ratios as they apply to right triangles.

SINE RATIO

Take several similar right triangles and overlap them so that the acute angles at *A* match up. Since the triangles are all similar, the sides are in proportion.

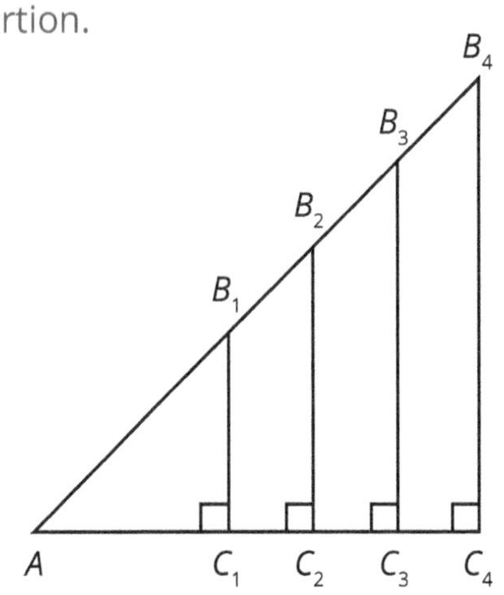

A special ratio that is formed by taking the side opposite $\angle A$ over the hypotenuse is called the **sine ratio** with respect to angle *A*.

This measure is written

$\sin \angle A = \frac{\text{side opposite } \angle A}{\text{hypotenuse}}$: $\sin \angle A = \frac{B_1C_1}{AB_1}$ or

$\sin \angle A = \frac{B_2C_2}{AB_2}$ or $\sin \angle A = \frac{B_3C_3}{AB_3}$ or

$\sin \angle A = \frac{B_4C_4}{AB_4}$.

Since these triangles are similar, we know that $\frac{B_1C_1}{AB_1} = \frac{B_2C_2}{AB_2} = \frac{B_3C_3}{AB_3} = \frac{B_4C_4}{AB_4}$.

As long as we keep the same acute angle at *A*, the $\sin \angle A$ is the same number whatever right triangle we use.

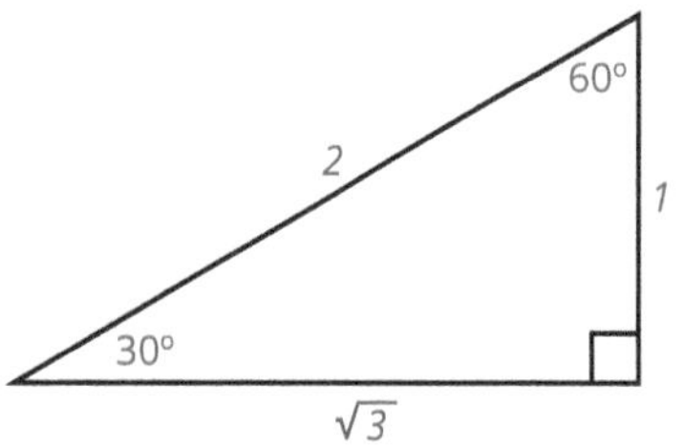

Take a 30°-60°-90° triangle. We know the hypotenuse is the short leg times two; therefore, with respect to the 30° angle, the $\sin 30° = \frac{1}{2}$. With respect to the 60° angle, the sin 60° is $\frac{\sqrt{3}}{2}$.

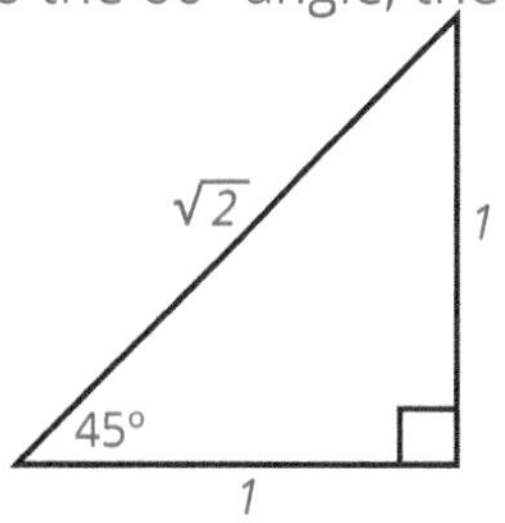

In a 45°-45°-90° triangle, the legs are equal and the hypotenuse is the square root of two, times the leg. Therefore, $\sin 45° = \frac{1}{\sqrt{2}} = \frac{1}{2}\sqrt{2}$.

Mathematicians have found the approximate values of the sine ratio for all acute angles. These values are put into a table in decimal notation along with the cosine and tangent ratio numbers. Of course, many calculators today perform this role also.

Notice that as the angle gets larger, so does the sine ratio number. The sine ratio number will never be larger than 1. In a right triangle, the hypotenuse is the longest side and any fraction (ratio) with the denominator larger than the numerator will be less than 1.

TABLE OF TRIGONOMETRIC RATIOS							
ANGLE	SINE	COSINE	TANGENT	ANGLE	SINE	COSINE	TANGENT
1°	.0175	.9998	.0175	46°	.7193	.6947	1.0355
2°	.0349	.9994	.0349	47°	.7314	.6820	1.0724
3°	.0523	.9986	.0524	48°	.7431	.6691	1.1106
4°	.0698	.9976	.0699	49°	.7547	.6561	1.1504
5°	.0872	.9962	.0875	50°	.7660	.6428	1.1918
6°	.1045	.9945	.1051	51°	.7771	.6293	1.2349
7°	.1219	.9925	.1228	52°	.7880	.6157	1.2799
8°	.1392	.9903	.1405	53°	.7986	.6018	1.3270
9°	.1564	.9877	.1584	54°	.8090	.5878	1.3764
10°	.1736	.9848	.1763	55°	.8192	.5736	1.4281
11°	.1908	.9816	.1944	56°	.8290	.5592	1.4826
12°	.2079	.9781	.2126	57°	.8387	.5446	1.5399
13°	.2250	.9744	.2309	58°	.8480	.5299	1.6003
14°	.2419	.9703	.2493	59°	.8572	.5150	1.6643
15°	.2588	.9659	.2679	60°	.8660	.5000	1.7321
16°	.2756	.9613	.2867	61°	.8746	.4848	1.8040
17°	.2924	.9563	.3057	62°	.8829	.4695	1.8807
18°	.3090	.9511	.3249	63°	.8910	.4540	1.9626
19°	.3256	.9455	.3443	64°	.8988	.4384	2.0503
20°	.3420	.9397	.3640	65°	.9063	.4226	2.1445
21°	.3584	.9336	.3839	66°	.9135	.4067	2.2460
22°	.3746	.9272	.4040	67°	.9205	.3907	2.3559
23°	.3907	.9205	.4245	68°	.9272	.3746	2.4751
24°	.4067	.9135	.4452	69°	.9336	.3584	2.6051
25°	.4226	.9063	.4663	70°	.9397	.3420	2.7475
26°	.4384	.8988	.4877	71°	.9455	.3256	2.9042
27°	.4540	.8910	.5095	72°	.9511	.3090	3.0777
28°	.4695	.8829	.5317	73°	.9563	.2924	3.2709
29°	.4848	.8746	.5543	74°	.9613	.2756	3.4874
30°	.5000	.8660	.5774	75°	.9659	.2588	3.7321
31°	.5150	.8572	.6009	76°	.9703	.2419	4.0108
32°	.5299	.8480	.6249	77°	.9744	.2250	4.3315
33°	.5446	.8387	.6494	78°	.9781	.2079	4.7046
34°	.5592	.8290	.6745	79°	.9816	.1908	5.1446
35°	.5736	.8192	.7002	80°	.9848	.1736	5.6713
36°	.5878	.8090	.7265	81°	.9877	.1564	6.3138
37°	.6018	.7986	.7536	82°	.9903	.1392	7.1154
38°	.6157	.7880	.7813	83°	.9925	.1219	8.1443
39°	.6293	.7771	.8098	84°	.9945	.1045	9.5144
40°	.6428	.7660	.8391	85°	.9962	.0872	11.4301
41°	.6561	.7547	.8693	86°	.9976	.0698	14.3007
42°	.6691	.7431	.9004	87°	.9986	.0523	19.0811
43°	.6820	.7314	.9325	88°	.9994	.0349	28.6363
44°	.6947	.7193	.9657	89°	.9998	.0175	57.2900
45°	.7071	.7071	1.0000				

We use the sine ratio to find the dimension of some parts of a right triangle.

$\sin = \frac{\text{side opposite}}{\text{hypotenuse}}$

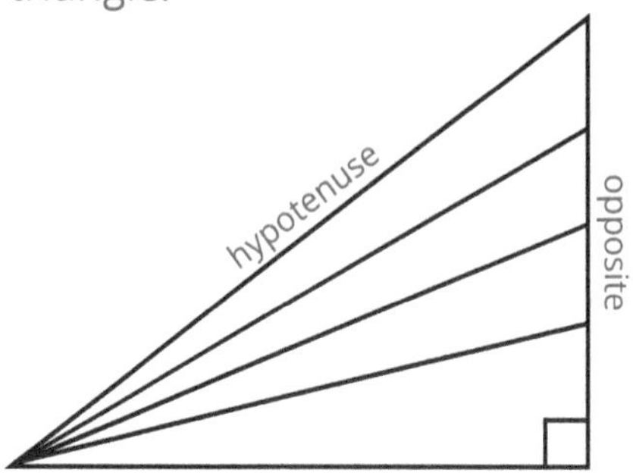

Model 1: $\sin 40° = \frac{x}{8}$

from our table, $\sin 40° = 0.6428$, so

$0.6428 = \frac{x}{8}$

$x = 8(0.6428)$

$x = 5.1424$

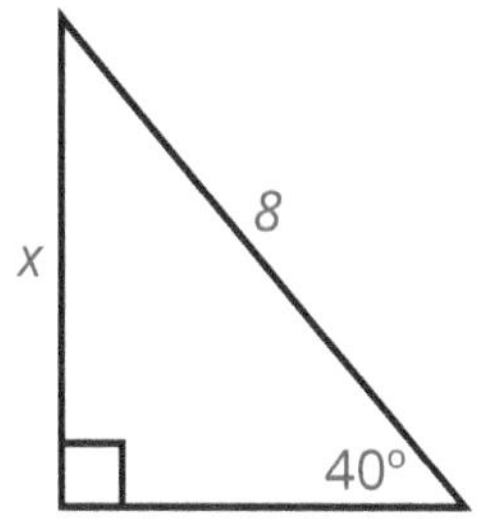

Model 2: $\sin 50° = \frac{y}{10}$

$0.766 = \frac{y}{10}$

$y = 7.66$

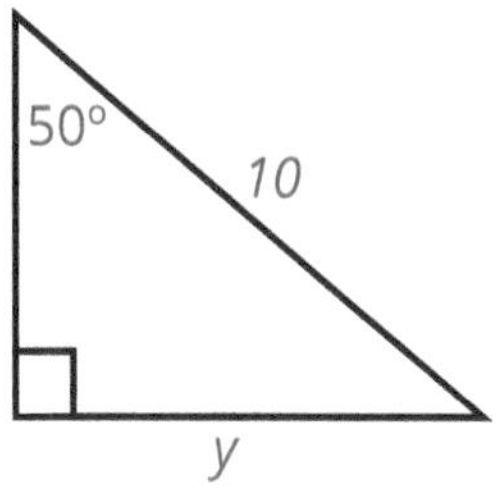

Model 3: $\sin x° = \frac{3}{5}$

$\sin x° = 0.600$

$x = 37°$

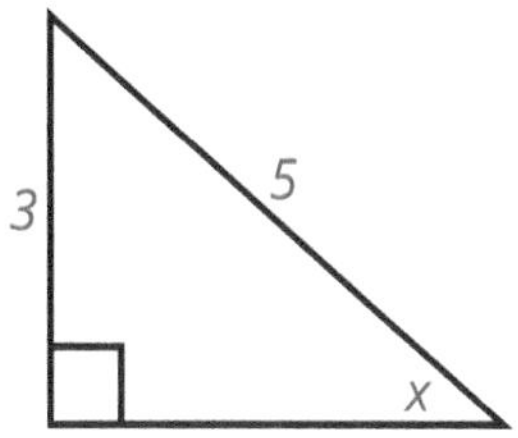

Model 4: $\sin z° = \frac{x}{8}$ $\qquad$ $\sin 70° = \frac{y}{8}$

$z = 90° - 70°$

$z = 20°$

$\sin 20° = \frac{x}{8}$ $\qquad$ $0.9397 = \frac{y}{8}$

$0.342 = \frac{x}{8}$ $\qquad$ $y = 7.5176$

$x = 2.736$

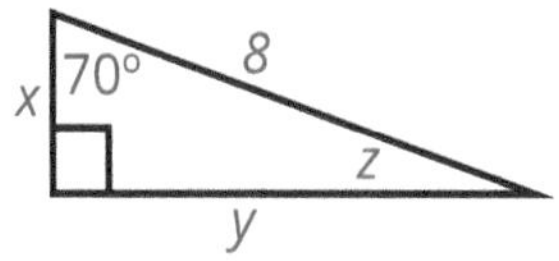

Your answers to these problems will only be approximations since most of the sine ratio numbers are approximate.

State the sine ratio for each labeled angle. Leave your answer in reduced fraction form.

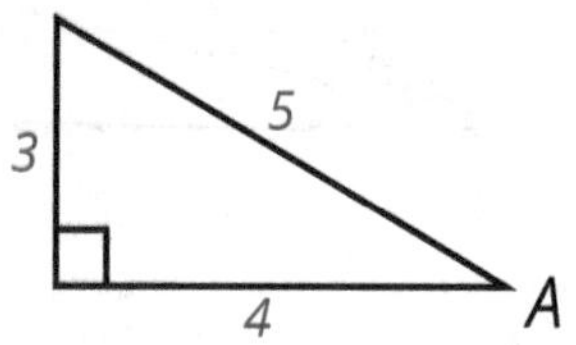

3.35 sin ∠A = ______________

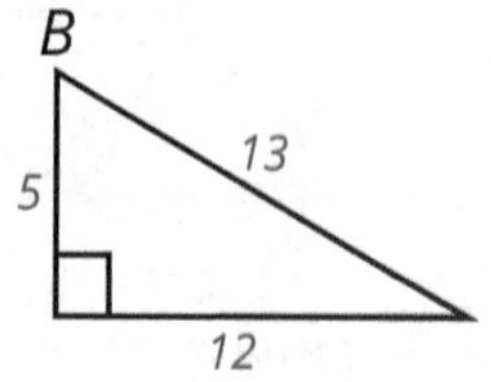

3.36 sin ∠B = ______________

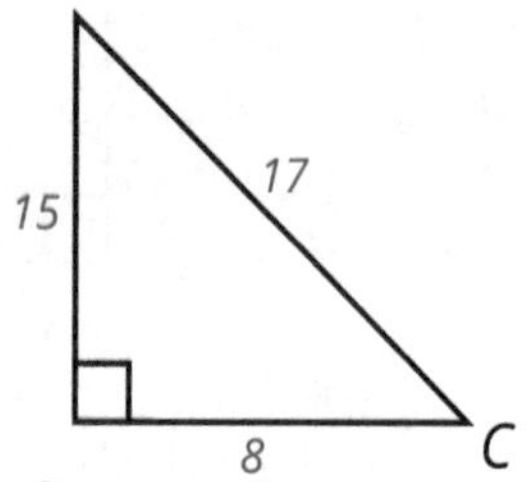

3.37 sin ∠C = ______________

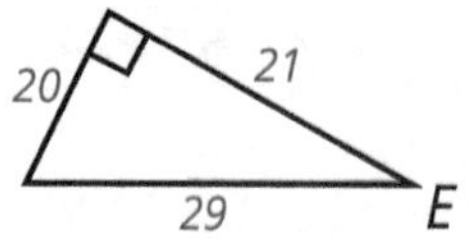

3.38 sin ∠E = ______________

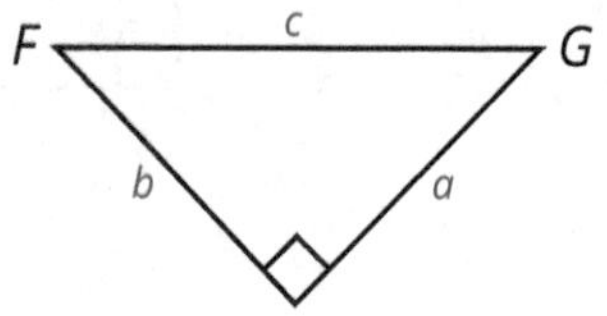

3.39 a. sin ∠F = ______________

b. sin ∠G = ______________

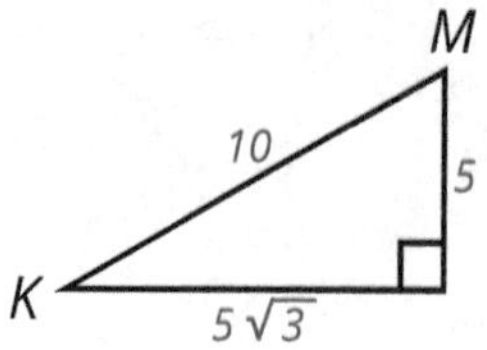

3.40 a. sin ∠K = ______________

b. sin ∠M = ______________

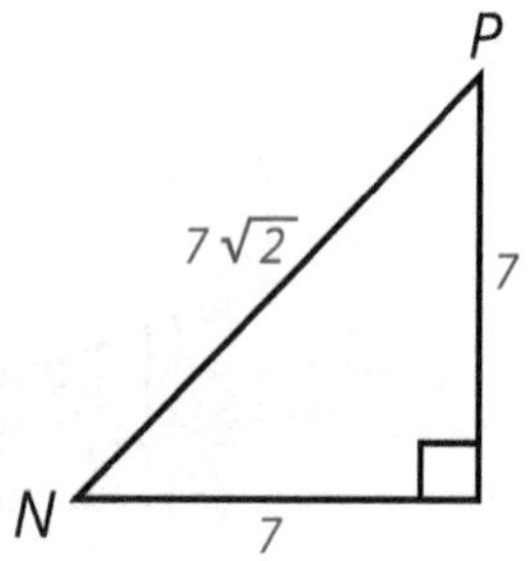

3.41 a. sin ∠N = ______________

b. sin ∠P = ______________

State the equation you can use to find x. Do not solve the equation.

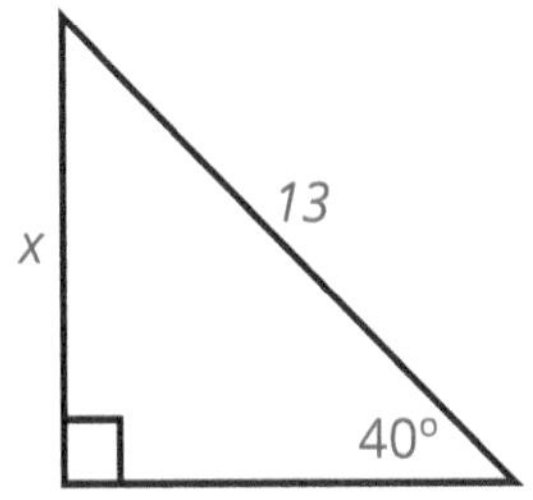

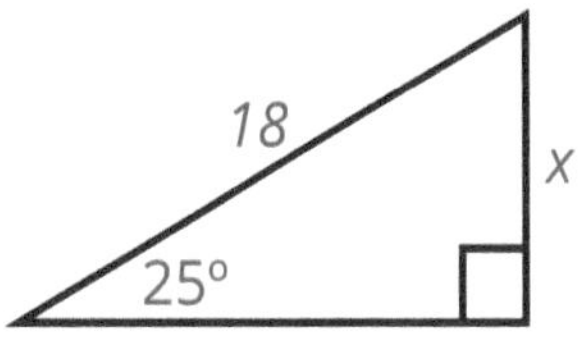

3.42 ______________________________

3.43 ______________________________

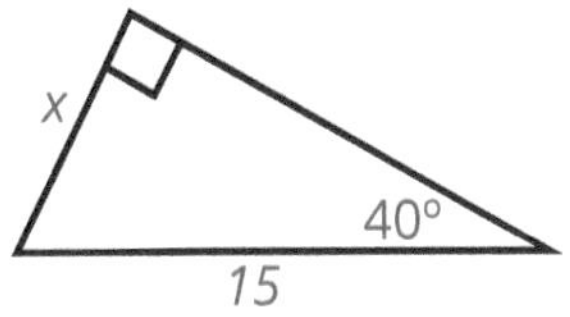

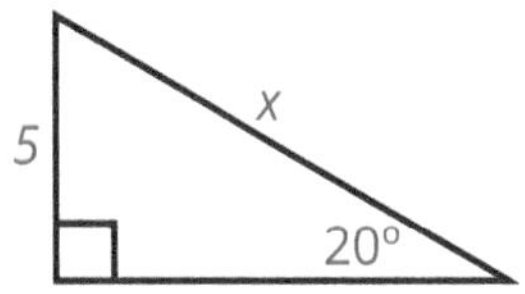

3.44 ______________________________

3.45 ______________________________

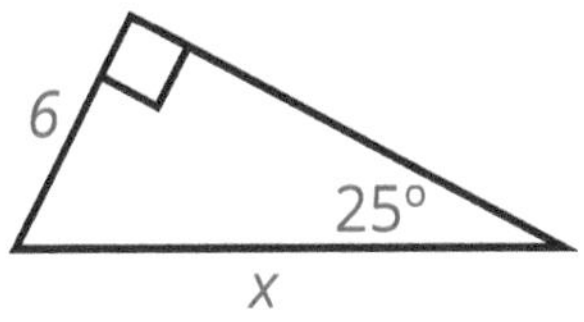

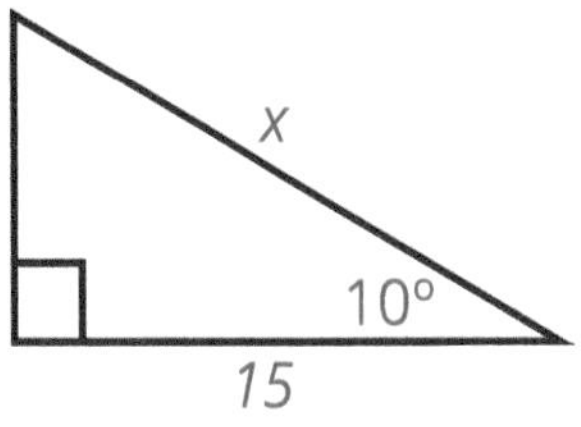

3.46 ______________________________

3.47 ______________________________

Use the table for sine and find x to the nearest tenth.

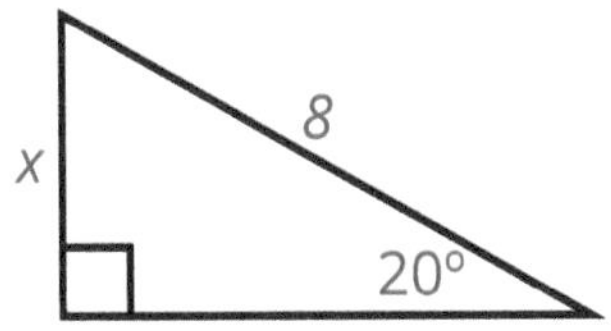

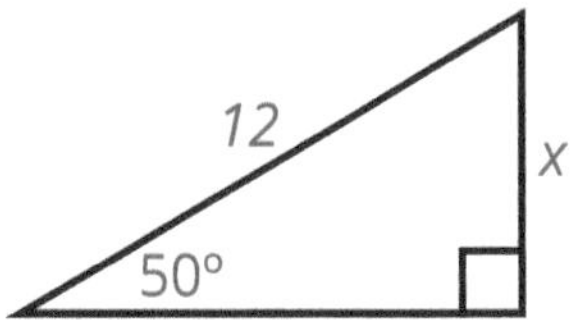

3.48 x = ________________

3.49 x = ________________

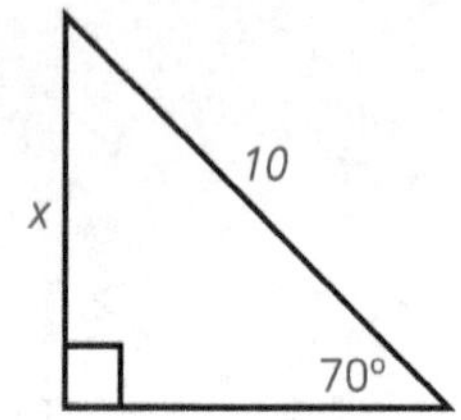

3.50 $x =$ ________________

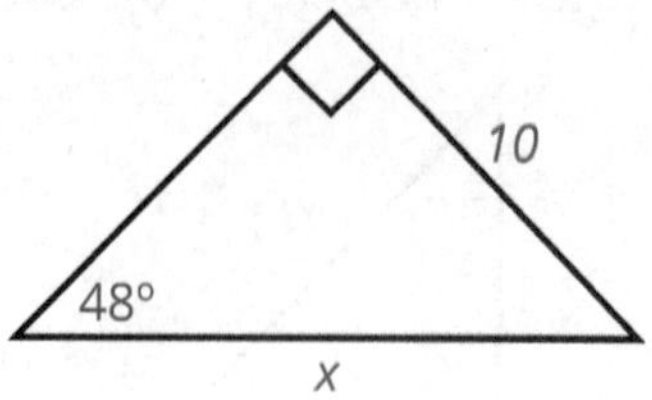

3.51 $x =$ ________________

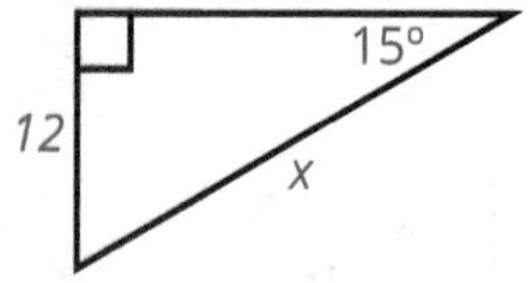

3.52 $x =$ ________________

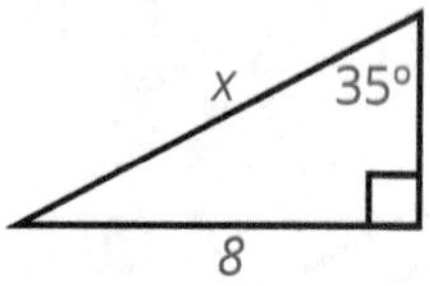

3.53 $x =$ ________________

Find the measure of $\angle A$ to the nearest degree. Use the table for sine.

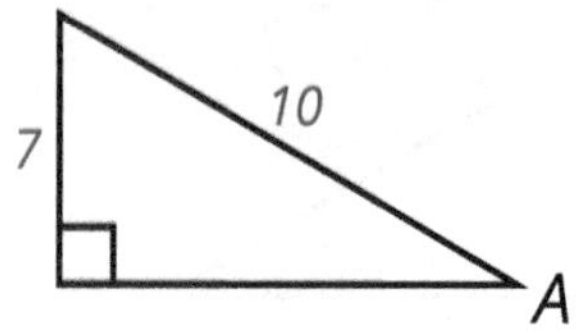

3.54 $\angle A =$ ________________

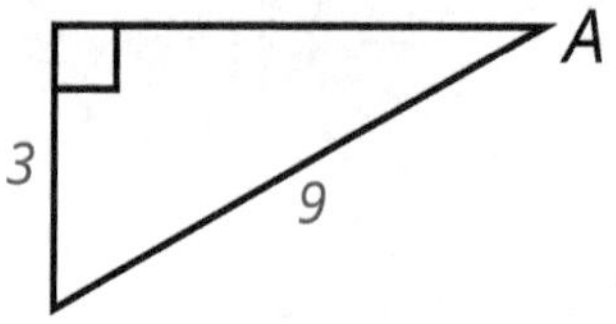

3.55 $\angle A =$ ________________

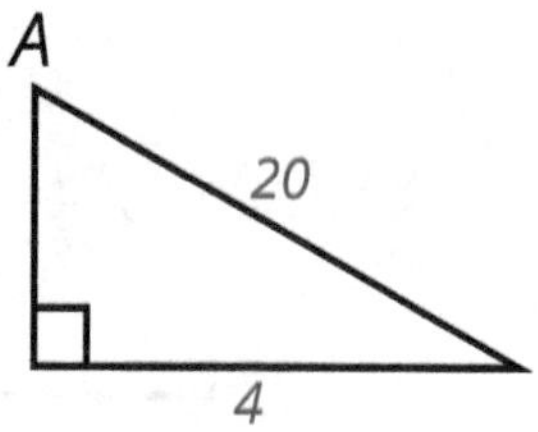

3.56 $\angle A =$ ________________

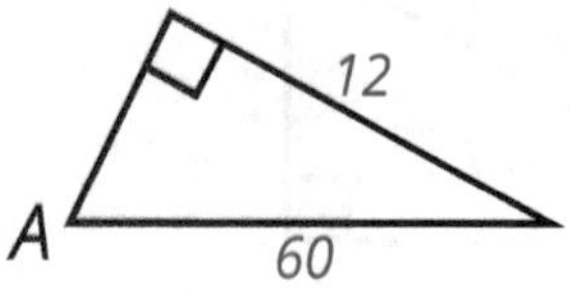

3.57 $\angle A =$ ________________

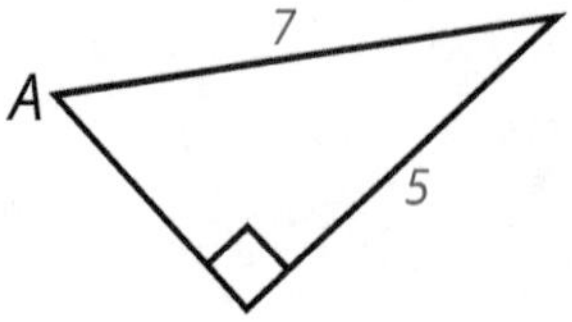

3.58 $\angle A =$ ________________

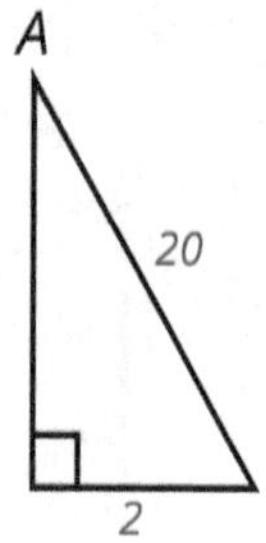

3.59 $\angle A =$ ________________

COSINE RATIO

Another ratio that can be made with the similar right triangles is the side adjacent to the acute angle over the hypotenuse.

$$\frac{AC_1}{AB_1} = \frac{AC_2}{AB_2} = \frac{AC_3}{AB_3} = \frac{AC_4}{AB_4}$$

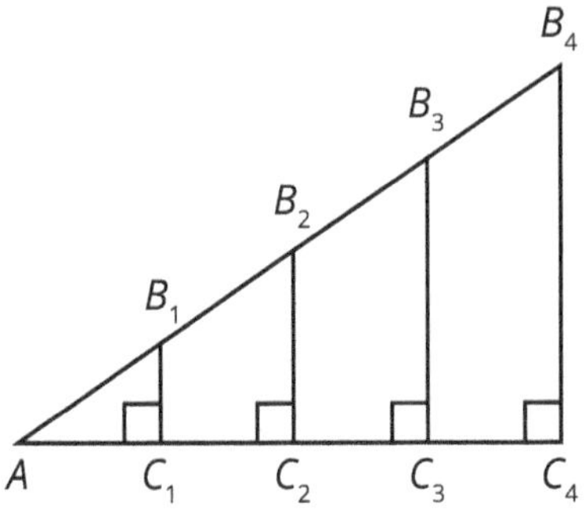

This ratio is called the **cosine ratio** with respect to angle *A*.

This measure is written

$\cos \angle A = \frac{\text{side adjacent to } \angle A}{\text{hypotenuse}}$: $\cos \angle A = \frac{AC_1}{AB_1}$ or $\cos \angle A = \frac{AC_2}{AB_2}$ or $\cos \angle A = \frac{AC_3}{AB_3}$ or $\cos \angle A = \frac{AC_4}{AB_4}$.

Since the ratios are all equal, the cosine of angle *A* is the same number, whichever triangle we use.

Model 1: $\cos 30° = \frac{\text{side adjacent}}{\text{hypotenuse}}$

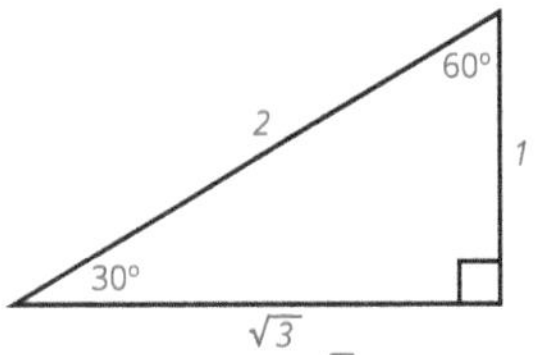

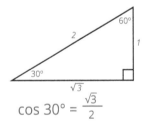

$\cos 30° = \frac{\sqrt{3}}{2}$

Model 2: $\cos 60° = \frac{\text{side adjacent}}{\text{hypotenuse}}$

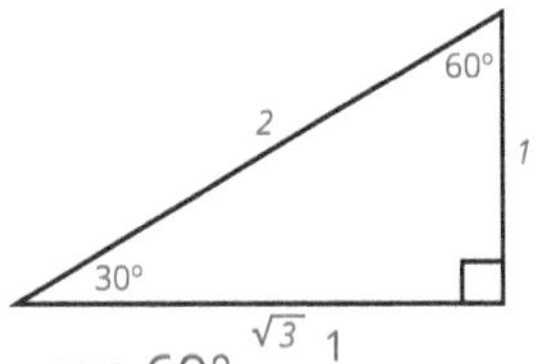

$\cos 60° = \frac{1}{2}$

Model 3: $\cos 45° = \frac{\text{side adjacent}}{\text{hypotenuse}}$

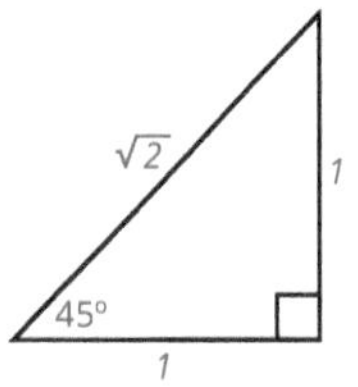

$\cos 45° = \frac{1}{\sqrt{2}} = \frac{\sqrt{2}}{2}$

Look at the table under the cosine heading. Notice that as the size of the angle gets larger, the cosine number gets smaller. Still, the cosine number will always be less than 1. Also notice that the sine of an angle and the cosine of the complement of that angle are the same number.

Models: $\sin 30° = \cos 60°$

$\sin 60° = \cos 30°$

$\sin 40° = \cos 50°$

$\sin 45° = \cos 45°$

Solving problems using the cosine equation is the same process as for the sine equation.

Model 1: $\cos 20° = \frac{x}{5}$

$0.9397 = \frac{x}{5}$

$x = 4.6985$

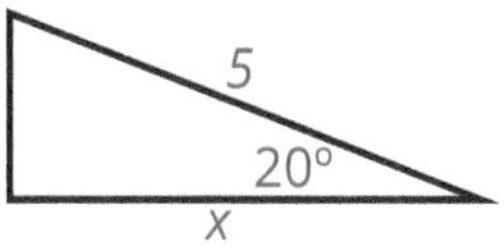

Model 2: $\cos 40° = \frac{10}{x}$

$0.766 = \frac{10}{x}$

$0.766x = 10$

$x = 13.05$

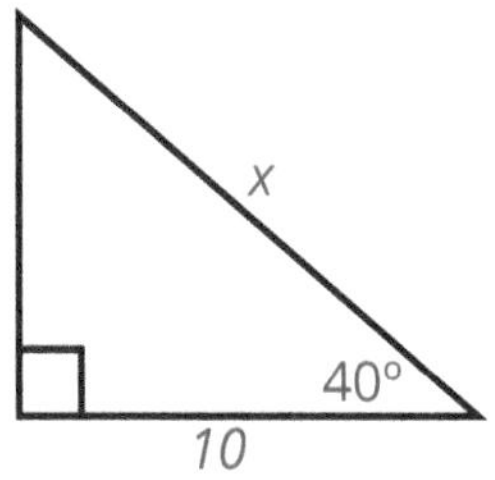

Model 3: $\cos x° = \frac{8}{12}$

$\cos x° = 0.6666$

$x = 48°$

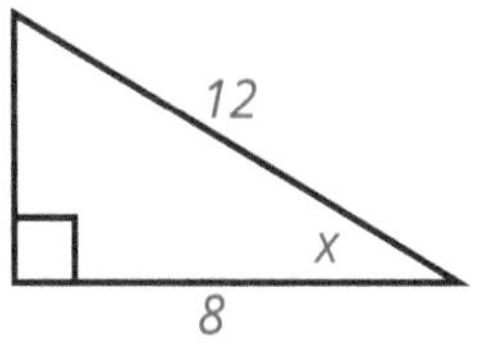

Find x to the nearest tenth.

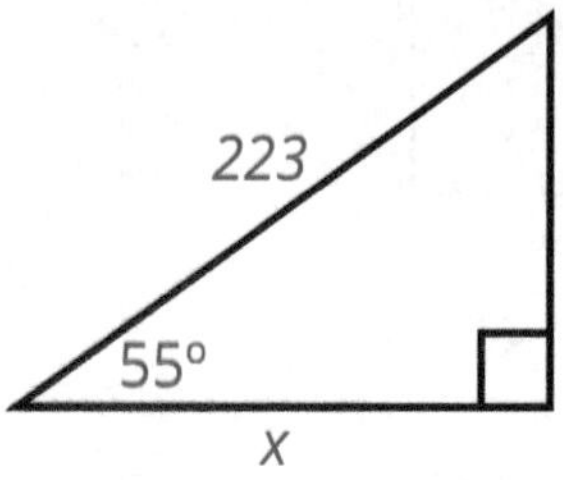

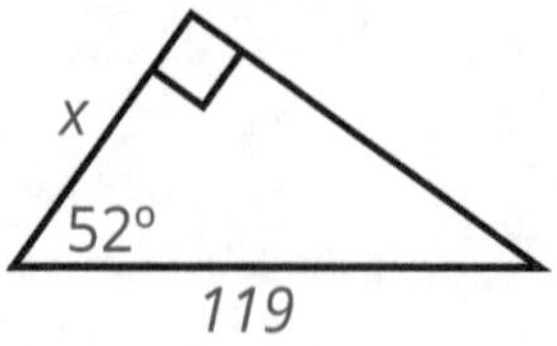

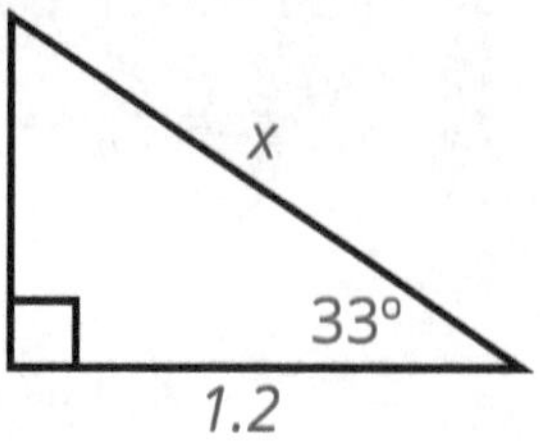

3.60 x = ____________

3.61 x = ____________

3.62 x = ____________

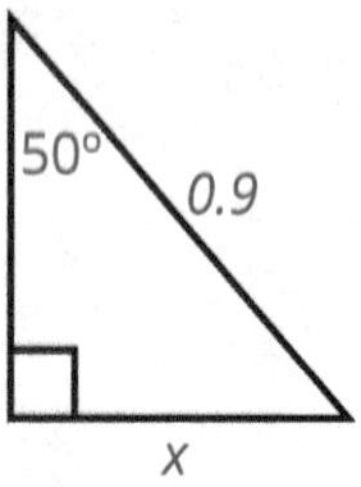

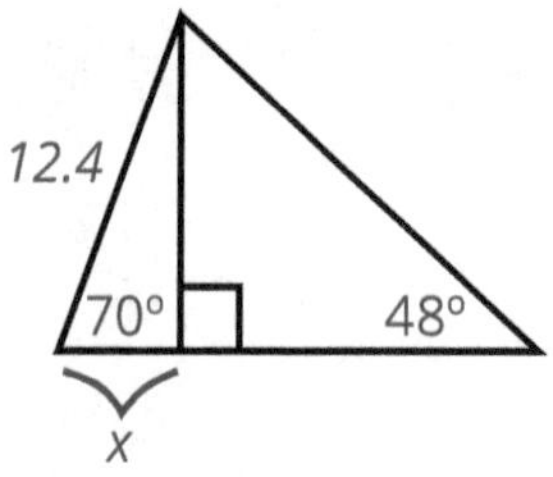

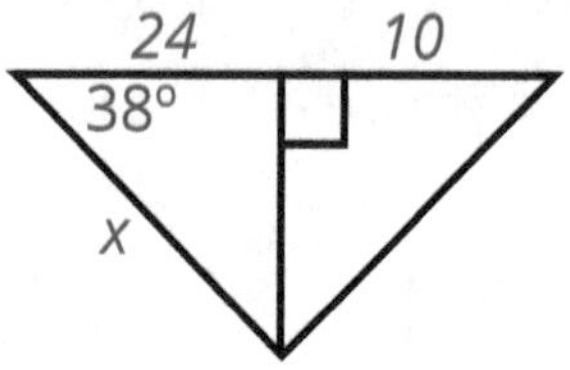

3.63 x = ____________

3.64 x = ____________

3.65 x = ____________

Find $\angle A$ to the nearest degree.

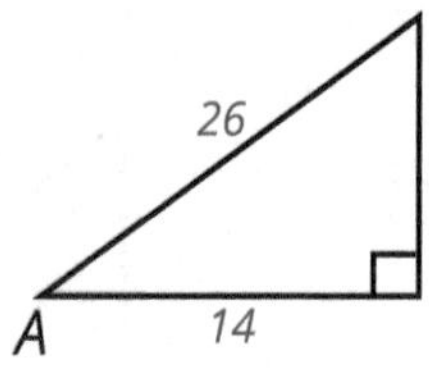

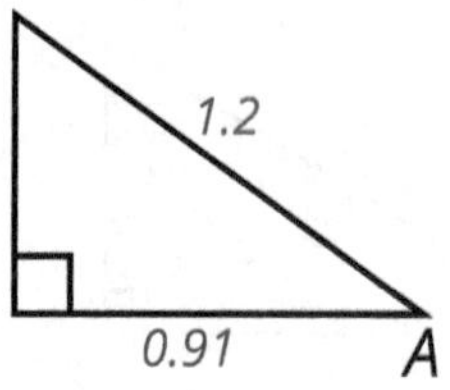

3.66 $\angle A$ = ____________

3.67 $\angle A$ = ____________

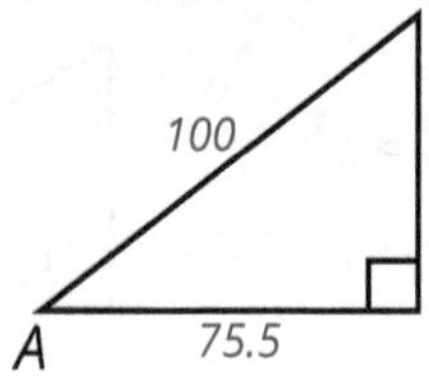

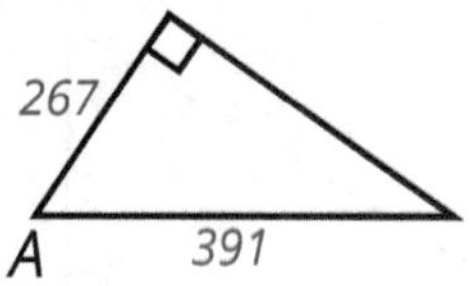

3.68 $\angle A$ = ____________

3.69 $\angle A$ = ____________

TANGENT RATIO

The third ratio that we will use is formed by taking the side opposite angle *A* over the side adjacent to angle *A*.

$$\frac{B_1C_1}{AC_1} = \frac{B_2C_2}{AC_2} = \frac{B_3C_3}{AC_3} = \frac{B_4C_4}{AC_4}$$

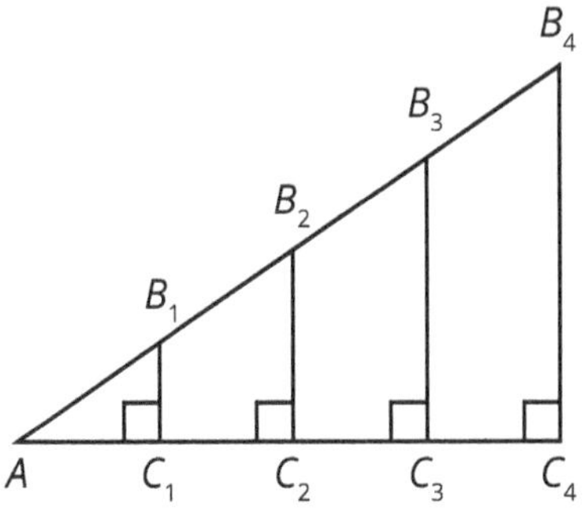

This ratio is called the **tangent ratio** with respect to angle *A*.

We write

$\tan \angle A = \frac{B_1C_1}{AC_1}$ or $\tan \angle A = \frac{B_2C_2}{AC_2}$ or

$\tan \angle A = \frac{B_3C_3}{AC_3}$ or $\tan \angle A = \frac{B_4C_4}{AC_4}$.

Just as with the sine and the cosine, the tangent ratio is the same for a given angle no matter how large the sides of the triangle become. Look again at the table for tangent ratio. Unlike the sine and cosine ratio numbers, the tangent ratio number can be greater than one. As the angle increases so does the tangent number without a limit.

$$\tan \angle A = \frac{\text{opposite side } \angle A}{\text{adjacent side } \angle A}$$

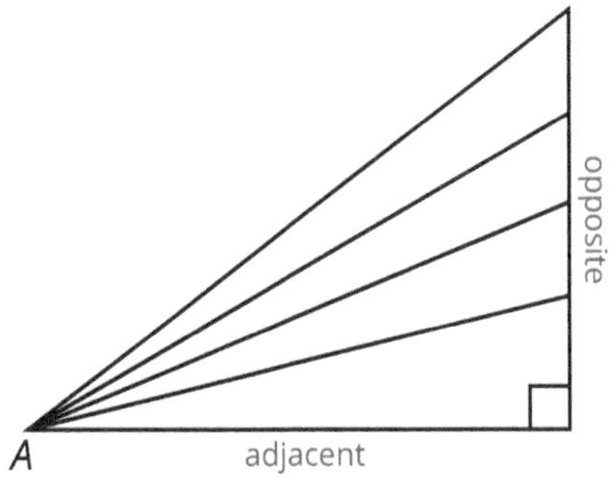

$\tan 30° = \frac{1}{\sqrt{3}} = \frac{\sqrt{3}}{3}$

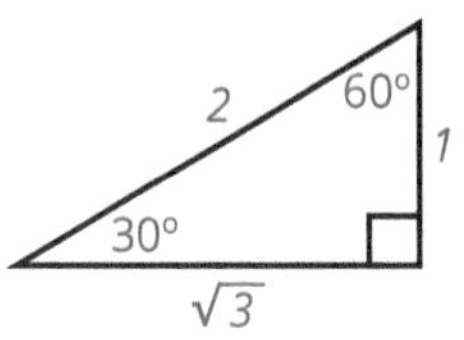

$\tan 60° = \frac{\sqrt{3}}{1}$

$\tan 45° = \frac{1}{1}$

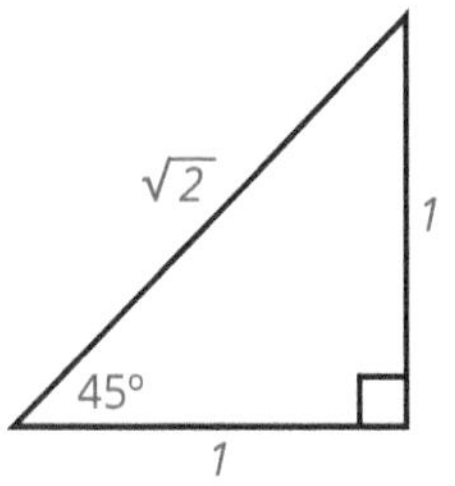

Model 1: $\tan 30° = \frac{6}{x}$

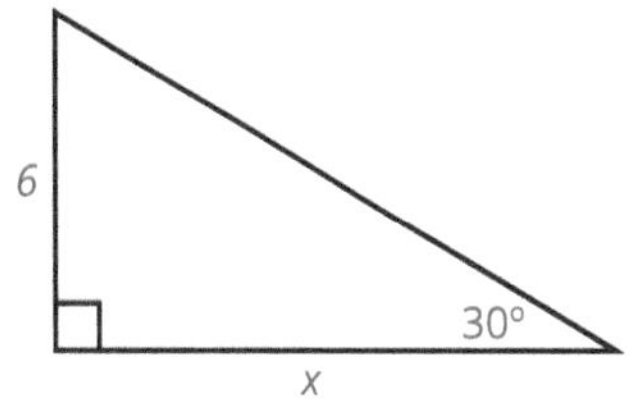

$0.5774 = \frac{6}{x}$

$0.5774x = 6$

$x = 10.39$

Model 2: $\tan 40° = \frac{x}{12}$

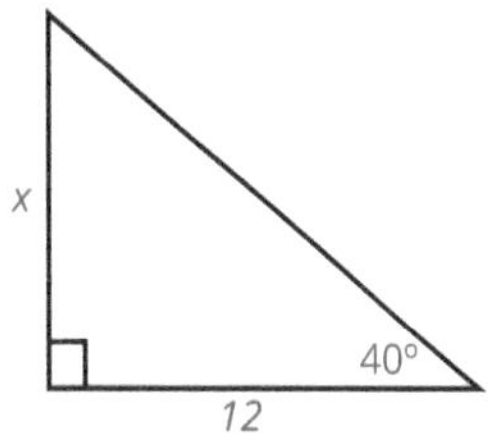

$0.8391 = \frac{x}{12}$

$x = 10.06$

Model 3: $\tan x° = \frac{6}{4}$

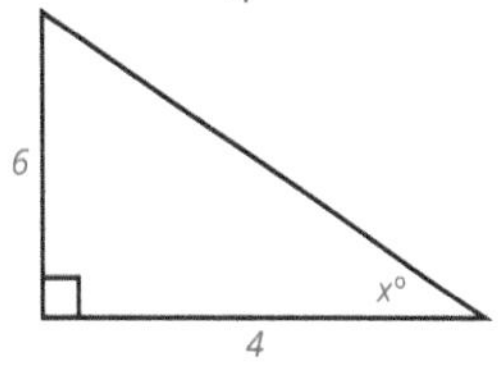

$\tan x° = 1.500$

$x = 56°$

Find *x* to the nearest tenth.

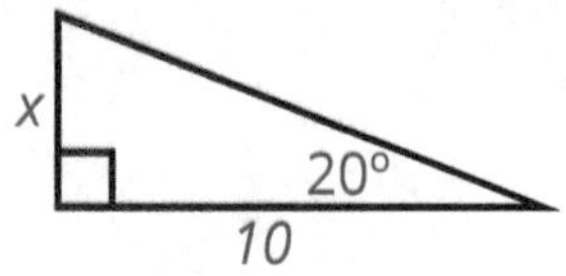

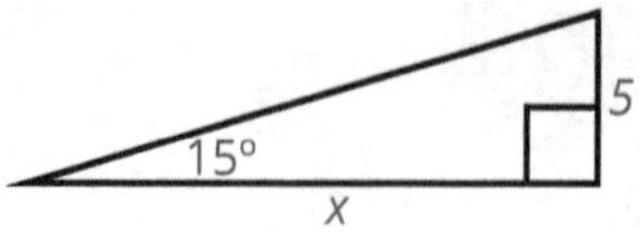

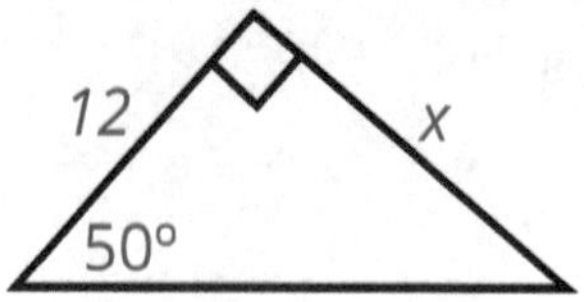

3.70 x = ____________

3.71 x = ____________

3.72 x = ____________

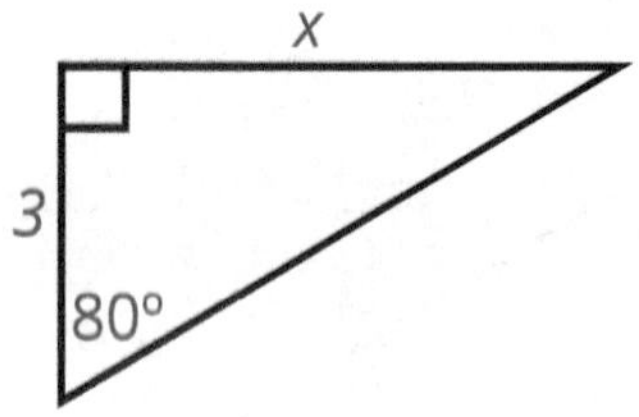

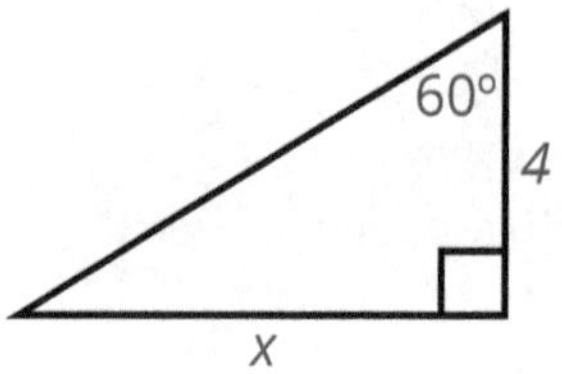

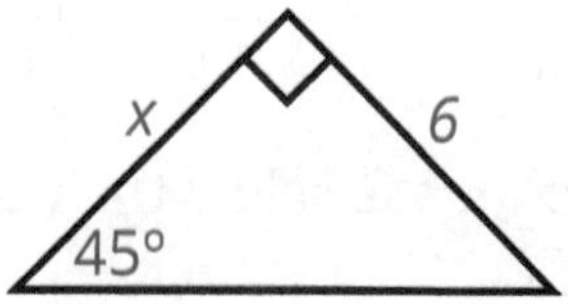

3.73 x = ____________

3.74 x = ____________

3.75 x = ____________

Find ∠*A* to the nearest degree.

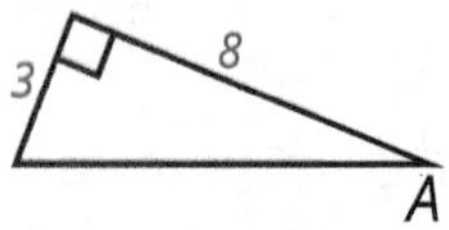

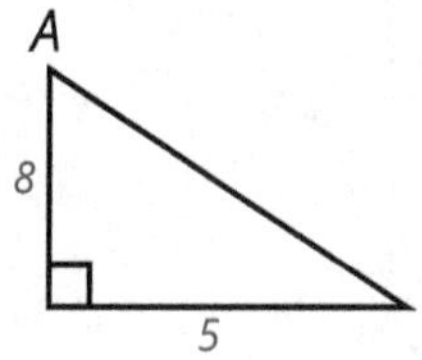

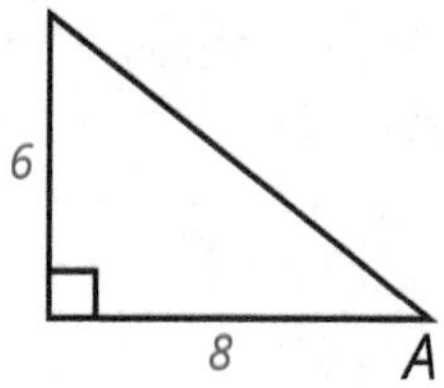

3.76 ∠A = ____________

3.77 ∠A = ____________

3.78 ∠A = ____________

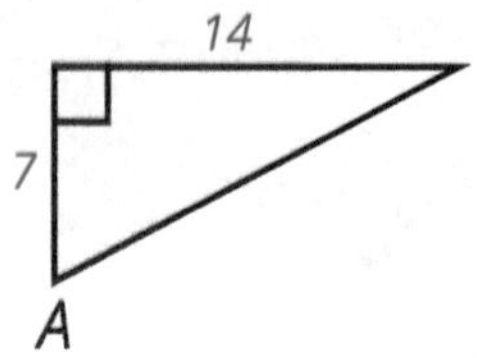

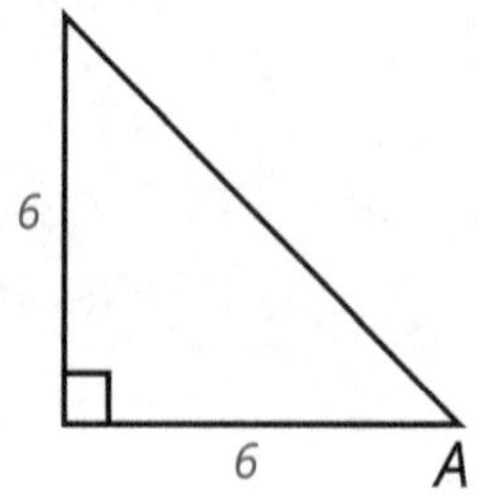

3.79 ∠A = ____________

3.80 ∠A = ____________

INDIRECT MEASURE

Many times we would like to find the length of an object but cannot place a ruler on it and measure it directly. We can use similar right triangles and trigonometry to find the measure indirectly.

USING SIMILAR TRIANGLES

Suppose we want to find the height of an object like a flagpole using similar triangles.

Proceed in this way: $\triangle ABC \sim \triangle DEF$ because the angle of elevation (looking up) of the sun is the same and each forms a right angle with the ground. So $\frac{BC}{EF} = \frac{AB}{DE}$. We can find the length of *BC* (your height), *AB* (your shadow), and *DE* (shadow of flagpole), and solve the proportion. Suppose you are 5 ft. tall, your shadow is 3 ft. and the shadow of the flagpole is 10 ft.

$$\frac{5}{x} = \frac{3}{10}$$

$$3x = 50$$

$x = 16\frac{2}{3}$ ft. (height of the flagpole)

What if the sun is not out or the weather is too cloudy to cast a shadow? Then we can use the mirror method and similar triangles.

Place the mirror on the ground and then move backward or forward until you can see the top of the tree in the mirror. When you see the top of the tree, stop and mark the spot on the ground where you are. $\triangle ACB$ and $\triangle EDB$ are similar because the angles at the mirror are the same and right angles are formed where you stand and where the tree is. We can now measure directly *AC*, *AB*, and *BE*. Find *DE* from the proportion $\frac{AC}{DE} = \frac{AB}{BE}$.

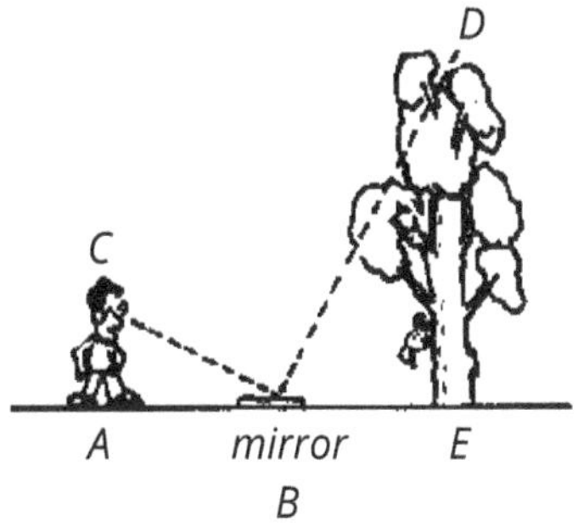

Suppose *AC* = 4 ft., *AB* = 6 ft., and *BE* = 12 ft.

$$\frac{4}{DE} = \frac{6}{12}$$

$$6DE = 48$$

DE = 8 ft. (height of tree)

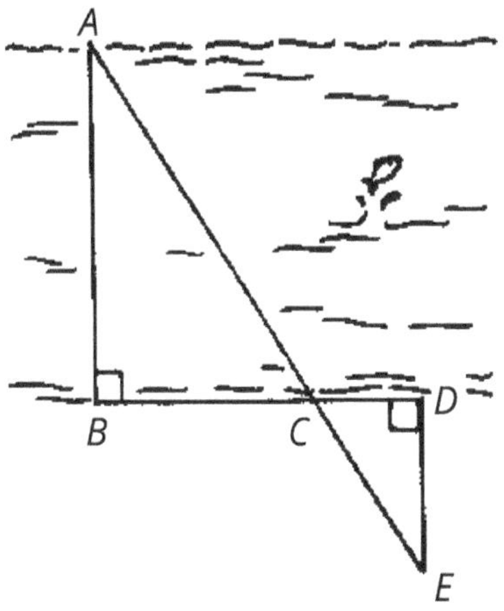

To find the distance across the river, use *ABC* and *EDC*. The vertical angles are equal and the right angles are equal so the triangles are similar and $\frac{AB}{DE} = \frac{BC}{CD}$, if *BC* = 12 ft., *CD* = 3 ft., and *DE* = 5 ft.

$$\frac{AB}{5} = \frac{12}{3}$$

$$3AB = 60$$

AB = 20 ft. (width of river)

Make a sketch if you need to and solve these problems using similar triangles. Show your work and circle your answer.

3.81 If the shadow of a tree is 14 m long and the shadow of a person who is 1.8 m tall is 4 m long, how tall is the tree?

3.82 A pole 3 m high has a shadow 5 m long when the shadow of a nearby building is 110 m long. How tall is the building?

3.83 A telephone pole has a shadow of 16 ft. when a person 5 ft. tall has a shadow of 6 ft. How tall is the pole?

3.84 At the bank of a river, by measurement, a = 9 ft., b = 15 ft., c = 12 ft., and d = 7 ft. How long is x? How long is y?

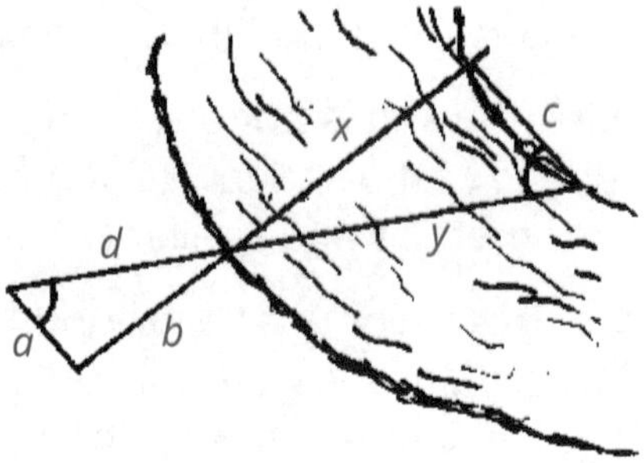

3.85 Boy is 6 ft. tall. Boy to mirror is 8 ft. Mirror to house is 16 ft. How high is the top of the house?

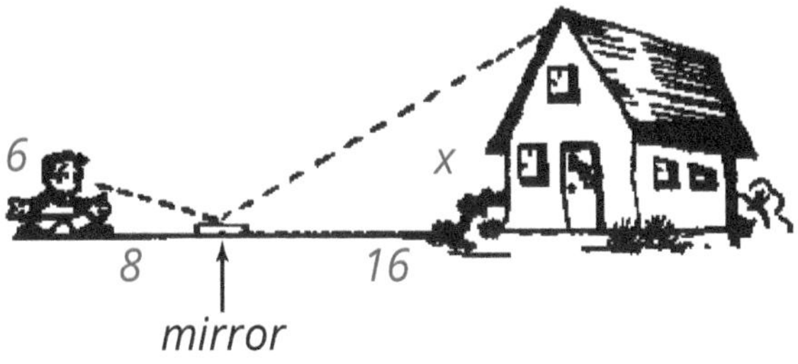

USING TRIGONOMETRY

We can also measure indirectly if we can set up a right triangle and have some way to measure an acute angle.

Knowing the measure of one of the acute angles, we can apply one of the trigonometric ratios to solve the right triangle.

Model 1: How far above the ground is the kite if 300 feet of string is out and a 40-degree angle is formed with the string and the ground?

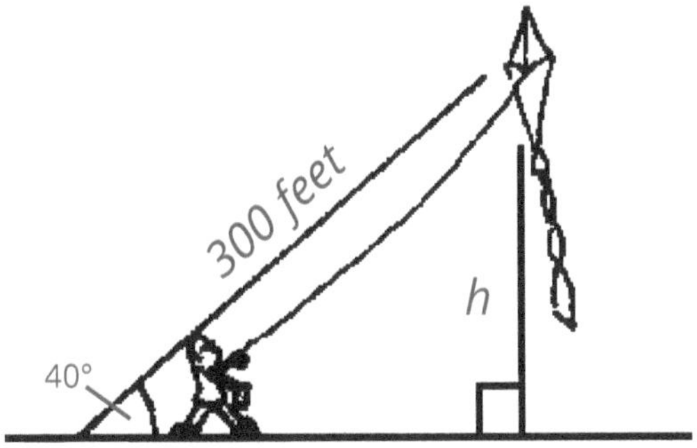

$\sin 40° = \frac{h}{300}$

$0.6428 = \frac{h}{300}$

$h = 192.8$ ft.

Model 2: How wide is the river?

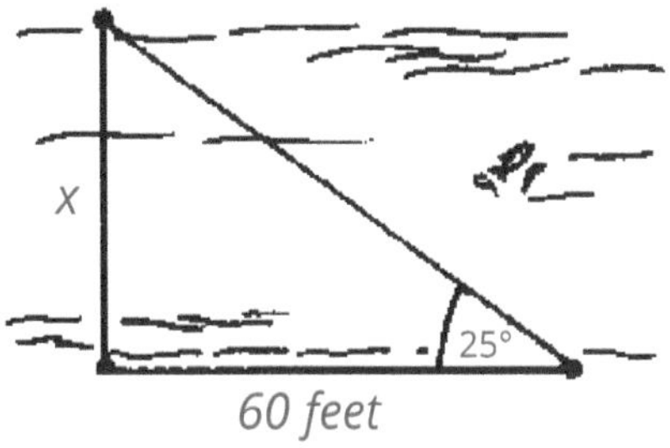

$\tan 25° = \frac{x}{60}$

$0.4663 = \frac{x}{60}$

$x = 28.0$ ft.

Model 3: How tall is the tower?

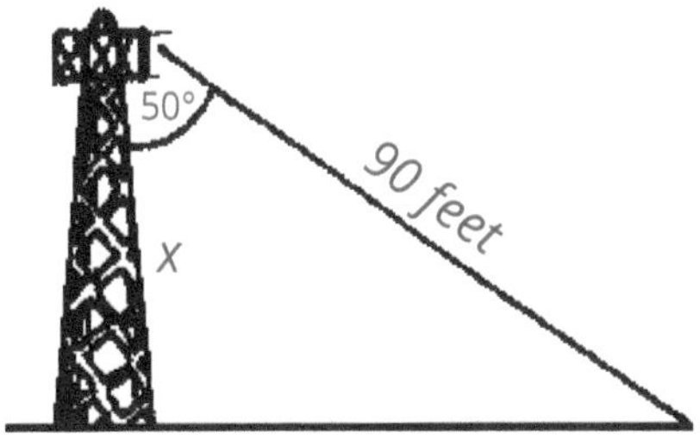

$\cos 50° = \frac{x}{90}$

$0.6428 = \frac{x}{90}$

$x = 57.9$ ft.

Set up a right triangle model for the following problems and solve them by using the trigonometric ratio that applies. Show your work and circle your answer.

3.86 The angle looking up at the sun is 70°. A flagpole casts a shadow of 15 ft. Find the height of the flagpole.

3.87 The shadow of a building is 40 ft. long. The angle between the ground and the line to the sun is 35°. Find the height of the building.

3.88 A guy wire is stretched from the top of a tower to a point 10 yards from the base of the tower. The wire makes an angle of 65° with the ground. Find the length of the guy wire.

3.89 How much string is out if a kite is 100 feet above the ground and the string makes an angle of 65° with the ground?

3.90 A vertical pole 6 feet long casts a shadow 55 inches long. Find the angle of elevation of the sun.

3.91 Find the altitude of an isosceles triangle with a vertex angle of 70° and a base of 246.

3.92 Who gains altitude more quickly, a pilot traveling 400 mph and rising at an angle of 30°, or a pilot traveling 300 mph and rising at an angle of 40°? How much more quickly (in mph) does he gain altitude?

Work this challenge exercise. Show your work and circle your answer.

3.93 Find the height of the mountain peak. *A* is known to be 6,500 feet above sea level; *AB* = 600 feet. The angle at *A* looking up at *P* is 20°. The angle at *B* looking up at *P* is 35°. How far above sea level is the peak *P*?

(Hint: Draw a perpendicular $\overline{BJ}$ from *B* to $\overline{AP}$. Label the various angles. Compute *BJ*, then *BP*, then *PQ*; and finally find 6,500 + *PQ*.)

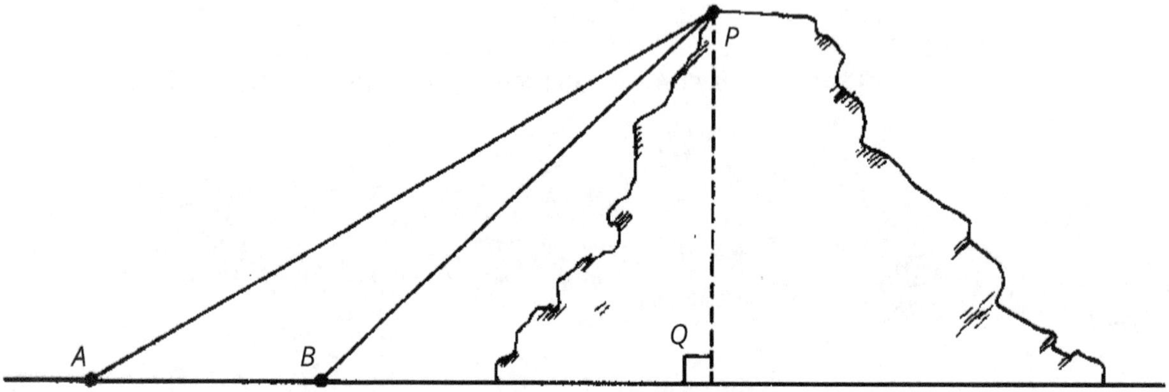

TEACHER CHECK ____________ initials ____________ date

Before you take this last Self Test, you may want to do one or more of the following self checks.

1. ________ Read the objectives. Determine if you can do them.
2. ________ Restudy the material related to any objectives that you cannot do.
3. ________ Use the **SQ3R** study procedure to review the material:
   a. **S**can the sections.
   b. **Q**uestion yourself.
   c. **R**ead to answer your questions.
   d. **R**ecite the answers to yourself.
   e. **R**eview areas you did not understand.
4. ________ Review all activities and Self Tests, writing a correct answer for every wrong answer.

SELF TEST 3

Write *always, sometimes,* **or** *never* **to make each statement true** (each answer, 2 points).

3.01 A ratio is ______________________ a comparison of two numbers by addition.

3.02 Two ratios are ______________________ equal to each other.

3.03 The first and fourth terms of a proportion are ______________________ called the means.

3.04 If two angles of one polygon are equal to two angles of a second polygon, then the two polygons are ______________________ similar.

3.05 The altitude to the hypotenuse of a right triangle is ______________________ the geometric mean between the segments on the hypotenuse.

3.06 In a 30°-60°-90° triangle, the long leg is ______________________ half the hypotenuse.

3.07 The slant height of a regular square pyramid is ______________________ longer than its altitude.

3.08 The faces of a rectangular solid are ______________________ square.

3.09 The sine ratio of an angle is ______________________ the opposite side over the adjacent side.

3.010 The tangent ratio number is ______________________ greater than one.

Find the missing parts (each answer, 3 points).

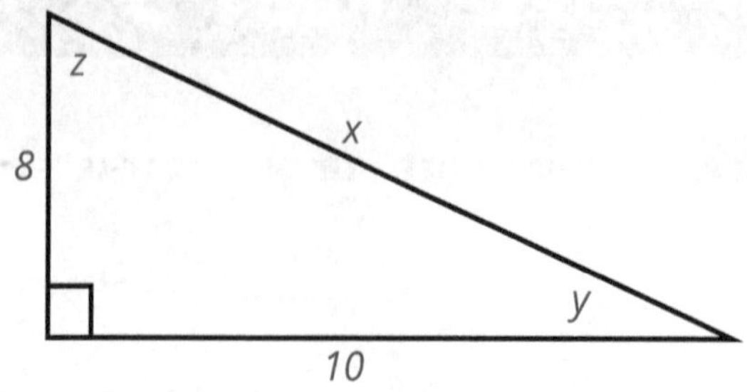

3.011 x = ____________ **3.012** y = ____________ **3.013** z = ____________

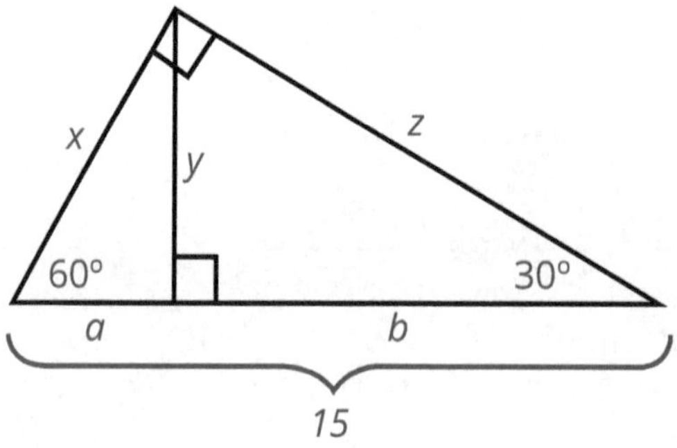

3.014 x = ____________ **3.015** y = ____________ **3.016** z = ____________

3.017 a = ____________ **3.018** b = ____________

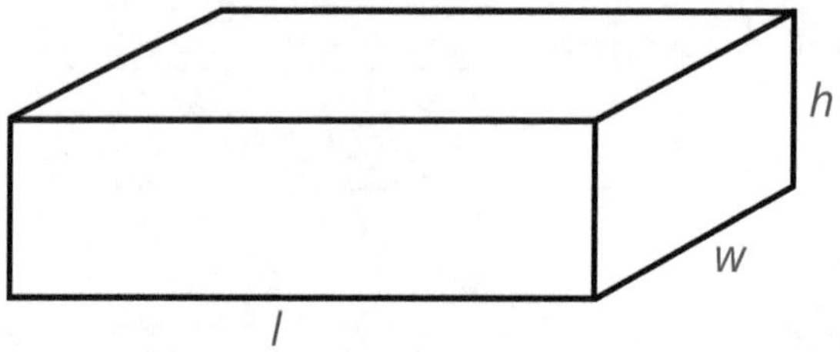

$l = 8$, $w = 4$, $h = 2$

3.019 Find the diagonal of the base. ______________________

3.020 Find the diagonal of the rectangular solid. ______________________

Given: regular square pyramid

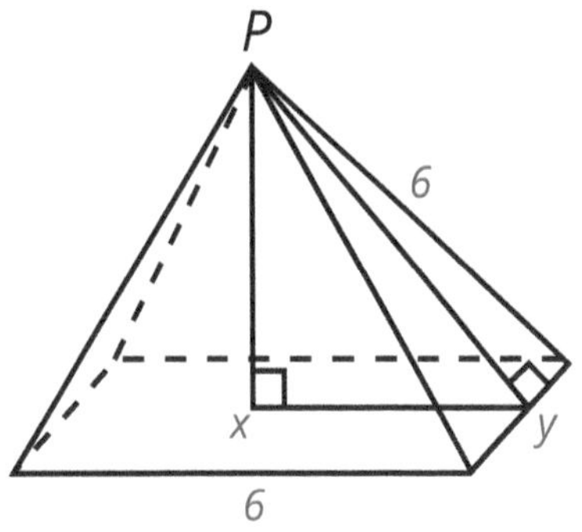

3.021 Find *Py*. ____________

3.022 Find *Px*. ____________

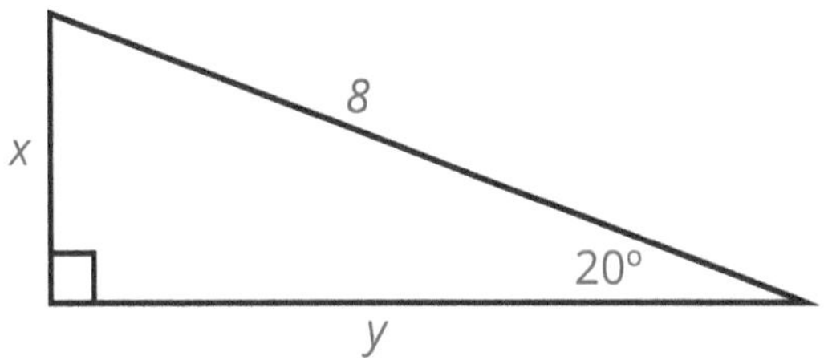

3.023 Find *x* to the nearest tenth. ____________________

3.024 Find *y* to the nearest tenth. ____________________

3.025 Find *h*. ____________________

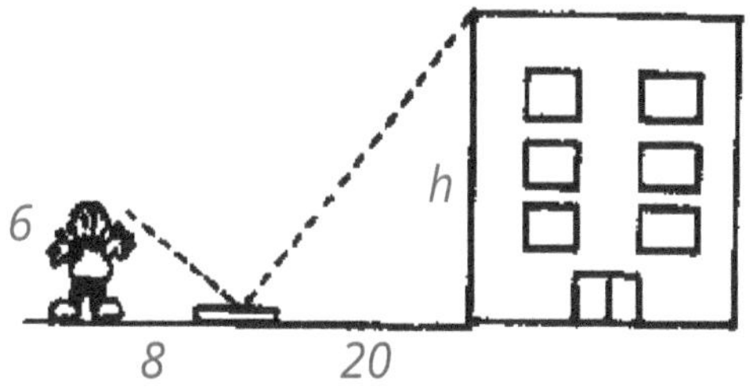

52/65	**SCORE** ________	**TEACHER** ________ initials	________ date

Before taking the LIFEPAC Test, you may want to do one or more of the following self checks.

1. ________ Read the objectives. Check to see if you can do them.
2. ________ Restudy the material related to any objectives that you cannot do.
3. ________ Use the **SQ3R** study procedure to review the material.
4. ________ Review activities, Self Tests, and LIFEPAC Glossary.
5. ________ Restudy areas of weakness indicated by the last Self Test.

GLOSSARY

altitude of a triangle .... The perpendicular distance from a vertex to the opposite side.

cosine ratio .... With respect to an acute angle of a right triangle, the ratio of the side adjacent to the angle over the hypotenuse.

cube .... A solid figure with squares for all faces.

diagonal of rectangular solid .... A segment whose end points are not in the same plane.

divided proportionally .... Two segments divided into two parts such that the ratios of the parts are equal.

edge .... In a solid figure, the intersection of any two faces.

extended proportion .... A proportion showing more than two ratios equal.

extremes .... The first and fourth terms of a proportion.

faces .... The sides of a solid figure.

geometric mean .... In a proportion, the number in both means positions: in $\frac{a}{x} = \frac{x}{b}$, x is the geometric mean between a and b.

lateral face .... Any face that intersects the base of a solid figure.

means .... The second and third terms of a proportion.

perimeter .... The distance around a polygon.

projection .... The point or segment formed by extending a perpendicular from the end points of a segment to a linear plane.

proportion .... An equation that states that two ratios are equal.

pyramid .... A solid figure having one base and lateral faces that are triangles.

ratio .... A comparison of two numbers by division.

rectangular solid .... A solid figure whose faces are all rectangles.

similar polygons .... Polygons that have corresponding angles equal and corresponding sides in proportion.

sine ratio .... With respect to an acute angle of a right triangle, the ratio formed by the side opposite the acute angle over the hypotenuse.

slant height .... In a pyramid, the altitude of any lateral face.

tangent ratio.. With respect to an acute angle of a right triangle, the ratio of the side opposite the acute angle over the side adjacent to the acute angle.

vertex .... In a solid figure, any point where two edges intersect.

NOTES

MATH 1005

LIFEPAC TEST

NAME ______________________________

DATE ______________________________

SCORE ______________________________

MATH 1005: LIFEPAC Test

Find the ratio in simplest form (each answer, 2 points).

1. 5 to 15 ________________

2. 15 minutes to 2 hours ________________

3. 30:6 ________________

4. $\frac{2}{3}$ to $\frac{3}{2}$ ________________

Solve for the variable (each answer, 2 points).

5. $\frac{x}{3} = \frac{5}{8}$ $x =$ ________________

6. 3:12 = x:16 $x =$ ________________

7. $\frac{2}{x} = \frac{6}{2}$ $x =$ ________________

8. $\frac{x}{5} = \frac{2}{3} = \frac{5}{y}$ $x =$ a. ________________

$y =$ b. ________________

Which property of proportion is illustrated? (each answer, 3 points)

9. If $\frac{x}{y} = \frac{r}{s}$, then $\frac{x+y}{y} = \frac{r+s}{s}$. ________________

10. If $\frac{x}{y} = \frac{a}{b} = \frac{c}{d}$, then $\frac{x+a+c}{y+b+d} = \frac{c}{d}$. ________________

11. If $\frac{x+z}{y} = \frac{a}{b}$, then $ay = bx + bz$. ________________

12. If $\frac{a}{b} = \frac{c}{d}$, then $\frac{b}{a} = \frac{d}{c}$. ________________

Answer the following questions (each answer, 3 points).

13. Which polygons are similar? ________________

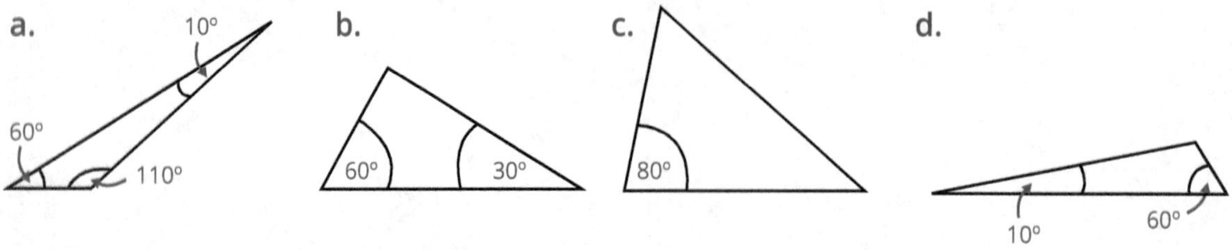

14. Which triangles are similar? ______________________

a. b. c. d.

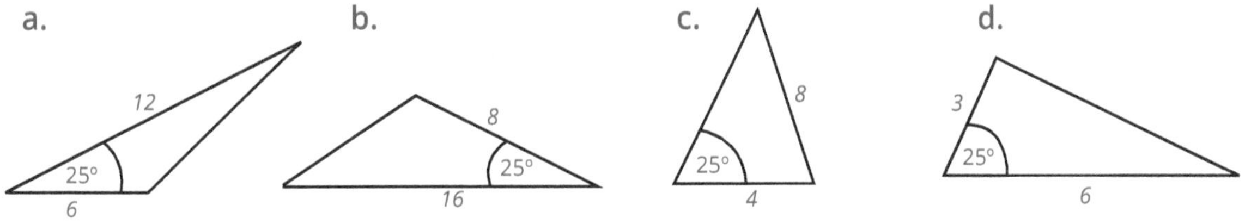

15. Which of the triangles are right triangles? ______________________

a. b. c. d.

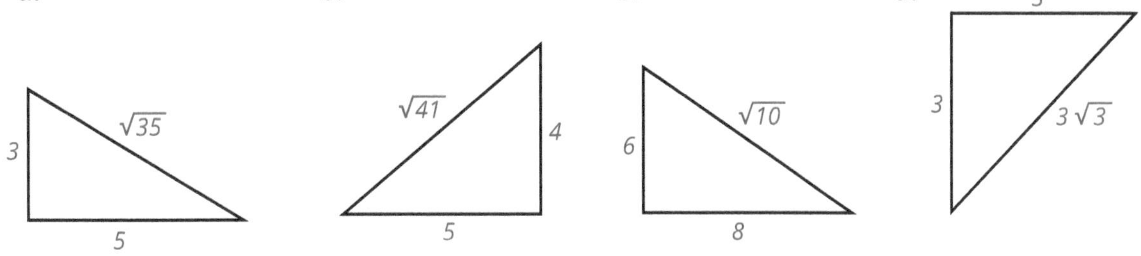

Complete the following items (each answer, 4 points).

16. The side of one polygon is 20 ft. Find the corresponding side of a similar polygon with corresponding sides 3 ft. and 9 ft.

17. Find the ratio of the perimeters in Problem 16. ______________

18. Find *x*. $x =$ ______________

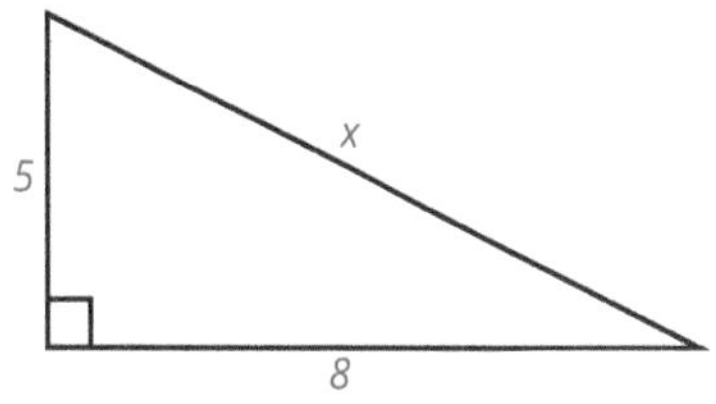

19. Find *x* and *y*. $x =$ a. ______________

$y =$ b. ______________

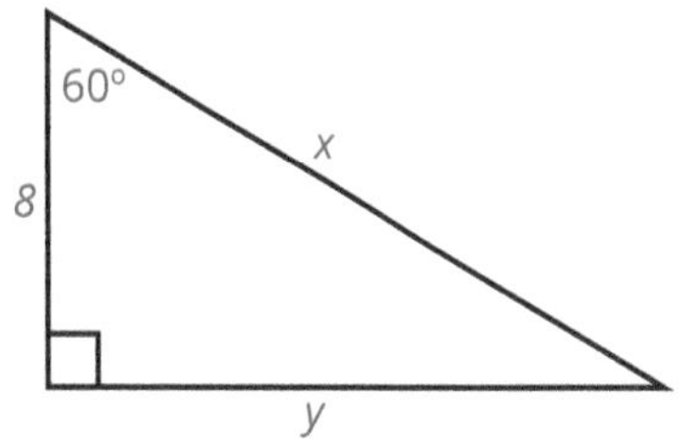

20. Find the diagonal of the rectangular solid.

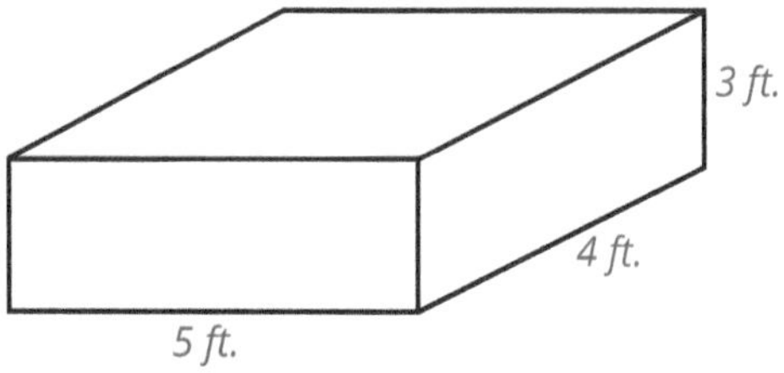

21. Find the slant height of this square pyramid.

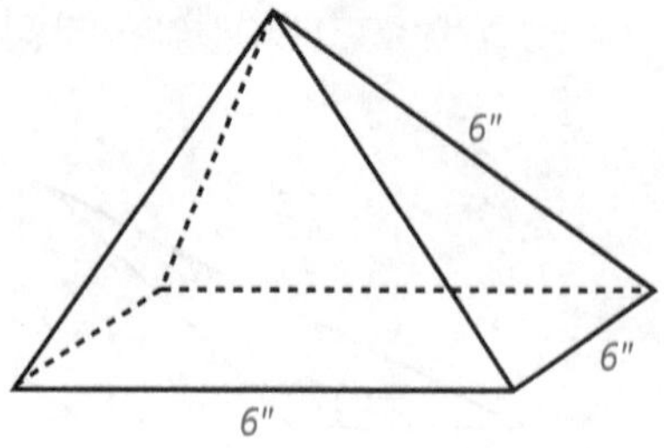

22. Find *x* and *y*.

x = a. ________________

y = b. ________________

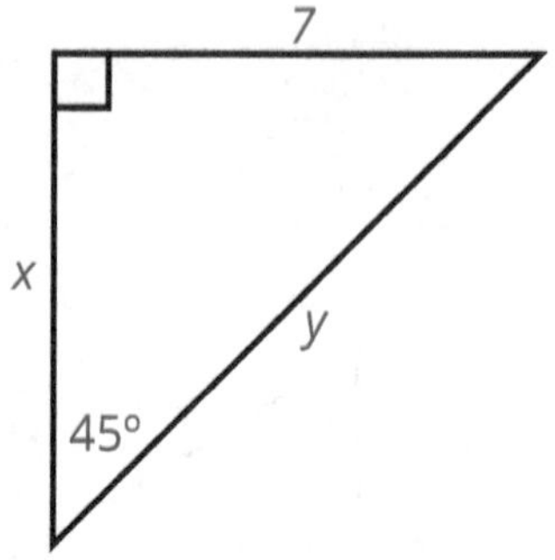

23. Write the equation you would use to find the altitude of the airplane.

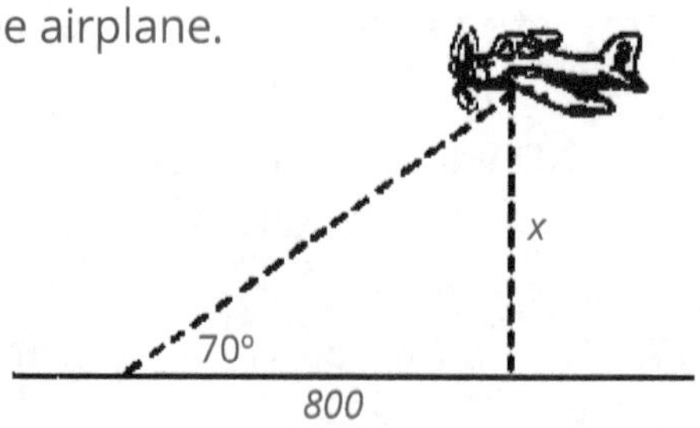

24. Write the equation you would use to find the distance to the iceberg.

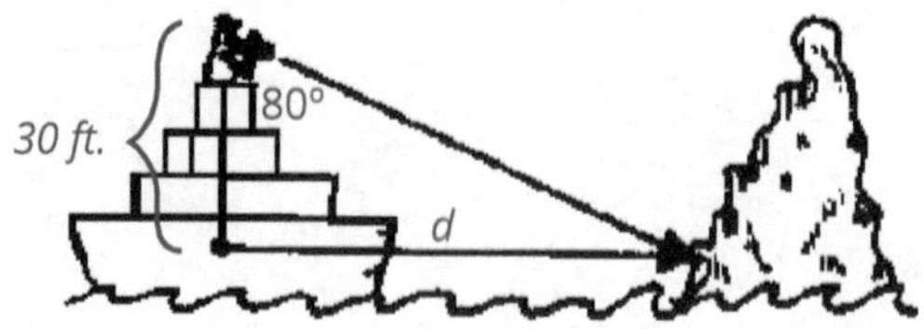

25. Find the height of the cross if the shadow of a boy 5 ft. 6 in. tall is 2 ft., and the shadow of the cross is 2 yards.

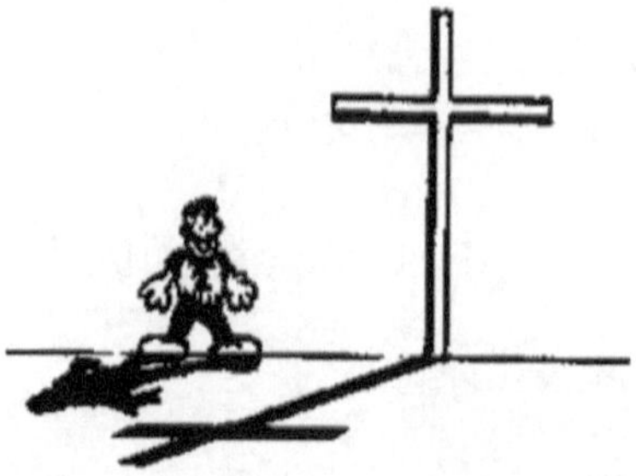

Circles

Introduction

The circle is one of the basic geometric shapes that we study. The circle and its space partner, the sphere, can be found in all phases of life. The circle is even referred to in the Bible: Ezekiel chapter 1, mentions Ezekiel's vision of a wheel in a wheel; Isaiah 40:22 refers to God's power over "the circle of the earth." We use ideas related to circles in our cars, from the steering wheel to the gears that make them run.

Industry would be at a standstill if not for ideas based on the circle. Many games and sports activities depend on circles and spheres.

In our study of the circle, we shall learn about the different parts of a circle and how angles and segments are related to circles. We shall learn how to measure arcs, angles, and segment lengths that are formed in circles.

Objectives

Read these objectives. The objectives tell you what you will be able to do when you have successfully completed this LIFEPAC. When you have finished this LIFEPAC, you should be able to:

1. Identify the characteristics of circles and spheres.
2. Define tangents.
3. Use theorems related to tangents.
4. Use arcs to measure central angles and central angles to measure arcs.
5. Find the measure of the angle formed by the hands of a clock at any given time.
6. Solve problems related to chords and secants.
7. Solve problems related to inscribed angles.
8. Find the measures of angles formed by segments related to circles.
9. Find the measures of segments formed by chords, secants, and tangents.

Survey the LIFEPAC. Ask yourself some questions about this study and write your questions here.

1. CIRCLES AND SPHERES

To learn about circles and spheres we need to define the parts of the figures and the relationship those parts have to each other. Some of these terms you may already know; others will be completely new to you.

Section Objective

Review this objective. When you have finished this section, you should be able to:

1. Identify the characteristics of circles and spheres.

CHARACTERISTICS OF CIRCLES

Circles have specific parts, each with a geometric definition. After the parts of the circle have been learned, then the different relationships dealing with circles become easy to define.

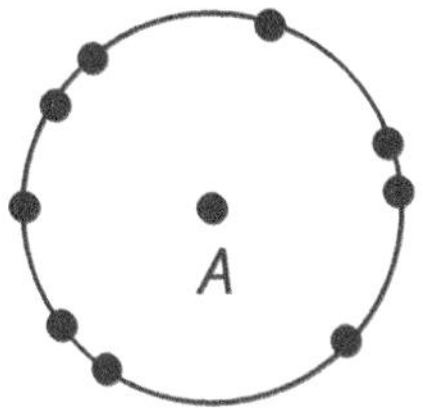

Circle *A*

First we need to agree on a definition of a circle. A good definition of a circle follows.

> **DEFINITION**
> **Circle:** the set of all points in a plane that are the same distance from a given point in that plane.

A circle, by this definition, consists of all the points in a plane that meet the requirement of being equally distant from some point in the plane. We call the other point the center of the circle. If we measure the distance from the center to the circle at any point, the distance will remain the same.

A circle is named by using its center point.

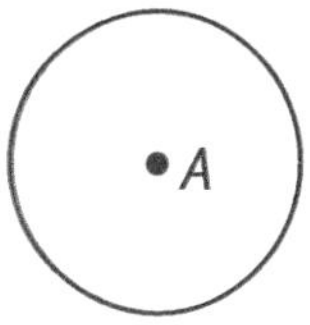

Circle *A*

RADIUS

One important part of the circle is the radius.

> **DEFINITION**
> **Radius:** a segment with endpoints on the circle and at the center of the circle.

The word **radius** will be used in two ways. First, as the definition states, a radius is a segment. Therefore, when we talk about the radius of a circle, we are referring to a segment. A second use of the word radius refers us to the length of that segment: The radius is a number. No confusion should arise as to which radius we mean because of the way it will be used in a sentence.

Model 1: The radius of circle *R* is 3". (measure)

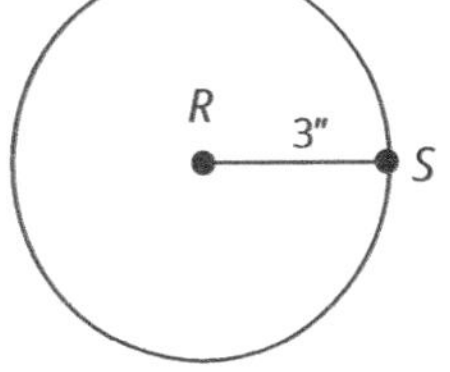

Model 2: The radius of circle *R* is *RS*. (segment)

When a doubt might exist as to which radius is intended, we will specify the *length* or the *measure* of the radius to mean the number.

Notice that all radii (plural of radius) in the same circle will have the same length.
RA = *RB* = *RC* = *RD* in circle *R*.
Radii of a circle are equal.

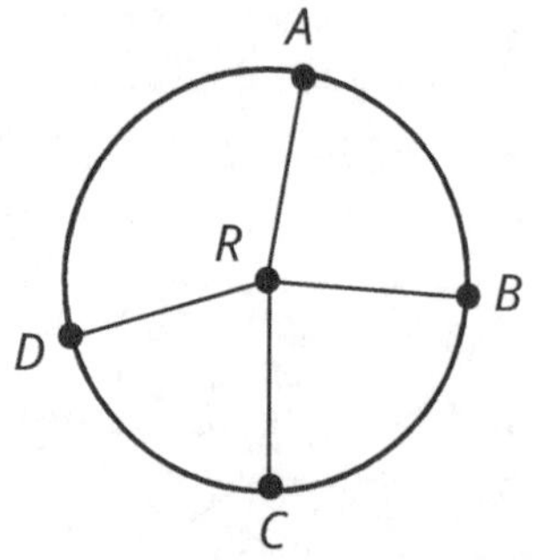

DIAMETER

Another part of the circle is the diameter.

> **DEFINITION**
> **Diameter:** a segment passing through the center with endpoints on the circle.

The word **diameter** will also be used in two ways, just as radius is used. The segment $\overline{RA}$ is the diameter of circle *O*. The diameter of circle *O* is 6 inches.

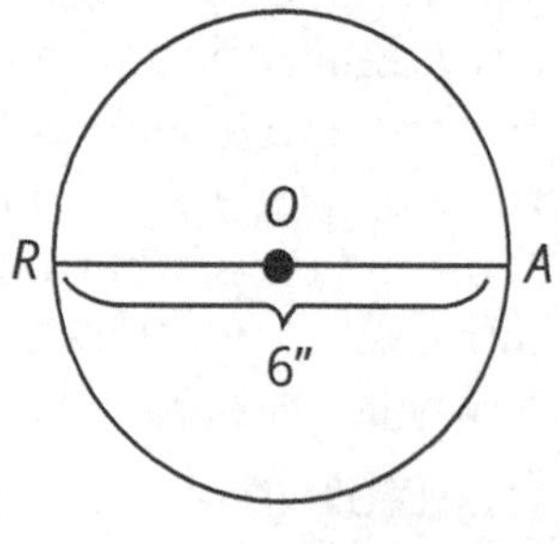

Since the diameter passes through the center of the circle, it is made up of two radii. $\overline{OR}$ and $\overline{OA}$ are radii and the three points *R*, *O*, and *A* are collinear with *O* being the midpoint of $\overline{RA}$. We then have *RO* + *OA* = *RA* or radii + radii = diameter. Two radii equal a diameter. Therefore, the length of a diameter is twice the length of a radius.

CONGRUENT CIRCLES

One way in which circles can be related is to be **congruent**.

> **DEFINITION**
> **Congruent circles:** circles that have equal radii.

We studied congruent triangles in a previous LIFEPAC, and you should remember that congruent triangles are the same shape and size. Since all circles are the same shape, their size depends only on their radii. When we use this definition of congruent circles in a proof we can express it in this form: Radii of congruent circles are equal.

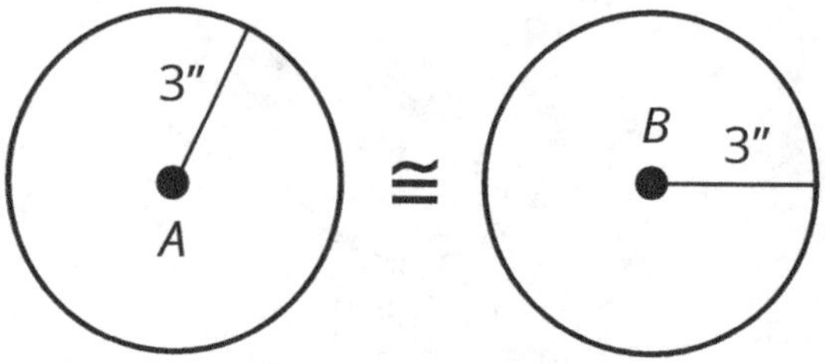

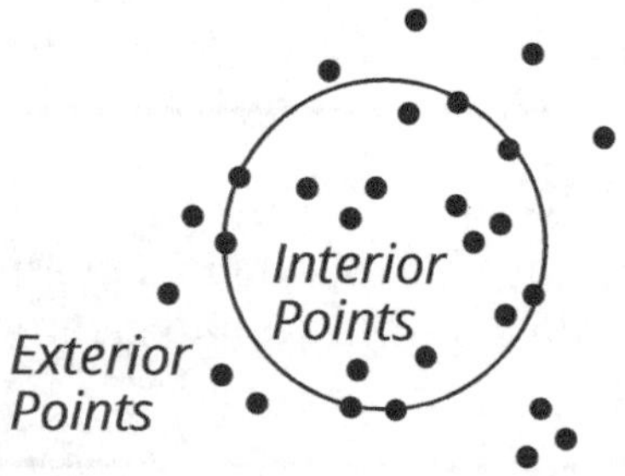

Our definition of a circle states that it lies in a plane. The circle divides the points of that plane into three sets: the points of the plane that are interior to the circle, the points that are exterior to the circle, and the points that are the circle itself.

CONCENTRIC CIRCLES

Circles can also be related by being *concentric*.

> **DEFINITION**
>
> **Concentric circles:** two or more circles that lie in the same plane and have the same center.

You see many examples of concentric circles every day. A bicycle wheel, a car wheel and tire, a bullseye target, and designs on clothing are a few.

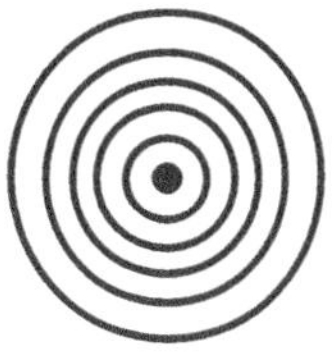

Refer to the circles to complete the following activities.

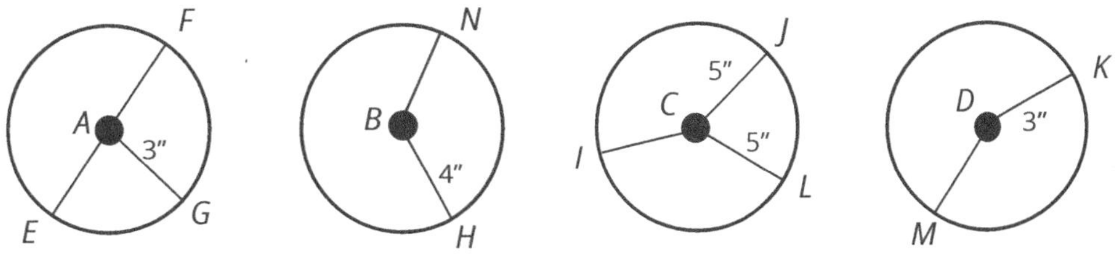

1.1 Name two radii of circle *D*. ______________________

1.2 Name a diameter of circle *A*. ______________________

1.3 Name two radii of circle *B*. ______________________

1.4 What is the name of the circle that has radius $\overline{CL}$? ______________________

1.5 Name three radii of circle *A*. ______________________

1.6 What is the length of the radius in circle *C*? ______________________

1.7 What is the length of diameter $\overline{EF}$? ______________________

1.8 What circles have the same length radii? ______________________

1.9 What circles are congruent? ______________________

1.10 What circles are concentric? ______________________

Refer to this circle to complete the following activities.

Given: $AB = 4$

$AC = 6$

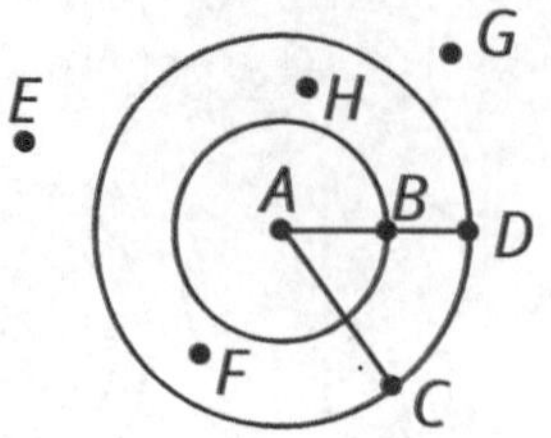

1.11 What is the name of the radius of the smaller circle? ____________________

1.12 What is the name of the radius of the larger circle? ____________________

1.13 Name six points in the exterior of the smaller circle. ____________________

1.14 Name four points in the interior of the larger circle. ____________________

1.15 What is the length of $\overline{BD}$? ____________________

1.16 What points are in the exterior of both circles? ____________________

1.17 What point is the center of both circles? ____________________

1.18 Does $AC = AB + BD$? ____________________

1.19 If $AC = 20$ and $BD = 8$, what is the radius of the smaller circle? ____________________

1.20 If $BD = 7$ and the radius of the smaller circle is 7, what is the diameter of the larger circle?

____

CHARACTERISTICS OF SPHERES

Many properties and parts of a circle suggest similar properties and parts of a sphere. Notice, for example, how close the definition of a circle and a sphere are to each other.

> **DEFINITION**
>
> **Sphere:** the set of all points that are the same distance from a given point.

Omitting the words **in a plane** from the definition of a circle gives the definition of a sphere. A sphere is named by its center just like a circle.

Spheres and spherically shaped objects are all about us. Many sports and games are played with balls that are spheres: baseball, tennis, golf, marbles. We eat spherically shaped foods; apples, oranges, tomatoes, cherries. We even live on a sphere.

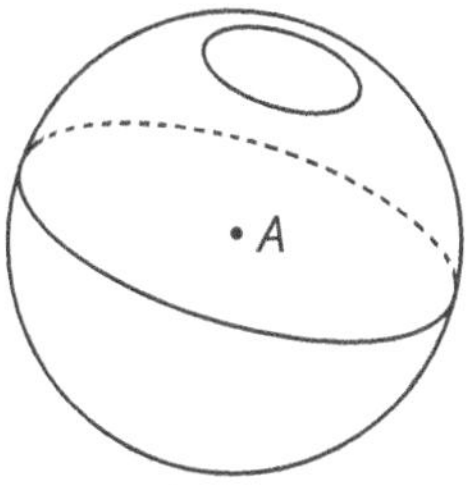

Sphere A

We can often define terms used for spheres by replacing the word **circle** with **sphere** in the definitions for the circle. The center of a sphere is the point from which all the rest are equidistant.

> **DEFINITIONS**
>
> **Radius of Sphere:** a segment with endpoints at the center of the sphere and a point on the sphere
>
> **Diameter of a sphere:** a segment passing through the center with endpoints on the sphere.
>
> **Congruent spheres:** spheres that have equal radii.

A sphere divides space into three sets. Points that are exterior to the sphere have a distance greater than the radius from the sphere. Points that are interior to the sphere have a distance that is less than the radius. Points of the sphere have a distance equal to the radius.

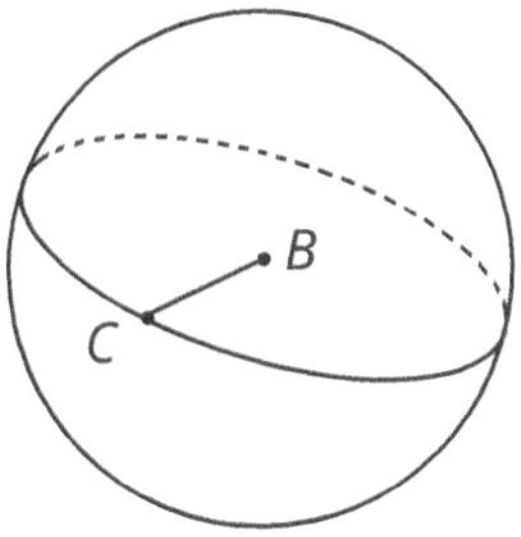

Remember, the sphere itself is only the shell of points around its center.

If a plane intersects a sphere at many points, the intersection will be a circle. If the plane does not contain the center of the sphere, the intersection is called a **small circle**. If the plane contains the center, the intersection is called a **great circle**. The equator of our earth is a great circle.

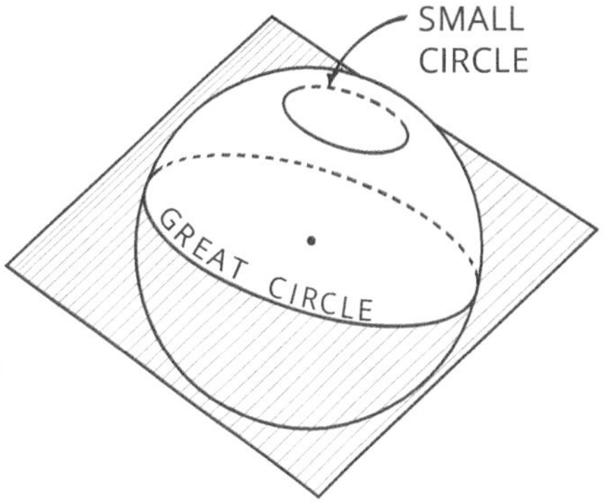

Spheres may be concentric to one another, similar to concentric circles.

> **DEFINITIONS**
>
> **Great circle:** the intersection of a sphere and a plane containing the center of the sphere.
>
> **Small circle:** the intersection of a sphere and a plane not containing the center of the sphere.
>
> **Concentric spheres:** two or more spheres that have the same center.

Refer to the spheres to complete the following activities.

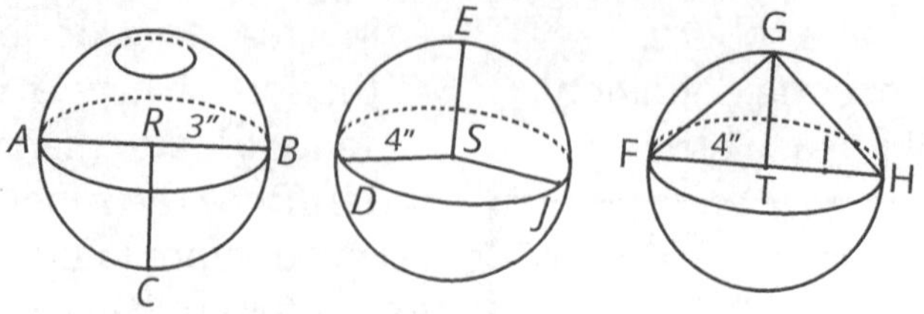

1.21 Name the three spheres. ____________________

1.22 Name a radius of sphere *S*. ____________________

1.23 Name three radii of sphere *T*. ____________________

1.24 Name a diameter of sphere *R*. ____________________

1.25 Name two congruent spheres. ____________________

1.26 How long is the diameter of sphere *S*? ____________________

1.27 If $\overline{GT}$ is perpendicular to $\overline{FT}$, what kind of triangle is triangle *GFT*? ____________________

1.28 Name the interior points of sphere *T*. ____________________

1.29 Name the points on sphere *R*. ____________________

1.30 *DS* + *SJ* = ____________________.

Review the material in this section in preparation for the Self Test. The Self Test will check your mastery of this particular section. The items missed on this Self Test will indicate specific areas where restudy is needed for mastery.

SELF TEST 1

Complete each sentence (each answer, 3 points).

1.01 A circle is named by its ____________________ .

1.02 A sphere is named by its ____________________ .

1.03 A diameter equals ____________________ radii.

1.04 Circles in the same plane and having the same center are called ____________________ circles.

1.05 All points of a sphere are ________________ distances to its center.

1.06 The center is in the ____________________ of a circle.

1.07 The center of a great circle is also the center of a ____________________ .

1.08 All radii of a circle are ____________________ .

1.09 Two circles are congruent if their ____________________ are equal.

1.010 If two spheres have the same center but different radii, they are called ____________________ spheres.

Refer to the circles to complete the following items (each answer, 3 points).

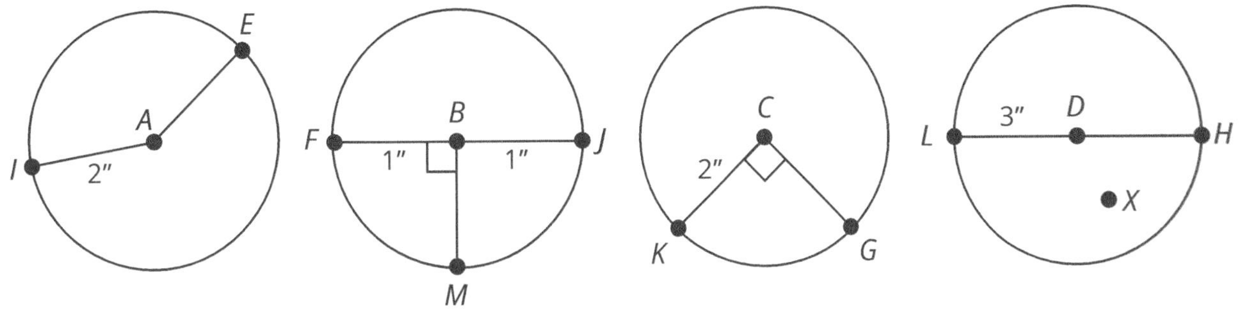

1.011 Find the diameter of circle *C*. ____________________

1.012 Name two congruent circles. ____________________

1.013 *FJ* = ____________________

1.014 Name the interior points of circle *D*. ____________________

1.015 Name an angle equal to $\angle FBM$. ____________________

1.016 Name the points on circle *B*. ____________________

1.017 *FB* + *BM* = ____________________

1.018 What segments in circle *B* are equal? ____________________

1.019 *LH* = ____________________

1.020 Does *IA* = *LD*? ____________________

Draw a sphere and show the following parts (each part, 2 points).

1.021 Center *S*

1.022 Radius *SM*

1.023 A great circle

1.024 A diameter *MN*

1.025 Exterior point *B*

Draw two concentric circles and show the following parts (each part, 2 points).

1.026 Radius of smaller circle *AB*

1.027 Radius of larger circle *AC*

1.028 Point *D* in the exterior of the smaller circle but in the interior of the larger circle

1.029 Diameter of the smaller circle, *BE*

1.030 Point *F*, interior to both circles

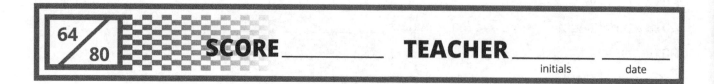

64/80 **SCORE** ________ **TEACHER** ________ initials ________ date

2. TANGENTS, ARCS, AND CHORDS

Three important concepts related to circles are **tangents**, **arcs**, and **chords**. In this section we shall define these terms and learn some theorems and postulates that deal with them.

Section Objectives

Review these objectives. When you have finished this section, you should be able to:

2. Define tangents.
3. Use theorems related to tangents.
4. Use arcs to measure central angles and central angles to measure arcs.
5. Find the measure of the angle formed by the hands of a clock at any given time.
6. Solve problems related to chords, and secants.

TANGENTS

The word **tangent** is used in several ways. We have already used it in another LIFEPAC to mean a specific ratio of the sides of a right triangle. We shall now define the tangent as it relates to a circle and a line.

Consider a line and a circle in the same plane. They may intersect in one point, in two points, or in no points. In a plane, a line that intersects a circle in exactly one point is **tangent** to the circle. The line is called a tangent line and the point of intersection is called the **point of tangency.** Segments and rays may also be tangent to a circle.

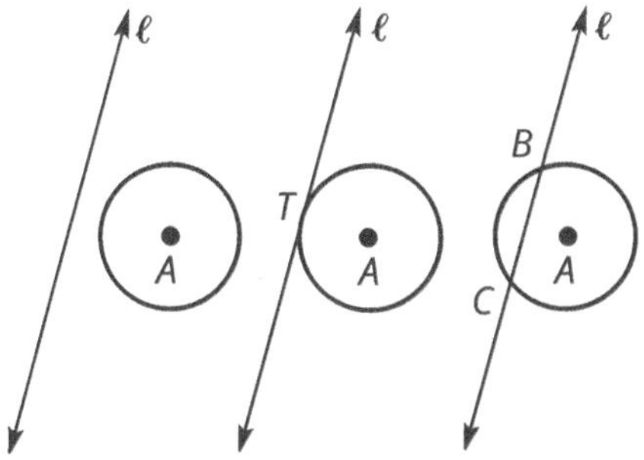

DEFINITION

Tangent line: a line in the plane of a circle that intersects the circle in one point.

Model: $\overleftrightarrow{CD}$, $\overrightarrow{DE}$, $\overline{CD}$, and $\overline{DE}$ are all tangent to circle *A* at point *D*. They are all in the plane and intersect the circle at point *D*.

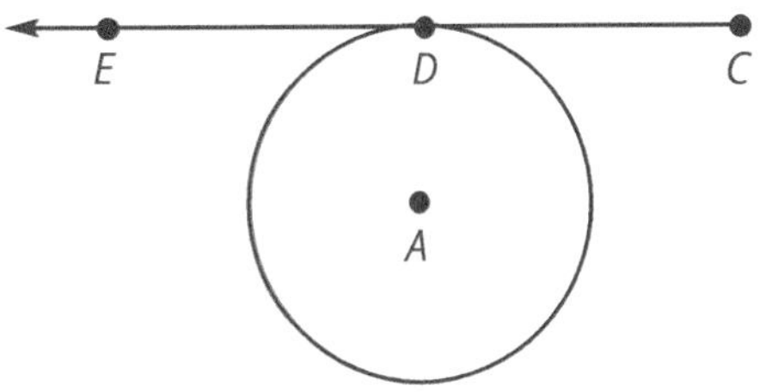

A tangent to a sphere is a line (ray or segment) or a plane that intersects the sphere in exactly one point. The point of intersection with the sphere is the point of tangency.

Line ℓ, $\overline{AB}$, $\overrightarrow{AB}$, and plane *M* are all tangent to sphere *S*.

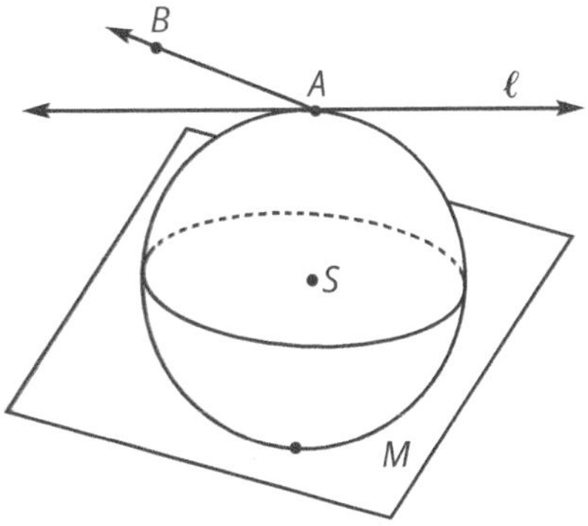

Notice that at a point on a circle, only one tangent line exists. However, at a point on a sphere, an infinite number of tangent lines exist in only one tangent plane.

A line that is tangent to each of two circles or spheres is called a **common tangent**.

In the case of circles, if the common tangent intersects the segment joining the centers, it is a **common internal tangent**. If it does not intersect the segment joining the centers, it is called a **common external tangent**.

DEFINITIONS FOR CIRCLES OR SPHERES

Common internal tangent: the common tangent intersecting the line segment joining the centers of circles.

Common external tangent: a common tangent that does not intersect the line segment joining the centers of circles.

Spheres can also have common tangents.

Notice that for circles the maximum number of common tangents is four: two internal and two external.

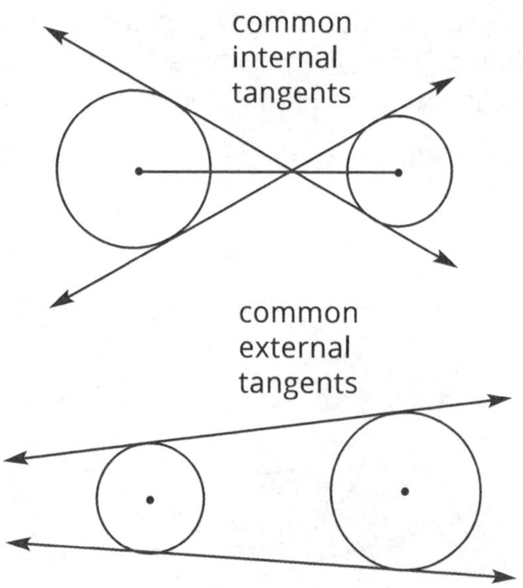

For spheres, however, the number of common tangent lines and planes is infinite.

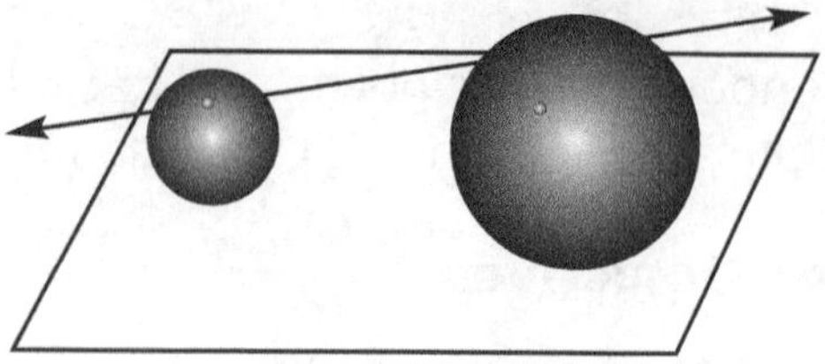

We also refer to circles being tangent to each other. Two coplanar circles are tangent to each other if both circles are tangent to the same line at the same point.

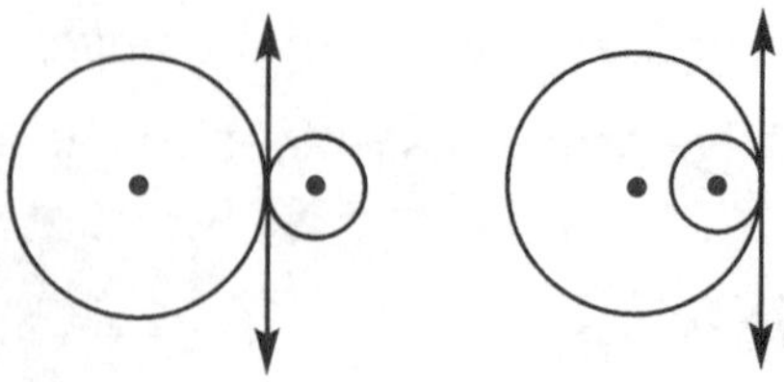

DEFINITIONS FOR TWO CIRCLES WITH A COMMON TANGENT

Externally tangent circles: tangent circles where their centers are on opposite sides of the common tangent line. They have one common internal tangent.

Internally tangent circles: two tangent circles where their centers are on the same side of the common tangent line. They have one common external tangent.

A polygon that has each of its sides tangent to a circle is **circumscribed** about the circle. The circle is also said to be *inscribed* in the polygon.

DEFINITION

Circumscribed polygon: a polygon with all sides tangent to a circle contained within the polygon.

Model 1: Each side of the polygon is tangent to circle *M*; therefore, quadrilateral *ABCD* is circumscribed about circle *M*.

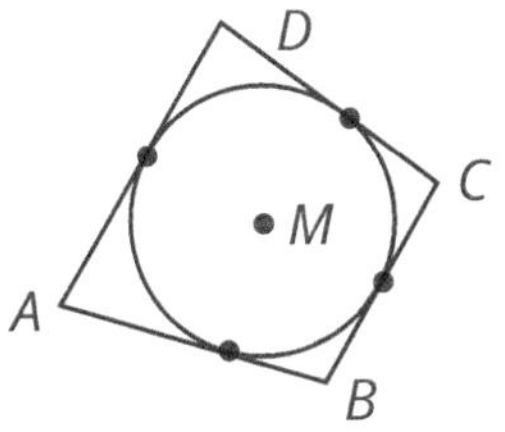

Model 2: Circle *R* is inscribed in triangle *ABC*. All three sides are tangent to the circle.

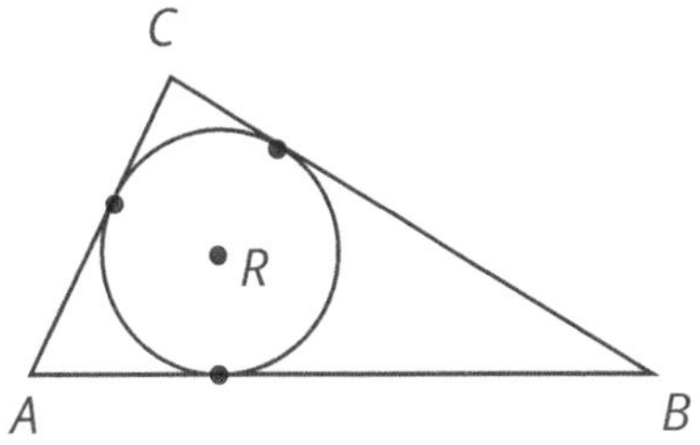

Refer to the figure to complete the following activities.

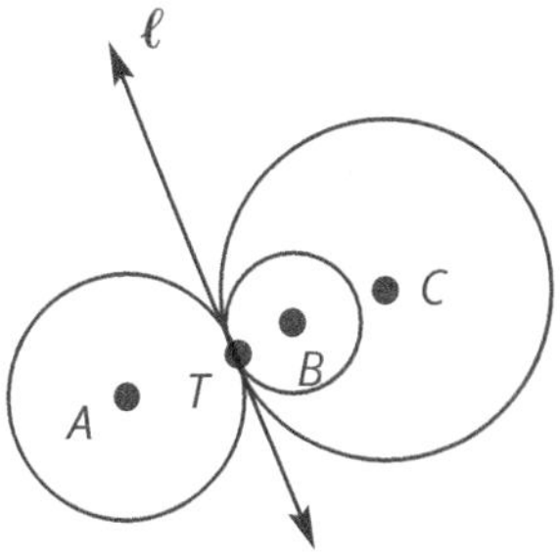

2.1 Name two internally tangent circles.

2.2 Name two externally tangent circles.

2.3 Name two circles to which ℓ is a common external tangent. ____________________

2.4 Name two circles to which ℓ is a common internal tangent. ____________________

2.5 Are any concentric circles shown? ____________

Refer to the figures to complete the following activities.

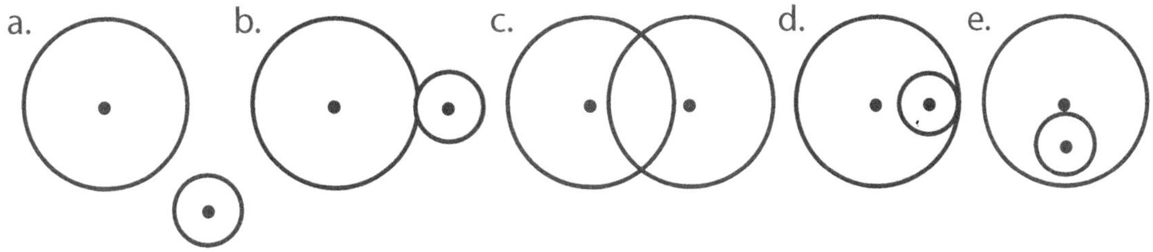

2.6 How many common internal tangents can be drawn for illustration?

a. ______________ b. ______________ c. ______________

d. ______________ e. ______________

2.7 How many common external tangents can be drawn for illustration?

a. ______________ b. ______________ c. ______________

d. ______________ e. ______________

Think of a., b., c., d., and e. as being spheres for Problems 2.8 and 2.9.

2.8 How many common tangent planes can be drawn for illustration?

a. ____________ b. ____________ c. ____________

d. ____________ e. ____________

2.9 How many common tangent lines can be drawn for illustration?

a. ____________ b. ____________ c. ____________

d. ____________ e. ____________

Sketch the required figures.

2.10 A right triangle circumscribed about a circle

2.11 An obtuse triangle circumscribed about a circle

2.12 An isosceles trapezoid circumscribed about a circle

2.13 A non-isosceles trapezoid circumscribed about a circle

2.14 a. A rhombus circumscribed about a circle

b. Must the rhombus be a square?

____

2.15 a. A rectangle circumscribed about a circle

b. Must the rectangle be a square?

____

2.16 Two circles that cannot have a common tangent

2.17 Two circles that have two common external tangents but no common internal tangents

2.18 Two circles that have exactly four common tangents

2.19 Two circles that have exactly three common tangents

2.20 Two circles that have exactly two common tangents

2.21 Two circles that have exactly one common tangent

Refer to the figure to name the following parts.

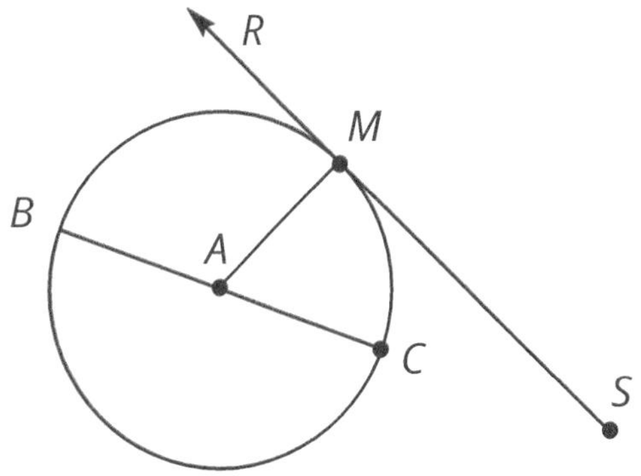

2.22 A segment tangent to circle *A*

____

2.23 A diameter of circle *A*

____

2.24 A point of tangency ______________________________

2.25 Why is *BC* not a tangent to circle *A*?

____

Find the required lengths.

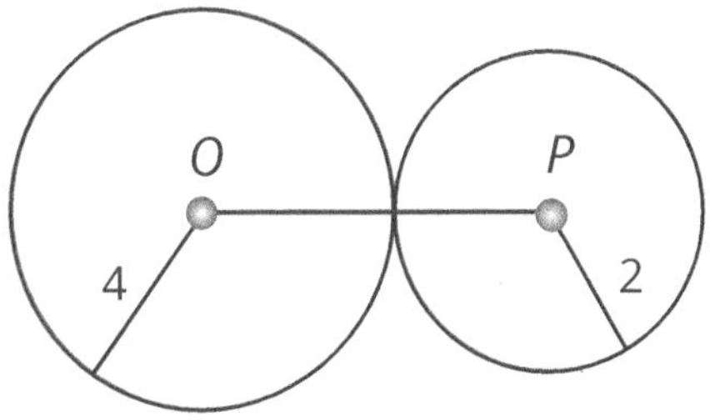

2.26 *OP* = ______________________________

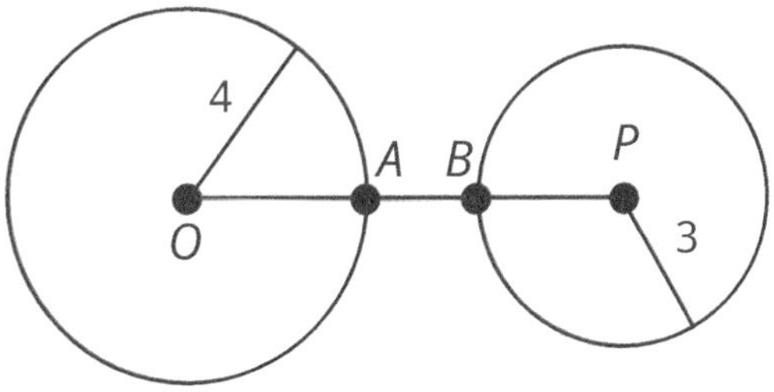

2.27 *OP* = 9

a. *BP* = ______________________________

b. *OA* = ______________________________

c. *AB* = ______________________________

2.28 $OA = 8$

$OP =$ ______________________

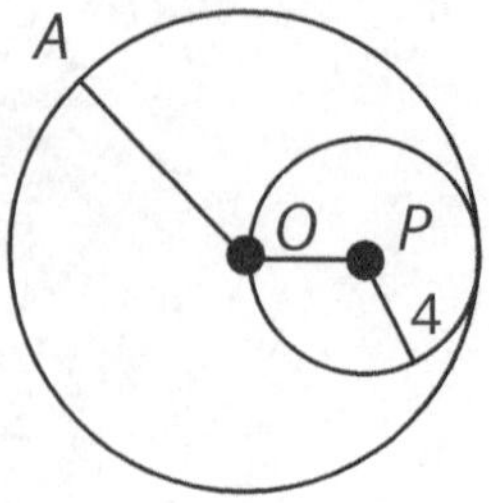

2.29 $AP =$ ______________________

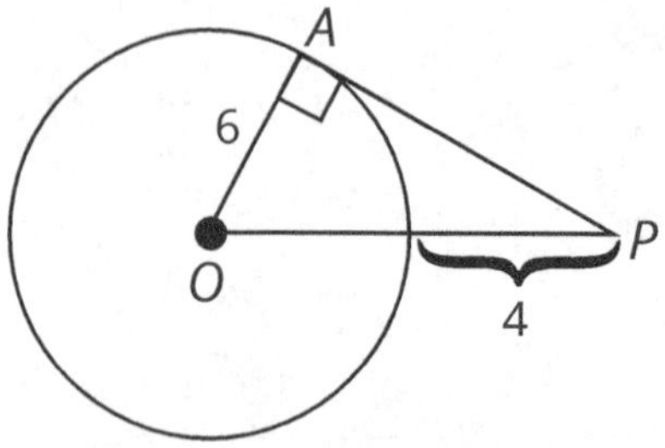

2.30 $ON =$ ______________________

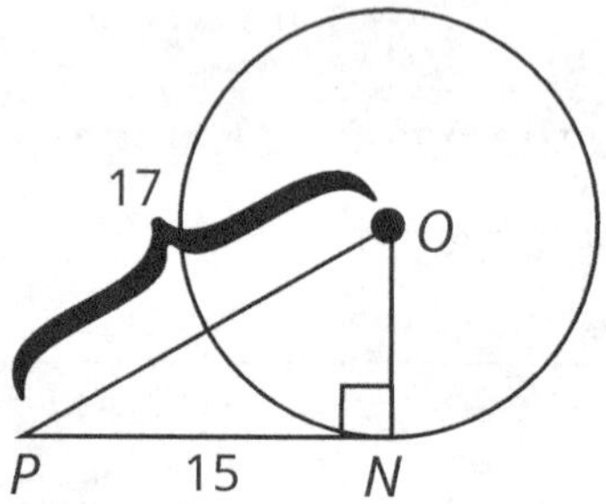

ARCS

We know that a circle is the set of all points equidistant from the center. It is the ring formed around a point. If we were to take just a part of that ring or circle, we would then have what we call an arc. The rainbow that God used as a sign of his covenant with Noah after the Flood was an arc.

We will study three kinds of arcs: the minor arc, the major arc, and the semicircle.

MINOR ARC

To define an arc, we must first define a special angle that is related to a circle.

> **DEFINITION**
>
> **Central angle:** an angle in the plane of a circle with the vertex at the center of the circle.

Models: Central angles of circle *R* are $\angle 1$ and $\angle 2$.

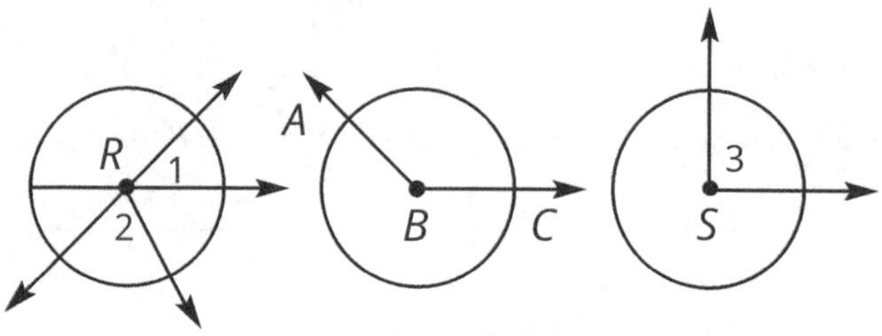

A central angle of circle *B* is $\angle ABC$.

A central angle of circle *S* is $\angle 3$.

Now we can define the first type of arcs.

> **DEFINITION**
>
> **Minor arc:** the union of two points of a circle, not end points of a diameter, and all points of the circle that are in the interior of the central angle whose sides contain the two points.

We name a minor arc by using the points where the central angle intersects the circle and then putting an $\frown$ over the letters.

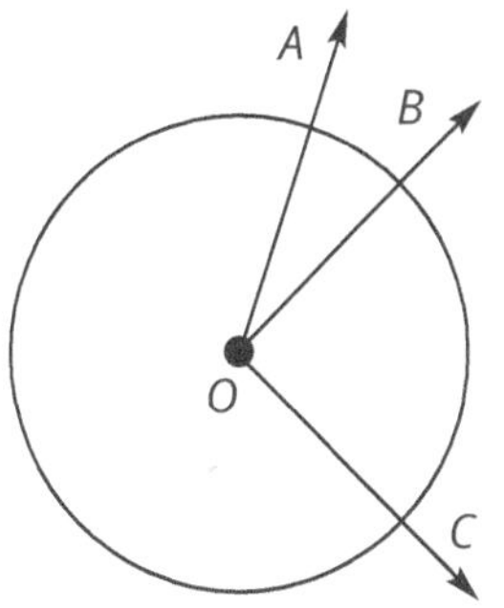

Minor arc $\overset{\frown}{AB}$ is the part of the circle that is in the interior of $\angle AOB$. Minor arc $\overset{\frown}{BC}$ is the part of the circle in the interior of $\angle BOC$. Minor arc $\overset{\frown}{ABC}$ or $\overset{\frown}{AC}$ is the part of the circle in the interior of $\angle AOC$. We usually use only two letters to name a minor arc, but we can use three if necessary.

MAJOR ARC

Do you think you can guess what a major arc is?

> **DEFINITION**
>
> **Major arc:** the union of two points of a circle, not the end points of a diameter; and all points of the circle that are in the exterior of the central angle whose sides contain the two points.

We name a major arc by using three points of the circle. We use the two points where the central angle intersects the circle and a point of the circle in the exterior of the central angle.

Model 1: $\overset{\frown}{AB}$ is a minor arc.

$\overset{\frown}{AXB}$ is a major arc.

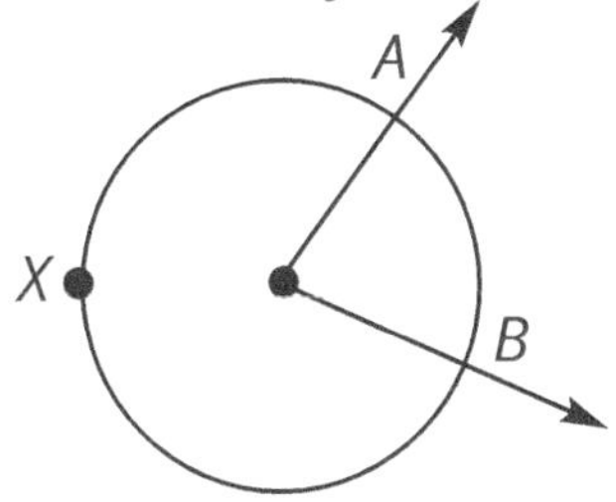

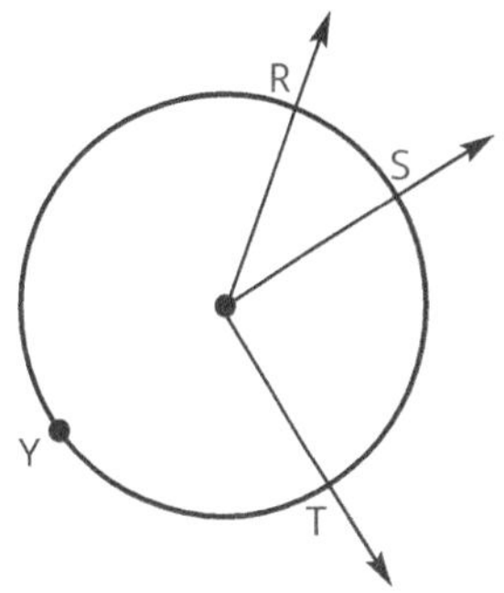

Model 2: $\overset{\frown}{RS}$ is a minor arc.

$\overset{\frown}{RYS}$ or $\overset{\frown}{RTS}$ is a major arc.

$\overset{\frown}{ST}$ is a minor arc.

$\overset{\frown}{SYT}$ or $\overset{\frown}{SRT}$ is a major arc.

$\overset{\frown}{RT}$ is a minor arc.

$\overset{\frown}{RYT}$ is a major arc.

We must always use three letters to name a major arc.

SEMICIRCLE

The third type of arc is a semicircle.

> **DEFINITION**
>
> **Semicircle:** the union of the end points of a diameter and all points of the circle lying on one side of the diameter.

$\overset{\frown}{RXS}$ is one semicircle and $\overset{\frown}{RYS}$ is another semicircle of circle *A*.

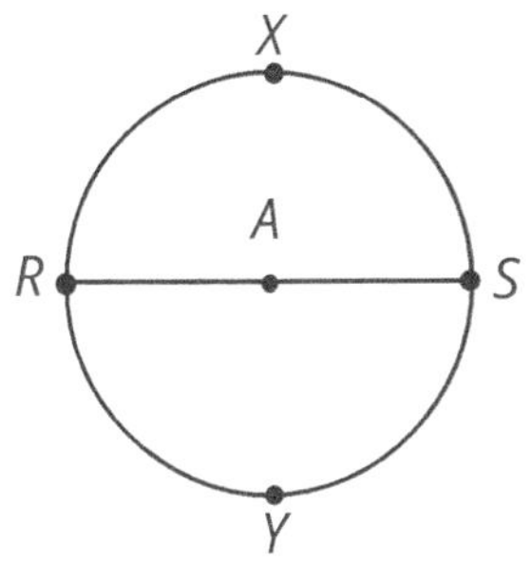

If we take a minor arc and its major arc and put them together, we get the complete circle. Minor arc $\overset{\frown}{AB}$ and major arc $\overset{\frown}{BCA}$ together give us the complete circle *O*.

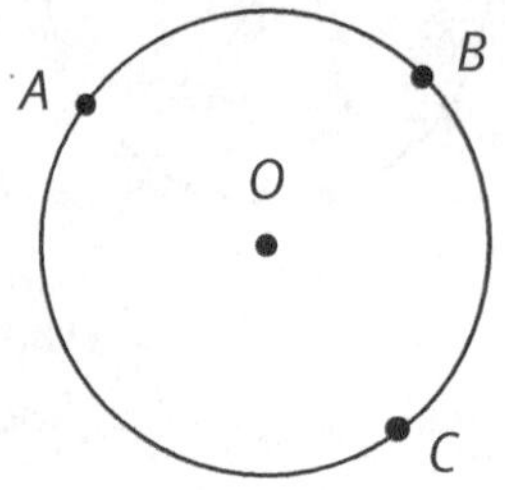

Both semicircles of a circle will also give us the complete circle. Semicircle $\overset{\frown}{MXN}$ and semicircle $\overset{\frown}{NYM}$ together give us the complete circle *P*.

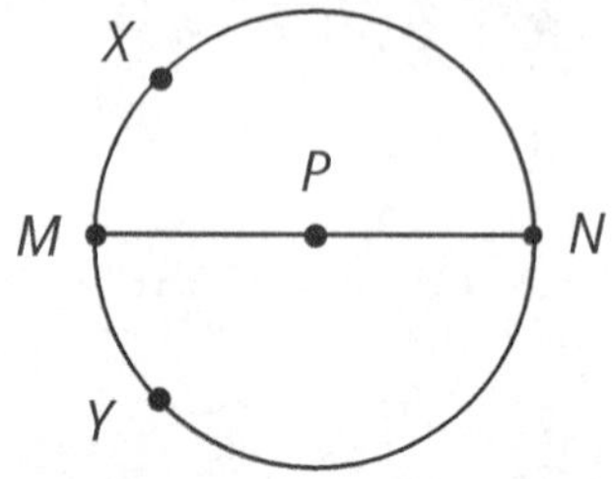

Next we shall find a way to measure these arcs. We define the measure of a minor arc to be the same as the measure of its central angle.

If $m\angle 1 = 60°$, then $m\,\overset{\frown}{AB} = 60°$.

If $m\angle 2 = 50°$, then $m\,\overset{\frown}{BC} = 50°$.

If $m\angle 3 = 150°$, then $m\,\overset{\frown}{CD} = 150°$.

If $m\,\overset{\frown}{AD} = 100°$, then $m\angle 4 = 100°$.

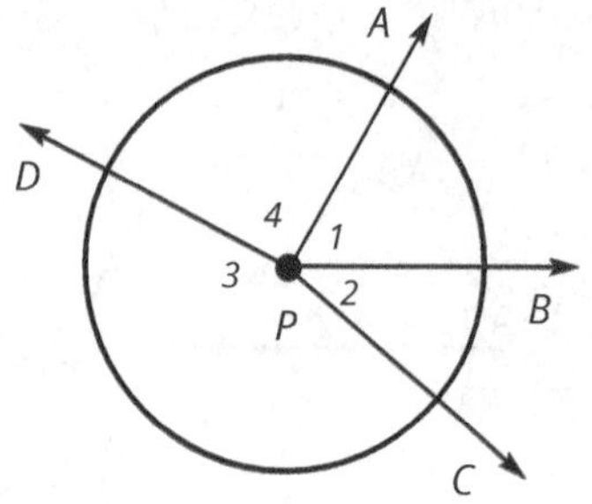

The measure of a minor arc equals the measure of its central angle. Since a complete circle contains 360 degrees, we know that the measure of a major arc equals 360° minus the measure of its minor arc.

If $m\angle 1 = 70°$, then minor arc $\overset{\frown}{PQ} = 70°$ and major arc $\overset{\frown}{PSQ} = 360° - 70° = 290°$.

If $m\angle 2 = 90°$, then minor arc $\overset{\frown}{RQ} = 90°$ and major arc $\overset{\frown}{RSQ} = 360° - 90° = 270°$.

If major arc $\overset{\frown}{PSR} = 200°$, then minor arc $\overset{\frown}{PR} = 360° - 200° = 160°$.

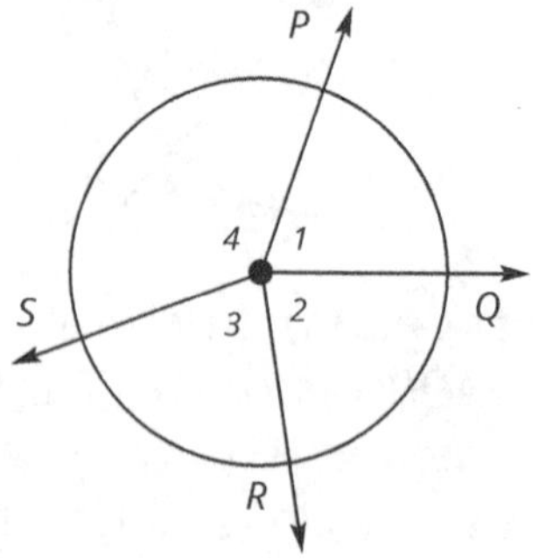

A minor arc and its major arc measure a total of 360°.

Since a circle has two related semicircles, we can measure each semicircle as 180 degrees.

MEASURES

Measure of minor arc equals measure of central angle.

Measure of major arc equals 360° minus measure of minor arc.

Measure of semicircle equals 180°.

Remember that these measures are angular measures of the arcs and not linear measures. In another LIFEPAC we shall measure arcs with feet, inches, meters and other linear units; but for now we are measuring arcs using degrees.

CLOCK ANGLES

An interesting application to the measure of arcs and central angles has to do with the hands of a clock. At different times during the day, the hands of a clock form different central angles. The angular distance that the tip of the hands travel can be thought of as an arc of a circle.

The problem is to find the angle formed by the hands of the clock at different times of the day. Some of the angles are easy to find; others require more thought.

At 3:00 and at 9:00 the hands form a 90-degree central angle. At 6:00 they form opposite rays. At 12:00 they are together and no angle is formed.

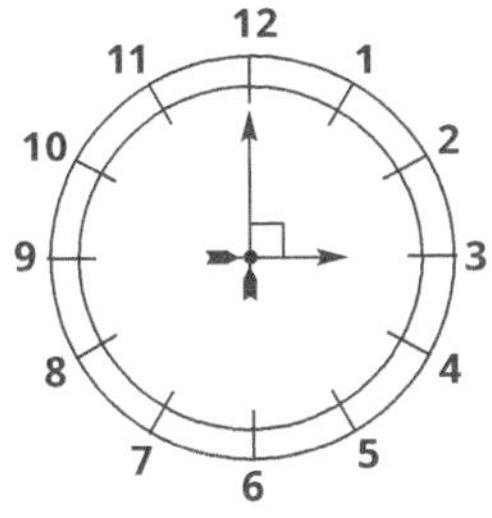

Most people think that at 3:30, 9:30, 12:15, and 11:45 the hands are perpendicular and form 90-degree angles; but the hands are not perpendicular at these times. Remember that as the tip of the minute hand moves through an arc of 360 degrees, the tip of the hour hand moves 30 degrees: 360 ÷ 12 = 30. The arc between each hour number equals 30°. So at 3:30 the minute hand is on the 6 and the hour hand is halfway between 3 and 4. The arc for the central angle at 3:30 would be 75 degrees.

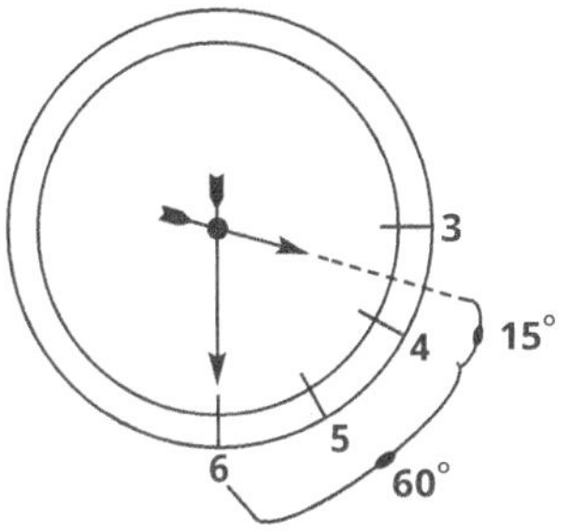

At 9:30 the hour hand is halfway from the 9 to the 10. The minute hand is on the 6. So the arc that is used measures 90° + 15° = 105°. The angle formed by the hands of a clock at 9:30 is 105 degrees.

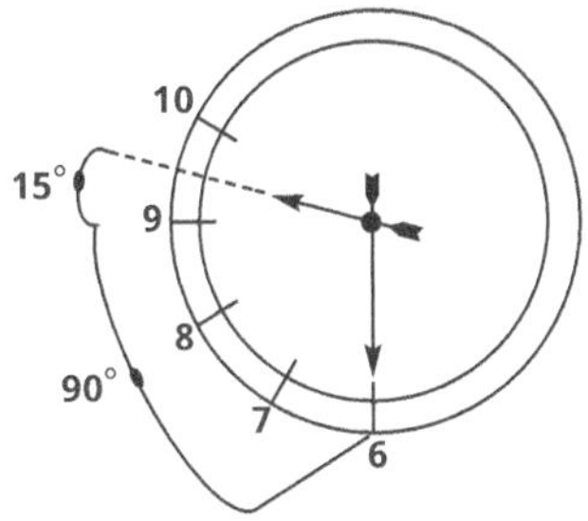

At 12:15 the hour hand has moved $\frac{15}{60}$, or $\frac{1}{4}$, of the way from 12 to 1. The minute hand is on the 3. One fourth of 30°= $7\frac{1}{2}$°. The arc between the hands is 60° + $22\frac{1}{2}$° = $82\frac{1}{2}$°.

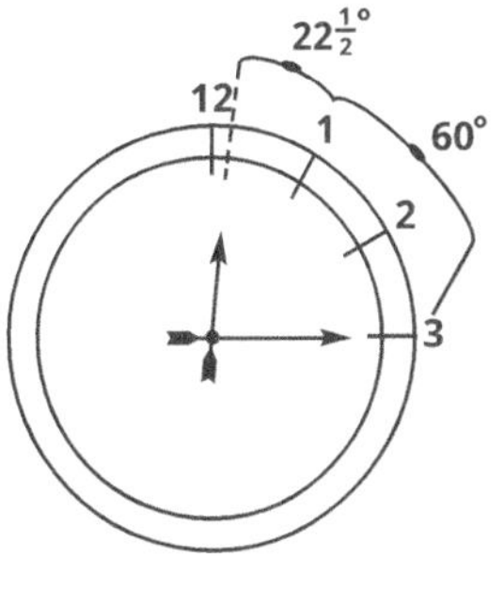

At 11:45 the hour hand is $\frac{45}{60}$ or $\frac{3}{4}$, of the way from 11 to 12. The minute hand is on the 9. Since $\frac{3}{4}$ of 30° = $22\frac{1}{2}$°, the hands form a central angle of 60° + $22\frac{1}{2}$° = $82\frac{1}{2}$°.

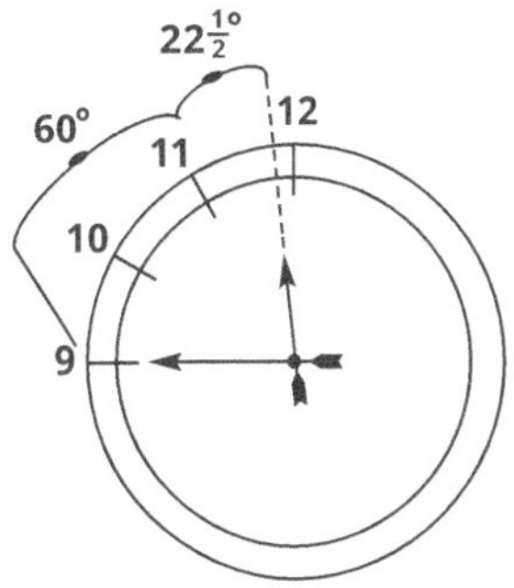

Now try one a little harder. Find the angle formed by the hands of a clock at 2:28. The hour hand is $\frac{28}{60}$, or $\frac{7}{15}$ of the way from 2 to 3: $\frac{7}{15}$ of 30° = 14°. The minute hand is $\frac{3}{5}$ of the way from 5 to 6: $\frac{3}{5}$ of 30° = 18°. The total arc would be 16° + 60° + 18° = 94°. The angle formed by the hands of the clock at 2:28 is 94°.

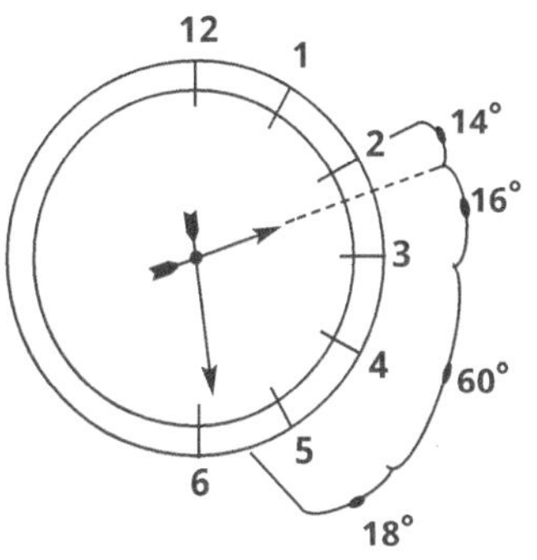

Refer to the figure to complete the following activities.

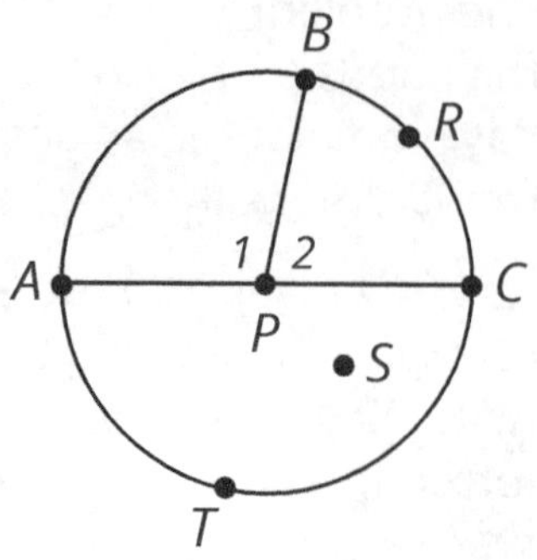

2.31 Is S a point of the circle? ____________

2.32 Is P a point of the circle? ____________

2.33 If $\overline{BP} \perp \overline{PC}$, what is m $\overset{\frown}{BC}$? ____________

2.34 If m$\angle 1 = 90°$, what is m $\overset{\frown}{ACB}$? ____________

2.35 If $\overline{AC}$ is a diameter, name two semicircles.

____________ ____________

2.36 If $\overline{AC}$ is a diameter, name two minor arcs. ____________ .

2.37 If $\overline{AC}$ is a diameter, name two major arcs. ____________ .

2.38 If m$\angle 1 = 110°$, name an arc with a measure of 110°: a. ____________

Name an arc with a measure of 250°: b. ____________

2.39 In a circle with an 8-inch radius, a central angle has a measure of 60°.

How long is the segment joining the endpoints of the arc cut off by the angle?

____

Complete these activities by finding the measure of the angle formed by the hands of a clock at the given times.

2.40 ____________ 9:50

2.41 ____________ 8:00

2.42 ____________ 2:00

2.43 ____________ 3:20

2.44 ____________ 10:15

2.45 ____________ 8:30

2.46 ____________ 4:52

2.47 ____________ 11:00

2.48 ____________ 2:40

2.49 ____________ 10:50

2.50 ____________ 12:01

Refer to the figure to find the following measures.

Given: *BD* is a diameter
$m\angle 1 = 100^\circ$
$m\,\overset{\frown}{BC} = 30^\circ$

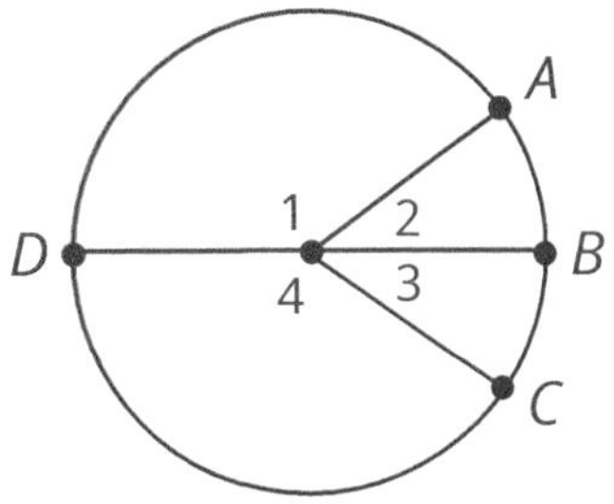

2.51 $m\angle 2$ = ____________________

2.52 $m\angle 3$ = ____________________

2.53 $m\angle 4$ = ____________________

2.54 $m\,\overset{\frown}{AD}$ = ____________________

2.55 $m\,\overset{\frown}{AC}$ = ____________________

2.56 $m\,\overset{\frown}{DC}$ = ____________________

2.57 $m\,\overset{\frown}{ADB}$ = ____________________

2.58 $m\,\overset{\frown}{DAB}$ = ____________________

2.59 $m\,\overset{\frown}{DAC}$ = ____________________

2.60 $m\,\overset{\frown}{CAB}$ = ____________________

CHORDS

If we connect the end points of an arc or a semicircle we form a segment that lies in the interior of the circle. This figure is called a **chord**.

> **DEFINITION**
> **Chord:** a segment with end points on the circle.

Model: $\overline{DE}$, $\overline{GH}$, and $\overline{IJ}$ are chords. Their endpoints are on the circle. Notice that chord $\overline{IJ}$ passes through the center of the circle. Therefore, chord $\overline{IJ}$ is also a diameter of the circle.

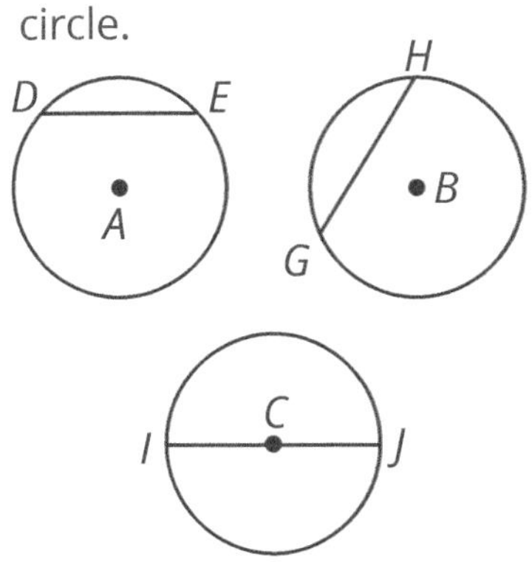

An alternate definition of diameter uses the idea of a chord: a diameter is a chord that passes through the center of the circle.

If we make a line out of our chord by extending both ends, we get another figure called a **secant**.

> **DEFINITION**
> **Secant:** a line that contains a chord.

Model: $\overleftrightarrow{DE}$, $\overleftrightarrow{GH}$, and $\overleftrightarrow{IJ}$ are secants to the circle. Notice that the secant intersects the circle in two points.

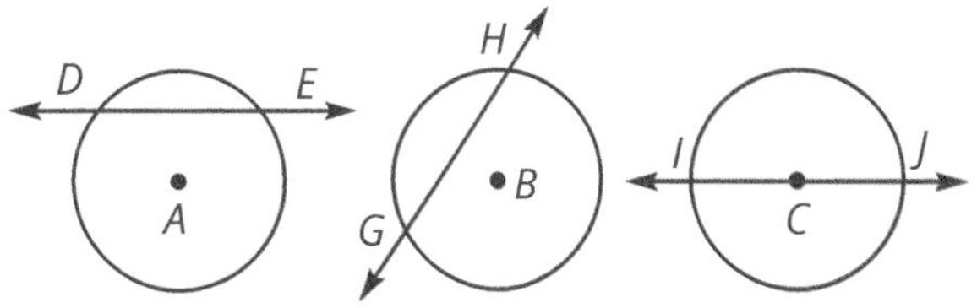

The definitions for chords and secants to a sphere are almost identical to those for a circle. A chord of a sphere is a segment with end points on the sphere. A secant to a sphere is a line that contains a chord of the sphere.

One other definition we will need is that for an **inscribed polygon**. A polygon is said to be inscribed in a circle when each side of the polygon is a chord of the circle. Each vertex will be a point of the circle. We also can say that the circle circumscribes the polygon.

> **DEFINITION**
> **Inscribed polygon:** a polygon contained within a circle, with each side being a chord of the circle.

Models: Triangle *ABC* is inscribed in circle *W*.

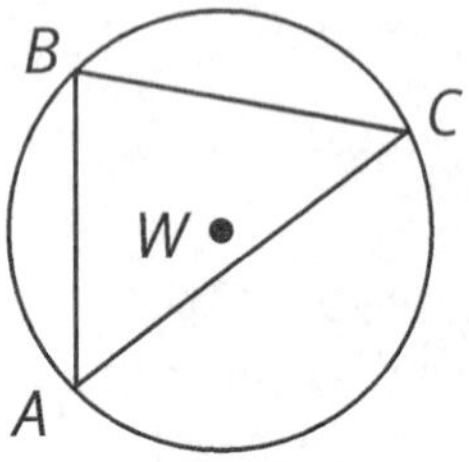

Quadrilateral *DEFG* is inscribed in circle *X*.

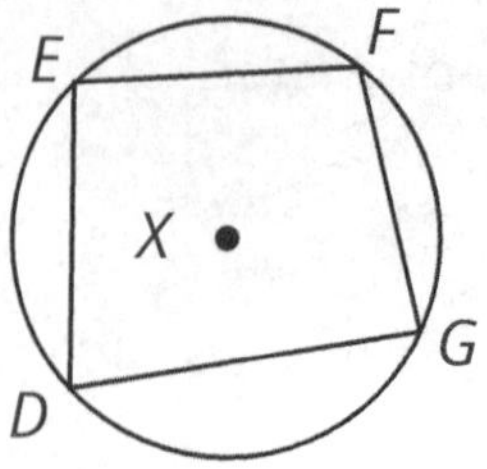

Circle *Y* circumscribes polygon *HIJKL*.

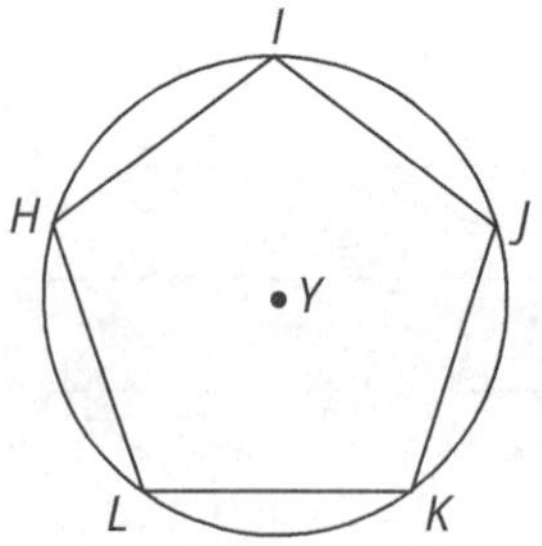

Refer to the figure to complete the following activities.

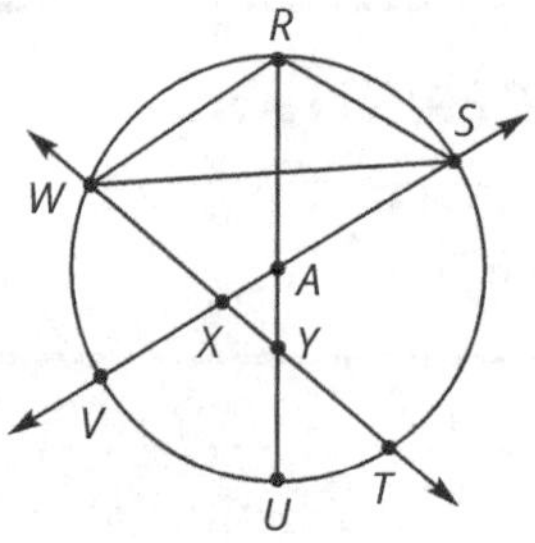

2.61 Name all the chords shown. ____________________

2.62 Name all the secants shown. ____________________

2.63 Name all the tangents shown. ____________________

2.64 Is triangle *AXY* inscribed in circle *A*? __________

2.65 Is triangle *WSR* inscribed in circle *A*? __________

2.66 Name all the diameters shown. ____________________

2.67 Name all the radii shown. ____________________

Refer to the figure to complete the following items.

2.68 Name three radii. ________________________

2.69 Name three chords. ________________________

2.70 Name two secants. ________________________

2.71 Name a diameter. ________________________

2.72 Name a tangent. ________________________

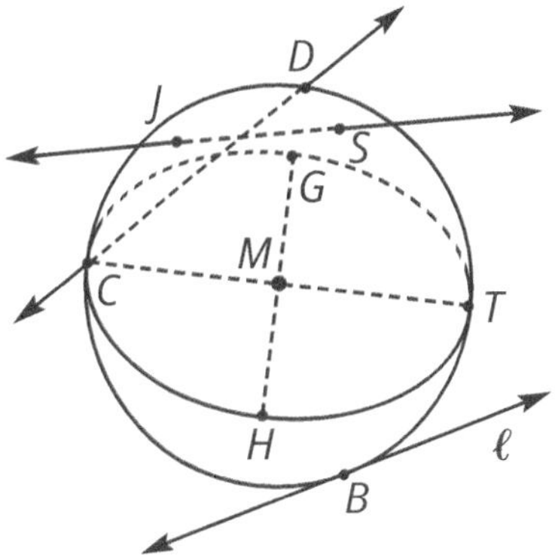

Complete these items.

2.73 State a definition for a polygon inscribed in a sphere.

____

____

____

2.74 Draw a sketch of triangle *ABC* inscribed in sphere *P*.

Write whether each triangle is inscribed in the circle, circumscribed about the circle, or neither.

2.75 ________________________

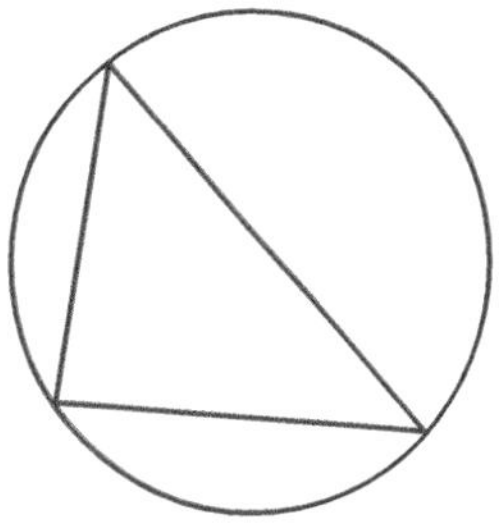

2.76 ________________________

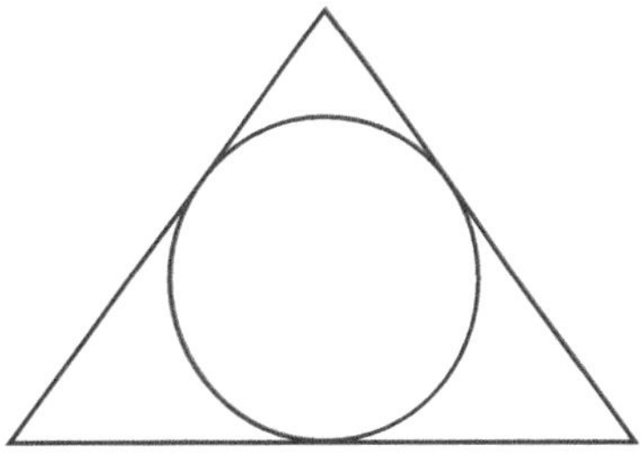

2.77 ______________________________

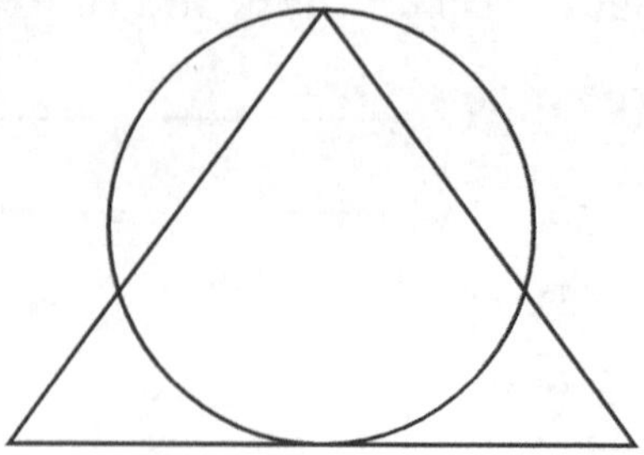

2.78 ______________________________

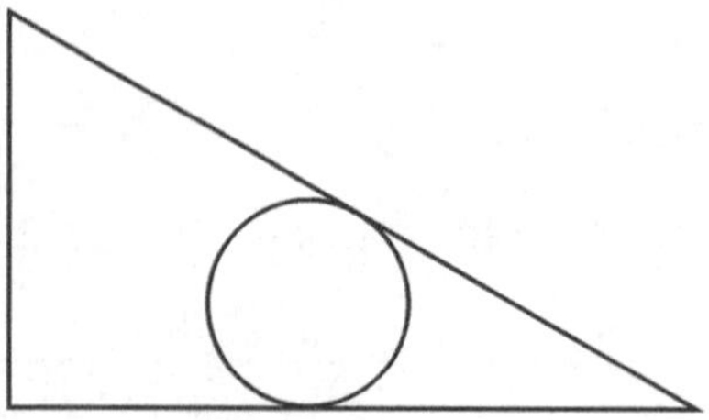

2.79 ______________________________

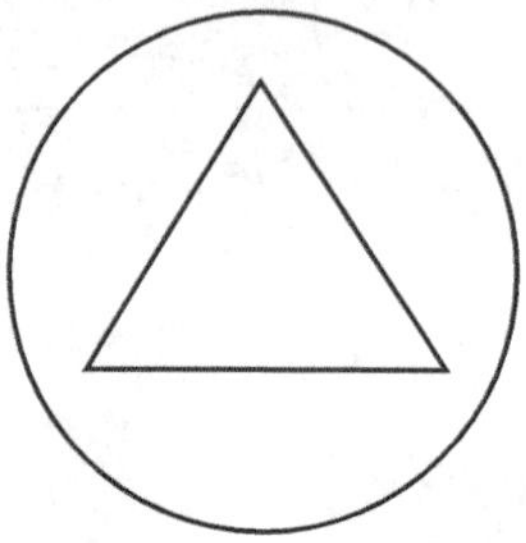

THEOREMS

We now will study several theorems that relate to tangents, arcs, and chords of a circle.

> **THEOREM 6-1**
>
> A radius drawn to a point of tangency is perpendicular to the tangent.

Given: t tangent to circle P at A.

To Prove: $\overline{PA} \perp t$

Plan: Use an indirect proof

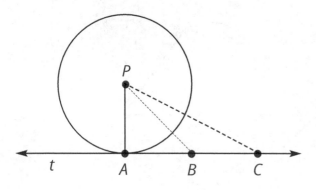

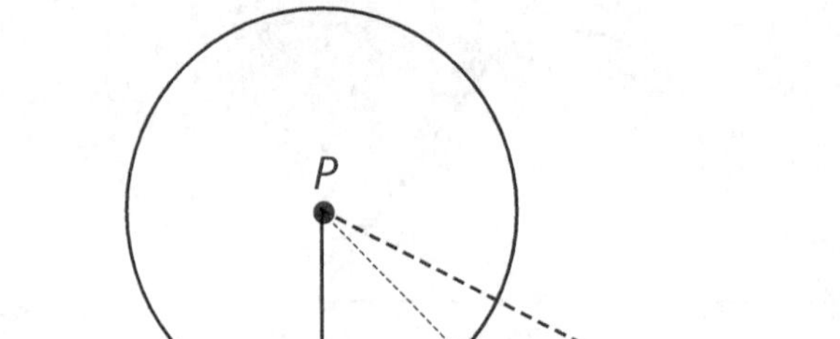

Suppose t is not perpendicular to $\overline{PA}$. Let $\overline{PB}$ be perpendicular to t because exactly one perpendicular goes from a point to a line. Next choose a point C on the ray opposite $\overrightarrow{BA}$ so that $BC = AB$.

Draw $\overline{PC}$. Now $\triangle PAB \cong \triangle PCB$ by *SAS*, so $PA = PC$ by *CPCTE*. Therefore, $\overline{PC}$ is also a radius of the circle and point C is on the circle. Thus t intersects the circle in two points, A and C. This condition, however, contradicts the given information that t is a tangent. Therefore, our supposition that t is not perpendicular to $\overline{PA}$ is false; and the statement that t is perpendicular to $\overline{PA}$ is true.

The converse of this theorem is also true.

> **THEOREM 6-2**
>
> A line in the plane of a circle and perpendicular to a radius at its outer endpoint is tangent to the circle.

Complete the following proofs.

2.80 Given: $\overline{AB}$ is diameter of circle O

$\overleftrightarrow{AC}$ and $\overleftrightarrow{BD}$ are tangents

Prove: $\overleftrightarrow{AC} \parallel \overleftrightarrow{BD}$

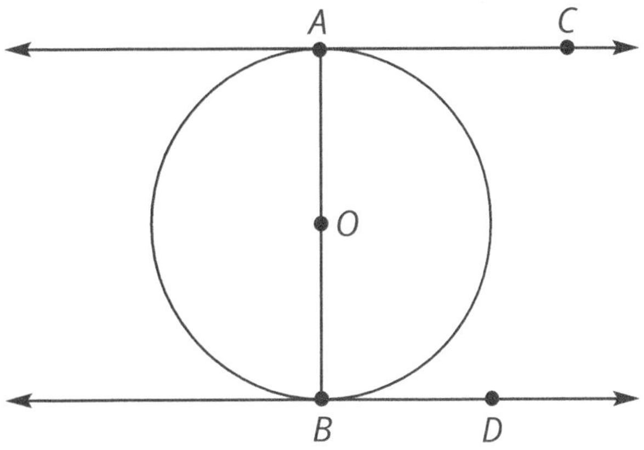

STATEMENT	REASON

2.81 Given: $\overleftrightarrow{RS}$ tangent to $\odot A$ and $\odot B$ at points R and S.

Prove: $\overline{AR} \parallel \overline{BS}$

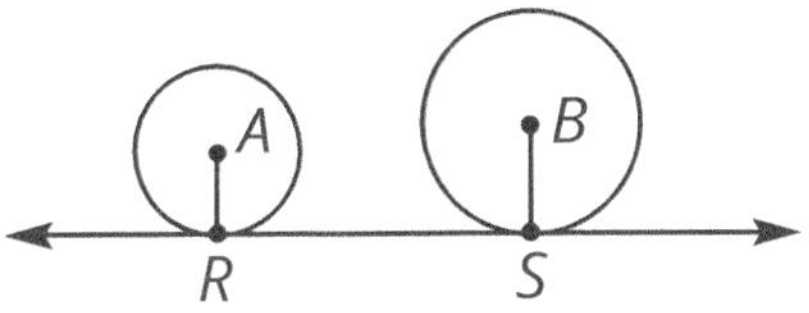

STATEMENT	REASON

2.82 Given: $\overline{PA}$, $\overline{PB}$ tangent to $\odot R$ at points A and B

Prove: $PA = PB$
(Hint: Draw $\overline{RA}$, $\overline{RB}$, $\overline{RP}$, and prove $\triangle$'s $\cong$).

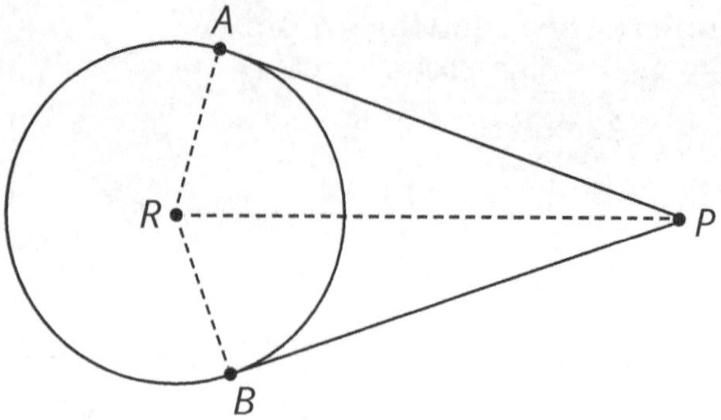

STATEMENT	REASON

2.83 Given: $\overline{AE}$ tangent to $\odot R$ at A and to circle S at E

Proven: $\angle R = \angle S$

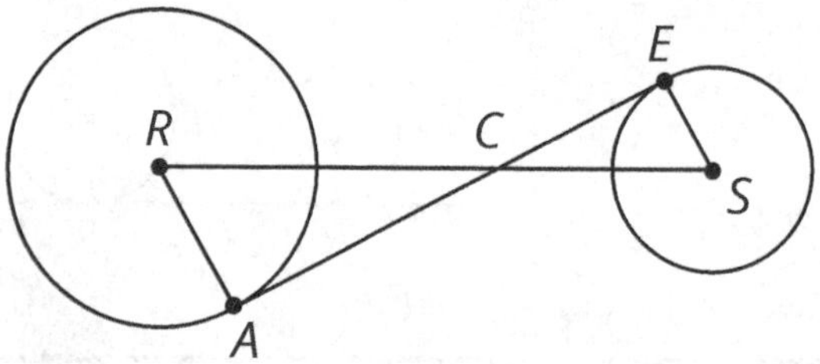

STATEMENT	REASON

2.84 Given: Two concentric circles with $\overline{AB}$ tangent to smaller circle at R

Prove: $AR = RB$

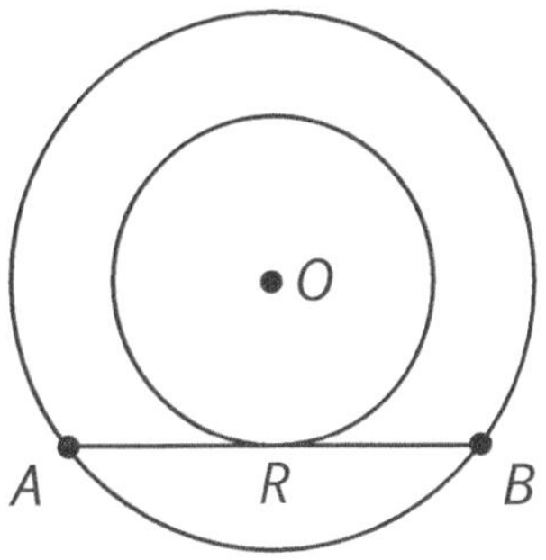

STATEMENT	REASON

Recall that we have a method of adding the lengths of segments by using the betweenness definition. We can add the measures of angles by using the angle addition theorem. We will now state a postulate that will allow us to add arcs.

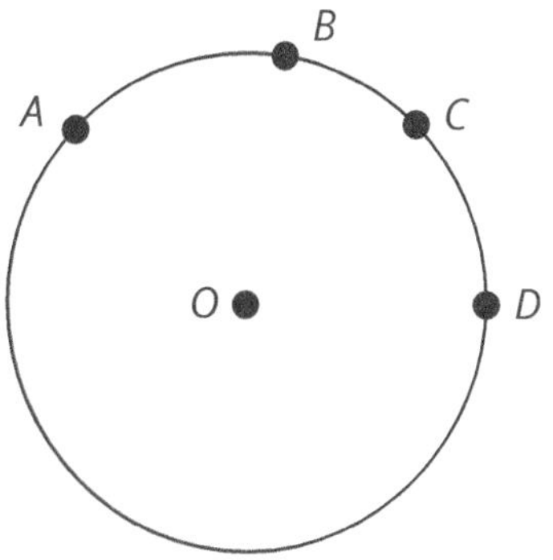

POSTULATE 16

P16: If the intersection of $\widehat{AB}$ and $\widehat{BC}$ of a circle is the single point B, then $m\,\widehat{AB} + m\,\widehat{BC} = m\,\widehat{ABC}$.

(Arc addition postulate)

When using the arc addition postulate, we must make sure the intersection of the arcs is a single point. We could not add $\widehat{AB}$ and $\widehat{CD}$ because their intersection is empty. We cannot add $\widehat{AC}$ and $\widehat{BD}$ because their intersection is more than one point: it is $\widehat{BC}$.

Models: $m\,\widehat{AB} + m\,\widehat{BC} = m\,\widehat{ABC}$

$m\,\widehat{AC} + m\,\widehat{CD} = m\,\widehat{ACD}$

$m\,\widehat{BC} + m\,\widehat{CD} = m\,\widehat{BCD}$

THEOREM 6-3

If in the same circle or congruent circles two central angles are equal, then their arcs are equal.

Given: $\odot A \cong \odot B$
$\angle 1 = \angle 2$

Prove: $m\overset{\frown}{RS} = m\overset{\frown}{TU}$

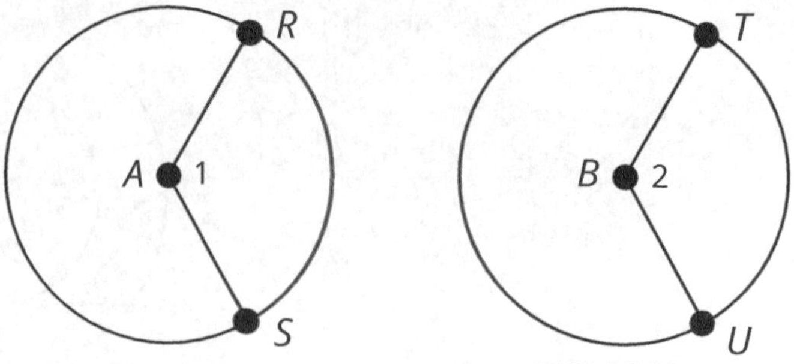

STATEMENT	REASON
1. $\odot A \cong \odot B$ $\angle 1 = \angle 2$	1. Given
2. $m\overset{\frown}{RS} = m\angle 1$ $m\overset{\frown}{TU} = m\angle 2$	2. Measure of arc = central angle
3. $m\overset{\frown}{RS} = m\overset{\frown}{TU}$	3. Substitution

The converse of Theorem 6-3 is also true.

THEOREM 6-4

If in the same circle or congruent circles two minor arcs are equal, then their central angles are equal.

Complete the following proofs.

2.85 Given: Points *R*, *S*, *T*, *Q* on circle *O*

Prove: $m\overset{\frown}{RS} + m\overset{\frown}{ST} + m\overset{\frown}{TQ} = m\overset{\frown}{RQ}$

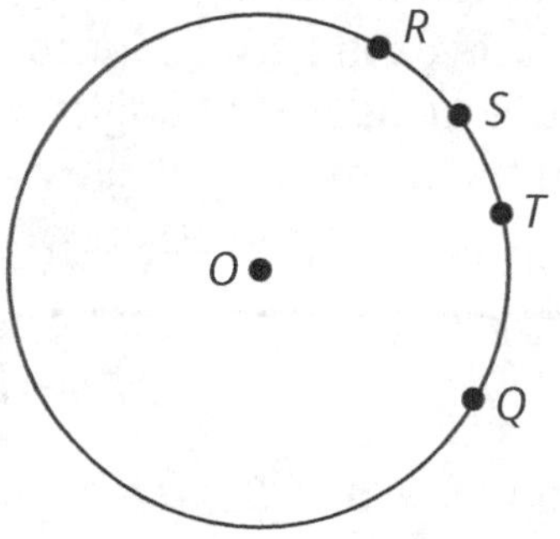

STATEMENT	REASON

2.86 Given: $\overline{AB}$, $\overline{CD}$ are diameters

Prove: $BD = CA$

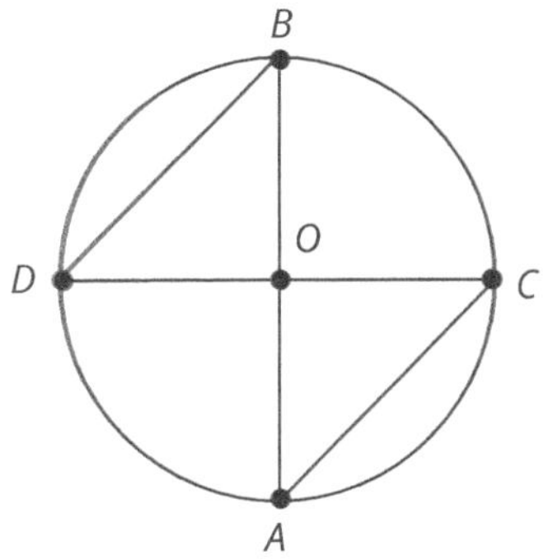

STATEMENT	REASON

2.87 Given: $m\angle XOY = m\angle WOV$

$m\,\widehat{YZ} = m\,\widehat{ZW}$

Prove: $m\,\widehat{XZ} = m\,\widehat{ZV}$

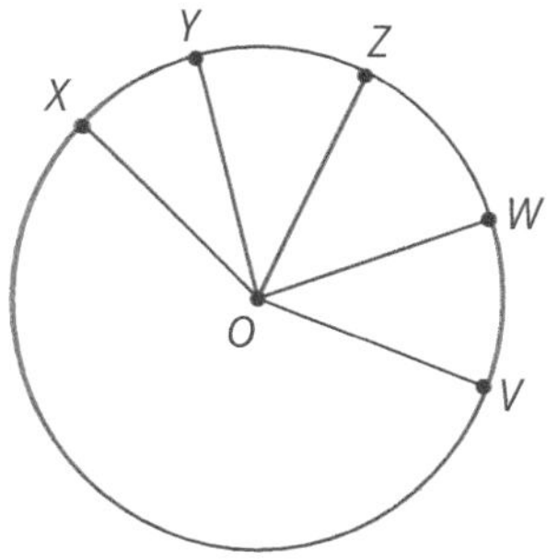

STATEMENT	REASON

2.88 Given: *SW* is diameter of $\odot R$

$m\overset{\frown}{TS} = 30°$

Prove: $m\angle T = 15°$

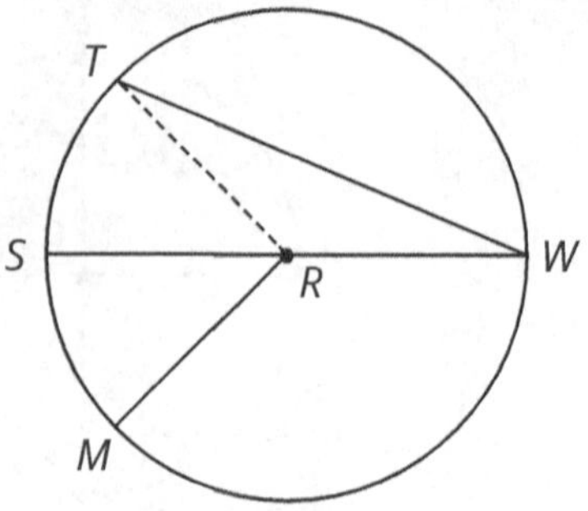

STATEMENT	REASON

Identify each arc as a major arc, a minor arc, or a semicircle for a.; find its measure for b.

2.89 $\overset{\frown}{QR}$ a. ______________________ b.______________

2.90 $\overset{\frown}{QSP}$ a. ______________________ b. ______________

2.91 $\overset{\frown}{PQR}$ a. ______________________ b. ______________

2.92 $\overset{\frown}{PQ}$ a. ______________________ b. ______________

2.93 $\overset{\frown}{PQS}$ a. ______________________ b. ______________

2.94 $\overset{\frown}{QRS}$ a. ______________________ b. ______________

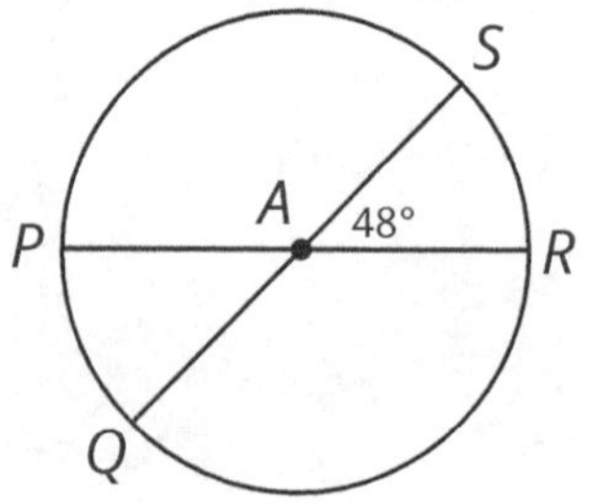

THEOREM 6-5

In the same circle or congruent circles if the chords are equal, then the arcs are equal.

Given: $\odot A \cong \odot B$

$CD = EF$

Prove: $m\,\overset{\frown}{CD} = m\,\overset{\frown}{EF}$

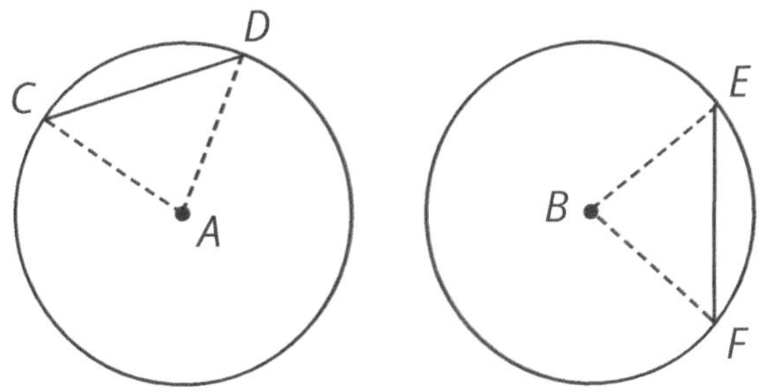

STATEMENT	REASON
1. Draw $\overline{AC}, \overline{AD}, \overline{BE}, \overline{BF}$	1. Auxiliary lines
2. $AC = BE, AD = BF$	2. Radii of congruent circles are equal.
3. $CD = EF$	3. Given
4. $\triangle ACD \cong \triangle BEF$	4. SSS
5. $\angle A = \angle B$	5. CPCTE
6. $m\,\overset{\frown}{CD} = m\,\overset{\frown}{EF}$	6. If central angles =, then arcs =.

The converse of Theorem 6–5 is also true.

THEOREM 6-6

In the same circle or in congruent circles if the arcs are equal, then the chords are equal.

The next theorem, Theorem 6–7, gives us three very useful equations dealing with diameters, chords, and arcs. First, however, we need to know the difference between the midpoint of an arc and the center of an arc.

DEFINITIONS

Midpoint of arc: a point X on the arc $\overset{\frown}{AB}$ such that $m\,\overset{\frown}{AX} = m\,\overset{\frown}{XB}$.

Center of an arc: the center of the circle that contains the arc.

Any line, ray, or segment that contains the midpoint of an arc *bisects* the arc.

Models: If $\overset{\frown}{AX} = \overset{\frown}{XB}$, then X is the midpoint of $\overset{\frown}{AB}$.

P is the center of $\overset{\frown}{AB}$.

t is a secant that bisects $\overset{\frown}{AB}$.

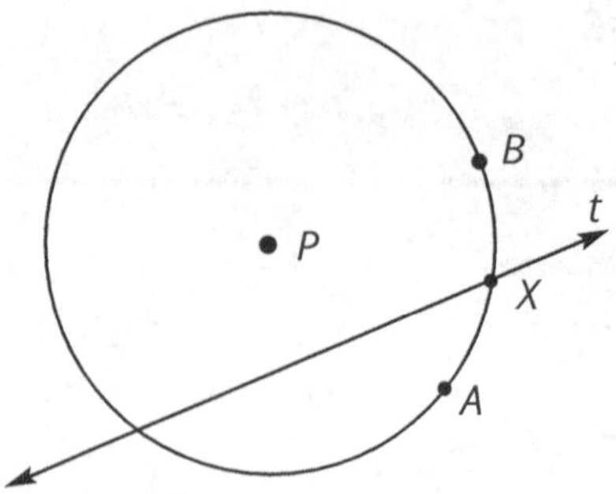

THEOREM 6-7

If a diameter is perpendicular to a chord, then it bisects the chord and its two arcs.

Given: $\overline{XY} \perp \overline{AB}$

Prove: $AC = CB$

$m\,\overset{\frown}{AX} = m\,\overset{\frown}{XB}$

$m\,\overset{\frown}{AY} = m\,\overset{\frown}{BY}$

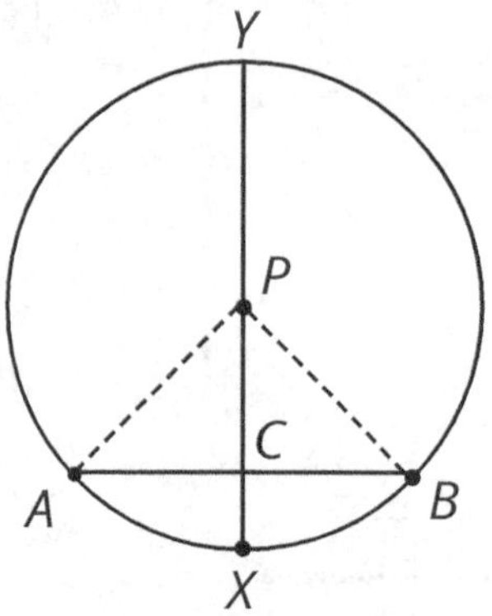

STATEMENT	REASON
1. Draw $\overline{PA}$, $\overline{PB}$,	1. Auxiliary lines
2. $\overline{XY} \perp \overline{AB}$	2. Given
3. $PA = PB$	3. Radii of circle are =
4. $PC = PC$	4. Reflexive
5. $\angle PCA, \angle PCB$ are rt $\angle$'s	5. $\perp$'s form rt angles
6. rt $\triangle PCA \cong$ rt $\triangle PCB$	6. HL
7. $AC = CB$ $\angle APX = \angle BPX$	7. CPCTE
8. $m\,\overset{\frown}{AX} = m\,\overset{\frown}{XB}$	8. If central angles =, arcs are =
9. $\angle APY, \angle APX$ are supplementary $\angle BPY, \angle BPX$ are supplementary	9. Exterior sides in opposite rays
10. $\angle APY = \angle BPY$	10. Two angles supplementary to = $\angle$'s are =
11. $m\,\overset{\frown}{AY} = m\,\overset{\frown}{BY}$	11. If central angles =, arcs are =

MATH 1006

LIFEPAC TEST

NAME ____________________

DATE ____________________

SCORE ____________________

63
78

MATH 1006: LIFEPAC TEST

Refer to the figure to complete the following items (each answer, 3 points).

Given: ⊙A externally tangent to ⊙B

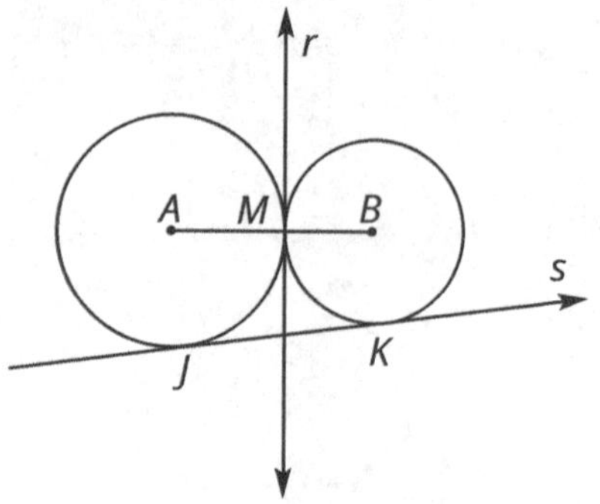

1. Name a common internal tangent.

   ____

2. Name a common external tangent.

   ____

3. $\overline{AM}$ __________ *r*.
4. Name the point of tangency of *s* to circle *A*. __________
5. How many possible common tangents to circles *A* and *B* can exist? __________

Refer to the figure and state the theorem that supports the statement (each answer, 4 points).

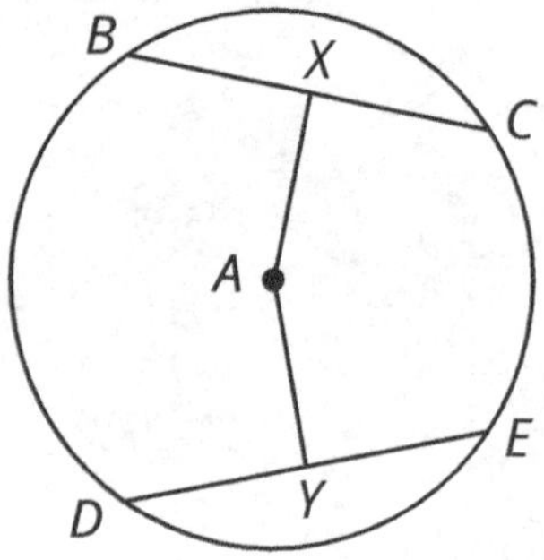

6. If *BC* = *DE*, then $\overset{\frown}{BC} = \overset{\frown}{DE}$.

   ____

7. If m $\overset{\frown}{BC}$ = m $\overset{\frown}{DE}$, then *BC* = *DE*.

   ____

8. If $\overline{AX}$ is perpendicular to $\overline{BC}$, then *BX* = *XC*.

   ____

Refer to the figures to find the following measures (each answer, 3 points).

Given: $\overline{DR}$ tangent to ⊙*O*

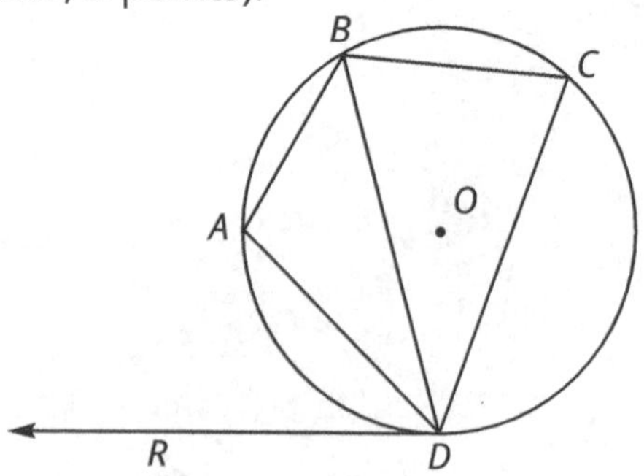

9. If m $\overset{\frown}{BD}$ = 150°, then ∠A = ____________________.
10. If m ∠*C* = 63°, then m ∠*BDR* = ____________________.
11. If m ∠*RDC* = 120°, then m $\overset{\frown}{DC}$ = ____________________.

Given: $\overline{PB}$ tangent
$\overline{PV}$, $\overline{PU}$ secants

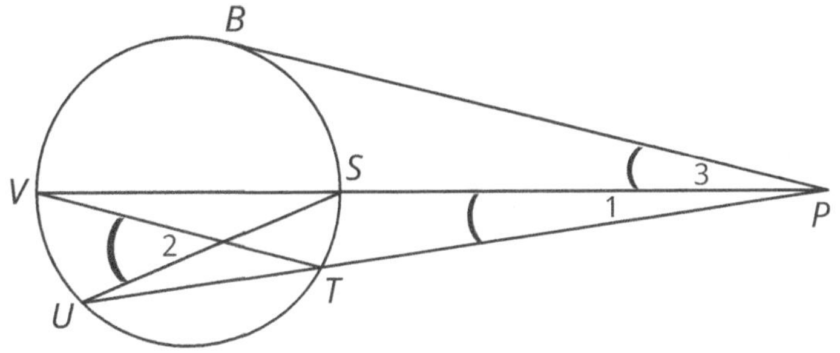

12. If m $\widehat{VU}$ = 80° and m $\widehat{ST}$ = 40°, then m∠1 = ________________ .

13. If m $\widehat{UV}$ = 70° and m $\widehat{ST}$ = 30°, then m∠2 = ________________ .

14. If m $\widehat{VB}$ = 60° and m $\widehat{BS}$ = 30°, then m∠3 = ________________ .

15. If m∠1 = 30° and m $\widehat{ST}$ = 20°, then m $\widehat{UV}$ = ________________ .

Given: $\overline{AD}$ diameter of ⊙P

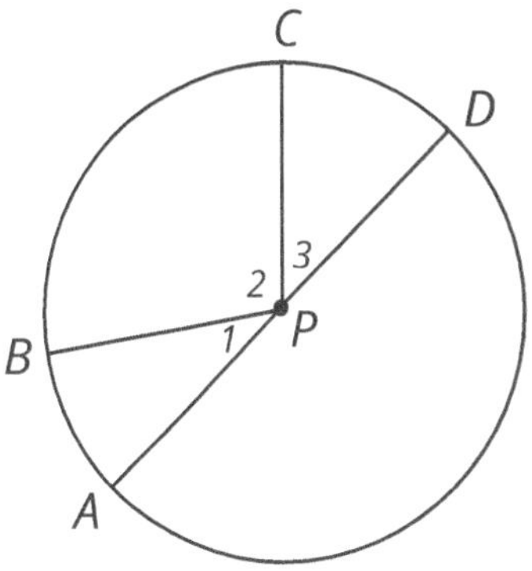

16. If m∠1 = 40°, then m $\widehat{AB}$ = ____________ .

17. m $\widehat{AB}$ + m $\widehat{BC}$ = m ____________ .

18. If m∠1 = m∠3 = 20°, then m $\widehat{BC}$ = ____________ .

19. If m∠3 = 30°, then m $\widehat{ABC}$ = ____________ .

Find *x* in the given figures (each answer, 3 points).

20. x = ______________________

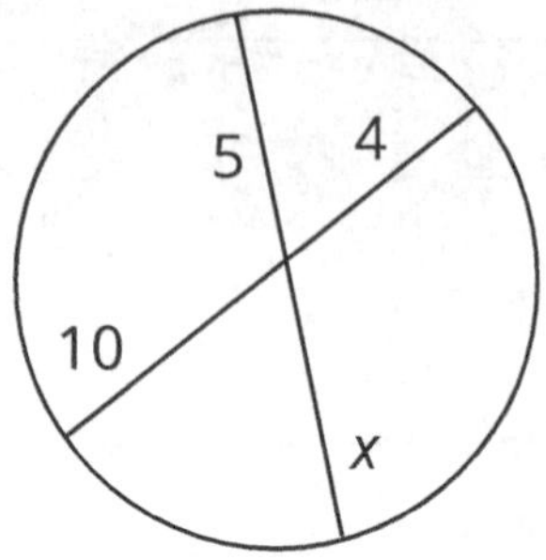

21. x = ______________________

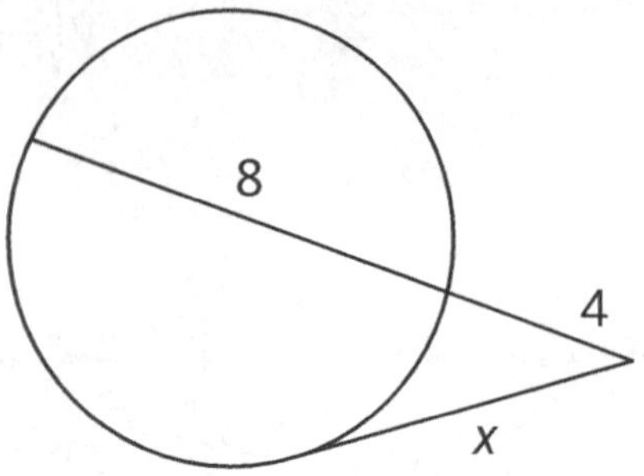

22. x = ______________________

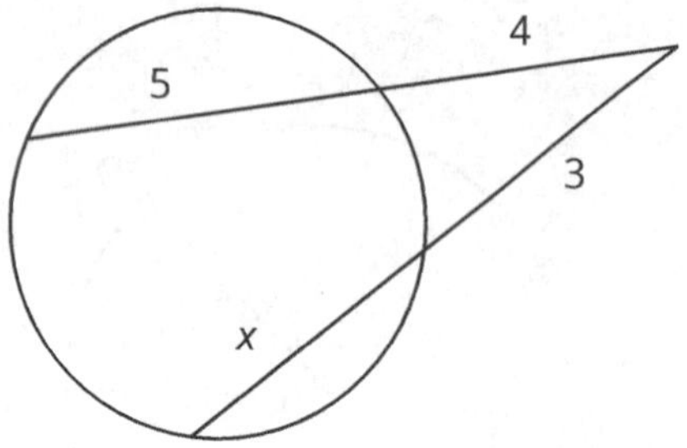

23. x = ______________________

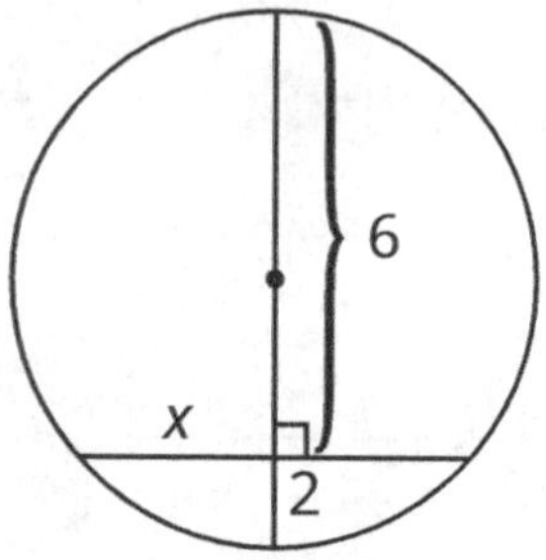

24. x = ______________________

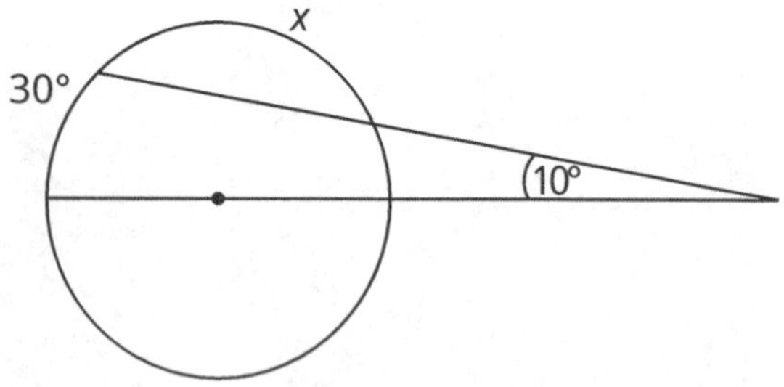

25. x = ______________________

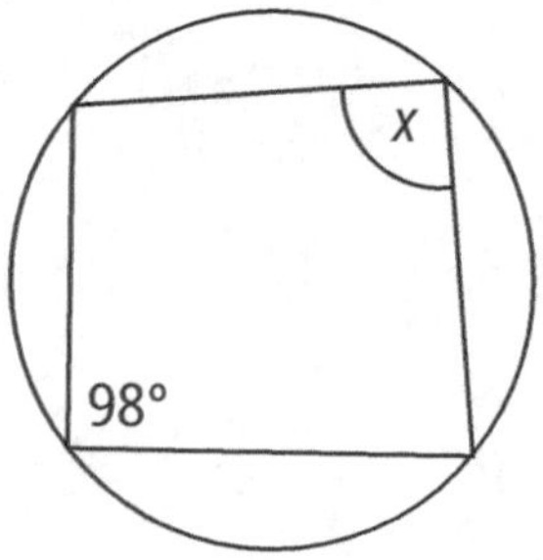

The next two theorems tell us something about the length of chords and their distance from the center of a circle. Remember that distance means the shortest path from one point to another; distance from a chord to the center is measured with the line from the center that is perpendicular to the chord.

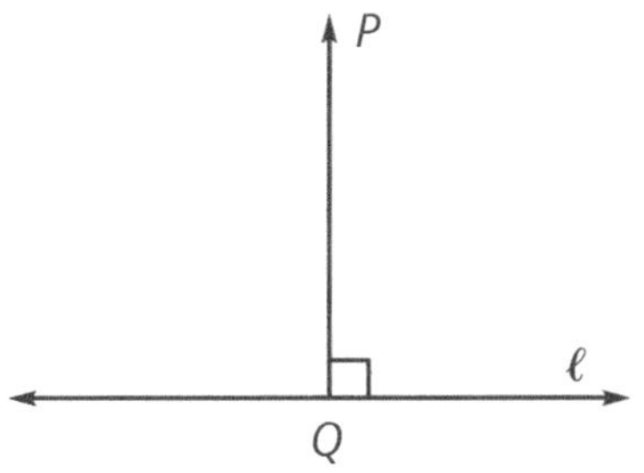

THEOREM 6-8

In the same circle or in congruent circles if the chords are equidistant from the center, then their lengths are equal.

Given: $AX = AY$

$\angle AXC$ & $\angle AYE$ are right angles

Prove: $BC = DE$

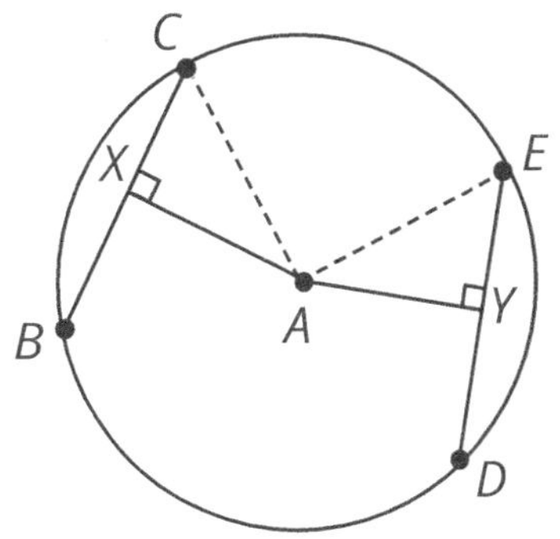

STATEMENT	REASON
1. $AX = AY$ $\angle AXC$ & $\angle AYE$ are right angles	1. Given
2. Draw $\overline{AC}$, $\overline{AE}$	2. Auxiliary line
3. $AC = AE$	3. All radii equal
4. rt $\triangle AXC \cong$ rt $\triangle AYE$	4. HL
5. $XC = YE$	5. CPCTE
6. $BX = XC$ $DY = YE$	6. Diameter $\perp$ to chord bisects chord
7. $BX = DY$	7. Substitution
8. $BX + XC = DY + YE$	8. Addition property of equality
9. $BC = DE$	9. Betweeness and substitution

The converse of Theorem 6–8 is also true.

THEOREM 6-9

In the same circle or in congruent circles if the chords have the same length, then they are equidistant from the center.

Write the following proofs.

2.95 Prove Theorem 6–4.

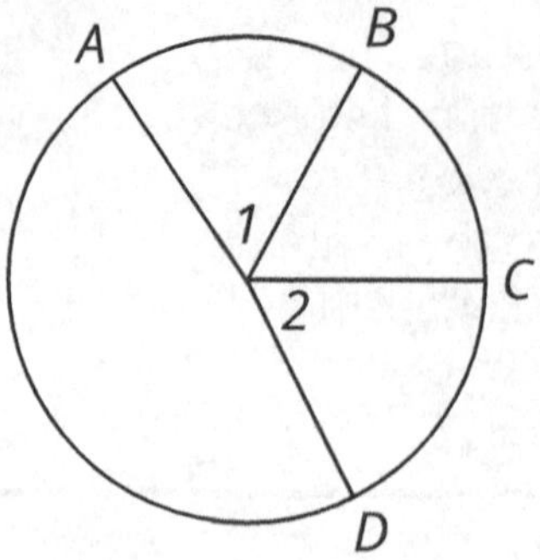

Given: ______________________

Prove: ______________________

STATEMENT	REASON

2.96 Prove Theorem 6–6.

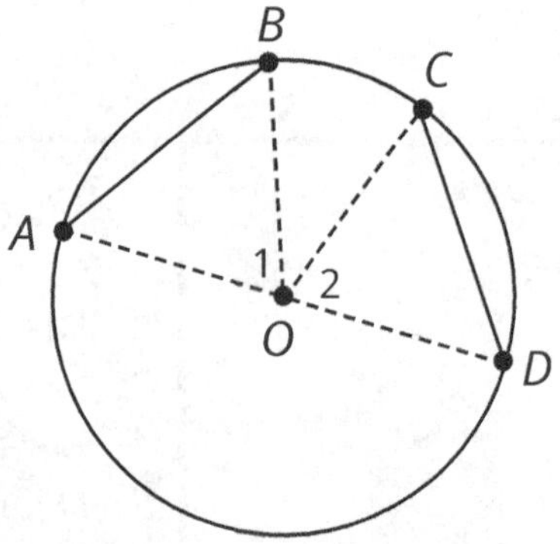

Given: ______________________

Prove: ______________________

STATEMENT	REASON

Find the following measures.

2.97 If a chord 10 inches long is 5 inches from the center of a circle, find the radius of the circle.

____

2.98 In a circle with a 12-inch radius, find the length of a segment joining the midpoint of a 20-inch chord and the center of the circle.

____

2.99 Find the radius of a circle in which an inscribed square has a side of 8 inches.

____

Refer to the figure to complete the following activities.

2.100 If $RB = 5$, then $AB =$ ______________________________.

2.101 If $AB = 12$, then $AR =$ ______________________________.

2.102 If $RB = 4$ and $OR = 3$, then $OB =$ ______________________________.

2.103 If $OB = 10$ and $RB = 8$, then $OR =$ ______________________________.

2.104 If $OB = 10$ and $AR = 6$, then $OR =$ ______________________________.

2.105 If $OB = 17$ and $AB = 30$, then $OR =$ ______________________________.

2.106 If m $\overset{\frown}{BC} = 20°$, then m $\overset{\frown}{AC} =$ ______________________________.

2.107 If m $\angle BOC = 30°$, then m $\overset{\frown}{BAC} =$ ______________________________.

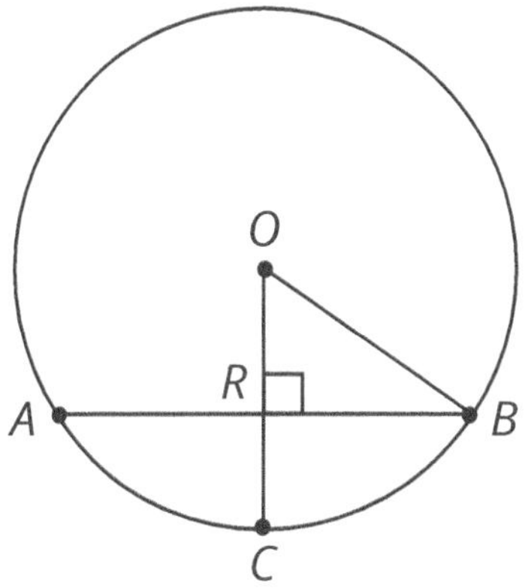

Review the material in this section in preparation for the Self Test. This Self Test will check your mastery of this particular section as well as your knowledge of the previous section.

SELF TEST 2

Can you conclude that $\widehat{AB} = \widehat{BC}$? Write *yes* or *no* (each answer, 3 points).

2.01 ____________________

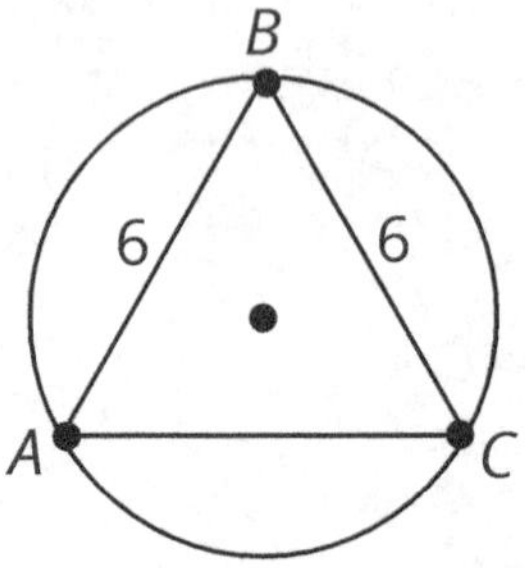

2.02 ____________________

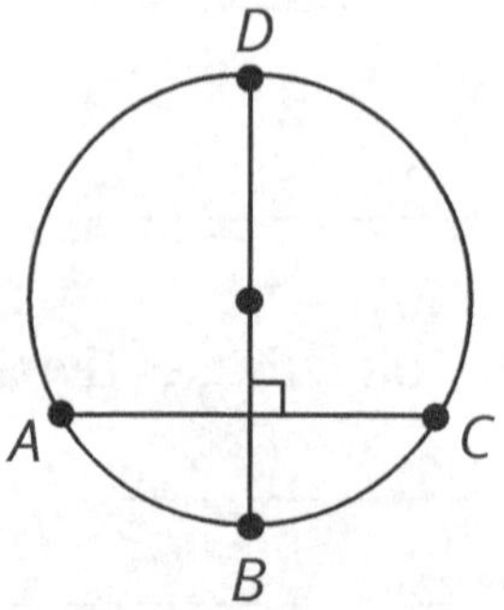

2.03 ____________________

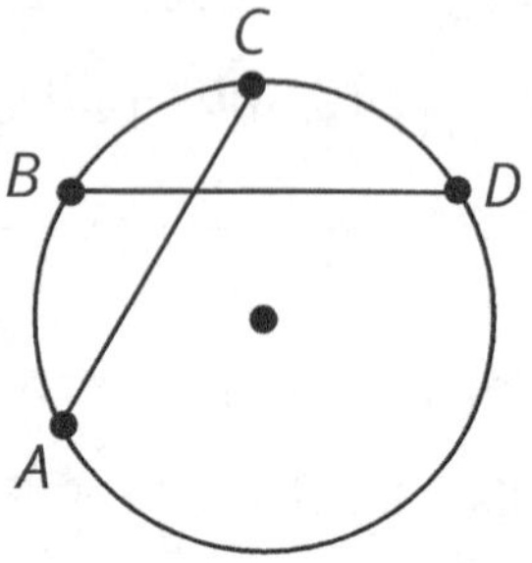

2.04 ____________________

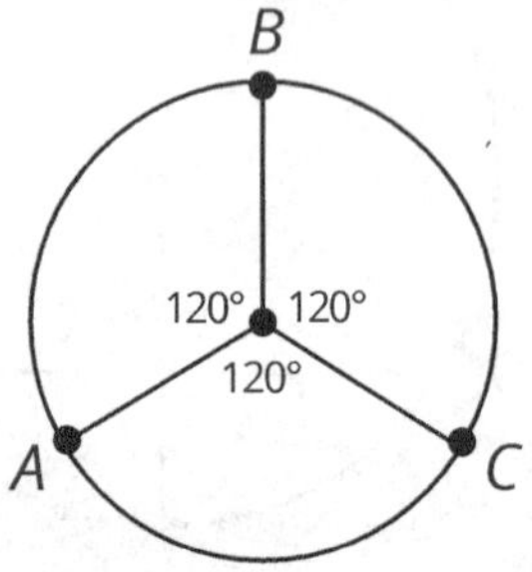

2.05 ____________________

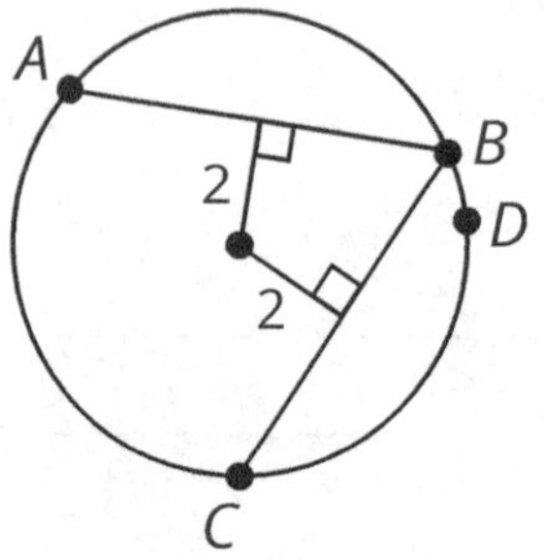

Sketch the following figures (each answer, 4 points).

2.06 A circle inscribed in a triangle

2.07 A square circumscribed about a circle

2.08 Two circles with exactly three common tangents

2.09 Two tangent circles with one common external tangent

2.010 An equilateral triangle inscribed in one of two concentric circles and circumscribed about the other circle

Complete these items (each answer, 3 points).

2.011 Find the angle between the hands of a clock at 5:15. ________________

2.012 A circle is divided into 12 equal arcs. Find the measure of one of those arcs.

____

2.013 The radius of a sphere is 6 inches. Find the length of a chord connecting two perpendicular radii. ________________

2.014 If $\overset{\frown}{AXB}$ names a major arc of a circle, name the minor arc. ________________

2.015 If chord $\overline{AB}$ is 3 inches from the center and chord $\overline{CD}$ is 5 inches from the center of the same circle, which chord is longer? ________________

Refer to the figure to complete the following items (each answer, 3 points).

Given: *t* is tangent at *B*
$\overline{AB}$ is diameter

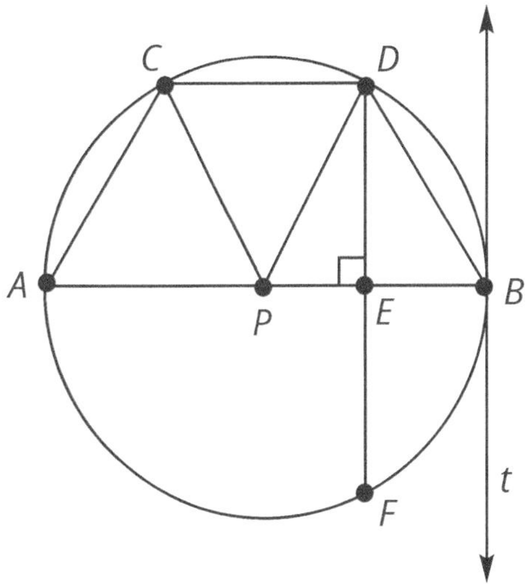

2.016 If m $\angle DPB$ = 60°, then m $\overset{\frown}{DB}$ = ________________.

2.017 If m $\overset{\frown}{AF}$ = 110°, then m $\overset{\frown}{DB}$ = ________________.

2.018 If *AC* = *CD* = *DB*, then m $\angle CPD$ = ________________.

2.019 If $\overline{AB} \perp \overline{DF}$, then $\overline{DF}$ | | ________________.

2.020 If m $\overset{\frown}{DB}$ = 60° and PE = 3, then *PB* = ________________.

Complete the proof (each numbered item, 3 points).

Given: Circle *P* with diameter $\overline{RS} \perp \overline{TW}$

Prove: $\triangle RTW$ is isosceles.

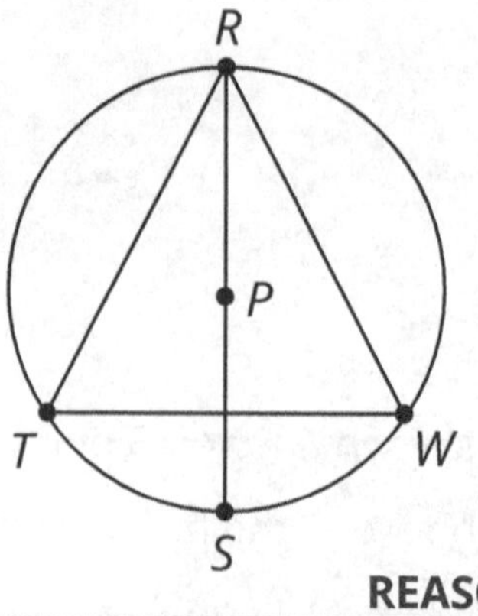

STATEMENT	REASON
2.021 ______________________	______________________
2.022 ______________________	______________________
2.023 ______________________	______________________
2.024 ______________________	______________________

62/77 **SCORE** __________ **TEACHER** __________ __________
initials date

3. SPECIAL ANGLES AND SEGMENTS RELATED TO CIRCLES

You may have been curious about some of the special angles and segments related to circles. In this section we shall learn theorems that tell us how to find the measures of these special angles and segments.

Section Objectives

Review these objectives. When you have finished this section, you should be able to:

7. Solve problems related to inscribed angles.
8. Find the measure of angles formed by segments related to circles.
9. Find the measure of segments formed by chords, secants, and tangents.

SPECIAL ANGLES

Three groups of special angles are related to circles: those with measure equal to half the intercepted arc, those with measure equal to half the **sum** of the intercepted arcs, and those with measure equal to half the **difference** of the intercepted arcs. We need two definitions to be able to understand these three groups.

We have learned that a central angle has its vertex at the center of the circle. If we move the vertex to be on the circle and have its sides pass through the endpoints of an arc, we have produced an **inscribed angle** along with an **intercepted arc**.

> **DEFINITIONS**
>
> **Inscribed angle:** an angle with sides containing the endpoints of an arc and with a vertex that is a point of the arc other than an endpoint of the arc.
>
> **Intercepted arc:** an angle intercepts an arc if the endpoints of the arc lie on the sides of the angle and all points of the arc except the endpoints lie in the interior of the angle.

The arc that is in the exterior of the angle is the arc in which the angle is inscribed. The arc in the interior of the angle is the intercepted arc.

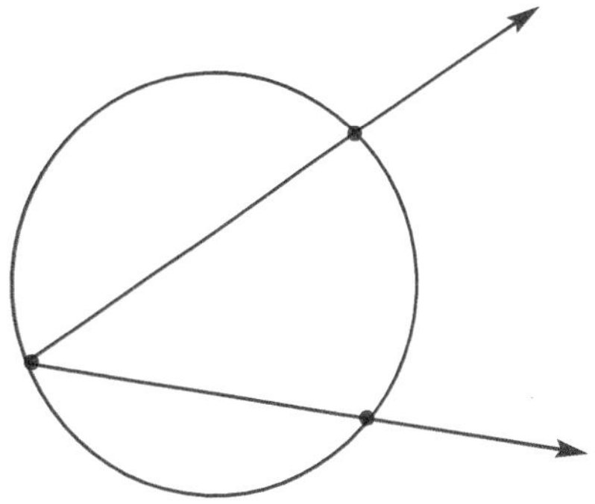

Model 1: $\angle ABC$ is inscribed in $\overset{\frown}{ABC}$.

$\angle ABC$ intercepts $\overset{\frown}{AC}$.

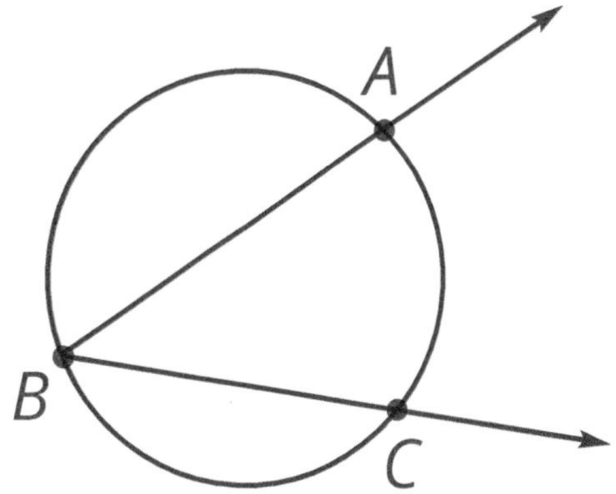

Model 2: In the circles shown, only ∠1 is an inscribed angle.

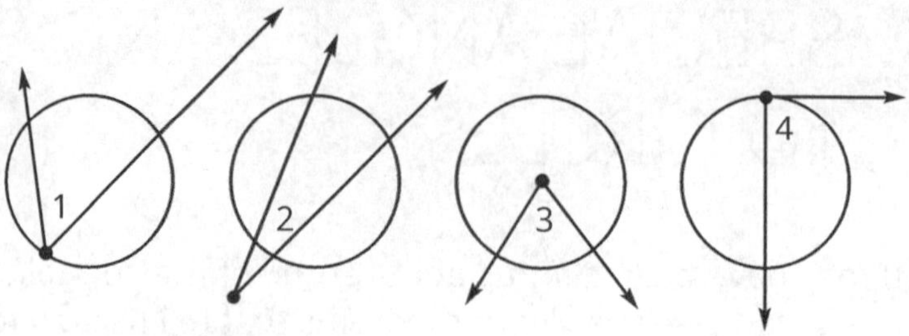

Model 3: ∠1 is inscribed in a minor arc.
∠1 intercepts a major arc.

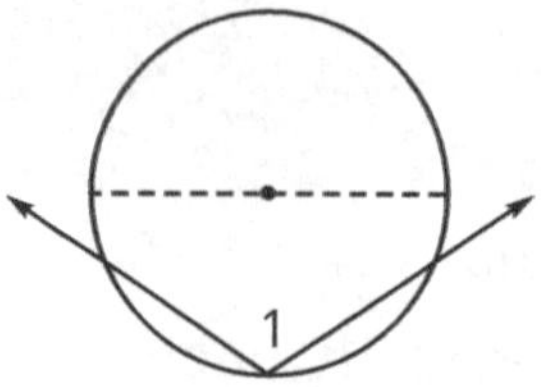

Model 4: ∠2 is inscribed in a major arc.
∠2 intercepts a minor arc.

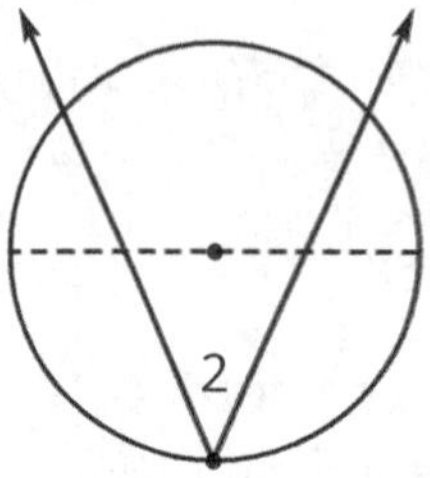

Model 5: ∠3 is inscribed in a semicircle.
∠3 intercepts a semicircle.

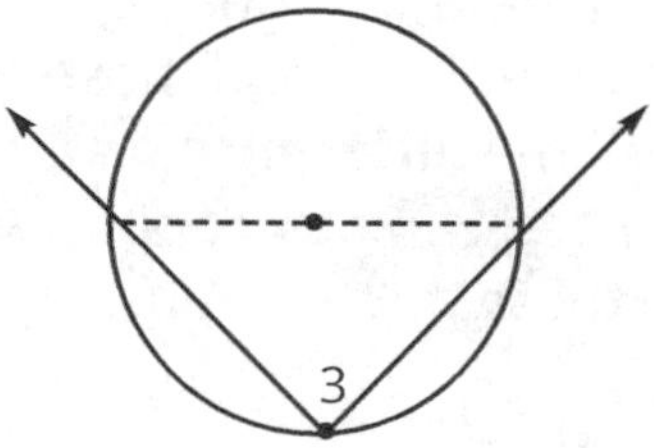

TYPE ONE

Now we can begin with theorems about angles that measure half of the arc they intercept.

> **THEOREM 6-10**
> The measure of an inscribed angle is equal to half the measure of its intercepted arc.

Given: ∠*ABC* inscribed in circle *P*

Prove: $m\angle ABC = \frac{1}{2} m\widehat{AC}$

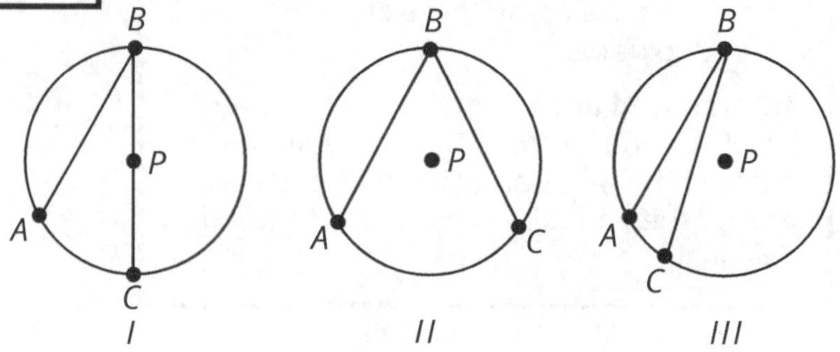

Three possible cases to consider are shown: that the center of the circle lies on a side of the inscribed angle (I), that it lies in the interior of the angle (II), and that it lies in the exterior of the angle (III).

We shall prove Case I at this time.

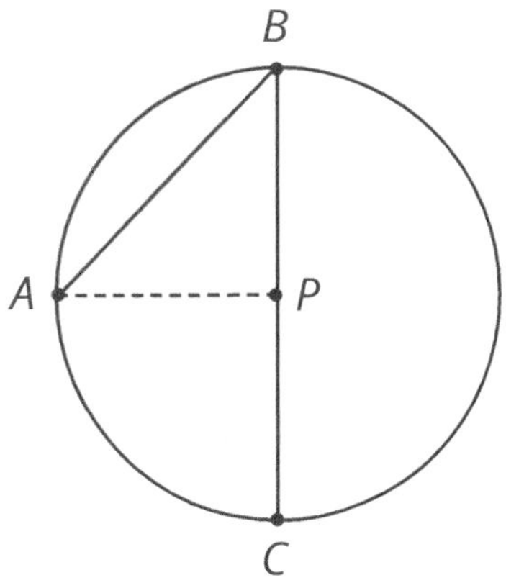

Case I STATEMENT	REASON
1. Draw PA	1. Auxiliary line
2. $PA = PB$	2. Radii of same circle =
3. $\angle ABC = \angle BAP$	3. Base angles of isosceles triangles =
4. $\angle APC = \angle BAP + \angle ABC$	4. Exterior angle of $\triangle$ = sum of remote interior angles
5. $\angle APC = 2\ \angle ABC$	5. Substitution
6. $\angle ABC = \frac{1}{2}\ \angle APC$	6. Division property of equality
7. $\angle APC = \text{m}\ \overset{\frown}{AC}$	7. Central angle = intercepted arc
8. $\angle ABC = \frac{1}{2}\ \text{m}\ \overset{\frown}{AC}$	8. Substitution

Case II can now be proved by using diameter $\overline{BX}$ and the angle addition theorem.

Case III can be proved in the same way as Case II using subtraction of angles.

We have three very useful corollaries to this theorem.

> **Corollary 1:** An angle inscribed in a semicircle is a right angle.
>
> **Corollary 2:** The opposite angles of an inscribed quadrilateral are supplementary.
>
> **Corollary 3:** If two angles intercept the same or equal arcs, the angles are equal.

Model 1: If $\overline{RT}$ is a diameter, then $\angle RST$ is a right angle.

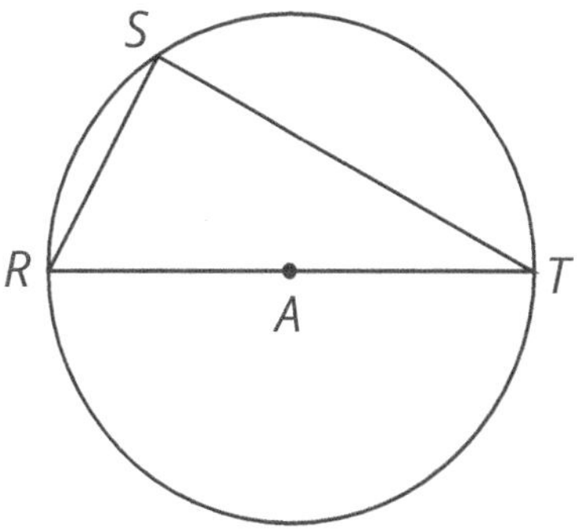

Model 2: If *ABCD* is inscribed in circle *O*, then ∠A and ∠C are supplementary and ∠B and ∠D are supplementary.

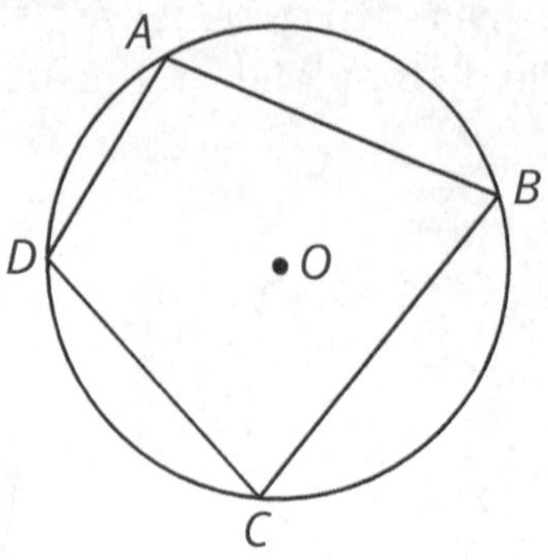

Model 3: m∠1 = m∠2 = m∠3.

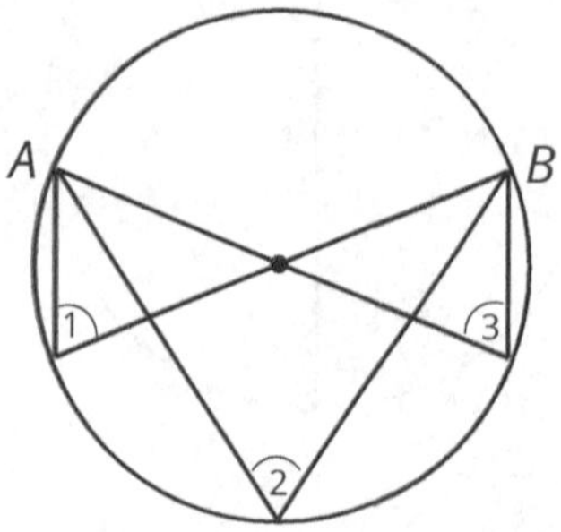

In describing the position of angles in relation to a circle, we use the terms **secant ray** and **tangent ray**.

DEFINITIONS

Secant ray: a ray that lies on a secant line and contains both points of intersection with the circle.

Tangent ray: a ray that lies on a tangent line and contains the point of tangency.

Model 1: $\overrightarrow{RS}$ and $\overrightarrow{AB}$ are secant rays.

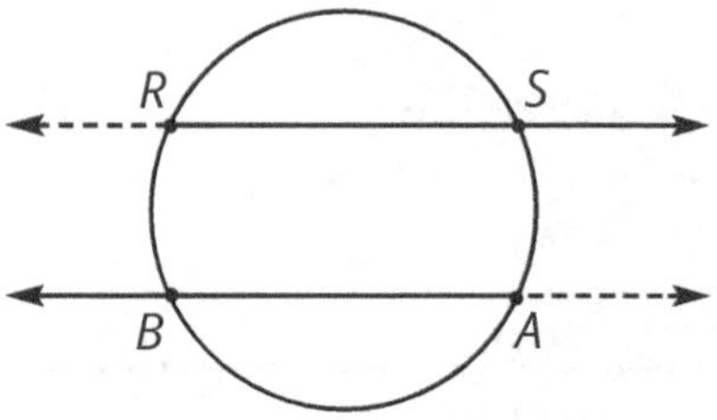

Model 2: $\overrightarrow{PQ}$ and $\overrightarrow{CD}$ are tangent rays.

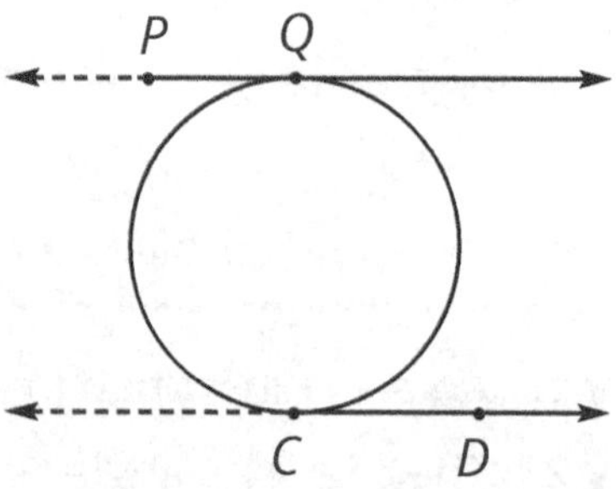

These terms lead us to our next theorem.

THEOREM 6-11

The measure of an angle formed by a secant ray and a tangent ray drawn from a point on a circle is equal to half the measure of its intercepted arc.

Given: Circle A with $\overrightarrow{RT}$ a tangent ray and $\overrightarrow{RS}$ a secant ray.

Prove: $m\angle SRT = \frac{1}{2}\overset{\frown}{SR}$

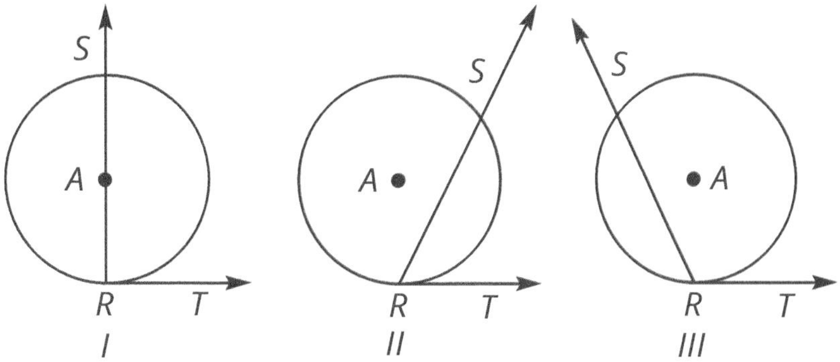

Again we must consider three possible positions for this secant-tangent angle.

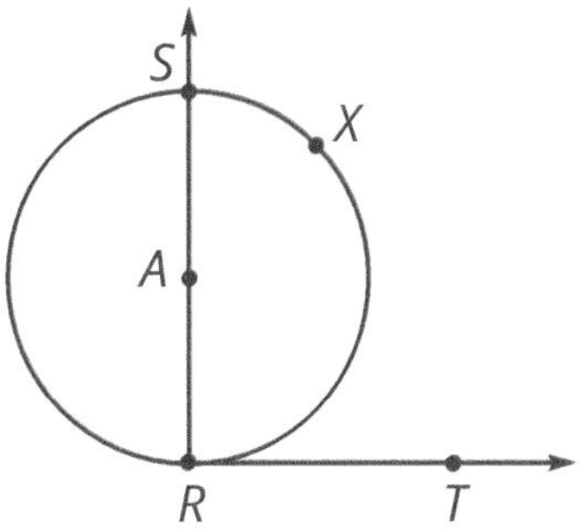

Case I **STATEMENT**	**REASON**
1. $\overline{RS}$ is diameter	1. Given
2. $\overline{RS} \perp \overline{RT}$	2. Radius $\perp$ to tangent
3. $\angle SRT = 90°$	3. $\perp$'s form right angles
4. $\overset{\frown}{SXR}$ is a semicircle	4. Definition of semicircle
5. $m\overset{\frown}{SXR} = 180°$	5. Measure of semicircle = 180°
6. $\frac{1}{2} m\overset{\frown}{SXR} = 90°$	6. Division property of equality
7. $m\angle SRT = \frac{1}{2} m\overset{\frown}{SXR}$	7. Substitution

Case II and Case III can be proved by drawing $\overrightarrow{RA}$ and using angle addition, arc addition, Case I, and the measure of inscribed angle theorem.

Refer to the figure to complete the following activities.

Given: $\overline{AD}$ is diameter

3.1 If m $\overset{\frown}{CDA}$ = 260° and m $\overset{\frown}{BC}$ = 30°,

then m $\overset{\frown}{BA}$ = a. ____________

m $\overset{\frown}{CD}$ = b. ____________

∠*BAD* = c. ____________

∠*BAC* = d. ____________

∠*CAD* = e. ____________

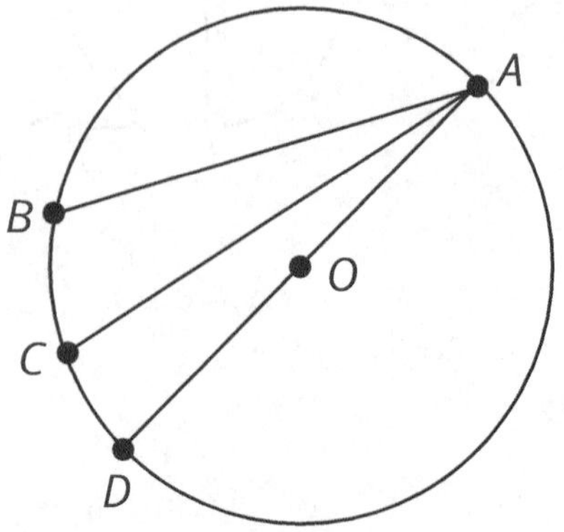

3.2 If ∠*BAD* = 70° and m $\overset{\frown}{BC}$ = 50°,

then m $\overset{\frown}{BD}$ = a. ____________

m $\overset{\frown}{BA}$ = b. ____________

∠*CAD* = c. ____________

∠*BAC* = d. ____________

Refer to the figure to complete the following items.

Given: $\overleftrightarrow{RT}$ is tangent at *S*

3.3 If ∠*U* = 70° and ∠*USR* = 50°,

then ∠*VST* = a. ____________

∠*V* = b. ____________

m $\overset{\frown}{SV}$ = c. ____________

m $\overset{\frown}{US}$ = d. ____________

m $\overset{\frown}{UV}$ = e. ____________

∠*USV* = f. ____________

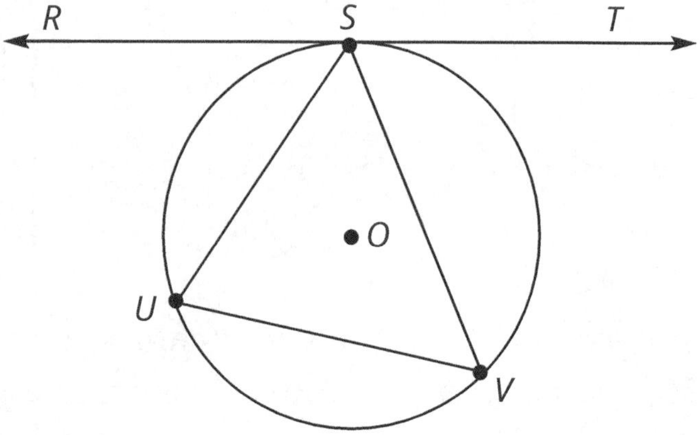

3.4 If ∠*RSV* = 125°, ____________

then m $\overset{\frown}{SUV}$ = a. ____________

m $\overset{\frown}{SV}$ = b. ____________

∠*TSV* = c. ____________

∠*U* = d. ____________

Refer to the figure to complete the following activities.

Given: $\overline{AB}$, $\overline{BC}$, $\overline{CD}$, $\overline{DA}$ are chords

$\overline{BD}$ is a diameter

$\overleftrightarrow{EF}$ is tangent at C

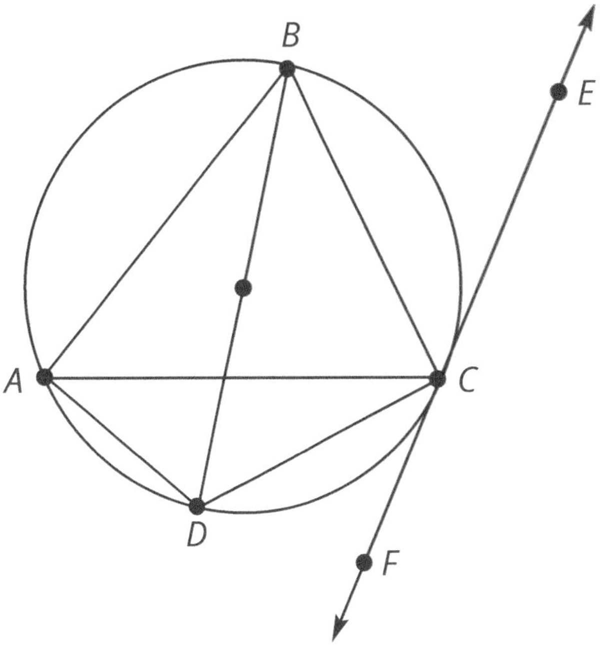

3.5 $\angle BAD$ = a. ____________

$\angle ABD + \angle ADB$ = b. ____________

3.6 If m $\widehat{AB}$ = 120°,
then $\angle ADB$ = a. ____________

m $\widehat{AD}$ = b. ____________

$\angle ACD$ = c. ____________

3.7 If $\angle ADB$ = 70°,
then $\angle ABD$ = a. ____________

m $\widehat{AB}$ = b. ____________

m $\widehat{AD}$ = c. ____________

3.8 If $\angle DBC$ = 40°,
then m $\widehat{DC}$ = a. ____________

m $\widehat{BC}$ = b. ____________

$\angle ECB$ = c. ____________

$\angle DCF$ = d. ____________

$\angle BDC$ = e. ____________

Refer to the figure to complete the following activities.

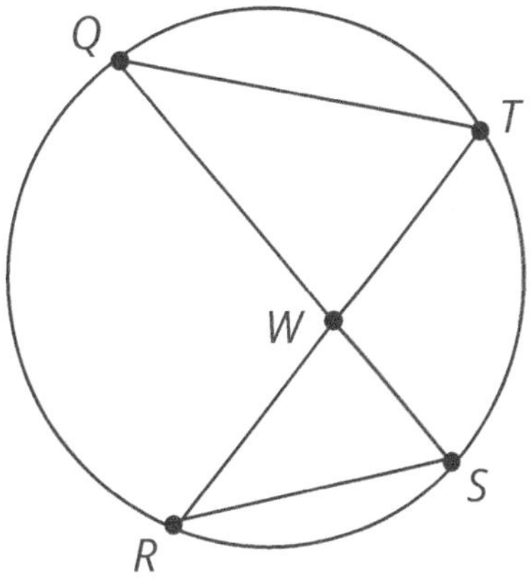

3.9 If m $\widehat{TS}$ = 96°,
then $\angle Q$ = a. ____________

$\angle R$ = b. ____________

3.10 If m $\widehat{QR}$ = 118°,
then $\angle T$ = a. ____________

$\angle S$ = b. ____________

3.11 If $\angle Q = 44°$

then m $\overset{\frown}{TS}$ = a. ____________________

$\angle R$ = b. ____________________

3.12 If $\angle Q = 47°$,

then m $\overset{\frown}{TS}$ = a. ____________________

$\angle R$ = b. ____________________

3.13 Is $\triangle RWS \sim \triangle TWQ$? ____________________

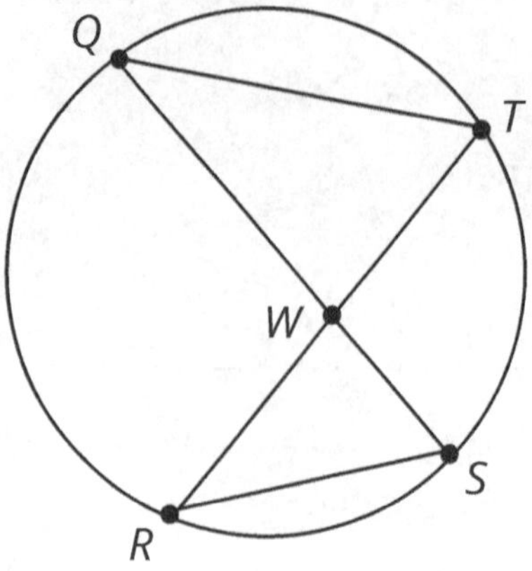

Find the measure of $\angle 1$.

3.14 m$\angle 1$ = ____________________

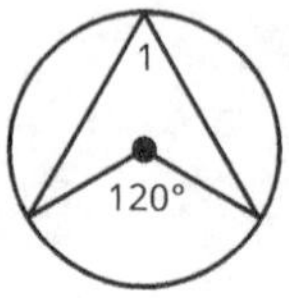

3.15 m$\angle 1$ = ____________________

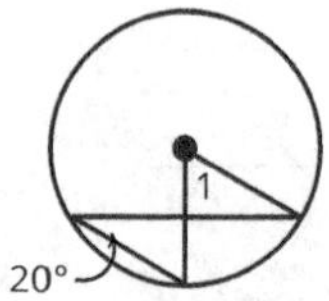

3.16 m$\angle 1$ = ____________________

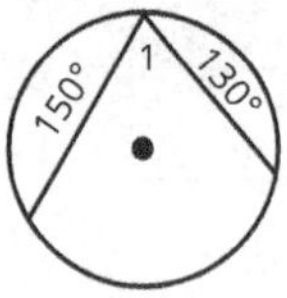

3.17 m$\angle 1$ = ____________________

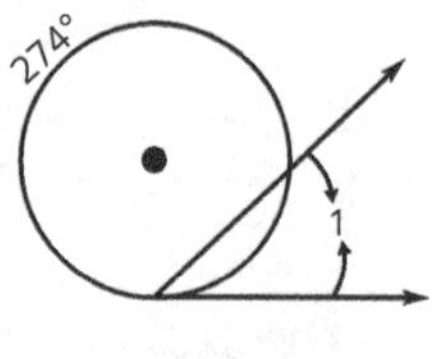

3.18 m$\angle 1$ = ____________________

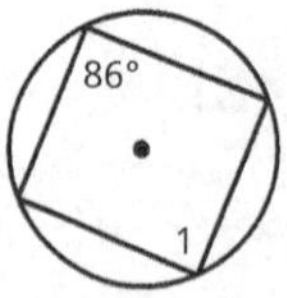

3.19 m$\angle 1$ = ____________________

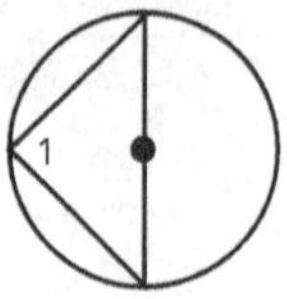

3.20 m$\angle 1$ = ____________________

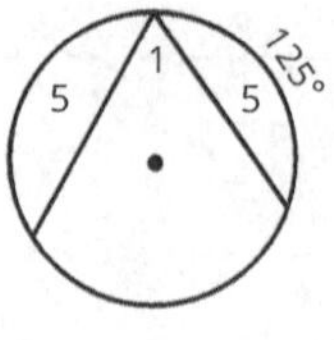

TYPE TWO

The second type of angle measures half the sum of the arcs it intercepts.

> **THEOREM 6-12**
> The measure of an angle formed by two secants that intersect inside the circle is equal to half the sum of the intercepted arcs.

Given: Secants $\overleftrightarrow{AC}$, $\overleftrightarrow{BD}$ intersect at P inside circle

Prove: $\angle 1 = \frac{1}{2}(m\,\overset{\frown}{AD} + m\,\overset{\frown}{BC})$

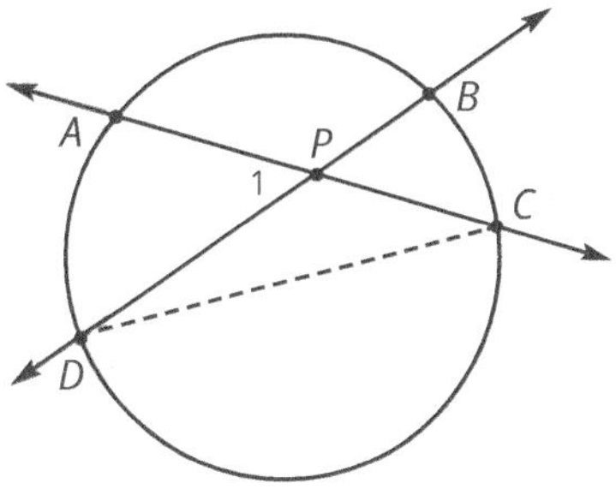

STATEMENT	REASON
1. Draw $\overline{DC}$	1. Auxiliary line
2. $\angle 1 = \angle D + \angle C$	2. Exterior angle of Δ = sum of remote interior angles
3. $\angle D = \frac{1}{2}\overset{\frown}{BC}$ $\angle C = \frac{1}{2}\overset{\frown}{AD}$	3. Measure of inscribed angle
4. $\angle 1 = \frac{1}{2}\,m\,\overset{\frown}{BC} + \frac{1}{2}m\,\overset{\frown}{AD}$	4. Substitution
5. $\angle 1 = \frac{1}{2}\,(m\,\overset{\frown}{BC} + m\,\overset{\frown}{AD})$	5. Algebra

Actually, four angles are formed by the two secants. Angle 1 and $\angle 3$ would have the same measure since they are vertical. The same is true for $\angle 2$ and $\angle 4$. Angle 2 is a supplement of 1 so after finding the measure of one angle by using Theorem 6–12, it is an easy matter to find the measures of the other three.

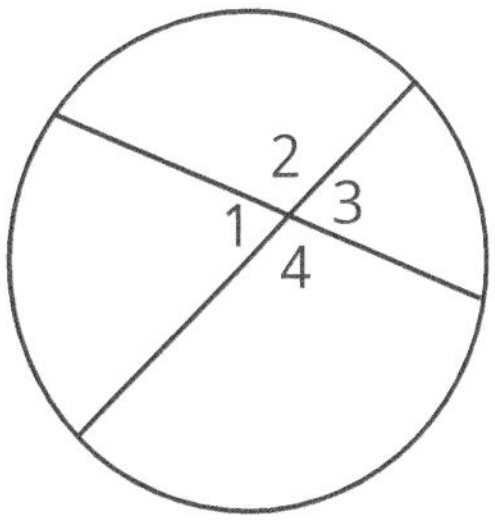

Find the measures of each angle using the theorems.

3.21 a. m ∠1 = ______________

b. m ∠2 = ______________

c. m ∠3 = ______________

d. m ∠4 = ______________

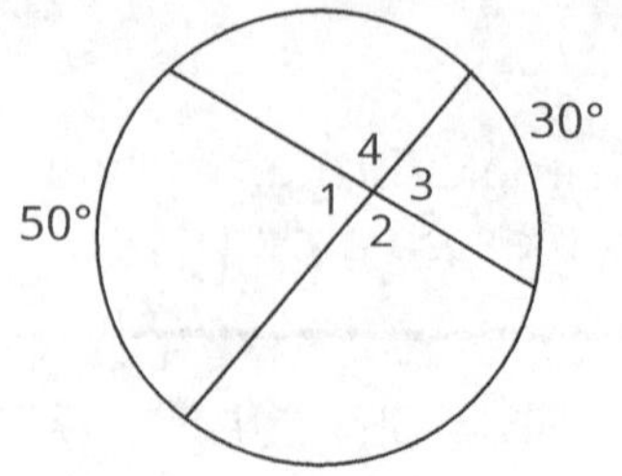

3.22 a. m ∠1 = ______________

b. m ∠2 = ______________

c. m ∠3 = ______________

d. m ∠4 = ______________

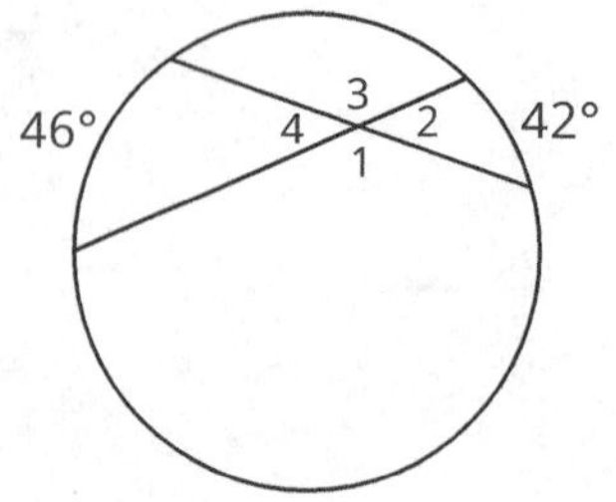

3.23 a. m ∠1 = ______________

b. m ∠2 = ______________

c. m ∠3 = ______________

d. m ∠4 = ______________

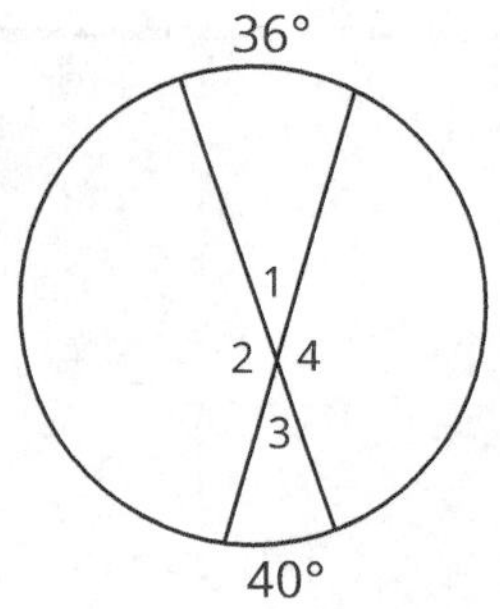

Given: $\overline{AC}$ and $\overline{BD}$ are diameters.

3.24 a. m ∠1 = ______________

b. m ∠2 = ______________

c. m ∠3 = ______________

d. m ∠4 = ______________

e. m $\overset{\frown}{AB}$ = ______________

f. m $\overset{\frown}{BC}$ = ______________

g. m $\overset{\frown}{DC}$ = ______________

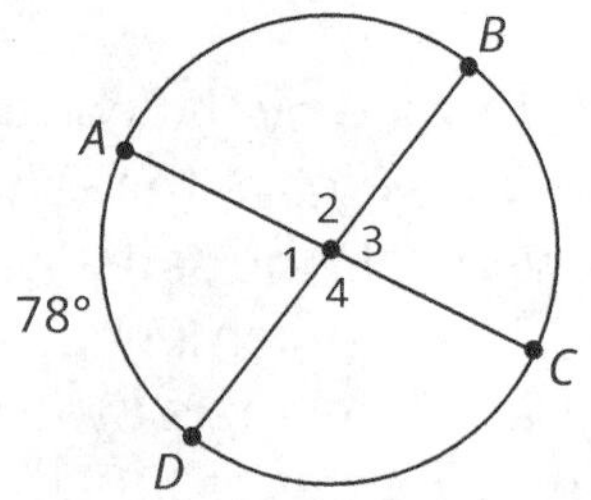

3.25 a. m $\angle 1$ = ____________________

b. m $\angle 2$ = ____________________

c. m $\angle 3$ = ____________________

d. m $\angle 4$ = ____________________

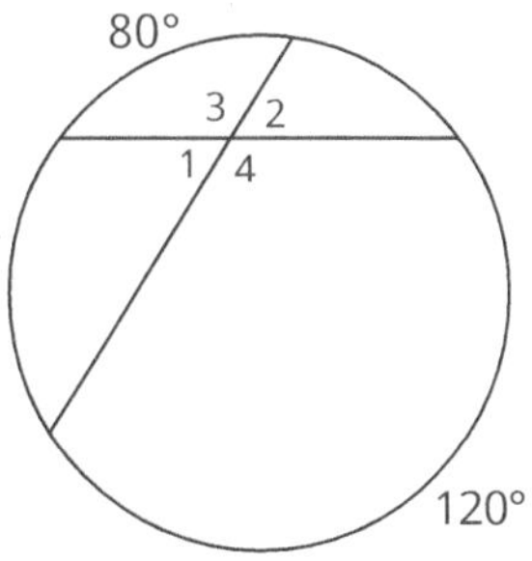

Complete the following activities by finding *x*.

Model 1: Find x

$32° = \frac{1}{2}(x + 35°)$

$64° = x + 35°$

$x = 29°$

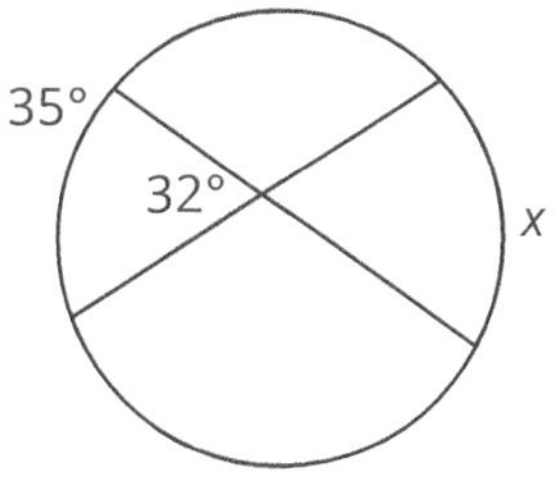

3.26 x = ____________

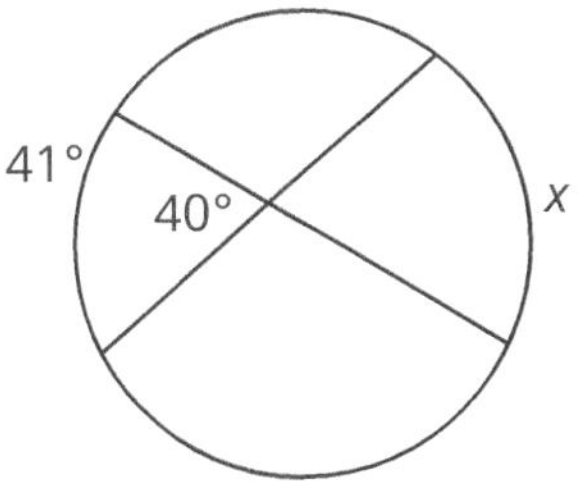

3.27 x = ____________

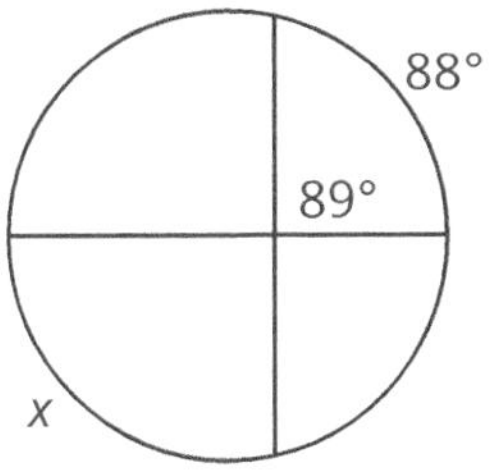

3.28 x = ____________

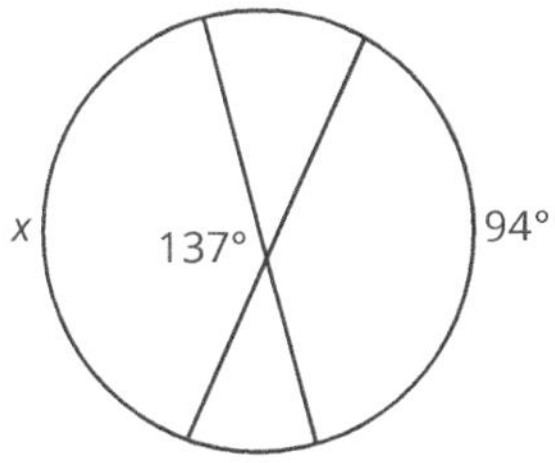

3.29 $x =$ ____________

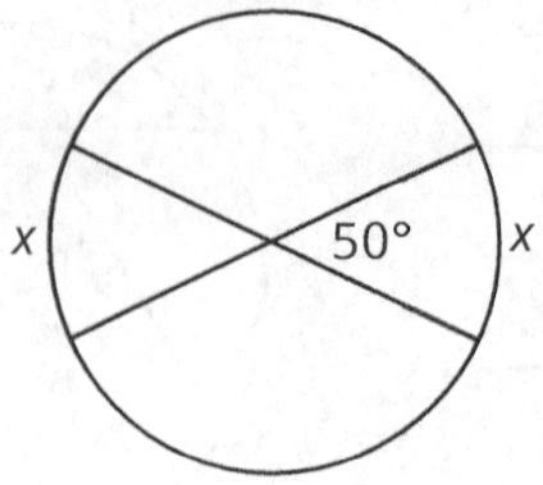

3.30 $x =$ ____________

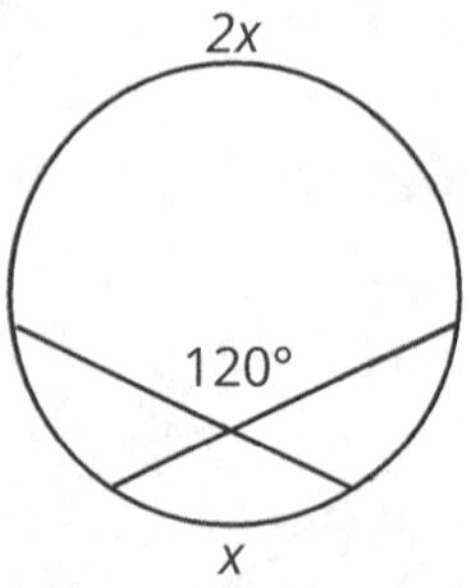

3.31 $x =$ ____________

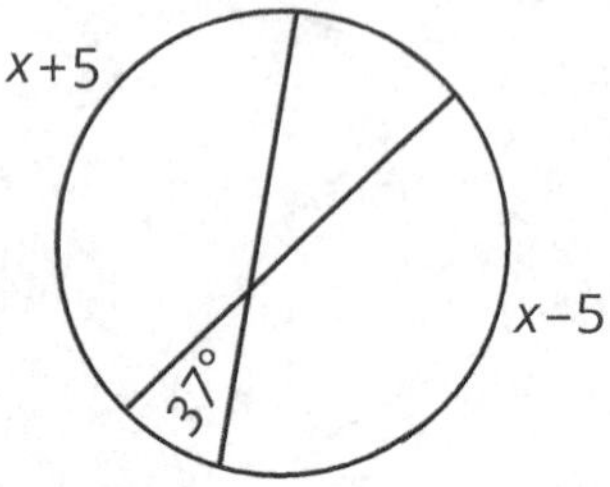

3.32 $x =$ ____________

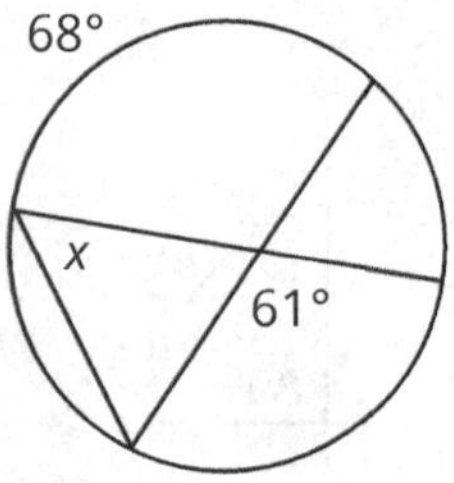

3.33 $x =$ ____________

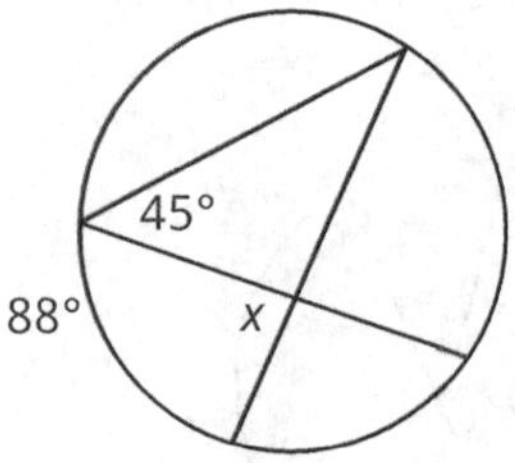

TYPE THREE

The final group of angles measure half the difference of the arcs they intercept.

> **THEOREM 6-13**
> The measure of the angle formed by two secants intersecting outside the circle equals half the difference of the intercepted arcs.

Given: Secant rays $\overrightarrow{PA}$ and $\overrightarrow{PD}$

Prove: $\angle 1 = \frac{1}{2}$ (m $\overset{\frown}{AD}$ − $\overset{\frown}{BC}$)

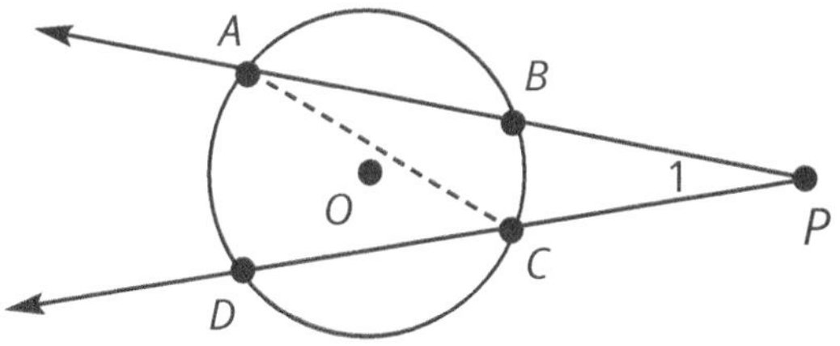

STATEMENT	REASON
1. Draw $\overline{AC}$	1. Auxiliary line
2. $\angle DCA = \angle 1 + \angle PAC$	2. Exterior angle of triangle = sum of 2 interior, opposite ∠'s
3. $\angle DCA = \frac{1}{2}$m $\overset{\frown}{AD}$ $\angle PAC = \frac{1}{2}$m $\overset{\frown}{BC}$	3. Measure of inscribed angle = $\frac{1}{2}$ intercepted arc
4. $\frac{1}{2}$m $\overset{\frown}{AD} = \angle 1 + \frac{1}{2}$m $\overset{\frown}{BC}$	4. Substitution
5. $\angle 1 = \frac{1}{2}$(m $\overset{\frown}{AD}$ – m $\overset{\frown}{BC}$)	5. Factoring

If we take one of the secant rays and make it a tangent ray, we have use for Theorem 6-14.

> **THEOREM 6-14**
> The measure of the angle formed by a tangent ray and a secant ray intersecting outside the circle is equal to half the difference of the intercepted arcs.

Given: Secant $\overrightarrow{PA}$, tangent $\overrightarrow{PC}$

Prove: $\angle 1 = \frac{1}{2}$(m $\overset{\frown}{AC}$ – m $\overset{\frown}{BC}$)

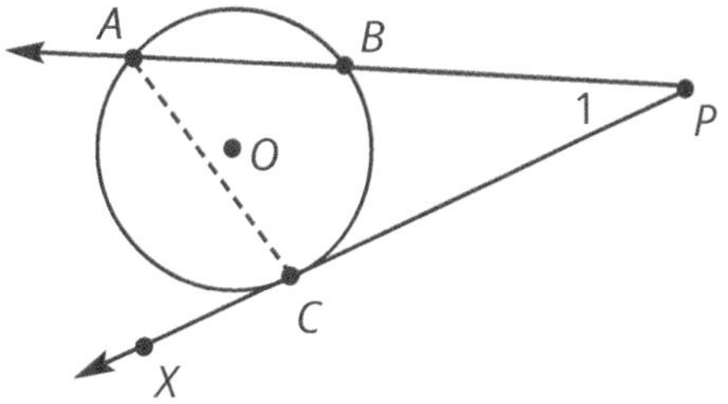

STATEMENT	REASON
1. Draw $\overline{AC}$	1. Auxiliary line
2. $\angle ACX = \angle PAC + \angle 1$	2. Exterior angle of triangle
3. $\angle PAC = \frac{1}{2} m\,\overset{\frown}{BC}$	3. Inscribed angle measure
4. $\angle ACX = \frac{1}{2} m\,\overset{\frown}{AC}$	4. Tangent-Secant angle (Theorem 6-11)
5. $\frac{1}{2} m\,\overset{\frown}{AC} = \angle \frac{1}{2} m\,\overset{\frown}{BC} + \angle 1$	5. Substitution
6. $\angle 1 = \frac{1}{2}(m\,\overset{\frown}{AC} - m\,\overset{\frown}{BC})$	6. Algebra

Now, if we change the other secant ray to a tangent ray, we have Theorem 6-15.

THEOREM 6-15

The measure of the angle formed by two tangent rays intersecting outside the circle is half the difference of the intercepted arcs.

Given: tangents $\overrightarrow{PA}$, $\overrightarrow{PB}$

Prove: $m\angle 1 = \frac{1}{2}(m\,\overset{\frown}{AXB} - m\,\overset{\frown}{AYB})$

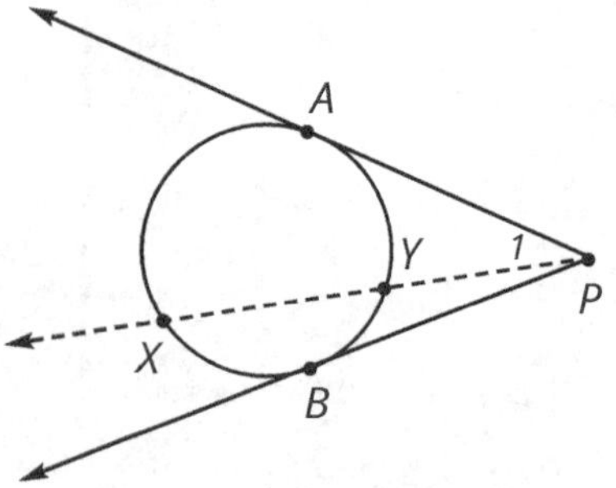

STATEMENT	REASON
1. Draw $\overrightarrow{PX}$	1. Auxiliary line
2. $m\angle 1 = m\angle APX + m\angle XPB$	2. Angle addition theorem
3. $m\angle APX = \frac{1}{2}(m\,\overset{\frown}{AX} - m\,\overset{\frown}{XY})$ $m\angle XPB = \frac{1}{2}(m\,\overset{\frown}{XB} - m\,\overset{\frown}{BY})$	3. Tangent-Secant outside circle angle
4. $m\angle 1 = \frac{1}{2}(m\,\overset{\frown}{AX} - m\,\overset{\frown}{AY}) + \frac{1}{2}(m\,\overset{\frown}{XB} - m\,\overset{\frown}{BY})$	4. Substitution
5. $m\angle 1 = \frac{1}{2}[(\overset{\frown}{AX} + \overset{\frown}{XB}) - (\overset{\frown}{AY} + \overset{\frown}{YB})]$	5. Algebra
6. $\overset{\frown}{AX} + \overset{\frown}{XB} = \overset{\frown}{AXB}$ $\overset{\frown}{AY} + \overset{\frown}{YB} = \overset{\frown}{AYB}$	6. Arc addition
7. $m\angle 1 = \frac{1}{2}(\overset{\frown}{AXB} - \overset{\frown}{AYB})$	7. Substitution

The following summary of angle and arc relationships should be useful for learning and review.

Central Angle = intercepted arc

$m\angle 1 = m\overset{\frown}{AB}$

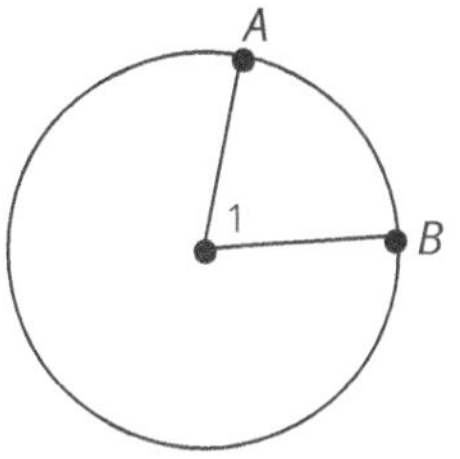

Inscribed angle = $\frac{1}{2}$ intercepted arc

$m\angle 1 = \frac{1}{2}\, m\overset{\frown}{AB}$

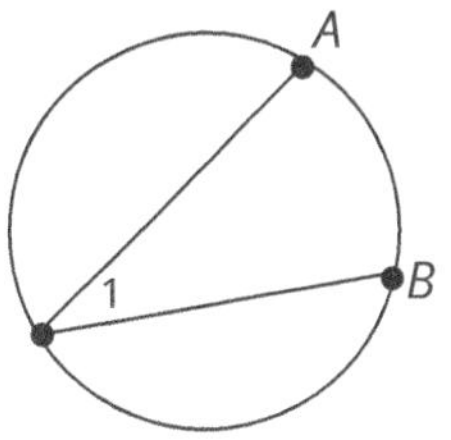

Angle formed by tangent and secant with vertex on circle = $\frac{1}{2}$ intercepted arc

$m\angle 1 = \frac{1}{2}\, m\overset{\frown}{AB}$

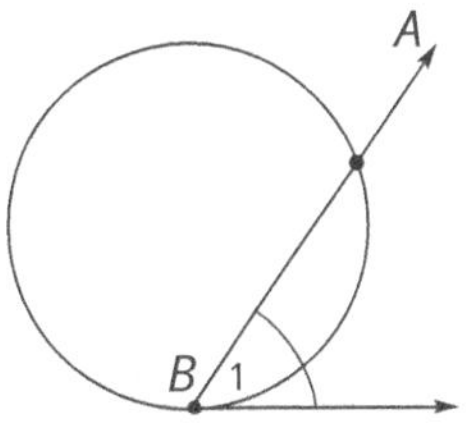

Angle formed by two secants with vertex inside circle = $\frac{1}{2}$ sum of intercepted arc

$m\angle 1 = \frac{1}{2}\,(m\overset{\frown}{AB} + m\overset{\frown}{CD})$

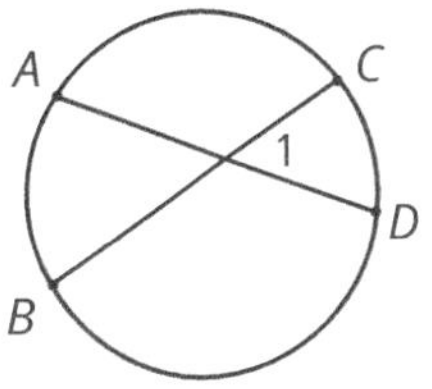

Angle formed by two secants with vertex outside the circle = $\frac{1}{2}$ difference of intercepted arcs

$m\angle 1 = \frac{1}{2}\,(m\overset{\frown}{AB} - m\overset{\frown}{CD})$

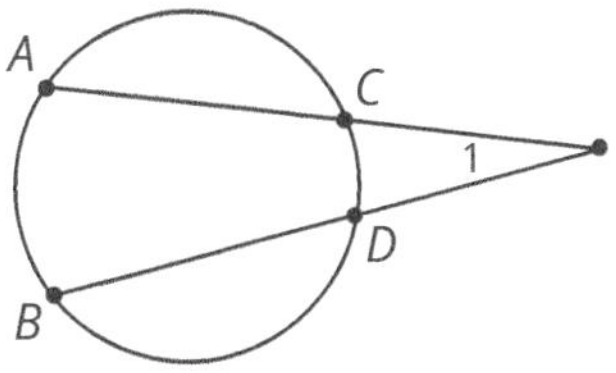

Angle formed by secant & tangent with vertex outside the circle = $\frac{1}{2}$ difference of intercepted arcs

$m\angle 1 = \frac{1}{2}\,(m\overset{\frown}{AB} - m\overset{\frown}{CB})$

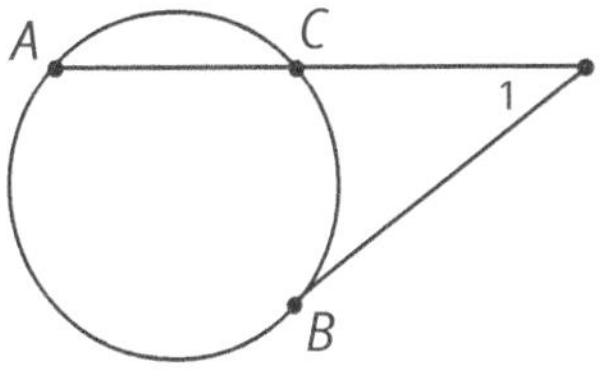

Angle formed by two tangents with vertex outside the circle = $\frac{1}{2}$ difference of intercepted arcs

$m\angle 1 = \frac{1}{2}\,(m\overset{\frown}{AXB} - m\overset{\frown}{AB})$

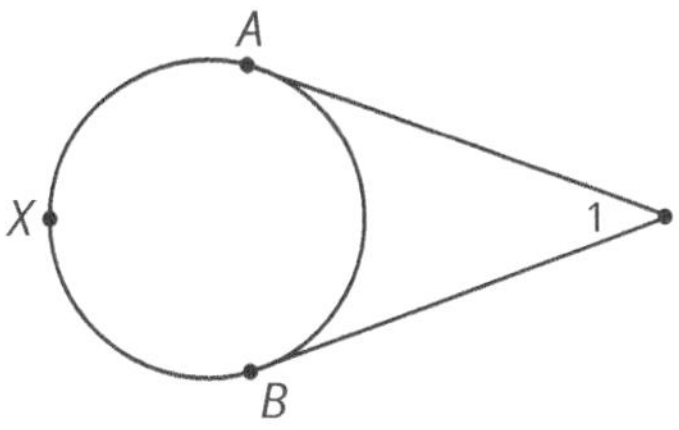

Use the angle measure theorems to find the measure of angle 1.

3.34 m∠1 = ______________

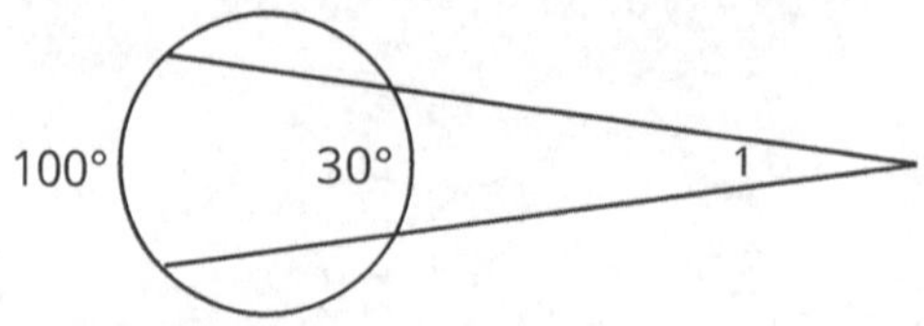

3.35 m∠1 = ______________

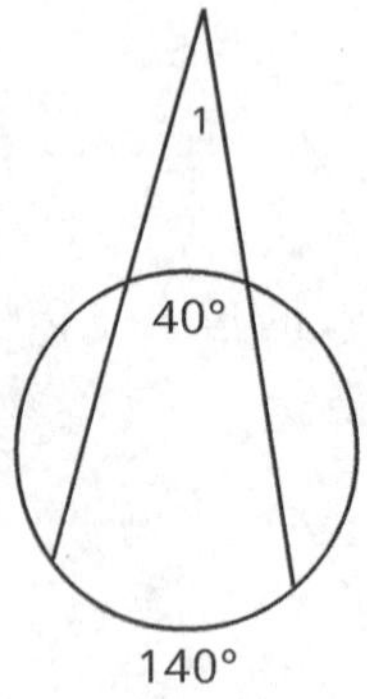

3.36 m∠1 = ______________

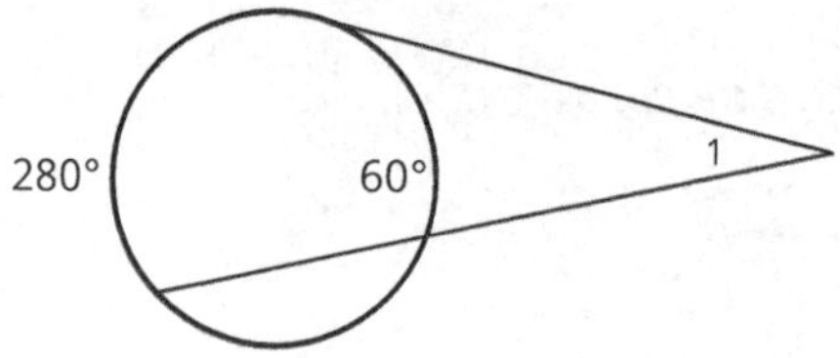

3.37 m∠1 = ______________

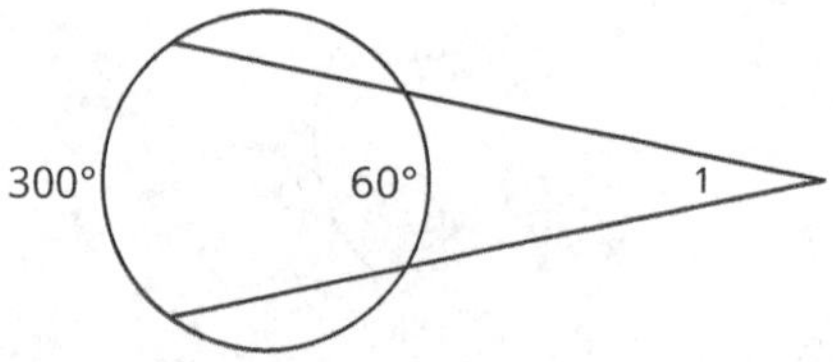

3.38 m∠1 = ______________

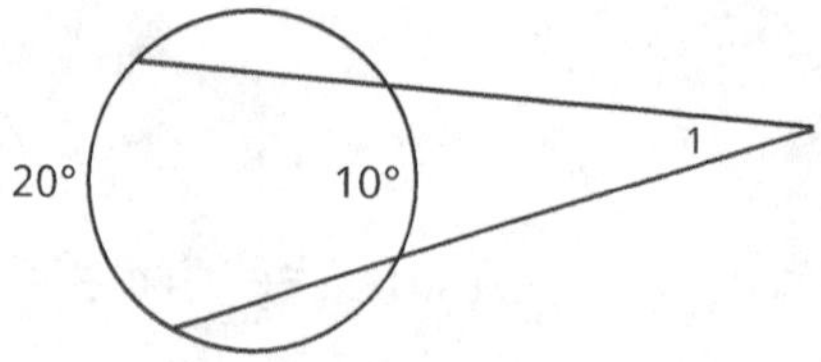

Find *x* in the following problems.

3.39 $x =$ ____________

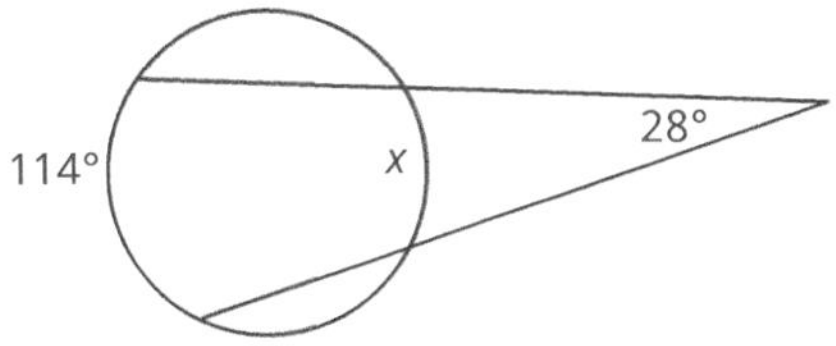

3.40 $x =$ ____________

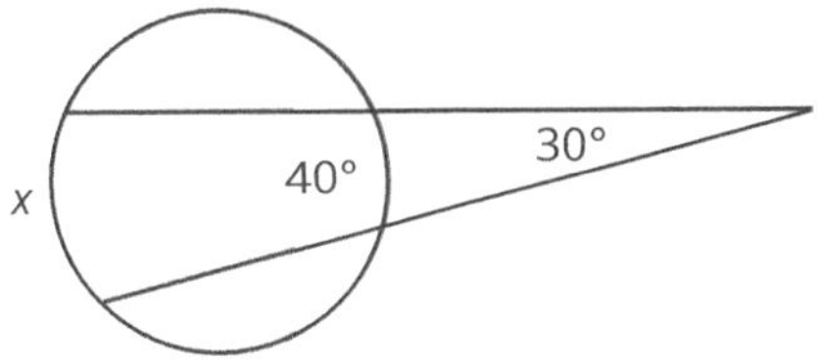

3.41 $x =$ ____________

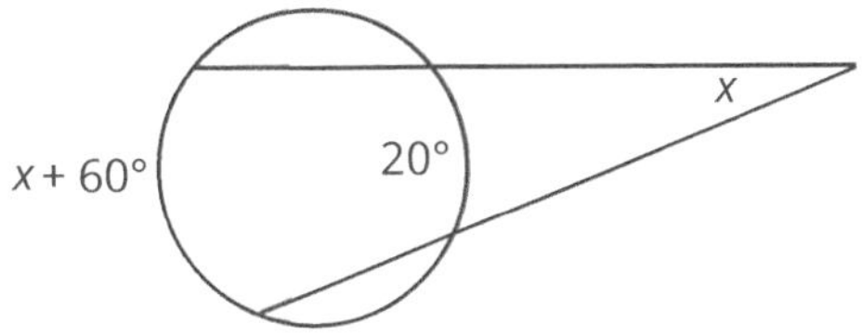

3.42 $x =$ ____________

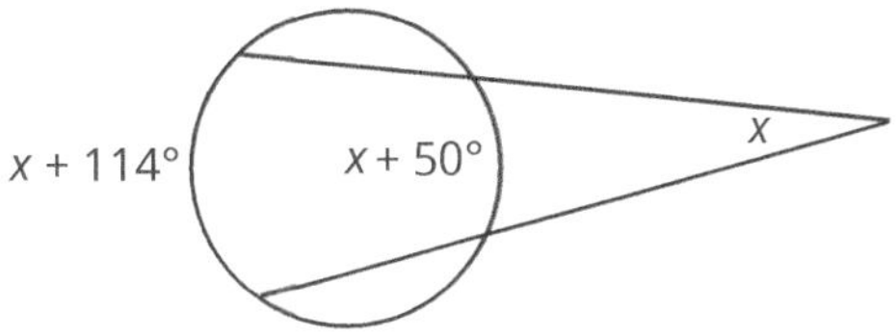

3.43 $x =$ ____________

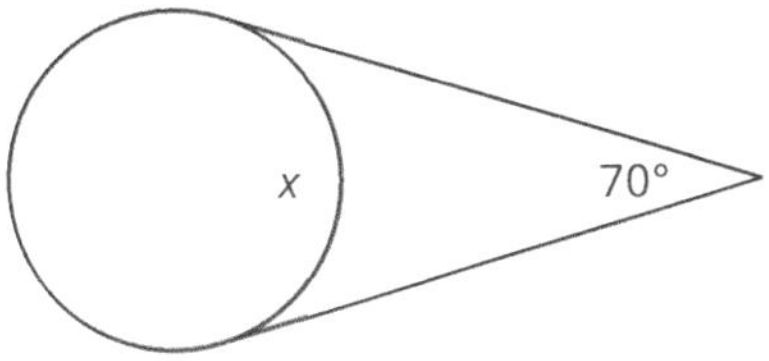

3.44 $x =$ ____________

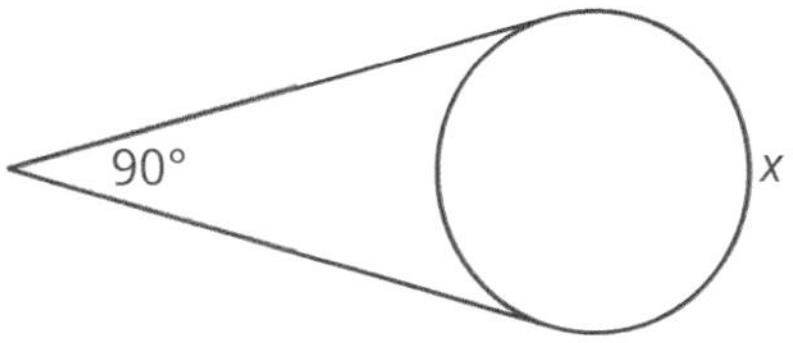

Find the measure of the following numbered angles in circle P when $\overset{\frown}{AE} = 53°$, $\overset{\frown}{BA} = 68°$, and $\overset{\frown}{CB} = 72°$.

3.45 m∠1 = ____________

3.46 m∠2 = ____________

3.47 m∠3 = ____________

3.48 m∠4 = ____________

3 49 m∠5 = ____________

3.50 m∠6 = ____________

3.51 m∠7 = ____________

3.52 m∠8 = ____________

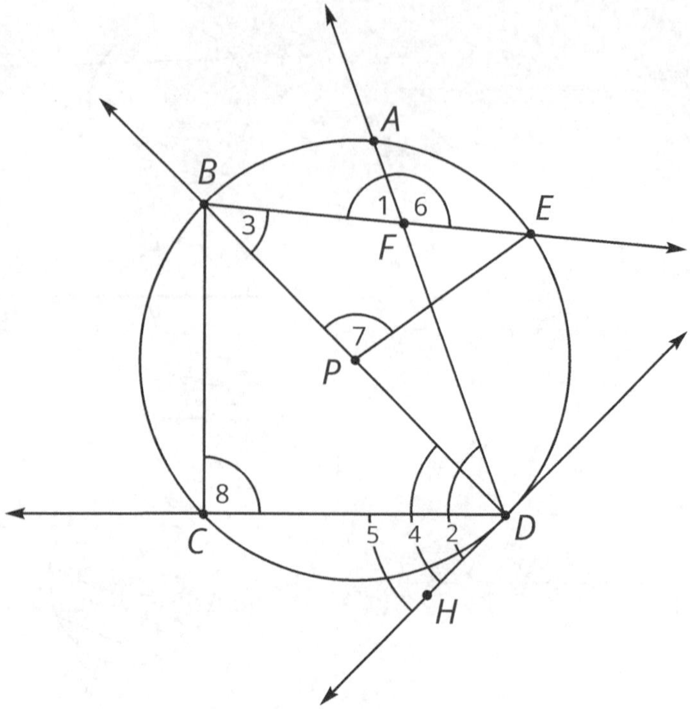

SPECIAL SEGMENTS

We have learned how to measure angles that are formed by chords, secants, and tangents to a circle. We shall now learn methods of finding the length of parts of chords, secants, and tangents.

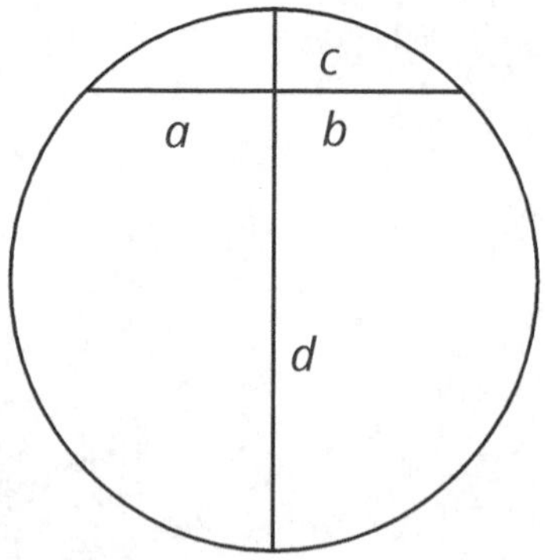

Many theorems that we have studied so far have been statements that you intuitively know are true. In this section, however, you will prove theorems with statements that are quite surprising. Do you believe that $ab = cd$? Theorem 6-16 proves this statement.

> **THEOREM 6-16**
>
> If two chords intersect in a circle, the product of the lengths of the segments of one chord is equal to the product of the lengths of the other chord.

Given: Chords $\overline{AC}$ and $\overline{BD}$ intersect at P

Prove: $AP \cdot PC = BP \cdot PD$

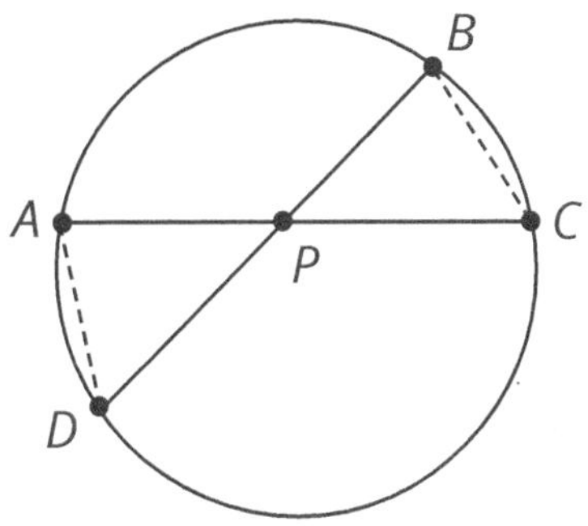

STATEMENT	REASON
1. Draw $\overline{AD}$, $\overline{BC}$	1. Auxiliary lines
2. $\angle A = \angle B$ $\angle D = \angle C$	2. Angles intercept same arc
3. $\triangle APD \sim \triangle BPC$	3. AA
4. $\frac{AP}{BP} = \frac{PD}{PC}$	4. Corresponding sides of similar $\triangle$'s are proportional
5. $AP \bullet PC = BP \bullet PD$	5. POP (Cross product)

THEOREM 6-17

If two secants intersect at a point outside a circle, the length of one secant times the length of its external part is equal to the length of the other secant times the length of its external part.

Given: Secants $\overrightarrow{CA}$ and $\overrightarrow{CD}$ intersect at C

Prove: $AC \cdot BC = DC \cdot EC$

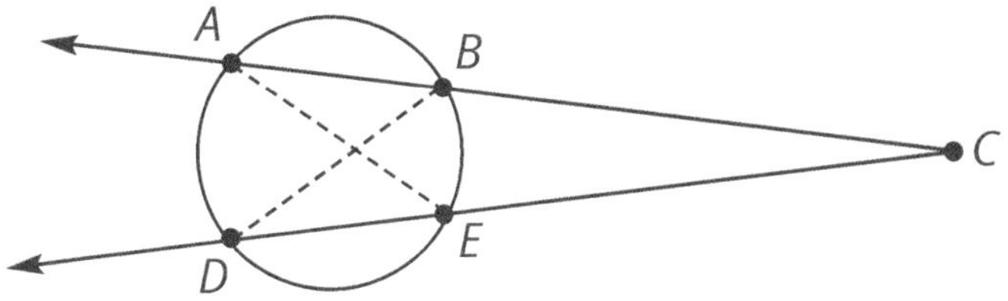

STATEMENT	REASON
1. Draw $\overline{AE}$ and $\overline{DB}$	1. Auxiliary lines
2. $\angle CAE = \angle CDB$	2. Angles intercept same arc
3. $\angle C = \angle C$	3. Reflexive
4. $\triangle DBC \sim \triangle AEC$	4. AA
5. $\frac{AC}{DC} = \frac{EC}{BC}$	5. Corresponding sides of similar $\triangle$'s are proportional
6. $AC \bullet BC = DC \bullet EC$	6. POP

> **THEOREM 6-18**
> If a tangent segment and a secant segment intersect outside a circle, the length of the tangent segment is the geometric mean between the secant segment and the external part of the secant segment.

Given: Secant $\overrightarrow{PA}$, tangent $\overrightarrow{PC}$ intersect at P

Prove: $\frac{AP}{PC} = \frac{PC}{BP}$

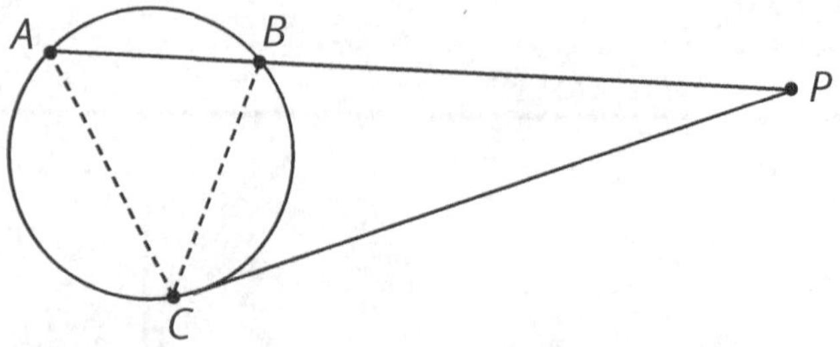

STATEMENT	REASON
1. Draw $\overline{BC}$ and $\overline{AC}$	1. Auxiliary lines
2. $\angle P = \angle P$	2. Reflexive
3. $\angle BCP = \frac{1}{2}\text{m}\,\overset{\frown}{BC}$	3. Tangent-secant angle with vertex on circle
4. $\angle A = \frac{1}{2}\text{m}\,\overset{\frown}{BC}$	4. Inscribed angle measure
5. $\angle A = \angle BCP$	5. Substitution
6. $\triangle APC \sim \triangle CPB$	6. AA
7. $\frac{AP}{PC} = \frac{PC}{PB}$	7. Corresponding sides of similar $\triangle$'s are proportional

Knowledge of these three theorems can be helpful in finding measures that we were previously unable to find.

Model 1: Find x.

$2x = 30$

$x = 15$

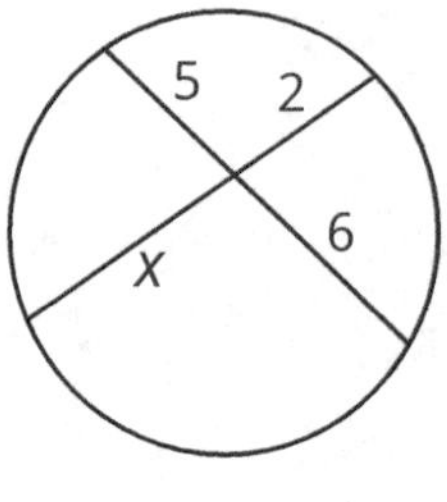

Model 2: Find x.

$12x = 16(8)$

$12x = 128$

$x = 10\frac{2}{3}$

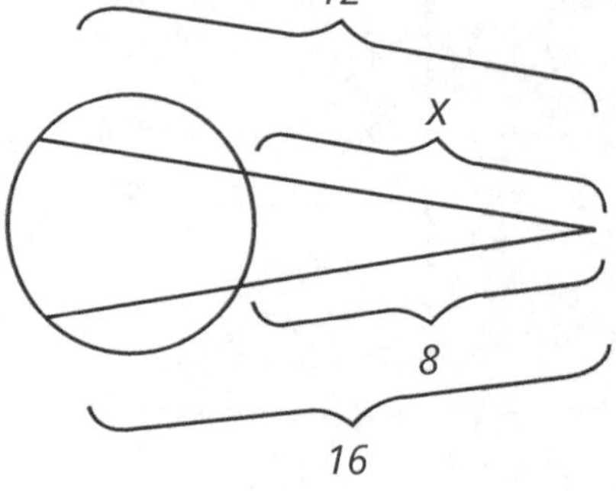

Model 3: Find x.

$\frac{12}{x} = \frac{x}{3}$

$x^2 = 36$

$x = 6$

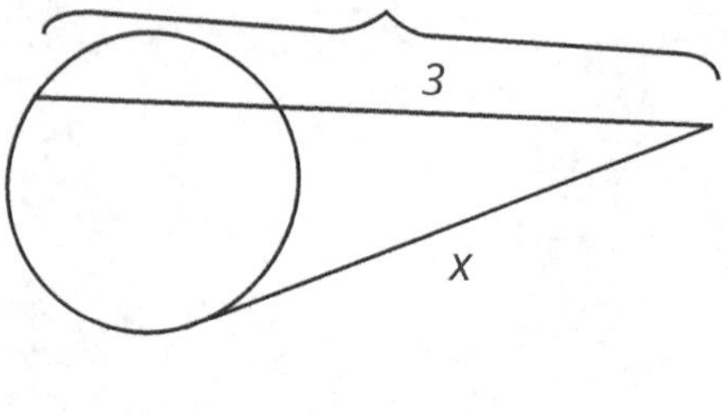

Use the theorems to find x in the following circles.

3.53 x = ______________________

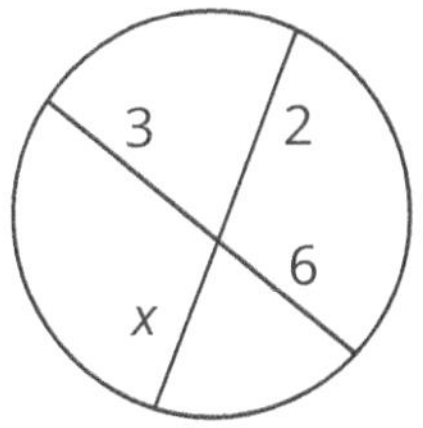

3.54 x = ______________________

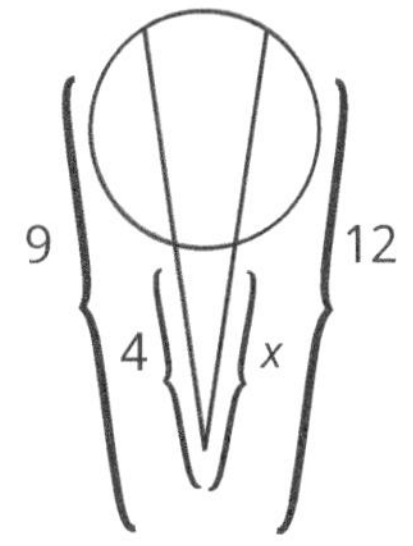

3.55 *x* = ______________________

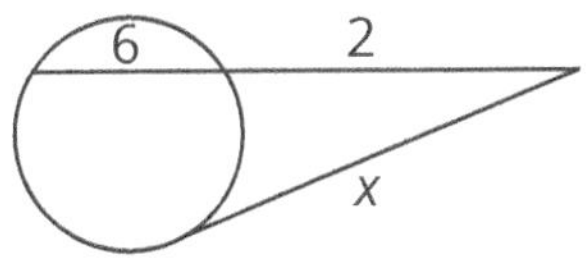

3.56 *x* = ______________________

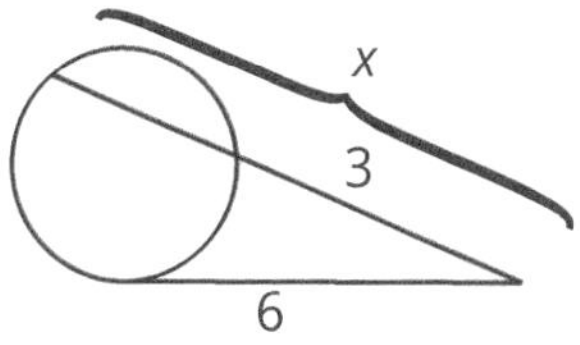

3.57 *x* = ______________________

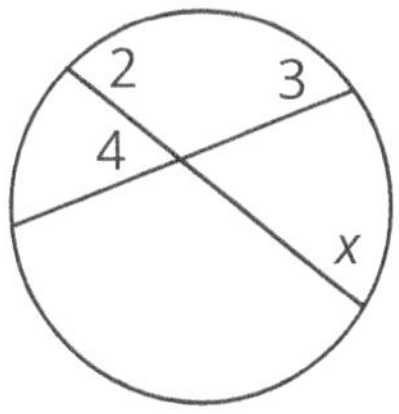

3.58 *x* = ______________________

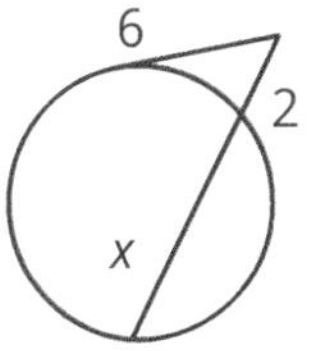

3.59 *x* = ______________________

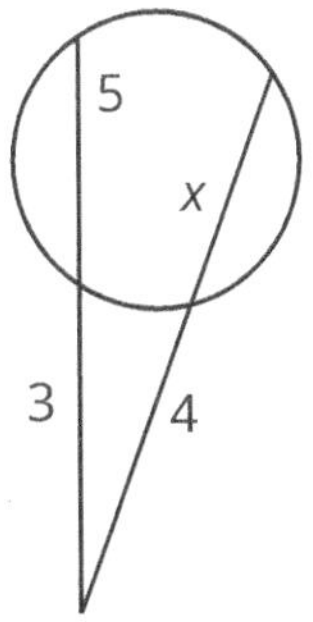

3.60 *x* = ______________________

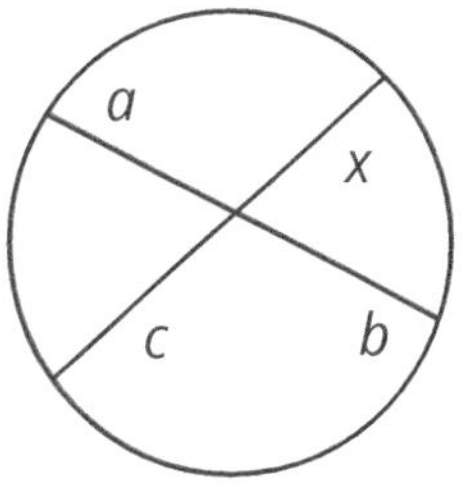

Refer to the figure to complete the following activities.

3.61 If $AM = 7$, $MB = 6$, and $CM = 8$, find CD. ____________

3.62 If $CM = 8$, $DM = 6$, and $AB = 16$, find AM. ____________

3.63 If $AM = 8$, $AB = 16$, and $CD = 20$, find CM. ____________

3.64 If $AB = 12$, $CD = 12$, and $MD = 3$, find AM. ____________

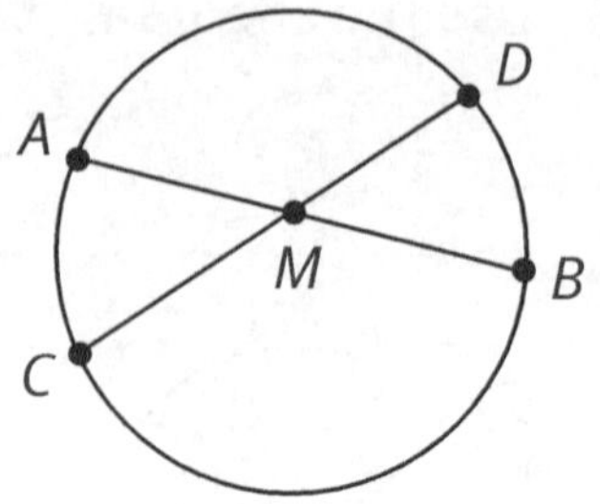

Refer to the figure to complete the following activities.

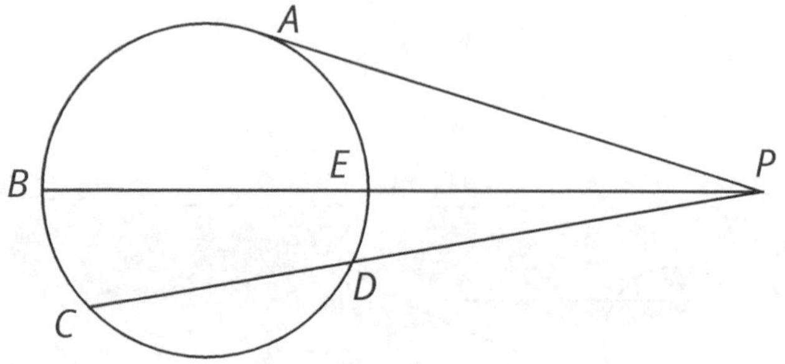

3.65 If $\overline{PA} = 6$ and $\overline{PE} = 4$, find $\overline{BE}$. ____________________

3.66 If $\overline{PD} = 5\sqrt{2}$ and $\overline{DC} = 7\sqrt{2}$ find $\overline{PA}$. ____________________

3.67 If $\overline{PA} = 10$ and $\overline{BE} = 21$, find $\overline{BP}$. ____________________

3.68 If $\overline{PC} = 6$, $\overline{PD} = 4$, and $\overline{BE} = 5$, find $\overline{PE}$. ____________________

Complete the following proofs.

3.69 Given: $\overline{PA} = \overline{PB}$
Prove: $\overline{PC} = \overline{PD}$

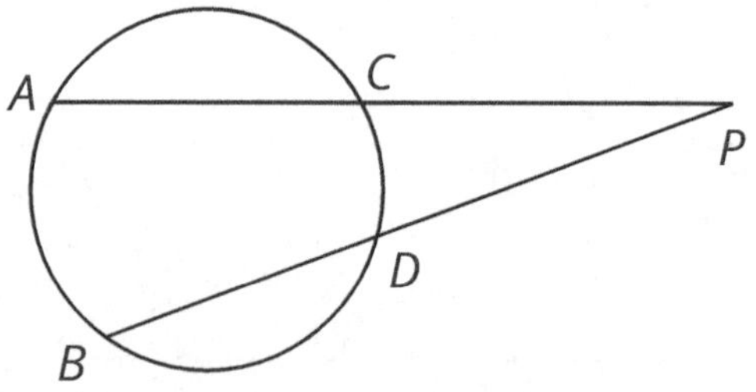

STATEMENT	REASON

3.70 Given: $\overline{AB}$ is diameter, $\overline{BC}$ is tangent to circle O.

Prove: $\triangle AXB \sim \triangle ABC$

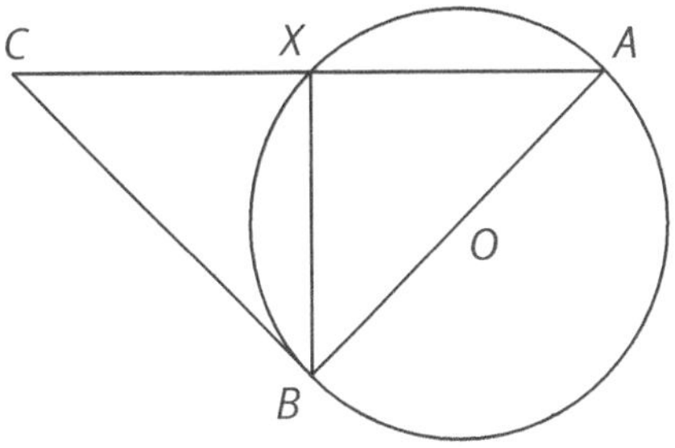

STATEMENT	REASON

Before you take this last Self Test, you may want to do one or more of these self checks.

1. ________ Read the objectives. See if you can do them.
2. ________ Restudy the material related to any objectives that you cannot do.
3. ________ Use the **SQ3R** study procedure to review the material:
   a. **S**can the sections.
   b. **Q**uestion yourself.
   c. **R**ead to answer your questions.
   d. **R**ecite the answers to yourself.
   e. **R**eview areas you did not understand.
4. ________ Review all vocabulary, activities, and Self Tests, writing a correct answer for every wrong answer.

SELF TEST 3

Refer to the figures to complete the following items (each answer, 3 points).

Given: $\triangle RST$ is circumscribed about $\odot A$

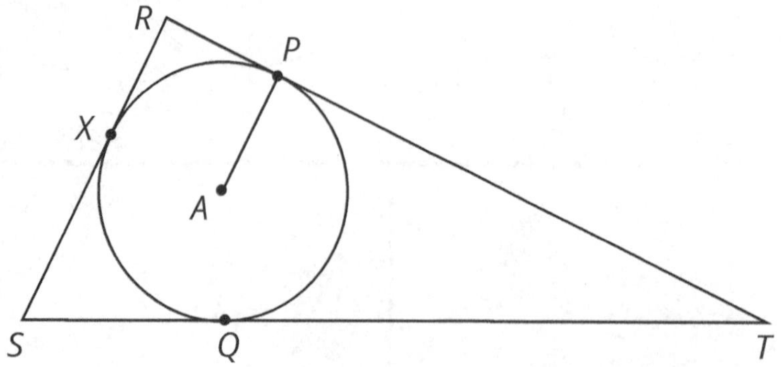

3.01 Circle *A* is ________________ in $\triangle RST$.

3.02 $\overline{RS}$ is ________________ to circle *A* at *X*.

3.03 $m\angle APT =$ ________________ .

3.04 $m\angle S =$ ________________ .

Write the correct answer in the blank (each answer, 3 points).

3.05 Radii of congruent circles are ________________ .

3.06 Measures of minor arcs equal measures of ________________ .

3.07 If $\angle T$ is inscribed in a semicircle, then the measure of angle *T* is ________________ .

3.08 The measure of an angle formed by two secants intersecting inside the circle equals

________________________________ .

3.09 The measure of an angle formed by two secants intersecting outside the circle equals

________________________________ .

3.010 A diameter that is perpendicular to a chord ________________ the chord.

Refer to the figure to name the following parts (each answer, 3 points).

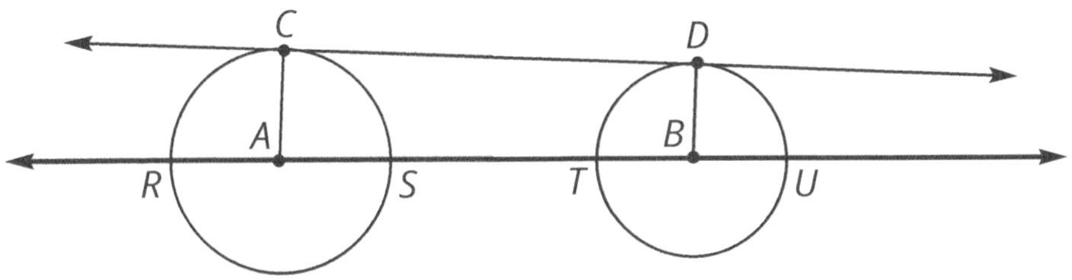

3.011 Radius of circle *B*. ____________________

3.012 Diameter of circle *A*. ____________________

3.013 Common tangent. ____________________

3.014 An angle whose measure equals $\widehat{DU}$. ____________________

3.015 Is circle *A* tangent to circle *B*? __________

Refer to the figures to complete the following items (each answer, 3 points).

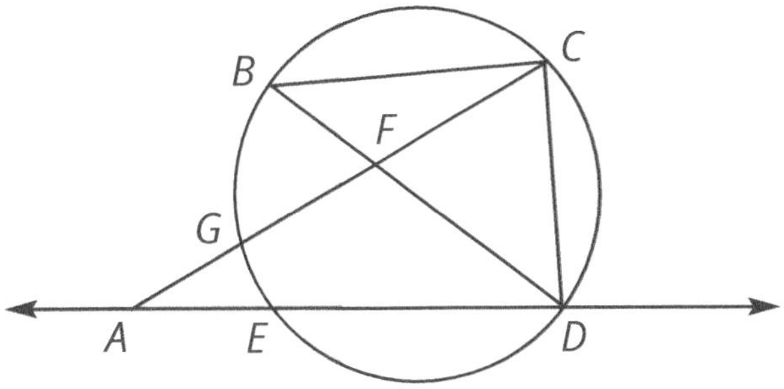

3.016 m$\angle BFG$ = ____________________

3.017 m$\angle CAD$ = ____________________

3.018 If m$\angle DFC$ = 40° and m $\widehat{CD}$ = 55°, then m $\widehat{BG}$ = ____________________ .

3.019 If m $\angle A$ = 15° and m $\widehat{CD}$ = 55°, then m $\widehat{GE}$ = ____________________ .

3.020 If $\overline{BD}$ is diameter, then $\triangle BCD$ is a ____________________ triangle.

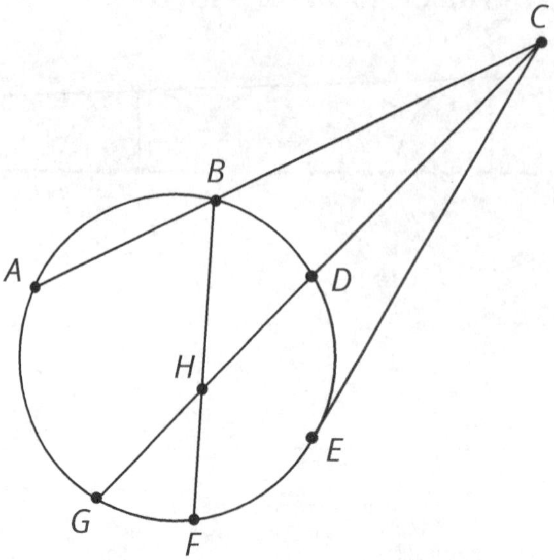

3.021 If $BH = 3$, $BF = 10$, and $GH = 2$, find HD. ____________________

3.022 If $AC = 12$ and $BC = 3$, find CE. ____________________

3.023 If $CG = 10$, $AC = 8$, and $BC = 5$, find DC. ____________________

3.024 If $GC = 16$, and $CE = 8$, find DC. ____________________

3.025 If $BC = 3$, $AB = 5$, and $CD = 2$, find DG. ____________________

60/75	**SCORE** ________	**TEACHER** ________ initials	________ date

Before you take the LIFEPAC Test, you may want to do one or more of these self checks.

1. ________ Read the objectives. See if you can do them.
2. ________ Restudy the material related to any objectives that you cannot do.
3. ________ Use the **SQ3R** study procedure to review the material.
4. ________ Review activities, Self Tests, and LIFEPAC Glossary.
5. ________ Restudy areas of weakness indicated by the last Self Test.

GLOSSARY

center of an arc .... The center of the circle that contains the arc.

center of a circle .... The point in the plane equidistant from all points of the circle.

central angle .... An angle with its vertex at the center of a circle.

chord .... A segment with end points on the circle.

circle .... The set of all points in a plane that are at a given distance from a given point in the plane.

circumscribed polygon .... A polygon with each side tangent to the circle contained within.

common external tangent .... A tangent to two coplanar circles such that a segment connecting the centers of the circles does not intersect the tangent.

common internal tangent .... A tangent to two coplanar circles such that a segment connecting the centers of the circles intersects the tangent.

concentric circles .... Two or more circles that lie in the same plane and have the same center.

congruent circles .... Circles that have equal radii.

diameter .... A chord of a circle that contains the center of the circle.

midpoint of an arc .... A point x on the arc $\widehat{AB}$ such that m $\widehat{AX}$ = m $\widehat{XB}$.

great circle .... The intersection of a sphere and a plane that passes through the center of the sphere.

inscribed angle .... An angle with vertex that is a point of an arc other than the end points and with sides that pass through the end points of the arc.

intercepted arc .... The arc with end points that are points of the sides of the angle and including all points on the arc in the interior of the angle.

major arc .... The union of two points of a circle, not the end points of a diameter; and all points of the circle that lie in the exterior of the central angle with sides that contain the two points.

minor arc .... The union of two points of the circle, not the ends of a diameter; and all points of the circle that lie in the interior of the central angle with sides that contain the two points.

radius .... A segment joining the center of a circle to a point of the circle.

secant .... A line that contains a chord of a circle.

secant ray .... A ray that lies on a secant line and contains both points of intersection with the circle.

semicircle .... The union of the endpoints of a diameter of a circle and all points of the circle lying on the same side of the diameter.

small circle .... The intersection of a sphere and a plane that does not pass through the center of the sphere.

sphere .... The set of all points at a given distance from a given point.

tangent line .... A line that lies in the plane of the circle and intersects the circle in exactly one point.

tangent circles .... Two coplanar circles that are tangent to the same line at the same point.

tangent ray .... A ray that lies on a tangent line and contains the point of tangency.

MATH 1007
Construction and Locus

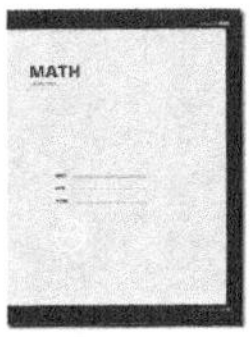

LIFEPAC Test is located in the center of the booklet. Please remove before starting the unit.

Author:
Milton R. Christen, M.A.

Editor-in-Chief:
Richard W. Wheeler, M.A.Ed.

Editor:
Robin Hintze Kreutzberg, M.B.A.

Consulting Editor:
Robert L. Zenor, M.A., M.S.

Revision Editor:
Alan Christopherson, M.S.

Alpha Omega PUBLICATIONS

804 N. 2nd Ave. E.
Rock Rapids, IA 51246-1759

Construction and Locus

Introduction

In your previous LIFEPACs you have represented geometric figures by sketching them on your paper. You had no particular concern for the accuracy of the figures, as long as they did not give misleading information.

Some of you may have made accurate drawings using a ruler, compass, and protractor. You may be surprised to learn that in many situations you can make these figures with the same or greater accuracy using only the compass and an unmarked straightedge.

In this LIFEPAC® you will learn how to construct a variety of figures using only the compass and straightedge. You will also learn a technique to locate and describe sets of points that satisfy one or more given conditions.

Objectives

Read these objectives. The objectives tell you what you will be able to do when you have successfully completed this LIFEPAC. When you have finished this LIFEPAC, you should be able to:

1. Copy segments and angles.
2. Bisect angles, segments, and arcs.
3. Construct perpendiculars to a line.
4. Construct tangents to a circle.
5. Construct parallel lines.
6. Divide a segment into a given number of equal segments.
7. Construct a fourth proportional.
8. Construct a geometric mean.
9. Divide a segment into a given ratio.
10. Construct triangles.
11. Construct special circles.
12. Construct certain polygons.
13. Define locus.
14. Solve locus problems.
15. Construct figures using locus concepts.

Survey the LIFEPAC. Ask yourself some questions about this study and write your questions here.

1. BASIC CONSTRUCTION

You will learn five basic constructions in this section: copying figures, bisecting figures, constructing perpendiculars, constructing parallels, and constructing with measurements. Each of these constructions will be done using only the compass and the straightedge. With these five basic constructions you can then construct other geometric figures such as triangles, rectangles, and parallelograms.

Section Objectives

Review these objectives. When you have finished this section, you should be able to:

1. Copy segments and angles.
2. Bisect angles, segments, and arcs.
3. Construct perpendiculars to a line.
4. Construct tangents to a circle.
5. Construct parallel lines.
6. Divide a segment into a given number of equal segments.
7. Construct a fourth proportional.
8. Construct a geometric mean.
9. Divide a segment into a given ratio.

COPYING FIGURES

To copy a figure means to duplicate it on your paper so that the segments and angles of the copy are exactly the same size as the original. Copying is done with just two tools: a compass and an unmarked straightedge.

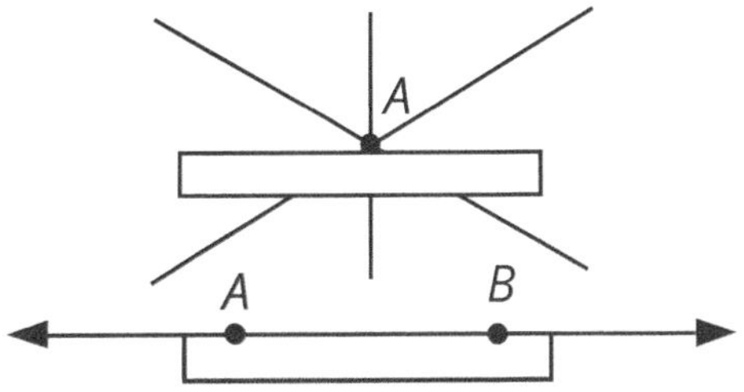

> **DEFINITION**
> **Straightedge**: an instrument used only to draw lines through one given point and draw the unique line through two given points.

> **DEFINITION**
> **Compass:** an instrument used only to draw circles or arcs of a circle having a given center and to draw the unique circle having a given center and a given radius.

We can use many items to draw lines, if they are straight. The edge of a book, the edge of a piece of cardboard, a piece of plastic, or a ruler will all serve. We can use the ruler so long as we do not use the numbers on it for measuring.

A compass can take many forms, but the two main parts of any compass are its points. One point is a fixed sharp metal point that you stick into your paper at the center of the circle. The other point contains the writing tool, usually a pencil. The pencil point is adjustable up and down. The compass should be adjusted so that the tip of the pencil is the same length as the tip of the center point. The distance between the two points will be the radius of the circle you are drawing.

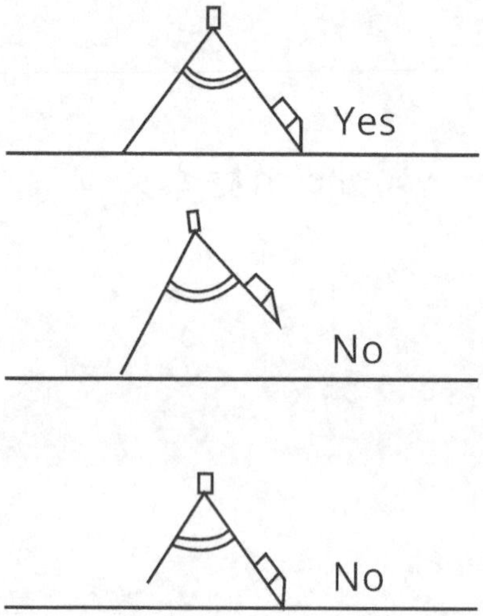

When using a compass, you may wish to back your paper with some thin cardboard so that the center point of the compass will stick in and not slide off your paper.

When drawing a circle, hold the compass at the top. Do not hold the legs of the compass, or you may change the radius of your circle.

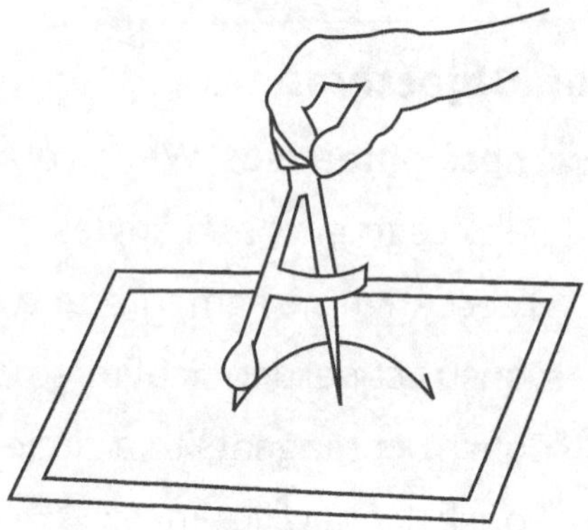

Tip the compass slightly in the direction you are drawing so that it is not perpendicular to the paper and pull the compass through your circle. Never push the compass, because pushing may tear your paper.

Use your straightedge to construct lines through the given points. Use your compass to construct circles.

1.1 $\overline{AB}$

1.2 $\overrightarrow{BC}$

1.3 $\overleftrightarrow{DC}$

1.4 $\overleftrightarrow{BD}$

1.5 $\overline{AD}$

1.6 $\overrightarrow{AC}$

1.7 Circle *A*, any radius

1.8 Circle *B*, any radius

1.9 Circle *C*, same radius as circle *B*

1.10 Circle *D*, same radius as circle *A*

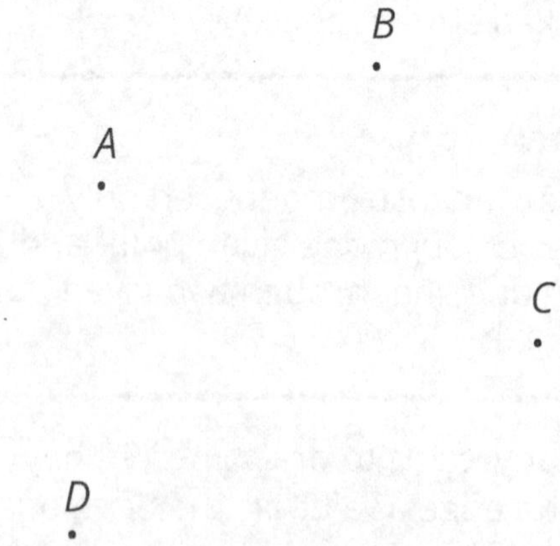

Construct circles with the given segment as radius and the given point as center.

1.11 circle *A*

1.12 circle *B*

1.13 circle *C*

1.14 circle *D*

1.15 circle *E*

1.16 circle *F*

To copy any segment, use Construction 1.

CONSTRUCTION 1

Given a segment, construct another segment with a length equal to the given segment.

Given: $\overline{AB}$

To construct: segment $\overline{RS}$ with length equal to AB

Steps: Draw a work line t. Pick a point on t; call it R. Put point of compass on A and pencil on B. This distance will be the radius of an arc. Place point of compass at R and, using radius from previous step, make an arc that intersects t at S.
$\overline{RS}$ is the required segment.

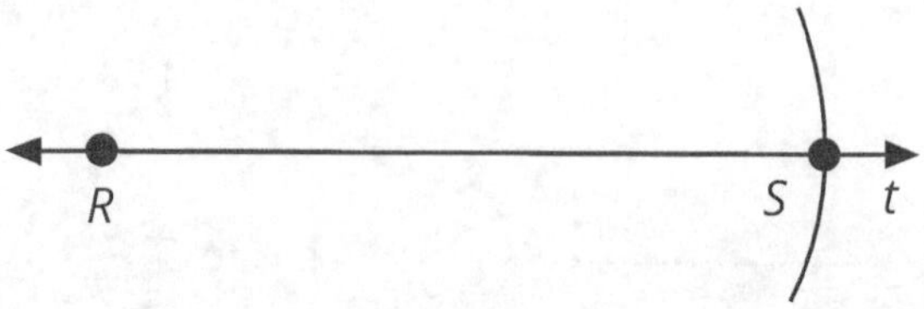

To copy any angle, use Construction 2.

CONSTRUCTION 2

Given a segment, construct another angle with measure equal to the given angle.

Given: $\angle ABC$

To construct: $\angle RST$ with measure equal to $\angle ABC$

Steps: Construct a ray $\overrightarrow{ST}$. With B as center and a convenient radius, construct an arc that intersects $\overrightarrow{BA}$ at X and $\overrightarrow{BC}$ at Y. With the same radius and center at S, construct an arc intersecting $\overrightarrow{ST}$ at Z. With center at Z and radius YX, construct an arc that intersects the arc from S. Call this point R.

$\angle RST$ is the required angle.

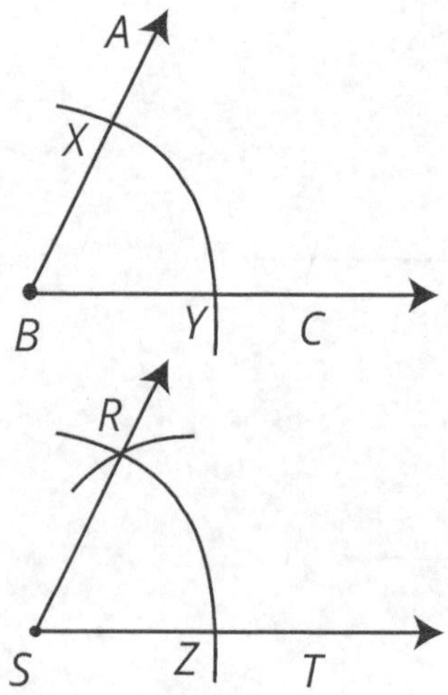

Use segments *a*, *b*, and *c* to complete the following constructions of segments with length equal to the indicated segments.

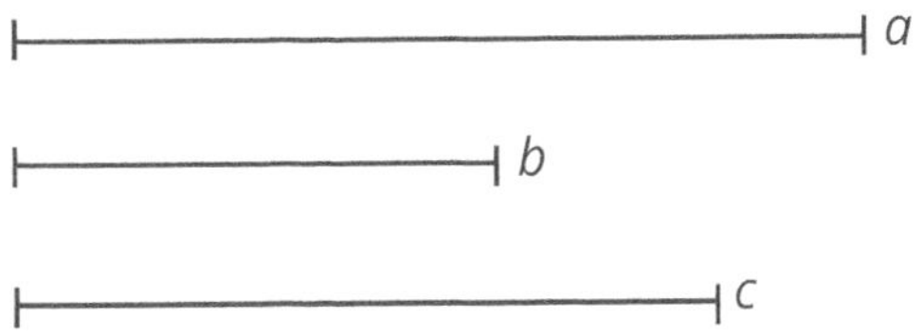

1.17 $a + b$

1.18 $a - b$

1.19 $2b + a$

1.20 $a + b + c$

1.21 $a + 2b - c$

1.22 $a - b + c$

1.23 $a + c - b$

By construction, copy the angles given. Leave all construction arcs in your final figure.

1.24

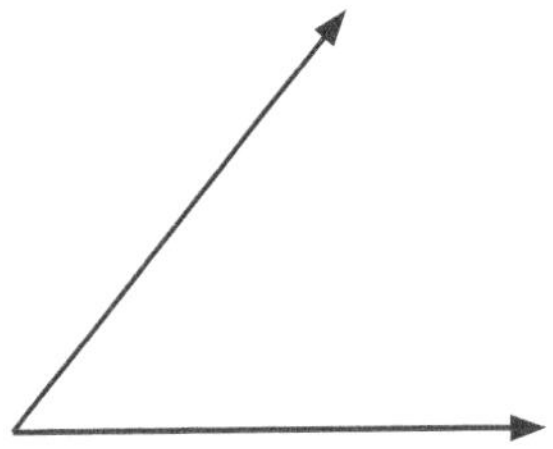

1.25

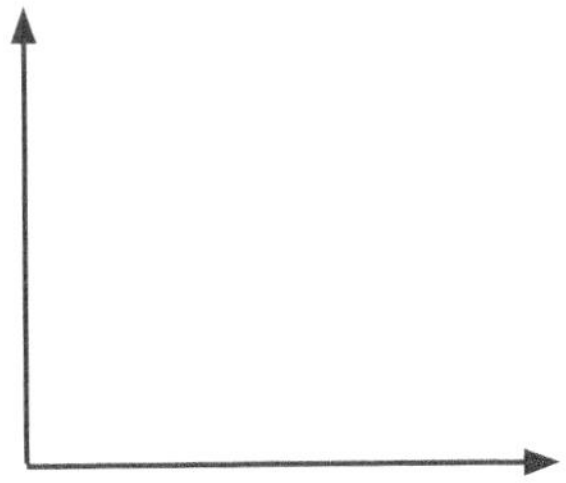

1.26

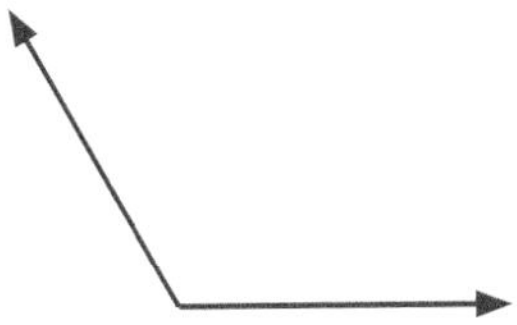

1.27

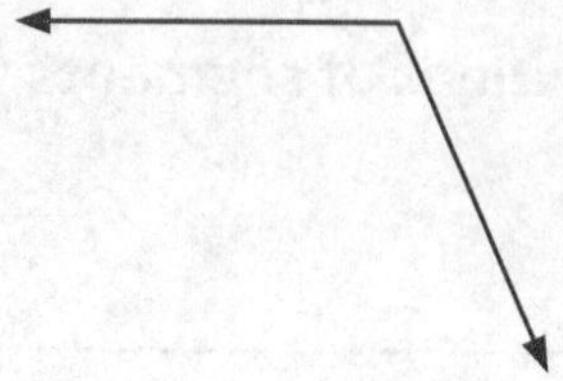

1.28

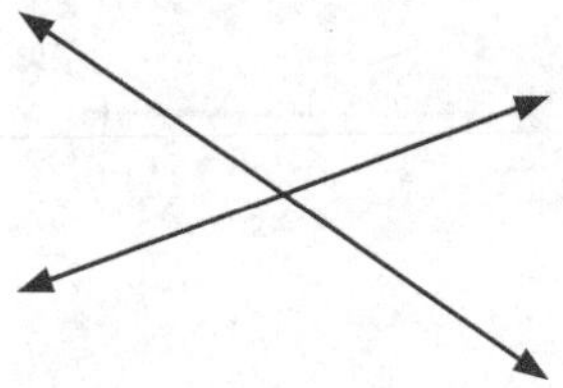

1.29

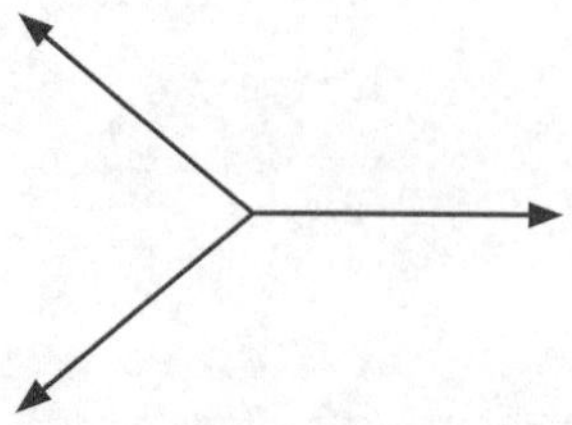

1.30

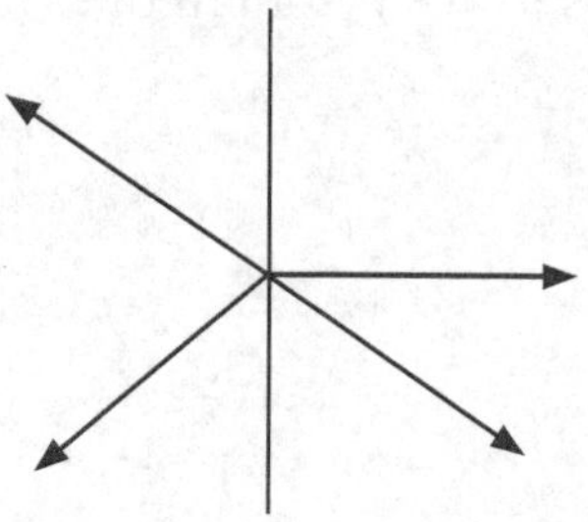

1.31 Construct an angle equal to $2x$.

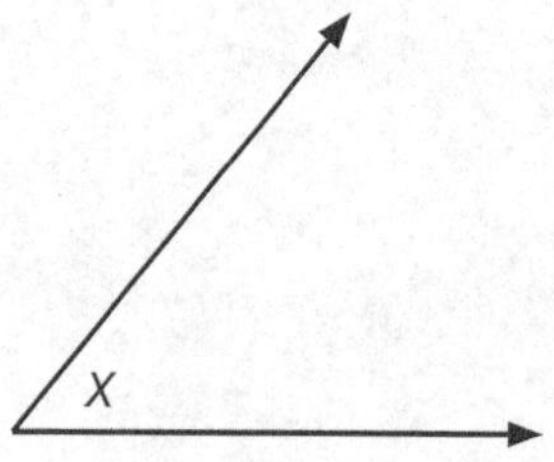

1.32 Construct a supplement to to $\angle Y$.

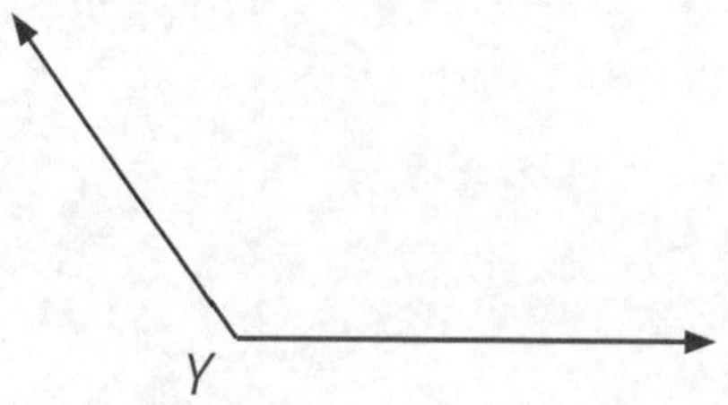

BISECTING

In many of our constructions, we want to divide a segment, an angle, or an arc into two equal parts. When this division has been accomplished, we have bisected the segment, angle, or arc.

To bisect a segment, follow Construction 3.

CONSTRUCTION 3

Given a segment, construct a bisector of the segment.

Given: $\overline{AB}$

To construct: a bisector of $\overline{AB}$

Steps: Take a radius greater than half of AB and construct intersecting arcs using A as center and then B as center.

Let X and Y be the two points of intersection of the arcs. Draw $\overleftrightarrow{XY}$. $\overleftrightarrow{XY}$ is the required bisector of $\overline{AB}$.

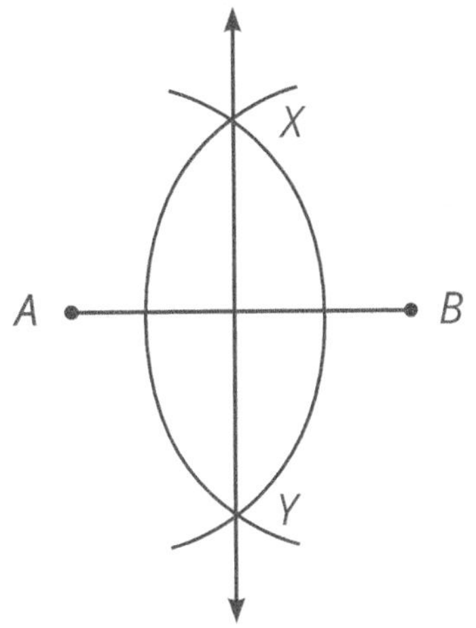

This bisector of the segment is also perpendicular to the segment at its midpoint. It is sometimes called the *perpendicular bisector* of the segment.

The point where $\overleftrightarrow{XY}$ intersects $\overline{AB}$ is the *midpoint* of $\overline{AB}$.

Therefore, any segment, line, or ray passing through this point would also be a bisector of the segment.

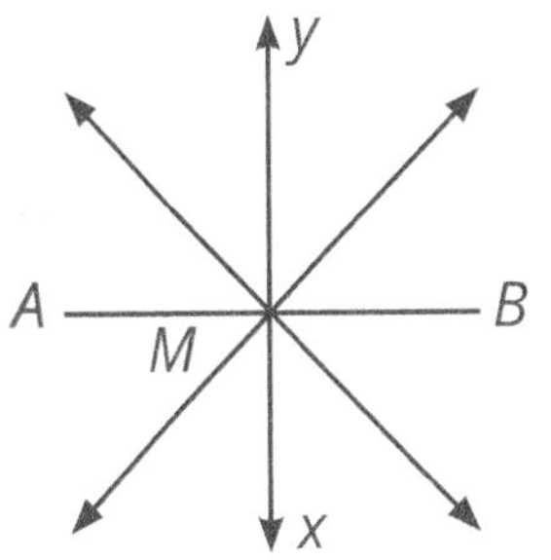

Bisecting an angle is a bit more involved. Follow Construction 4 to bisect an angle.

CONSTRUCTION 4

Given an angle, construct a ray that bisects the angle.

To construct: $\overrightarrow{BD}$ that bisects $\angle ABC$

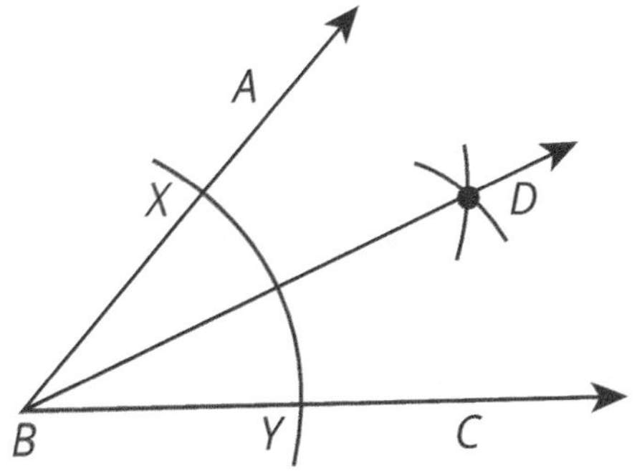

Steps: Using a convenient radius and the vertex of the angle B as center, construct an arc that intersects both sides of the angle. Call these points X and Y as centers and a radius greater than half of XY, construct two arcs that intersect in the interior of $\angle ABC$. Call this point D.

Draw $\overrightarrow{BD}$. $\overrightarrow{BD}$ is the ray that bisects $\angle ABC$.

Make sure that the radius you use to make the arcs from *X* and *Y* is long enough. If it is not long enough, then the arcs will not intersect. Remember that we need two points to determine a line, segment, or ray.

Constructing the bisector of an arc is very similar to bisecting a segment. Construction 5 shows you how.

CONSTRUCTION 5

Given an arc, construct a line that bisects the given arc.

Given: $\overset{\frown}{AB}$

To construct: $\overleftrightarrow{XY}$ that bisects $\overset{\frown}{AB}$

Steps: Using *A* and *B* as centers and a radius greater than half of $\overset{\frown}{AB}$, construct two arcs that intersect.Let X and Y be the points of intersection of the arcs. Draw $\overleftrightarrow{XY}$. $\overleftrightarrow{XY}$ is the desired line that bisects $\overset{\frown}{AB}$.

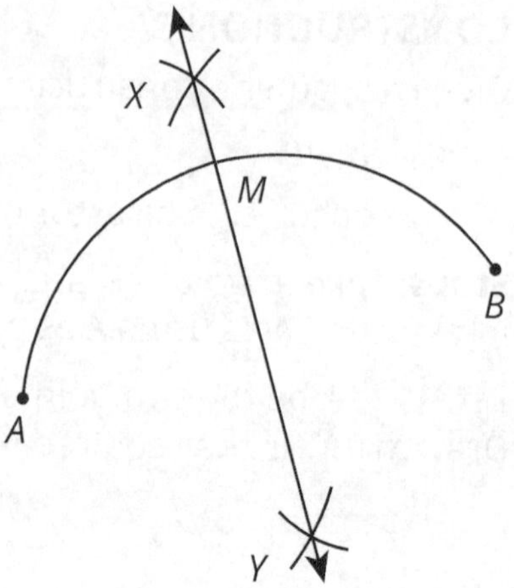

The point *M* where the bisector intersects the arc is called the *midpoint of the arc*. Any line, segment, or ray, that passes through this midpoint is also a bisector of the arc.

Construct the bisector of the following figures.

1.33

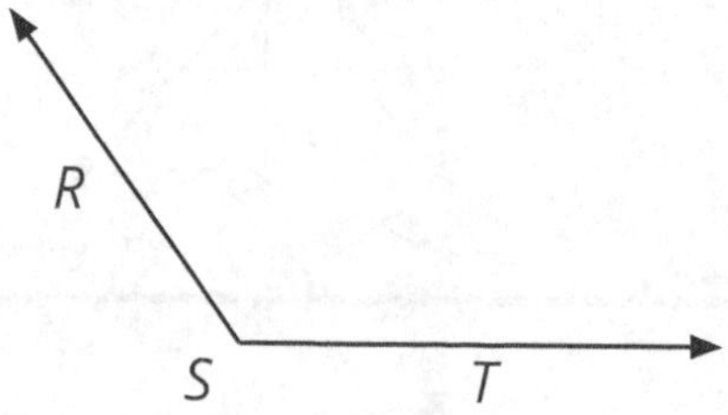

1.34

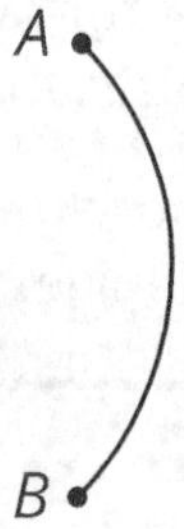

1.35

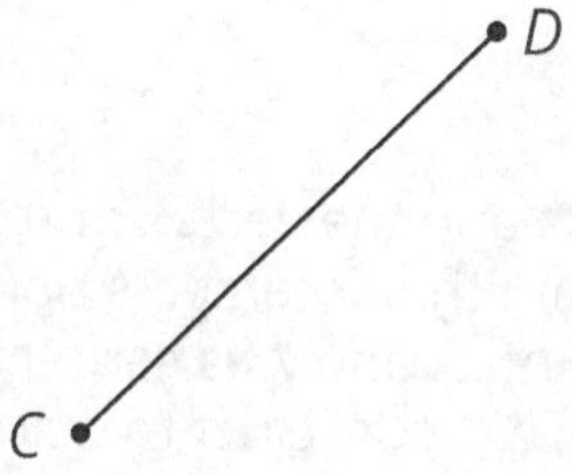

1.36

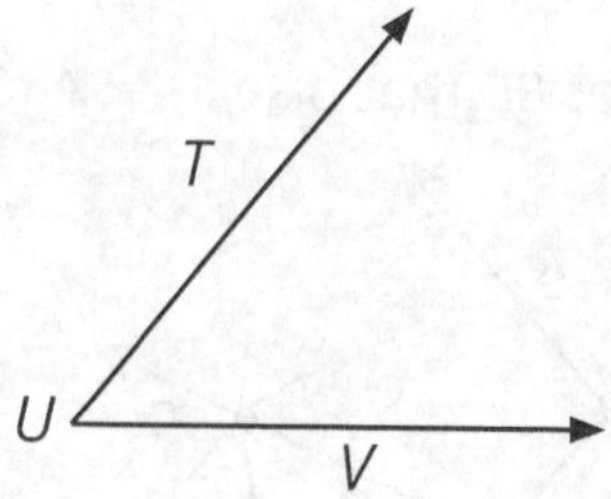

1.37

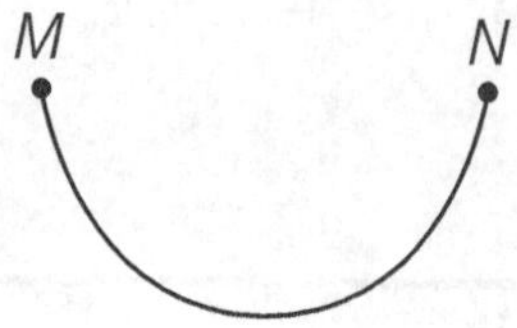

1.38

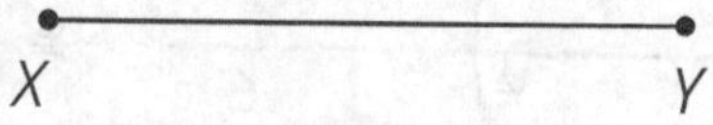

Complete the following activities.

1.39 Find the midpoint of $\overline{AB}$. Name it R.

1.40 Find the midpoint of $\overset{\frown}{AB}$. Name it S.

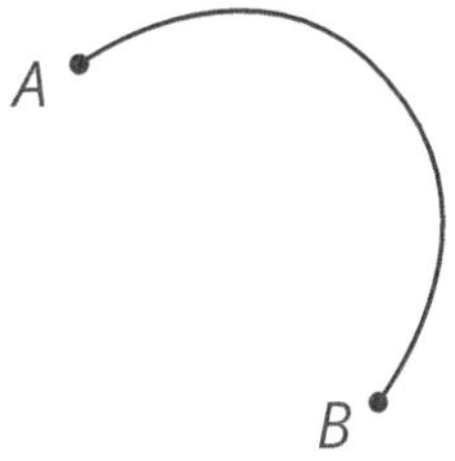

1.41 Find the angle bisector of each angle in this triangle. Extend the bisectors until they intersect each other.

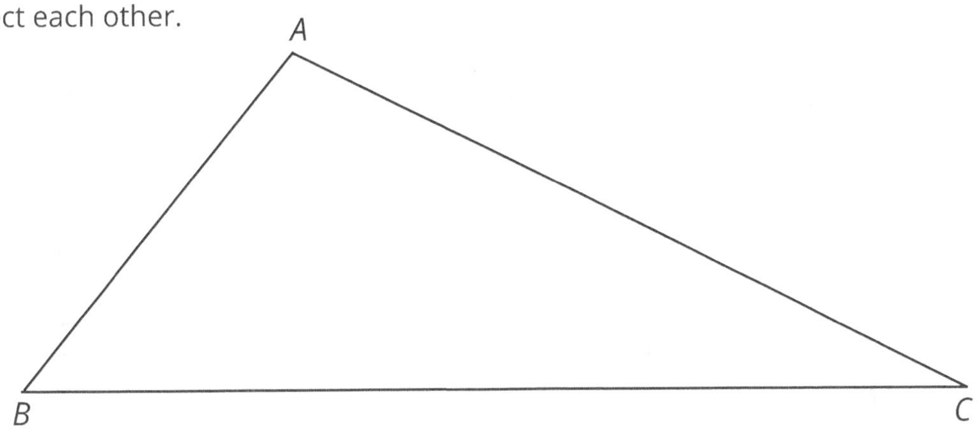

1.42 Find the bisector of $\overset{\frown}{AB}$ and of $\overset{\frown}{BC}$. Extend the bisectors until they intersect. What do you think the point of intersection is in relation to the arc?

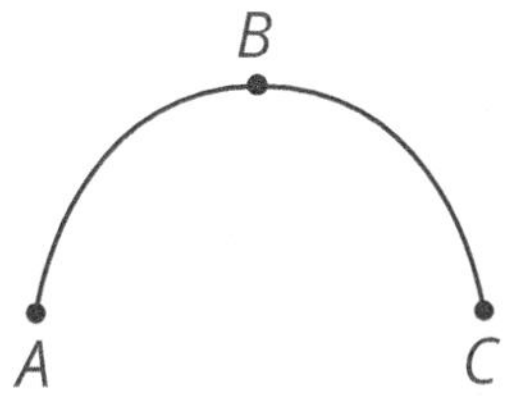

1.43 Divide $\angle ABC$ into four equal angles. (Hint: Use bisectors)

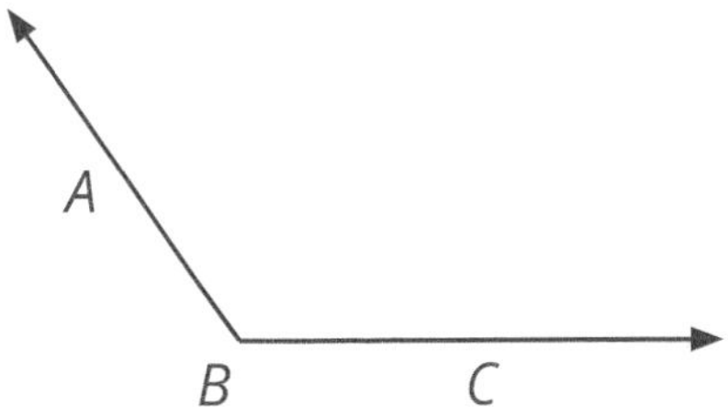

1.44 Divide $\overline{AB}$ into four equal segments.

1.45 Find the center of the circle that AC is a part of.

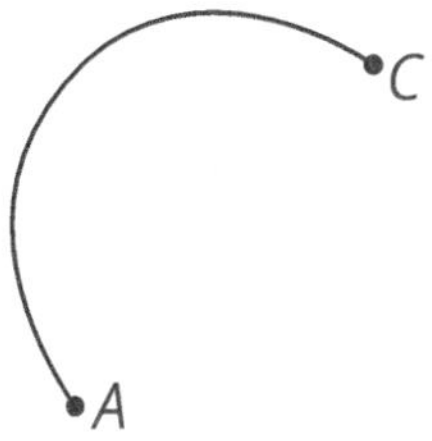

CONSTRUCTING PERPENDICULARS

The next constructions involve perpendiculars. Recall that by definition two lines are perpendicular if equal adjacent angles are formed. Perpendicular lines also form right angles. You will learn to construct a line perpendicular to another line at a point on the line, to construct a perpendicular to a line from a point off the line, and to construct tangents to a circle.

CONSTRUCTION 6

Given a point on a line, construct a line perpendicular to the line at the given point.

Given: point P on line t

To construct: $\overleftrightarrow{ZP} \perp t$

Steps: Use a convenient radius; and with P as center, make arcs that intersect t on both sides of P. Call these points X and Y. With a radius greater than half of XY, and with X and Y as centers, construct arcs that intersect at Z. Draw $\overleftrightarrow{ZP}$. $\overleftrightarrow{ZP}$ is the required line that is perpendicular to t at P.

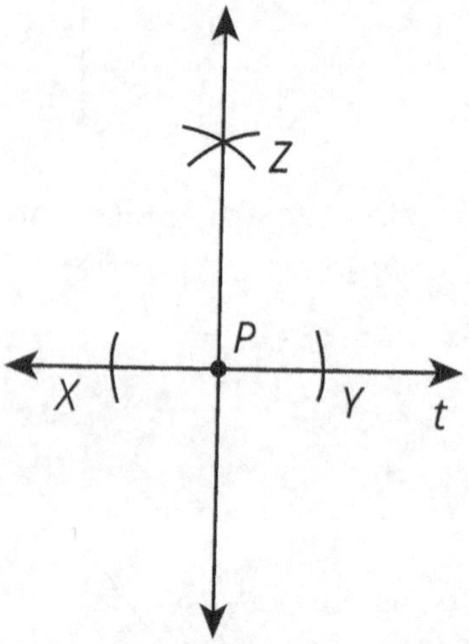

CONSTRUCTION 7

Given a point off a line, construct a line perpendicular to the line through the point.

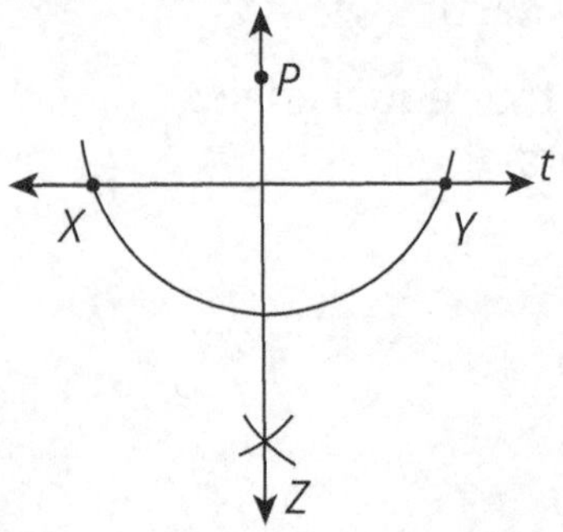

Given: point P not on line t

To construct: $\overleftrightarrow{ZP} \perp t$

Steps: With P as center and a radius greater than the distance to t; construct an arc that intersects t in two points, X and Y. With radius greater than half of $\overline{XY}$, and with X and Y as centers, construct arcs that intersect at Z. Draw $\overleftrightarrow{ZP}$. $\overleftrightarrow{ZP}$ is the required line perpendicular to t and through P.

Complete the following constructions. Leave all construction arcs on your paper.

1.46 Construct a perpendicular to t through A.

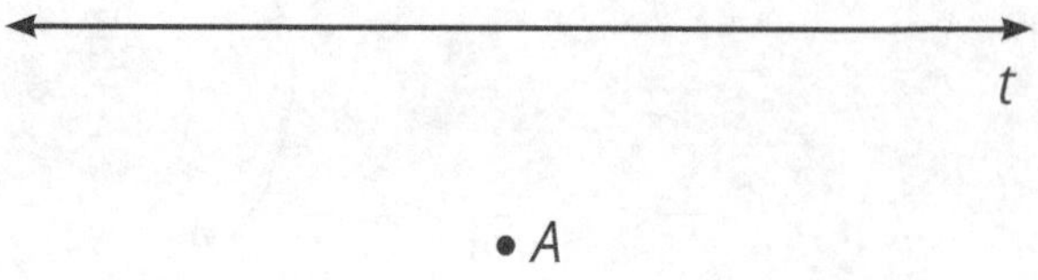

1.47 Construct a perpendicular to *t* through *B*.

1.48 Construct a perpendicular to $\overline{AB}$ at *A* and at *B*. (Hint: Extend $\overline{AB}$.)

1.49 Construct the perpendicular bisectors of each side of this triangle. Extend the bisectors until they intersect each other.

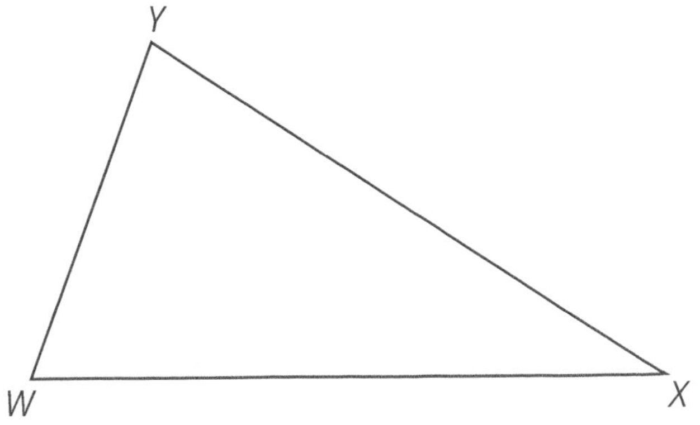

1.50 Construct perpendiculars from A to $\overline{BC}$; from *B* to $\overline{AC}$; and from C to $\overline{AB}$. Do these perpendiculars all intersect in one point? ______________________

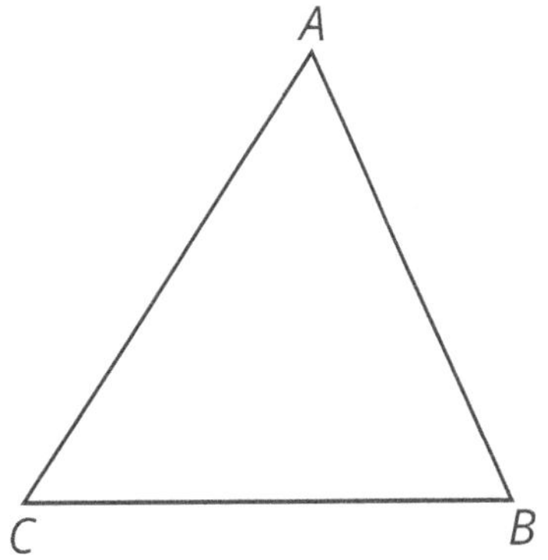

1.51 Construct perpendiculars to line *t* from *A*, *B*, *C*, and *D*.

What can you say about these lines? ______________________________________

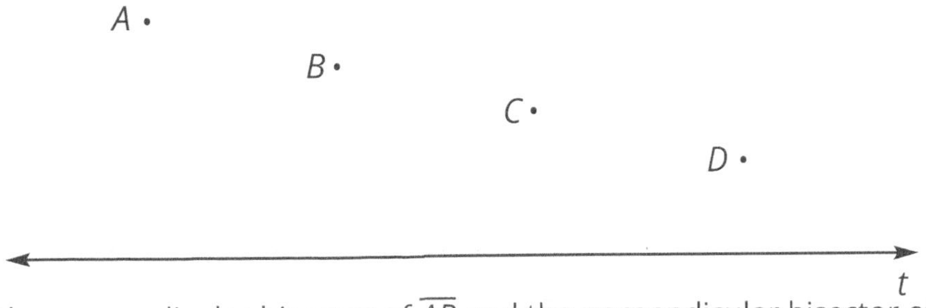

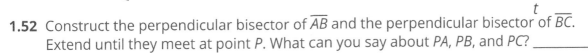

1.52 Construct the perpendicular bisector of $\overline{AB}$ and the perpendicular bisector of $\overline{BC}$. Extend until they meet at point *P*. What can you say about *PA*, *PB*, and *PC*? ______________

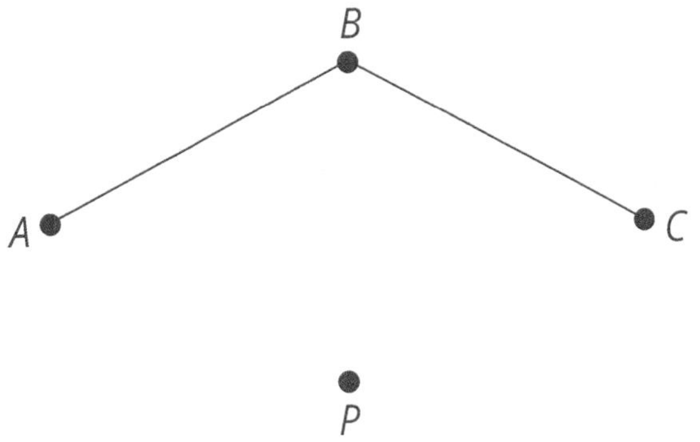

1.53 Construct a perpendicular to the diameter at both end points.

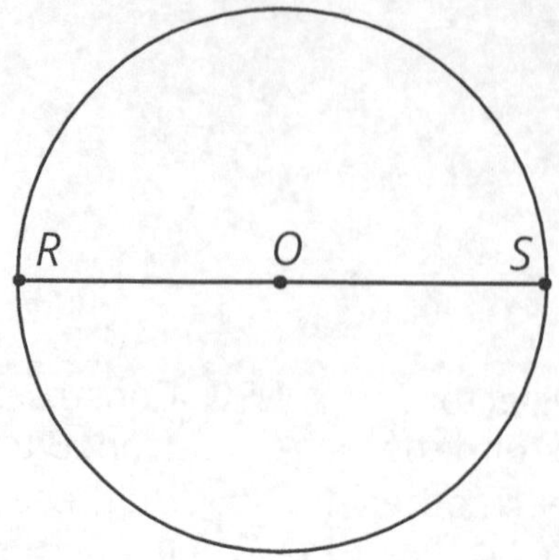

The next two constructions will involve tangents to a circle. Remember that a tangent to a circle is perpendicular to a radius at the point of tangency.

CONSTRUCTION 8

Given a point on a circle, construct a tangent to the circle through that point.

Given: circle *O*; point *A* on the circle

To construct: a tangent to the circle through *A*

Steps: Draw line $\overleftrightarrow{OA}$. At *A* construct a perpendicular to $\overleftrightarrow{OA}$. The perpendicular *t* is the required tangent to the circle.

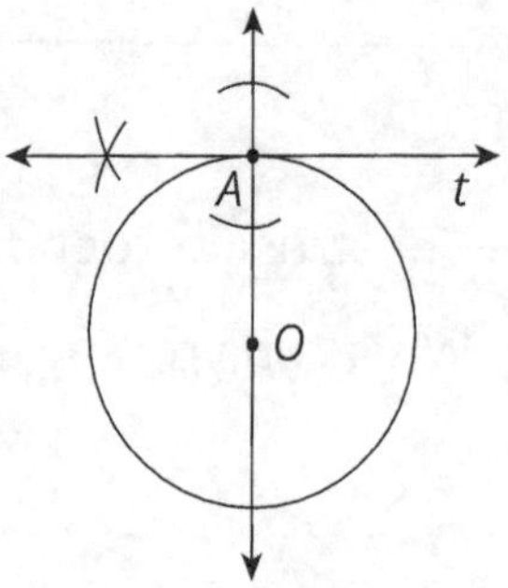

CONSTRUCTION 9

Given a point in the exterior of a circle, construct a tangent to the circle through the point.

Given: circle *O* with the point *A* in the exterior of the circle.

To construct: a tangent to the circle through *A*

Steps: Draw line $\overline{OA}$. Find the midpoint of $\overline{OA}$. Call it *M*. Using *M* as center and $\overline{MO}$ as radius, construct an arc that intersects the circle at *X* and *Y*. Draw $\overleftrightarrow{AY}$ and $\overleftrightarrow{AX}$. $\overleftrightarrow{AY}$ and $\overleftrightarrow{AX}$ both fit the requirement of a tangent to circle *O*.

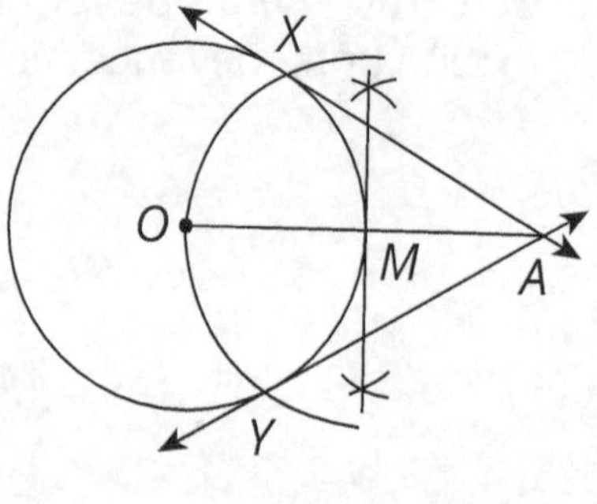

Complete the following constructions. Leave all construction arcs on your paper.

1.54 Construct a tangent to circle *O* at *A*.

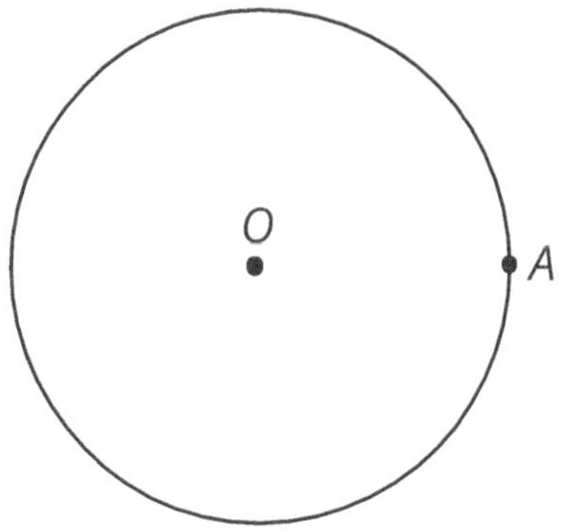

1.55 Construct two tangents to circle *O* through *P*.

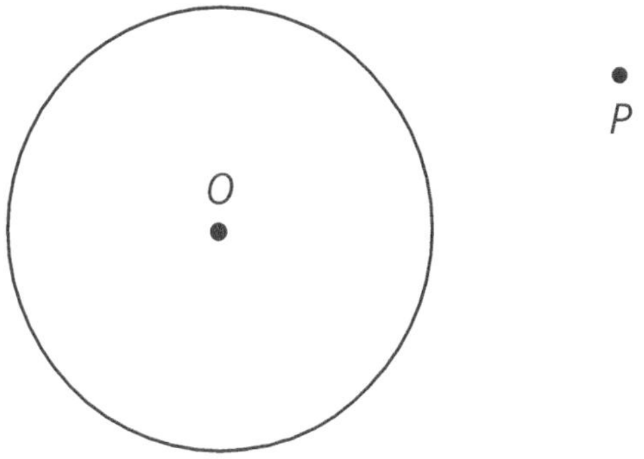

1.56 Construct two tangents to circle *O*, at *A* and at *B*, where $\overline{AB}$ is a diameter. What relationship exists between the two tangents? ____________________

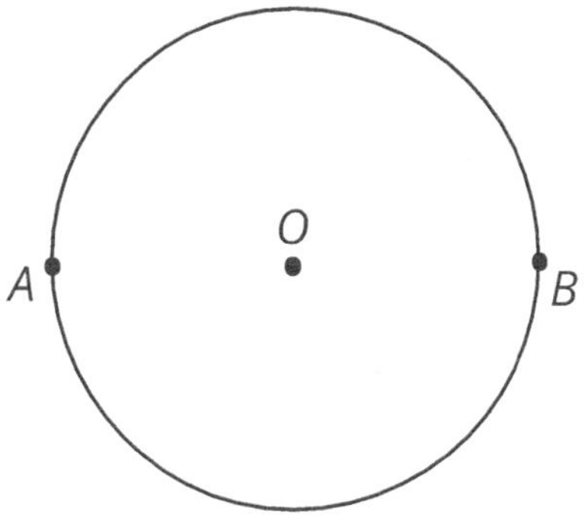

1.57 Construct tangents to circle *O* at *A* and *B*. If $\overline{OA}$ and $\overline{OB}$ are perpendicular radii, what relationship exists between the two tangents? ____________________

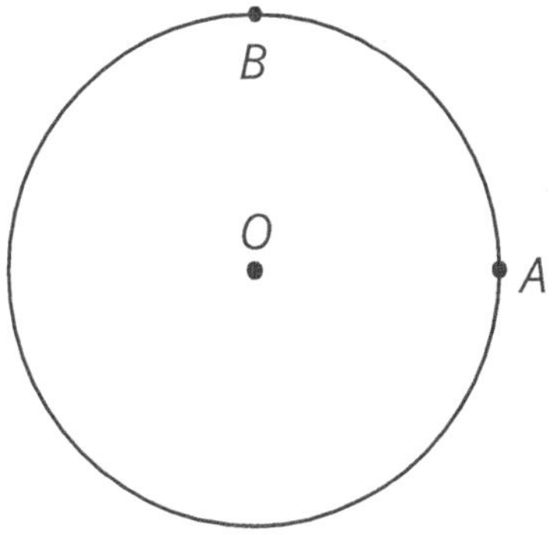

1.58 Construct tangents to circle *O* at *A*, *B*, and *C*. Extend the tangents until they intersect and form a triangle. What relationship exists between the sides of the triangle and the circle?

____

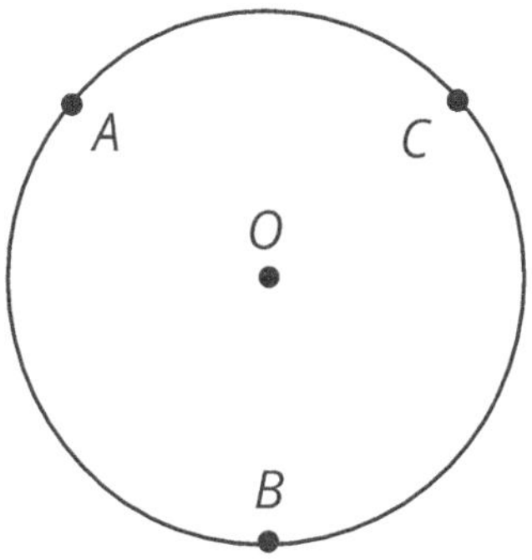

1.59 Construct two tangents to circle *O* through point *P* and one tangent through point *A*. Extend the tangents until they intersect. What relationship exists between the triangle and the ?

____

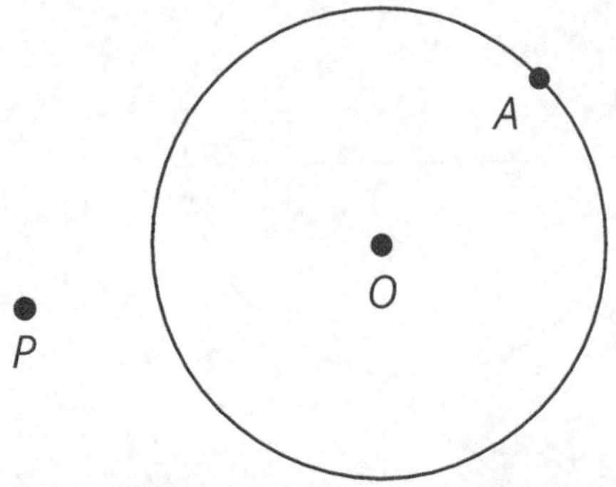

1.60 Construct a common internal tangent for circle *A* and circle *B*.

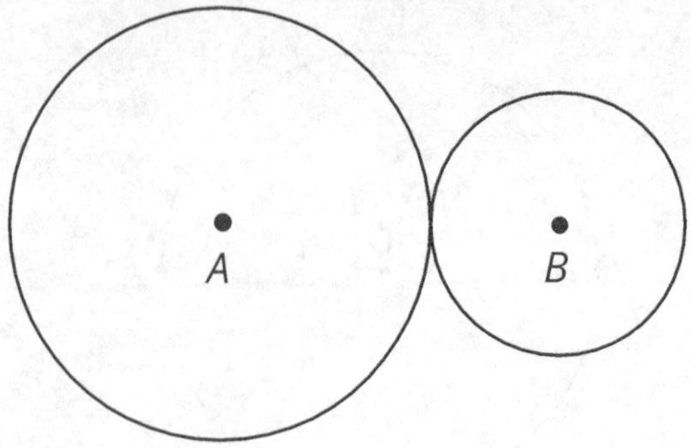

CONSTRUCTING PARALLELS

Construction of parallels uses the theorem stating that if alternate interior angles are equal, or if alternate exterior angles are equal, or if corresponding angles are equal, then the lines are parallel.

CONSTRUCTION 10

Given a line and a point off the line, construct a line parallel to the given line passing through the given point.

Given: line *m*; point *P* not on *m*

To construct: line *n*, parallel to *m* and through *P*

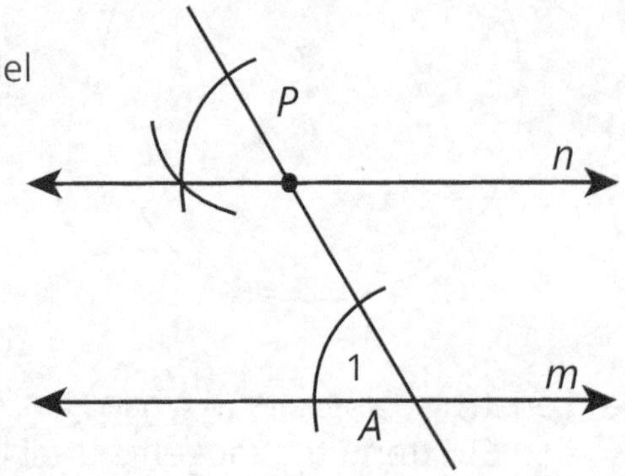

Steps: Draw a line through *P* intersecting m at *A*. (This line will be the transversal) Copy angle 1 in the corresponding position using *P* as a vertex. (Refer to Construction 2 if necessary.)
Extend this side of the angle at *P*. This line is the required line *n* parallel to *m*.

You may also copy ∠1 in the alternate interior position to construct the parallel; or you may use an exterior angle if you wish, copying it in the alternate position or the corresponding position

Complete the following constructions. Leave all constructing arcs on your paper.

1.61 Construct a parallel to *l* through *P*.

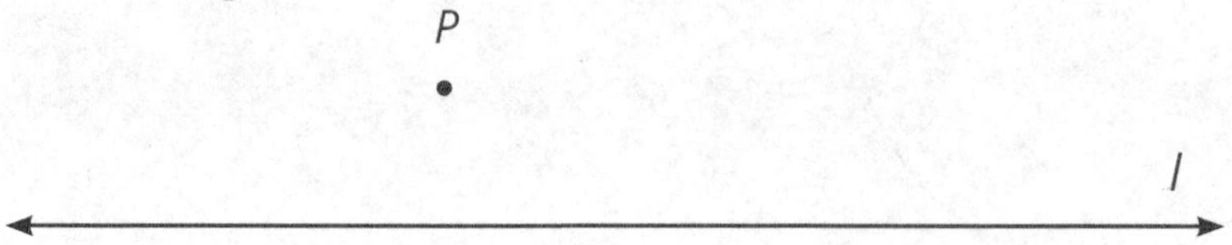

1.62 Construct parallels to *l* through *A* and *B*. What relationship exists between the two lines you constructed? ______________________________

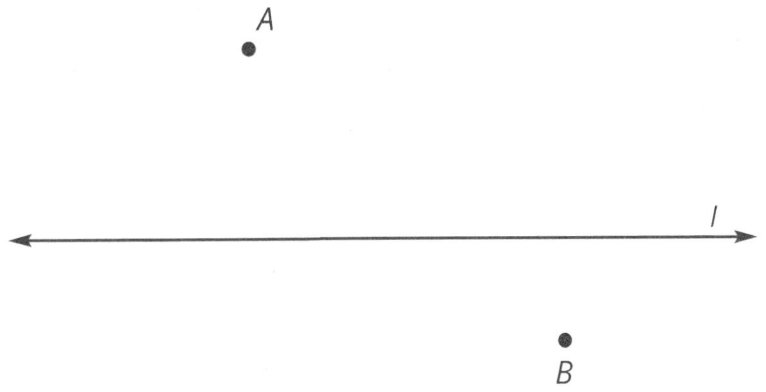

1.63 Through *R* construct a perpendicular to *l*. Call it *m*. Construct a parallel to *l* through *R*. Call it *n*. What relationship exists between *m* and *n*? ______________________________

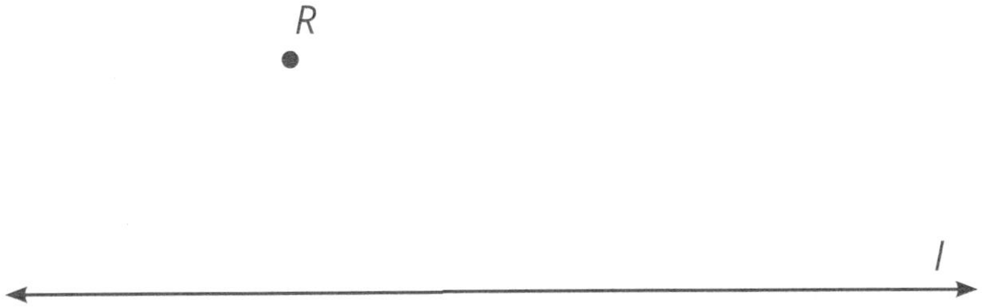

1.64 Through C construct a parallel to $\overline{AB}$. Through *A* construct a parallel to $\overline{BC}$. Through *B* construct a parallel to $\overline{AC}$. Extend these lines to form a new triangle. What relationship exists between the two triangles? ______________________________

1.65 Construct a line through *R* that is parallel to a line through *S*. You construct the line through *S*.

CONSTRUCTING WITH MEASURES

In this section we shall learn some constructions that have to do with measurements of segments. These constructions will be done without the use of a ruler.

CONSTRUCTION 11

Given a segment, divide the segment into a given number of equal parts. Use three parts as an example.

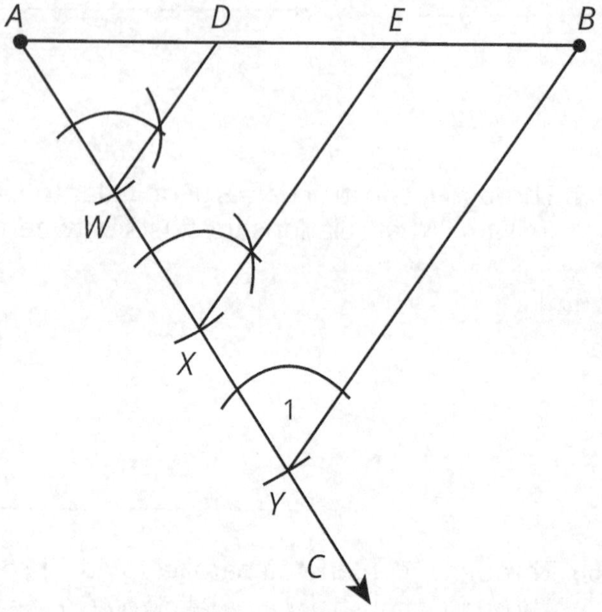

Given: $\overline{AB}$

To construct: Divide $\overline{AB}$ into three equal segments.

Steps: Draw a $\overrightarrow{AC}$ at a convenient angle to $\overline{AB}$. With a convenient radius and A as center, draw an arc intersecting $\overrightarrow{AC}$ at W. With the same radius and W as center, draw an arc intersecting $\overrightarrow{AC}$ at X. With same radius and X center at X, draw an arc intersecting $\overrightarrow{AC}$ at Y. Draw segment $\overleftrightarrow{YB}$.

Construct parallels to $\overline{YB}$ through X and W. (Use Construction 10: Copy $\angle 1$ at X and W in the corresponding position.) Call the points D and E where the parallels intersect $\overline{AB}$. Segments $\overline{AD}$, $\overline{DE}$, and $\overline{EB}$ will be equal in length.

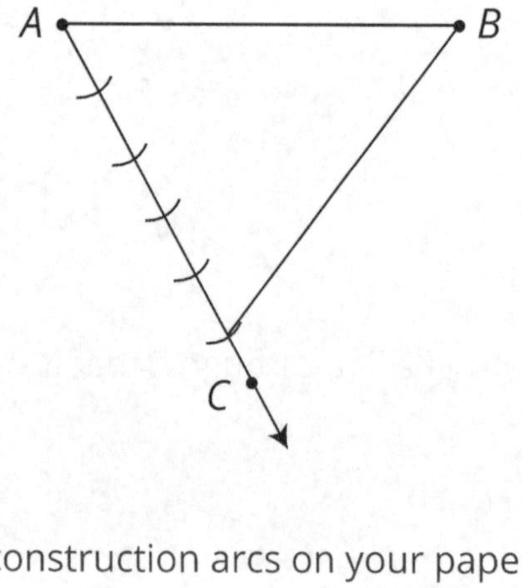

If you want to divide $\overline{AB}$ into five equal parts, then five arcs would be marked off on $\overline{AC}$ and the last arc intersection point would be connected to B. Four parallels would then be constructed. The number of arcs you mark on $\overline{AC}$ is the number of equal parts you will have on the given segment.

If you want to divide a segment into an even number of equal parts, you may wish to use the bisecting method of Construction 3.

Complete the following constructions. Leave all construction arcs on your paper.

1.66 Divide segment $\overline{AB}$ into three equal parts.

1.67 Divide segment $\overline{CD}$ into five equal parts.

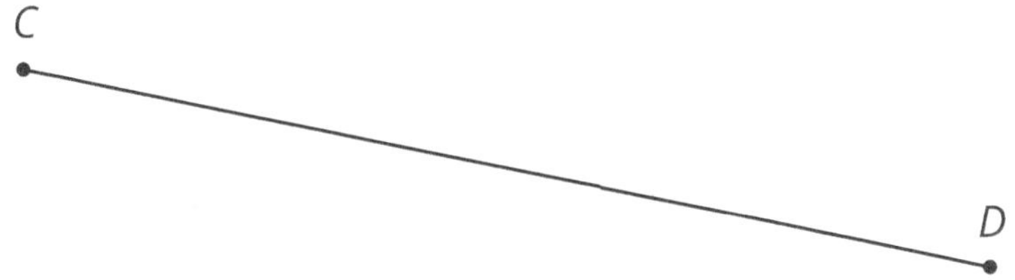

1.68 Divide $\overline{AB}$ into four equal parts using Construction 11.

1.69 Divide $\overline{AB}$ into four equal parts using the bisecting method of Construction 3.

1.70 Divide $\overline{AB}$ into two parts that are in the ratio of 1 to 2. (Hint: Divide $\overline{AB}$ into three equal parts and mark $\overline{AB}$ so the ratio of parts is 1:2.)

1.71 Divide $\overline{RS}$ into two parts that are in the ratio of 2 to 3.

In the equation $\frac{a}{b} = \frac{c}{x}$, *x* is the *fourth proportional* between *a*, *b*, and *c*. Proportionals *a*, *b*, *c*, *b* and *x* represent the length of four segments. We want to find by construction the length of the fourth proportional, *x*. Construction 12 shows this process.

CONSTRUCTION 12

Given three segments, construct a segment whose length is the fourth proportional to the length of the other three segments.

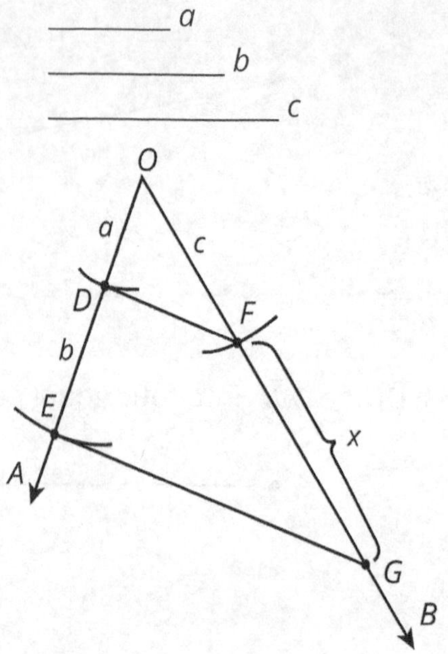

Given: three segments, with length a, b, and c

To construct: a segment with length x, the fourth proportional to a, b, and c

Steps: Draw a convenient angle $\angle AOB$. On $\overrightarrow{OA}$ copy the segment whose length is a. Add to that segment another segment whose length is equal to b. On $\overrightarrow{OB}$; copy the segment whose length is equal to c. Call these points D, E, and F. Draw $\overline{DF}$. Construct a parallel to $\overline{DF}$ through E. This parallel intersects $\overrightarrow{OF}$ at G. The length of segment FG is the required fourth proportional.

Leave all construction arcs on your paper when doing these construction problems.

1.72 Given a, b, and c, the length of three segments. Find the fourth proportional.

____________________ a

_____________________________ b

________________________ c

1.73 Find the fourth proportional to r, s, and t.

_______________________ r

_________ s

________________ t

1.74 $x = \frac{b^2}{a}$; find x. (Hint: $\frac{a}{b} = \frac{b}{x}$)

______________________ *a*

______________________________ *b*

1.75 $x = \frac{cd}{a}$; find x.

________________ *a*

______________________ *c*

__________ *d*

CONSTRUCTION 13

Given two segments, construct a segment whose length is the geometric mean between the lengths of the given segments.

Given: segments whose lengths are *a* and *b*

To construct: a segment whose length *x* is the mean proportional between *a* and *b*

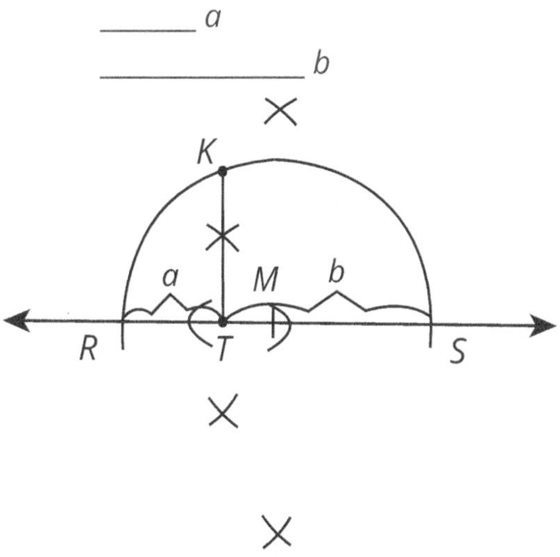

Steps: On a work line construct $\overline{RS}$, whose length is ($a + b$). Find the midpoint *M* of $\overline{RS}$. With *M* as center and radius *MR*, construct a semicircle. At point *T*, where *a* and *b* intersect, construct a perpendicular that intersects the semicircle at *K*. $\overline{TK}$ is the desired segment whose length is the geometric mean between *a* and *b*.

Remember that the geometric mean is the number such that $\frac{a}{x} = \frac{x}{b}$ or $x^2 = ab$ or $x = \sqrt{ab}$. If we were given some unit length on a scale, we would be able to construct segments with lengths of $\sqrt{2}$, $\sqrt{3}$, $\sqrt{5}$, or any other irrational length, by using Construction 13.

Complete these constructions. Leave all construction arcs on your paper.

1.76 Construct x such that $\frac{a}{x} = \frac{x}{b}$.

______________ a

______________________ b

1.77 Construct x such that $x = \sqrt{rs}$.

______________ s

______________________ r

1.78 Construct x such that $x = 2\sqrt{rs}$.

____________ r

____________________ s

Complete the following proofs.

1.79 Write a proof for Construction 3

Given: $\overline{AB}$

Prove: $\overleftrightarrow{XY}$ bisects $\overline{AB}$

Hint: Prove $\overline{AM} = \overline{MB}$ by using congruent triangles.

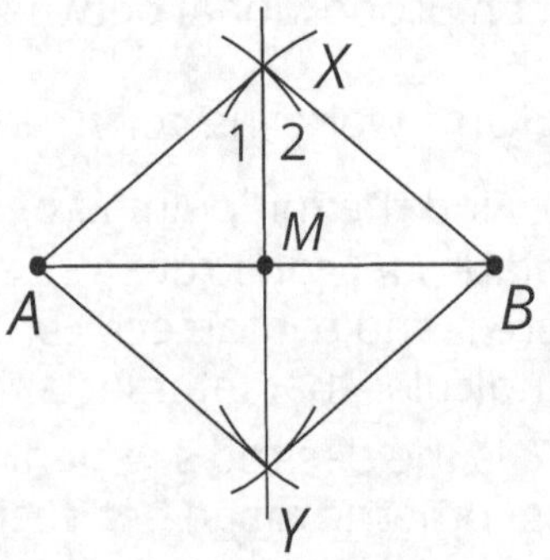

STATEMENT	REASON

STATEMENT	REASON

1.80 Write a proof for Construction 4.

Given: $\angle ABC$

Prove: $\overrightarrow{BD}$ bisects $\angle ABC$

Hint: Show $\angle 1 = \angle 2$ by using congruent triangles

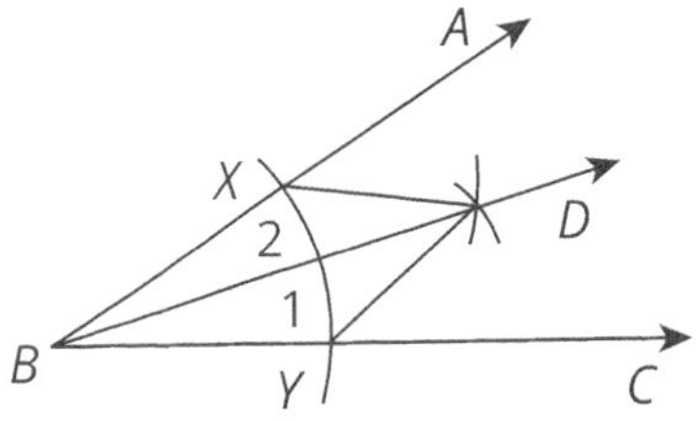

STATEMENT	REASON

1.81 Write a proof for Construction 5.

Given: $\overset{\frown}{AB}$

Prove: $\overleftrightarrow{XY}$ bisects $\overset{\frown}{AB}$

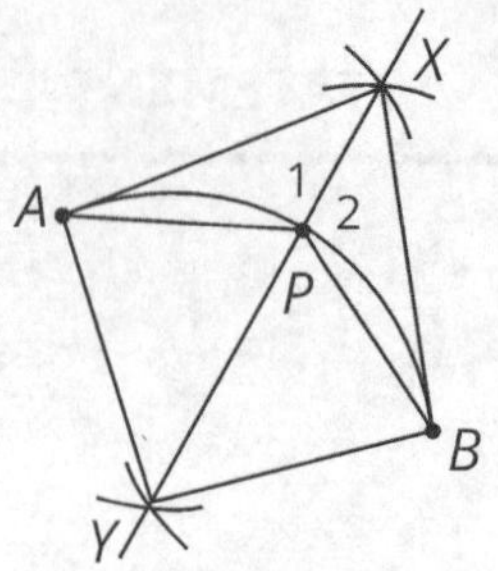

STATEMENT	REASON

1.82 Write a proof for Construction 9.

Given: circle O; point A

Prove: $\overleftrightarrow{AX}$ tangent to circle O

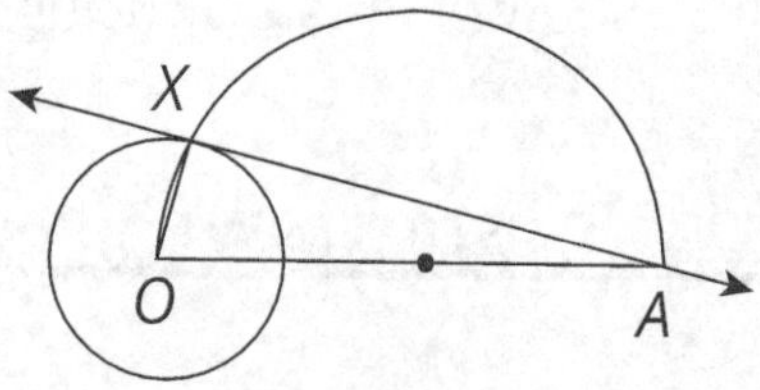

STATEMENT	REASON

1.83 Write a proof for Construction 10.

Given: line m; point P not on m

Prove: $m \parallel n$

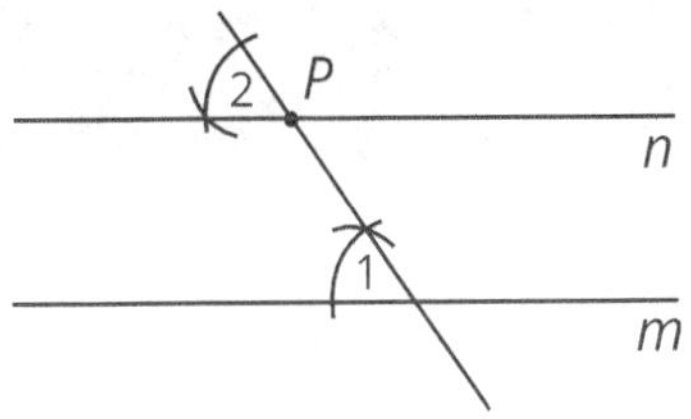

STATEMENT	REASON

1.84 Write a proof for Construction 11.

Given: $\overline{AB}$

Prove: $AD = DE = EB$

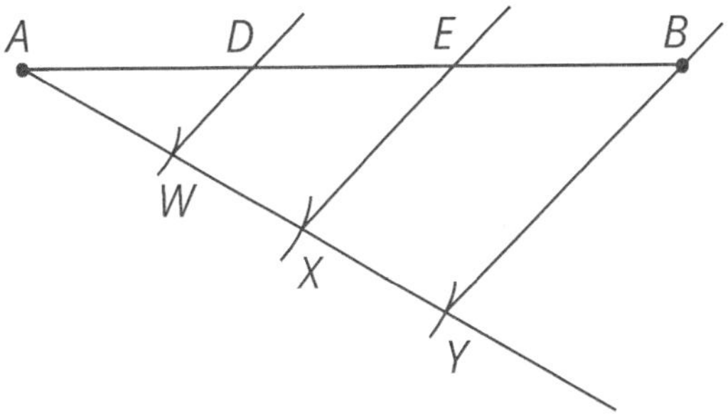

STATEMENT	REASON

Review the material in this section in preparation for the Self Test. The Self Test will check your mastery of this particular section. The items missed on this Self Test will indicate specific areas where restudy is needed for mastery.

SELF TEST 1

Complete these constructions. Leave all construction arcs on your paper (each construction, 5 points).

1.01 Construct segment $MN = 3a$.

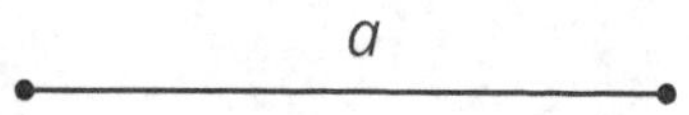

1.02 Construct an angle, $\angle ABC = 2x$.

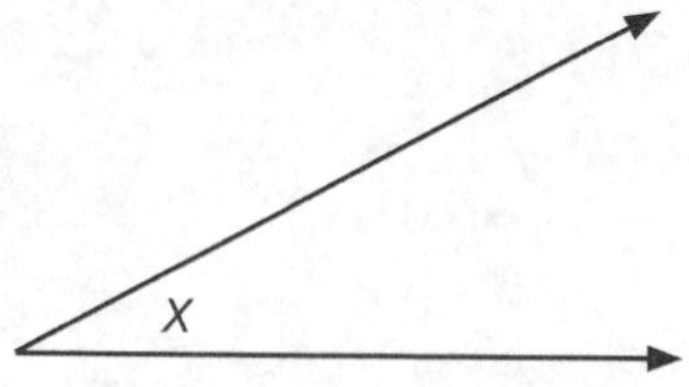

1.03 Bisect $\overline{AB}$ with $\overleftrightarrow{CD}$.

1.04 Bisect $\angle ROS$ with $\overrightarrow{OT}$.

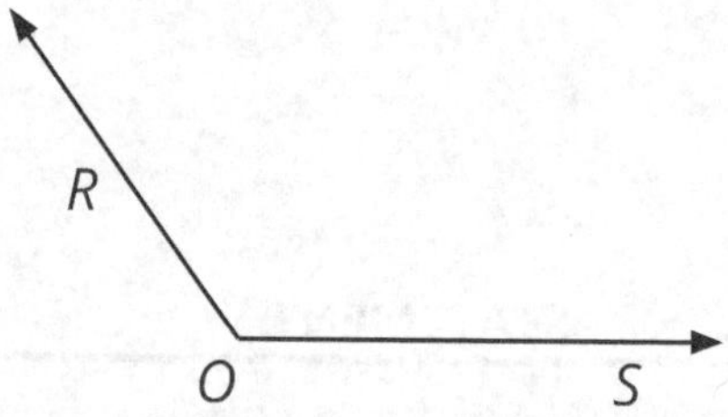

1.05 Find the midpoint, M, of $\overset{\frown}{ST}$.

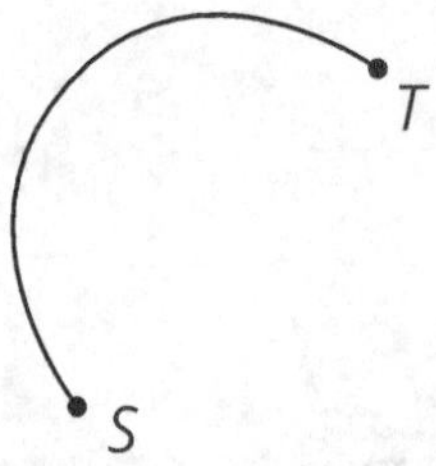

1.06 Construct $\overleftrightarrow{CT}$ perpendicular to $\overleftrightarrow{RS}$ at M.

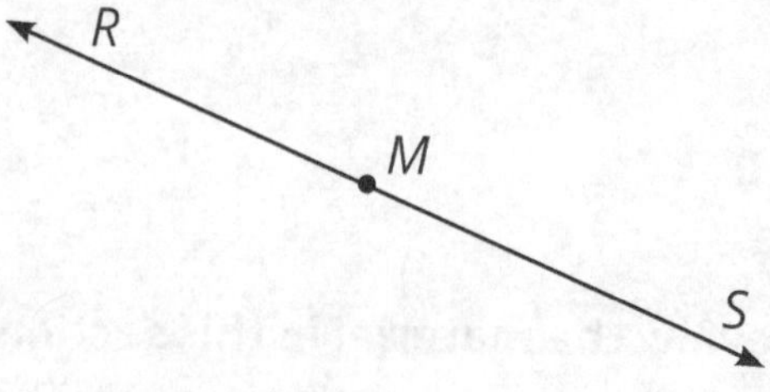

1.07 Construct $\overleftrightarrow{CT}$ perpendicular to $\overleftrightarrow{RS}$ at N.

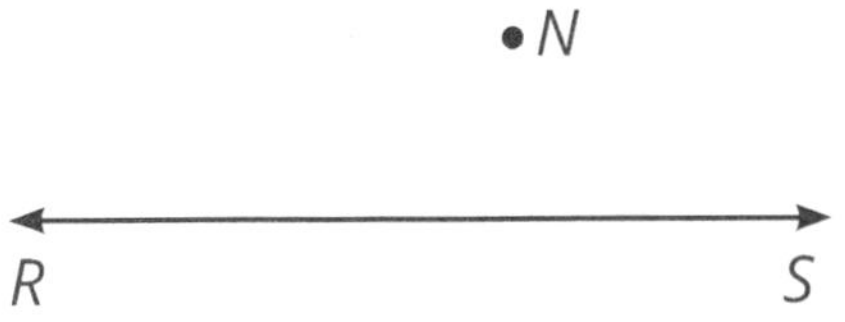

1.08 Construct a tangent, t, to circle A at B.

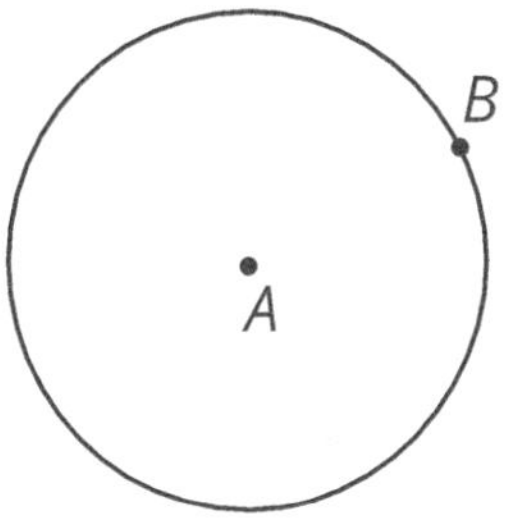

1.09 Construct a tangent, $\overrightarrow{PX}$, to circle B.

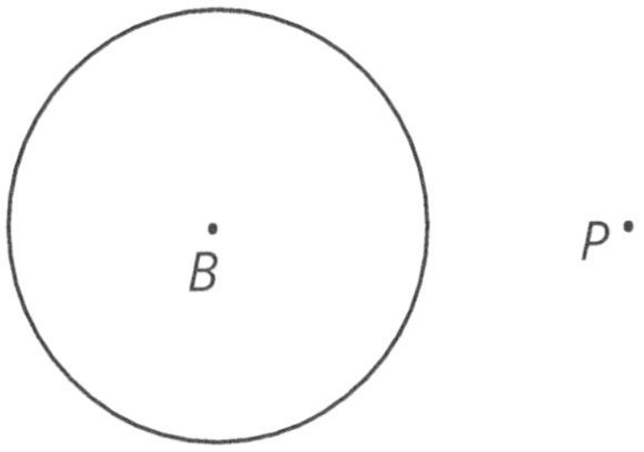

1.010 Construct l parallel to m through P.

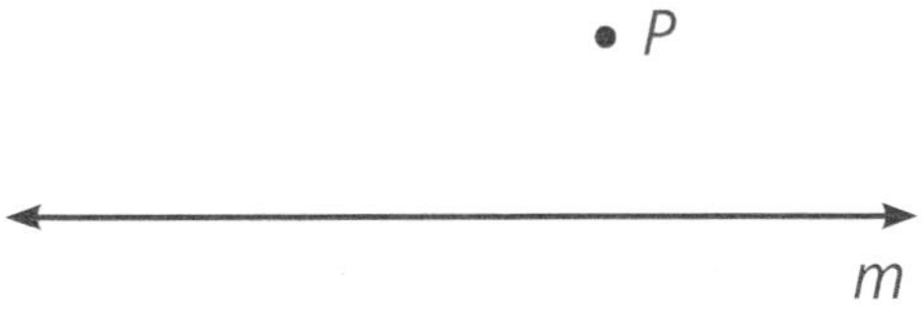

1.011 Divide $\overline{AB}$ into five equal parts.

1.012 Find x, the fourth proportional between r, s, and t.

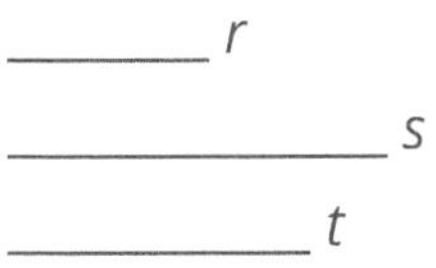

1.013 Find x, the geometric mean between c and d.

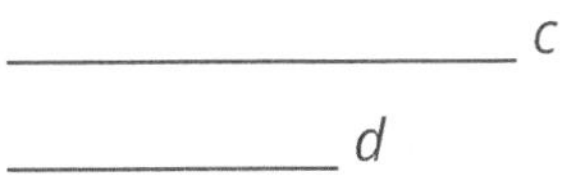

52/65 **SCORE** ________ **TEACHER** ________ ________
initials date

2. FIGURE CONSTRUCTION

Using the basic construction concepts that you have just learned, you will now be able to construct some more advanced figures. Special circles, triangles, and other polygons will be presented in this section.

Section Objectives

Review these objectives. When you have completed this section, you should be able to:

10. Construct triangles.
11. Construct special circles.
12. Construct certain polygons.

TRIANGLES

First you will see how to construct triangles with specific parts. Sometimes the lengths of the sides will be given; sometimes an angle measure will also be stated.

Construct a triangle given its three sides.

Given: ________ *a*
________________ *b*
__________ *c*

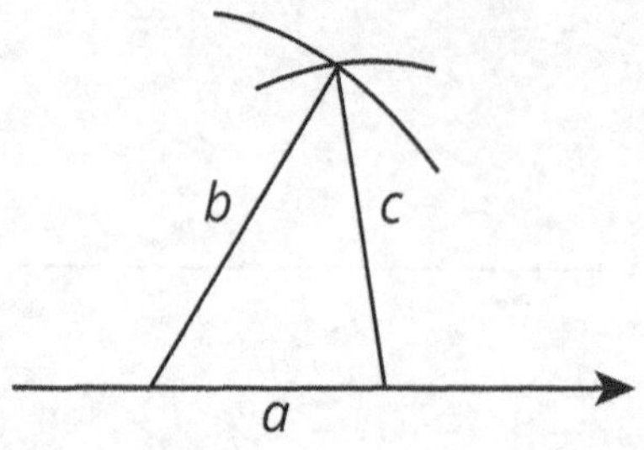

Steps: Copy *a* on your work line.
With *b* as a radius and one end point of *a* as center, draw an arc. With *c* as radius and the other end point of *a* as center, draw another arc that intersects the first arc. This point is the third vertex of the triangle.

To think about constructing a triangle given its three sides, remember the triangle inequality theorem. It states that the sum of two sides of a triangle is greater than the third side. This statement lets you know that the other two sides will intersect somewhere off of the third side.

MATH 1007

LIFEPAC TEST

NAME ______________________

DATE ______________________

SCORE ______________________

40

50

MATH 1007: LIFEPAC TEST

Complete the following items. Use only straightedge and compass for constructions, and leave all construction arcs on your paper (each numbered item, 5 points).

1. Construct a triangle with sides equal to *a*, *b*, and *c*.

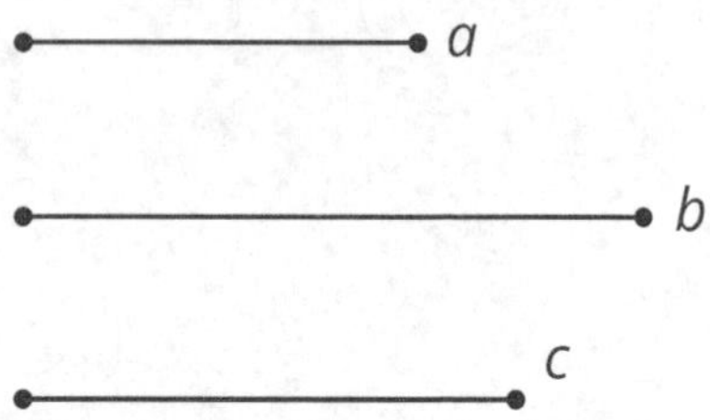

2. Construct a rectangle with sides equal to *a* and *c*.

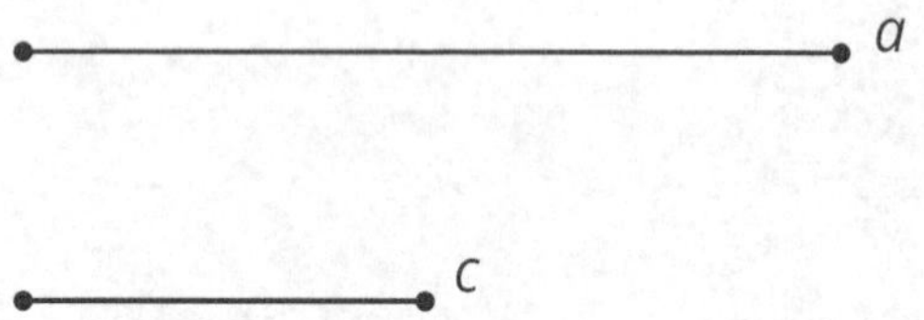

3. Construct a parallelogram with an angle equal to $\angle 1$ and sides equal to *a* and *b*.

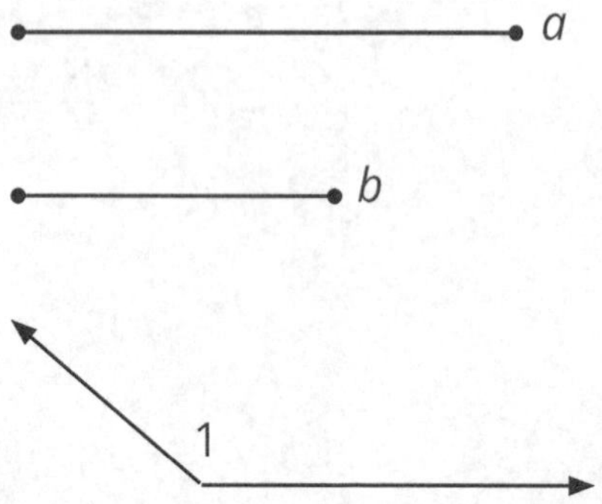

4. Construct a segment equal to $\frac{1}{3}(a + b)$.

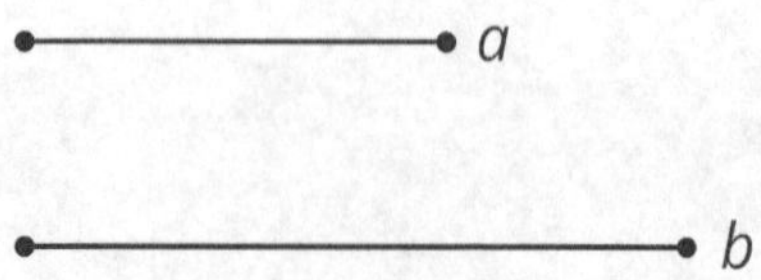

5. Construct the fourth proportional between *a*, *b*, and *c*.

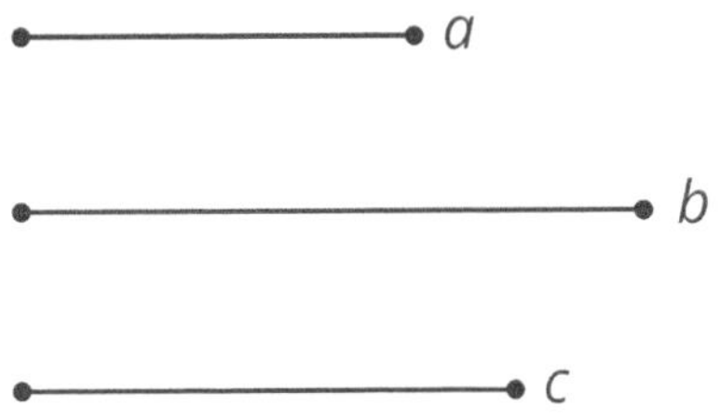

6. Construct a geometric mean between *a* and *c*.

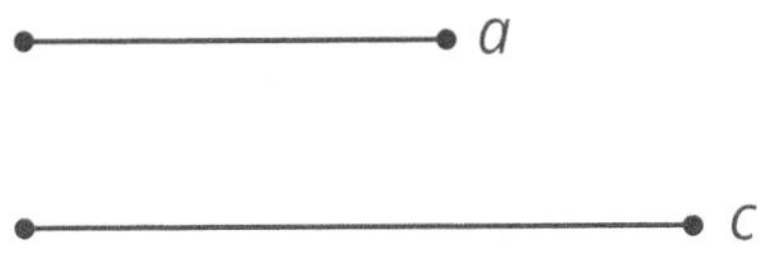

7. What is the locus of points in a plane equidistant from two parallel lines and a given distance *d* from a point *P*? Sketch all solutions.

8. Construct a rhombus with diagonals *b* and *c*. (Hint: The diagonals of a rhombus are perpendicular bisectors of each other.)

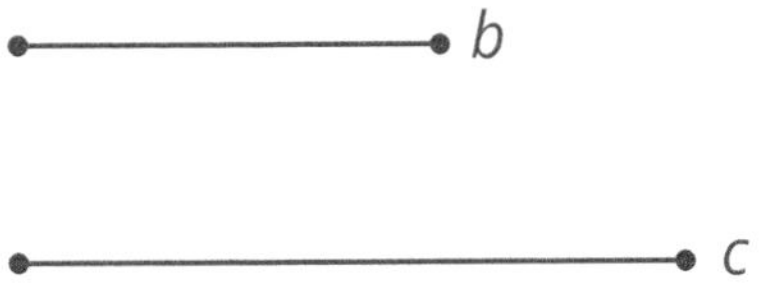

9. What is the locus of points three inches above the top of a table that measures four feet by eight feet?

10. Construct the locus of points in a plane that are equidistant from the sides of $\angle A$ and at a distance *d* from point *P*. Label the locus points *X*.

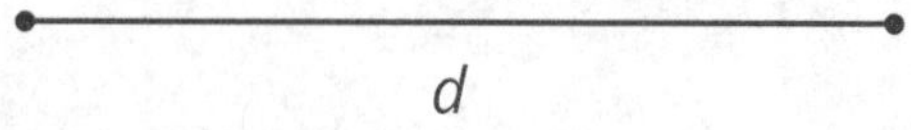

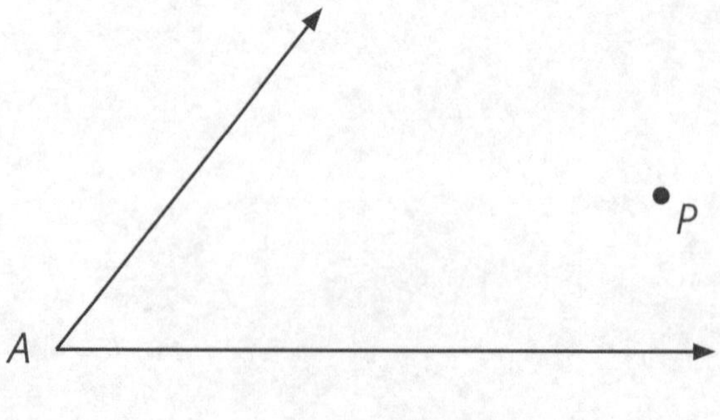

Construct a triangle given two sides and the included angle.

Given: ________ *a*

____________ *b*

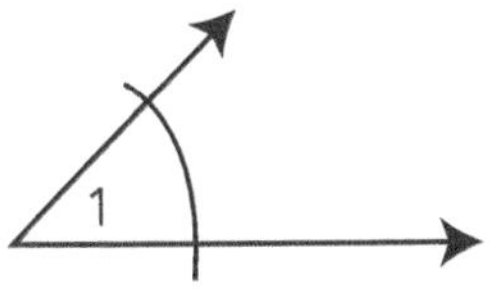

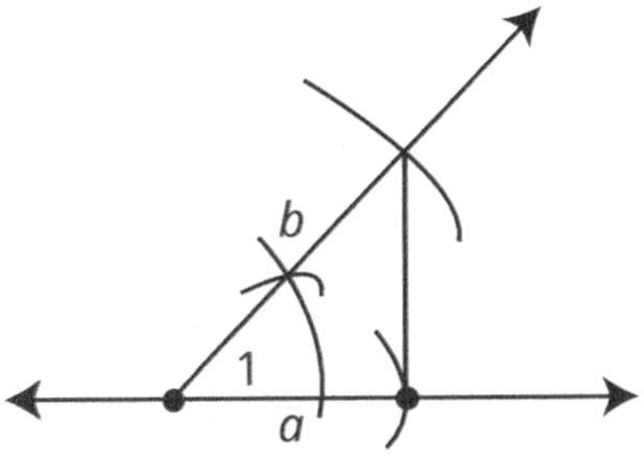

Steps: On your work line copy ∠1. With *a* as radius and the vertex of ∠1 as center, draw an arc that intersects one of the rays of the angle. With *b* as radius and the vertex of ∠1 as center, draw an arc that intersects the other ray of the angle. Connect these two points of intersection to form the third side of the triangle.

Construct a 30° - 60° - 90° triangle.

Steps: Construct an equilateral triangle.
Each angle will have a measure of 60°.
Bisect one angle; this step will form the 30° angle.
The third angle of the triangle formed will be 90°, thus completing the 30°-60°-90° construction.

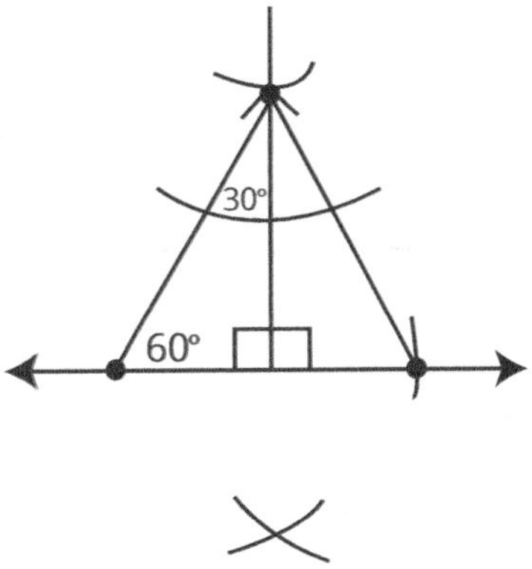

Construct a 45° - 45° - 90° triangle.

Steps: Construct a perpendicular to a work line; this step forms the 90° angle. With the vertex of the 90° angle as center and radius equal to the side of the triangle, draw an arc that intersects both sides of the right angle. Connect these points of intersection to form the hypotenuse of the triangle. The triangle formed is an isosceles right triangle, thus making the acute angles equal to 45 °.

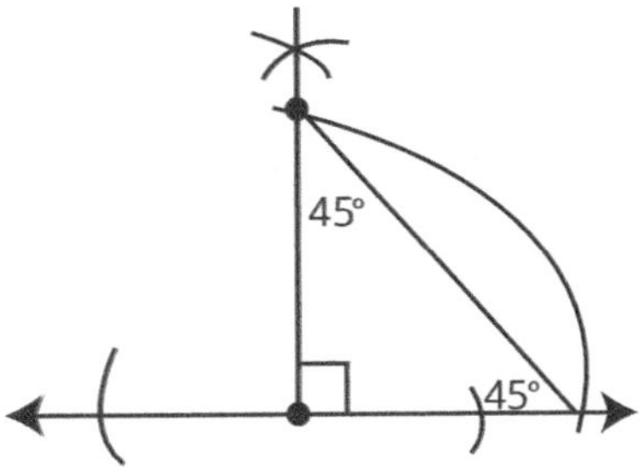

Construct the median of a triangle.

Given: Triangle *ABC*

Steps: The *median* of a triangle is a segment whose end points are the vertex of an angle and the midpoint of the opposite side. Find the midpoint of $\overline{AB}$. Connect the opposite vertex, *C*, to this midpoint. This segment is a median to the triangle. The triangle has two other medians that are found in the same way.

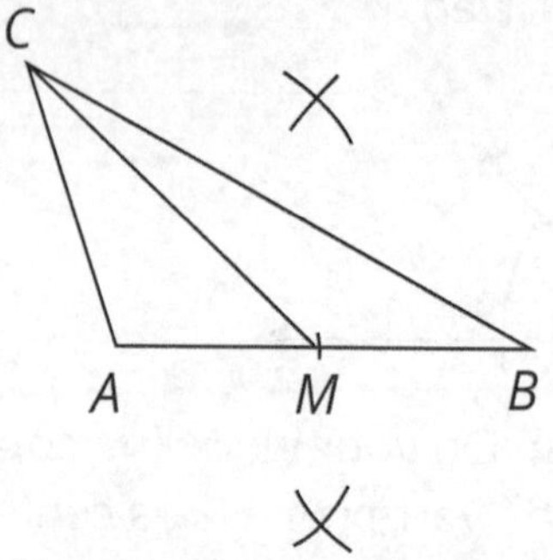

Construct the altitude of a triangle.

Given: Triangle *ABC*

Steps: The *altitude* of a triangle is a segment from a vertex perpendicular to the opposite side. From *C* construct a perpendicular to $\overline{AB}$. This segment is the altitude to side $\overline{AB}$. Each triangle has three altitudes, one from each vertex.

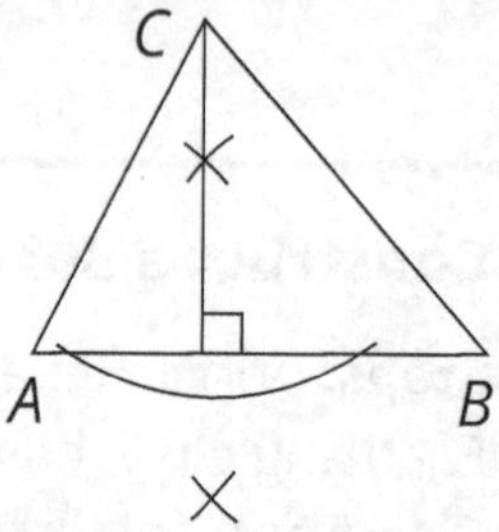

Complete these constructions. Leave all construction arcs on your paper.

2.1 Construct a triangle with sides equal to *a*, *b*, and *c*.

______________________ *a*

______________________ *b*

_________________ *c*

2.2 Construct a 30°- 60°- 90° triangle with hypotenuse equal to *AB*.

A ______________________________ *B*

2.3 Construct a triangle with sides equal to a and b and having $\angle C$ as the included angle.

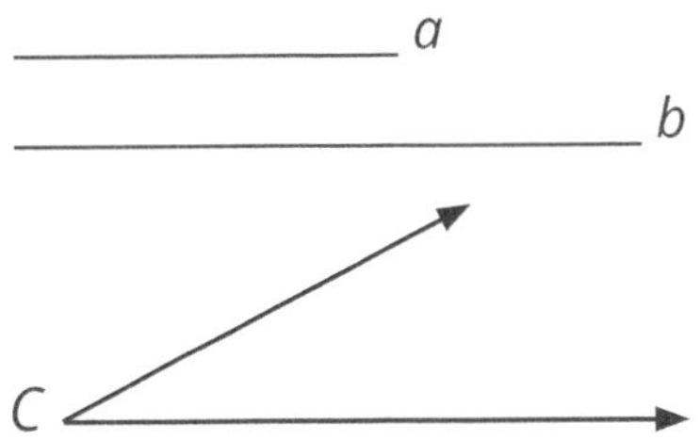

2.4 Construct a 45°- 45°- 90° triangle with leg equal to AB.

2.5 Construct the median to side $\overline{AB}$ of triangle ABC.

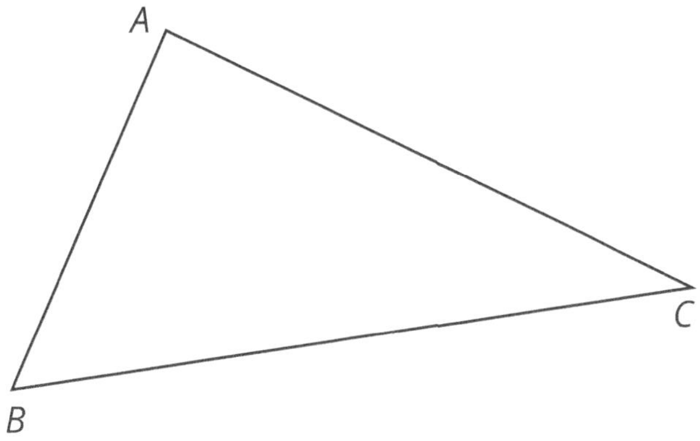

2.6 Construct the altitude to side $\overline{AB}$ of triangle ABC.

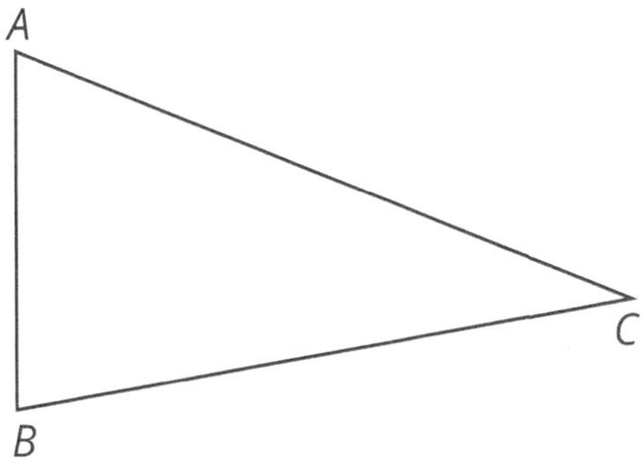

2.7 Construct a 30°- 60°- 90° triangle with short leg equal to *AB*. (Hint: In a 30°- 60°- 90° triangle, H = 2S.)

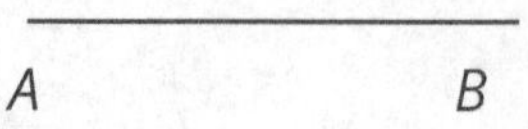

2.8 Construct the altitude to side $\overline{AB}$ of triangle *ABC* (Hint: Extend $\overline{AB}$ to the left.)

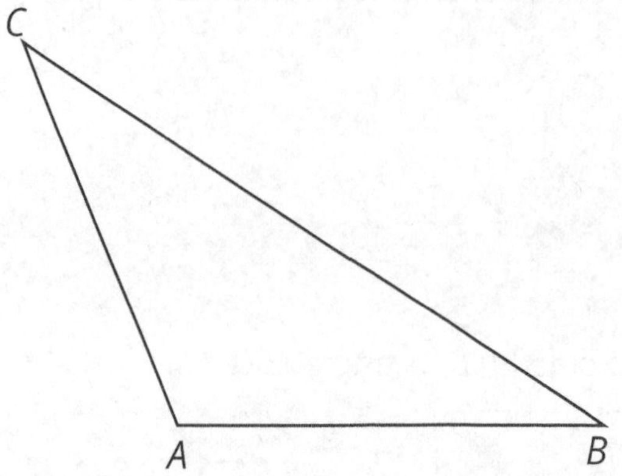

2.9 Construct all three medians of an equilateral triangle with side equal to RS.

2.10 Construct an isosceles triangle with sides equal to *AB* and vertex angle equal to ∠1.

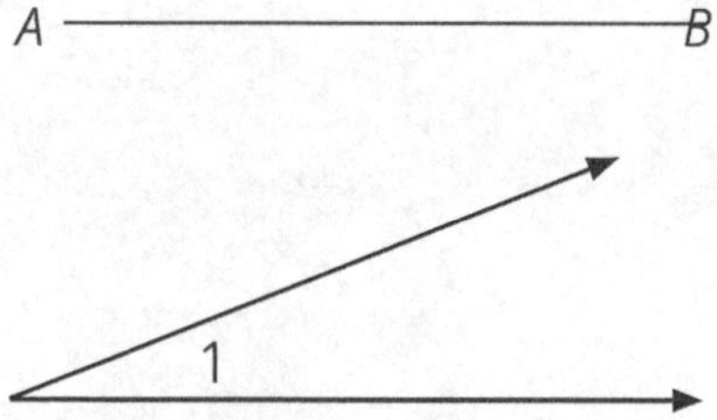

2.11 Construct a 60° angle, a 30° angle, a 15° angle, and a 120° angle.

2.12 Construct an isosceles triangle with side equal to *AB* and vertex angle equal to 120°.

A ______________________________ *B*

2.13 Construct a right triangle. Construct the altitude to all three sides.

Where do the altitudes intersect? ____________________

2.14 Construct an acute triangle. Construct the altitudes to all three sides. Where in relationship to the triangle do the altitudes intersect? ____________________

2.15 Construct an obtuse triangle. Construct the altitudes to all three sides. Where in relationship to the triangle do the altitudes intersect? ____________________

CIRCLES

Some special cases of the circle can now be considered for construction. You will learn to draw a circle given three points on the circle and to construct inscribed or circumscribed circles.

Construct a circle given three points of the circle.

Given: *A*, *B*, *C*

Steps: To construct a circle, we need to know where the center is located and the length of the radius. The center is found by constructing the perpendicular bisector of any two segments formed by the three points. The drawing uses segments *AB* and *BC*. The intersection of these two perpendicular bisectors is the center of the desired circle. The radius is the distance from the center point to any of the three given points.

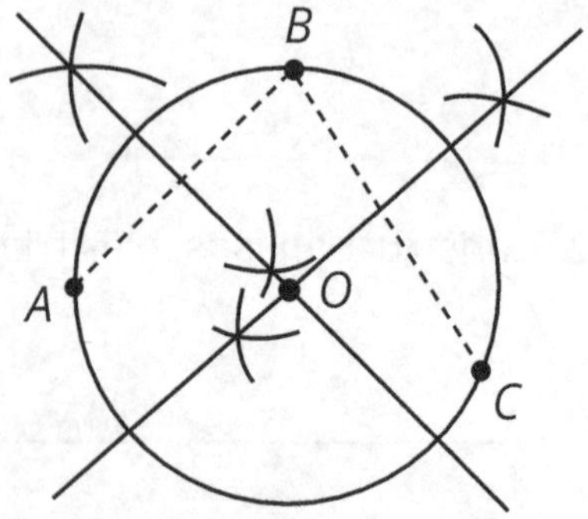

Construct a circle that is inscribed in a given triangle.

Given: Triangle *ABC*

Steps: We need to find the center and radius of the desired circle. First, the center is the intersection of the bisectors of any two angles; construct the bisectors to find the center. Next, the circle must be tangent to the sides of the triangle; therefore, the radius is perpendicular to any side of the triangle. Construct a perpendicular from the center to any side. The length of this perpendicular is our radius.

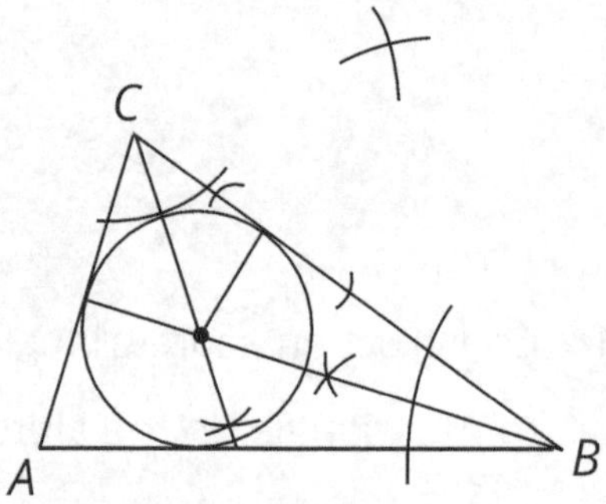

Construct a circle that circumscribes in a given triangle.

Given: Triangle *ABC*

Steps: We need to find the center and the radius of the desired circle. Consider the three vertices of the triangle as three points of the circle, and use the first construction of this section.

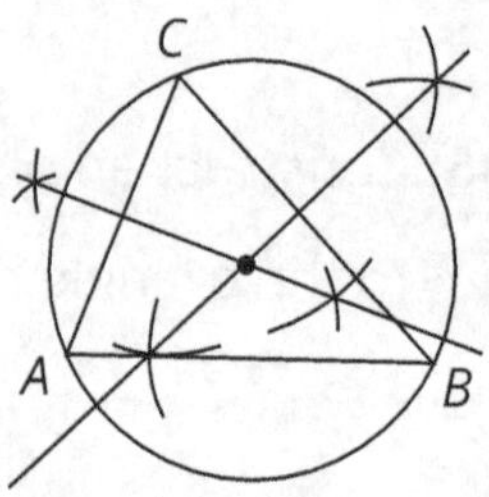

Complete the following constructions. Leave all construction arcs on your paper.

2.16 Inscribe a circle in triangle *ABC*.

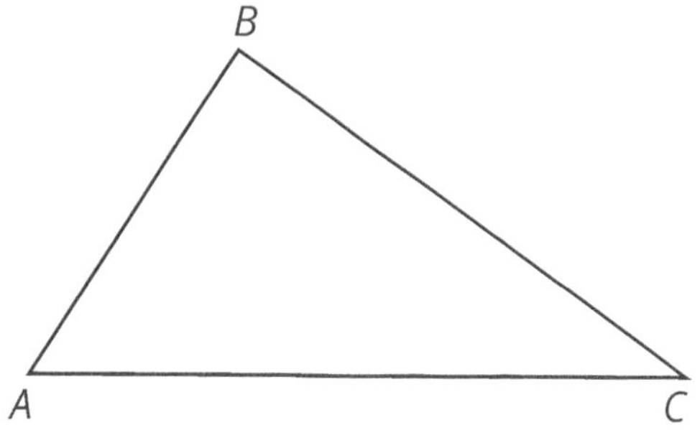

2.17 Construct a circle through points *R*, *S*, and *T*.

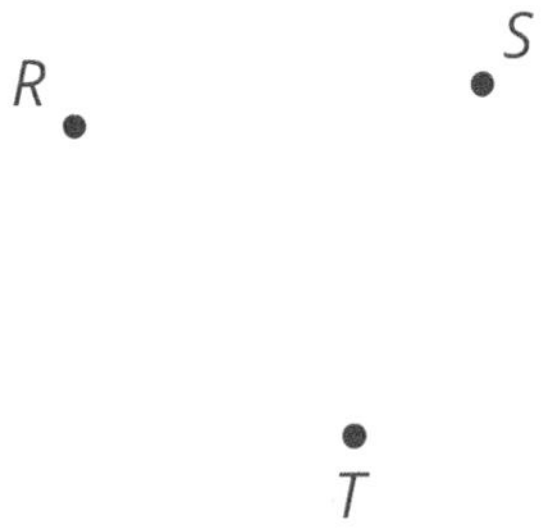

2.18 Circumscribe a circle about triangle *DEF*.

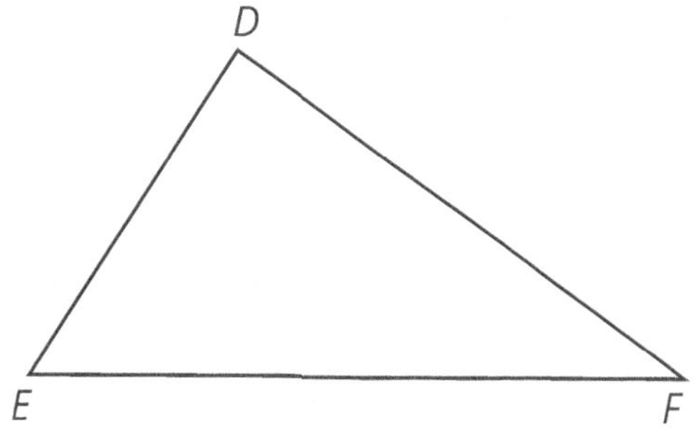

2.19 Construct an equilateral triangle with side equal to *r*. Inscribe a circle in the triangle.

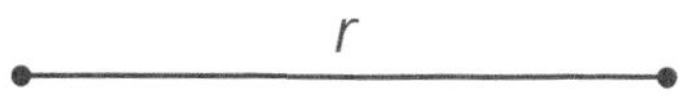

2.20 Construct a right triangle. Circumscribe a circle about the right triangle.

a. What relationship does the hypotenuse have with the circle? ____________________

b. What would be a quick way to find the center of the circle? ____________________

POLYGONS

Some other polygons besides triangles can be constructed using the basic construction ideas. You will see how to construct rectangles, parallelograms, regular hexagons, and octagons.

Construct a rectangle given its sides.

Given: two segments, *l* and *w*

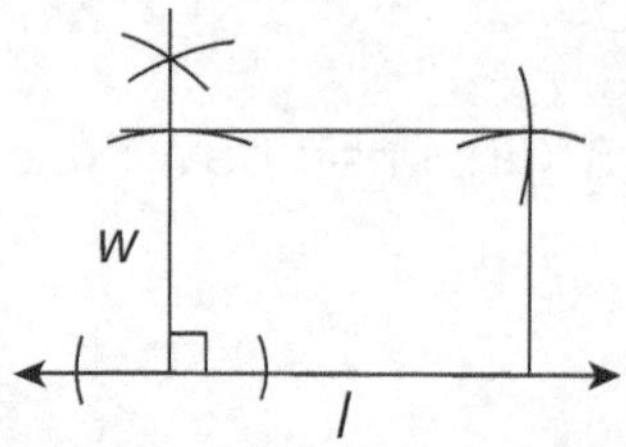

Steps: A rectangle has four right angles; therefore, we start by constructing a perpendicular to a work line. Copy the segment for the length on one ray of the right angle and copy the segment for the width on the other ray. With end of l as center and w as radius, construct an arc. With the end of w as center and l as radius, construct an arc that intersects the first arc. The intersection of the two arcs is the fourth corner of the rectangle.

Construct a parallelogram given its sides and an angle.

Given: two sides, *a* and *b*; ____________ *b*

∠1 ____________ *a*

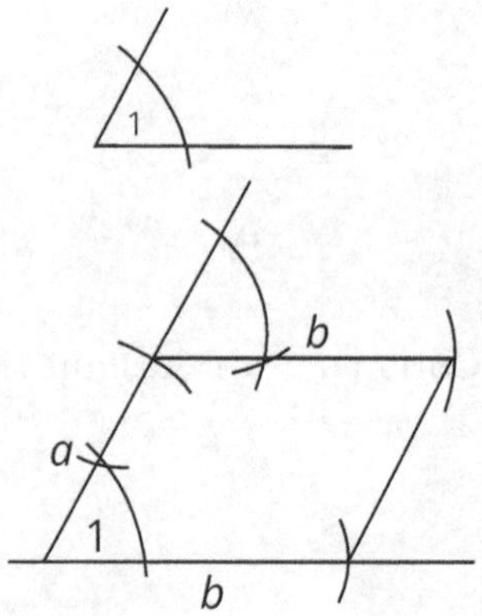

Steps: Copy ∠1. Copy *a* on one side of ∠1 and copy *b* on the other side of ∠1. Construct *a* parallel to *b* through the end of *a*. Copy *b* on this parallel. Construct the fourth side to form the parallelogram.

A rhombus would be constructed the same way as a parallelogram, but with all sides being the same length.

Construct a regular hexagon with given side.

Given: side *a*

Steps: Construct a circle with radius equal to *a***.** With the compass set on length *a*, mark off consecutive arcs around the circle, measuring each new arc from the previous intersection. You will mark exactly six arcs. Connect these six points in order to form the hexagon.

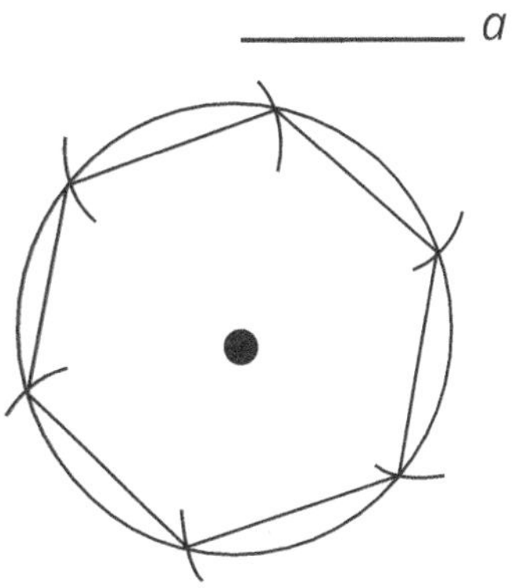

Construct a regular octagon with given side.

Given: side equal to *a*

Steps: On a work line copy *a*. At one end of *a*, construct a 45° angle. Mark off *a* on that ray. Copy the 45° angle at the end of this *a*. Continue in this way until you get back to the original work line. The completed figure is a regular octagon.

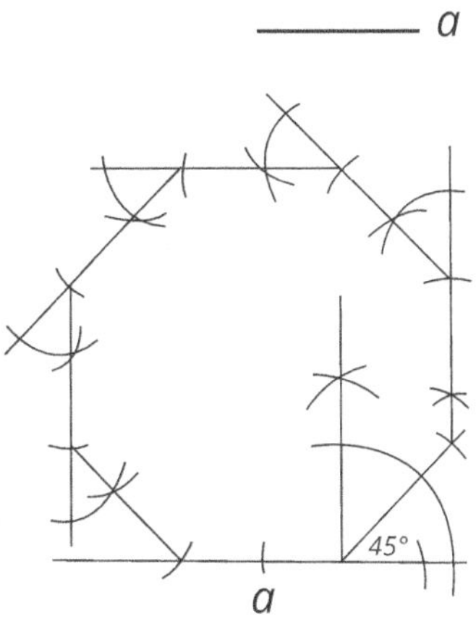

Complete these constructions. Leave all construction arcs on your paper.

2.21 Construct a square with side equal to *r*.

_______________ *r*

2.22 Construct a hexagon with side equal to *r*.

_______________ *r*

2.23 Construct a rhombus with a 45° angle and sides equal to r.

________________________ r

2.24 Construct an octagon with sides equal to r.

__________ r

2.25 Construct a rectangle with length twice the width and with width equal to r.

____________ r

2.26 Construct a square with side equal to r, and circumscribe a circle about it.

_______________ r

2.27 Construct a hexagon of side r. Connect opposite vertices.

a. What figures are formed inside the hexagon? ______________________________

b. Does this construction suggest another way to construct a hexagon? ______________

__________ r

2.28 Construct an octagon of side *r*. Label the vertices *A, B, C, D, E, F, G,* and *H*. Connect *A* to *C* to *E* to *G* to *A*. Connect *B* to *D* to *F* to *H* to *B*. What figures are formed inside the octagon?

____

__________ r

Complete this activity.

2.29 Write a proof for the construction of a regular hexagon.

Given: side equal to *a*

Prove: Polygon *ABCDEF* is a regular hexagon.

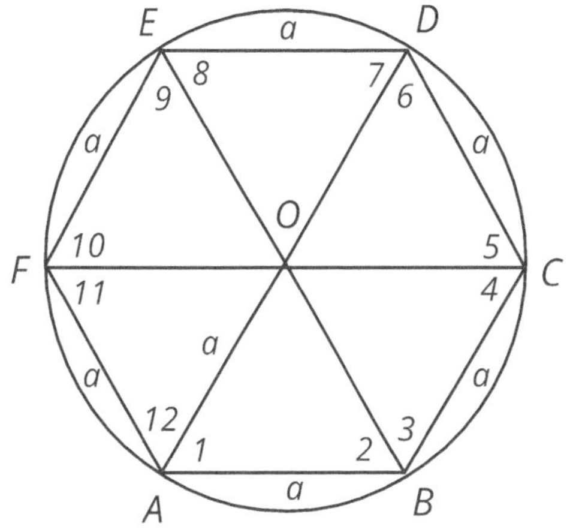

Review the material in this section in preparation for the Self Test. This Self Test will check your mastery of this particular section as well as your knowledge of the previous section.

SELF TEST 2

Complete these constructions. Leave all construction arcs on your paper (each construction, 5 points).

2.01 Construct an equilateral triangle with side equal to *s*.

2.02 Construct an isosceles triangle with leg equal to *t* and vertex angle equal to ∠1.

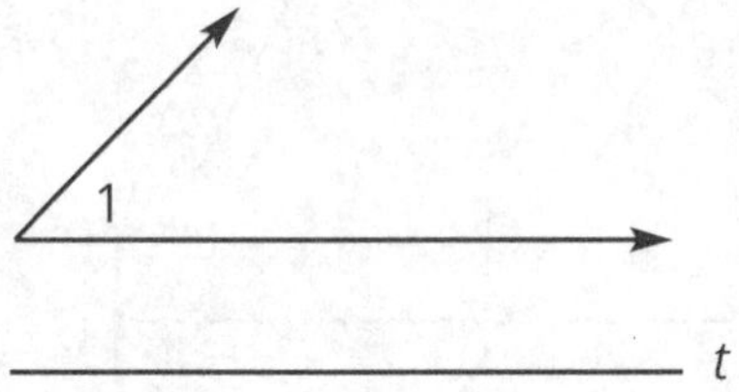

2.03 Construct the three medians to triangle *ABC*.

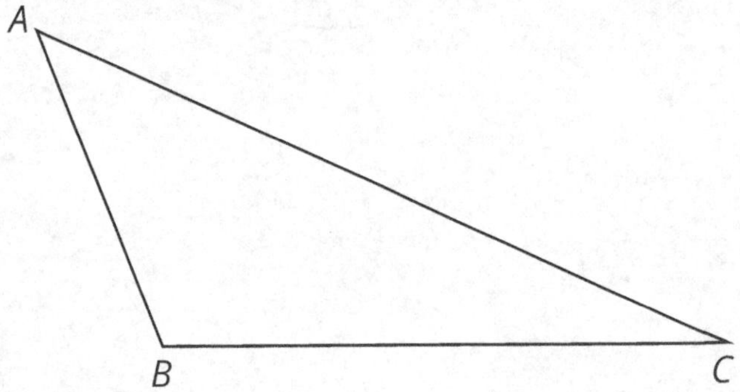

2.04 Construct a square with sides equal to *r*.

2.05 Inscribe a circle in triangle *ABC*.

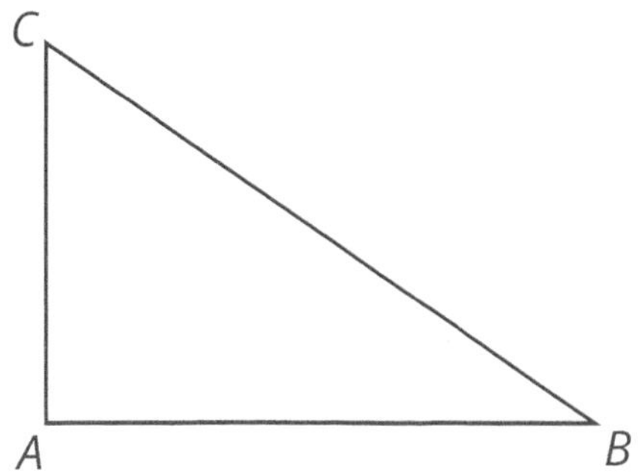

2.06 Construct a regular hexagon with sides equal to *t*.

2.07 Construct a 30°- 60°- 90° triangle.

2.08 Construct the three altitudes to right triangle *CDE*.

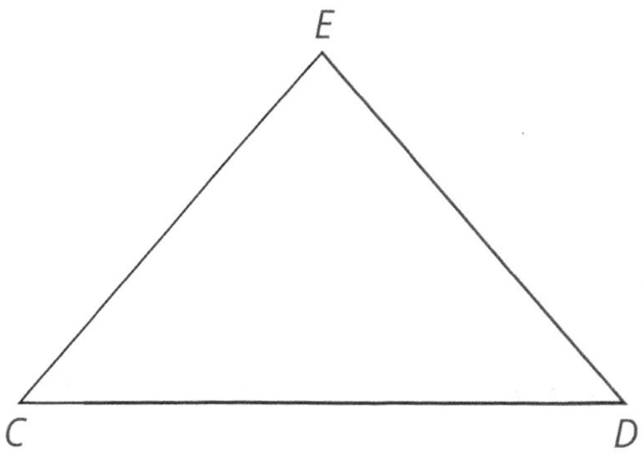

2.09 Circumscribe a circle about triangle *RST*.

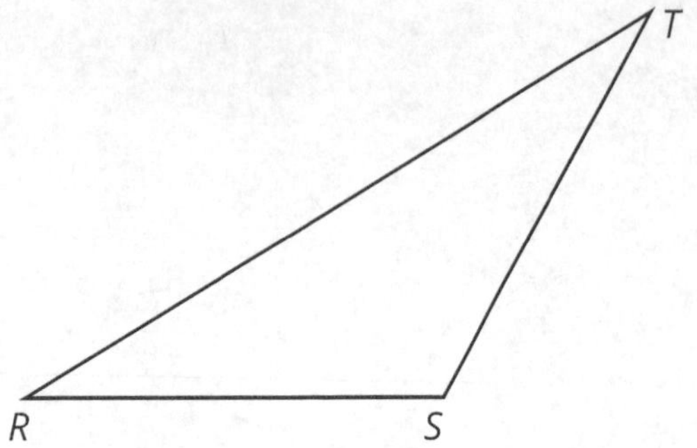

2.010 Construct a parallelogram with sides equal to *a* and *b* and having an angle equal to 45°.

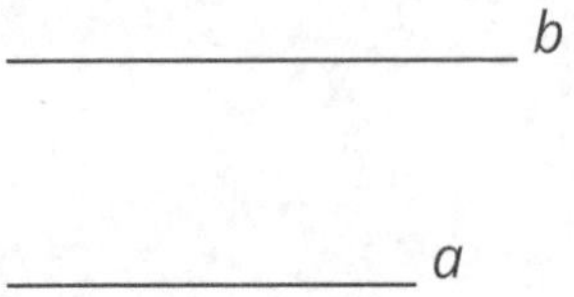

2.011 Construct a 45°- 45°- 90° isosceles triangle with leg equal to *a*.

2.012 Construct a regular octagon with side equal to *r*.

48/60 **SCORE** ________ **TEACHER** ________ ________
initials date

3. LOCUS

To complete many of the constructions, we had to use points that were formed by the intersection of lines and arcs. These points or sets of points satisfied some condition given in the problem. Many of our definitions have to do with sets of points that meet certain conditions. In this section you will describe and construct geometric figures that satisfy one or more given conditions.

Section Objectives

Review these objectives. When you have completed this section, you should be able to:

13. Define locus.
14. Solve locus problems.
15. Construct figures using locus concepts.

MEANING

Consider this problem: Make a sketch and then describe the location of all points that are coplanar with points *A* and *B* and are equidistant from *A* and *B*.

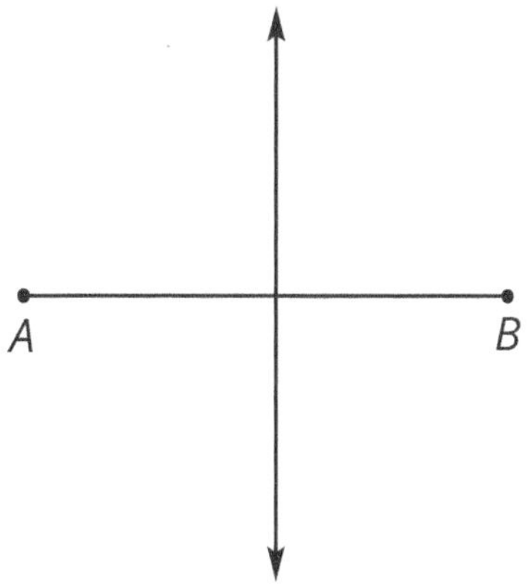

Two or three points that meet the given conditions are not too hard to find. If you mentally consider all points that meet the conditions, you should come to the conclusion that all the points form a line. An accurate description of the location of these points must tell what geometric figure they form (what it is) and its location with respect to *A* and *B* (where it is). One good description of the figure might be "a line in the same plane as *A* and *B* that is also the perpendicular bisector of $\overline{AB}$."

If the condition that all the points be coplanar were removed, then both sketch and description would be changed. The description would be "<u>a</u> plane that is the perpendicular bisector of $\overline{AB}$." From these descriptions, a definition of locus should be easy to understand.

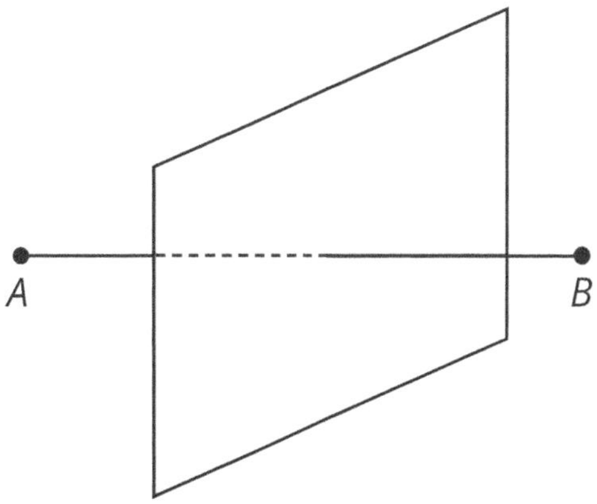

> **DEFINITION**
> **Locus:** the set of all those and only those points that satisfy a given condition.

The plural of *locus* is *loci*. A locus is a geometric figure, a set of points. It contains all the points that make the condition true and contains no points that do not satisfy the condition.

The solution to a locus problem consists of two parts: (1) a sketch in which the points representing the locus are clearly shown and (2) an accurate word description in which all details of the "what" and "where" of the locus are mentioned.

Unless the statement of a problem restricts a locus to a plane, you should always think in terms of three dimensions, or space.

Model 1: Find the locus of points that lie in the plane of two parallel lines r and t and are equidistant from r and t.

Solution: A line s, in the plane of and parallel to r and t and located midway between r and t.

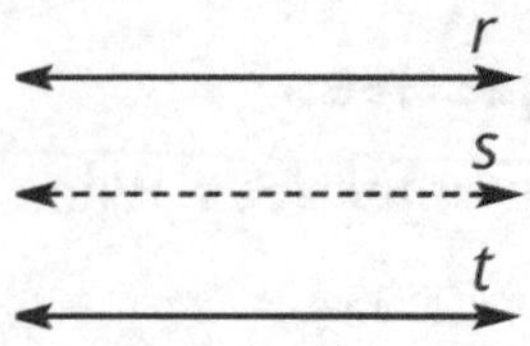

Model 2: Find the locus of points three inches from P.

Solution: A sphere with center at P and radius of three inches.

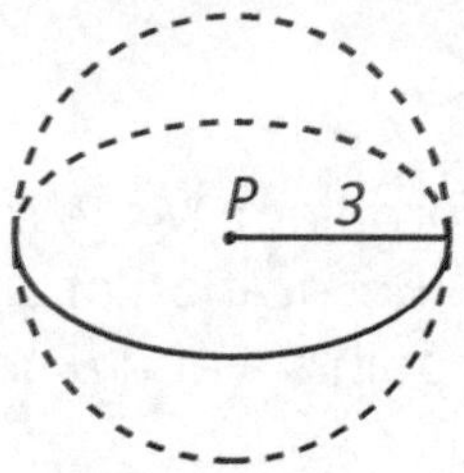

Make a sketch and give a description in words for these locus problems.

3.1 A given circle has center at *P* and a radius of four inches. What is the locus of the midpoints of all radii of the circle? ______________________________

3.2 What is the locus of points in a plane and six inches from a given line t in the plane?

____

3.3 What is the locus of the centers of all circles that are tangent to each of two parallel lines?

____

3.4 Find the locus of the centers of all circles that are tangent to both sides of a given angle.

____

3.5 What is the locus of points 3 inches from a given segment? ____________________

3.6 Given two concentric circles with radii of 5" and 7", what is the locus of points in the plane of the two circles and equidistant from them? ____________________

3.7 Given two intersecting lines *a* and *b*, what is the locus of points in the plane of *a* and *b* and equidistant from *a* and *b*? ____________________

3.8 What is the locus of points in a plane and two inches from a point *P*?

____

3.9 What is the locus of points in the plane of and equidistant from the sides of an angle?

____

3.10 What is the locus of points three inches from a given plane *R*?

____

3.11 Given two points *R* and *S* lying in plane *T*, what is the locus of the centers of all circles that lie in *T* and pass through line *RS* only once at the midpoint of segment *RS*?

____

3.12 Given two perpendicular lines *l* and *m*, what is the locus of the centers of all circles tangent to both *l* and *m*? ____

3.13 Given a circle with radius of five inches, what is the locus of all points in the plane of the circle and at a distance of two inches from the circle?

____

3.14 A sphere of radius 4 is internally tangent to a sphere of radius 8.
What is the locus of the possible centers of the internal sphere?

____

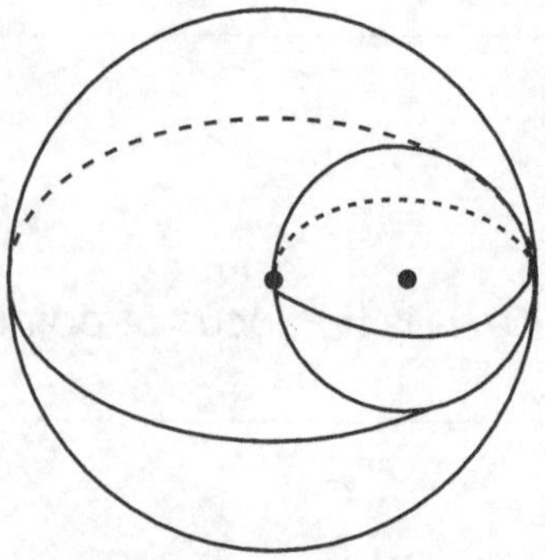

INTERSECTION

Occasionally more than one condition is given for a set of points. In that situation the locus is the set of points and only those points that are common to the loci for the separate conditions. The points of intersection, if any, of each locus are the needed points. All possible positions of the separate loci must be considered.

Model 1: In a plane find the locus of points that are equidistant from two given points *R* and *S* and at a given distance *t* from a given point *P*.

Solution: The locus of the first condition is a line that is the perpendicular bisector of *RS*. The locus of the second condition is a circle with radius *t* and center at *P*.

The possible solutions are based on the relative position of *R*, *S*, and *P*.

Possible solutions:

(1) The locus is the set of two points *X* and *Y*.

(2) The locus is the set of one point *X*.

(3) The locus is the empty set.

(1)

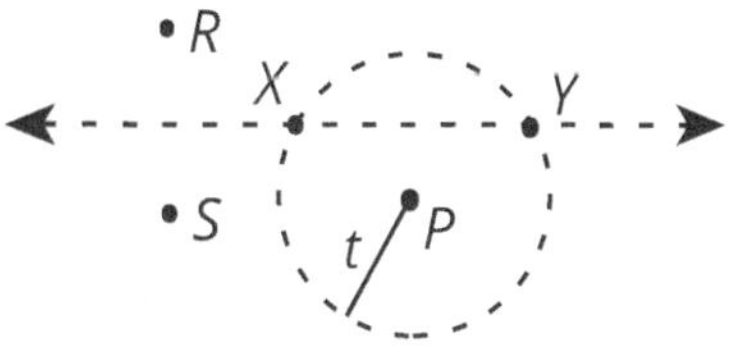

(2)

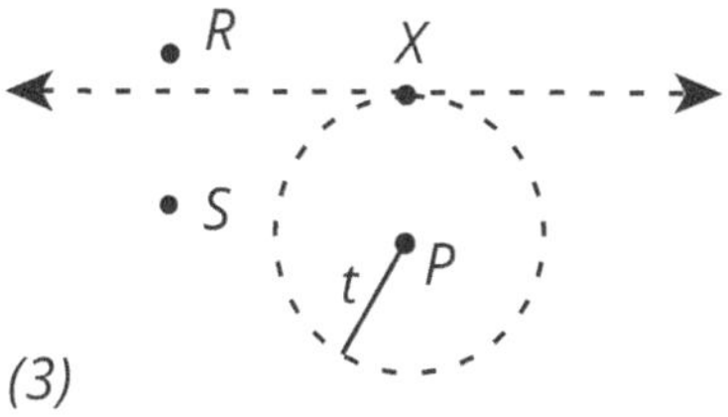

(3)

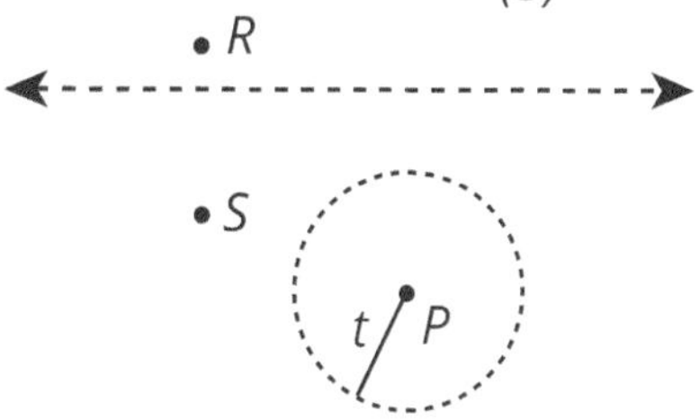

Model 2: Find the locus of points equidistant from two parallel planes *R* and *S* and at a given distance *d* from point *P*.

Solution: The locus of the first condition is a plane *X* parallel to *R* and *S* and halfway between them. The second is a sphere of radius *d* and center *P*. The possible solutions are based on the relative positions of *R*, *S*, and *P*.

(1) The empty set. The two loci do not intersect.

(2) One point A. The sphere is tangent to the plane.

(3) A circle. The plane intersects the sphere in a circle.

(1)

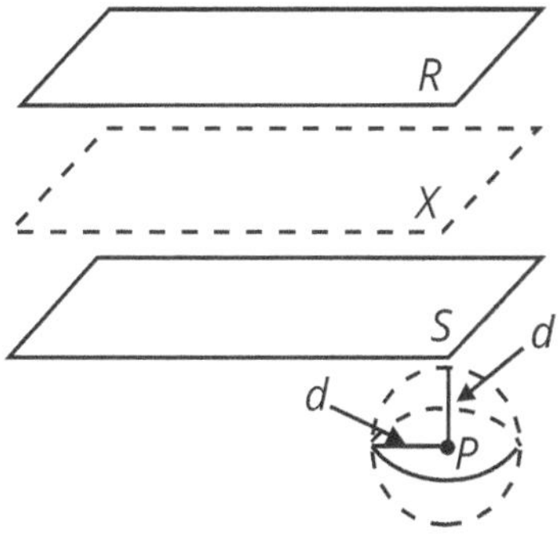

(2)

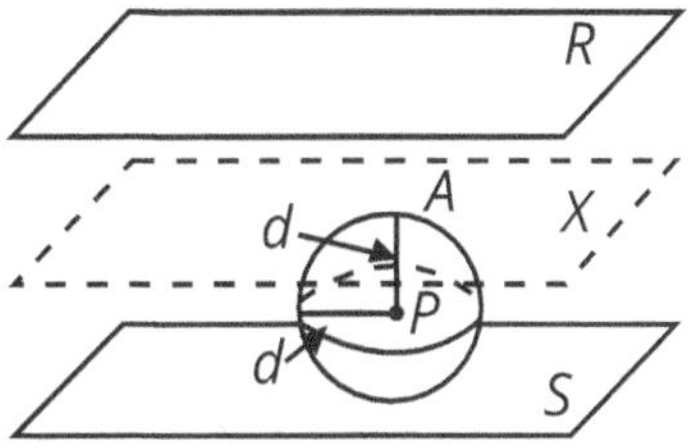

(3)

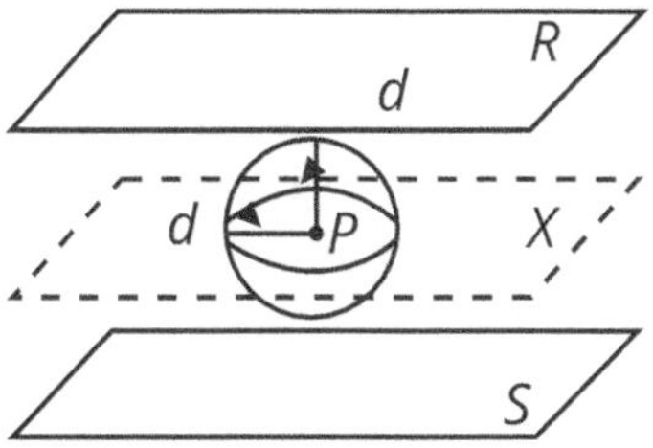

Give all possible solutions to these problems. Make a sketch and describe the solution set.

3.15 Given *R* in the interior of $\angle CDE$, find the locus of points that are in the interior of $\angle CDE$, are equidistant from the sides of $\angle CDE$, and are a given distance *d* from point *R*.

3.16 Given two points *X* and *Y* in the plane of two parallel lines *l* and *m*, find the locus of points that are in the plane, are equidistant from *X* and *Y*, and are equidistant from *l* and *m*.

3.17 Given two points *A* and *B* on the plane of $\angle RST$, find the locus of points that are in the interior of $\angle RST$, are equidistant from the sides of $\angle RST$, and are equidistant from *A* and *B*.

3.18 Given two parallel lines *l* and *m* and a third line *t*, all in a plane, find the locus of points that are in the plane, are equidistant from *l* and *m*, and are a given distance *d* from *t*.

3.19 What is the locus of points that are equidistant from two given points *A* and *B* and are also equidistant from two intersecting lines, all in a plane?

3.20 Given a point *B* in plane *N*, what is the locus of points five inches from *B* and three inches from plane *N*?

CONSTRUCTION

The solution to many problems involving constructions depends on finding points that satisfy more than one condition. These problems are best solved by constructing separate loci for each condition. Then you can use the intersection points, for they meet all the given conditions.

When doing a construction problem of this type, you will want to sketch the final figure so that you can see the relationship between the various parts.

Model 1: Given: $\overline{AB}$, $\overline{CD}$, $\angle 1$

Construct: Triangle *XYZ* so that
$XY = AB$, $\angle X = \angle 1$ and
the altitude to *XY* equals *CD*

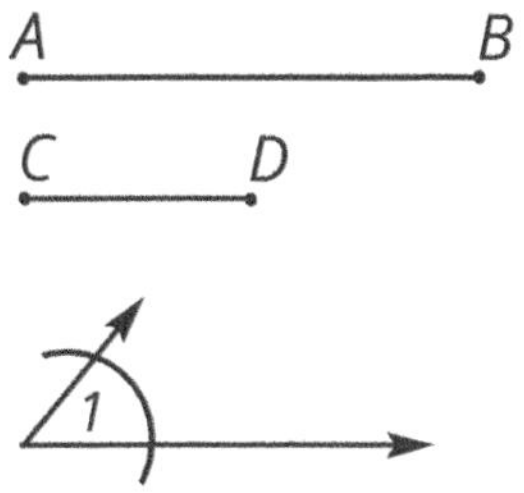

Initial sketch:

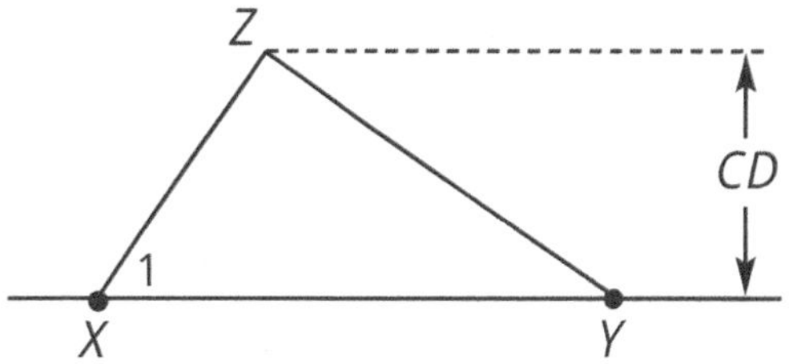

Steps: Copy $\overline{AB}$ on a work line. This line will be side *XY* of the triangle. Copy $\angle 1$ in both positions shown. The locus of points meeting the condition that $\angle X$ be equal to $\angle 1$ is $\overrightarrow{XW}$ and $\overrightarrow{XV}$. Construct two lines *j* and *k* parallel to $\overline{XY}$ at the distance of *CD*. This locus meets the condition of the altitude to *XY*. Call the intersection of these two loci points *Z* and *Z'*. Triangle *XZY* and triangle *XZ'Y* both meet all the given conditions.

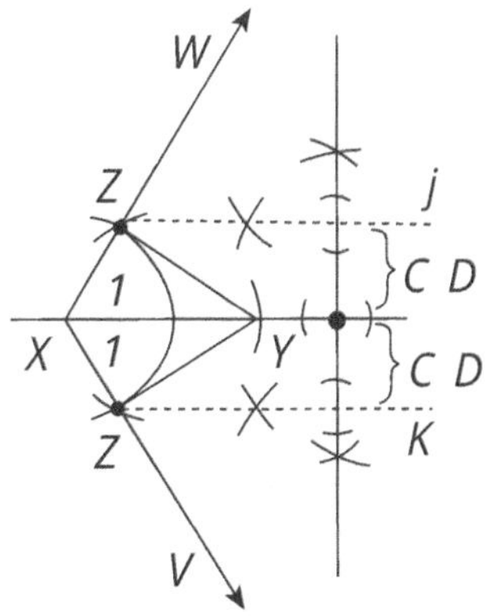

Model 2: Given: $\overline{AB}$ and $\overline{CD}$

Construct a right triangle *RST* whose hypotenuse $\overline{RS}$ is equal to *AB* and for which the altitude to the hypotenuse equals *CD*.

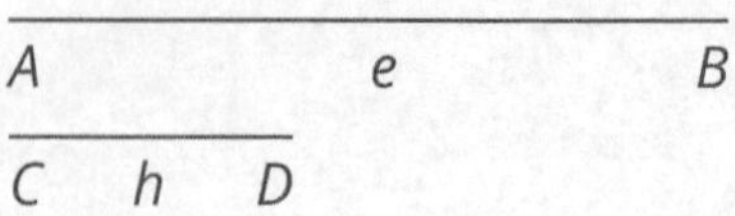

Initial Sketch:

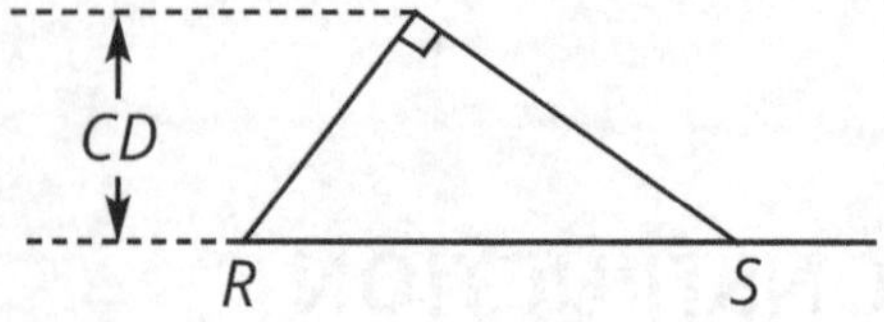

Steps: For convenience call the length of *AB*, *e*, and the length of *CD*, *h*.

Copy $\overline{AB}$ on your work line. This line will be the hypotenuse $\overline{RS}$. Find the midpoint of $\overline{RS}$ and make a circle with center at the midpoint of $\overline{RS}$ and with radius equal to half of $\overline{RS}$. The right angle of our triangle will be on this locus since any angle inscribed in a semicircle is a right angle. Construct two lines *l* and *m* parallel to $\overline{RS}$ and a distance h from $\overline{RS}$. The intersection of the circle locus and the parallel locus gives us four points, any one of which can be *T*, the right angle of our triangle *RST*.

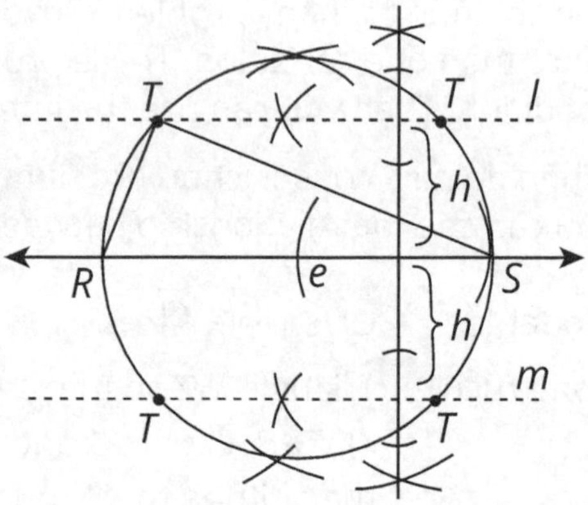

Use these segments and angles to complete each of the following constructions.
Leave all construction arcs on your paper.

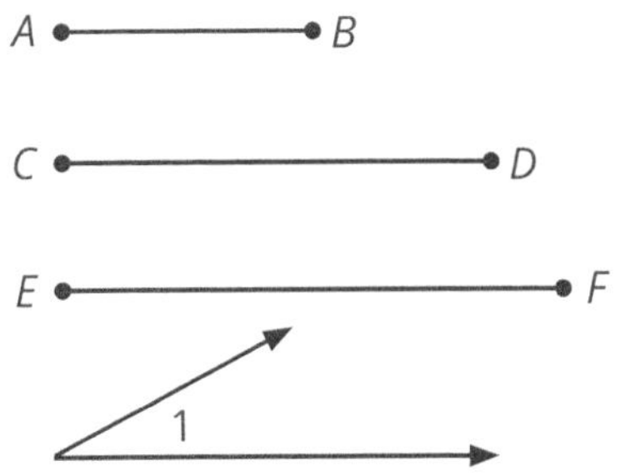

3.21 Construct an isosceles triangle with base angle equal to $\angle 1$ and the altitude to the base equal to *AB*.

3.22 Construct a right triangle with acute angle equal to $\angle 1$ and the altitude to the hypotenuse equal to *AB*.

3.23 Construct a triangle with two sides equal to *CD* and *EF* and the altitude to *EF* equal to *AB*.

3.24 Construct a right triangle with a leg equal to *CD* and the altitude to the hypotenuse equal to *AB*.

3.25 Construct an isosceles triangle such that the radius of the circumscribed circle is equal to *AB* and the base equals *CD*.

3.26 Draw a line *t*. Choose a point *R* on t and a point *S* not on *t*. Construct a circle that passes through *R* and *S* and is tangent to *t*.

Complete this challenge exercise.

3.27 a. An *X* is painted at the top of an automobile tire. The tire rolls along a smooth road. Sketch the locus of point *X*. (The curve is called a cycloid.)

b. Sketch the locus if *X* is halfway from the center to the edge of the wheel.

c. Sketch the locus if *X* is at the center of the wheel.

Before you take this last Self Test, you may want to do one or more of these self checks.

1. ________ Read the objectives. See if you can do them.
2. ________ Restudy the material related to any objectives that you cannot do.
3. ________ Use the **SQ3R** study procedure to review the material:
   a. **S**can the sections.
   b. **Q**uestion yourself.
   c. **R**ead to answer your questions.
   d. **R**ecite the answers to yourself.
   e. **R**eview areas you did not understand.
4. ________ Review all vocabulary, activities, and Self Tests, writing a correct answer for every wrong answer.

SELF TEST 3

Sketch and describe the following loci (each answer, 5 points).

3.01 Describe the locus of points in your classroom one foot from the floor.

____

3.02 What is the locus of points in a plane and six inches from a given line *t* in that plane?

____

3.03 What is the locus of points equidistant from the four vertices of a square?

____

3.04 Describe the locus of points that are equidistant from two parallel planes.

____

3.05 What is the locus of the centers of all circles that are tangent to both of two parallel lines?

____

Suppose you found required loci to be the figures indicated. Describe the different possible sets of points the two loci could have in common (each numbered item, 5 points).

3.06 Two lines.

3.07 A line and a plane.

3.08 Two unequal circles in the same plane.

3.09 A plane and a sphere.

3.010 Two parallel lines and a sphere.

3.011 Two unequal spheres.

Sketch and describe all the five possible solutions (each answer, 5 points).

3.012 Given two intersecting lines *s* and *t* and point *O* all in a plane; find the locus of points that are in the plane, are equidistant from *s* and *t*, and are a given distance *d* from point *O*.

Complete these constructions. Leave all construction arcs on your paper (each construction, 5 points).

3.013 Given: $\angle 1$, $\overline{AB}$, $\overline{CD}$; construct a parallelogram with an angle equal to $\angle 1$, a side equal to $\overline{AB}$, and the altitude to $\overline{AB}$ equal to $\overline{CD}$.

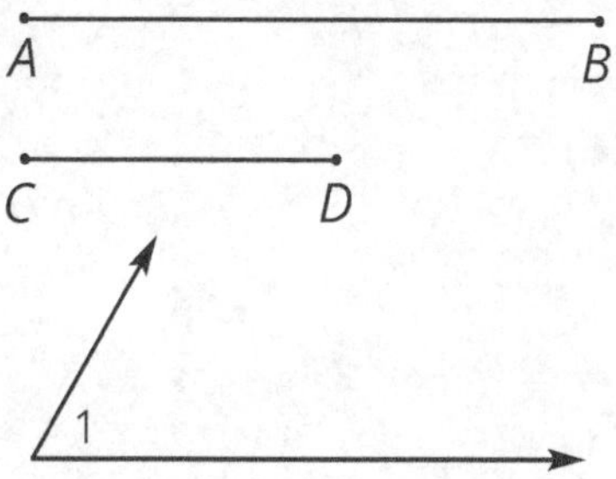

3.014 Given: $\angle 1$, $\overline{AB}$; construct an isosceles triangle with base angles equal to $\angle 1$ and altitude to the base equal to $\overline{AB}$.

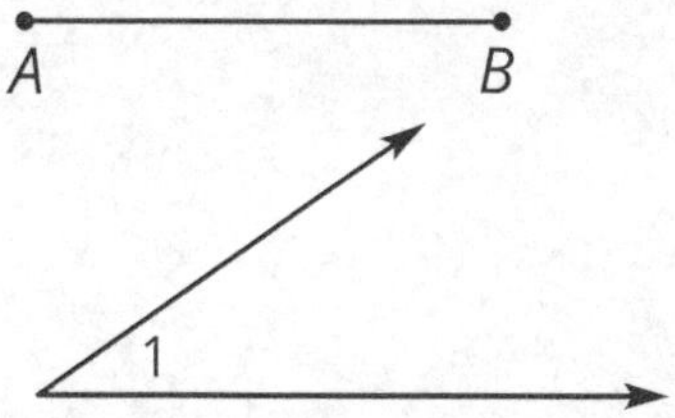

3.015 Given: $\angle 1$, $\overline{AB}$; construct a right triangle with leg equal to AB and acute angle equal to $\angle 1$.

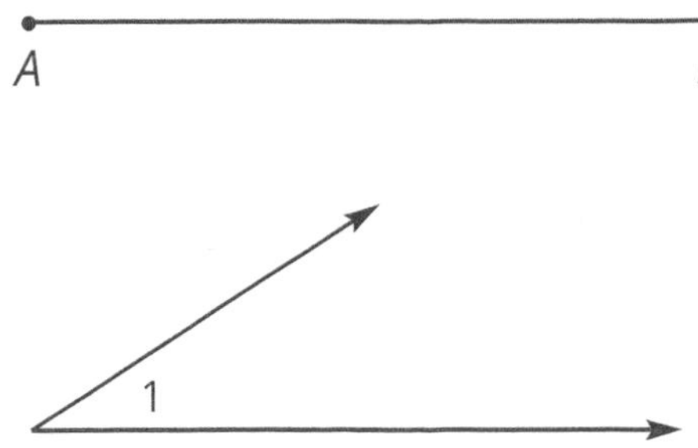

76/95 **SCORE** ________ **TEACHER** ________ ________
initials date

Before you take the LIFEPAC Test, you may want to do one or more of these self checks.

1. ________ Read the objectives. See if you can do them.
2. ________ Restudy the material related to any objectives that you cannot do.
3. ________ Use the **SQ3R** study procedure to review the material.
4. ________ Review activities, Self Tests, and LIFEPAC vocabulary words.
5. ________ Restudy areas of weakness indicated by the last Self Test.

GLOSSARY

construction .... To draw a figure with only a straightedge and a compass.

compass .... An instrument used to construct circles and arcs of circles.

circumscribed circle .... A circle passing through each vertex of a polygon.

inscribed circle .... A circle to which all the sides of a polygon are tangent.

locus .... A set of points that satisfy a certain condition.

regular hexagon .... A six-sided polygon with all sides equal and all angles equal.

regular octagon .... An eight-sided polygon with all sides equal and all angles equal.

straightedge .... An instrument used to construct straight lines.

MATH 1008
Area and Volume

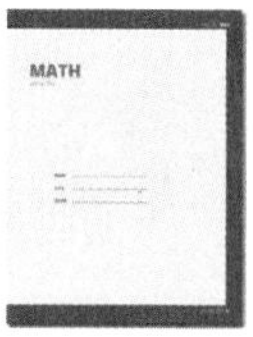

LIFEPAC Test is located in the center of the booklet. Please remove before starting the unit.

Author:
Milton R. Christen, M.A.

Editor-in-Chief:
Richard W. Wheeler, M.A.Ed.

Editor:
Robin Hintze Kreutzberg, M.B.A.

Consulting Editor:
Robert L. Zenor, M.A., M.S.

Revision Editor:
Alan Christopherson, M.S.

AOP

804 N. 2nd Ave. E.
Rock Rapids, IA 51246-1759

Area and Volume

Introduction

In other math LIFEPACs, you have learned how to find the area and volume of many geometric shapes. You were given a formula or a rule and some numbers to substitute into it. You then did the computations and came out with an answer.

In this LIFEPAC®, you will study area and volume as a part of our deductive system. You will learn why the formulas for area and volume are written as they are rather than simply using them. We shall define some terms, state some postulates, and prove theorems about area and volume. Some of the theorems will be the familiar formulas you have used in the past.

Objectives

Read these objectives. The objectives tell you what you will be able to do when you have successfully completed this LIFEPAC. When you have finished this LIFEPAC, you should be able to:

1. Define area.
2. Calculate the area of certain polygons.
3. Compare areas of similar polygons.
4. Calculate the circumference of a circle.
5. Calculate the area of a circle.
6. Calculate the area of a sector of a circle.
7. Calculate the area of a segment of a circle.
8. Calculate the surface areas of certain solid figures.
9. Calculate the volumes of certain solid figures.

Survey the LIFEPAC. Ask yourself some questions about this study and write your questions here.

1. POLYGONS

In this section we shall derive the formulas for the areas of some quadrilaterals, triangles, and regular polygons. We shall also compare the areas of similar polygons using proportions.

Section Objectives

Review these objectives. When you have completed this section, you should be able to:

1. Define area.
2. Calculate the area of certain polygons.
3. Compare areas of similar polygons.

AREA CONCEPTS

When we speak of the area of figures, we are referring to the measure of what can go inside the figure. This "inside" of a figure is called a *region*. A *triangular region* is the union of a triangle and its interior. A *polygonal region* is the union of the nonoverlapping triangular regions. Every polygon can be broken into triangular regions in different ways.

Region

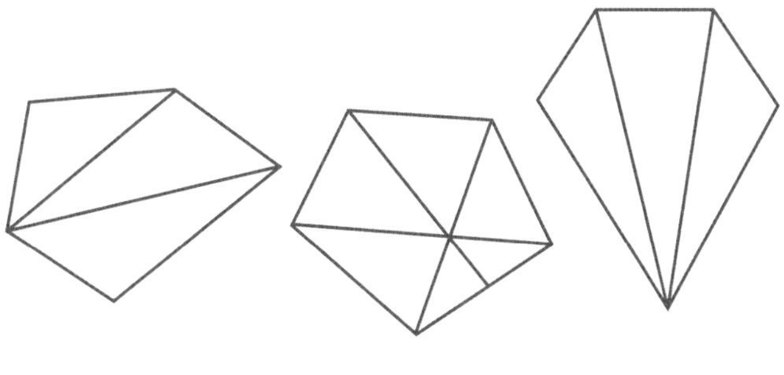

DEFINITIONS

Area the measure of the space inside a geometric figure.

Region the space inside and including the sides of a figure.

You will now learn three postulates that have to do with area and regions.

POSTULATE 17

P17: For every polygonal region there exists one unique positive number that is called the area of that region.

Postulate 17 gives us a number that can be used to represent area.

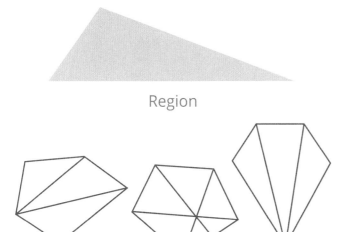

POSTULATE 18

P18: If two triangles are congruent, then their areas are the same number.

Postulate 18 seems reasonable, since congruent triangles have the same shape and the same size and since area is a number that measures the size of the triangle.

POSTULATE 19:

P19: The area of a polygonal region is the sum of the areas of the triangular regions that form the polygonal region.

(Area Addition Postulate)

Postulate 19 gives us a way of adding areas of triangles to find the area of any polygon. This postulate is similar both to the angle addition theorem that allows us to add angle measures and to the definition of betweenness in which we add lengths of segments.

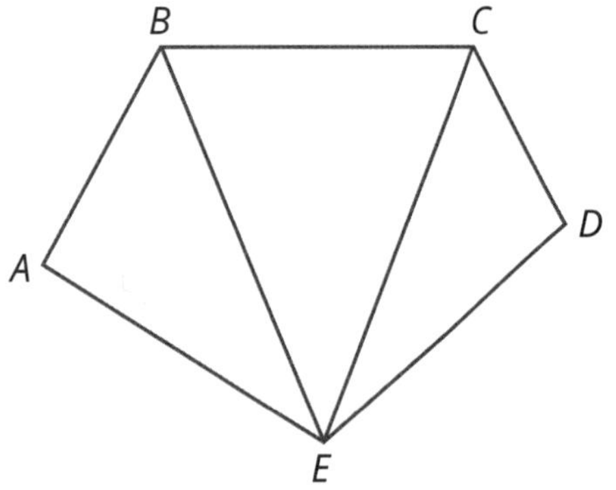

Area *ABCDE* =
Area *AEB* + Area *BEC* + Area *CED*.

To make use of the idea of area in the physical world, we need to agree on a unit for measuring area. The *square unit* has been developed in the following manner.

Consider a square one unit on each side. We shall agree that the area of this square is one square unit. When we find the area of a region, we are looking for the number of these square units that will fit onto the surface of that region. The unit of measurement used could be inches, feet, yards, or any other unit of length. The corresponding unit for area would be square inch, square foot, and square yard.

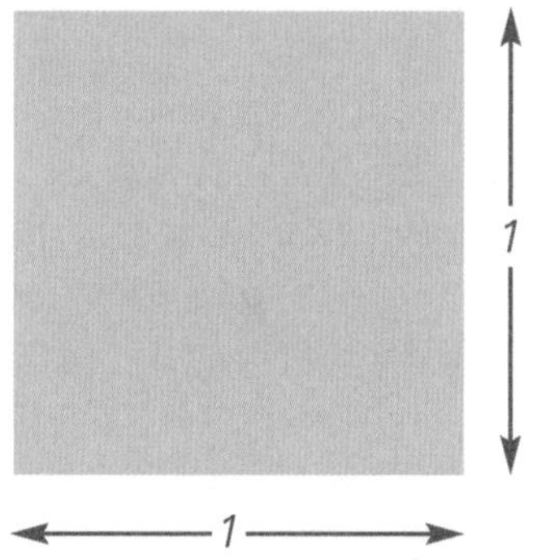

1 square unit

Complete the following activities.

1.1 Divide the three similar polygons into triangular regions in three different ways.

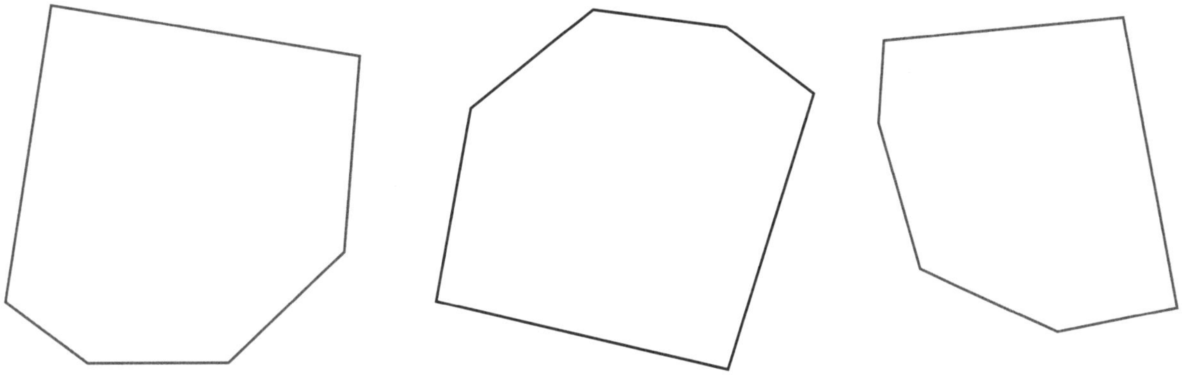

1.2 If the area of each of the triangular regions is as shown, what is the area (A) of each polygon?

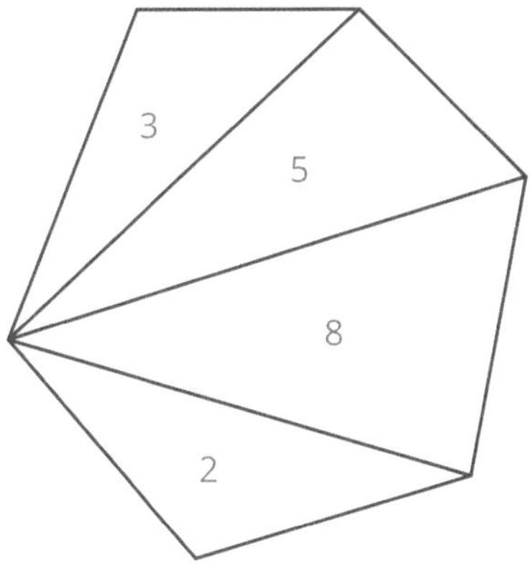

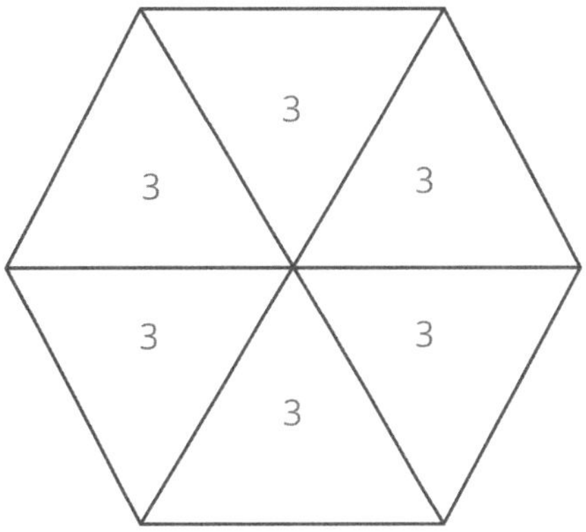

a. A = ________________ b. A = ________________

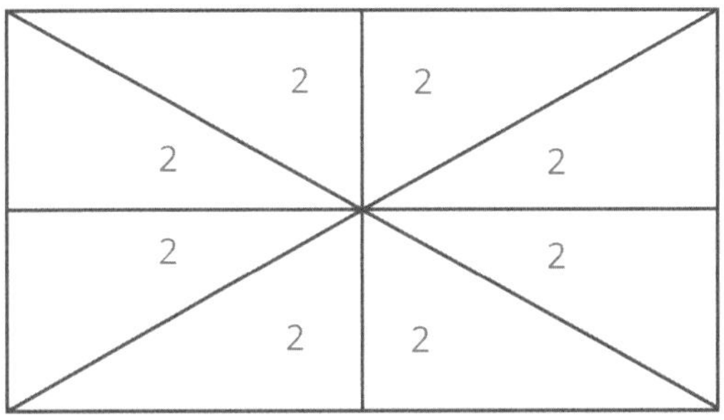

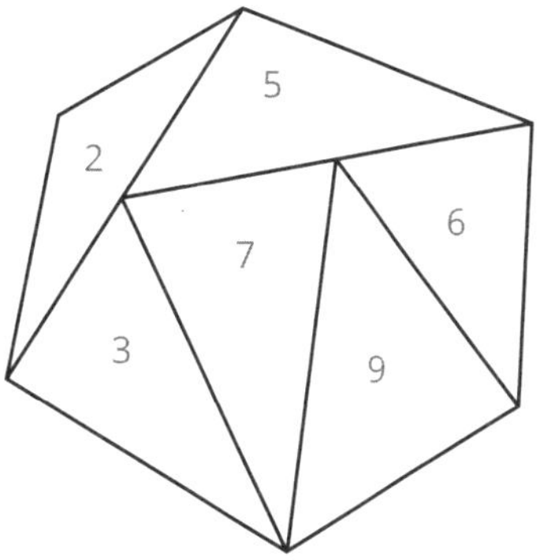

c. A = ________________ d. A = ________________

1.3 If triangle *RST* is congruent to triangle *WXY* and the area of triangle *WXY* is 20 square inches, what is the area of triangle *RST*? ____________________

1.4 Which three of the following numbers cannot represent the area of a polygon? __________

a. 68 b. 40 c. -5 d. $\sqrt{30}$

e. 0 f. -200

1.5 If two triangles have the same area, must they be congruent? ____________________

1.6 Can a rectangle and a triangle have the same area? ____________________

1.7 When a diagonal is drawn in a rectangle, what is true of the areas of the two triangles into which it divides the rectangle? Why? ____________________

____

1.8 Do the diagonals of a rhombus divide it into four triangles of equal area? ____________________

1.9 If two equilateral triangles have equal perimeters, must they also have equal areas?

____

1.10 If two polygons have the same area, must they have the same number of sides? __________

RECTANGLE

Suppose we take a rectangle with length of six inches and width of three inches.

We can place 18 square inches inside this region, as the figure shows. Therefore, the area of the rectangle is 18 sq. in.

Model 1:

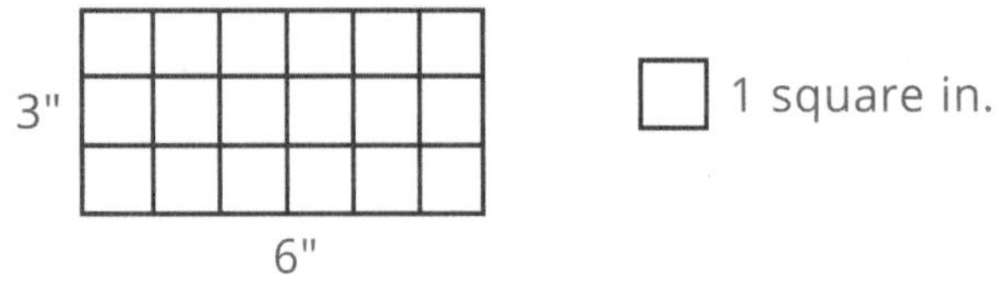

Suppose we take a rectangle that measures 5 ft. by 3 ft.

Model 2:

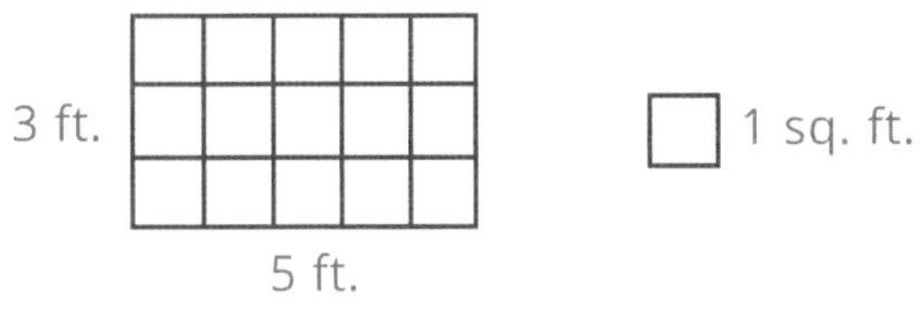

We can put 15 sq. ft. in the rectangle. The area of the rectangle would be 15 sq. ft.

If a rectangle were $3\frac{1}{2}$ cm long and 2 cm wide, its area would be 7 sq. cm.

Model 3:

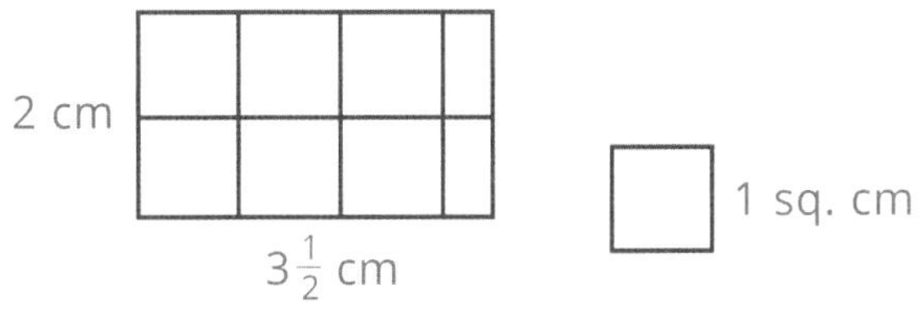

We can calculate the area number in each case by multiplying the length of the base of the rectangle by the length of the altitude to that base.

Model 1: $6 \times 3 = 18$

Model 2: $3 \times 5 = 15$

Model 3: $3\frac{1}{2} \times 2 = 7$

This fact suggests the next postulate.

POSTULATE 20:

P20: The area of a rectangle is the product of the length of a base and the length of the altitude to that base:

$A = bh$

Any side of a rectangle can be considered to be the base. Then each side adjacent to that base is an altitude to that base. Another way of saying Postulate 20 is that the area is the product of the length and the width.

A useful corollary to Postulate 20 tells how to find the area of a square.

Corollary: The area of a square is the square of the length of its side: $A = s^2$.

Since a square is a rectangle with base and altitude equal, we can replace *s* for *b* and *h* in the formula for area of a rectangle.

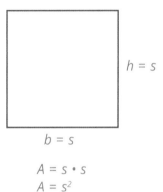

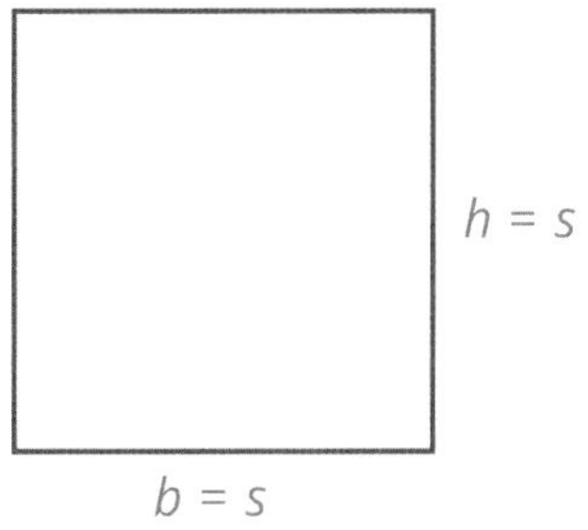

$A = s \cdot s$

$A = s^2$

When using an area formula in an application problem, you may use any practical unit of length. However, within any particular problem all dimensions must be in the same unit of length.

Model 1: Find the area of a rectangle with length of 2 yds. and width of 3 feet.

Solution: Let the linear unit be feet. Therefore, the length is 2 yds. × 3 = 6 ft.

$A = bh$

$A = 6(3)$

$A = 18$ sq. ft.

Model 2: Find the area of a rectangle if its base is 2 ft. and its height is 18 inches.

Solution: Let the linear unit be inches. Therefore, the base is 2 ft. × 12 = 24 inches.

$A = bh$

$A = 24(18)$

$A = 432$ sq. in.

Alternatively, let the linear unit be feet. Then the height is 18 inches divided by 12 = $1\frac{1}{2}$ft.

$A = bh$

$A = 2(1\frac{1}{2})$

$A = 3$ sq. ft.

Complete the following activities.

1.11 Find the area of a rectangle with base of 12 inches and height of 8 inches.

____

1.12 Find the area of a square with side of 7 feet. ______________

1.13 Find the area of a rectangle with length of 6 inches and width of 2 feet.

a. In sq. ft.: ______________ b. In sq. in.: ______________

1.14 Find the length of a rectangle with area of 16 sq. cm and width of 8 cm.

____

1.15 Find the side of a square with area of 25 sq. ft. ______________

1.16 Find the number of square inches in one square foot. ______________

1.17 The area of a desk top is $8\frac{3}{4}$ square feet. If the length is $3\frac{1}{2}$ ft., find the width.

____

1.18 The Smiths plan to recarpet their family room, which measures 15 ft. by 20 ft. How many square yards of carpet are needed?

____

1.19 The roof of a cabin is to be shingled at a cost of $70 a square. (A *square*, in shingling, is a region with an area of 100 sq. ft.) Find the cost of shingling the roof shown.

____

1.20 A wooden fence 6 ft. high and 300 ft. long is to be painted. How many gallons of paint are needed if one gallon covers 400 sq. ft.?

____

1.21 A piece of sheet metal is cut and bent to form a box, as shown. The box has no top.

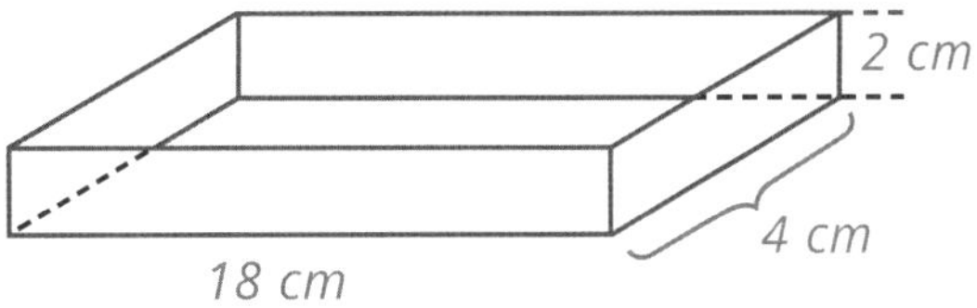

Find the area of:

a. the bottom: _______________

b. the two longer sides: _______________

c. the two shorter sides: _______________

1.22 A 3-ft.-wide sidewalk surrounds a rectangular plot that measures 20 ft. by 30 ft.

Find the area of the sidewalk. _______________

1.23 A rectangle is twice as long as it is wide. If its area is 50 sq. yds., find the length and the width.

____

1.24 Some pleated draperies must be twice as wide as the window they cover. How many square yards of material are needed to cover a window 2 ft. wide and 3 ft. long?

____

1.25 Find the area of grass in the home landscape diagram below.

____

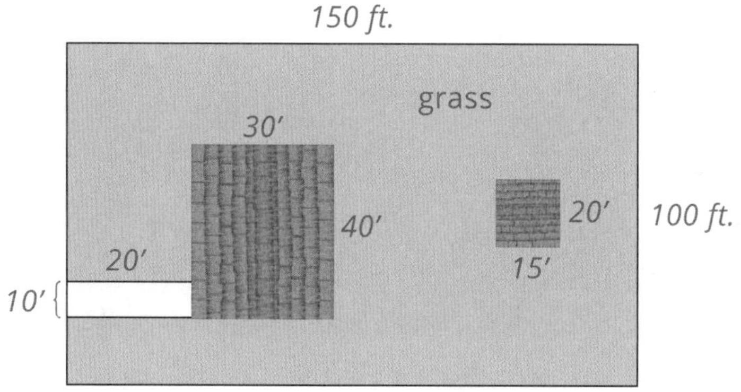

PARALLELOGRAM

Any side of a parallelogram can be called its *base*. The *altitude* to that base is the length of the perpendicular segment between the *D* base and its opposite side.

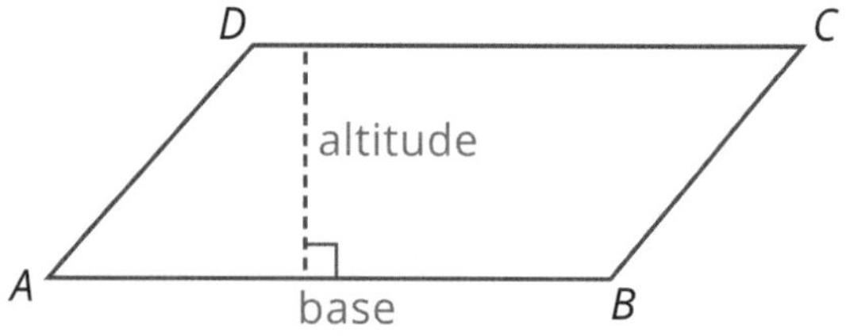

THEOREM 8-1

The area of a parallelogram is the product of any base and the altitude to that base:

$A = bh$

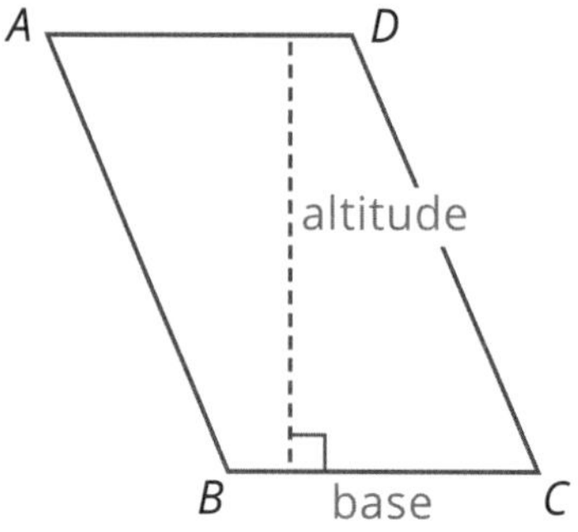

Given: $\square RSTU$ with $RS = b$ = base
$\overline{SX} \perp \overline{UT}$ and $SX = h$ = altitude

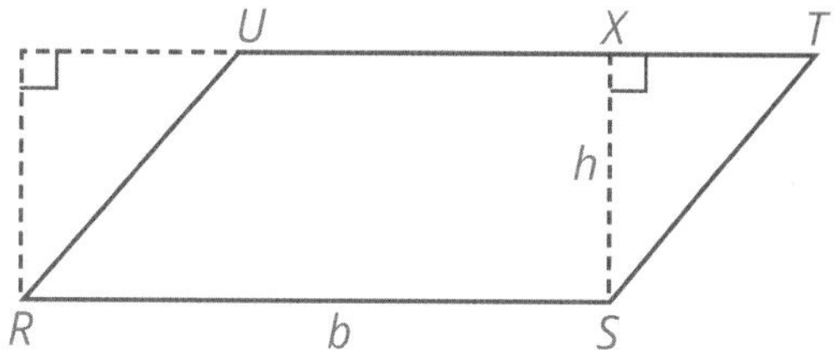

To Prove: Area of $\square RSTU = bh$

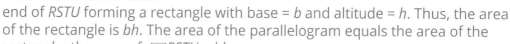

Outline of Proof: Move $\triangle STX$ to the other end of $RSTU$ forming a rectangle with base = b and altitude = h. Thus, the area of the rectangle is bh. The area of the parallelogram equals the area of the rectangle; the area of $\square RSTU = bh$.

Find the area of a parallelogram if a base and corresponding altitude have the indicated lengths.

1.26 Base $3\frac{1}{2}$ feet, altitude $\frac{3}{4}$ feet — Area = ____________

1.27 Base 8 inches, altitude 4 inches — Area = ____________

1.28 Base $1\frac{1}{2}$ feet, altitude 6 inches — Area = ____________

1.29 Base x yards, altitude y feet — Area = ____________

Find the area of $\square ABCD$ given m $\angle A = 30°$ and the following measures.

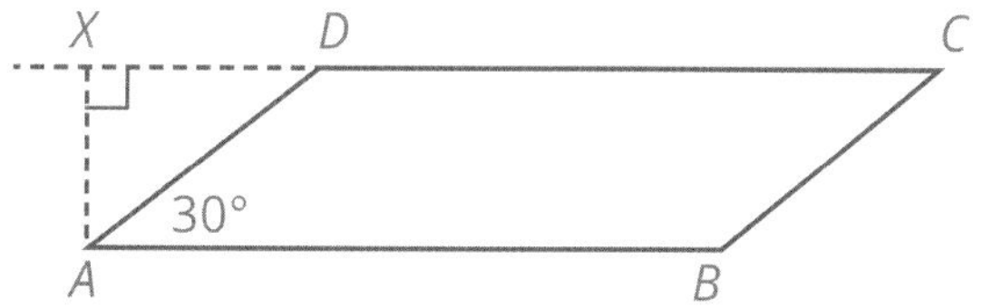

1.30 $AB = 10$ in. $AD = 6$ in. Area = ____________

1.31 $AB = 6$ ft. $AX = 3\sqrt{3}$ ft. Area = ____________

1.32 $AD = 4\sqrt{3}$ in. $AB = 8$ in. Area = ____________

1.33 $AX = 3$ ft. $AB = 4\sqrt{2}$ ft. Area = ____________

Complete the following activities.

1.34 Find the area of a parallelogram with sides of 12 inches and 8 inches if one of the angles is 120°.

____

1.35 A parallelogram with sides of 6 and 10 has an area of $30\sqrt{2}$. Find the measure of each angle of the parallelogram.

____

1.36 If the area of a parallelogram is to remain constant, what change must take place in the base if the altitude is multiplied by three?

a. ______________________________

If the altitude is divided by two? b. ______________________________

TRIANGLE

Theorem 8–2 will prove a formula for finding the area of triangles.

THEOREM 8-2

The area of a triangle is one-half the product of the length of a base and the altitude to that base:

$A = \frac{1}{2}bh$

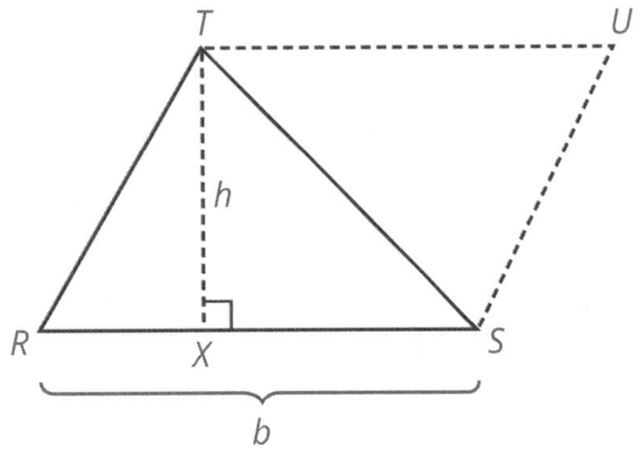

Given: $\triangle RST$ with $RS = b$, $\overline{TX} \perp \overline{RS}$, and $TX = h$ = altitude

To Prove: Area of $\triangle RST$ $\frac{1}{2}$ $= bh$

Outline of Proof:

Use auxiliary lines to complete the parallelogram shown. $\overline{TS}$, the diagonal of the parallelogram, divides it into two congruent triangles whose areas are equal.

The area of $\triangle RST$ would be $\frac{1}{2}$ the area of the parallelogram. The area of the parallelogram is bh; therefore, the area of $\triangle RST = \frac{1}{2}bh$.

Any side of the triangle can be considered its base. The altitude of the triangle to that base is the height in our formula.

Theorem 8–2 has two very useful corollaries.

Corollary 1: The area of an equilateral triangle with side of length s is one-fourth the product of the square of s and $\sqrt{3}$: $A = \frac{1}{4}s^2\sqrt{3}$.

Corollary 2: The area of a rhombus is one-half the product of the lengths of its diagonals: $A = \frac{1}{2}d_1d_2$.

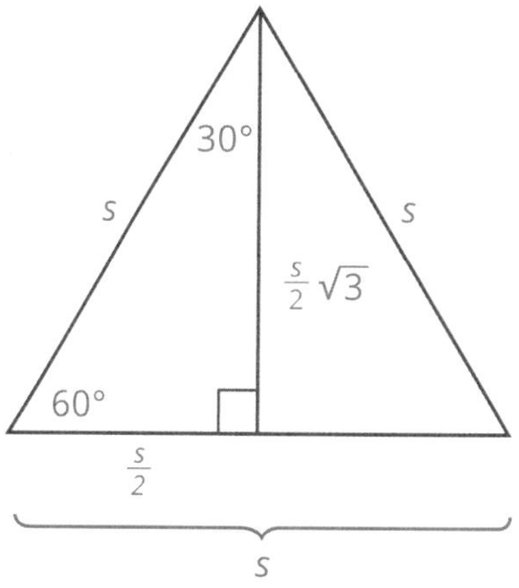

Proof of Corollary 1: Take an equilateral triangle with side s. The altitude of the triangle would be $\frac{1}{2}s\sqrt{3}$ because of the 30°-60°-90° relationship. Using the formula for area of a triangle, we then have

$A = \frac{1}{2}bh$

$A = \frac{1}{2}(s)\frac{1}{2}s\sqrt{3}$

$A = \frac{1}{4}s^2\sqrt{3}$

Complete these activities.

1.37 Write a paragraph proof for Corollary 2. (Hint: Draw the diagonals of the rhombus. What kind of triangles are formed? Add the areas of the triangles to get the area of the rhombus.)

The length of the base of the triangle is b, the length of the corresponding altitude is h, and the area is A. Find the missing part.

	b	h	A
1.38	4 in.	6 in.	________
1.39	________	5 in.	10 sq. in.
1.40	5 ft.	________	12 sq. ft.
1.41	$2\sqrt{3}$ in.	$3\sqrt{3}$ in.	________

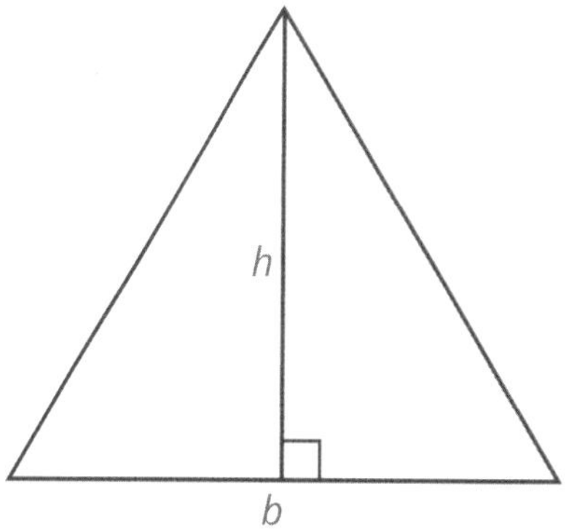

The lengths of the sides of a right **triangle are *a* and *b*, and the hypotenuse is *c*. Find the area of the triangle.**

1.42 $a = 6$ in. $b = 4$ in. $A =$ __________

1.43 $a = 5$ ft. $c = 13$ ft. $A =$ __________

1.44 $b = 2$ in. $c = 6$ in. $A =$ __________

1.45 $a = 2\sqrt{3}$ ft. $c = 4$ ft. $A =$ __________

1.46 $a = 5\sqrt{2}$ cm $b = 4\sqrt{2}$ cm $A =$ __________

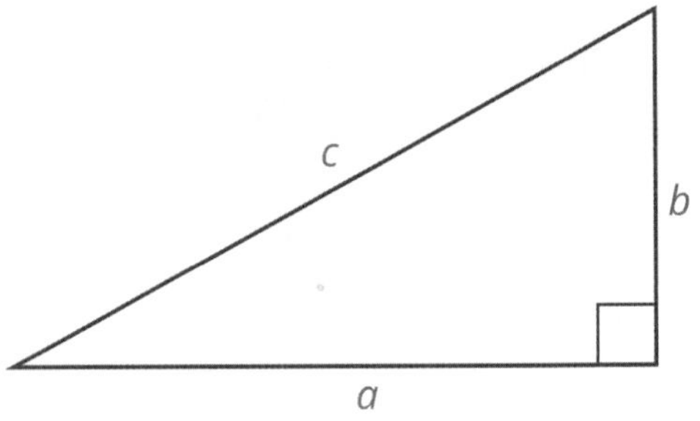

Think of an equilateral triangle in which the length of a side is *s*, the perimeter (distance around the triangle) is *p*, and the area is *A*. Find the missing parts.

	s	*p*	*A*
1.47	6 in.	a. ________	b. ________
1.48	5 in.	a. ________	b. ________
1.49	a. ________	12 ft.	b. ________
1.50	a. ________	b. ________	$9\sqrt{3}$ sq. ft.
1.51	a. ________	30 ft.	b. ________

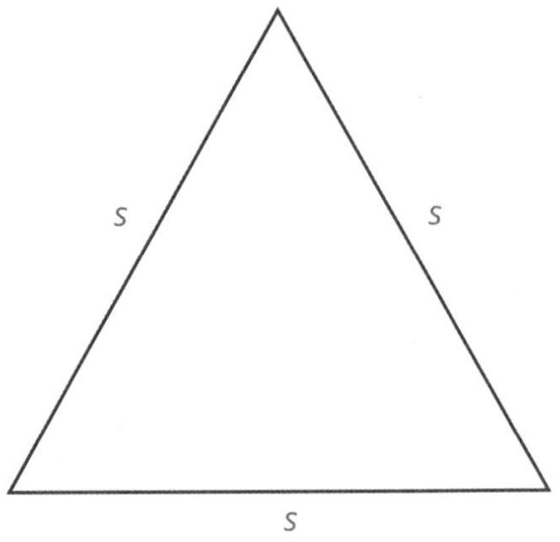

1.52 Find the area of a rhombus with diagonals 9 ft. and 12 ft. ____________________

1.53 Find the area of a rhombus with sides 13 in. and one diagonal 10 in. long.

____

1.54 The shorter diagonal of a rhombus has the same length as a side. Find the area of the rhombus if the longer diagonal is 12 in. long.

____

TRAPEZOID

Any side of a rectangle, triangle, or parallelogram can be taken as the base, but only the parallel sides of a trapezoid are called bases. Remember that the altitude of a trapezoid is a segment perpendicular from any point in one base to a point in the line containing the other base.

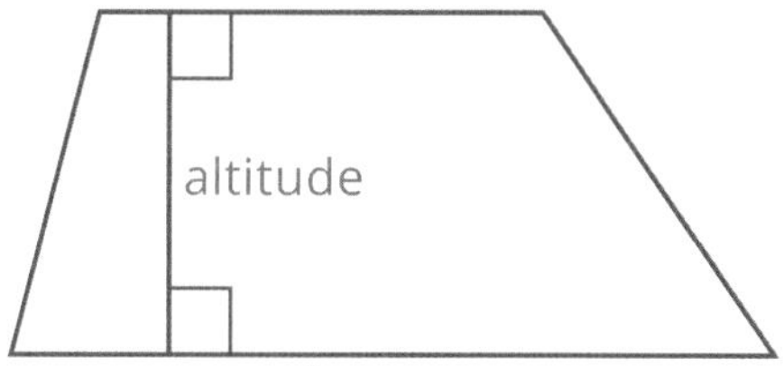

Theorem 8–3 proves the formula for the area of a trapezoid.

> **THEOREM 8-3**
> The area of a trapezoid is one-half the product of the length of an altitude and the sum of the lengths of the bases:
> $A = \frac{1}{2}h(b_1 + b_2)$.

Given: Trapezoid *ABCD* with $AB = b_1$, $DC = b_2$, and $\overline{DX} \perp \overline{AB}$; $DX = h$

To Prove: Area of $ABCD = \frac{1}{2}h(b_1 + b_2)$

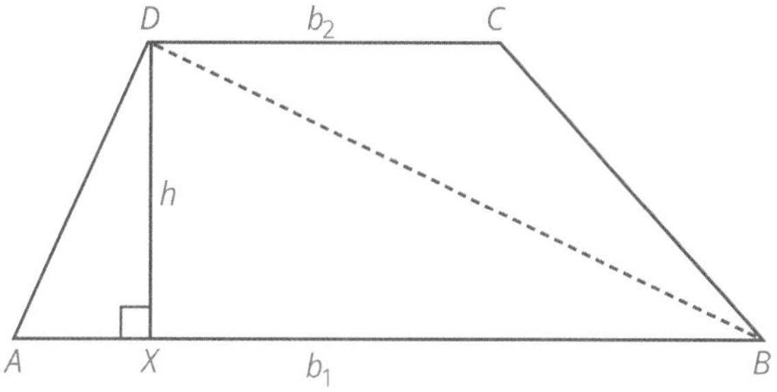

STATEMENT	REASON
1. Trapezoid *ABCD* with $AB = b_1$, $DC = b_2$, $DX = h$	1. Given
2. Draw $\overline{DB}$	2. Auxiliary line
3. Area $\triangle ABD = \frac{1}{2}b_1h$ Area $\triangle DBC = \frac{1}{2}b_2h$	3. Theorem 8–2, area of triangle
4. Area $ABCD$ = Area $\triangle ABD$ + Area $\triangle DBC$	4. Area addition postulate
5. Area $ABCD = \frac{1}{2}b_1h + \frac{1}{2}b_2h$	5. Substitution
6. Area $ABCD = \frac{1}{2}h(b_1 + b_2)$	6. Algebra

Think of a trapezoid with b_1 and b_2 as the length of the bases, h as the length of the altitude, and A as the area. Find the missing parts.

	b_1	b_2	h	A
1.55	10	6	4	________
1.56	6	________	2	18
1.57	________	5	3	12
1.58	5	3	________	24
1.59	$\frac{1}{2}$	$\frac{1}{4}$	1	________
1.60	$5\sqrt{2}$	$3\sqrt{2}$	________	$4\sqrt{6}$

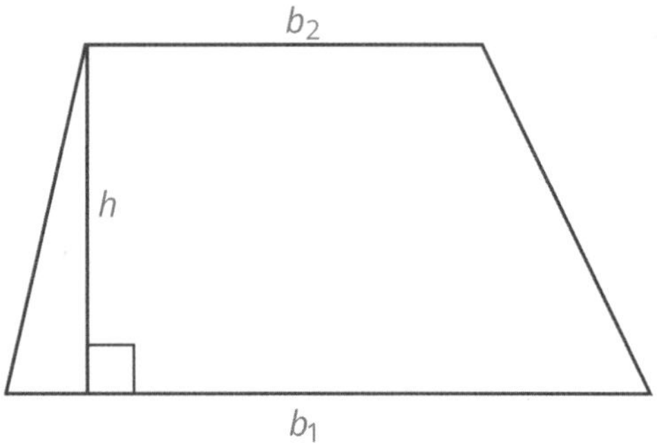

Complete the following activities.

1.61 An isosceles trapezoid has base angles equal to 45° and bases of lengths 6 and 12. Find the area of the trapezoid.

____

1.62 Find the area of a trapezoid if the altitude is 6" and the median is 8".

____

1.63 Find the area of the trapezoid shown.

A = ________________________

1.64 Find the area of the trapezoid shown.

A = ________________________

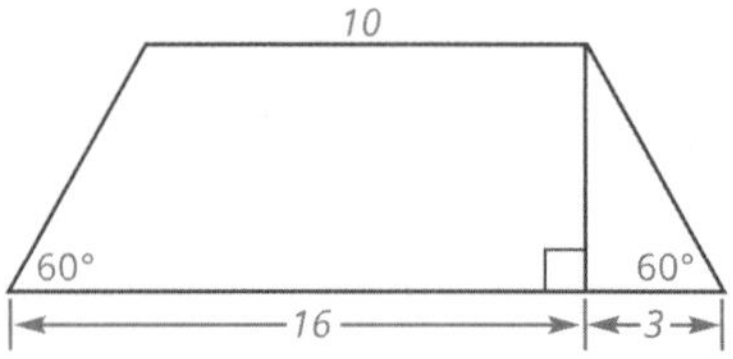

1.65 Find the area of the trapezoid shown.

A = ________________________

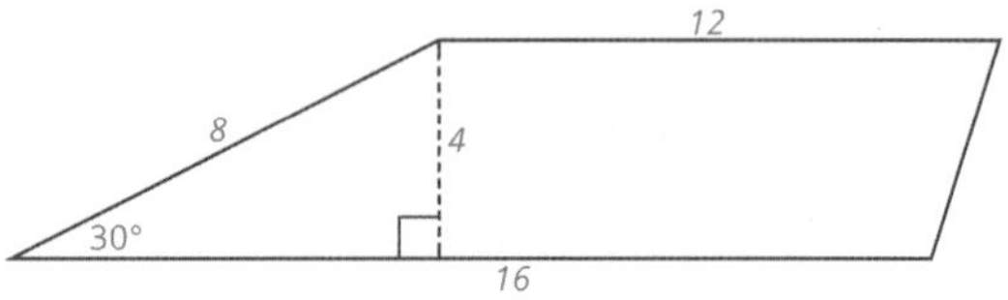

REGULAR POLYGON

Recall that a regular polygon has all sides equal and all angles equal. An equilateral triangle is a regular polygon. A square is a regular polygon. We already know formulas for area of a triangle and a square. We shall now find formulas for the area of any regular polygon. First we need some definitions for parts of a regular polygon.

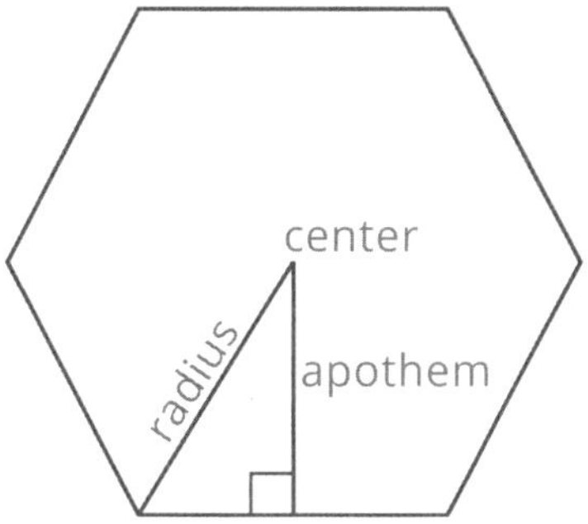

> **DEFINITIONS**
>
> **Center of a regular polygon** is the common center of its inscribed and circumscribed circles.
>
> **Radius of a regular polygon** is the distance from the center of the polygon to a vertex.
>
> **Apothem of a regular polygon** is the perpendicular distance from the center of the polygon to a side.
>
> **Central angle of a regular polygon** is an angle whose vertex is the center of the polygon and whose sides contain consecutive vertices of the polygon.

Corollary: A central angle of a regular n-gon has a measure equal to $\frac{360°}{n}$.

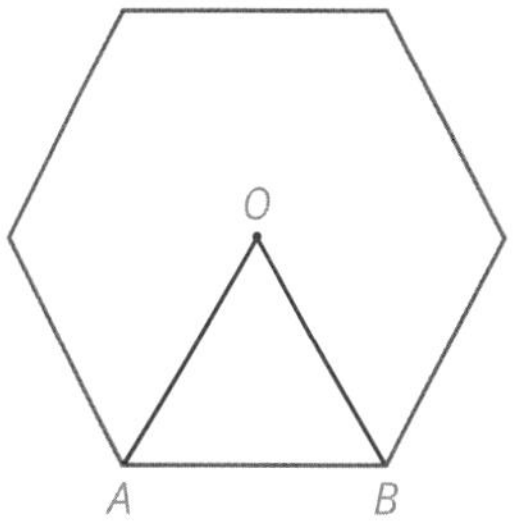

$\angle AOB$ is central $\angle$.

If we draw the radii to all the vertices of a regular polygon of n sides, we divide it into n congruent triangles. A formula for the area bounded by a regular polygon is derived in Theorem 8–4.

> **THEOREM 8-4**
>
> The area of a regular polygon is one-half the product of the apothem and the perimeter: $A = \frac{1}{2}ap$

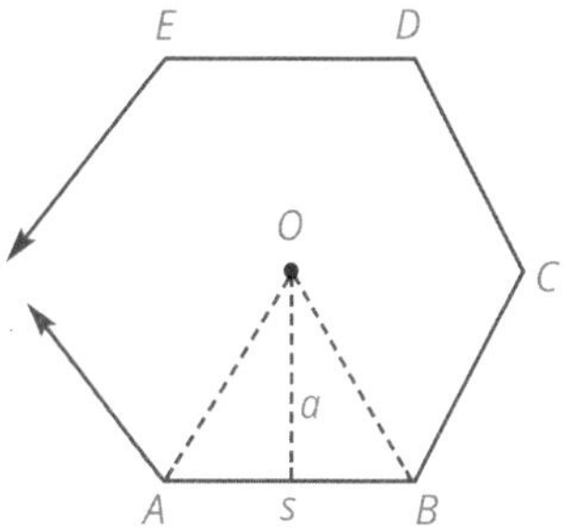

Given: Regular n-gon with vertices A, B, C, ..., apothem a, sides of length s, perimeter p, and area A.

To Prove: $A = \frac{1}{2}ap$

Outline of Proof:

If all radii are drawn to the vertices, then the n-gon is divided into n congruent triangles (SSS). The area of one of these triangles is $\frac{1}{2}sa$. The area of the n-gon is $n(\frac{1}{2}sa)$ or $\frac{1}{2}a(ns)$. Since $ns = p$, the area of the n-gon is $\frac{1}{2}ap$.

Find the area of an equilateral triangle (regular 3-gon) with the given measurement.

1.66 6-inch side $A =$ ____________

1.67 6-inch radius $A =$ ____________

1.68 6-inch apothem $A =$ ____________

1.69 9-inch perimeter $A =$ ____________

1.70 3-inch radius $A =$ ____________

Find the area of a regular hexagon with the given measurement.

1.71 4-inch side $A =$ ____________

1.72 48-inch perimeter $A =$ ____________

1.73 $2\sqrt{3}$ apothem $A =$ ____________

1.74 6-inch radius $A =$ ____________

Complete the following activities.

1.75 Find the area of a regular octagon with apothem *K* and side of 10.

$A =$ ____________

1.76 Find the length of a side of a regular hexagon with area equal to that of an equilateral triangle with perimeter of 36 inches.

$s =$ ____________

AREA COMPARISONS

Many times we would like to find a way to compare the area of one polygon with that of a similar polygon. Recall that similar polygons are those that have corresponding angles equal and corresponding sides in proportion.

We shall first prove a theorem that compares areas of similar triangles. Remember that the ratio of corresponding altitudes of similar triangles is equal to the ratio of corresponding sides.

> **THEOREM 8-5**
>
> The ratio of the area of two similar triangles is equal to the square of the ratio of the length of any two corresponding sides.

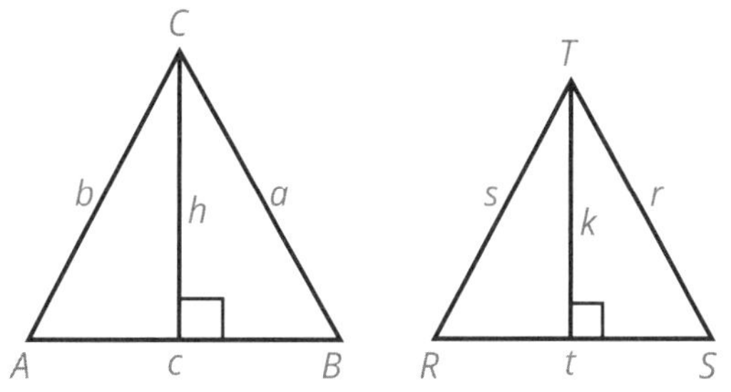

Given: $\triangle ABC \sim \triangle RST$

To Prove: $\frac{\text{Area } \triangle ABC}{\text{Area } \triangle RST} = (\frac{c}{t})^2 = (\frac{a}{r})^2 = (\frac{b}{s})^2$

Outline of Proof: Area $\triangle ABC = \frac{1}{2}ch$,

Area $\triangle RST = \frac{1}{2}tk$

$\frac{\text{Area } \triangle ABC}{\text{Area } \triangle RST} = \frac{\frac{1}{2}ch}{\frac{1}{2}tk} = \frac{ch}{tk}$

and $\frac{c}{t} = \frac{h}{k}$; therefore,

$\frac{\text{Area } \triangle ABC}{\text{Area } \triangle RST} = (\frac{c}{t})(\frac{c}{t}) = (\frac{c}{t})^2$

Since $\frac{c}{t} = \frac{a}{r} = \frac{b}{s}$,

$\frac{\text{Area } \triangle ABC}{\text{Area } \triangle RST} = (\frac{c}{t})^2 = (\frac{a}{r})^2 = (\frac{b}{s})^2 = (\frac{h}{k})^2$

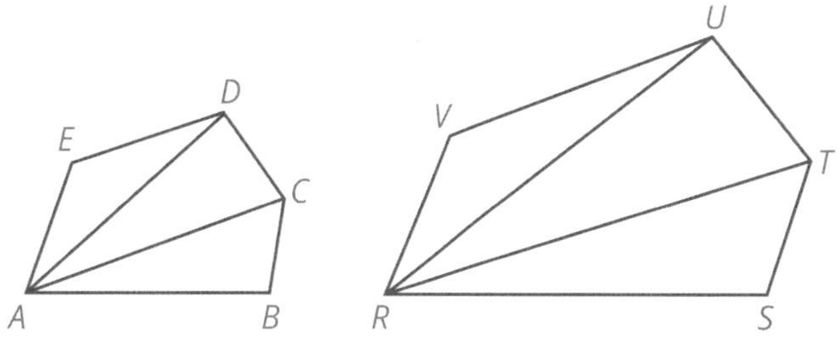

Pictured are two similar polygons. If we draw the diagonals from vertex *A* and from vertex *R*, we divide the polygons into triangles that seem to be similar. This fact suggests the next postulate.

> **POSTULATE 21**
>
> P21: If two polygons are similar, they can be separated into an equal number of triangles. These triangles will be similar to one another and in corresponding positions.

With Postulate 21 and Theorem 8-5 we can now prove a theorem about the areas of similar polygons.

> **THEOREM 8-6**
>
> The ratio of the areas of two similar polygons is equal to the square of the ratio of the lengths of any pair of corresponding sides.

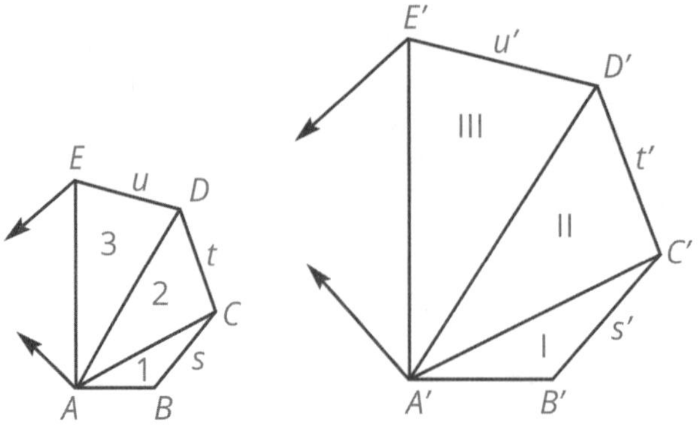

Given: *n*-gon *ABCD*... similar to *n*-gon *A'B'C'D'*... with corresponding sides $s, s'; t, t'; u, u'$; and so on.

To Prove: $\frac{\text{Area } ABCD}{\text{Area } A'B'C'D' \ldots} = (\frac{s}{s'})^2$

Outline of Proof: By Postulate 21, $\frac{\text{Area } \triangle 1}{\text{Area } \triangle \text{I}} = (\frac{s}{s'})^2$, $\frac{\text{Area } \triangle 2}{\text{Area } \triangle \text{II}} = (\frac{t}{t'})^2$, $\frac{\text{Area } \triangle 3}{\text{Area } \triangle \text{III}} = (\frac{u}{u'})^2$, and so on.

Also, since $\frac{s}{s'} = \frac{t}{t'} = \frac{u}{u'}$, then $(\frac{s}{s'})^2 = (\frac{t}{t'})^2 = (\frac{u}{u'})^2$.

By substitution, $\frac{\text{Area } \triangle 1}{\text{Area } \triangle \text{I}} = \frac{\text{Area } \triangle 2}{\text{Area } \triangle \text{II}} = \frac{\text{Area } \triangle 3}{\text{Area } \triangle \text{III}} = \ldots = (\frac{s}{s'})^2$.

By using the numerator-denominator sum property of proportions,

$$\frac{\text{Area } \triangle 1 + \text{Area } \triangle 2 + \text{Area } \triangle 3 + \ldots}{\text{Area } \triangle \text{I} + \text{Area } \triangle \text{II} + \text{Area } \triangle \text{III} \ldots} = (\frac{s}{s'})^2.$$

Then, by the area addition postulate, $\frac{\text{Area } ABCD}{\text{Area } A'B'C'D' \ldots} = (\frac{s}{s'})^2$.

Complete the following activities.

1.77 Two similar polygons have areas of 50 and 100 sq. in. Find the ratio of the length of a pair of corresponding sides.

____

1.78 One side of a triangle is 15 inches, and the area of the triangle is 90 sq. inches. Find the area of a similar triangle in which the corresponding side is 9 inches.

____

1.79 The shortest side of a polygon of area 196 sq. in. is 4 in. long. Find the area of a similar polygon whose shortest side is 8 in. long.

____

1.80 The sides of a quadrilateral are 3, 4, 5, and 6. Find the length of the sides of a similar quadrilateral whose area is 9 times as great.

____

1.81 Two similar hexagons have areas 36 sq. in. and 64 sq. in. What is the ratio of a pair of corresponding sides?

____

1.82 A circle has a radius of 6 in. Find the ratio of the areas of its inscribed and circumscribed equilateral triangles.

____

Find the ratio of the area of triangle *XBY* **to the area of triangle** *ABC* **for the given measurements, if** $\overline{XY} \parallel \overline{AC}$.

1.83 $BY = 2$ $BC = 4$ ______________________

1.84 $XY = 2$ $AC = 3$ ______________________

1.85 $BY = 3$ $YC = 2$ ______________________

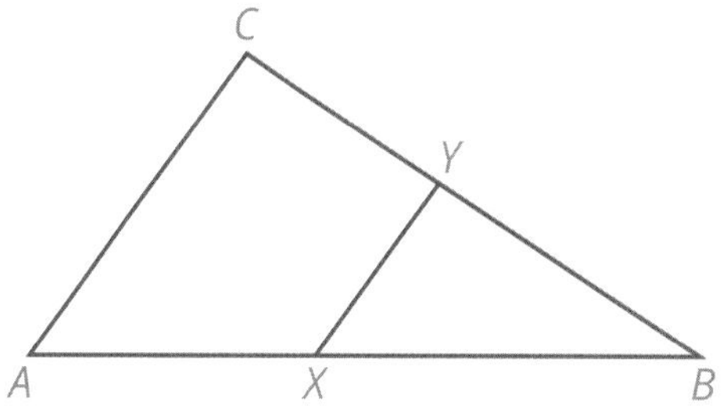

Review the material in this section in preparation for the Self Test. The Self Test will check your mastery of this particular section. The items missed on this Self Test will indicate specific areas where restudy is needed for mastery.

SELF TEST 1

Match the formula with the polygon (each answer, 2 points).

1.01	_______	Area of rectangle	a. $A = \frac{1}{2}bh$
1.02	_______	Area of parallelogram	b. $A = \frac{1}{2}h(b_1 + b_2)$
1.03	_______	Area of trapezoid	c. $A = \frac{1}{2}ap$
1.04	_______	Area of square	d. $A = \frac{1}{4}s^2\sqrt{3}$
1.05	_______	Area of rhombus	e. $A = bh$
1.06	_______	Area of regular polygon	f. $A = \frac{1}{2}d_1d_2$
1.07	_______	Area of triangle	g. $A = s^2$
1.08	_______	Area of equilateral triangle	

Complete the following items (each answer, 4 points).

1.09 Find the area of a regular pentagon with side equal to 3 and apothem equal to K.

____

1.010 Find the area of a regular hexagon with a 48-inch perimeter.

____

1.011 Find the area of a triangle with base of 10 inches and altitude to the base of 16 inches.

____

1.012 Find the area of a parallelogram with sides of 6 and 12 and an angle of 60°.

____

1.013 Find the area of a trapezoid with bases of 8 and 16 and a height of 10.

____

1.014 Find the area of an equilateral triangle with a side of 6 inches.

____

1.015 Two polygons are similar with the longest side of one 8 and the longest side of the other 10. Find the ratio of the areas.

____

1.016 The sides of a rhombus with angle of 60° are 6 inches. Find the area of the rhombus.

____

1.017 An isosceles trapezoid has bases of 4 and 10. If the base angle is 45°, find the area.

____

Find the area of the following figures (each answer, 4 points).

1.018 $A =$ ____________________

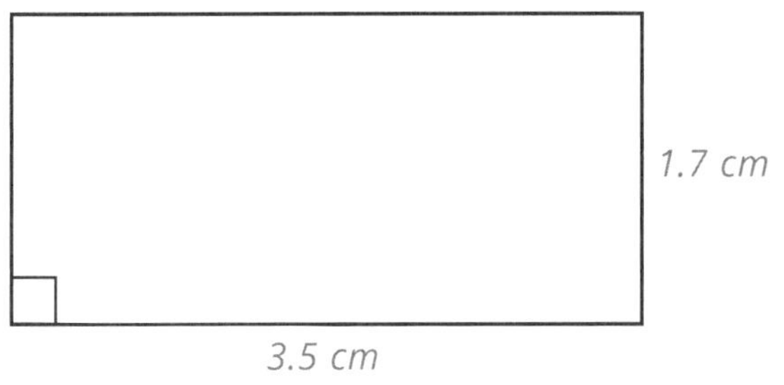

1.019 $A =$ ____________________

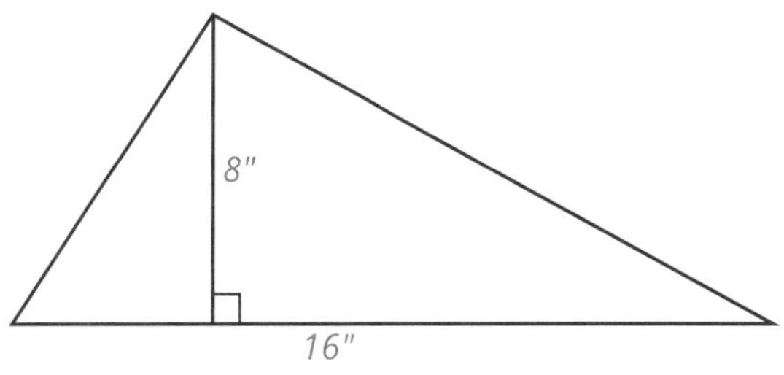

1.020 $A =$ ____________________

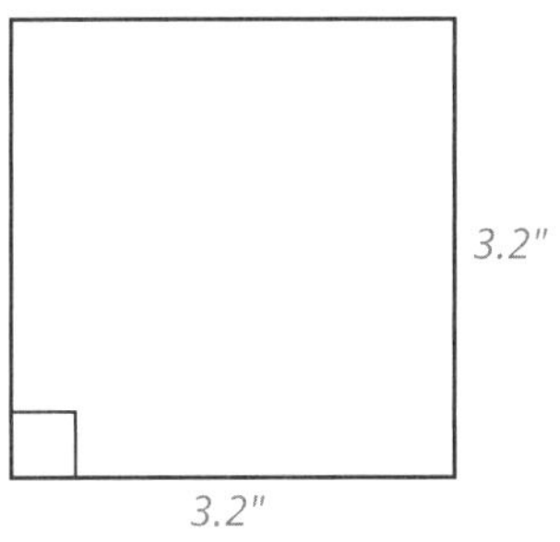

1.021 $A =$ ____________________

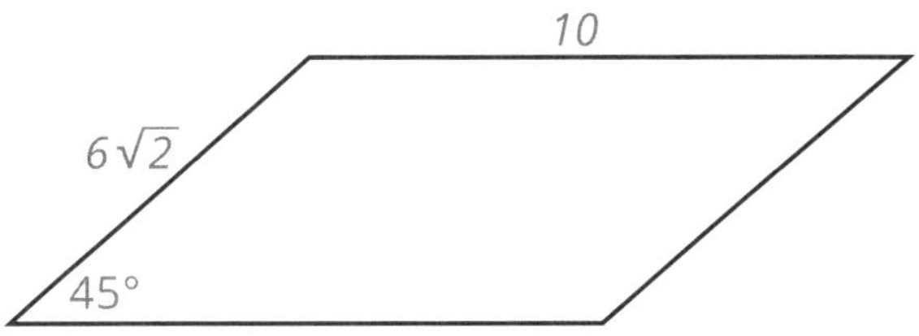

Solve the following problem (5 points).

1.022 Find the number of gallons of paint needed to cover the sides of the building shown with two coats of paint if one gallon covers 350 square feet. Disregard windows and doors. Round to the nearest gallon.

____

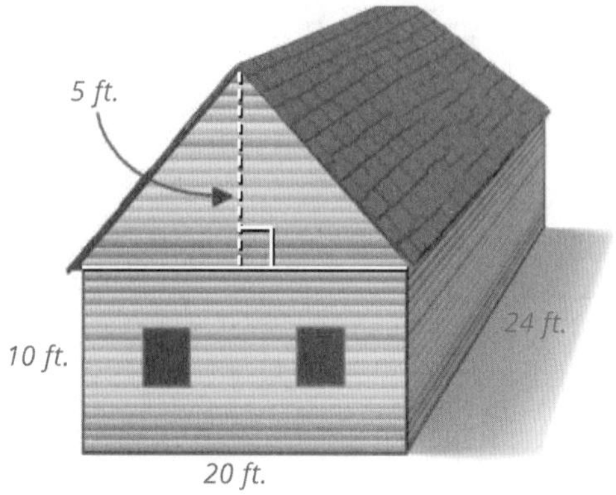

59/73 **SCORE** ____________ **TEACHER** ____________ ____________
initials date

2. CIRCLES

One of the most common geometric shapes we use is the circle. We shall now derive formulas for the area and circumference of circles and special parts of circles.

Section Objectives

Review these objectives. When you have completed this section, you should be able to:

4. Calculate the circumference of a circle.
5. Calculate the area of a circle.
6. Calculate the area of a sector of a circle.
7. Calculate the area of a segment of a circle.

CIRCUMFERENCE AND π

In this section we shall define the circumference of a circle and then show that the circumference of a circle is found by using the formula $C = 2\pi r$. We also must give a definition for π. To do these things, we must have some understanding of the idea of limits. We shall approach the idea of a limit by inductive reasoning.

Consider several congruent circles. Inscribe regular polygons with increasing numbers of sides in these circles.

Notice several facts:

1. The apothem, a, of the polygon increases, with its limit the radius of the circle: $a \to r$ (read, a approaches r as its limit).
2. The perimeter, p, of the polygon increases, with its limit the circumference of the circle: $p \to C$.
3. The area, A_p, of the polygon increases with its limit the area of the circle: $A_p \to A_o$. With these basic ideas of limits, we now define the circumference and area of a circle in terms of limit.

DEFINITIONS

Circumference of a circle (C) is the limit of the perimeters of the inscribed regular polygons. It is a positive number.

Area of a circle (A_o) is the limit of the areas of the inscribed regular polygons. It is a positive number.

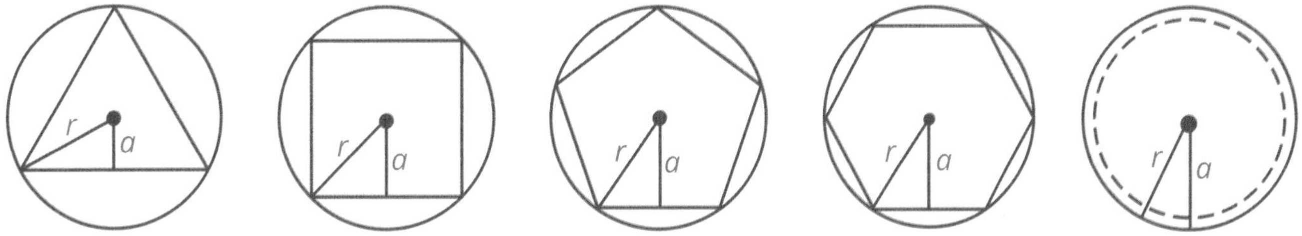

On the basis of these definitions an important relationship can be proved between the circumference and the diameter of any circle.

> **THEOREM 8-7**
>
> The ratio of the circumference to the diameter is the same for all circles.

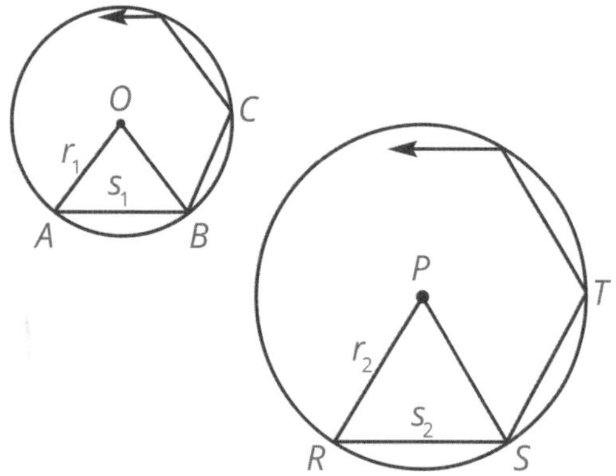

Given: Circle O with radius r_1, diameter d_1, and circumference C_1.

Circle P with radius r_2, diameter d_2, and circumference C_2.

To Prove: $\frac{C_1}{d_1} = \frac{C_2}{d_2}$

Outline of Proof:

Inscribe in each circle a regular n-gon with n the same for both circles. Let s_1 and s_2 be sides of polygons. $\angle O = \angle P$, for both have a measure of $\frac{360°}{n}$. $\angle A = \angle R$, for both have a measure of $\frac{1}{2}(180° - \frac{360°}{n})$.

Since $\triangle AOB$ and $\triangle RPS$ are isosceles triangles, then

$\triangle AOB \sim \triangle RPS$ and $\frac{s_1}{r_1} = \frac{s_2}{r_2}$ and $\frac{ns_1}{r_1} = \frac{ns_2}{r_2}$. Now ns_1 and ns_2 are the perimeters p_1 and p_2 of the inscribed polygons, so $\frac{p_1}{r_1} = \frac{p_2}{r_2}$.

Now as n increases, $p_1 \to C_1$ and $p_2 \to C_2$. Therefore, $\frac{p_1}{r_1} \to \frac{C_1}{r_1}$ and $\frac{p_2}{r_2} \to \frac{C_2}{r_2}$. Since we have shown $\frac{p_1}{r_1} = \frac{p_2}{r_2}$, we can reasonably assume that their limits are equal.

Therefore, $\frac{C_1}{r_1} = \frac{C_2}{r_2}$ or $\frac{C_1}{2r_1} = \frac{C_2}{2r_2}$ or $\frac{C_1}{d_1} = \frac{C_2}{d_2}$.

Since the number $\frac{C}{d}$ is the same for all circles whatever size the circles may be, we give this number a special name, π. This symbol, called *pi* and pronounced *pie*, is a letter from the Greek alphabet. In other words, π is defined to be the ratio of the circumference of a circle to the diameter of the circle. π is an irrational number. The relationship between C and d of any circle is such that when d is rational, C is not rational, and vice versa.

For practical problems we can approximate π as 3.14, $\frac{22}{7}$, or 3.1416. Two useful forms of our definition are $C = \pi d$ or $C = 2\pi r$. These equations are formulas for finding the circumference of a circle.

Notice some interesting facts about π:

a. In the Old Testament (I Kings 7:23) the value of the circumference/diameter ratio, or π, is given as 3.

b. Archimedes (287–212 BC) showed the value of the circumference/diameter ratio to lie between $3\frac{1}{7}$ and $3\frac{10}{71}$.

c. The symbol, π, for the circumference/diameter ratio was not used until the eighteenth century.

d. The value of π correct to 14 decimal places is 3.14159265358979.

e. Electronic computers have computed π correct to over ten trillion places.

f. π is used by biologists investigating laws of bacterial growth. Insurance actuaries use π in computing probabilities.

When finding the exact circumference of a circle, we do not replace π by an approximation but rather leave π in the answer.

Find the exact circumference of a circle with the given radius.

2.1 5 inches $C =$ ____________

2.2 7 feet $C =$ ____________

2.3 $3\frac{1}{2}$ cm $C =$ ____________

2.4 $3\frac{1}{4}$ inches $C =$ ____________

2.5 $\frac{x}{2}$ miles $C =$ ____________

2.6 36 inches $C =$ ____________

Find the approximate value of the circumference of a circle with the given radius. Use $\pi = 3.14$. Round your results to one more digit than the total number of digits in the given radius.

2.7 4 inches $C =$ ____________

2.8 6 ft. $C =$ ____________

2.9 5.1 cm $C =$ ____________

2.10 4.6 inches $C =$ ____________

2.11 3.21 ft. $C =$ ____________

2.12 6.53 cm $C =$ ____________

Find the radius of a circle with the given circumference.

2.13 12π in. $r =$ ____________

2.14 15π ft. $r =$ ____________

2.15 $6\sqrt{2}\pi$ in. $r =$ ____________

2.16 $5\sqrt{3}\pi$ cm $r =$ ____________

2.17 $8t\pi$ ft. $r =$ ____________

2.18 π yds. $r =$ ____________

Complete the following activities. Use an approximation for π only when instructed to do so.

2.19 How far does a rolling wheel with a 10-inch radius travel in ten revolutions?

____

2.20 Find the radius of a rolling wheel that makes six revolutions in traveling a distance of 66 ft. (Use $\pi = \frac{22}{7}$)

____

2.21 Given a square of perimeter 4, find the ratio of the circumference of the circumscribed circle to the circumference of the inscribed circle.

____

2.22 Find the radius of a circle whose circumference is equal to the sum of the circumferences of two circles with radii of 4 inches and 6 inches.

____

2.23 One man's waist has a diameter of 10 inches. A second man's waist has a diameter of 11 inches. How much longer is the second man's belt than the first man's belt? (Use $\pi = 3.14$)

____

2.24 Two boys run on a circular track that has a radius of 40 ft. One boy runs on the inside lane and the second boy runs 1 foot farther out. After 10 laps, how much farther has the boy on the outside run? (Use $\pi = 3.14$)

____

MATH 1008

LIFEPAC TEST

NAME ______________________

DATE ______________________

SCORE ______________________

80
100

MATH 1008: LIFEPAC TEST

Find the the following measures for these figures (each answer, 4 points).

1. Area of base ________________

2. Lateral area ________________

3. Total area ________________

4. Volume ________________

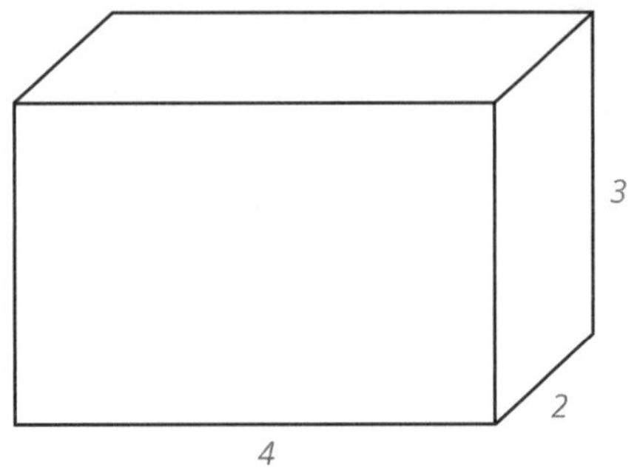

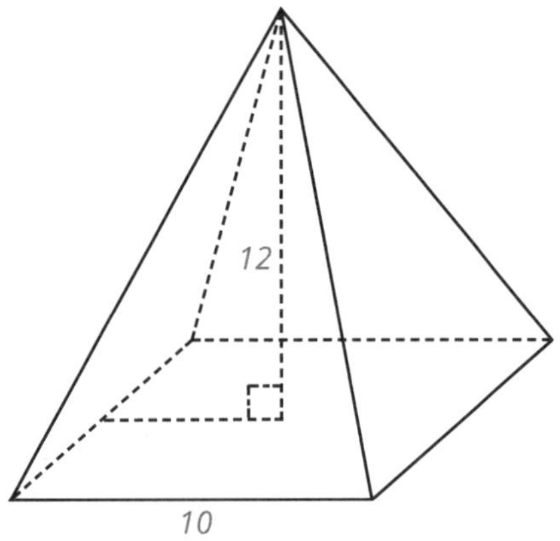

5. Slant height ________________

6. Lateral area ________________

7. Total area ________________

8. Volume ________________

9. Lateral area ______________________________

10. Total area ______________________________

11. Volume ______________________________

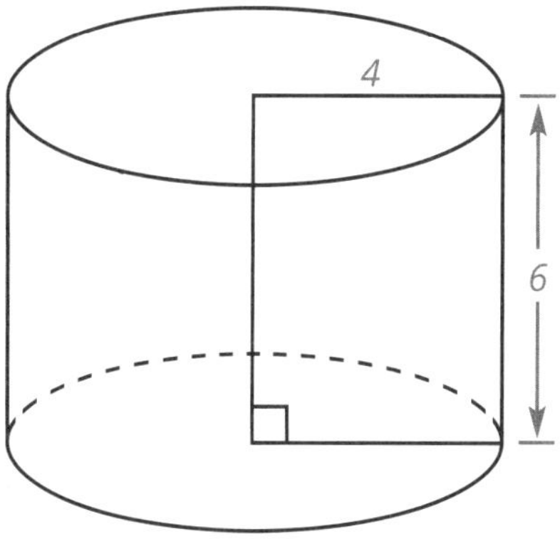

12. Slant height ______________________________

13. Lateral area ______________________________

14. Total area ______________________________

15. Volume ______________________________

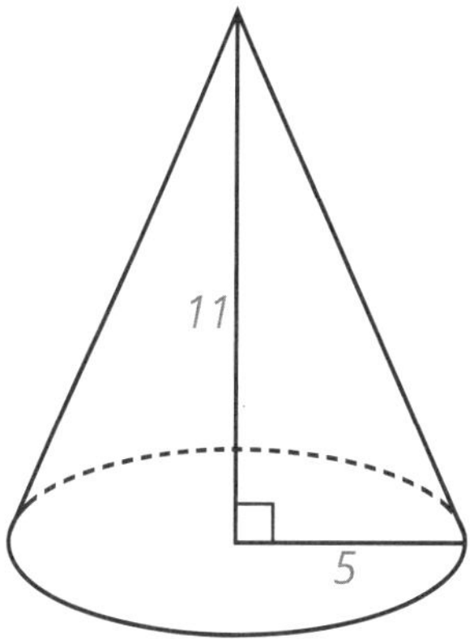

16. Surface area ______________________________

17. Volume ______________________________

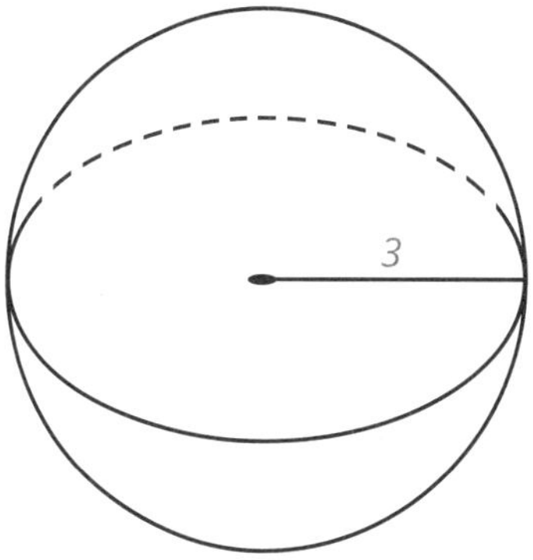

18. Area of circle ______________________

19. Area of sector *O-AXB* ______________________

20. Area of segment *AXB* ______________________

21. Circumference of circle ______________________

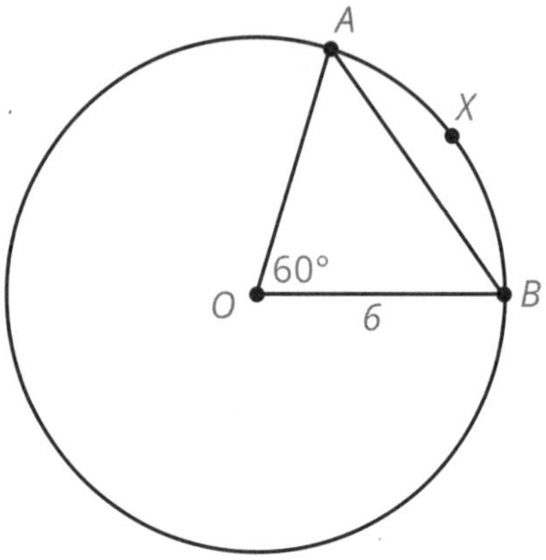

22. Apothem ______________________

23. Radius ______________________

24. Central angle ______________________

25. Area ______________________

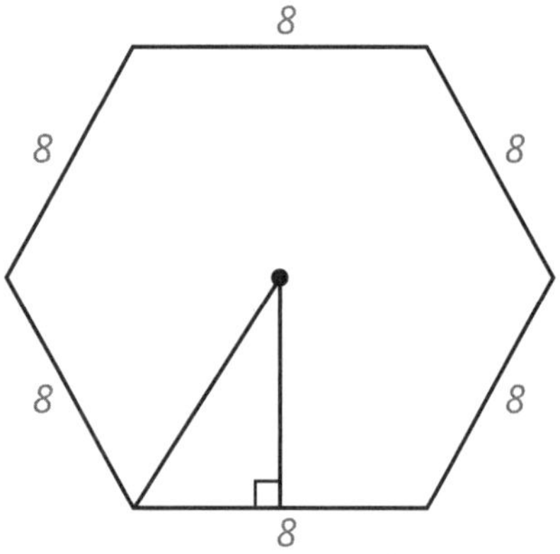

AREA OF CIRCLE

Our definition of the area of a circle and some clever thinking lead us to the formula for the area of a circle.

> **THEOREM 8-8**
>
> The area of a circle is the product of π and the square of the radius of the circle: $A = \pi r^2$.

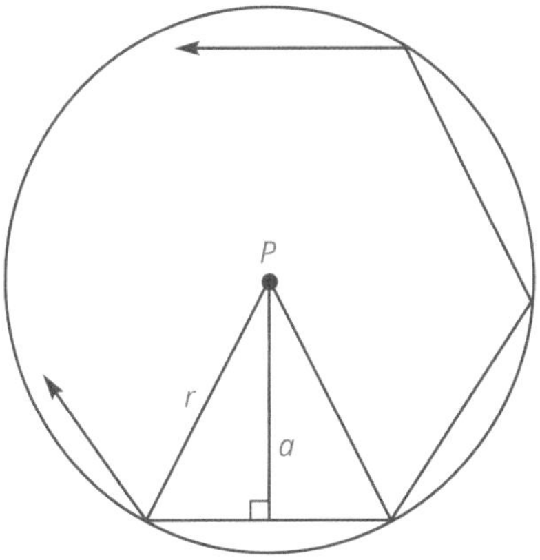

Given: Circle P with radius r and circumference C.

To Prove: $A = \pi r^2$

Outline of Proof:

Inscribe a regular n-gon in circle P. The area of the n-gon will be $A = \frac{1}{2}ap$.

As the number of sides of the n-gon increases without limit, $a \rightarrow r$ and $p \rightarrow C$. Therefore, area of n-gon $= \frac{1}{2}rC$.

By definition, area of n-gon $\rightarrow$ area of circle. Therefore, area of circle $= \frac{1}{2}rC$. Since $C = 2\pi r$, we then have A circle $= \frac{1}{2}r(2\pi r) = \pi r^2$.

Find the area of the circle with the given radius or diameter. (Use $\pi = 3.14$)

2.25 $r = 6$ $A =$ ____________ sq. units

2.26 $r = 4$ $A =$ ____________ sq. units

2.27 $r = 2$ $A =$ ____________ sq. units

2.28 $d = 10$ $A =$ ____________ sq. units

2.29 $d = 12$ $A =$ ____________ sq. units

2.30 $d = 13$ $A =$ ____________ sq. units

Find the exact area of a circle having the given circumference.

2.31 8π $A =$ ____________

2.32 3π $A =$ ____________

2.33 $4\sqrt{3}\pi$ $A =$ ____________

Complete the following activities.

2.34 Find the exact circumference of a circle with an area equal to 36π sq. in.

____

2.35 Find the area of a circle circumscribed about an equilateral triangle whose side is 18 inches long.

____

2.36 The radii of two circles are in the ratio of 3 to 1. Find the area of the smaller circle if the area of the larger circle is 27π sq. in.

____

2.37 Find the exact area of the region bounded by two concentric circles with radii 10 inches and 6 inches.

____

2.38 Find the radius of a circle whose area equals the sum of the areas of two circles with radii 2 and 3.

____

AREA OF SECTOR

In a previous Math LIFEPAC you learned that the measure of arc *AB* equals the measure of its central angle. If we take two circles with different radii but having the same central ∠, we get two arcs that have the same degree measure:

$$m\,\widehat{AB} = 60° \text{ and } m\,\widehat{RS} = 60°.$$

We are now going to be concerned about the *length of arcs*. Observation seems to tell us that the length of $\widehat{RS}$ is greater than the length of $\widehat{AB}$. To find the length of an arc, we must find what part of the circumference of the circle it is and then multiply the circumference by that fractional part. In dealing with length of arcs, an entire circle may conveniently be considered an arc of degree measure 360°. We can then tell what fractional part of the circle our arc is: $\frac{m\,\widehat{AB}}{360°}$. The length of arc *AB* is $\frac{m\,\widehat{AB}}{360°}$ times the circumference of the circle. Since the circumference of a circle is $2\pi r$, the length of $AB = \frac{m\,\widehat{AB}}{360°}(2\pi r)$.

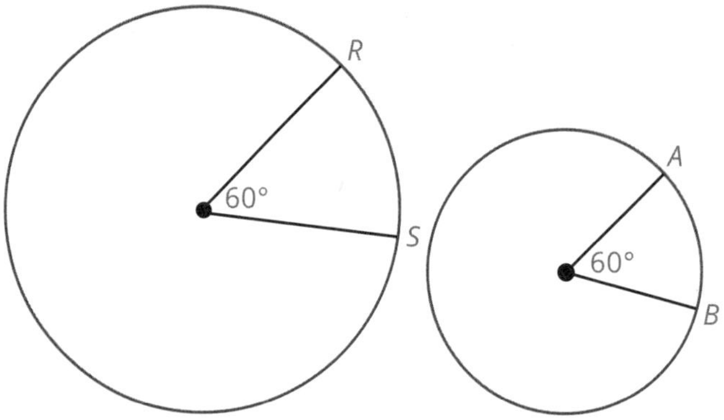

Model 1: Find the exact length of a 60° arc in a circle of radius 6".

Solution: length of arc $= \frac{60}{360}(2\pi \cdot 6)$
$= 2\pi$ inches

Model 2: Find the approximate length of a 90° arc in a circle of radius 14 ft. (Use $\pi = \frac{22}{7}$)

Solution: length of arc $= \frac{90}{360}(2)(\frac{22}{7})(14)$
$= 22$ ft.

Express the required measurements in exact form.

2.39 Find the length of an arc of 40° in a circle with an 8" radius.

____

2.40 Find the radius of a circle in which a 30° arc is 2π inches long.

____

2.41 Find the degree measure of an arc 4π ft. long in a circle of radius 10 ft.

____

2.42 A bicycle wheel with radius 26" rotates through an arc that measures 80°. What is the length of the arc of the tire that touched the ground?

____

2.43 If the length of an arc is 12π inches and the radius of the circle is 10 inches, find the measure of the arc.

____

2.44 What part of the circumference is an arc whose measure is:

a. 1°? _______________ b. 30°? _______________ c. 45°? _______________

d. 60°? _______________ e. 90°? _______________

A *sector* of a circle is defined to be the region bounded by two radii and an arc of the circle. A good model for a sector would be a piece of pie, cake, or pizza.

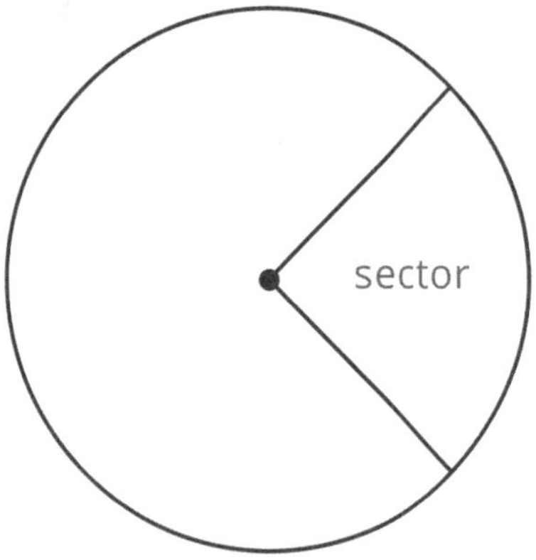

> **DEFINITION:**
>
> A **sector** is the portion of a circle bounded by two radii and one of the arcs they intercept.

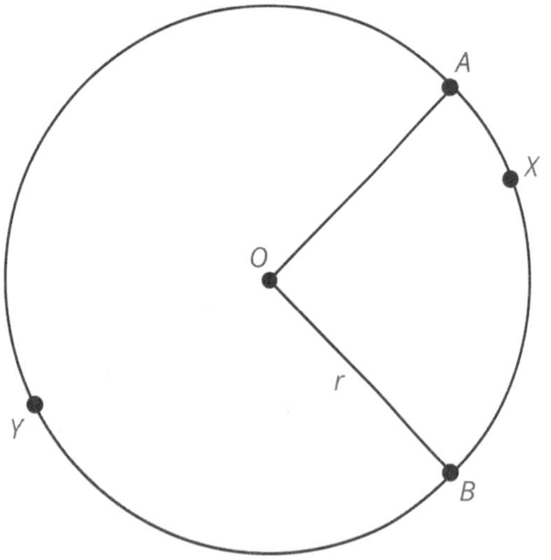

In circle *O*, *O-AXB* is a sector and *O-AYB* is a sector. *r* is the radius of both sectors. $\overset{\frown}{AXB}$ is the arc of sector *O-AXB*. $\overset{\frown}{AYB}$ is the arc of sector *O-AYB*.

To find the area of the sector we proceed as we did in finding the length of an arc. First, find out what fractional part of the circle the arc of the sector is by using the measure of the arc; then multiply this fractional part by the area of the circle.

$$\text{Area of sector} = \frac{m\overset{\frown}{AB}}{360°}(\pi r^2)$$

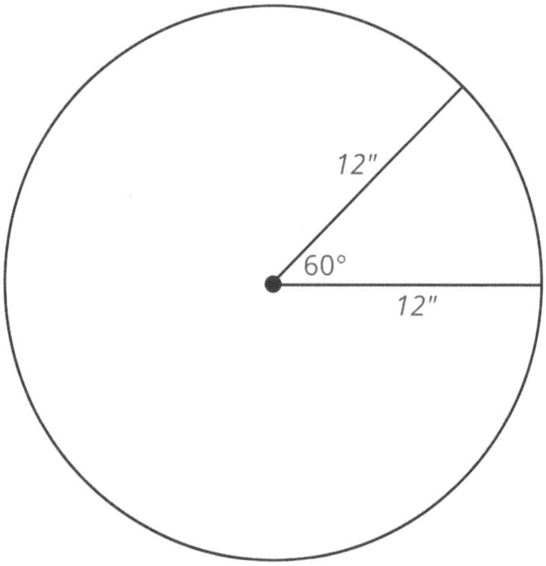

Model: Find the area and the perimeter of a sector with a 60° arc in a circle with radius equal to 12".

Solution: $A = \frac{60}{360}(\pi \cdot 12 \cdot 12)$

$A = 24\pi$ sq. in.

$p = \frac{60}{360}(2\pi \cdot 12) + 12 + 12$

$p = (4\pi + 24)$ inches

Express your answers in simplest exact form.

2.45 Find the area of a sector with radius 10" and measure of arc equal to 45°.

____

2.46 Find the area of a sector with measure of arc equal to 90° and radius equal to 1 foot.

____

2.47 Find the area of a sector with radius equal to 8 and measure of arc equal to 300°.

____

2.48 In a circle of radius 10 cm, a sector has an area of 40π sq. cm. Find the degree measure of the arc of the sector.

____

2.49 Find the radius of a circle with a sector area of 7π sq. ft. and an arc whose measure is 70°.

____

2.50 A 10" diameter pumpkin pie is cut into six equal servings. What is the area of the top of each piece of pie?

____

2.51 What is the area of the sector formed by the hands of a clock at 4 o'clock if the face of the clock is a circle with diameter of 12"?

____

2.52 An equilateral triangle with side of $2\sqrt{3}$ is inscribed in a circle. Find the area of one of the sectors formed by the radii to the vertices of the triangle.

____

2.53 A square with sides of $3\sqrt{2}$ is inscribed in a circle. Find the area of one of the sectors formed by the radii to the vertices of the square.

____

AREA OF SEGMENT

A **segment** of a circle is defined as the region bounded by a chord and the arc of the circle. In the following figure, two segments are shown: segment *ABX* and segment *ABY*.

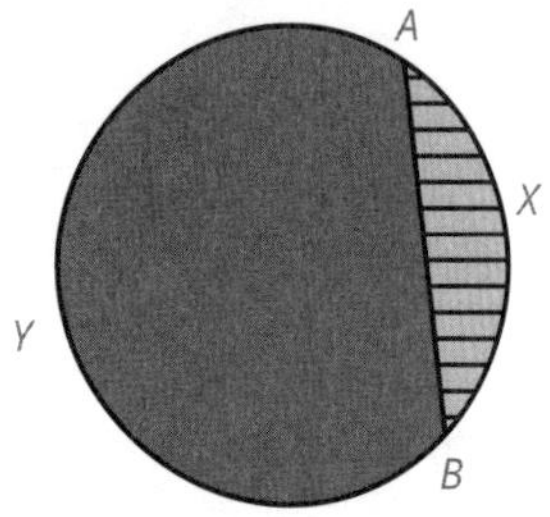

> **DEFINITION:**
> A **segment** is the portion of a circle bounded by a chord and one of the arcs it intercepts.

We have no set formula for finding the area of a segment. In general, to find the area of a segment, we subtract the area of a triangle from the area of a sector.

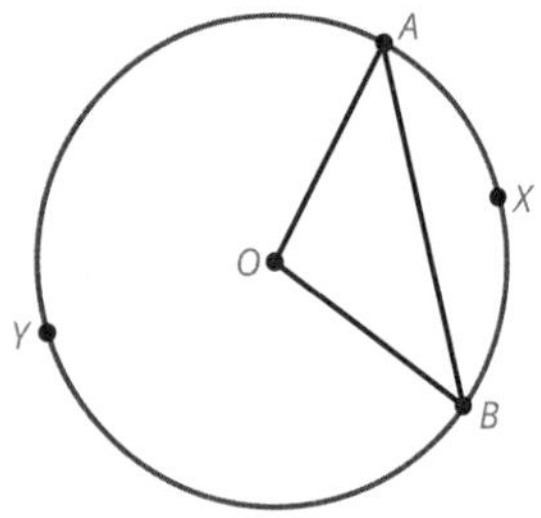

Area *ABX* = Area *O-AXB* – Area △*AOB*

The area of segment *ABY* can then be found by subtracting the area of segment *ABX* from the area of the circle, or by adding the area of triangle *AOB* to the area of sector *O-AYB*.

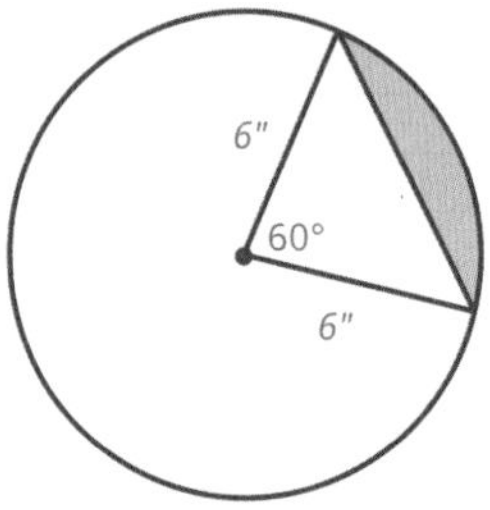

Model: Given a circle with a 6" radius, find the area of a segment that has a 60° arc.

Solution: Area of sector $\frac{60}{360}(\pi \cdot 36)$
$= 6\pi$ sq. in.

Area of triangle $= 9\sqrt{3}$ sq. in.

Area of segment = $(6\pi - 9\sqrt{3})$sq. in.

Express your answers in exact form.

2.54 Find the area of the smaller segment whose chord is 8" long in a circle with an 8" radius.

____

2.55 Find the area of the larger segment in Problem 2.54.

____

2.56 A segment of a circle has a 120° arc and a chord of $8\sqrt{3}$ in. Find the area of the segment.

____

2.57 Find the area of one segment formed by a square with sides of 6" inscribed in a circle.

____

2.58 A regular hexagon with sides of 3" is inscribed in a circle. Find the area of a segment formed by a side of the hexagon and the circle.

____

2.59 An equilateral triangle is inscribed in a circle with a radius of 6". Find the area of the segment cut off by one side of the triangle.

____

Find the area of the shaded portions in each figure.

2.60 $A =$ ______________________

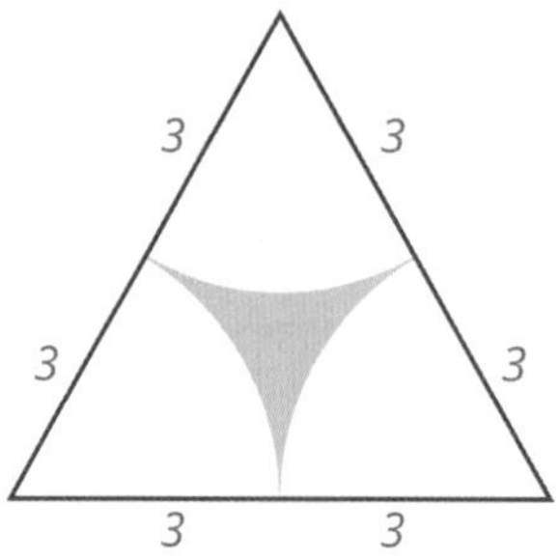

2.61 $A =$ ______________________

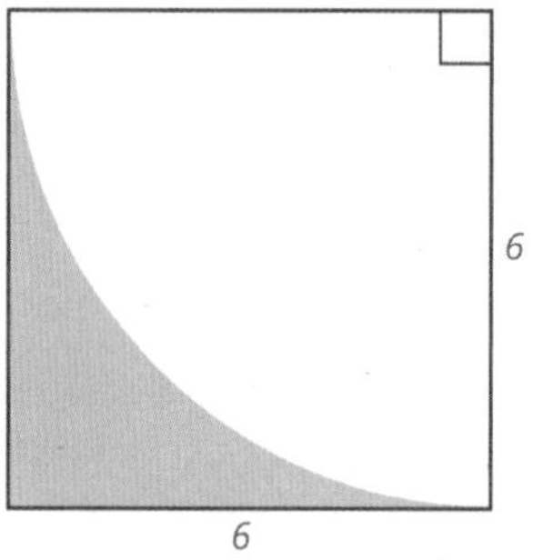

2.62 $A =$ ______________________

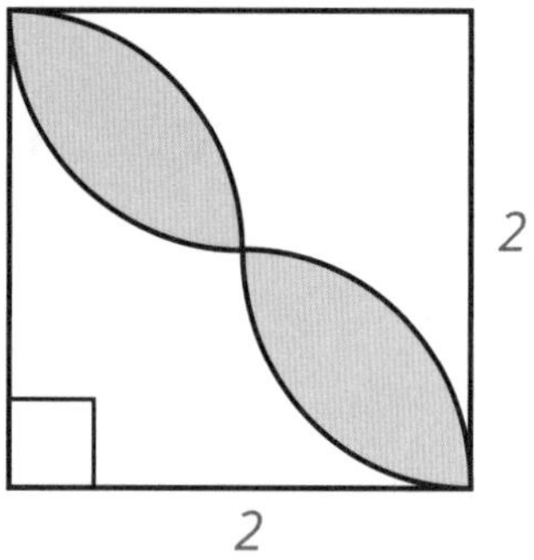

2.63 $A =$ ______________________

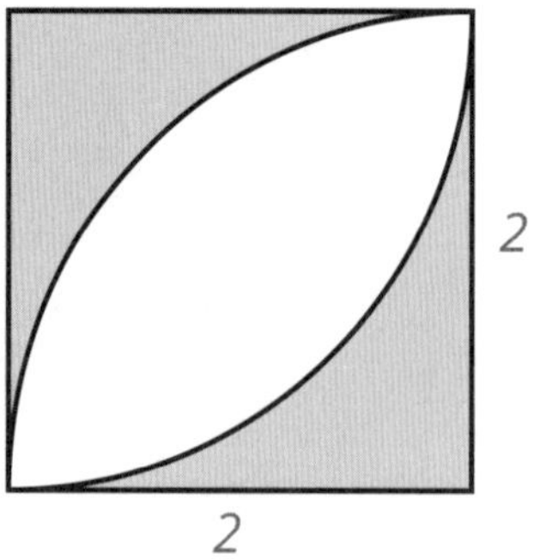

2.64 $A =$ ______________________

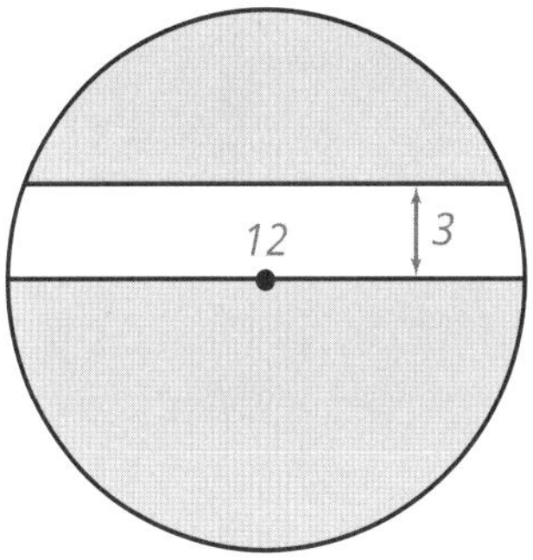

2.65 $A =$ ______________________

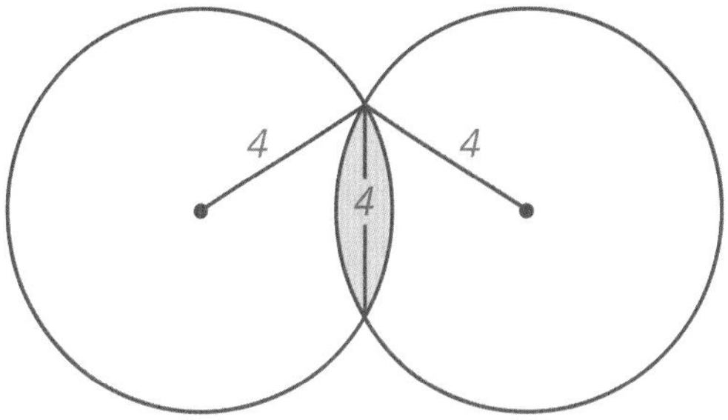

2.66 $A =$ ______________________

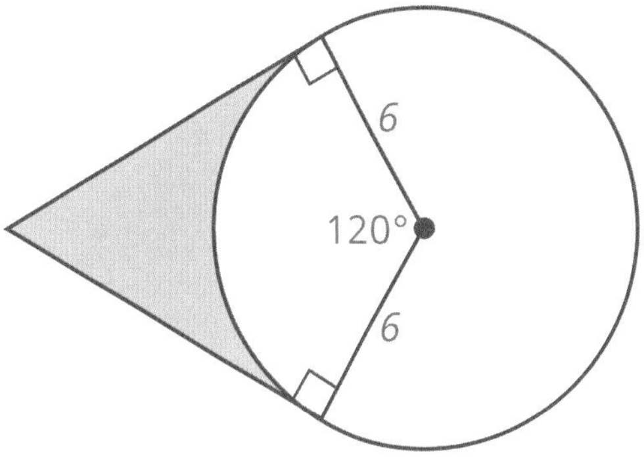

Review the material in this section in preparation for the Self Test. This Self Test will check your mastery of this particular section as well as your knowledge of the previous section.

SELF TEST 2

Solve the following problems. Leave answers in exact form unless otherwise indicated (each answer, 4 points).

2.01 Find the approximate area of a circle with radius equal to 8 ft. (Use $\pi = 3.14$)

____

2.02 Find the exact circumference of a circle with diameter equal to 8 ft.

____

2.03 Find the radius of a circle whose area equals the area of a rectangle that measures 2 ft. by 11 ft. (Use $\pi = \frac{22}{7}$)

____

2.04 Find the area of a sector of an 8" radius circle if the sector has an arc that measures 45°.

____

2.05 Find the length of the arc in Problem 2.04.

____

2.06 Find the area of a segment formed by a chord 8" long in a circle with radius of 8".

____

2.07 Find the area of the region between a regular hexagon with sides of 6" and its inscribed circle.

____

Find the area of the shaded portions in each figure (each answer, 4 points)**.**

2.08 $A =$ ______________________________

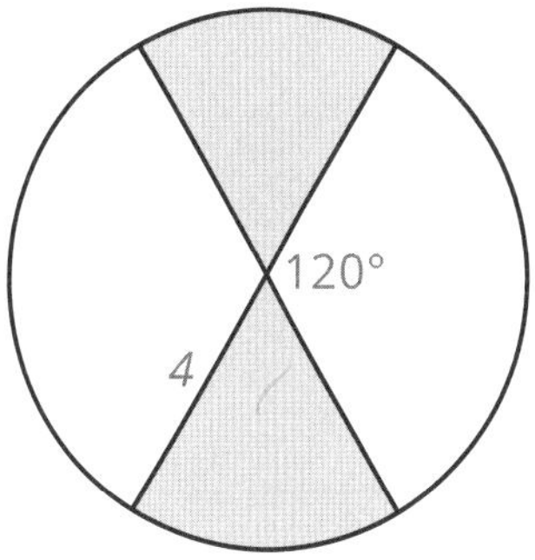

2.09 $A =$ ______________________________

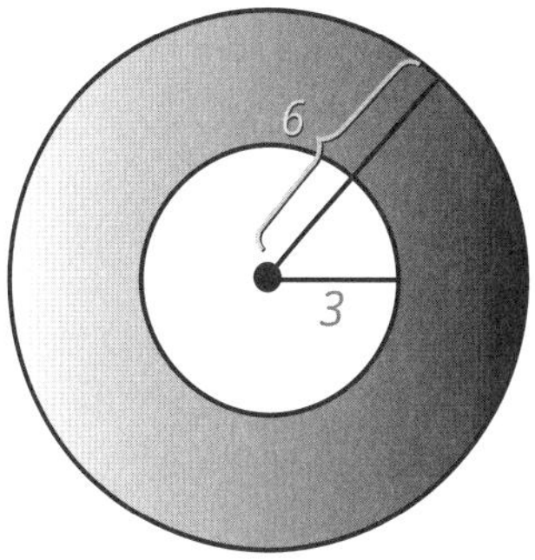

2.010 $A =$ ______________________________

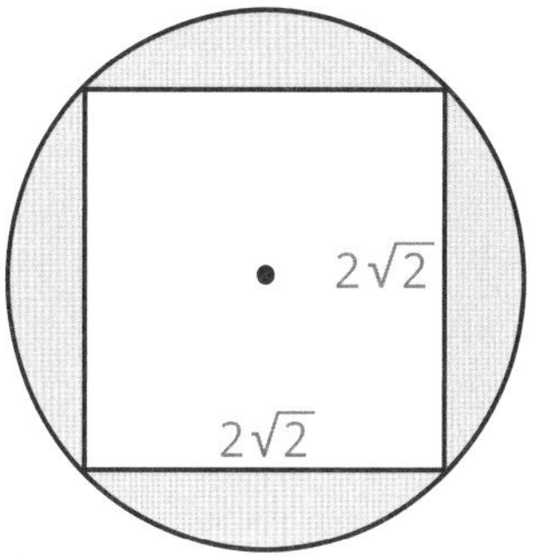

2.011 $A =$ ______________________________

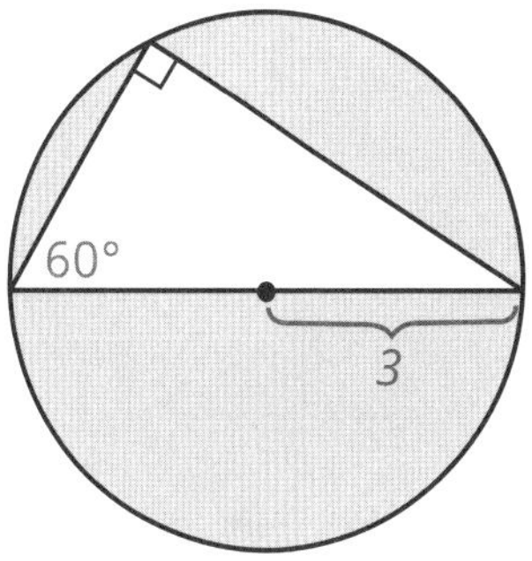

2.012 $A =$ ______________________

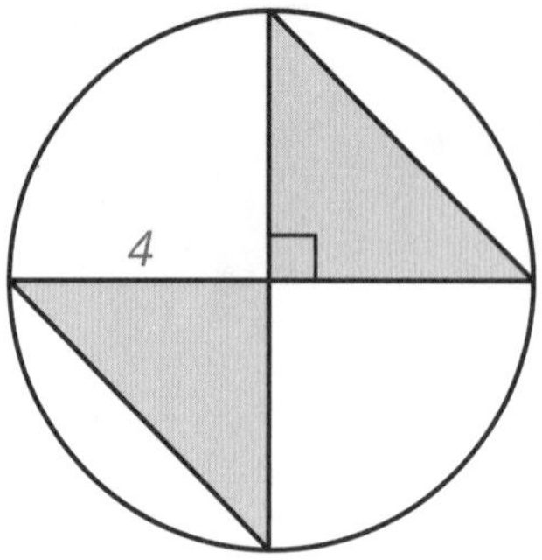

Match the figures to the appropriate formulas (each answer, 2 points).

2.013	_______	$A = \frac{1}{4}s^2\sqrt{3}$	a. circle circumference
2.014	_______	$A = bh$	b. equilateral triangle
2.015	_______	$A = \pi r^2$	c. circle area
2.016	_______	$A = \frac{m\,\widehat{AB}}{360°}(\pi r^2)$	d. circle sector
2.017	_______	$C = \pi d$	e. rectangle
2.018	_______	$A = \frac{m\,\widehat{AB}}{360°}(\pi r^2) - \frac{1}{2}bh$	f. regular polygon
2.019	_______	$A = \frac{1}{2}ap$	g. circle segment
2.020	_______	$A = \frac{1}{2}bh$	h. triangle

52/64 **SCORE** __________ **TEACHER** __________ __________
initials date

3. SOLIDS

We deal with two common measurements related to solid geometric figures: the area of the surface and the volume.

In finding volume we need to use a new unit of measure. This unit of measure for volume is a cube that measures one unit long, one unit wide, and one unit high.

When we find volume, we are finding the number of *cubic units* that can fit in the interior of the solid figure.

Section Objectives

Review these objectives. When you have completed this section, you should be able to:

8. Calculate the surface areas of certain solid figures.
9. Calculate the volumes of certain solid figures.

PRISM

Consider two parallel planes, each containing one of two congruent polygons. Connect the corresponding vertices with segments. If the placement of the polygons is such that these segments are parallel, then the solid figure formed is a *prism.*

A prism has two *bases*, the two congruent polygons. The segments connecting the corresponding vertices are called *lateral edges.* The *lateral faces* are the sides of the prism. They are parallelograms. If the lateral edges are perpendicular to the bases, then the prism is called a *right prism*. Prisms I and II are right prisms. If the lateral edges are not perpendicular to the bases, then the prism is called an *oblique prism.* Prisms III and IV are oblique prisms.

The *altitude* of a prism is the segment perpendicular to the plane of the bases with one endpoint in each plane. The length of an altitude is the *height* (h) of the prism.

The *lateral area* (L.A.) of a prism is the sum of the areas of its lateral faces. The *total area* (T.A.) of a prism is the sum of its lateral area and the area of its two bases.

We can find formulas for lateral area and total area of a prism in terms of its height (h), the perimeter of its base (p), and the area of its

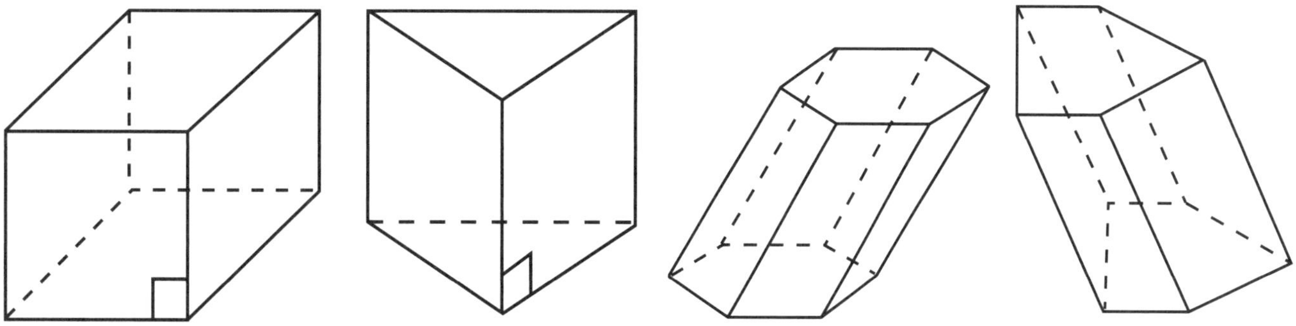

I. II. III. IV.

base (B). Think of unfolding a prism. The lateral faces form a parallelogram whose length is the perimeter of the base (p). The height of the parallelogram is the height of the prism (h).

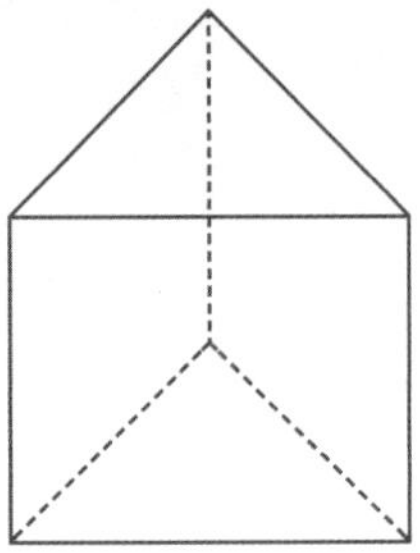

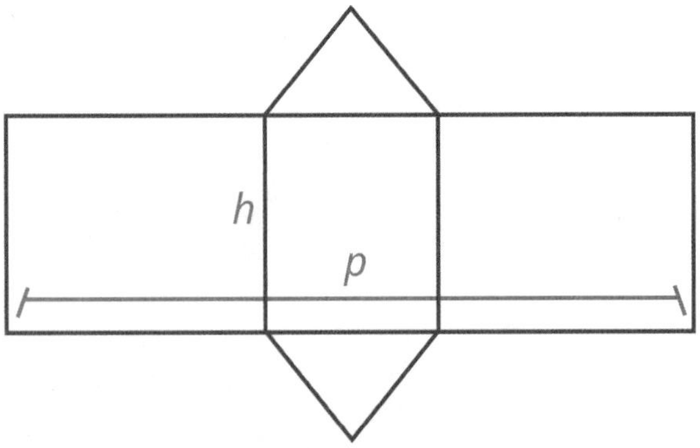

$L.A. = ph$

$T.A. = ph + 2B$

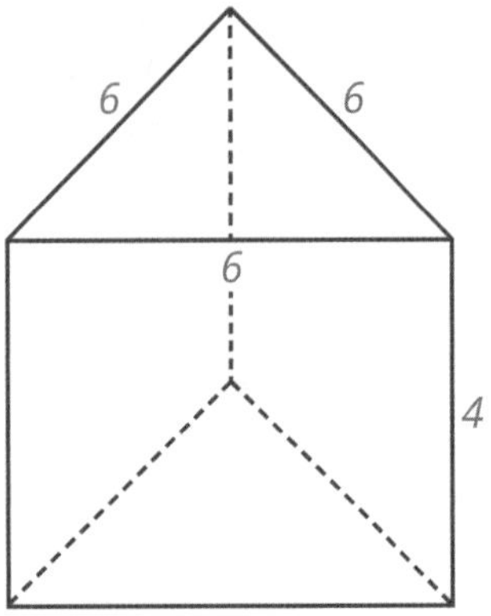

Model: Find the lateral area and the total area of a triangular prism if its height is 4" and its base is an equilateral triangle with side 6".

Solution:

$L.A. = ph$

$= 18(4)$

$= 72$ sq. in.

$T.A. = ph + 2B$

$= 72 + 2(9\sqrt{3})$

$= (72 + 18\sqrt{3})$ sq. in.

(Note: The lateral area of an oblique prism can only be found by using the perpendicular height, h, not the perimeter times the length of the parallelogram.)

The volume of a prism can be found by placing a layer of cubes on the base. The number of cubes will be the same as the area of the base (B). Then multiply this number by how many layers of cubes are in the prism. This number will be the height of the prism (h). Thus we have found a formula for the volume of a prism.

$V = Bh$

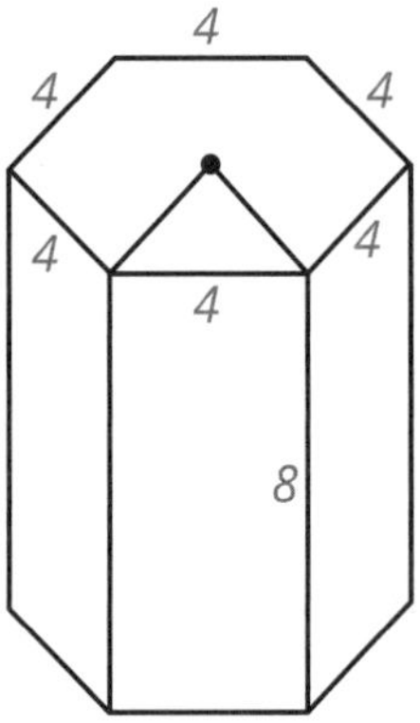

Model: Find the volume of a prism with height of 8" if its base is a regular hexagon with 4" side.

Solution: $B = \frac{1}{2}ap$

$= \frac{1}{2}(2\sqrt{3})(24)$

$= 24\sqrt{3}$ sq. in.

$h = 8$ inches

$V = Bh$

$= 24\sqrt{3}(8)$

$= 192\sqrt{3}$ cu. in.

Find the lateral area, total area, and volume for each prism.

3.1 a. $L.A.$ = ______________________

b. $T.A.$ = ______________________

c. V = ______________________

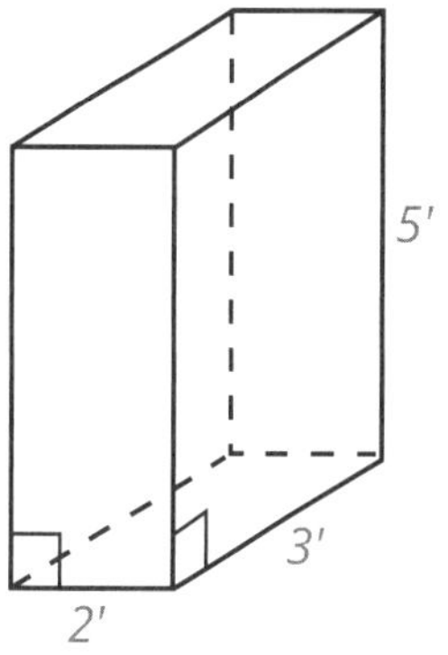

3.2 a. $L.A.$ = ______________________

b. $T.A.$ = ______________________

c. V = ______________________

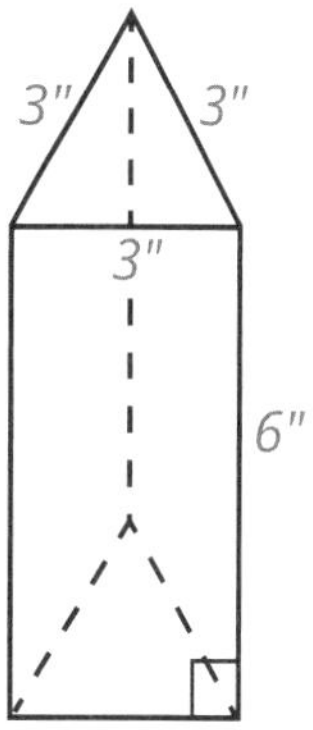

3.3 a. $L.A.$ = ______________________

b. $T.A.$ = ______________________

c. V = ______________________

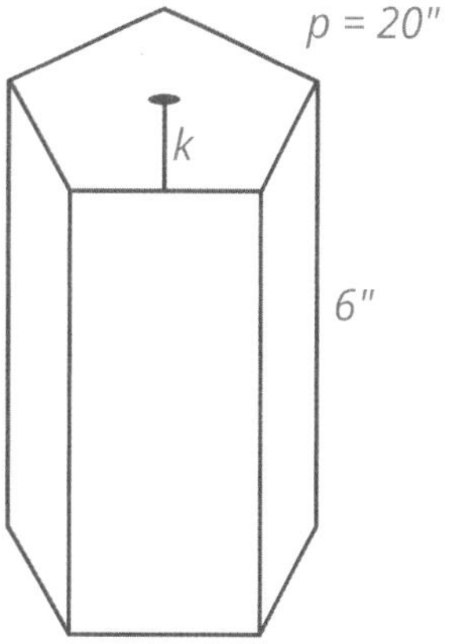

3.4 a. *L.A.* = ______________________

b. *T.A.* = ______________________

c. *V* = ______________________

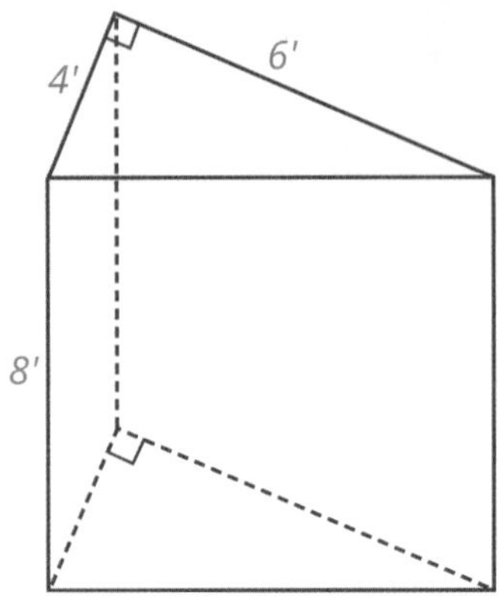

3.5 a. *L.A.* = ______________________

b. *T.A.* = ______________________

c. *V* = ______________________

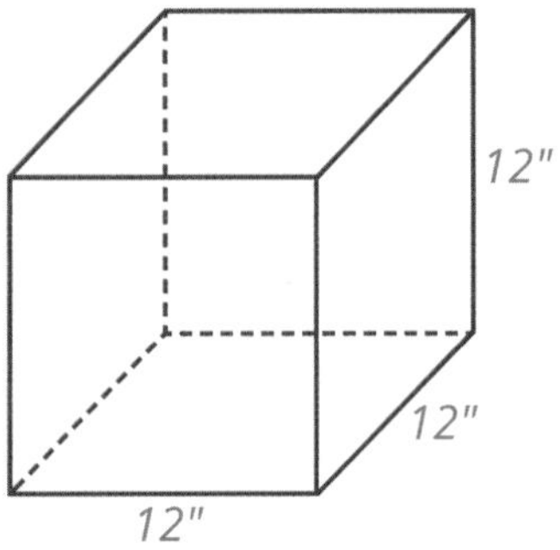

Complete the following activities.

3.6 Find the volume of a cube that has a total area of 96 sq. in. ______________________

3.7 A prism of height 12" has a rhombus with diagonals 6" and 8" for a base. Find the volume and the lateral area.

a. *V* = ______________________ b. *L.A.* = ______________________

3.8 Find the area of the base of a prism if its volume is 300 cu. in. and its height is 6 in.

____

3.9 Find the perimeter of the base of a prism if its lateral area is 88 sq. ft. and its height is 16 feet.

____

3.10 A brick wall measures 20 ft. by 6 ft. by 1 ft. and is made out of bricks that measure 8" by 4" by 2". If 10 percent of the wall is mortar, find the number of bricks needed.

____

PYRAMID

Consider a polygon and a point not in the plane of the polygon. Join the point to each vertex of the polygon. The solid figure formed is called a **pyramid**. The point outside the plane of the base polygon is the *vertex.* The segments joining the vertex to the base are *lateral edges.* Each of the triangular sides is called a *lateral face.* The *altitude* of the pyramid is a segment from the vertex perpendicular to the plane of the base. Its length is the height (h) of the pyramid.

A *regular pyramid* has a regular polygon for its base, and all its lateral edges are of equal lengths.

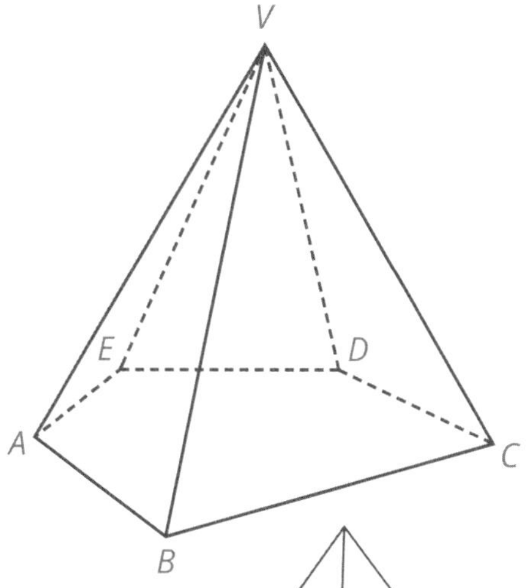

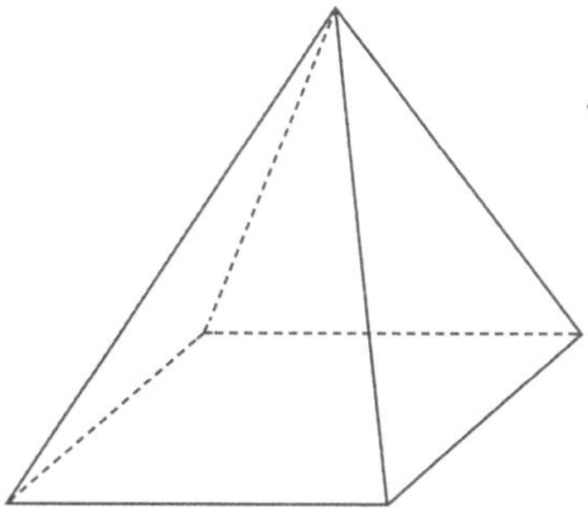

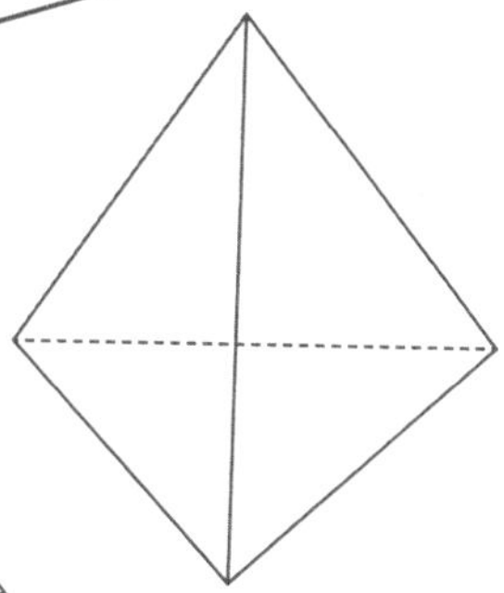

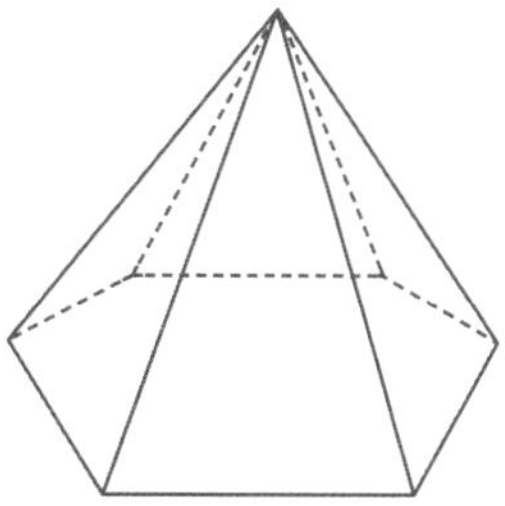

Regular Pyramids

The *slant height* (l) of a regular pyramid is the length of the altitude of any one of its lateral faces. The *lateral area* (*L.A.*) of a pyramid is the sum of the areas of the lateral faces. The *total area* (*T.A.*) of a pyramid is the sum of the lateral area and the area of the base.

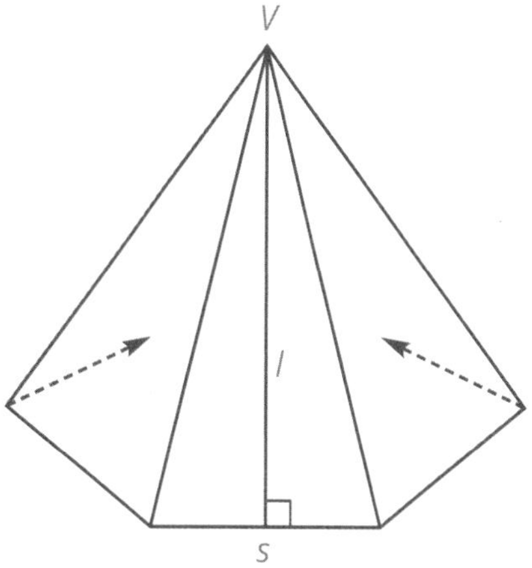

If a pyramid is nonregular, we must have enough measures given to find the area of each face. However, if a pyramid is regular, the area can be computed even if only enough measures are given to find the area of one face and the base.

Area of one lateral face = $\frac{1}{2}sl$

Area of n lateral faces = $n(\frac{1}{2}sl) = \frac{1}{2}(ns)l$

Because $ns = p$ of the base,

$L.A. = \frac{1}{2}pl$ and $T.A. = \frac{1}{2}pl + B$

We shall postulate the formula for finding the volume of a pyramid.

POSTULATE 22

P22: The volume of any pyramid is one-third the product of the area of the base (B) and the length of the altitude (h):

$V = \frac{1}{3}Bh$

Model: Find the lateral area, total area, and volume of a regular square-base pyramid with base edge 6" and height equal to 4".

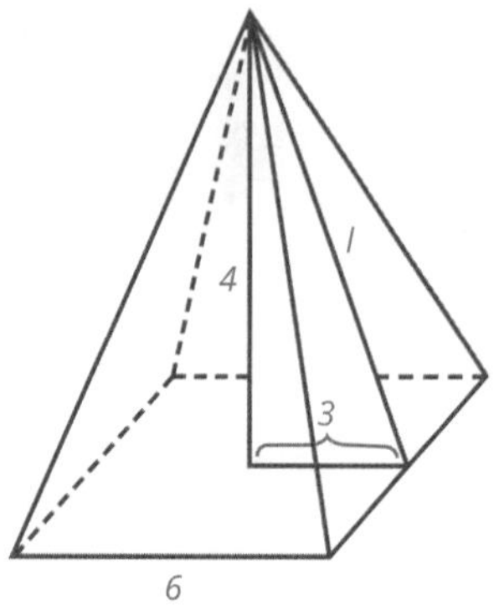

Solution: $l = \sqrt{3^2 + 4^2} = \sqrt{25}$

$l = 5$

$p = 4(6)$

$p = 24$

$B = 6^2$

$B = 36$

$L.A. = \frac{1}{2}pl$ $\quad T.A. = \frac{1}{2}pl + B$ $\quad V = \frac{1}{3}Bh$

$= \frac{1}{2}(24)(5)$ $\quad = 60 + 36$ $\quad = \frac{1}{3}(36)(4)$

$= 60$ sq. in. $\quad = 96$ sq. in. $\quad = 48$ cu. in.

Find the lateral area, total area, and volume for regular pyramid.

3.11 a. *L.A.* = ______________________

b. *T.A.* = ______________________

c. *V* = ______________________

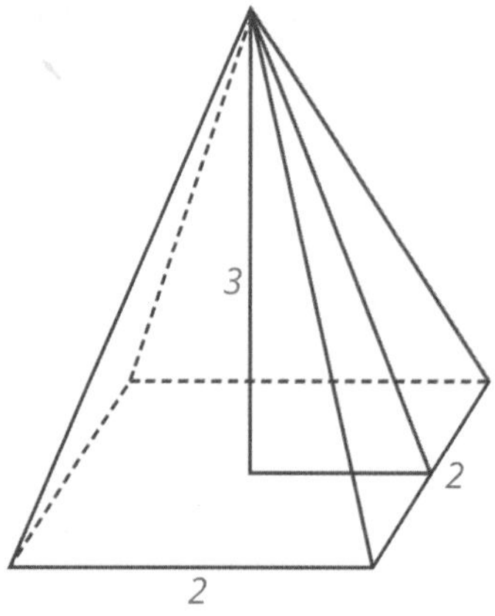

3.12 a. *L.A.* = ______________________

b. *T.A.* = ______________________

c. *V* = ______________________

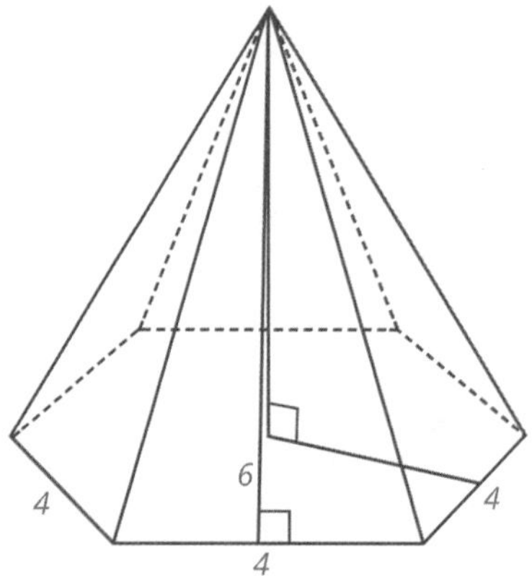

3.13 a. *L.A.* = ______________________

b. *T.A.* = ______________________

c. *V* = ______________________

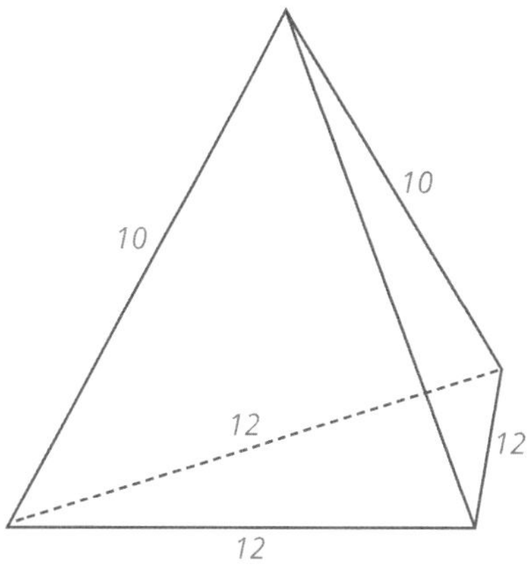

(Hint: The intersection of the medians for any triangle is $\frac{2}{3}$ of the distance from the vertex to the opposite side. In the triangle, a median is a line joining a vertex to the midpoint of the opposite side. It divides the triangle into two parts of equal area. The three medians intersect in the triangle's centroid of center of mass, and two-thirds of the length of each median is between the vertex and the centroid, while one-third is between the centroid and the midpoint of the opposite side. The centroid is the point where the altitude of a pyramid that has a triangle as its base would intersect the base.)

3.14 a. *L.A.* = ______________________

b. *T.A.* = ______________________

c. *V* = ______________________

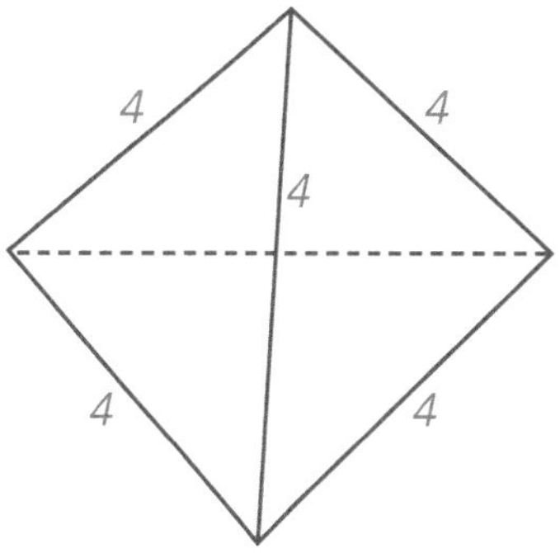

3.15 a. *L.A.* = ______________________

b. *T.A.* = ______________________

c. *V* = ______________________

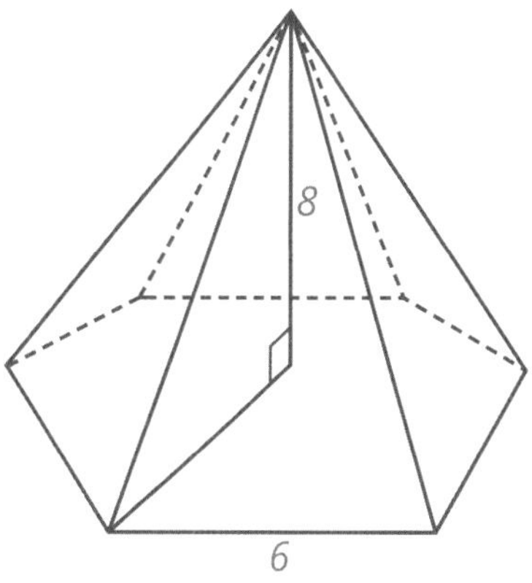

Complete the following activities.

3.16 Find the volume of a pyramid with base area $24\sqrt{3}$ and height of $6\sqrt{3}$.

____

3.17 A pyramid has a base area of 16 sq. in. and a volume of 32 cu. in. Find the length of the altitude.

____

3.18 The base of a pyramid is a square with sides 10 ft. long. Each lateral edge is 13 ft. long. Find the total area.

____

3.19 Find the volume of a regular square pyramid that has a base edge of 6 ft. long and a lateral edge 10 ft. long.

____

3.20 Find the volume of a regular triangular pyramid if all edges are 3" long.

____

CYLINDER

A circular cylinder can be defined in much the same way we defined a prism. Consider two parallel planes, each containing one of two congruent circles. Connect corresponding points of the two circles with segments. If the selection of the points is such that all the segments are parallel, then the solid figure formed is a circular cylinder.

The *bases* of cylinders are congruent circles. As in a prism, an *altitude* is a perpendicular segment whose end points are in the plane of the bases. A *right circular cylinder* is one in which the segments between the bases are perpendicular to the bases.

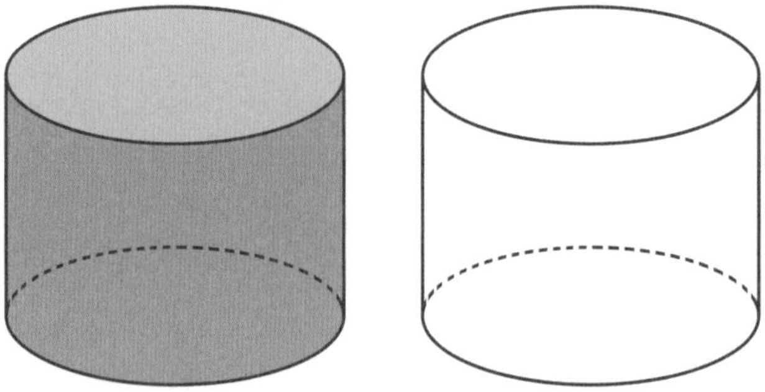

Right Cylinder

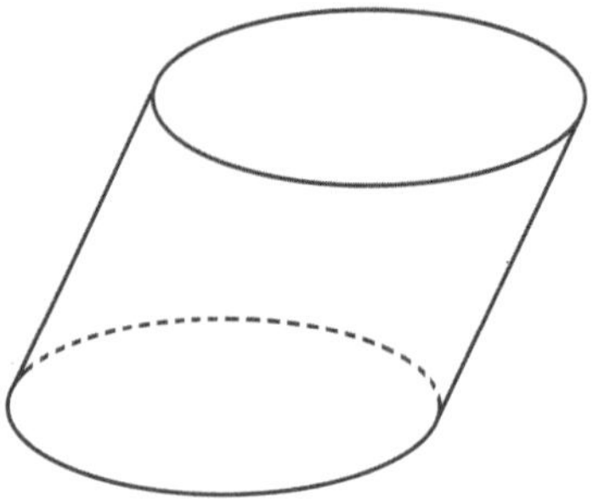

Oblique Cylinder

Just as we considered the circumference and area of a circle to be the limits of the perimeter and area of the inscribed polygons, we also take the area and volume of the cylinder to be the limits of the area and volume for the inscribed prism as we increase the number of sides.

Prism

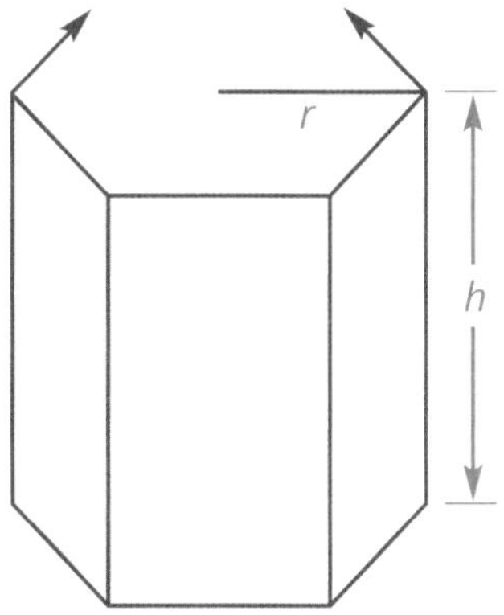

Cylinder

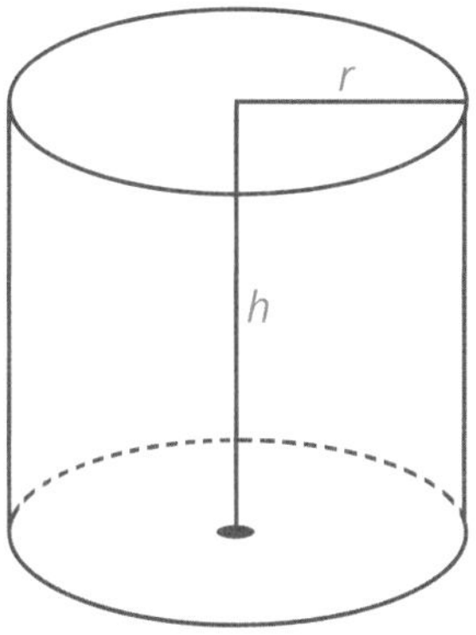

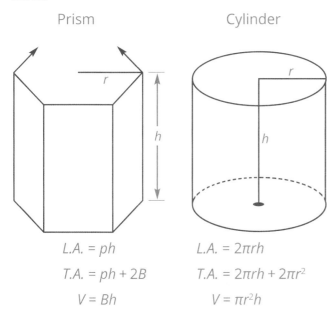

Prism	Cylinder
$L.A. = ph$	$L.A. = 2\pi rh$
$T.A. = ph + 2B$	$T.A. = 2\pi rh + 2\pi r^2$
$V = Bh$	$V = \pi r^2 h$

As the number of sides increases,

$p \rightarrow 2\pi r$

$B \rightarrow \pi r^2$

Model: Find the lateral area, total area, and volume of a circular cylinder with 4" radius and 6" height.

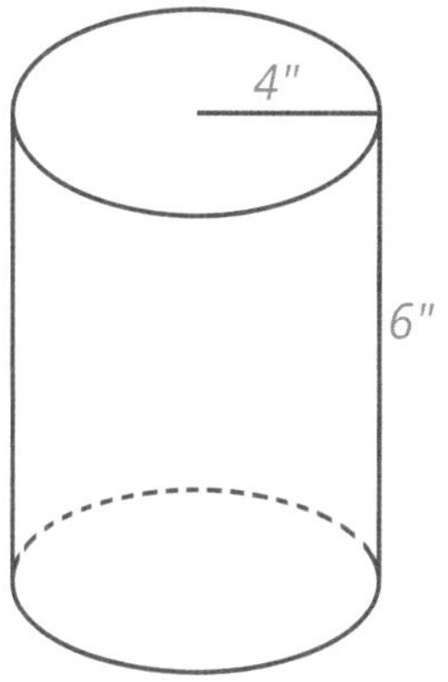

Solution:
$$L.A. = 2\pi rh$$
$$= 2\pi(4)(6)$$
$$= 48\pi \text{ sq. in.}$$

$$T.A. = 2\pi rh + 2\pi r^2$$
$$= 48\pi + 2\pi 4^2$$
$$= 80\pi \text{ sq. in.}$$

$$V = \pi r^2 h$$
$$= \pi(4)^2(6)$$
$$= 96\pi \text{ cu. in.}$$

Find the lateral area, total area, and volume for the cylinders with the given measurements.

3.21 $r = 4, h = 5$

a. $L.A.$ = ______ b. $T.A.$ = ______ c. V = ______

3.22 $r = 2, h = 4$

a. $L.A.$ = ______ b. $T.A.$ = ______ c. V = ______

3.23 $r = 2, h = 3$

a. $L.A.$ = ______ b. $T.A.$ = ______ c. V = ______

3.24 $r = 1, h = 1$

a. $L.A.$ = ______ b. $T.A.$ = ______ c. V = ______

3.25 $r = 6, h = 20$

a. $L.A.$ = ______ b. $T.A.$ = ______ c. V = ______

Complete the following activities.

3.26 Find the volume of a cylinder of height 6" and base with circumference 16π".

______

3.27 The radius of a cylinder is 5" and the lateral area is 70π sq. in. Find the length of the altitude.

______

3.28 A cylinder is inscribed in a cube. If the edge of the cube is 3" long, find the volume of the cylinder.

______

3.29 A cylinder has a volume of 320π cu. in. and a height of 5". Find the radius of the cylinder.

______

3.30 Which can contains more food?

______

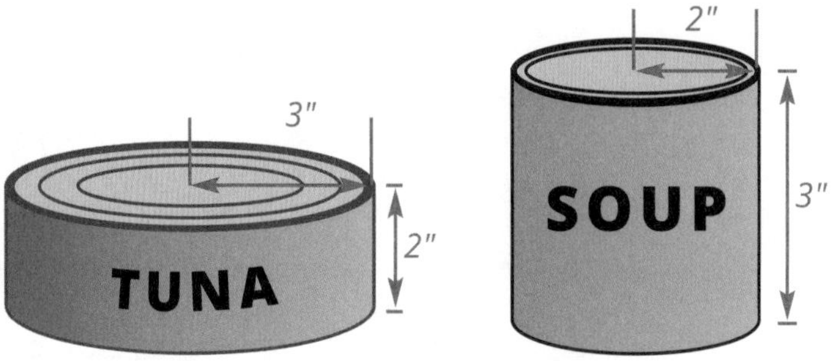

CONE

Consider a circle and a point not in the plane of the circle. The solid figure formed by joining the point to all points of the circle is a *circular cone*.

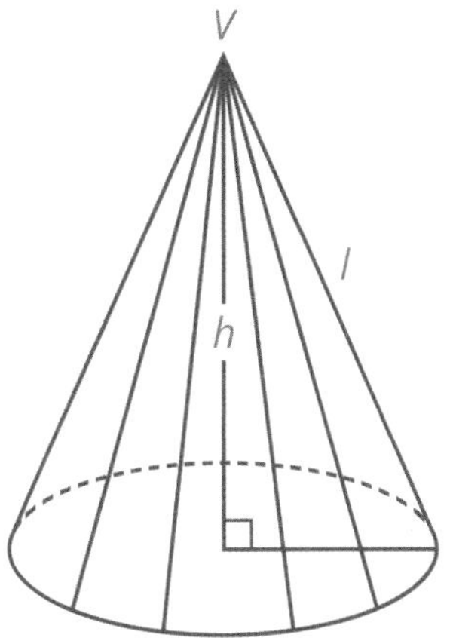

The point, V, is called the *vertex* of the cone, and the circle is its *base*. The *altitude* of the cone is the segment from the vertex perpendicular to the plane of the base. In a *right circular cone,* all the segments from the vertex to the points of the base are equal in length. In a right circular cone the distance from the vertex to a point on the base is called the *slant height* (l).

By assuming that the limits of the lateral area, total area, and volume of the inscribed pyramids to a cone are the lateral area, total area, and volume of the cone, we can obtain formulas for the cone.

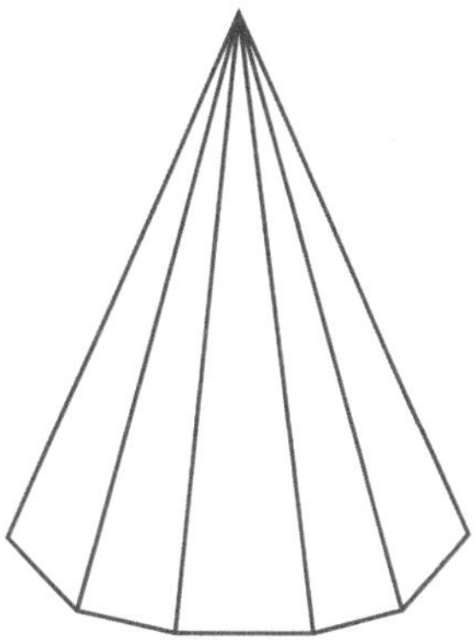

Regular Pyramid

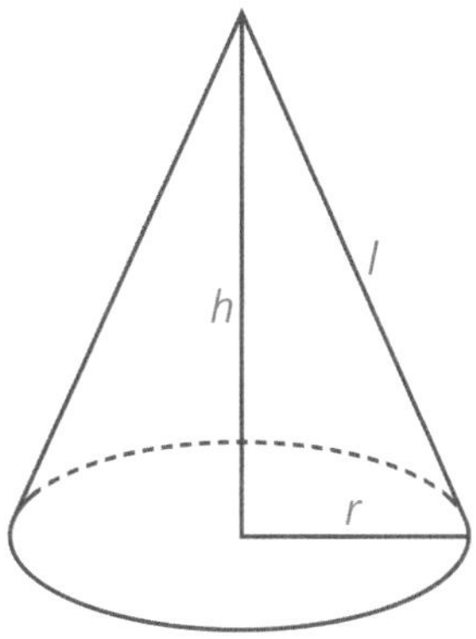

Right Circular Cone

Regular Pyramid	Right Circular Cone
$L.A. = \frac{1}{2}pl$	$L.A. = \pi rl$
$T.A. = \frac{1}{2}pl + B$	$T.A. = \pi rl + \pi r^2$
$V = \frac{1}{3}Bh$	$V = \frac{1}{3}\pi r^2 h$

As the number of sides of the base increases,

$$p \to 2\pi r$$

$$B \to \pi r^2$$

Model: Find the *L.A.*, *T.A.*, and *V* of a right circular cone with 3" radius and 4" height.

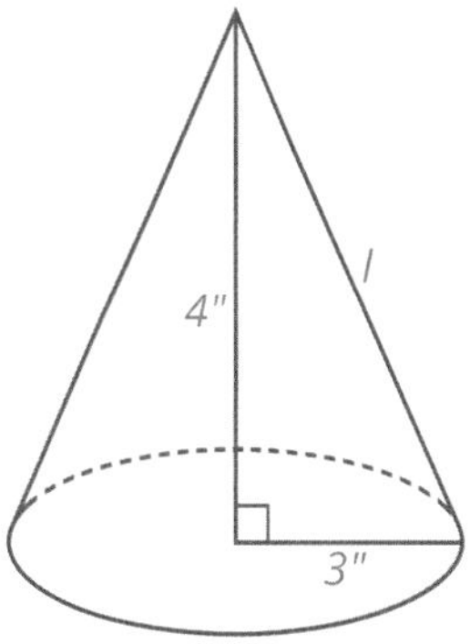

Solution: $L.A. = \pi rl \qquad l = \sqrt{4^2 + 3^2} = \sqrt{25}$

$= \pi(3)(5) \qquad l = 5$

$= 15\pi$ sq. in.

$T.A. = 15\pi + \pi 3^2$

$= 15\pi + 9\pi$

$= 24\pi$ sq. in.

$V = \frac{1}{3}Bh$

$= \frac{1}{3}\pi 3^2(4)$

$= 12\pi$ cu. in.

Find the missing measures for a right circular cone.

	r	l	h	$L.A.$	$T.A.$	V
3.31	3	a. ________	5	b. ________	c. ________	d. ________
3.32	6	10	a. ________	b. ________	c. ________	d. ________
3.33	2	a. ________	b. ________	12π	c. ________	d. ________
3.34	5	a. ________	b. ________	c. ________	d. ________	100π
3.35	a. ________	4	b. ________	8π	c. ________	d. ________

Complete the following activities.

3.36 A cone with radius of 3" has a total area of 24π sq. in. Find the volume of the cone.

____

3.37 A cone is inscribed in a regular square pyramid. If the pyramid has a base edge of 6" and a slant height of 9", find the volume of the cone.

____

3.38 A solid gold cube with edge of 2" is melted down and recast as a cone with a 3" radius base. Find the height of the cone.

____

3.39 A Native American tepee is a conical tent. Find the number of cubic feet of air in a tepee 10 ft. in diameter and 12 ft. high.

____

3.40 Find the number of buffalo skins needed to cover the tepee in Problem 3.39 if each skin covers 15 sq. ft. (Use $\pi = 3.14$)

____

SPHERE

Recall our definition of a sphere as the set of all points in space that are the same distance from a given point called the center. Since a sphere has no base, it will have no lateral area; only a *total area*, which we shall call the *surface area(s)*.

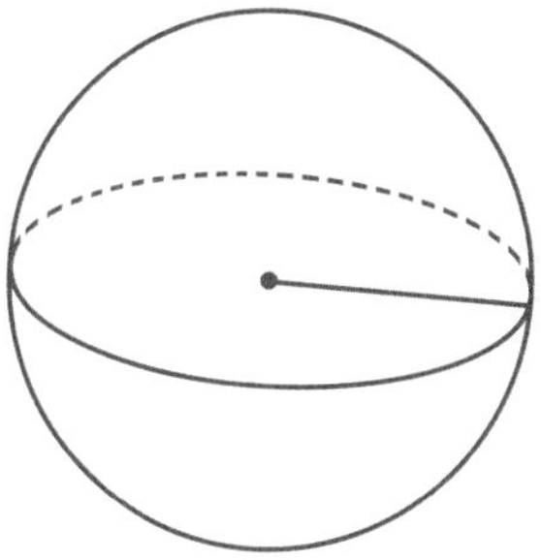

Formal proofs leading to formulas for the volume and surface area of a sphere are very involved and difficult. We shall, therefore, simply postulate these formulas.

POSTULATE 23

P23: The volume of a sphere with radius r is $\frac{4}{3}\pi r^3$.

POSTULATE 24

P24: The surface area of a sphere with radius r is $4\pi r^2$.

Model: Find the volume and surface area of a 5-inch sphere.

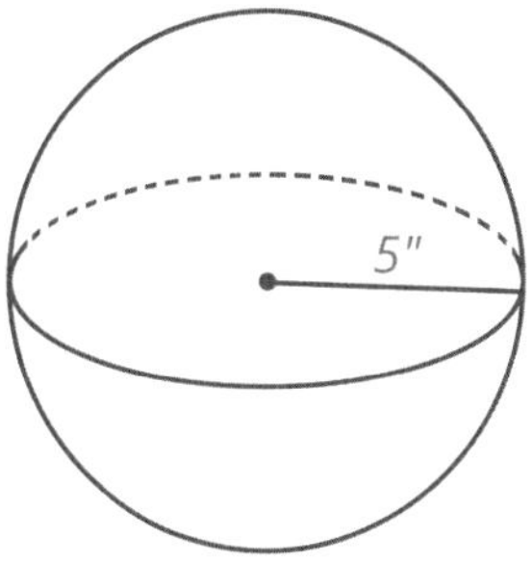

Solution: $V = \frac{4}{3}\pi r^3$

$V = \frac{4}{3}\pi(5)^3$

$V = \frac{500}{3}\pi$ cu. in.

$S = 4\pi r^2$

$S = 4\pi(5)^2$

$S = 100\pi$ sq. in.

Complete the following activities.

3.41 Find the surface area and volume of a sphere having a radius of 4".

$S =$ ____________________

$V =$ ____________________

3.42 The radius of one sphere is twice as great as the radius of a second sphere.

a. Find the ratio of their surface areas. ____________________

b. Find the ratio of their volumes. ____________________

3.43 A spherical storage tank has a diameter of 14 ft. How many cubic feet of water will it hold? (Use $\pi = \frac{22}{7}$) ____________________

3.44 Find the surface area of an orange with a 2" radius. ________________

3.45 If the amount of air in a spherical balloon is 288π cu. in.,

a. what is the radius of the balloon? ________________

b. what is the radius if half the air is let out? ________________

3.46 Find the volume of a sphere that has a surface area of 16π sq. in.

____

3.47 Find the surface area of a sphere that has a volume of 288π cu. in.

____

3.48 Two concentric spheres have radii of 5" and 6". Find the volume of the space between them.

____

3.49 A sphere is inscribed in a cylinder. Show that the surface area of the sphere and the lateral area of the cylinder are equal.

____

3.50 An ice cream cone is 5" deep and 2" in top diameter. One scoop of vanilla ice cream, 2" in diameter, is placed on the cone. If the ice cream melts into the cone, will it overflow?

____

Before you take this last Self Test, you may want to do one or more of the following self checks.

1. ________ Read the objectives. Determine if you can do them.
2. ________ Restudy the material related to any objectives that you cannot do.
3. ________ Use the **SQ3R** study procedure to review the material:
   a. **S**can the sections.
   b. **Q**uestion yourself again (review the questions you wrote initially).
   c. **R**ead to answer your questions.
   d. **R**ecite the answers to yourself.
   e. **R**eview areas you did not understand.
4. ________ Review all activities and Self Tests, writing a correct answer for every wrong answer.

SELF TEST 3

Match the appropriate formula to the solid figures (each answer, 2 points).

3.01 _______ cone

3.02 _______ sphere

3.03 _______ cylinder

3.04 _______ pyramid

3.05 _______ prism

a. $T.A. = 2\pi rh + 2\pi r^2$

b. $V = \frac{1}{3}Bh$

c. $V = \frac{4}{3}\pi r^3$

d. $L.A. = ph$

e. $L.A. = \pi rl$

f. $A = \frac{1}{2}h(b_1 + b_2)$

Match the figures to the appropriate formulas (each answer, 2 points).

3.06 _______ $A = \frac{1}{4}s^2\sqrt{3}$

3.07 _______ $A = bh$

3.08 _______ $A = \pi r^2$

3.09 _______ $A = \frac{m\widehat{AB}}{360°}(\pi r^2)$

3.010 _______ $C = \pi d$

3.011 _______ $A = \frac{m\widehat{AB}}{360°}(\pi r^2) - \frac{1}{2}bh$

3.012 _______ $A = \frac{1}{2}ap$

3.013 _______ $A = \frac{1}{2}bh$

a. circle circumference

b. equilateral triangle

c. circle area

d. circle sector

e. rectangle

f. regular polygon

g. circle segment

h. triangle

i. trapezoid

Find the lateral area, total area, and volume of each solid figure. Find the surface area and volume for the sphere. Leave answers in exact form (each measurement, 4 points).

3.014 a. $L.A.$ = ____________________

b. $T.A.$ = ____________________

c. V = ____________________

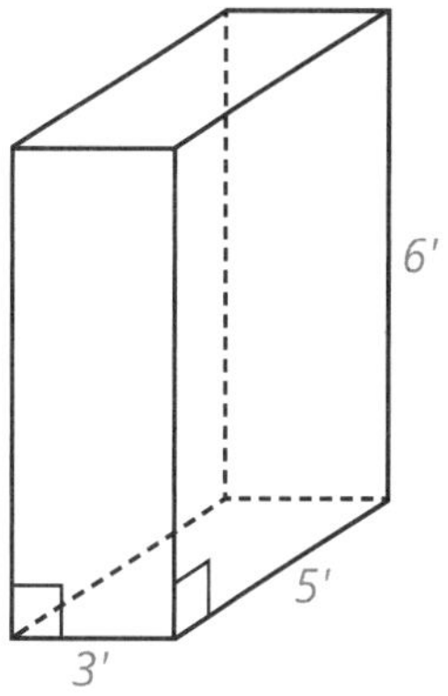

3.015 a. *L.A.* = ____________________

b. *T.A.* = ____________________

c. *V* = ____________________

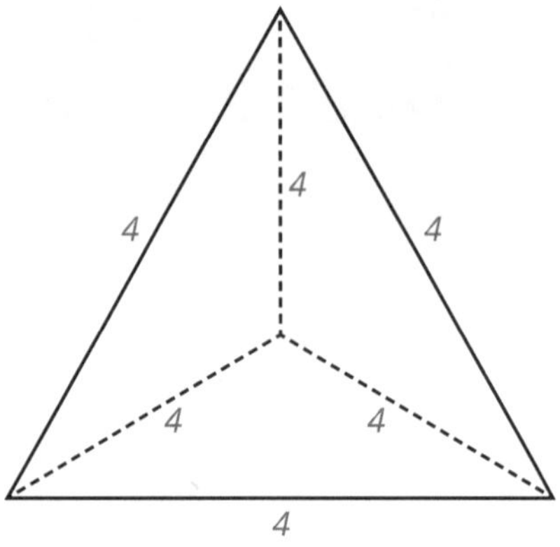

3.016 a. *L.A.* = ____________________

b. *T.A.* = ____________________

c. *V* = ____________________

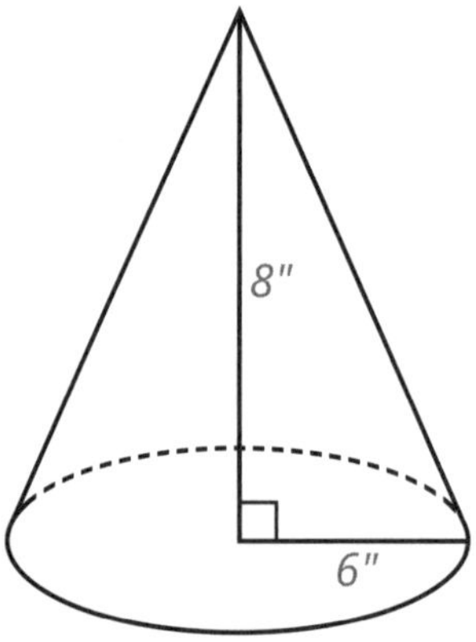

3.017 a. *L.A.* = ____________________

b. *T.A.* = ____________________

c. *V* = ____________________

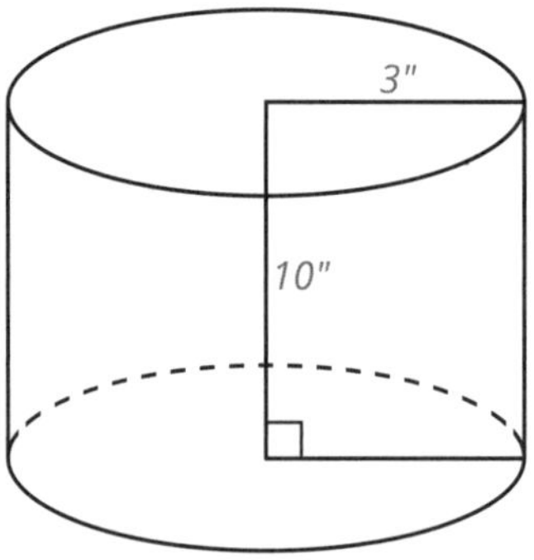

3.018 a. S = ______________________

b. V = ______________________

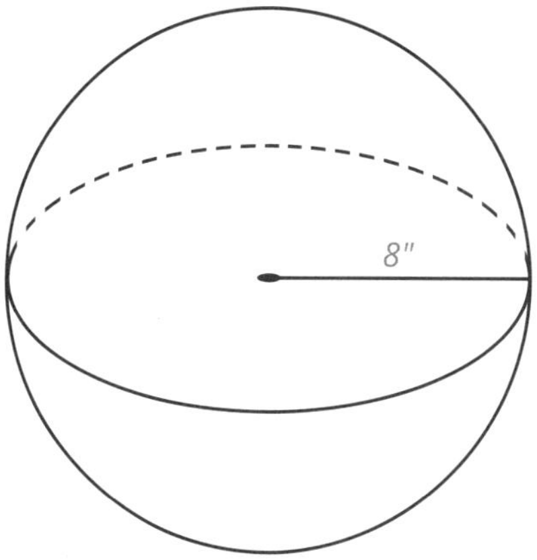

66/82	**SCORE** ________	**TEACHER** ________ initials	________ date

Before taking the LIFEPAC Test, you may want to do one or more of these self checks.

1. ________ Read the objectives. Check to see if you can do them.
2. ________ Restudy the material related to any objectives that you cannot do.
3. ________ Use the **SQ3R** study procedure to review the material.
4. ________ Review activities, Self Tests, and LIFEPAC Glossary.
5. ________ Restudy areas of weakness indicated by the last Self Test.

GLOSSARY

apothem .... A segment from the center of a regular polygon perpendicular to a side.

area .... A real number that measures the space inside a region.

circumference .... The distance around a circle.

cone .... A solid figure with a circular base and sides tapering to a point.

cubic unit .... The unit used to measure volume. It is a cube that measures one linear unit on a side.

cylinder .... A solid figure with two congruent parallel circles as bases.

lateral area .... The area of the sides of a solid figure.

length of arc .... The measure of an arc in linear units.

pi (π) .... The ratio of the circumference to the diameter in any circle.

prism .... A solid figure with two congruent parallel polygons for bases.

pyramid .... A solid figure with one polygon for a base and triangular sides.

region .... The space bounded by the sides of a polygon.

sector of a circle .... The part of a circle bounded by two radii and an arc.

segment of a circle .... The part of a circle bounded by a chord and its arc.

slant height .... The length of an altitude of a side of a pyramid.

square unit .... A unit that measures area. It is a square that measures one linear unit on a side.

total area .... The sum of the lateral area and the area of the base(s).

Coordinate Geometry

Introduction

Studying geometry with the use of coordinates is a relatively new approach. Geometry has been known and used even before the time of Christ. However, only in recent times (the 17th century) did Rene Descartes (1596-1650) publish the first book on analytical geometry. He showed how a systematic use of coordinates helped to attack problems. In coordinate geometry, geometric figures are studied by means of algebraic equations. The equations that are used involve numbers, called coordinates, which serve to locate points.

Objectives

Read these objectives. The objectives tell you what you will be able to do when you have successfully completed this LIFEPAC. When you have finished this LIFEPAC, you should be able to:

1. Plot points on the coordinate axes.
2. Identify a figure as having point, line, or plane symmetry.
3. Graph equations.
4. Graph inequalities.
5. Solve problems using the distance formula.
6. Find the equation of a circle.
7. Solve problems using the midpoint formula.
8. Find the slope of a line.
9. Identify parallel and perpendicular lines using slope.
10. Write the equation of a line.
11. Write geometric proofs by coordinate methods.

Survey the LIFEPAC. Ask yourself some questions about this study and write your questions here.

1. ORDERED PAIRS

To begin our study of coordinate geometry, we must set up a method of picturing points, lines, circles, and other figures in a plane.

Section Objectives

Review these objectives. When you have finished this section, you should be able to:

1. Plot points on the coordinate axes.
2. Identify a figure as having point, line, or plane symmetry.
3. Graph equations.
4. Graph inequalities.

POINTS IN A PLANE

To set up a system so that we might picture figures in a plane will require two number lines. We place them so that they are perpendicular to each other and intersect at their zero points. We usually name the horizontal line the *x*-axis and the vertical line the *y*-axis.

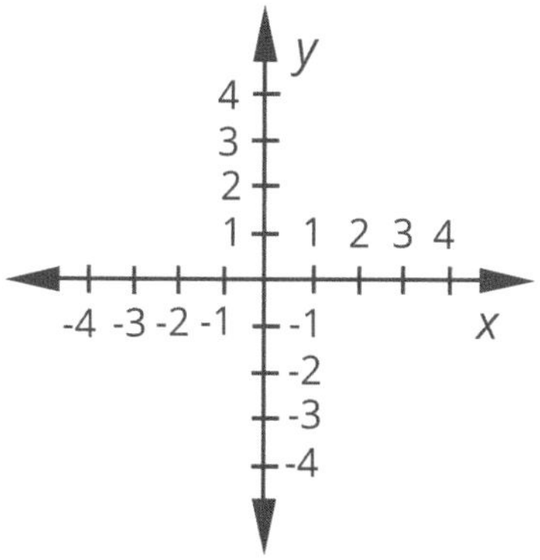

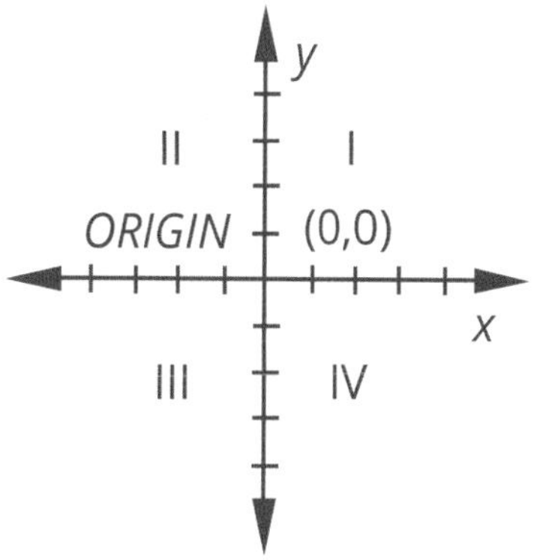

DEFINITIONS

***x*-axis**: the horizontal line.

***y*-axis:** the vertical line.

coordinate axes: the *x*-axis and *y*-axis together.

origin: the intersection of the coordinate axes at (0, 0).

The two lines, called *coordinate axes*, separate the plane into four regions, called *quadrants*, which are numbered as shown. The point where the two lines intersect is called the *origin*, and its location is given by the pair of numbers (0, 0). The positive numbers are to the right and above the origin. The negative numbers are to the left and below the origin.

To locate a point on the coordinate axes, we need to know its *x*-coordinate and its *y*-coordinate: its distance from the origin along each number line. These numbers are given as an ordered pair, (*x*, *y*).

The point (3, 2) is located 3 units to the right of the origin and 2 units above the origin. The point (-2, 5) is located 2 units to the left of the origin and 5 units above the origin.

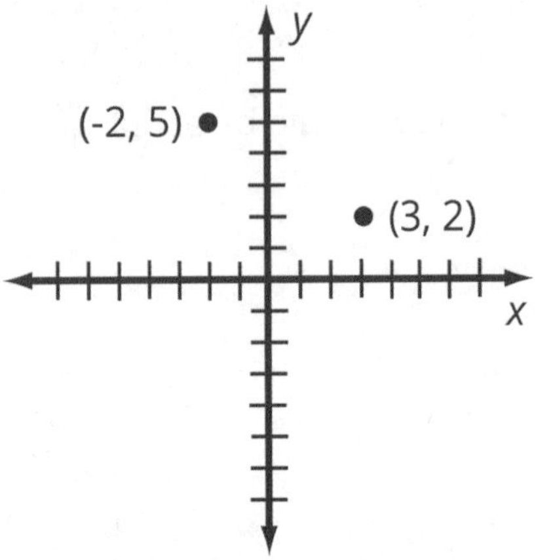

The order in which the coordinates are given is important: (3, 2) and (2, 3) are different points, as are (-4, -2) and (-2, -4). Remember that the first number given in the pair is the *x*-coordinate and the second number is the *y*-coordinate.

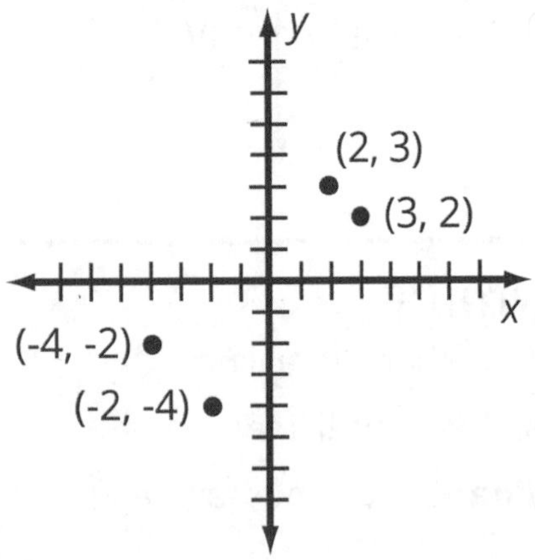

Model 1: Locate the following points.

A (2, 4) *D* (-4, -1)

B (-3, 7) *E* (4, -3)

C (0, 4) *F* (-3, 0)

Solution: Start at the origin and move 2 units to the right along the *x* axis, then 4 units up parallel to the *y*-axis. This location is point *A*.

Start at the origin and move 3 units to the left (-3), then 7 units up to locate point *B*.

Start at the origin; do not move right or left; then move 4 units up to locate point *C*.

Start at the origin and move 4 units to the left; then move 1 unit down to locate point *D*.

Start at the origin and move 4 right; then move 3 down to locate point *E*.

Start at origin and move 3 left; then do not move up or down to locate point *F*.

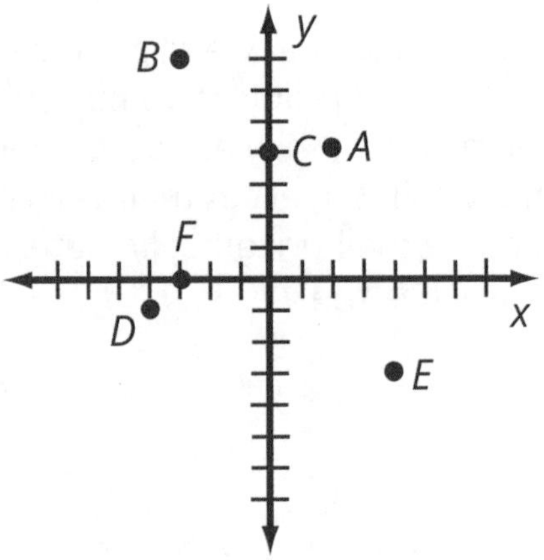

Notice that any point that has both coordinates positive would be in Quadrant I.

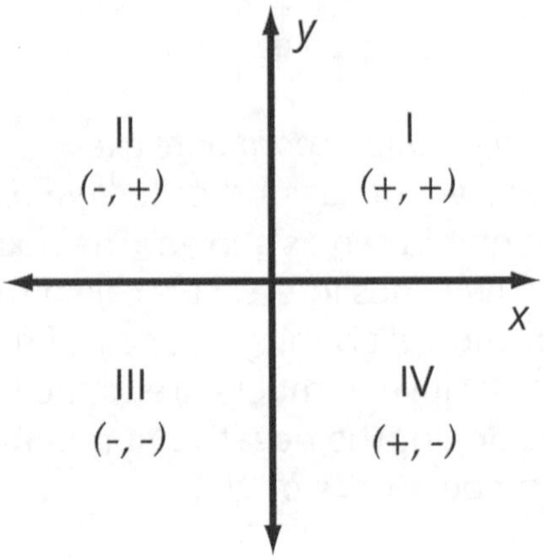

If the first coordinate is negative and the second is positive, then the point will be in the second quadrant. A point in the third quadrant would have both coordinates negative.

A point with the first coordinate positive and the second negative will be in Quadrant IV.

If the first coordinate is zero, the point lies on the *y*-axis. If the second coordinate is zero the point is on the *x*-axis.

Graph the points using one set of axes. Label the points.

1.1 *A* (1, 1), *B* (-3, 0), *C* (-4, -1), *D* (3, -2)

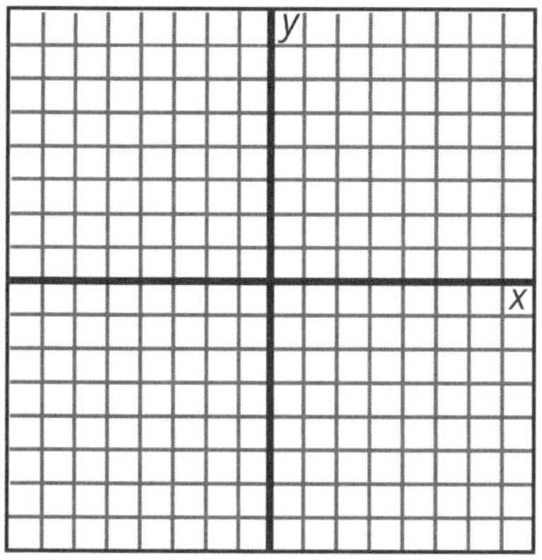

1.2 *R* (2, 0), *S* (2, -3) *T* (-2, 3), *U* (0, -4)

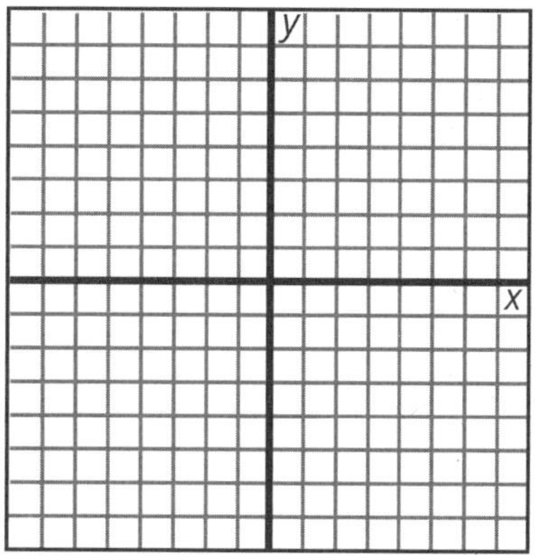

Complete the following activities.

1.3 Graph these points on one set of axes: *A* (0, 0), *B* (3, 4) and *C* (4, 2). Connect the points making segments. What geometric figure is formed?

____

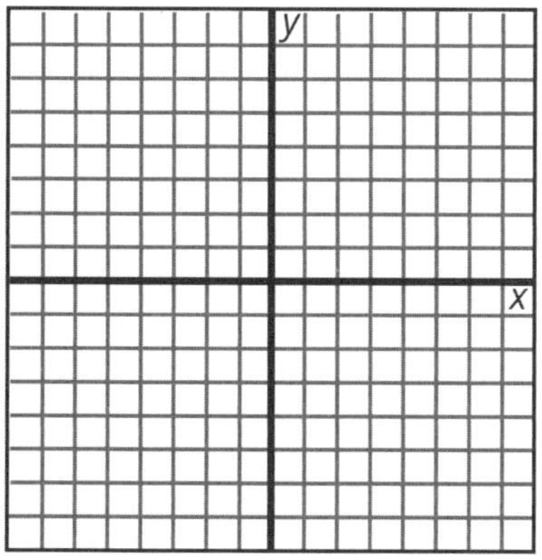

1.4 Graph these points on the same axes: *M* (-3, 4), *N* (4, 4), *O* (4, -2), and *P* (-3, -2). Connect the points to form quadrilateral *MNOP*. What special figure is formed?

____

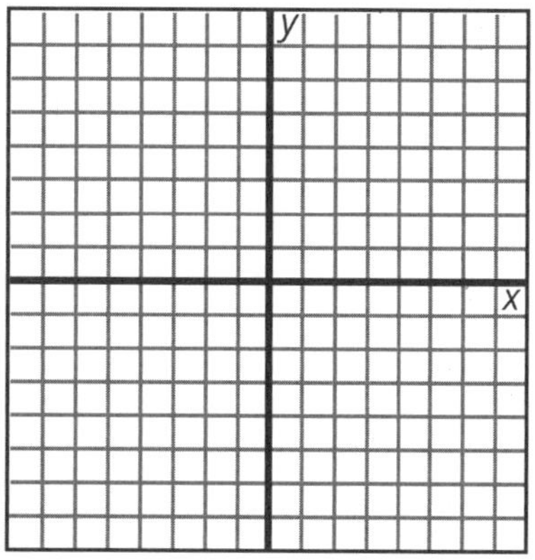

1.5 Graph these points on one set of axes: *R* (-1, 2), *S* (3, 2), *T* (5, -2), and *U* (-2, -2). Connect the points to form quadrilateral *RSTU*. What special quadrilateral is formed?

____

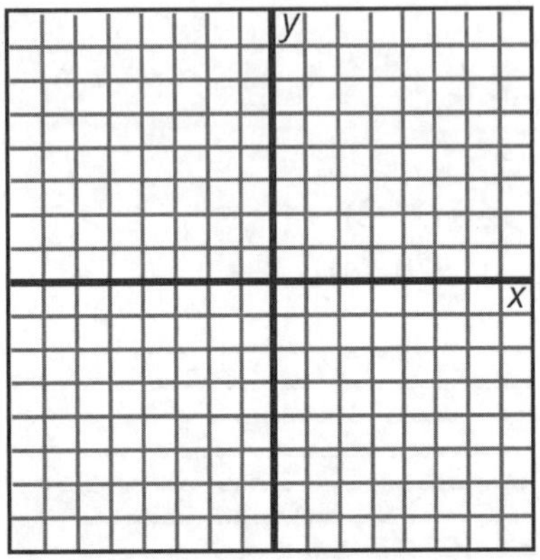

1.6 Graph these points on one set of axes: *A* (0, 0), *B* (0, 6), *C* (-6, 6), and *D* (-6, 0). Connect the points. What special quadrilateral is formed?

____

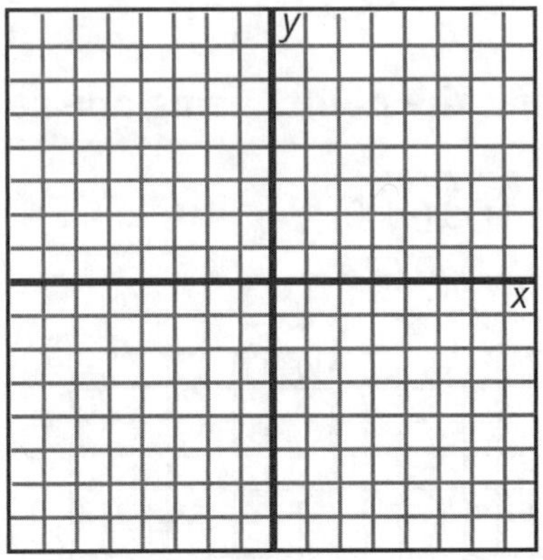

1.7 Graph these points on one set of axes: *A* (4, -6), *B* (4, 3), *C* (8, 3), *D* (8, 5), *E* (4, 5), *F* (4, 10), *G* (2, 10), *H* (2, 5), *I* (-2, 5), *J* (-2, 3) *K* (2, 3), and *L* (2, -6). Connect these points in alphabetical order.

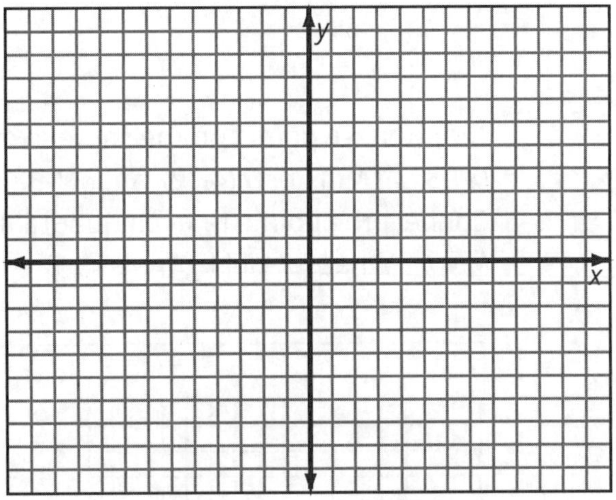

1.8 Graph these points on one set of axes: and connect them in the order given: (-2, -1), (-5, -1), (0, 4), (5, -1), (2, -1), (2, 1), (-2, 1), (-2, -1), (0, 5), (2, -1), (0, 1), (-2, -1).

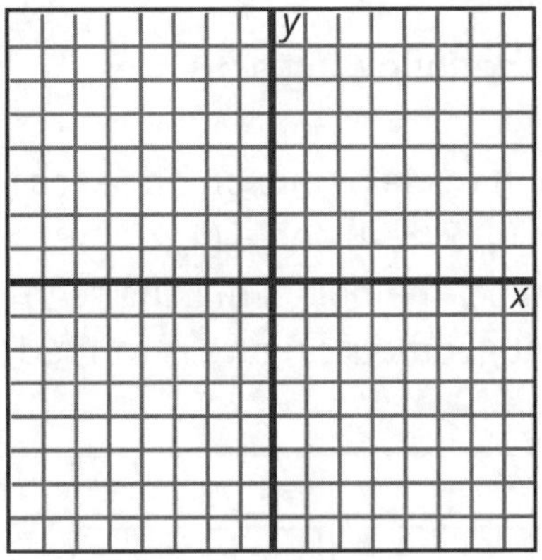

To find the ordered pair when we have the graph, we count to the axes. From the point count units perpendicular to the *x*-axis to find the *x*-coordinate. Also, from the point count units perpendicular to the *y*-axis to find the y-coordinate.
Point *A* has *x*-coordinate of 2 and *y*-coordinate of 3. Therefore, the ordered pair that is associated with point *A* is (2, 3).
The coordinates of *B* are (3, -1); of *C*, (- 3, -2); and of *D*, (-3, 5).

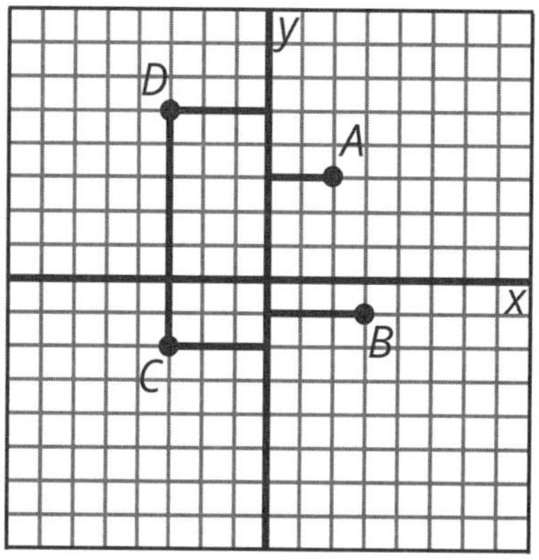

Find the coordinates of the following points.

1.9 *A* (________________)

B (________________)

C (________________)

D (________________)

E (________________)

F (________________)

G (________________)

H (________________)

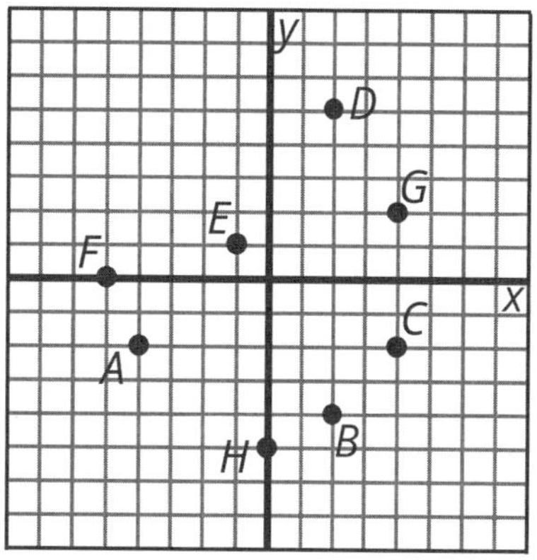

Draw a graph and write the answers.

1.10 Three of the vertices of a square are the points whose coordinates are (2, 3), (2, 6), and (5, 3). What are the coordinates of the fourth vertex?

____

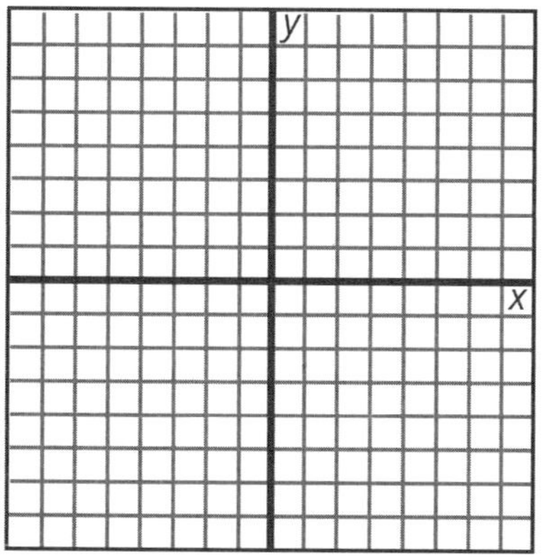

1.11 Three of the vertices of a rectangle have coordinates (-1, -1), (6, -1), and (-1, 2). What are the coordinates of the fourth vertex?

____

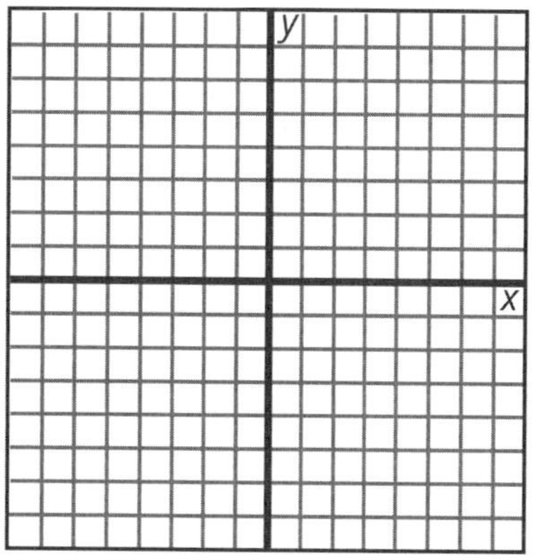

1.12 The longer base of an isosceles trapezoid joins points (-3, -2) and (7, -2). One end point of the shorter base is (-1, 4). What are the coordinates of the other end point?

____

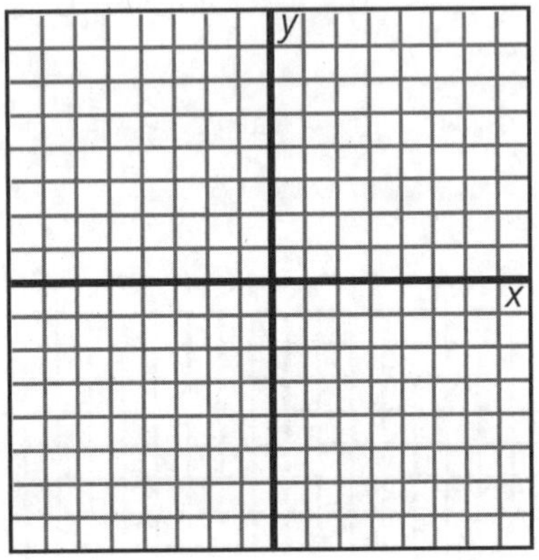

1.13 Two vertices of a square are (3, -2) and (3, 6). What are the coordinates of *two* pairs of points for the other vertices?

a. ________________

b. ________________

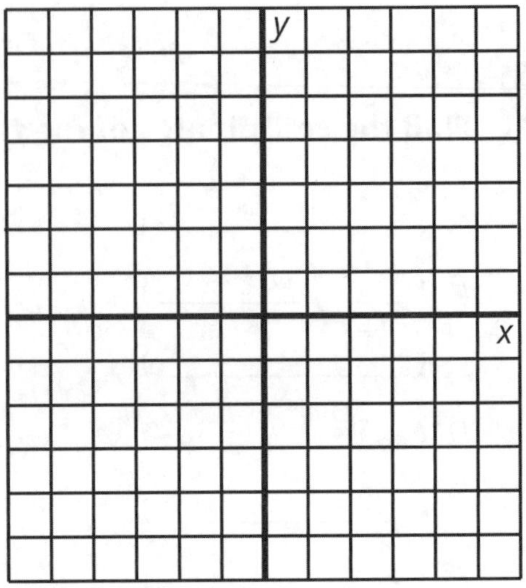

1.14 Write the coordinates of all the points in this figure.

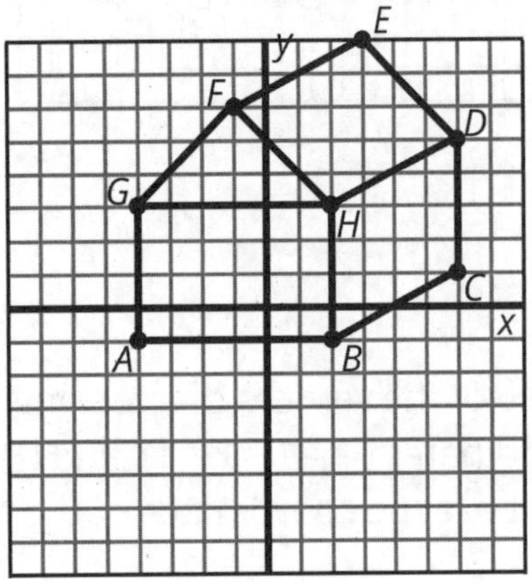

A (________)

B (________)

C (________)

D (________)

E (________)

F (________)

G (________)

H (________)

1.15 Write the coordinates of all the points in this figure.

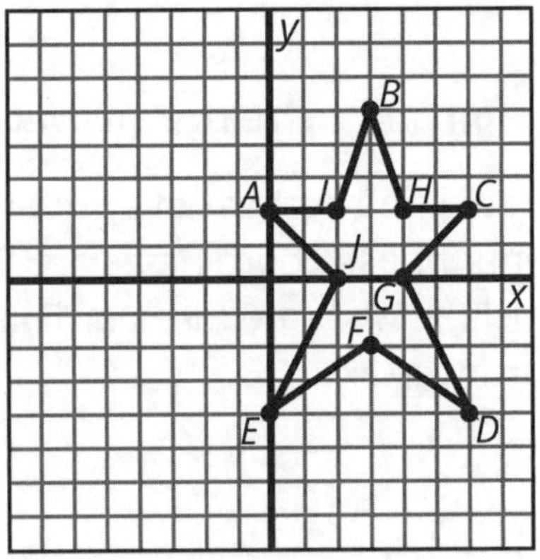

A (________) *B* (________)

C (________) *D* (________)

E (________) *F* (________)

G (________) *H* (________)

I (________) *J* (________)

1.16 Make your own segment figure and write the coordinates of the points.

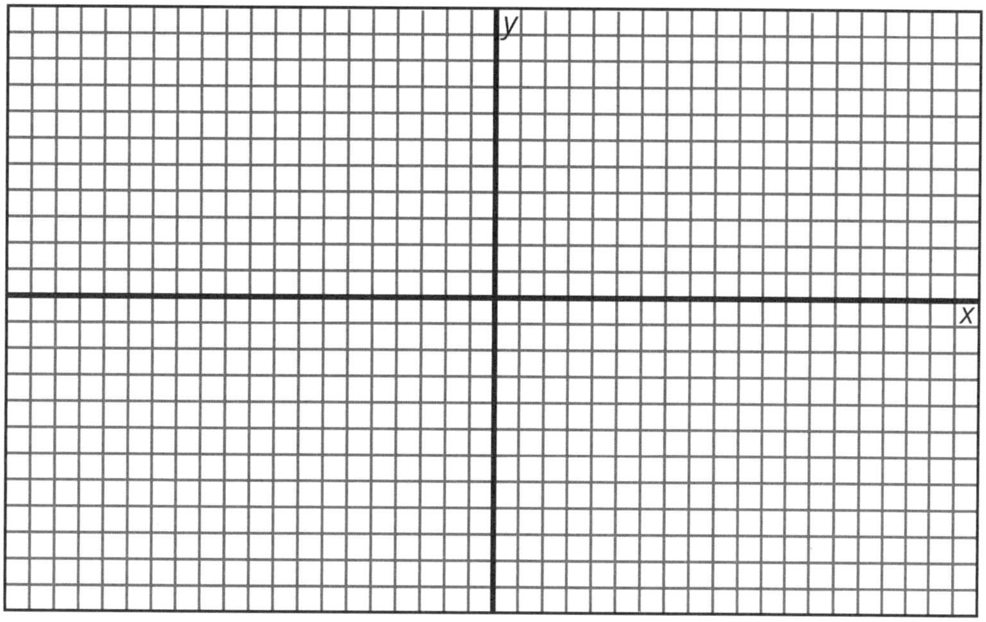

TEACHER CHECK ____________ initials ____________ date

SYMMETRY

People enjoy looking at certain objects partly because they have some sort of balance to them. A well-formed tree is balanced about its trunk. A church window has a certain balance to it. A snowflake and a butterfly are balanced.

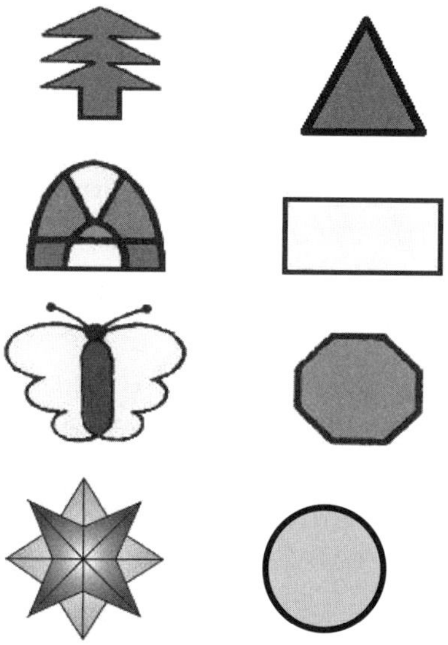

Some geometric figures are more pleasing to look at than others because they, too, have a special kind of balance to them.

An isosceles triangle is more pleasing to look at than a scalene triangle. A rectangle or a square is easier to look at than just any quadrilateral. Regular polygons are also more pleasing. Probably the most visually pleasing of all shapes is the circle. Isaiah 40:22, as you may recall, refers to God sitting upon the circle of the earth to judge it.

Although people speak of physical objects as being *symmetrical* when they appear to be well-balanced, mathematicians give the idea of *symmetry* exact meaning in three different cases.

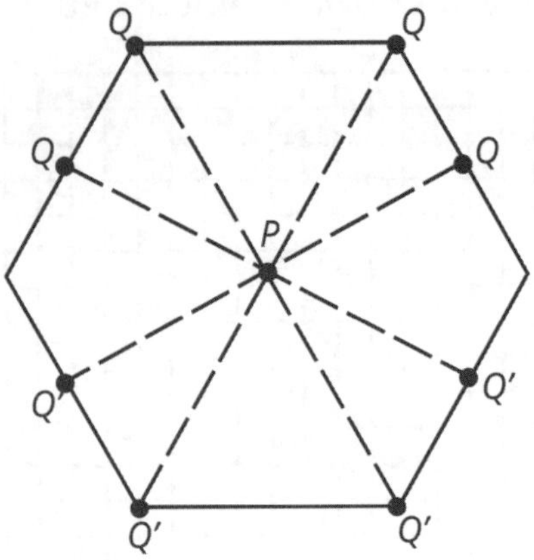

1. A figure has <u>symmetry with respect to a point *P*</u> if for every point of the figure a partner point *Q′* exists such that *P* is the midpoint of $\overline{QQ'}$. The regular hexagon shown has *point symmetry*. The point of symmetry is the center of the polygon, *P*.

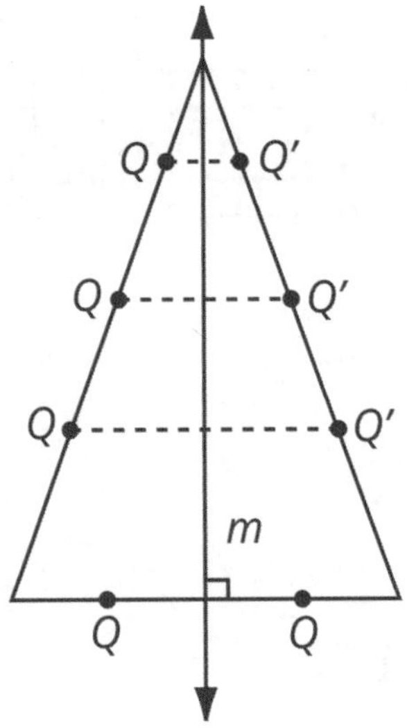

2. A figure has <u>symmetry with respect to a line *m*</u> if for every point *Q* of the figure a partner point *Q′* exists such that *m* is the perpendicular bisector of $\overline{QQ'}$. The isosceles triangle shown has *line symmetry*. The line of symmetry is the altitude to its base.

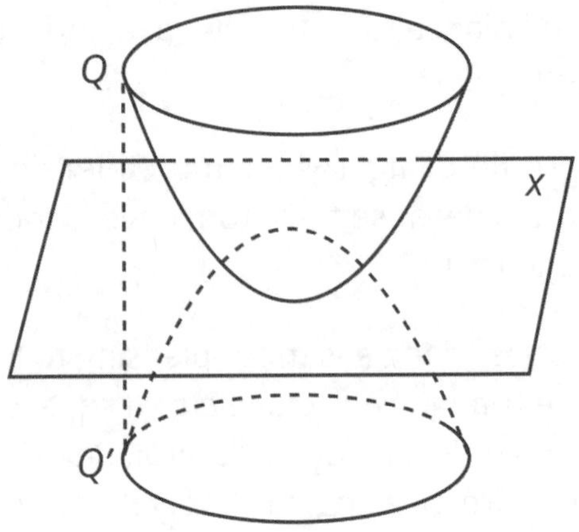

3. A figure has <u>symmetry with respect to a plane *X*</u> if for every point *Q* of the figure a partner point *Q′* exists such that *X* is the perpendicular bisector of $\overline{QQ'}$. The solid figure shown has *plane symmetry*. A plane of symmetry is *X*.

Some figures have more than one line of symmetry or more than one plane of symmetry. Some figures may have all three kinds of symmetry, but other figures may not be symmetrical at all.

Name the kind or kinds of symmetry the following figures have: point, line, plane, or none.

1.17 ______________ A

1.18 ______________ B

1.19 ______________ C

1.20 ______________ D

1.21 ______________ E

1.22 ______________ F

1.23 ______________ H

1.24 ______________ 2

1.25 ______________ 3

1.26 ______________ O

1.27 ______________ 8

1.28 ______________ 100

1.29 ______________ 7

Draw all the lines of symmetry you can find.

1.30

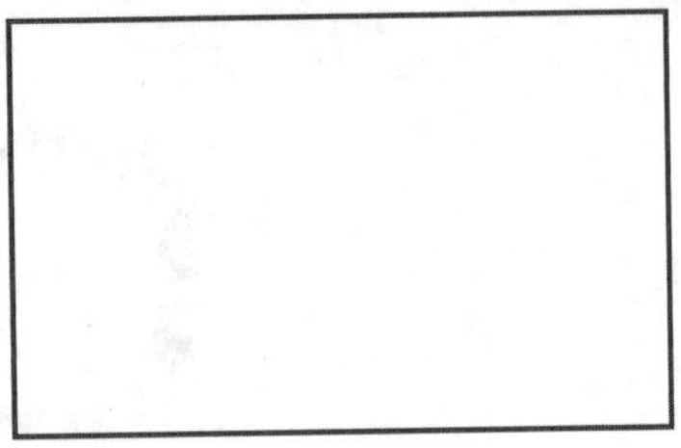

1.31

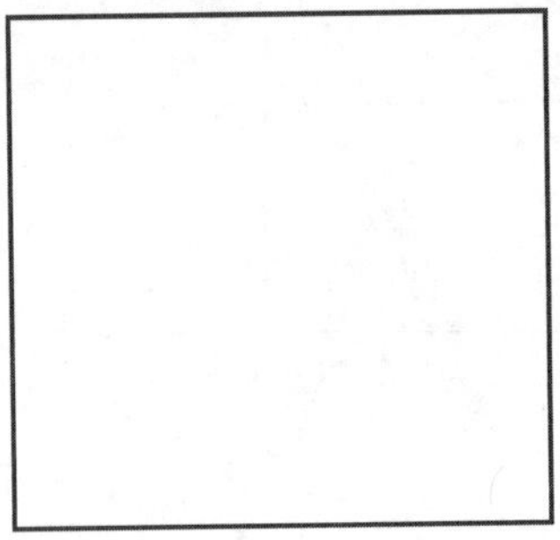

1.32

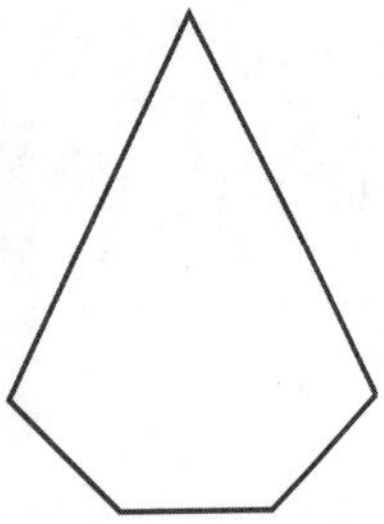

1.33

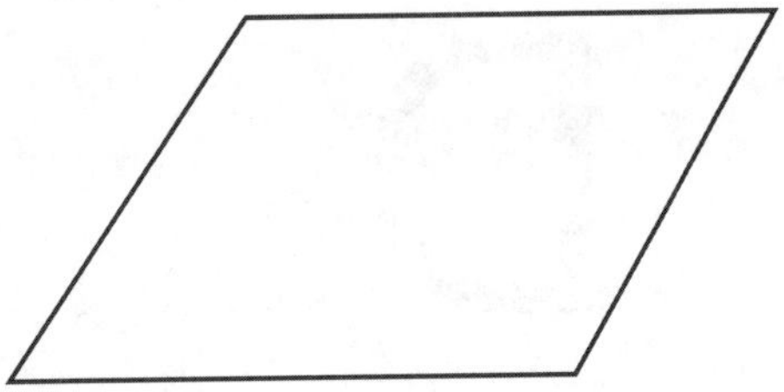

1.34

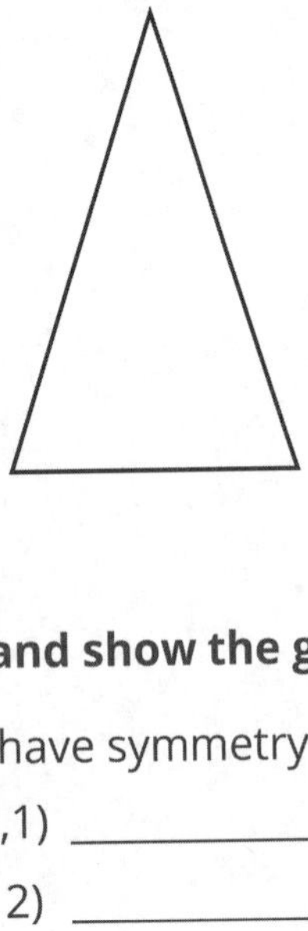

1.35

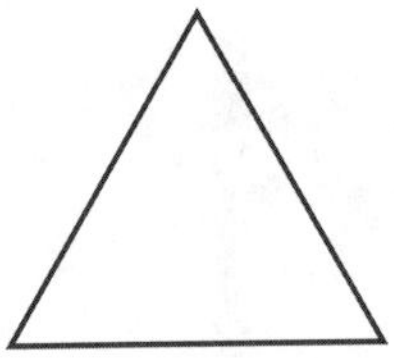

Write the answers and show the graph of the points mentioned.

1.36 Points *A* and *A'* have symmetry with respect to the *y*-axis. Find the coordinates of *A'*:

a. When *A* is (-2,1) ____________________

b. When *A* is (-3, -3) ____________________

c. When *A* is (4, 2) ____________________

d. When *A* is (3, -1) ____________________

a.

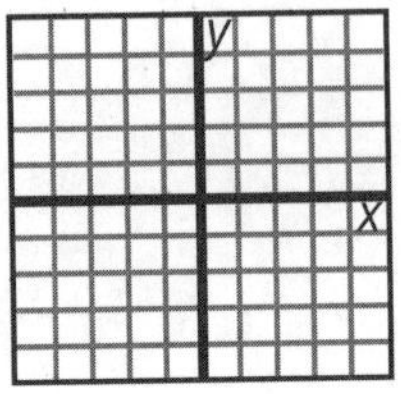

b.

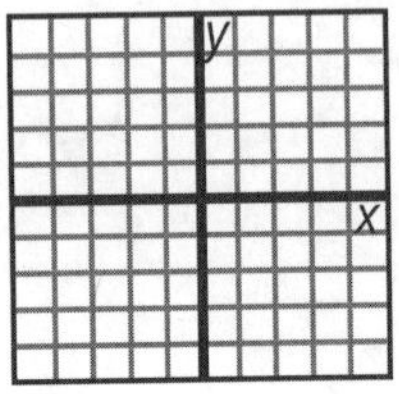

c.

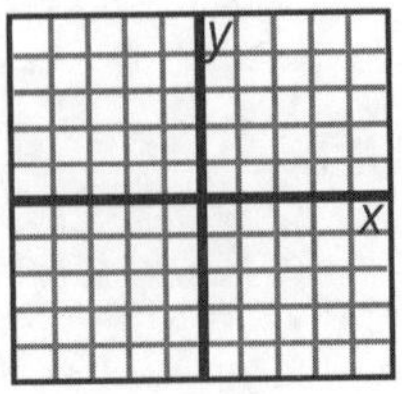

d.

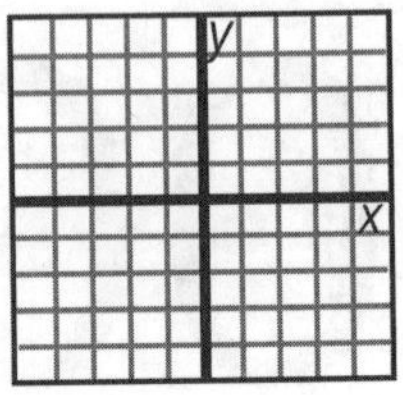

1.37 Points B and B' have symmetry with respect to the x-axis. Find the coordinates of B':

a. When B is (4, 3) ____________ b. When B is (4, 1) ____________

c. When B is (-3, 5) ____________ d. When B is (-3, -2) ____________

a.

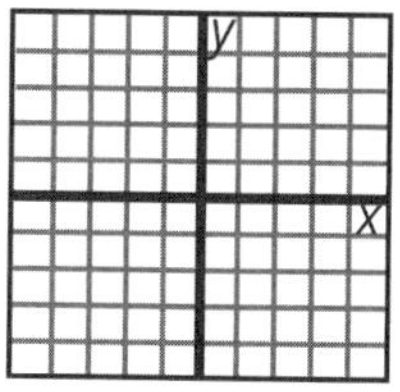

b.

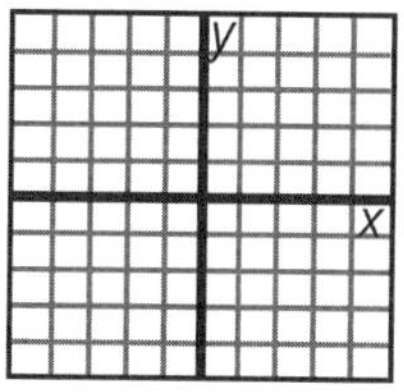

c.

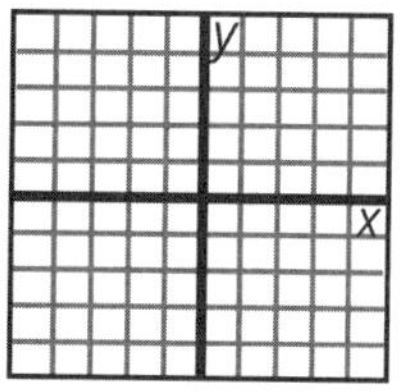

d.

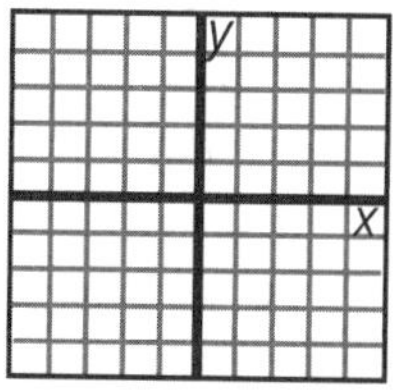

1.38 Points C and C' have symmetry with respect to the line parallel to, and two units above, the x-axis. Find the coordinates of C':

a. When C is (0,1) ____________ b. When C is (3, 5) ____________

c. When C is (-2, -1) ____________ d. When C is (-4, 3) ____________

a.

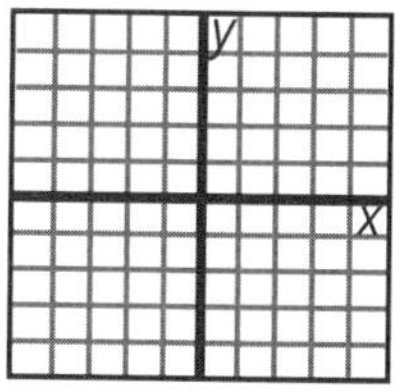

b.

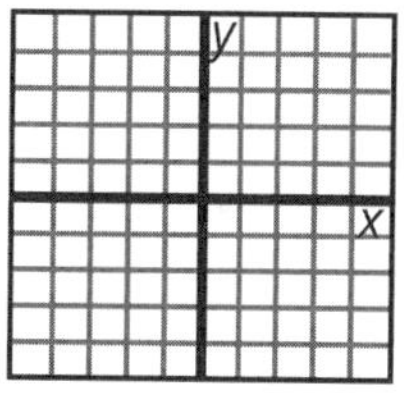

c.

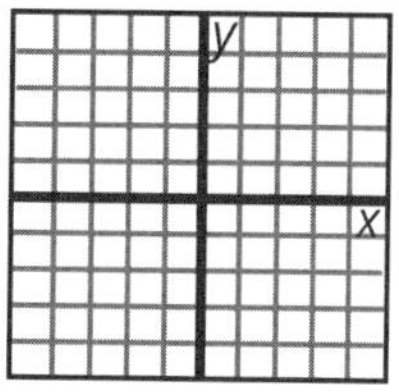

d.

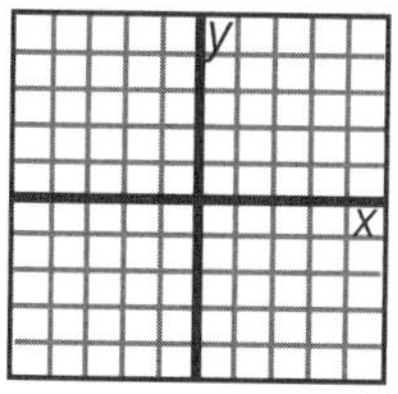

1.39 Points D and D' have symmetry with respect to the point (0, 0). Find the coordinates of D':

a. When D is (5, 0) ____________ b. When D is (0, 2) ____________

c. When D is (3, 3) ____________ d. When D is (2, -2) ____________

a.

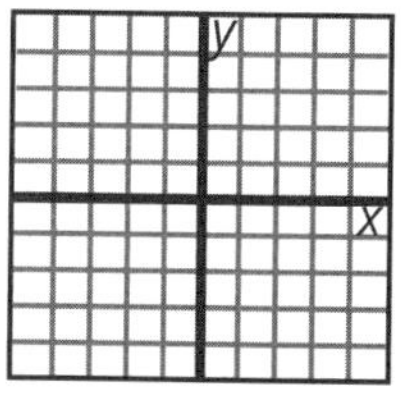

b.

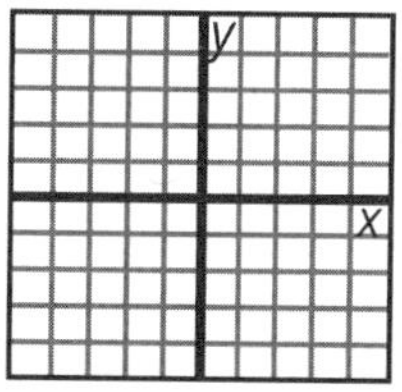

c.

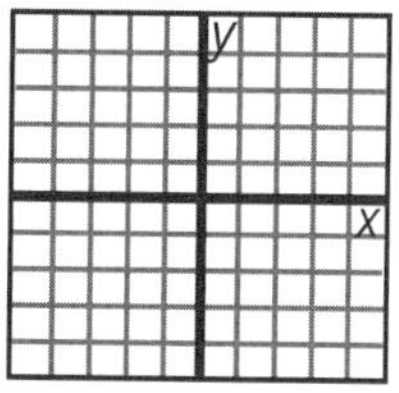

d.

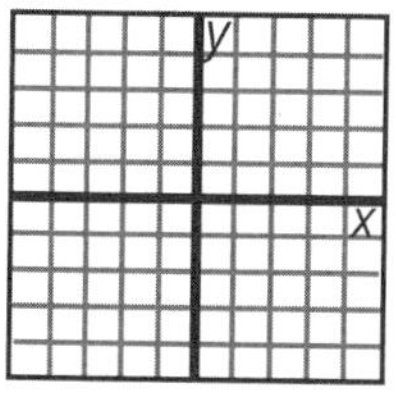

1.40 Points E and E' have symmetry with respect to the point (0, 3). Find the coordinates of E:

a. When E' is (0, 2) ____________ b. When E' is (0, 0) ____________

c. When E' is (-1, -1) ____________ d. When E' is (3, 3) ____________

a.

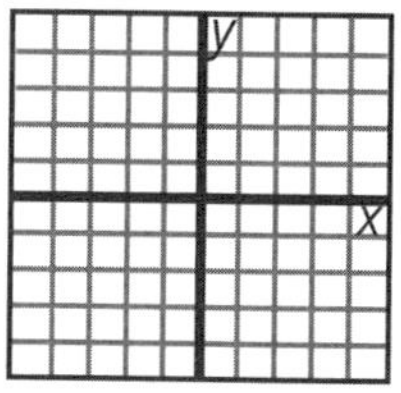

b.

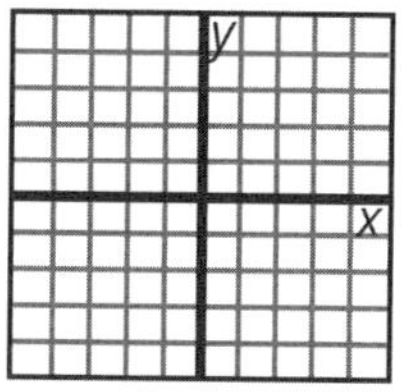

c.

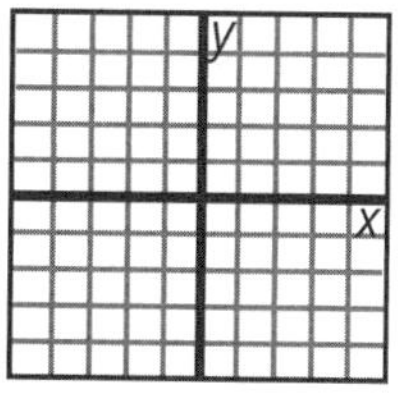

d.

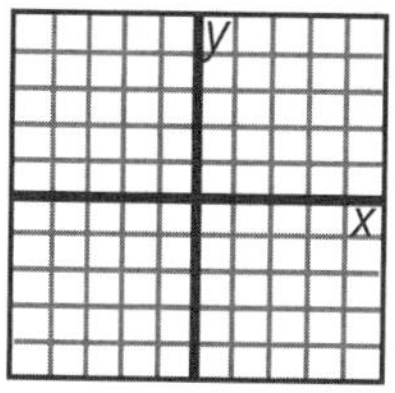

1.41 Points *F* and *F'* have symmetry with respect to point *S*. Find the coordinates of point *S*:

a. __________ when *F* is point (2, 5) and *F'* is point (4, 5).

b. __________ when *F* is point (2, 5) and *F'* is point (-4, 5).

c. __________ when *F* is point (3, 0) and *F'* is point (-3, 0).

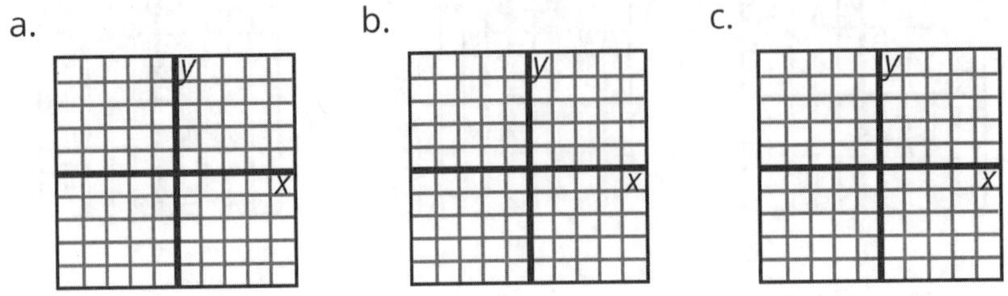

Complete the following activities.

1.42 If *m* is a line of symmetry, plot the partner points for the ones shown.

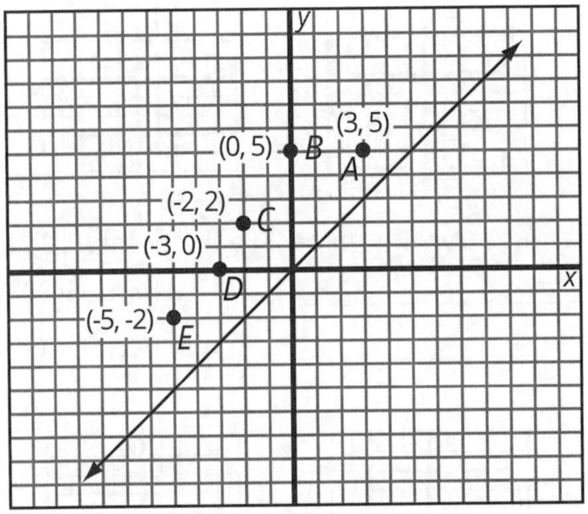

1.43 If *l* is a line of symmetry, sketch the rest of the figure so it is symmetrical to *l*.

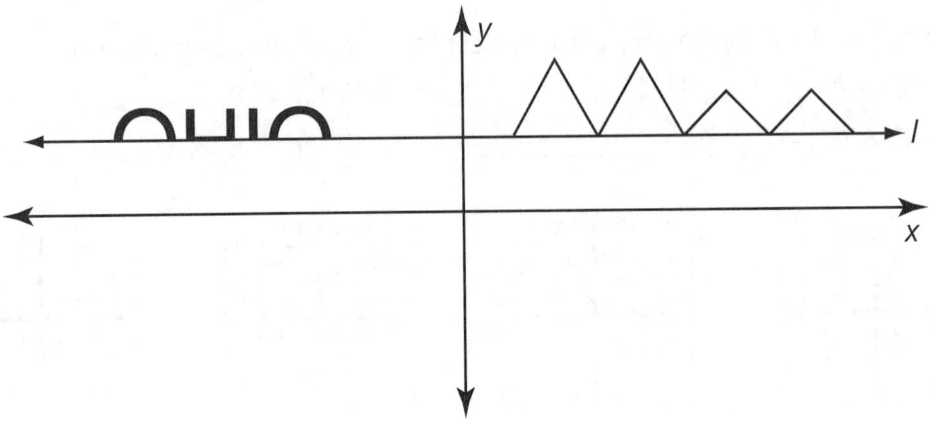

1.44 If n is a line of symmetry, sketch the rest of the figure so it is symmetrical to n.

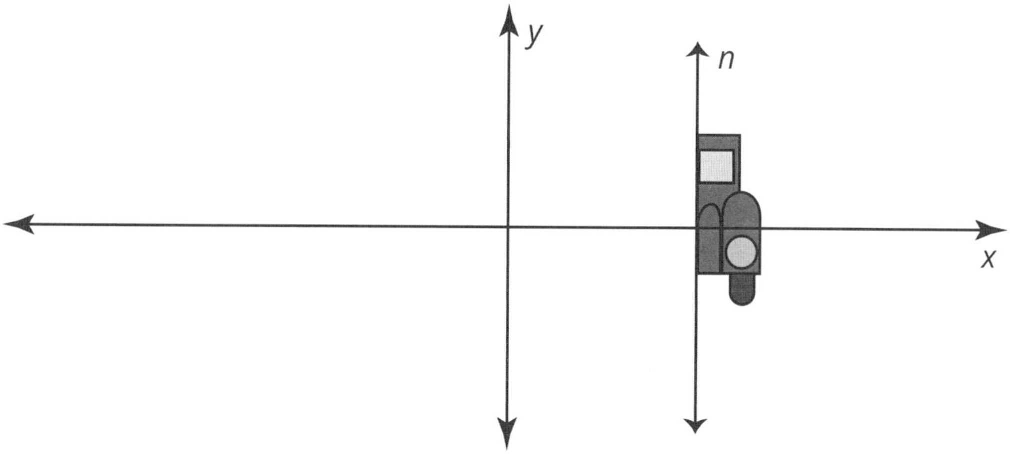

1.45 If P is a point of symmetry, sketch the rest of the figure so it is symmetrical to P.

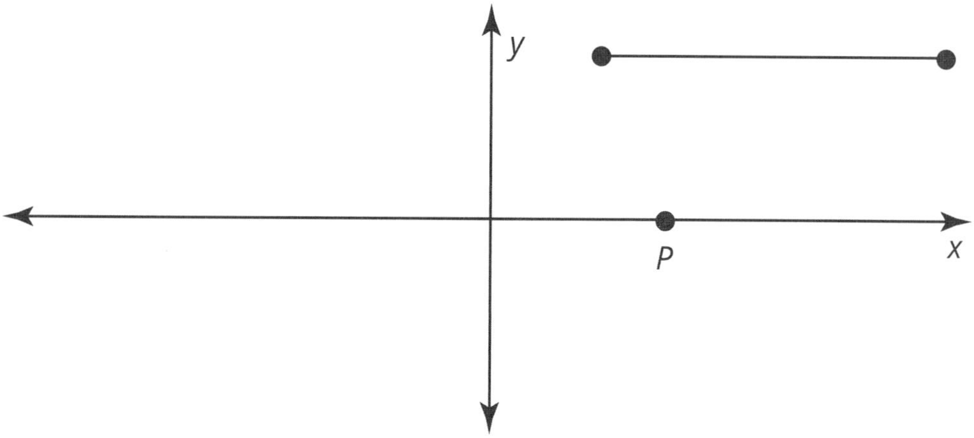

1.46 If Q is the point of symmetry, sketch the rest of the figure so it is symmetrical to Q.

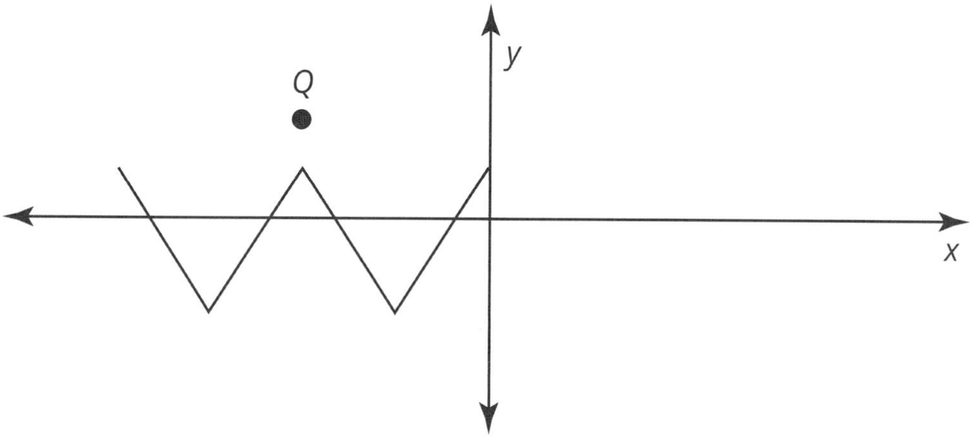

1.47 If R is the point of symmetry, sketch the rest of the figure so it is symmetrical to R .

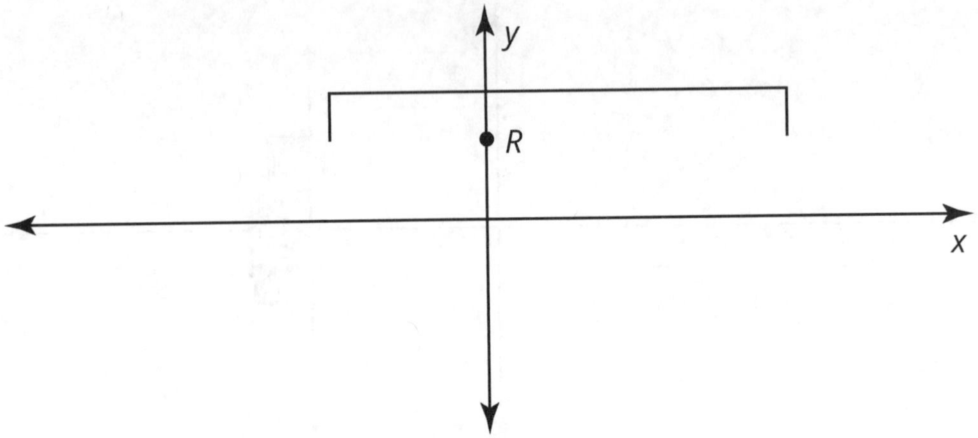

1.48 If N is the plane of symmetry, sketch the rest of the figure so it is symmetrical with respect to plane N.

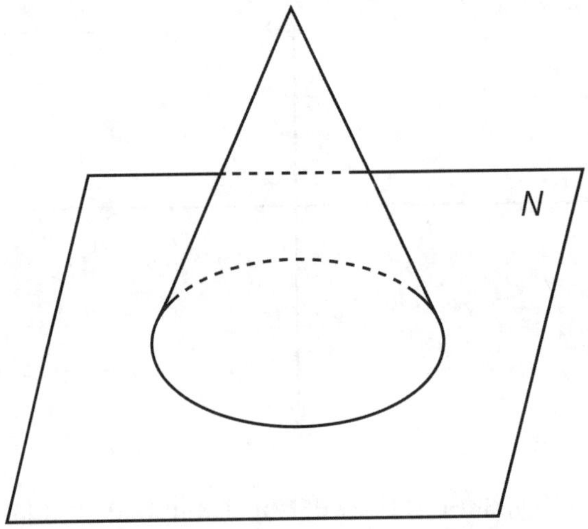

GRAPHS OF ALGEBRAIC CONDITIONS

A graph in a plane is a set of points. In a previous LIFEPAC we studied sets of points called *loci*. A locus is a set of points that meet certain geometric conditions. We often use the term *graph* for a set of points whose coordinates meet certain algebraic conditions.
The graph is represented by a drawing in a coordinate plane.

Model 1: Graph the set of points such that $x = 3$.

Solution: The condition here is that the x-coordinate of all the points must be 3. No restriction is placed on the y-coordinate. Some points that belong to the graph are (3, 1), (3, 2) (3, 0), (3, -1), (3, 4), and (3, -8). To show all such points, we draw a line.

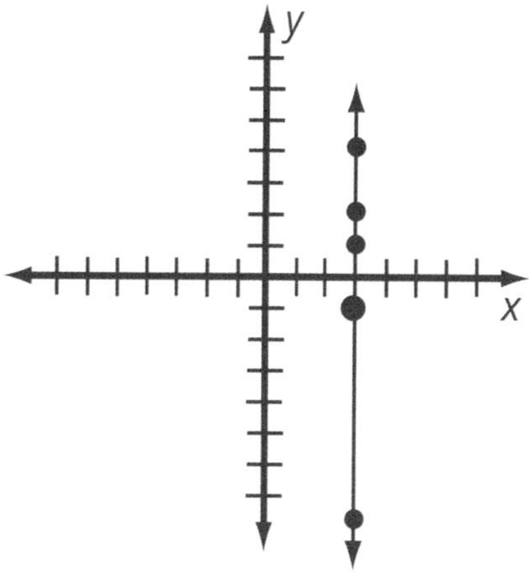

Model 2: Find $\{(x, y): x + y = 2\}$. Read this expression, "The set of all ordered pairs, or points, such that $x + y = 2$."

Solution: We solve the equation for y: $y = 2 - x$. The y-coordinate equals the x-coordinate subtracted from 2. Some points that satisfy this condition are (2, 0), (1, 1), (0, 2), (-1, 3), and (-2, 4). To show all points that make the conditions true, we draw a line through the points.

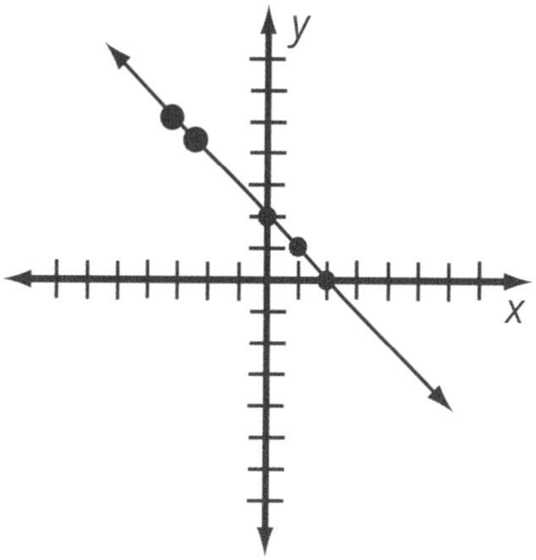

Model 3: Graph $\{(x, y): y \leq 2\}$.

Solution: All points on the line and in the shaded region have a y-coordinate that is less than or equal to 2. No restrictions are placed on the x-coordinate.

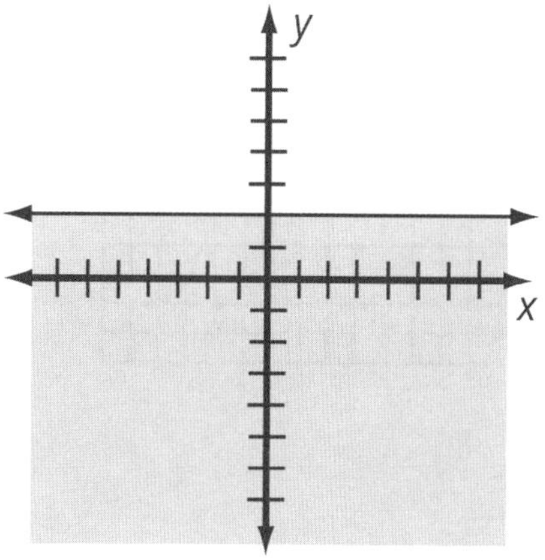

Model 4: Graph $\{(x, y): -5 < x \leq 1\}$.

Solution: All points on the solid line and in the shaded region meet the condition on x. The points on the broken line do not meet those conditions for x.

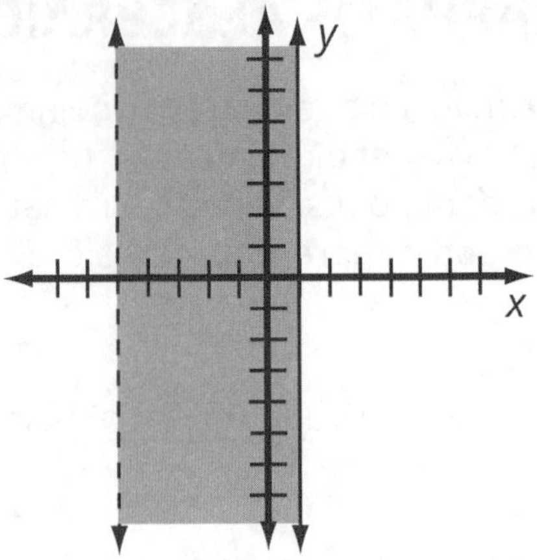

In the coordinate plane, draw the graph of the conditions given.

1.49 $x = 4$

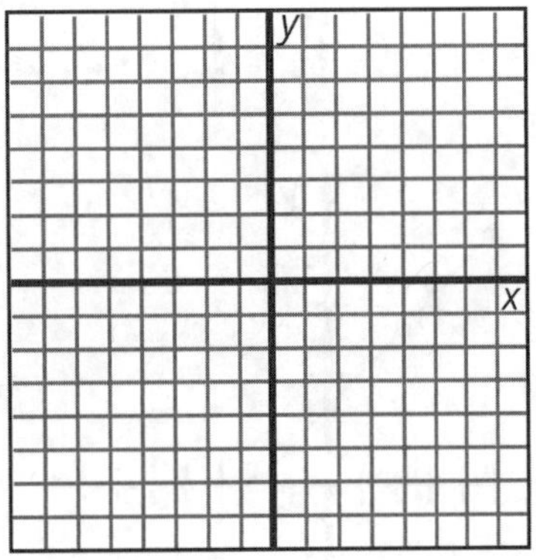

1.50 $x = -3$

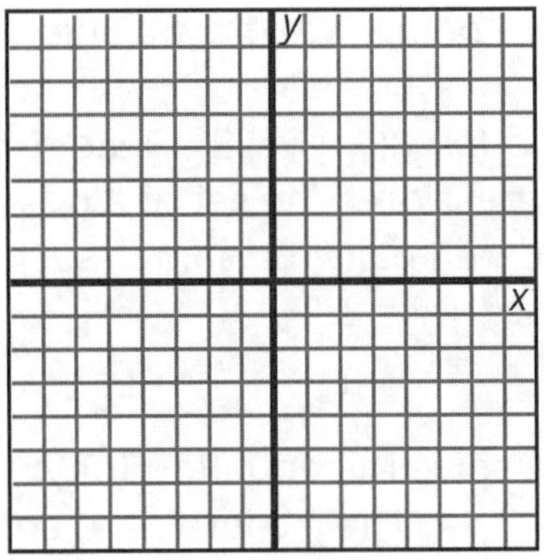

1.51 $x > -2$

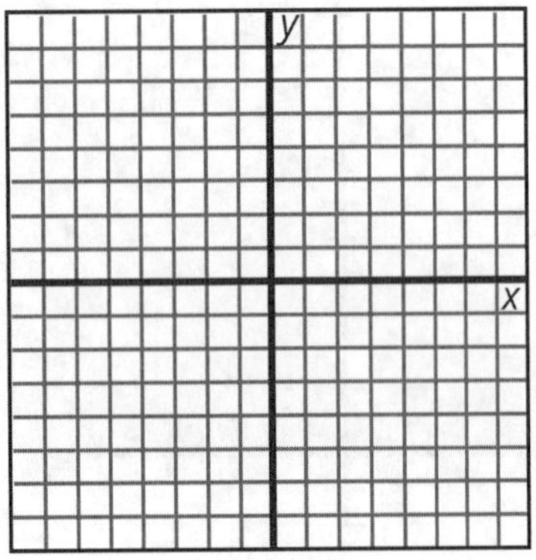

1.52 $y \leq 3$

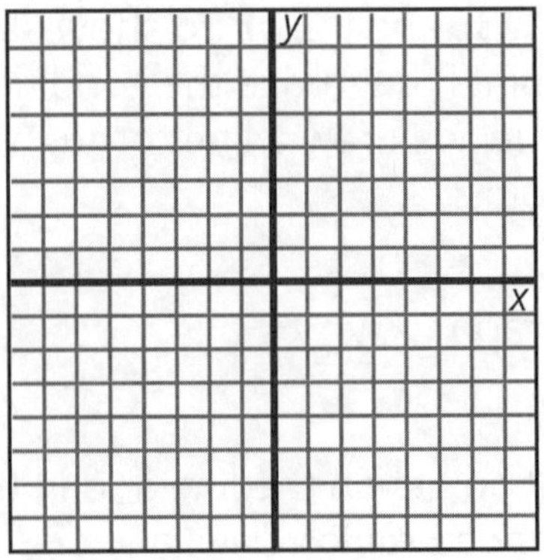

1.53 $x + y = 10$

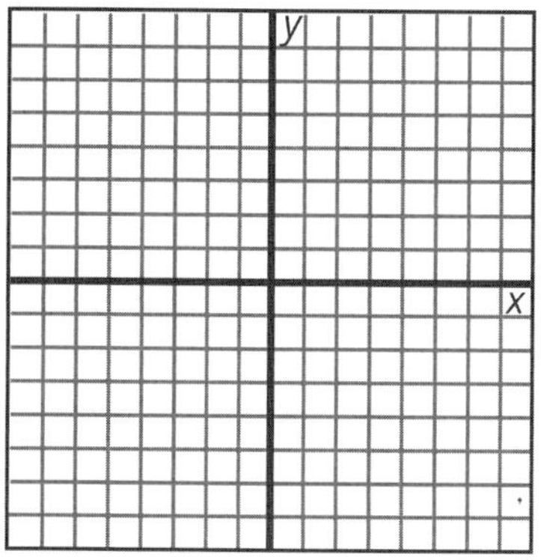

1.54 $3 \leq x \leq 5$

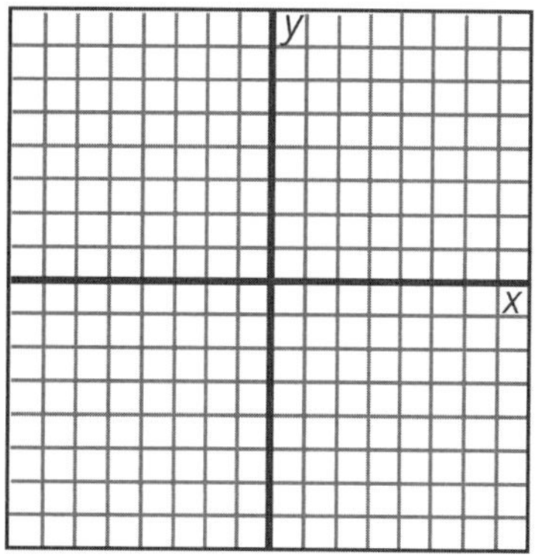

1.55 $-4 < y \leq 8$

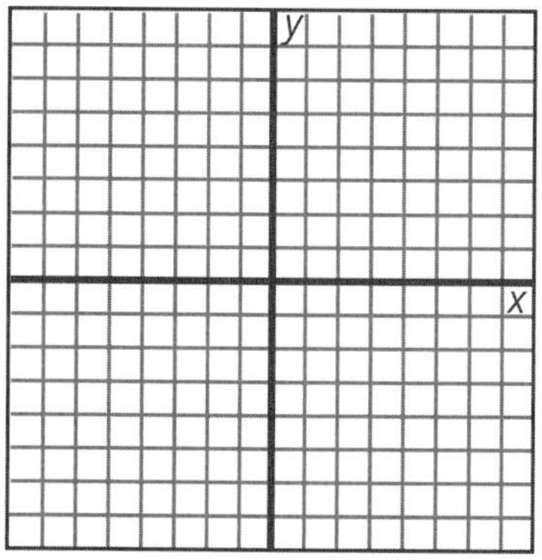

1.56 $x + y > 10$

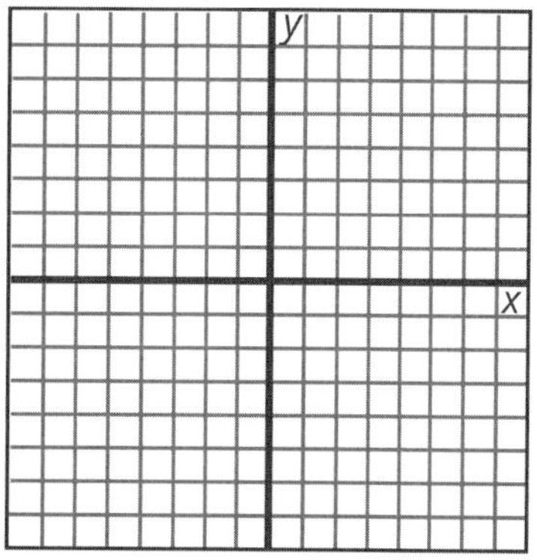

1.57 $x + y < 10$

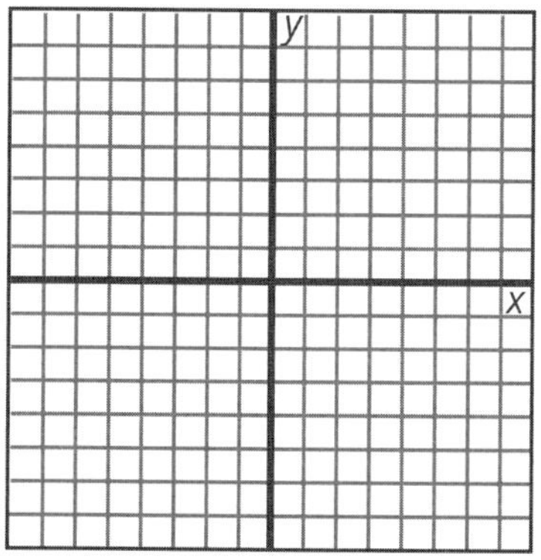

Model 1: Graph $\{(x, y): x = 3\} \cup \{(x, y): y \geq 2\}$.

Solution: Find the union of the two individual graphs.

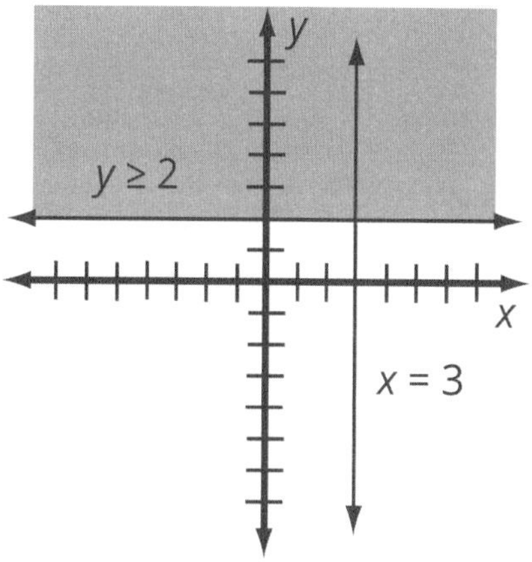

Model 2: Graph $\{(x, y): x = 3\} \cap \{(x, y)\ y \geq 2\}$.

Solution: Find the intersection of the two individual graphs.

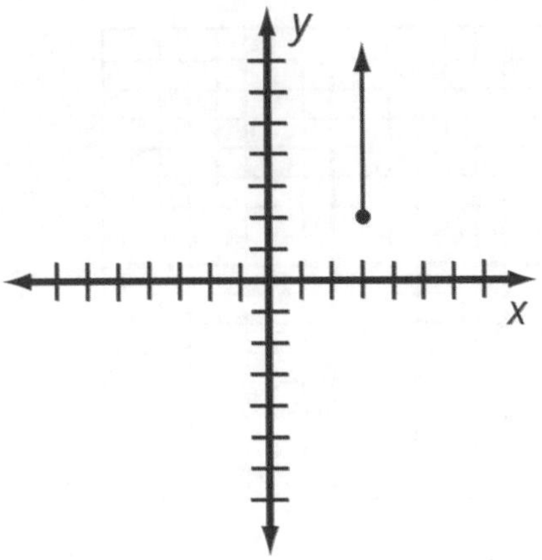

Draw the graph of the following conditions.

1.58 $\{(x, y): x = 2\} \cup \{(x, y): y = -2\}$

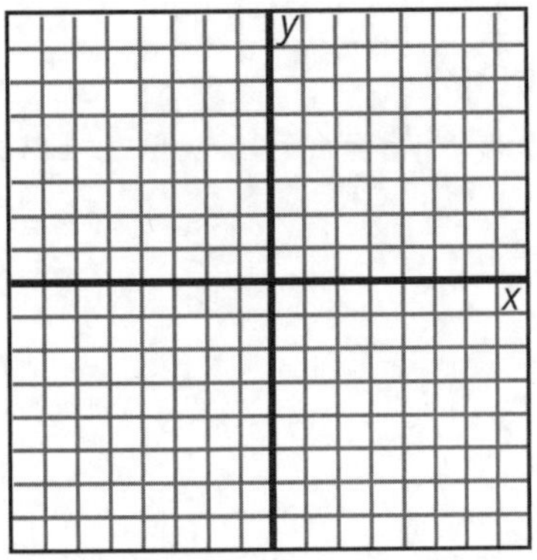

1.59 $\{(x, y): x \leq 2\} \cup \{(x, y): y \geq 1\}$

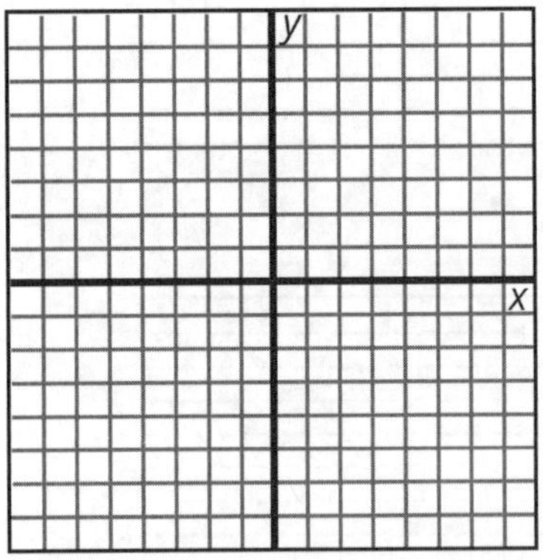

1.60 $\{(x, y): x = 2\} \cap \{(x, y): y \leq -3\}$

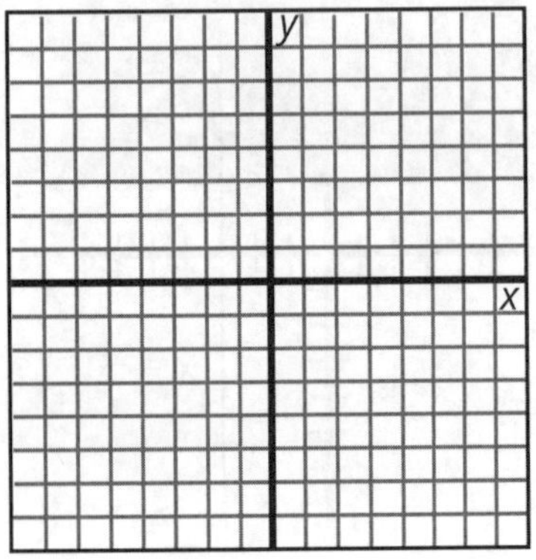

1.61 $\{(x, y): x \geq 2\} \cap \{(x, y): y \geq 2\}$

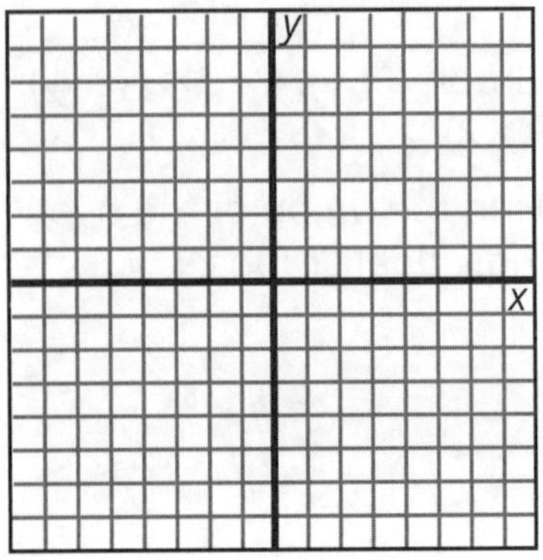

1.62 $\{(x, y): x \geq 3y\} \cap \{(x, y): x \geq 2\}$

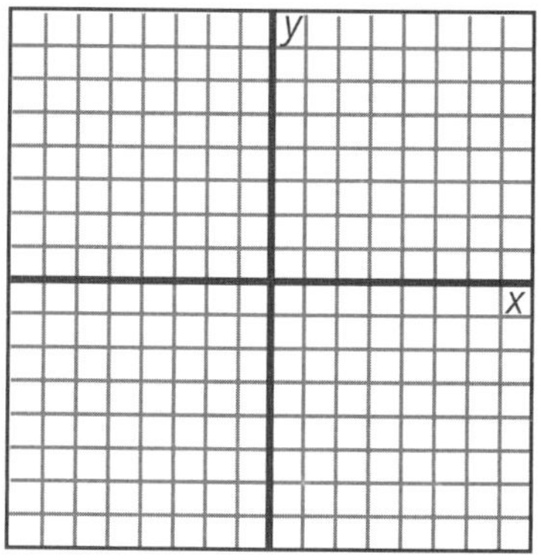

State the conditions that the following graphs meet.
Write the equation or inequality that is shown by the graph.

1.63 ______________________________

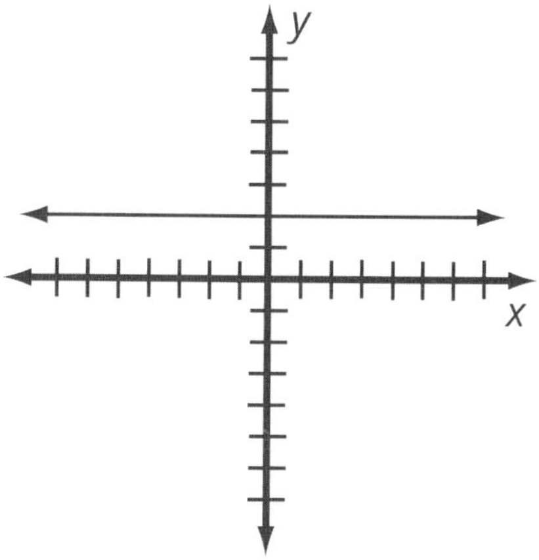

1.64 ______________________________

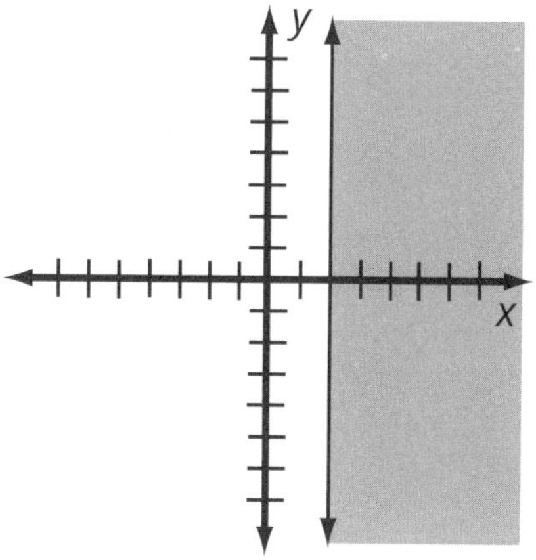

1.65 ______________________________

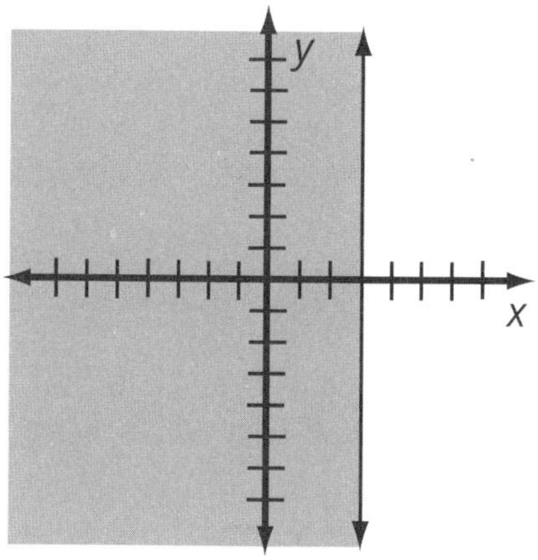

1.66 ______________________________

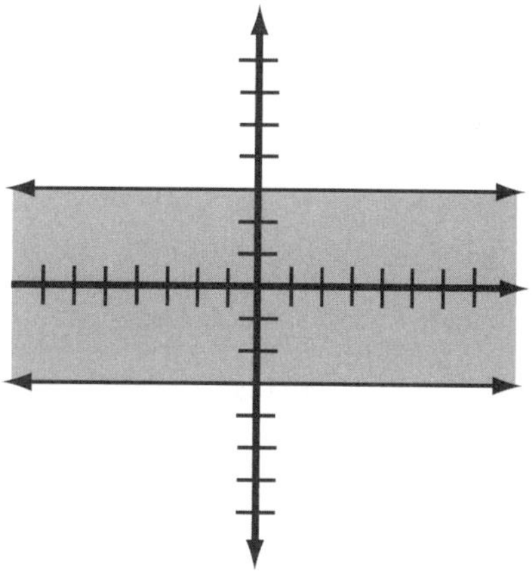

1.67 ____________________________

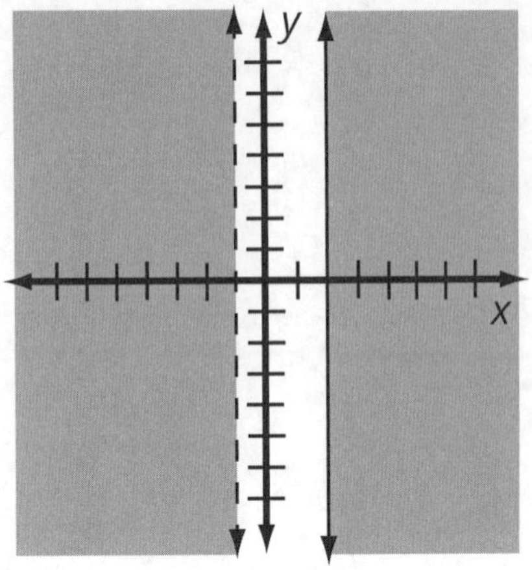

Review the material in this section in preparation for the Self Test. The Self Test will check your mastery of this particular section. The items missed on this Self Test will indicate specific areas where restudy is needed for mastery.

SELF TEST 1

Write the coordinates of these points (each answer, 2 points).

1.01 *A* (________________)

B (________________)

C (________________)

D (________________)

E (________________)

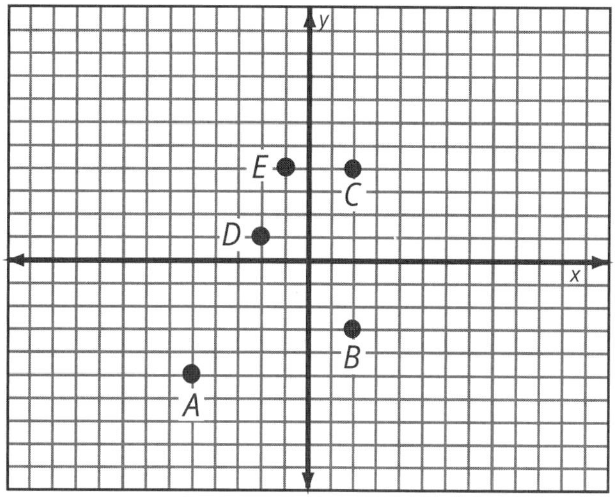

Graph these points on the axes given (each answer, 2 points).

1.02 *R* (3, 2) *U* (-2, -4)

S (5, 0) *V* (6, -3)

T (0, -4)

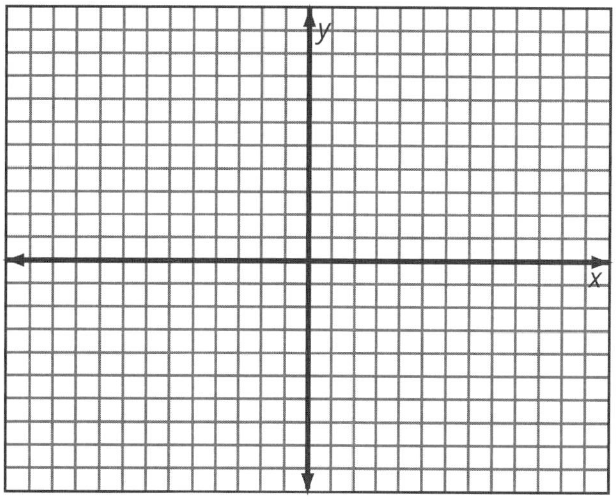

1.03 In which quadrant are these points located? (each answer, 2 points)

a. (2, 3) ________________ d. (-2, 5) ________________

b. (4, -2) ________________ e. (5, 1) ________________

c. (-3, -2) ________________

Tell the kind of symmetry these figures have: point, line, plane, or none (each answer, 2 points).

1.04 ______________________

1.05 ______________________

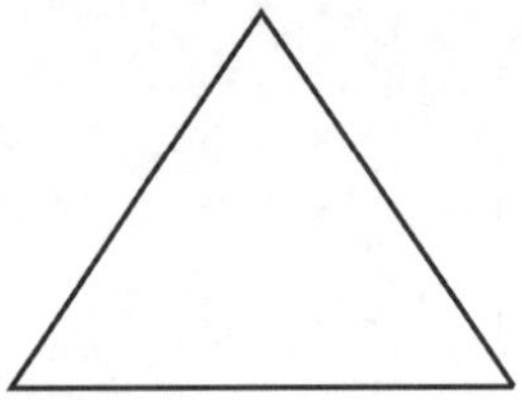

1.06 ______________________

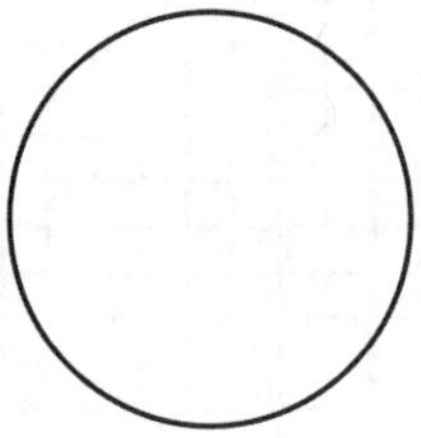

1.07 ______________________

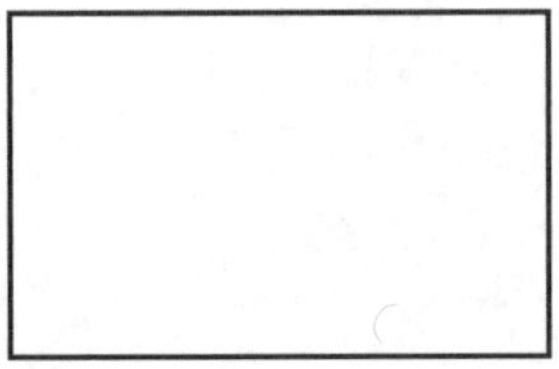

1.08 ______________________

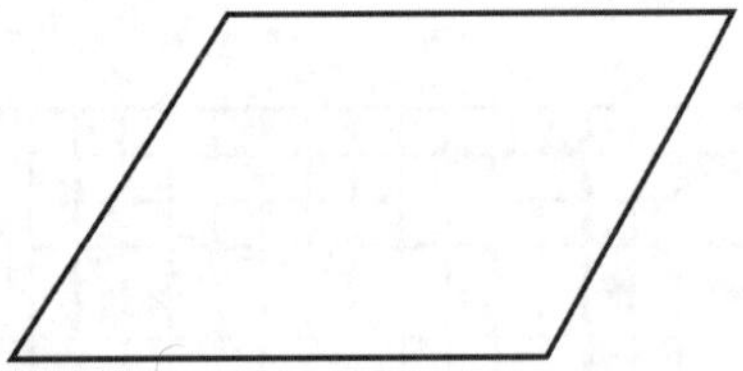

Complete these items (each answer, 3 points).

1.09 Points *A* and *A'* have symmetry with respect to the line two units above, and parallel to, the *x*-axis. Graph the points for *A'* when *A* is (1, 1), (-3, 0), (3, 4), and (-2, -1).

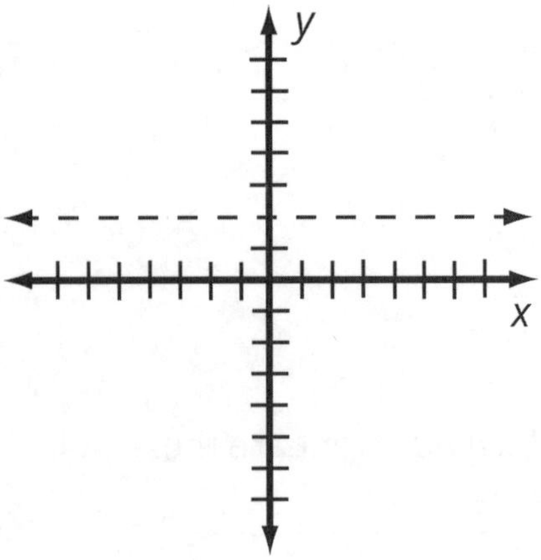

1.010 Points *B* and *B'* have symmetry with respect to *P*. Find the coordinates of *P* when *B* is (2, 8) and *B'* is (2, 2). ______________________

1.011 If l is a line of symmetry, plot the partner points for the ones shown.

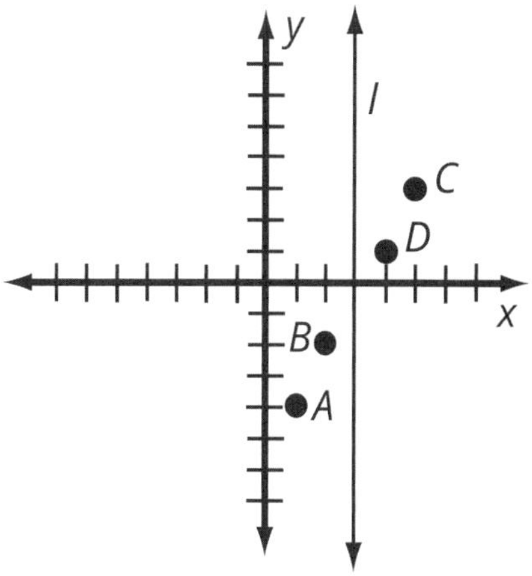

1.012 Graph the set of all points with x-coordinate twice the y-coordinate.

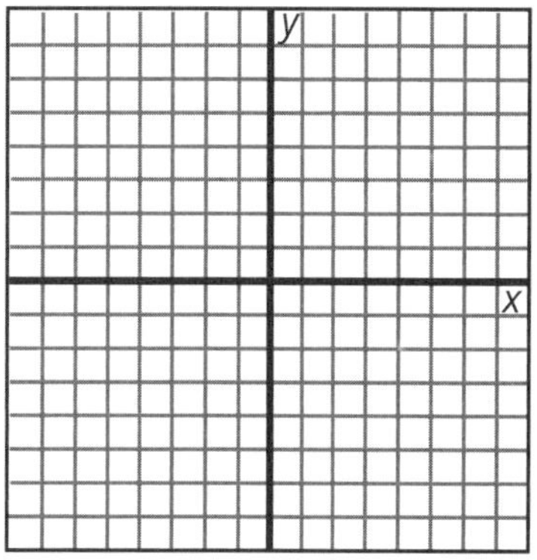

1.013 Three of the vertices of a parallelogram are (2, 1), (4, 7), and (6, 5). What are the two possible coordinates of the fourth vertex? ______________________

Graph the following conditions (each graph, 4 points).

1.014 $\{(x, y): x - y = 8\}$

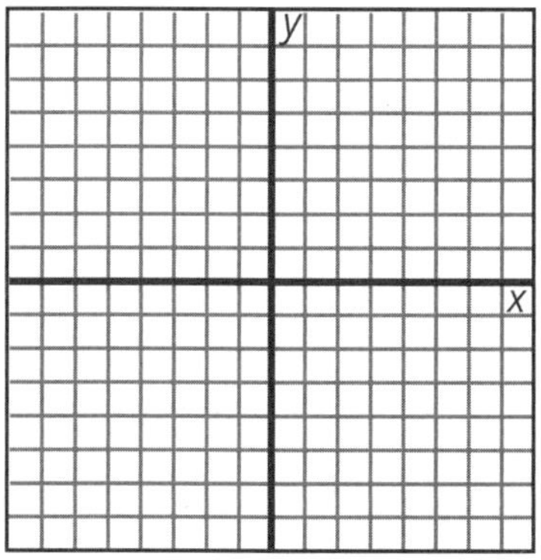

1.015 $\{(x, y); x \geq 4\}$

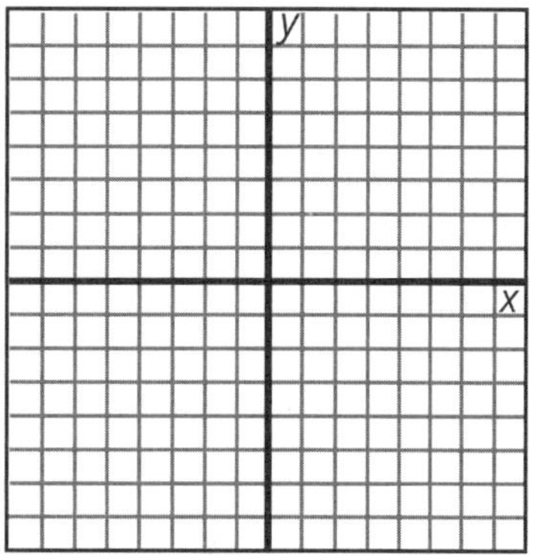

1.016 $\{(x, y): y \leq -4\}$

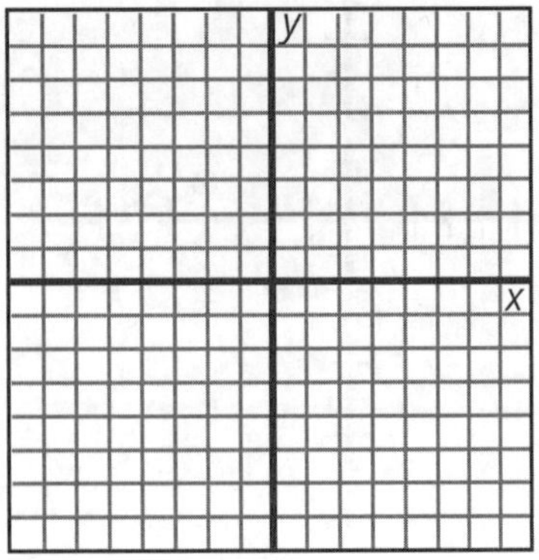

1.017 $\{(x, y): x - y \geq 8\}$

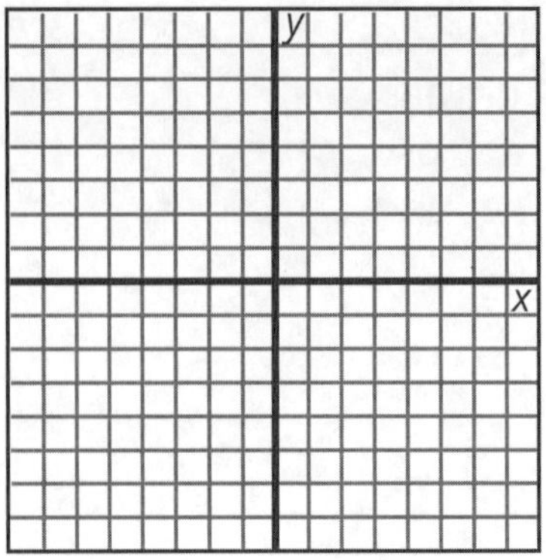

1.018 $\{(x, y): x \geq 2\} \cap \{(x, y): y \geq 2\}$

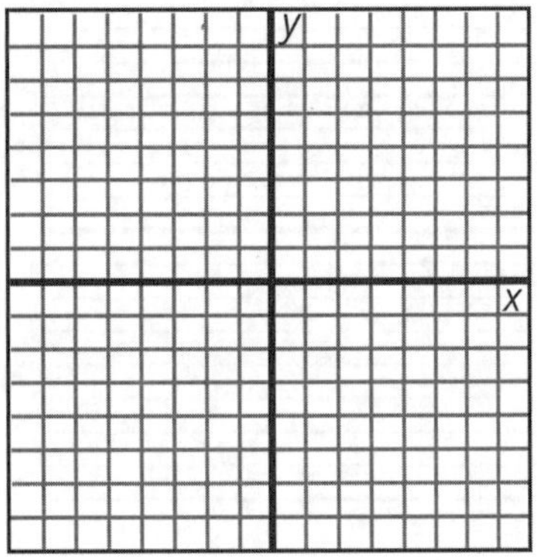

1.019 $\{(x, y)\} : x \leq 3 \} \cup \{ (x, y) : y \leq -3\}$

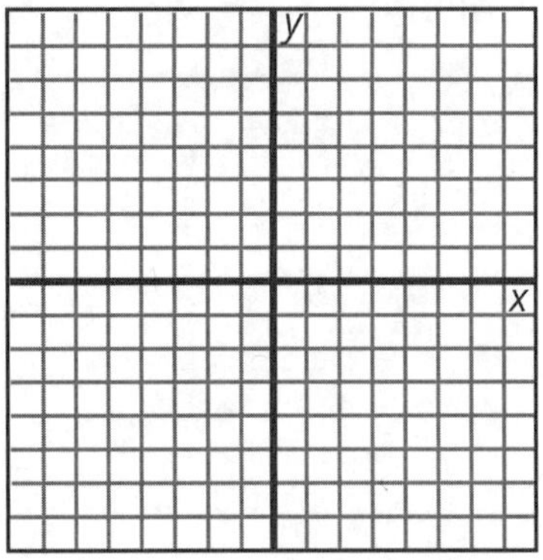

1.020 $\{(x, y) : x = 4\} \cap \{(x, y): y = 4\}$

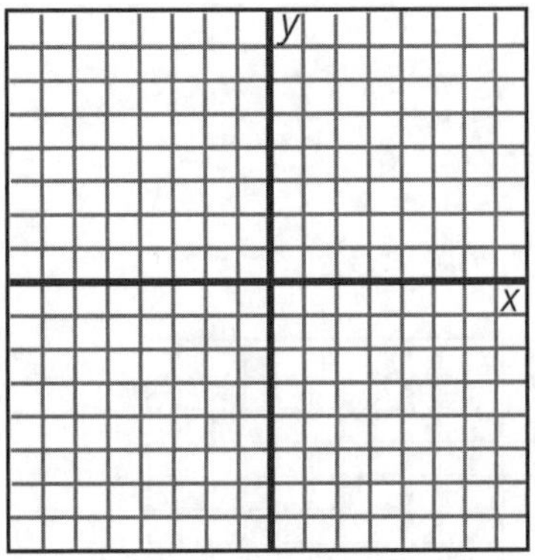

67/83 **SCORE**__________ **TEACHER**__________ __________

initials date

2. DISTANCE

Finding the distance between two points is an important concept in coordinate geometry. We use it in finding perimeters of polygons, in finding the equation of a circle, and in finding the midpoint of segments. Many other applications of the distance between points will be made.

Section Objectives

Review these objectives. When you have finished this section, you should be able to:

5. Solve problems using the distance formula.
6. Find the equation of a circle.
7. Solve problems using the midpoint formula.

DISTANCE FORMULA

To find the distance between two points that have the same *y*-coordinate, we take the absolute value of the difference in their *x*-coordinates.

$$P_1P_2 = |6 - 2| = |4| = 4$$
$$P_3P_4 = |-5 - (-2)| = |-3| = 3$$

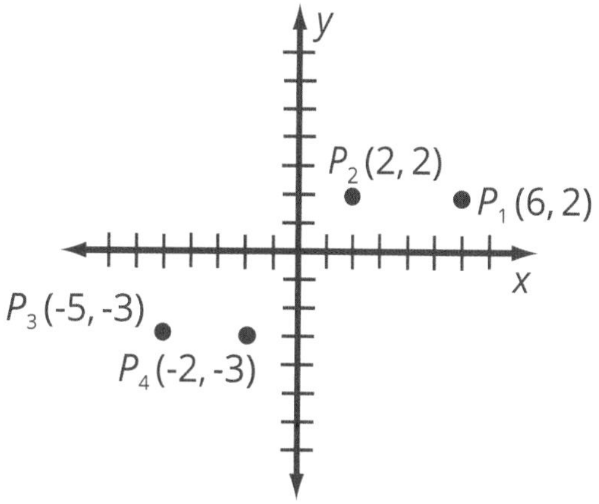

In general, when both points are on the same horizontal line, $P_1P_2 = |x_1 - x_2|$.

To find the distance between two points that have the same *x*-coordinate, we take the absolute value of the difference in their *y*-coordinates.

$$P_1P_2 = |2 - 5| = |-3| = 3$$
$$P_3P_4 = |2 - (-5)| = |2 + 5| = |7| = 7$$

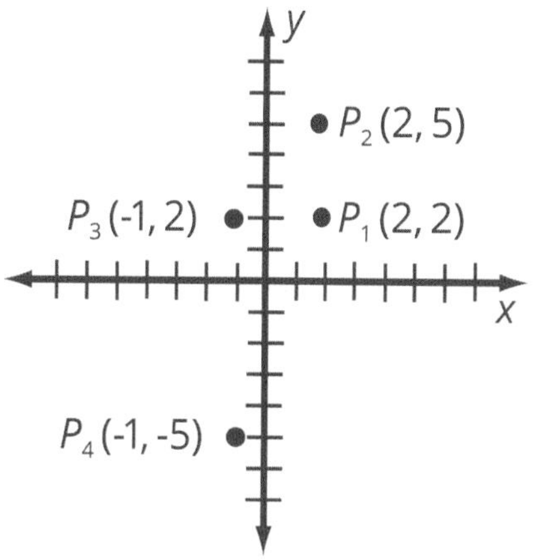

In general, when both points are on the same vertical line, $P_1P_2 = |y_1 - y_2|$.

A third possibility is that the two points are not on the same horizontal line or the same vertical line. We then find the distance with the help of the Pythagorean Theorem.

Complete a right triangle with P_1P_2 its hypotenuse and P_1Q, P_2Q its two legs. The coordinate of point Q will be (x_1, y_2). It has the same x-coordinate as P_1 and the same y-coordinate as P_2. Next we find the distances P_1Q and P_2Q. $P_1Q = |y_1 - y_2|$, $P_2Q = |x_1 - x_2|$. To find P_1P_2, we apply the Pythagorean Theorem to the right triangle:

$$(P_1P_2)^2 = (P_2Q)^2 + (P_1Q)^2$$

$$(P_1P_2)^2 = (x_1 - x_2)^2 + (y_1 - y_2)^2$$

$$P_1P_2 = \sqrt{(x_1 - x_2)^2 + (y_1 - y_2)^2}$$

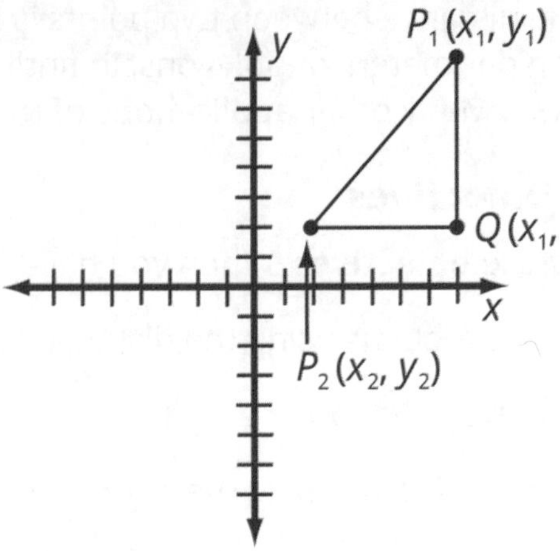

Thus, to find the distance between any two points on the coordinate plane, we use Theorem 9-1.

> **THEOREM 9-1**
>
> The distance between two points on the coordinate plane is $d = \sqrt{(x_1 - x_2)^2 + (y_1 - y_2)^2}$ where (x_1, y_1) and (x_2, y_2) are the coordinates of the two points.

Model 1: Find the distance between (3, 8) and (5, 3).

Solution:

$$d = \sqrt{(x_1 - x_2)^2 + (y_1 - y_2)^2}$$

$$d = \sqrt{(3 - 5)^2 + (8 - 3)^2}$$

$$d = \sqrt{4 + 25}$$

$$d = \sqrt{29}$$

Model 2: Find the distance between (-3, 2) and (9, -3).

Solution:

$$d = \sqrt{(x_1 - x_2)^2 + (y_1 - y_2)^2}$$

$$d = \sqrt{(-3 - 9) + (2 - [-3])^2}$$

$$d = \sqrt{144 + 25}$$

$$d = \sqrt{169}$$

$$d = 13$$

Find the distance between the points given. Simplify all irrational answers.

2.1 (2, 5) and (6, 8) $d =$ ____________

2.2 (3, 4) and (6, 8) $d =$ ____________

2.3 (-3, 2) and (9, -3) $d =$ ____________

2.4 (0, 6) and (5, 12) $d =$ ____________

2.5 (-3, -4) and (0, 0) $d =$ ____________

2.6 (0, -6) and (9, 6) $d =$ ____________

2.7 (4, 1) and (7, 5) $d =$ ____________

2.8 (-3, -6) and (3, 2) $d =$ ____________

2.9 (2, 3) and (-10, 12) $d =$ ____________

2.10 (2, 2) and (5, 5) $d =$ ____________

2.11 (0, 5) and (-5, 0) $d =$ ____________

2.12 (3, 4) and (4, 7) $d =$ ____________

2.13 (-1, -1) and (1, 3) $d =$ ____________

2.14 (-3, 0) and $(0, \sqrt{7})$ $d =$ ____________

2.15 (a, b) and $(2a, 2b)$ $d =$ ____________

Find the length of the sides of the triangles whose vertices have coordinates given. Identify the triangles as scalene, isosceles, or equilateral.

2.16 A (3, 5), B (6, 9), C (2, 6) ____________

2.17 R (1, 3), S (3, 1), T (5, 2) ____________

2.18 W (5, -5), X (-2, -2), Y (8, 2) ____________

2.19 P (0, 0), Q (6, 0), R $(3, 3\sqrt{3})$ ____________

2.20 K (7, 0), L (3, 4), M (2, -1) ____________

Find the length and width of the rectangles whose vertices are given.

2.21 *A* (2, 1), *B* (5, 4), *C* (0, 3), *D* (3, 6) ____________________

2.22 *R* (1, 1), *S* (9, 1), *T* (9, 5), *U* (1, 5) ____________________

2.23 *V* (-1, -2), *W* (3, -6), *X* (9, 0), *Y* (5, 4) ____________________

Find the perimeter and the length of the diagonals of these parallelograms.

2.24 *A* (1, 2), *B* (5, 4), *C* (6, 7), *D* (2, 5) ____________________

2.25 *R* (1, 4), *S* (0, -1), *T* (2, 2), *U* (-1, 1) ____________________

2.26 *E* (3, -2), *F* (-1, 4), *G* (-4, 1), *H* (0, -5) ____________________

Find the perimeter of these trapezoids.

2.27 *A* (2, 1), *B* (6, 5), *C* (3, 5), *D* (1, 3) ____________________

2.28 *E* (4, 2), *F* (2, 5), *G* (-2, 5), *H* (-4, 2) ____________________

2.29 *W* (-2, 1), *X* (-2, 4), *Y* (3, 7), *Z* (3, -1) ____________________

EQUATION OF A CIRCLE

We can find an equation for a circle by using the distance formula and the definition for a circle.

Remember that a circle is the set of points in a plane that are *equidistant* from a given point, called the center.

If we know the coordinates of the center and the length of the radius, we can use the distance formula, because the radius is the distance from the center to any point on the circle.

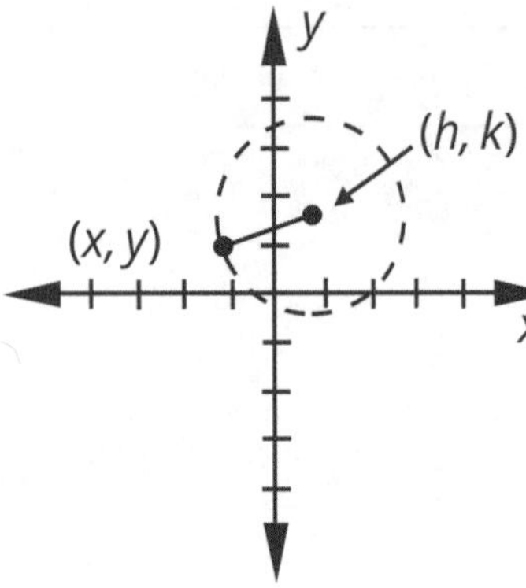

Let (h, k) be the coordinates of the center and the radius equal to r. (x, y) are the coordinates of any point on the circle.

$$d = \sqrt{(x_1 - x_2)^2 + (y_1 - y_2)^2}$$

$$r = \sqrt{(x - h)^2 + (y - k)^2}$$

$$r^2 = (x - h)^2 + (y - k)^2$$

This equation gives us the next theorem.

THEOREM 9-2

The formula for a circle is $(x - h)^2 + (y - k)^2 = r^2$, where (h, k) are the coordinates of the center and r is the length of the radius.

Corollary: The formula for a circle whose center is the origin is $x^2 + y^2 = r^2$.

Model 1: Find the equation of the circle whose center is (3, 2) and has a radius of 4.

Solution: $h = 3$, $k = 2$, and $r = 4$

$(x - h)^2 + (y - k)^2 = r^2$

$(x - 3)^2 + (y - 2)^2 = 16$

Any point with coordinates that satisfy this equation is on the circle; any point on the circle has coordinates that satisfy the equation.

Model 2: Find the equation of the circle with center at (4, 5) and radius of 3. Is the point (1, 5) on the circle? Is the point (5, 1) on the circle?

Solution: $(x - h)^2 + (y - h)^2 = r^2$
$(x - 4)^2 + (y - 5)^2 = 9$

Let $x = 1$, $y = 5$:
$(1 - 4)^2 + (5 - 5)^2 = 9$
$9 + 0 = 9$
$9 = 9$

(1, 5) is a point on the circle.

Let $x = 5$, $y = 1$:
$(5 - 4)^2 + (1 - 5)^2 = 9$
$1 + 16 = 9$
$17 = 9$
(5, 1) is not a point on the circle.

If a point is in the interior of the circle, it will satisfy the inequality $(x - h)^2 + (y - k)^2 < r^2$.
If a point is in the exterior of the circle, it will satisfy the inequality $(x - h)^2 + (y - k)^2 > r^2$.

Model 3: Given the circle $(x - 2)^2 + (y + 3)^2 = 25$, where are the following points with respect to the circle: *A* (2, 1), *B* (-2, 5), and *C* (2, 2)?

Solution: *A* (2, 1)

$(2 - 2)^2 + (1 + 3)^2 \quad ? \quad 25$
$0 + 16 \quad ? \quad 25$
$16 < 25$

The point is interior to the circle.

B (-2, 5)

$(-2 - 2)^2 + (5 + 3)^2 \quad ? \quad 25$
$16 + 64 \quad ? \quad 25$
$80 > 25$

The point is exterior to the circle.

C (2, 2)

$(2 - 2)^2 + (2 + 3)^2 \quad ? \quad 25$
$25 = 25$

The point is on the circle.

Write the equation of the circle described.

2.30 Center (5, 2), radius = 3 ______________________

2.31 Center (3, -2), radius = 5 ______________________

2.32 Center (0, 0), radius = 4 ______________________

2.33 Center (0, 4), radius $\sqrt{3}$ ______________________

2.34 Center (-3, 0), radius $\sqrt{5}$ ______________________

Find the coordinates of the center and the length of the radius of the following circles.

2.35 $(x - 3)^2 + (y - 7)^2 = 49$ a. center ______________ b. radius = ____________

2.36 $(x - 5)^2 + (y + 3)^2 = 25$ a. center ______________ b. radius = ____________

2.37 $(x + 2)^2 + y^2 = 10$ a. center ______________ b. radius = ____________

2.38 $x^2 + y^2 = 16$ a. center ______________ b. radius = ____________

2.39 $(x + 3)^2 + (y - 6)^2 = 24$ a. center ______________ b. radius = ____________

2.40 $x^2 + (y - 3)^2 = 8$ a. center ______________ b. radius = ____________

Write interior, exterior, or on the circle $(x - 5)^2 + (y + 3)^2 = 25$ for each of the following points.

2.41 A (3, 2) ____________________ **2.42** B (2, 3) ____________________

2.43 C (-2, 4) ____________________ **2.44** D (5, -3) ____________________

2.45 E (5, 2) ____________________ **2.46** F (0, - 3) ____________________

Graph the following expressions.

2.47 $(x + 2)^2 + (y - 2)^2 = 25$

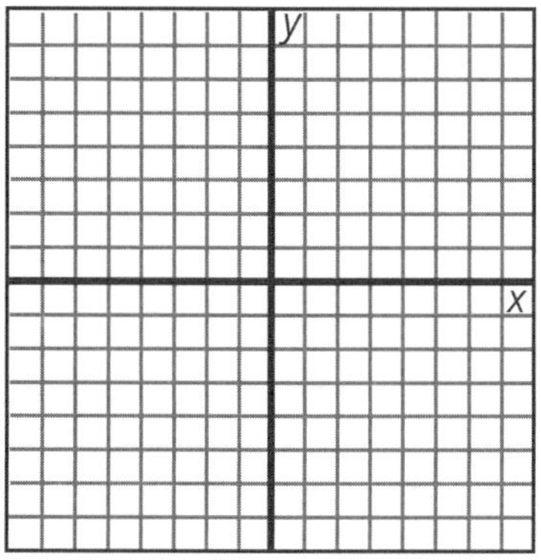

2.48 $(x - 3)^2 + y^2 = 4$

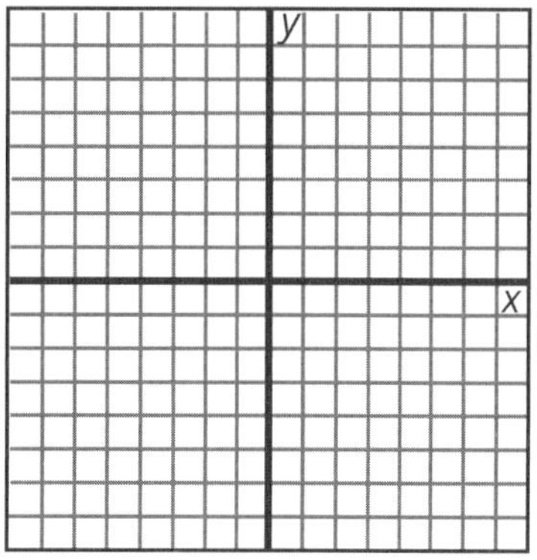

2.49 $x^2 + y^2 \geq 16$

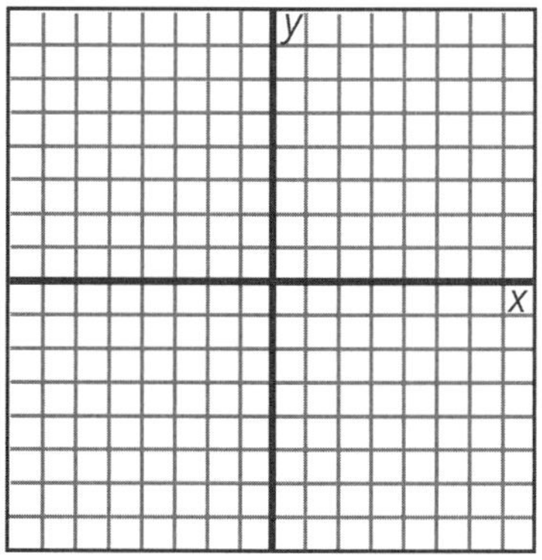

2.50 $(x + 1)^2 + (y - 3)^2 \leq 4$

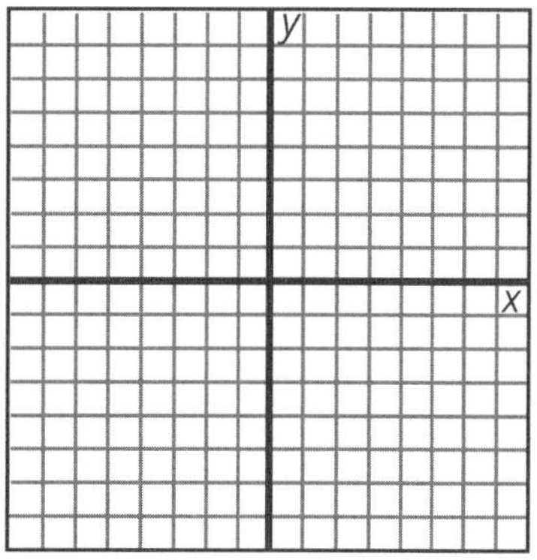

MIDPOINT FORMULA

The midpoint of a segment by definition is the point that divides the segment into two segments of equal length. We want to arrive at a method for finding the coordinates of the midpoint.

First, we shall find the coordinates of the midpoint of a horizontal segment, then a vertical segment, and finally a slanting segment.

Horizontal: $P_1P_2 = x_2 - x_1$

$P_1M = \frac{1}{2}(x_2 - x_1)$

$x_3 = x_1 + \frac{1}{2}(x_2 - x_1)$

$= x_1 - \frac{1}{2}x_1 + \frac{1}{2}x_2$

$x_3 = \frac{1}{2}x_1 + \frac{1}{2}x_2$

$x_3 = \frac{1}{2}(x_1 + x_2)$

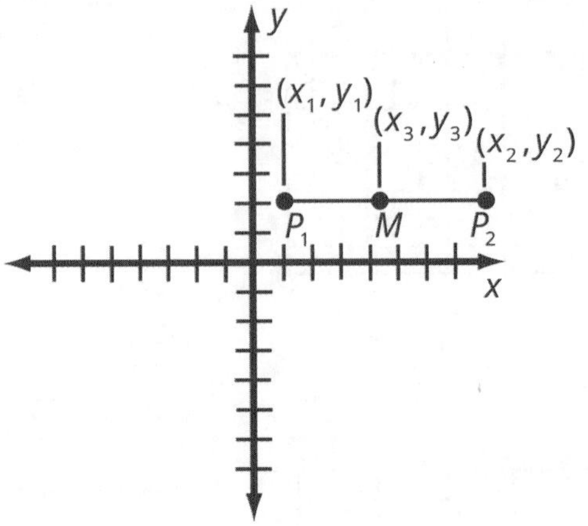

The x-coordinate of the midpoint is $\frac{1}{2}$ the sum of the x-coordinates of the endpoints.
The y-coordinate of all three points is the same.

Vertical:

$P_1P_2 = y_2 - y_1$

$P_1M = \frac{1}{2}(y_2 - y_1)$

$y_3 = y_1 + \frac{1}{2}(y_2 - y_1)$

$= y_1 + \frac{1}{2}y_2 - \frac{1}{2}y_1$

$= \frac{1}{2}y_2 + \frac{1}{2}y_1$

$y_3 = \frac{1}{2}(y_2 + y_1)$

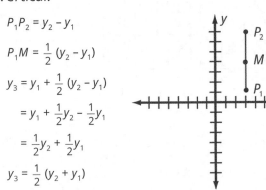

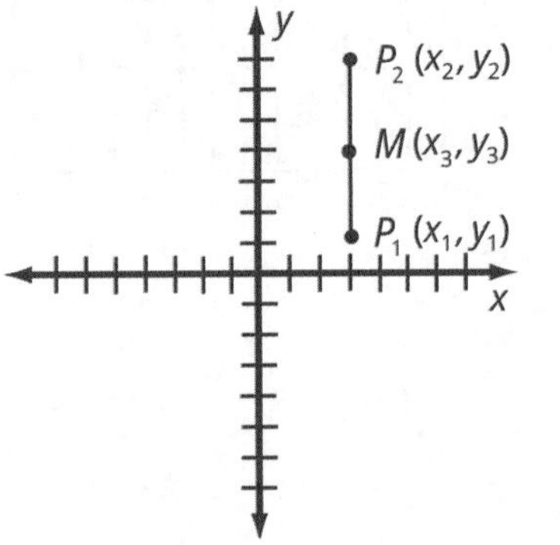

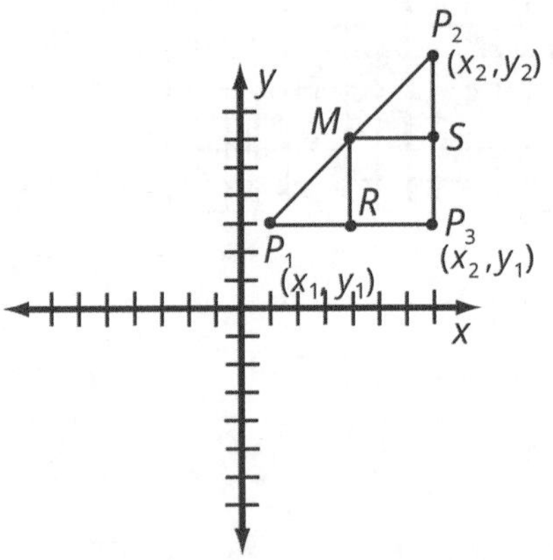

The y-coordinate of the midpoint is $\frac{1}{2}$ the sum of the y-coordinates of the endpoints.

The x-coordinates of all three points are the same.

The method for finding the midpoint of a slanting line may not be as apparent as the methods for horizontal or vertical lines, but it is actually just as easy.

The x-coordinate of R, the midpoint of P_1P_3, is $\frac{1}{2}(x_2 + x_1)$.

The y-coordinate of S, the midpoint of P_2P_3, is $\frac{1}{2}(y_2 + y_1)$.

The x-coordinate of M, the midpoint of P_1P_2, is the same as the x-coordinate of R, $\frac{1}{2}(x_2 + x_1)$.

The y-coordinate of M is the same as the y-coordinate of S, $\frac{1}{2}(y_2 + y_1)$.

Therefore, the coordinates of the midpoint are given by Theorem 9-3.

THEOREM 9-3

The coordinates of the midpoint of the segment connecting points (x_1, y_1) and (x_2, y_2) are $(\frac{1}{2}(x_2 + x_1), \frac{1}{2}(y_2 + y_1))$.

Model 1: Find the midpoint of the segment whose endpoints are (3, 2) and (5, 8).

Solution: $(\frac{1}{2}(3 + 5), \frac{1}{2}(2 + 8))$

(4, 5)

Model 2: If the midpoint of a segment is (-2, 4) and one endpoint is (1, 2), find the other endpoint.

Solution:

$x = \frac{1}{2}(x_2 + x_1)$	$y = \frac{1}{2}(y_2 + y_1)$
$-2 = \frac{1}{2}(1 + x_1)$	$4 = \frac{1}{2}(2 + y_1)$
$-4 = 1 + x_1$	$8 = 2 + y_1$
$-5 = x_1$	$6 = y_1$

The coordinates of the other endpoint are (-5, 6).

Find the coordinates of the midpoint of each segment whose endpoints are given.

	P_1	P_2	M
2.51	(3, 5),	(-2, 0)	______________
2.52	(5, 6),	(8, 2)	______________
2.53	(10, 6),	(-4, 8)	______________
2.54	(-16, 0),	(0, -16)	______________
2.55	(12, 4),	(-8, 8)	______________

Find the coordinates of the other endpoint when you are given the midpoint and one of the endpoints.

	P_1	M	P_2
2.56	(3, 5)	(-2, 0)	______________
2.57	(5, 6)	(8, 2)	______________
2.58	(10, 6)	(-4, 8)	______________
2.59	(-16, 0),	(0, -16)	______________
2.60	(12, 4)	(-8, 8)	______________

Complete these activities.

2.61 A rectangle has vertices whose coordinates are *A* (1, 4), *B* (4, -1), *C* (-1, -4), and *D* (-4, 1). Find the coordinates of the midpoints of each side. ______________________

____

2.62 A triangle has vertices whose coordinates are *A* (0, 0), *B* (5, 7), and *C* (3, 9) Find the coordinates of the midpoints of each side. ______________________

____

2.63 a. Find the midpoints of the diagonals of the rectangle in Problem 2.61.

____

b. What does your answer tell you about the diagonals of the rectangle?

____

2.64 If the vertices of a triangle are *A* (5, -1), *B* (-3, 1), and *C* (1, 5), what are the lengths of its medians?

____

2.65 The coordinates of the vertices of a square are *A* (-2, 5), *B* (3, 6), *C* (4, 1), and *D* (-1, 0). Find the coordinates of the midpoints of its sides and the midpoints of its diagonals.

a. sides: ______________________

b. diagonals: ______________________

2.66 A segment has endpoints *A* (-1, 1) and *B* (8, 4) . Find the coordinates of the three points that divide the segment into four equal parts. ______________________

2.67 The diameter of a circle has endpoints whose coordinates are *R* (-2, 2) and *S* (4, 2). Find the equation of the circle. ______________________

2.68 A circle is inscribed in a square whose vertices have coordinates *R* (0, 4), *S* (6, 2), *T* (4, -4), and *U* (-2, -2). Find the equation of the circle. ______________________

Review the material in this section in preparation for the Self Test. This Self Test will check your mastery of this particular section as well as your knowledge of the previous section.

MATH 1009

LIFEPAC TEST

NAME ______________________

DATE ______________________

SCORE ______________________

63
78

MATH 1009: LIFEPAC TEST

Complete these items (each answer, 3 points).

1. Point (-5, 5) lies in Quadrant ______________________ .

2. Point (0, 6) lies on the ________-axis.

3. Any line with no slope is parallel to the ______-axis.

4. On the graph of the equation $5x - y = 8$, the point whose y-coordinate is 7 has an x-coordinate of ____________________ .

5. If the equation of a circle is $(x + 4)^2 + (y - 6)^2 = 25$, its center is point a. ______________ and its radius is b. ______________ .

6. If the equation of a circle is $(x - 2)^2 + (y - 6)^2 = 4$, does it pass through point (5, 6)?

   ____

7. The distance between *A* (-4, 2) and *B* (4, 2) is ________________ .

8. The midpoint of *AB* of Problem 7 is ________________ .

9. The slope of *AB* of Problem 7 is ________________ .

10. The slope of a line parallel to *AB* of Problem 7 is ________________ .

11. The slope of a line perpendicular to *AB* of Problem 7 is ________________ .

12. Write the equation of the line through point (-5, 0) and parallel to the y-axis.

    ____

13. Write the equation of the line through (2, -4) and having slope of $\frac{3}{5}$. ______________________

14. Write the equation of the circle having a diameter with endpoints (-2, 1) and (6, 7).

    ____

15. Write the equation of the line that is the perpendicular bisector of the segment with endpoints (4, 1) and (2, -5) ____________________ .

16. In the figure, M and N are midpoints of $\overline{RT}$ and $\overline{ST}$. What is the length of $\overline{MN}$?

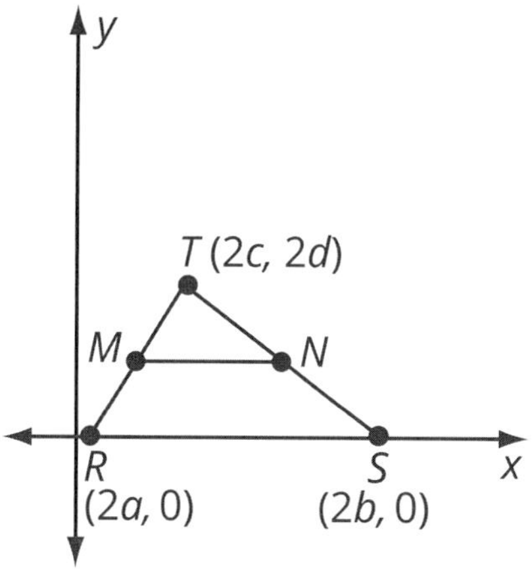

Sketch the following graphs (each graph, 4 points).

17. $4x - 3y = 12$

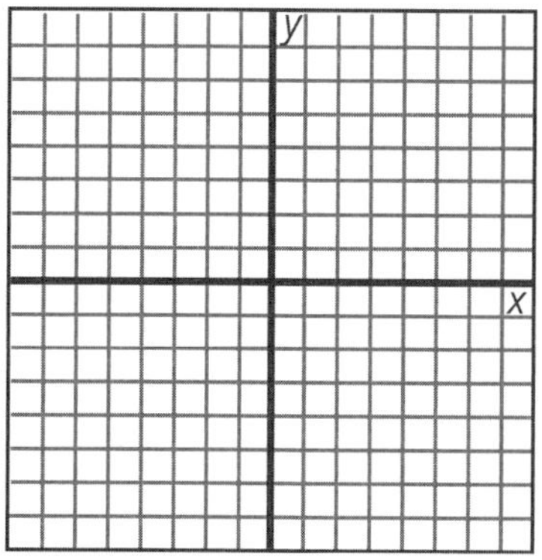

18. $|x| > 2$

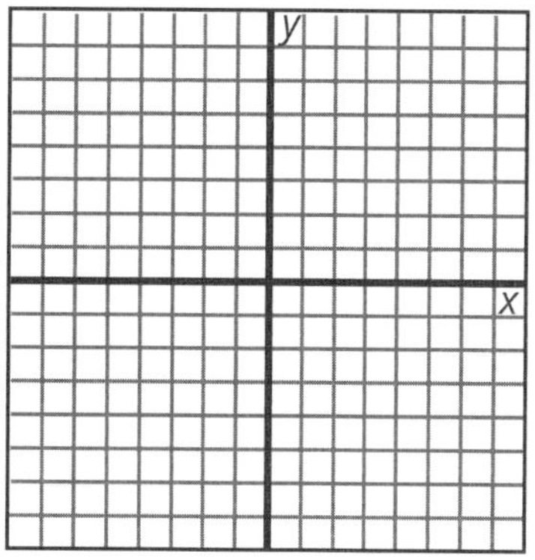

19. $\{(x, y): -1 \leq x \leq 3\}$

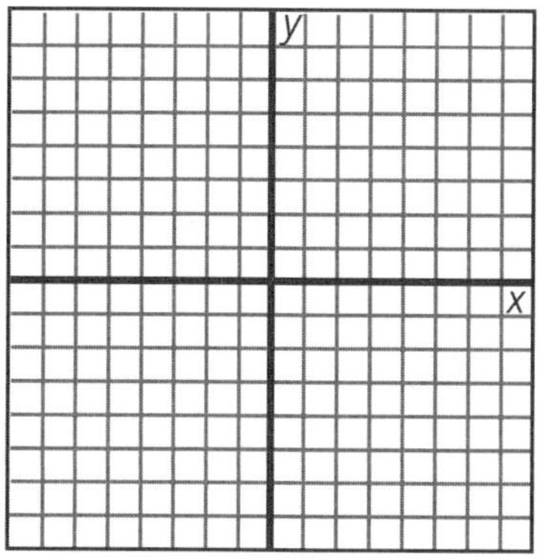

Answer true or false (each answer, 2 points).

20. ____________ A scalene triangle has symmetry with respect to a line containing a median of the triangle.

21. ____________ An equilateral triangle has symmetry with respect to a line containing an altitude of the triangle.

22. ____________ A circle has all three types of symmetry.

23. ____________ A parallelogram has symmetry with respect to the point of intersection of its diagonals.

24. ____________ A trapezoid has symmetry with respect to the median of the trapezoid.

Sketch and complete the proof (complete proof, 5 points).

25. Prove: The medians to the equal sides of an isosceles triangle are equal.

SELF TEST 2

Find the distance between these points (each answer, 3 points).

2.01 A (5, 8), B (-3, 4) AB = ____________

2.02 R (-1, 0), S (8, 6) RS = ____________

2.03 W (-6, -8), X (6, 8) WX = ____________

2.04 C (0, 4), T (-6, -3) CT = ____________

Find the equation of the circle whose center and radius are given (each answer, 3 points).

2.05 A (5, 6), radius = 3 ____________

2.06 B (7, -3), radius = $\sqrt{7}$ ____________

2.07 C (0, 8), radius = 8 ____________

2.08 D (-2, -5), radius = 1 ____________

Find the coordinates of the center and the length of the radius of these circles (each answer, 3 points).

2.09 $(x + 3)^2 + (y - 5)^2 = 25$

a. center ____________ b. radius ____________

2.010 $(x - 3)^2 + (y - 5)^2 = 8$

a. center ____________ b. radius ____________

2.011 $(x + 5)^2 + (y + 7)^2 = 16$

a. center ____________ b. radius ____________

2.012 $(x - 4)^2 + y^2 = 12$

a. center ____________ b. radius ____________

Is the given point interior, exterior, or on the circle $(x + 2)^2 + (y - 3)^2 = 81$? (each answer, 3 points).

2.013 P (8, 4) ____________ **2.014** Q (3, 0) ____________

2.015 R (6, 3) ____________ **2.016** S (-2, 12) ____________

Find the coordinates of the midpoint of the segment whose endpoints are given (each answer, 3 points).

2.017 A (2, 3) and B (6, 11) ________________

2.018 R (0, 5) and S (12, -5) ________________

2.019 W (-3, -7) and X (-8, -4) ________________

2.020 P (5, 5) and Q (-5, -5) ________________

Complete these items (each answer, 3 points).

2.021 Find the length of the medians of the triangle whose vertices are A (-1, -2), B (3, 6), and C (1, 0).

____

2.022 Find the length of the median of a trapezoid whose vertices have coordinates R (0, 3), S (2, 7), T (8, 7) and U (12, 3). ________________________

2.023 Find the coordinates of the point of symmetry of a circle whose equation is $x^2 + (y + 4)^2 = 12$. ________________________

2.024 A parallelogram whose vertices have coordinates R (1, -1), S (6, 1), T (8, 5) and U (3, 3) has a shorter diagonal of ________________________

Write the kind(s) of symmetry: point, line, plane, or none (each answer, 2 points).

2.025 ________________ **2.026** ________________ **2.027** ________________

D E F

2.028 ________________ **2.029** ________________ **2.030** ________________

H 2 3

Write the coordinates of the points shown (each answer, 2 points).

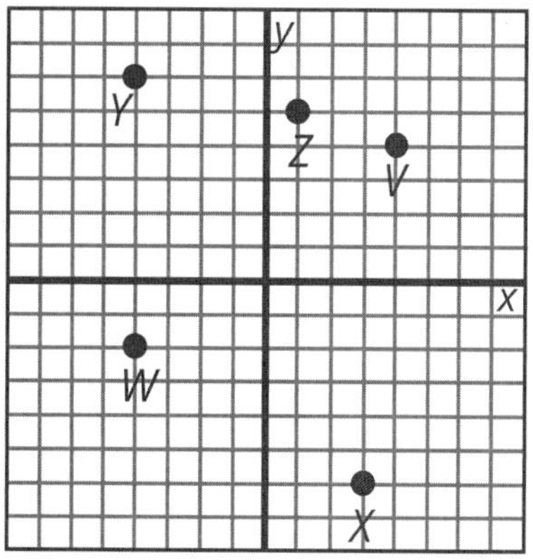

2.031 *V* ____________________

2.032 *W* ____________________

2.033 *X* ____________________

2.034 *Y* ____________________

2.035 *Z* ____________________

85/106 **SCORE** ____________ **TEACHER** ____________ ____________
initials date

3. LINES

One characteristic of lines that we are now interested in is their slope. Knowing the slopes of two lines, we can determine if they are parallel or perpendicular or if they intersect in some other way. With the help of slope, we can write the equation of a line.

Section Objectives

Review these objectives. When you have finished this section, you should be able to:

8. Find the slope of a line.
9. Identify parallel and perpendicular lines using slope.
10. Write the equation of a line.

SLOPE

If we place several lines on the coordinate axes, we notice that they slant different amounts and in different directions. This "slantiness" is called the *slope* of the line.

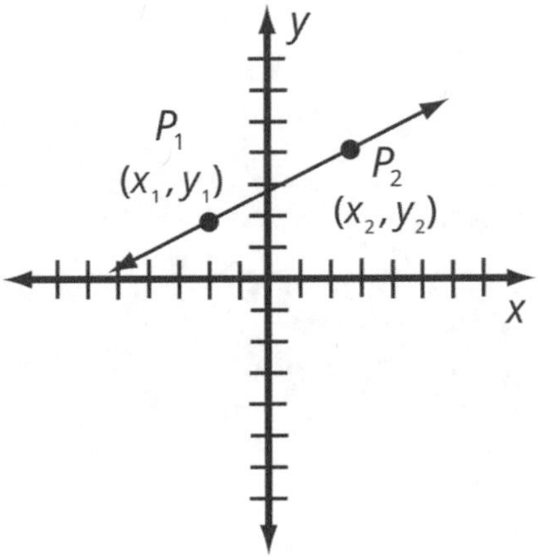

We define the slope of a line as the ratio of the difference in the *y*-coordinates to the difference in the *x*-coordinates of any two points on the line. We usually represent slope by the letter *m*.

DEFINITION

$$Slope = m = \frac{y_2 - y_1}{x_2 - x_1}$$

Since slope is a real number, it can be positive, negative, or zero depending on the coordinates of the two points.

Model 1: Slope of $\overleftrightarrow{AB}$

$$m = \frac{y_2 - y_1}{x_2 - x_1}$$

$$= \frac{9 - 4}{5 - (-1)}$$

$$= \frac{5}{6}$$

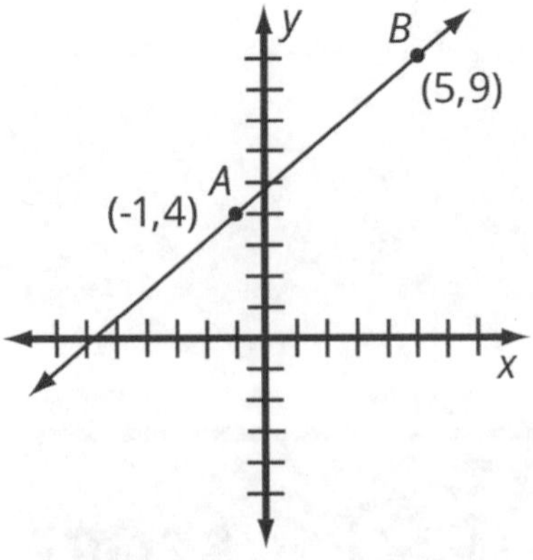

Model 2: Slope of $\overleftrightarrow{CD}$

$$m = \frac{y_2 - y_1}{x_2 - x_1} = \frac{6-3}{-2-2} = -\frac{3}{4}$$

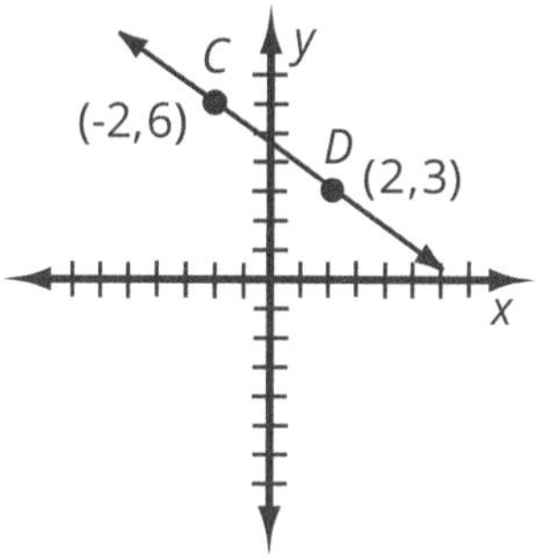

Model 3: Slope of $\overleftrightarrow{RS}$

$$m = \frac{y_2 - y_1}{x_2 - x_1} = \frac{2-3}{3-4} = \frac{-1}{-1} = 1$$

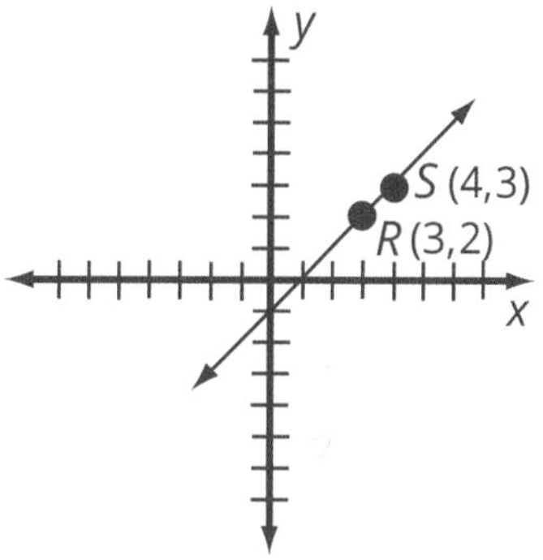

The order in which we subtract the coordinates is not important, but the order must stay the same for both *x*- and *y*-coordinates.

Model 1: Slope of $\overleftrightarrow{AB}$

$$m = \frac{4-9}{-1-5} = \frac{5}{6}$$

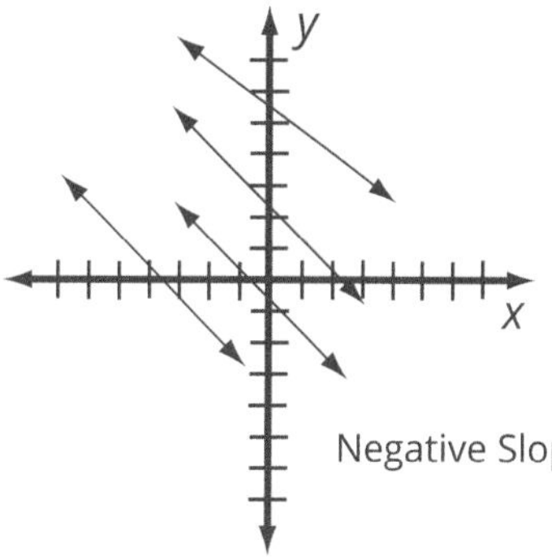

Negative Slope

Model 2: Slope of $\overleftrightarrow{CD}$

$$m = \frac{3-6}{2-(-2)} = -\frac{3}{4}$$

Model 3: Slope of $\overleftrightarrow{RS}$

$$m = \frac{3-2}{4-3} = \frac{1}{1} = 1$$

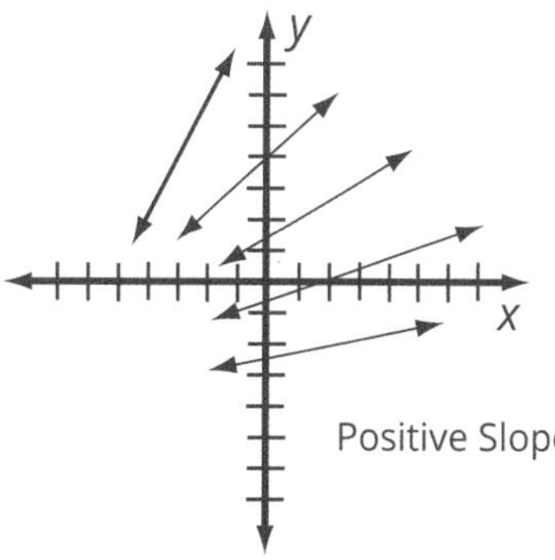

Positive Slope

We notice also that any line that goes from a lower left to an upper right direction will have a positive slope number. A line that goes from an upper left to a lower right direction will have a negative slope number.

A special case is that of a line that is parallel to the *y*-axis. If we apply the formula for slope, we get the following result.

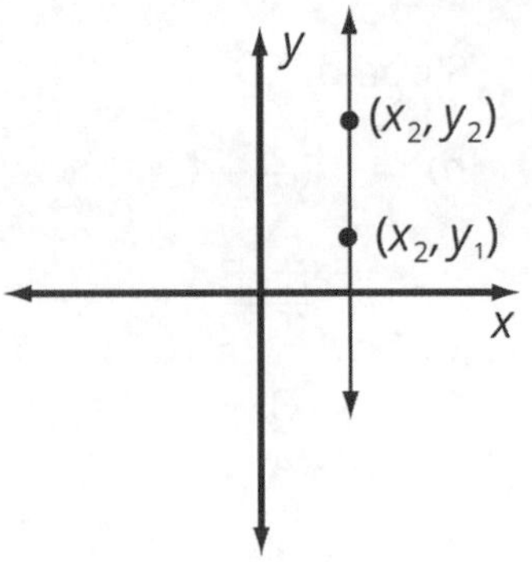

$$m = \frac{y_2 - y_1}{x_2 - x_2}$$

$$m = \frac{y_2 - y_1}{0}$$

Since division by zero is not defined, we say that any line parallel to the *y*-axis has *no slope*.

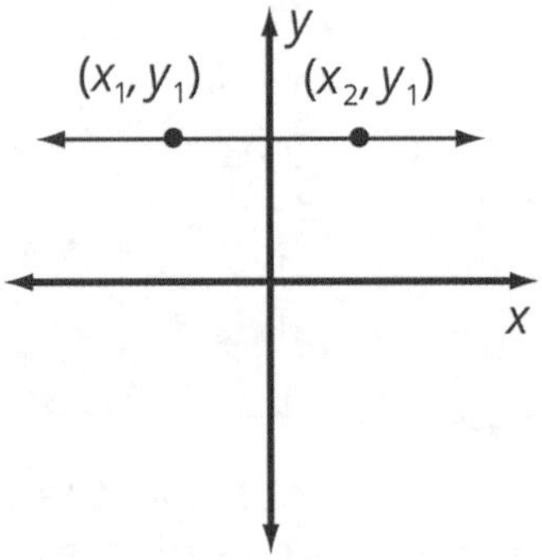

A line parallel to the *x*-axis, on the other hand, does have a slope number: *zero*.

$$m = \frac{y_1 - y_1}{x_2 - x_1} = \frac{0}{x_2 - x_1}$$

$$m = 0$$

Find the slope of the line that contains the points named.

3.1 *A* (3, 2), *B* (7, 8) $m =$ ______________

3.2 *R* (0, 4), *S* (5, 0) $m =$ ______________

3.3 *X* (2, -1), *Y* (0, 4) $m =$ ______________

3.4 *C* (3, 8), *D* (-2, 5) $m =$ ______________

3.5 *J* (1, -4), *K* (3, -1) $m =$ ______________

3.6 *G* (3, -2), *H* (7, -2) $m =$ ______________

3.7 *E* (0, 0), *F* (*a*, *b*) $m =$ ______________

3.8 *A* (0, *d*), *B* (*d*, 0) $m =$ ______________

3.9 *K* (*c* + *d*, *c* – *d*), *L* (*c* – *d*, *c* + *d*) $m =$ ______________

3.10 *P* (1, 2), *Q* (3, 4) $m =$ ______________

Use the slope formula to find the missing coordinate.

3.11 *P* (3, 2), *Q* (8, ____) $m = \frac{3}{5}$

3.12 *R* (0, _____), *S* (-4, 2) $m = 5$

3.13 *T* (13, 2), *W* (____ , -5) $m = -\frac{7}{2}$

3.14 A (________, 0), B (5, 10) $m = 2$

3.15 C (a, b), D (c, ________) $m = j$

The slope of a line is the same number whatever two points on the line we choose with which to calculate the slope. We can test a set of points to see if they are collinear.

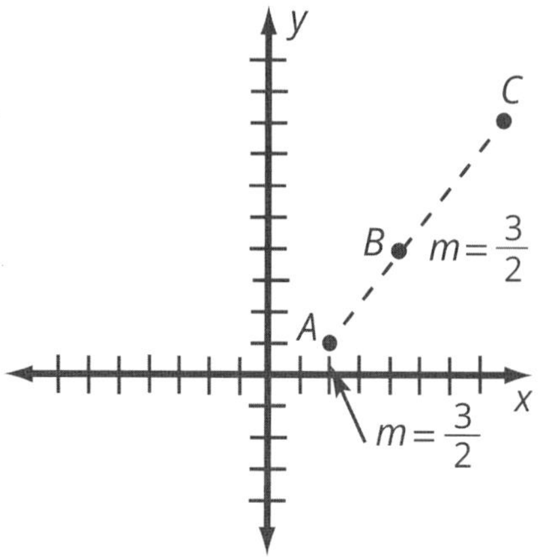

Model: Are the points A (2, 1), B (4, 4), and C (8, 10) collinear?

Solution: Find the slope of each pair of points.

All three segments have the same slope; therefore, points A, B, and C are collinear.

$$m_{AB} = \frac{4-1}{4-2} = \frac{3}{2};$$

$$m_{BC} = \frac{10-4}{8-4} = \frac{3}{2};$$

$$m_{AC} = \frac{10-1}{8-2} = \frac{3}{2}$$

Test the following sets of points to see if they are collinear. Write *yes* or *no*.

3.16 R (-1, 1), S (2, 4), T (6, 8) ________

3.17 C (1, -1), D (3, 4), E (5, 8) ________

3.18 W (4, 4), X (6, 2), Y (-8, 16) ________

3.19 A (3, 0), B (-2, 10), C (0, 5) ________

3.20 P (0, 3), Q (2, 0), R (4, -3) ________

Find the slope of the sides of the following quadrilaterals.

3.21 A (0, 0), B (2, 4), C (5, 4), D (4, 0)

m_{AB} = ________ m_{BC} = ________ m_{CD} = ________ m_{DA} = ________

3.22 R (-4, 0), S (-2, 6) , T (4, 4), U (2, -2)

m_{RS} = ________ m_{ST} = ________ m_{TU} = ________ m_{UR} = ________

3.23 M (0, 0), N (2, 4), P (8, 4), Q (12, 0)

m_{MN} = ________ m_{NP} = ________ m_{QP} = ________ m_{QM} = ________

Find the following slopes.

3.24 Find the slopes of the sides of a triangle whose vertices are P (1, 3), Q (3, 5), and R (6, 2).

m_{PQ} = ________________ m_{QR} = ________________ m_{RP} = ________________

3.25 Find the slopes of the medians of the triangle in Problem 3.24.

median to QR: m = ________________

median to PR: m = ________________

median to PQ: m = ________________

PARALLEL AND PERPENDICULAR LINES

A look at the graph of several nonvertical parallel lines suggests that their slopes are equal. We can prove this assumption to be true and obtain the next theorem.

THEOREM 9-4

Two nonvertical lines are parallel if, and only if, they have equal slopes:
$l_1 \| l_2$ if $m_1 = m_2$.

Given: $l \| k$
Prove: $m_l = m_k$

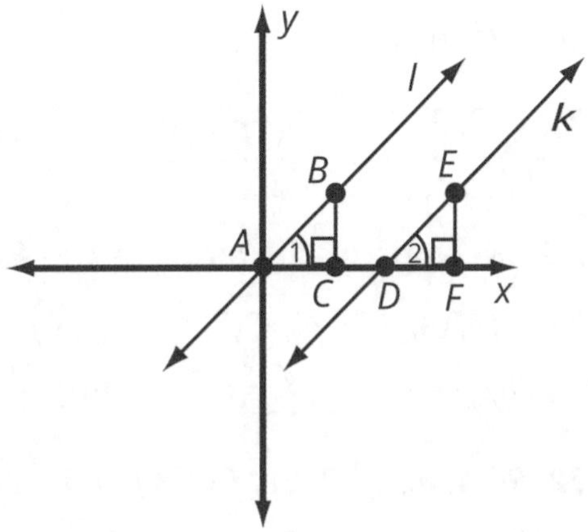

From B and E taken on l and k, draw $\overline{BC}$ and $\overline{EF}$ perpendicular to the x-axis.

AC is the difference of the x-coordinates of A and B and BC is the difference of the y-coordinates.

So $m_l = \frac{BC}{AC}$.

Similarly $m_k = \frac{EF}{DF}$. $\triangle ABC \sim \triangle DEF$ by $\angle 1 = \angle 2$ and $\angle C = \angle F$.

$\frac{BC}{AC} = \frac{EF}{DF}$ because corresponding sides of similar triangles are proportional.

By substitution, $m_l = m_k$.

The converse of Theorem 9-4 is also true.

Given: $m_l = m_k$

Prove: $l \parallel k$

Suppose $l \nparallel k$. Then the lines will intersect in some point P.
Draw $\overline{PQ}$ perpendicular to the x-axis; $m_l = \frac{PQ}{AQ}$ and $m_k = \frac{PQ}{DQ}$. Therefore, $m_l \neq m_k$. This statement is a contradiction of the given information, so $l \parallel k$ is false and $l \nparallel k$ is true.

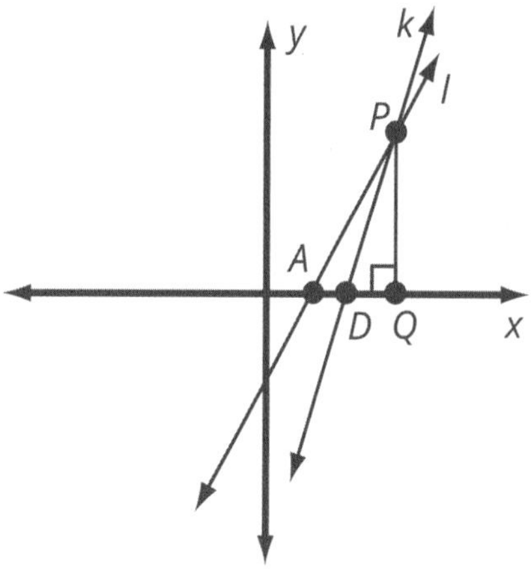

The phrase *if and only if* lets us use a statement and its converse by one theorem.

Our next theorem deals with the slopes of perpendicular lines.

THEOREM 9-5

Two nonvertical lines are perpendicular if, and only if, the slope of one is the negative reciprocal of the slope of the other line: $m_1 = -\frac{1}{m_2}$ or $m_1m_2 = -1$.

Given: $l_1 \perp l_2$

Prove: $m_1m_2 = -1$

Let points A, B, C have coordinates as shown.

$$m_1 = \frac{d}{c-a} \qquad m_2 = \frac{d}{c-b}$$

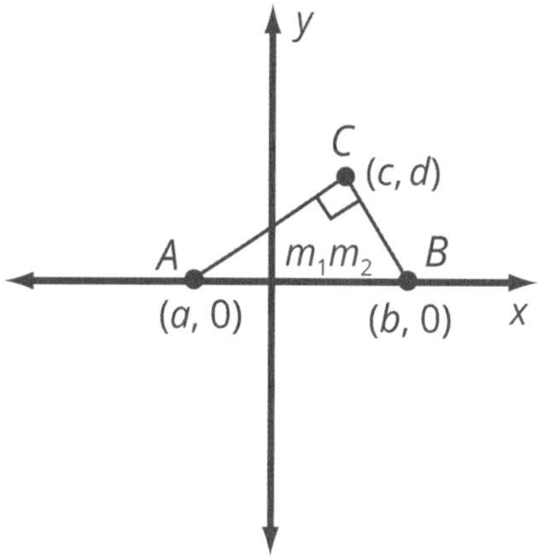

ABC is a right triangle so $(AC)^2 + (BC)^2 = (AB)^2$. Substitute the values for AC, BC, and AB in the formula and obtain the following results.

$$AC = \sqrt{d^2 + (c-a)^2}$$
$$BC = \sqrt{(c-b)^2 + d^2}$$
$$AB = \sqrt{(b-a)^2}$$
$$\left(\sqrt{d^2+(c-a)^2}\right)^2 + \left(\sqrt{(c-b)^2+d^2}\right)^2 = \left(\sqrt{(b-a)^2}\right)^2$$
$$d^2 + c^2 - 2ac + a^2 + c^2 - 2bc + b^2 + d^2 = b^2 - 2ab + a^2$$
$$2d^2 + 2c^2 - 2ac - 2bc + 2ab = 0$$
$$c^2 - ac + ab - bc + d^2 = 0$$
$$c(c-a) - b(c-a) + d^2 = 0$$
$$(c-a)(c-b) + d^2 = 0$$
$$1 + \frac{d^2}{(c-a)(c-b)} = 0 \text{ Divide by } (c-a)(c-b)$$
$$1 + \frac{d}{c-a} \cdot \frac{d}{c-b} = 0$$
$$m_1 \cdot m_2 = -1$$

The converse of Theorem 9-5 can also be proved true by reversing the order of the algebraic steps and showing that the triangle ABC is a right triangle by the converse of the Pythagorean Theorem.

Complete the following items.

3.26 Lines *k*, *l*, *m*, and *n* have slopes of $\frac{2}{3}$, -4, $-1\frac{1}{2}$ and $\frac{1}{4}$ respectively. Which pair of lines are perpendicular?

3.27 Show by using slope that the figure with vertices *A* (-5, -2), *B* (-4, 2), *C* (4, 5), and *D* (3, 1) is a parallelogram.

3.28 The vertices of a triangle are *A* (16, 0), *B* (9, 2), and *C* (0, 0).

a. What are the slopes of its sides? ______________________

b. What are the slopes of its altitudes? ______________________

3.29 Show that *A* (-2, 2), *B* (2, -2), *C* (4, 2), and *D* (2, 4) form a trapezoid with perpendicular diagonals.

3.30 Show that a line through (0, 0) and (*c*, *d*) is perpendicular to a line through (0, 0) and (-*d*, *c*).

3.31 State the slope of each side and each altitude of triangle *ABC* when *A* (2, 1), *B* (3, 5), and *C* (7, 2) are the vertices.

Given quadrilateral *RSTU*, tell which sides (if any) are parallel and which are perpendicular for the coordinates of the vertices.

3.32 *R* (0, 0), *S* (6, 3), *T* (5, 5), *U* (-1, 2)

3.33 *R* (1, -3), *S* (4, -1), *T* (2, 2), *U* (-4, -2)

3.34 *R* (-1, -5), *S* (8, 2), *T* (5, 5), *U* (-4, -2)

3.35 *R* (-1, 1), *S* (1, -2), *T* (4, 0), *U* (3, 3)

Answer these questions.

3.36 Given *A* (0, 1), *B* (3, 4), *C* (6, 1), *D* (3, -3),

a. What special kind of quadrilateral is *ABCD*? ____________________

b. Are its diagonals perpendicular? ____________________

Which of the following sets of coordinates form right triangles? Write *yes* or *no*.

3.37 *A* (2, 1), *B* (7, 1), *C* (2, 4) ____________________

3.38 *R* (1, -3), *S* (3, -1) *T* (5, -7) ____________________

3.39 *G* (7, 3), *H* (9, 0), *I* (5, -1) ____________________

3.40 *J* (2, 2), *K* (-1, 3), *L* (-2, -1) ____________________

3.41 *P* (0, 1), *Q* (3, 2), *R* (5, -4) ____________________

EQUATION OF A LINE

In an earlier part of the LIFEPAC, we drew graphs that met certain algebraic conditions.
Some conditions were written in the form of an equation in two variables; for example, $2x + 3y = 12$.

One way to find points that satisfy the equation is to assign any number to y and solve the equation for x. Let $y = 0$:

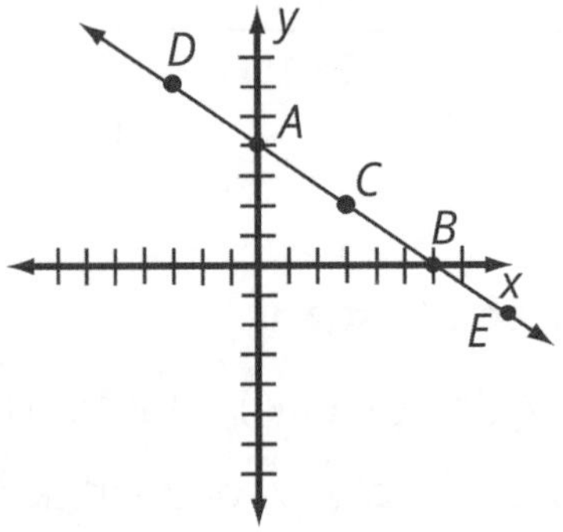

$$\begin{aligned} 2x + 3(0) &= 12 \\ 2x &= 12 \\ x &= 6 \end{aligned}$$

Therefore, (6, 0) is a point whose coordinates make the equation true.

Alternatively we can assign values to x and solve the resulting equation for y. Let $x = 0$:

$$\begin{aligned} 2(0) + 3y &= 12 \\ 3y &= 12 \\ y &= 4 \end{aligned}$$

Therefore, (0, 4) is also a point whose coordinates satisfy the equation.

A table of values for x and y that satisfy the equation $2x + 3y = 12$ is shown.

	x	y
A	0	4
B	6	0
C	3	2
D	-3	6
E	9	-2

If we find the slopes of $\overline{DA}$, $\overline{AC}$, $\overline{CB}$, $\overline{BE}$ as shown, we see that the points are all collinear, as the next theorem states.

$$m_{DA} = \frac{6-4}{-3-0} = -\frac{2}{3}$$

$$m_{AC} = \frac{4-2}{0-3} = -\frac{2}{3}$$

$$m_{CB} = \frac{2-0}{3-6} = -\frac{2}{3}$$

$$m_{BE} = \frac{0-(-2)}{6-9} = -\frac{2}{3}$$

> **THEOREM 9-6**
>
> The graph of any equation that can be written in the form $Ax + By = C$, where A and B are not both 0, is a line.

Next, we want to be able to write the algebraic condition (equation) when we know the coordinates of points that the line contains. This equation can be written by using Theorem 9-7.

> **THEOREM 9-7**
>
> The equation of the line passing through the point (x_1, y_1) and (x_2, y_2) is given by the formula $y - y_1 = m(x - x_1)$ where $m = \frac{y_2 - y_1}{x_2 - x_1}$ (point-slope form of the equation).

Given: P_1, P_2, P collinear with coordinates $(x_1, y_1), (x_2, y_2), (x, y)$

Prove: $y - y_1 = m(x - x_1)$

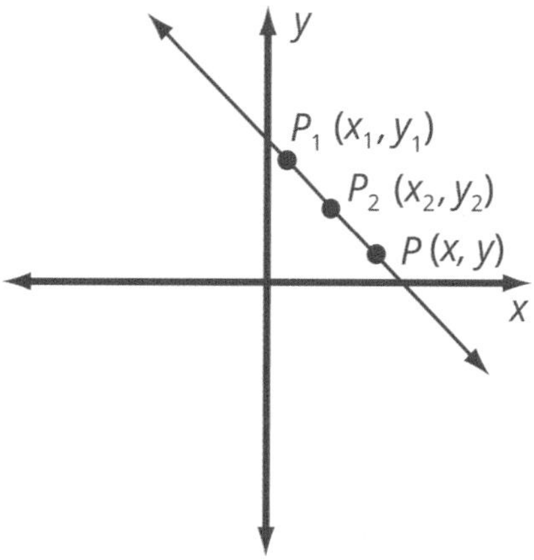

Find the slope of P_1P_2 and P_2P.

$$mP_1P_2 = \frac{y_2 - y_1}{x_2 - x_1}$$

$$mP_2P = \frac{y - y_1}{x - x_1}$$

Since the points are collinear, the slopes of the segments are equal.

$$\frac{y_2 - y_1}{x_2 - x_1} = \frac{y - y_1}{x - x_1}$$

$$(y - y_1)(x_2 - x_1) = (y_2 - y_1)(x - x_1)$$

$$y - y_1 = \frac{y_2 - y_1}{x_2 - x_1}(x - x_1)$$

$$y - y_1 = m(x - x_1)$$

Model 1: Find the equation of the line passing through points $A(3, 4)$ and $B(-2, -1)$. Express the equation in the form $Ax + By = C$ where A, B, C are integers. This form of the equation is called the *standard form*.

Solution:

$$y - y_1 = \frac{y_2 - y_1}{x_2 - x_1}(x - x_1)$$

$$y - 4 = \frac{-1 - 4}{-2 - 3}(x - 3)$$

$$y - 4 = \frac{-5}{-5}(x - 3)$$

$$y - 4 = x - 3$$

$$-x + y = 1$$

Model 2: Find the equation in standard form of the line containing *R* (0, 6) and *S* (4, -3).

Solution:

$$y - y_1 = \frac{y_2 - y_1}{x_2 - x_1}(x - x_1)$$

$$y - 6 = \frac{-3 - 6}{4 - 0}(x - 0)$$

$$y - 6 = \frac{-9}{4}x$$

$$4y - 24 = -9x$$

$$9x + 4y = 24$$

Write in standard form the equation of the line passing through the given points.

3.42 *A* (4, 1), *B* (5, 2) ____________________

3.43 *R* (3, 3), *S* (-6, -6) ____________________

3.44 *B* (0, 0), *C* (4, -4) ____________________

3.45 *P* (6, 2), *Q* (8, -4) ____________________

3.46 *M* (0, 6), *N* (6, 0) ____________________

3.47 *E* (-2, 2), *F* (5, 1) ____________________

3.48 *G* (4, 6), *H* (1, 5) ____________________

3.49 $S(\frac{1}{2}, 1)$, $T(\frac{1}{2}, 4)$ ____________________

3.50 *L* (5, 0), *M* (0, 5) ____________________

3.51 *X* (0, 6), *Y* (5, 6) ____________________

Write in standard form the equation of the line passing through the given point and having the given slope.

3.52 $A\ (5, 5), m = 3$ ____________________

3.53 $B\ (6, 2), m = -\frac{1}{2}$ ____________________

3.54 $C\ (0, 4), m = 0$ ____________________

3.55 $D\ (5, -2)\ m = \frac{2}{5}$ ____________________

3.56 $E\ (3, 5)$, m = no slope ____________________

Write the equation of the given line in standard form.

3.57 The line through (2, -1) and parallel to a line with slope of $\frac{3}{4}$.

3.58 The line through point (-3, 4) and perpendicular to a line that has slope $\frac{2}{5}$.

3.59 The line with slope $\frac{9}{7}$ and containing the midpoint of the segment whose end points are (2, -3) and (-6, 5).

3.60 The line through the midpoint of and perpendicular to the segment joining points (1, 0) and (5, -2).

3.61 The line containing the midpoints of the legs of right triangle *ABC* where *A* (-5, 5), *B* (1, 1), and *C* (3, 4) are the vertices.

3.62 The line containing the hypotenuse of right triangle *ABC* where *A* (-5, 5), *B* (1, 1), and *C* (3, 4) are the vertices.

3.63 The line containing the longer diagonal of a quadrilateral whose vertices are *A* (2, 2), *B* (-2, -2), *C* (1, -1), and *D* (6, 4).

3.64 The line containing the median of the trapezoid whose vertices are *R* (-1, 5) , *S* (1, 8), *T* (7, -2), and *U* (2, 0).

3.65 The line containing the altitude to the hypotenuse of a right triangle whose vertices are *P* (-1, 1), *Q* (3, 5), and *R* (5, -5).

3.66 The line containing the diagonal of a square whose vertices are *A* (-3, 3), *B* (3, 3), *C* (3, -3), and *D* (-3, -3). Find two equations, one for each diagonal.

Review the material in this section in preparation for the Self Test. This Self Test will check your mastery of this particular section as well as your knowledge of the previous sections.

SELF TEST 3

Find the slopes of the lines that contain the following points (each answer 3 points).

3.01 *A* (5, 6), *B* (10, 8) ____________________

3.02 *R* (-3, 5), *S* (3, -2) ____________________

3.03 *X* (0, 6), *Y* (-2, 4) ____________________

Find the slope of a line parallel to the line through the given points (each answer, 3 points).

3.04 *C* (0, 3), *D* (4, 6) ____________________

3.05 *M* (5, 5), *N* (6, -2) ____________________

3.06 *P* (-2, 4), *Q* (6, -2) ____________________

Find the slope of a line perpendicular to a line through the given points (each answer, 3 points).

3.07 *E* (5, 7), *F* (3, 1) ____________________

3.08 *G* (4, -2), *H* (8, 0) ____________________

3.09 *U* (6, 6), *V* (4, 4) ____________________

Write in standard form the equation of the line through the given points (each answer, 4 points).

3.010 *P* (0, -4), *Q* (5, 1) ____________________

3.011 *M* (-3, 2), *N* (5, 0) ____________________

3.012 *K* (6, 4), *L* (-6, 4) ____________________

Write in standard form the equation of the line passing through the given point and having the given slope (each answer, 4 points).

3.013 *R* (4, 0), $m = 5$ ____________________

3.014 *T* (-6, 1), $m = \frac{1}{2}$ ____________________

3.015 *W* (2, 5), $m = \frac{3}{2}$ ____________________

Write the equation of the given line in standard form (each answer, 4 points).

3.016 The line that contains the median to the base of an isosceles triangle with vertices *A* (2, 1), *B* (8, 4), and *C* (5, 7)

____

3.017 The line that is the perpendicular bisector of the segment whose endpoints are *R* (-1, 6) and *S* (5, 5)

____

3.018 The line that contains the point *Q* (1, -2) and is parallel to the line whose equation is $y - 4 = \frac{2}{3}(x - 3)$

____

3.019 The line that contains the diagonal of a rectangle with vertices *P* (2, -2), *Q* (2, -4), *R* (7, -2), and *S* (7, -4) and has a negative slope

____

Tell if the slope is positive, negative, zero, or no slope (each answer, 2 points).

3.020 ____________________

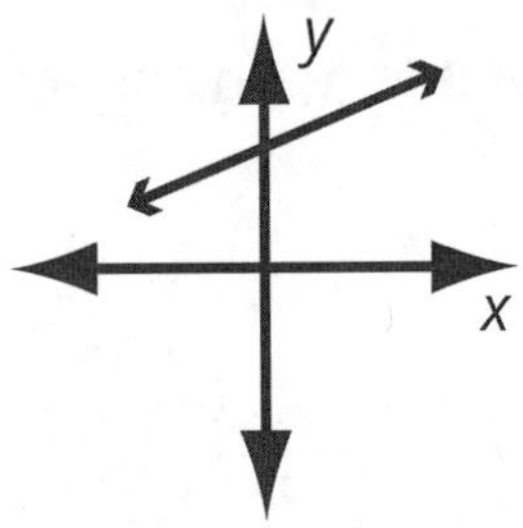

3.021 ____________________

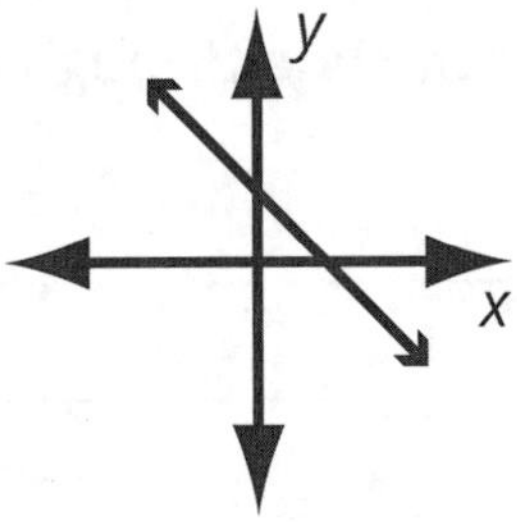

3.022 ____________________

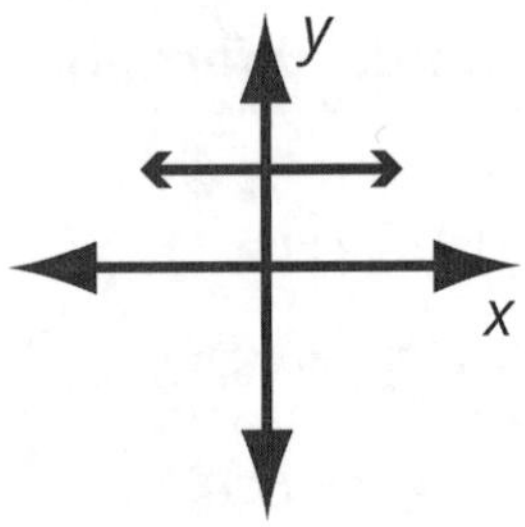

3.023 ____________________

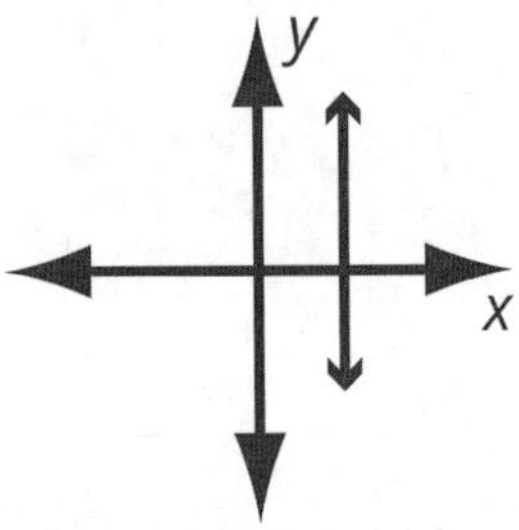

3.024 ____________________

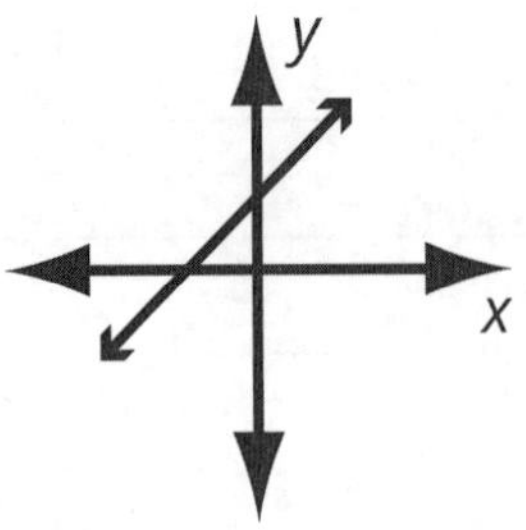

Graph the following conditions (each graph, 4 points).

3.025 $\{(x, y): x + y = 5\}$

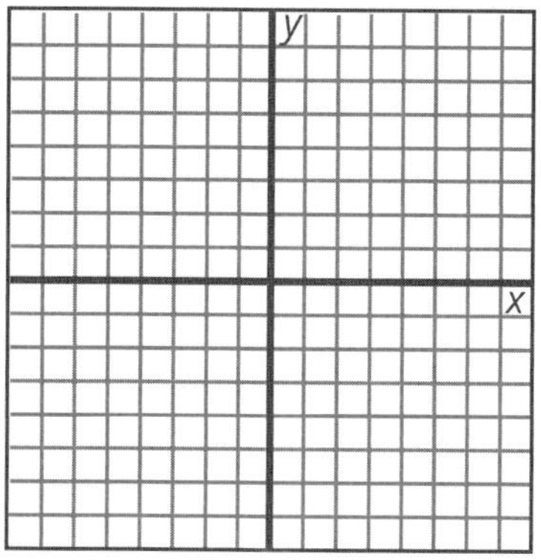

3.026 $\{(x, y): x + 2y \geq 6\}$

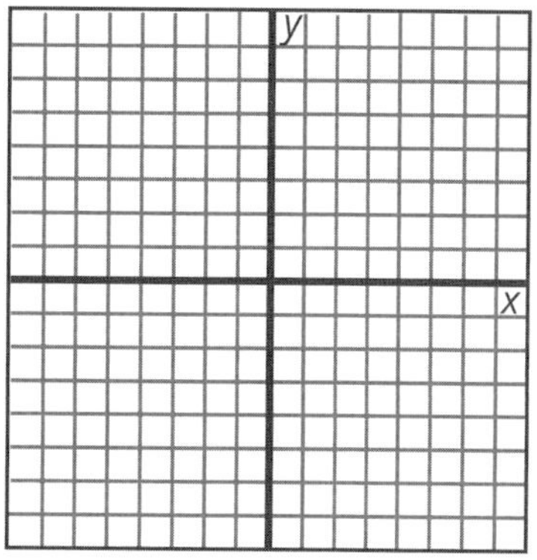

3.027 $\{(x, y): x = -3\} \cap \{(x, y): y = -3\}$

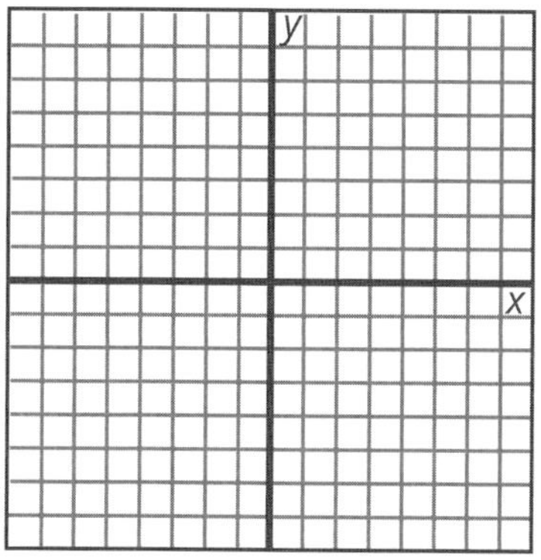

3.028 $\{(x, y): x \geq -4\} \cup \{(x, y): x \geq 4\}$

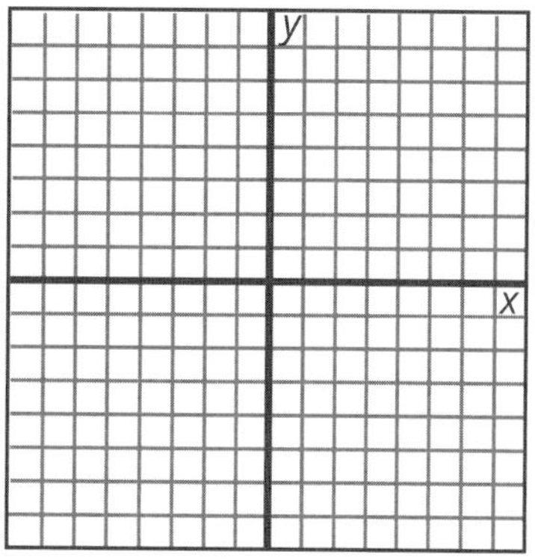

Find the coordinates of the center and the length of the radius of the following circles (each answer, 3 points).

3.029 $(x - 3)^2 + (y - 7)^2 = 49$ a. center ______________ b. radius = ______________

3.030 $(x + 2)^2 + y^2 = 10$ a. center ______________ b. radius = ______________

3.031 $(x + 3)^2 + (y - 6)^2 = 24$ a. center ______________ b. radius = ______________

Find the coordinates of the midpoint of the segment whose endpoints are given (each answer, 3 points).

	P_1	P_2	M
3.032	(3, 5)	(-2, 0)	______________________________
3.033	(10, 6)	(-4, 8)	______________________________
3.034	(3, 5)	(-7, -5)	______________________________

96/120 **SCORE** ______________ **TEACHER** ______________ ______________
initials date

4. PROOFS BY COORDINATE METHOD

In this section we shall use the distance and midpoint formulas along with equations of lines and circles to prove statements about figures in a coordinate plane. First, we shall observe some of the ways to place figures to make the proofs easier; then, we shall apply this information in proofs.

Section Objective

Review this objective. When you have finished this section, you should be able to:

11. Write geometric proofs by coordinate methods.

PLACEMENT OF FIGURES

The position of a figure with respect to the *x*- and *y*-axis is an important factor in a coordinate proof. If we do not choose the position of the figure with respect to the axes correctly, the equations which we will be using will be needlessly complicated. To learn how to place figures with respect to the axes so that the equations will be simpler will be to our advantage.

Suppose we want to prove some properties about a circle. We have several ways of placing the circle on the axes.

Model 1:

In Model 1 the circle has symmetry with respect to both axes. The equation of the circle has its simplest possible form: $x^2 + y^2 = r^2$.

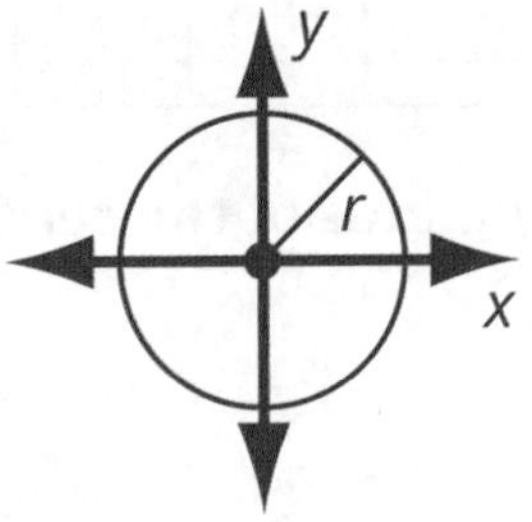

Model 2:

In Model 2 the circle has symmetry with respect to the *y*-axis only. Its equation is a little more involved: $x^2 + (y - r)^2 = r^2$.

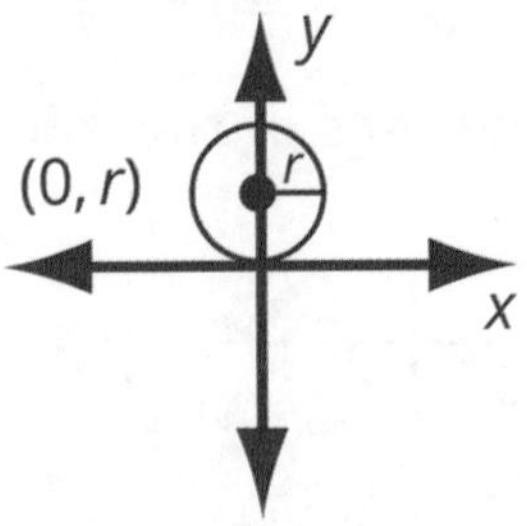

Model 3:

Model 3 is the least desirable because the circle is not symmetrical to either axis. Its equation is the most complicated: $(x - a)^2 + (y - b)^2 = r^2$.

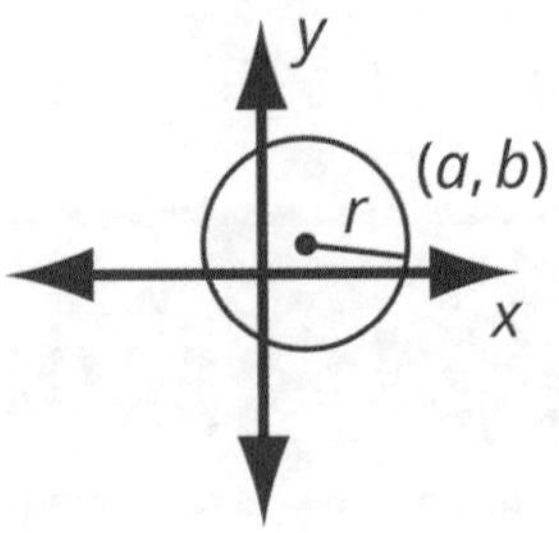

Consider isosceles triangle *ABC*. Two possible placements for the figure are shown. In Model 1 the base of the isosceles triangle lies on the *x*-axis and it has symmetry with respect to the *y*-axis. We can assign general coordinates to *B* and *C*, such as (0, *j*) and (*k*, 0). Since *A* is the partner point of *C*, its coordinates are (-*k*, 0).

Model 1:

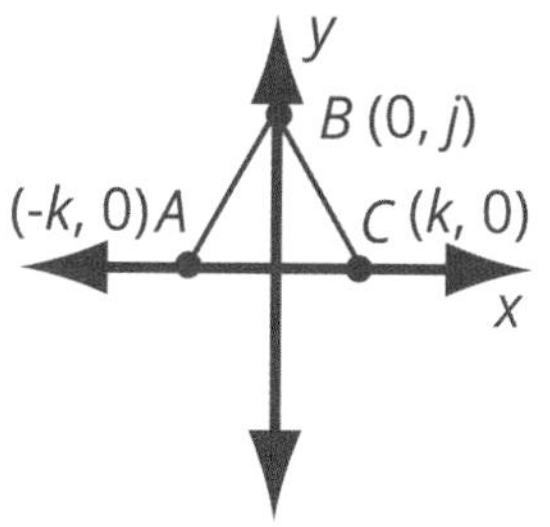

Model 2:

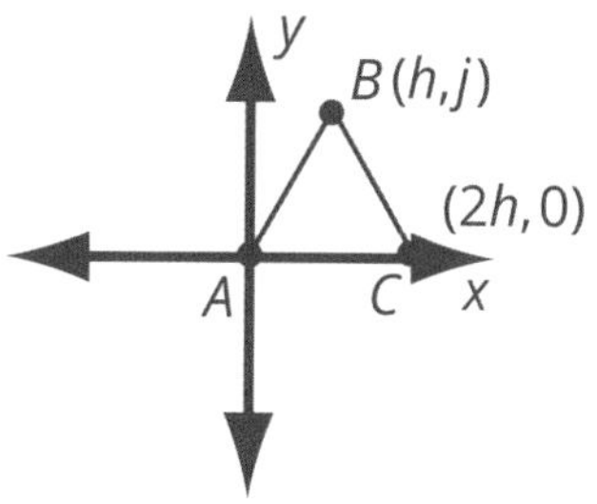

For Model 2, *A* would have coordinates (0, 0). *B* can be assigned any general coordinates, such as (*h*, *j*). The *x*-coordinate for *C* can be found by reasoning that the midpoint of *AC* must have the same *x*-coordinate as *B*; therefore, *C* would have coordinates (2*h*, 0).

When writing coordinate geometry proofs, you should use the more obvious properties of the figure in assigning coordinates to the vertices and other points.

For each figure which placement of the axes shown seems to be best?

4.1 Rectangle ____________________

a.

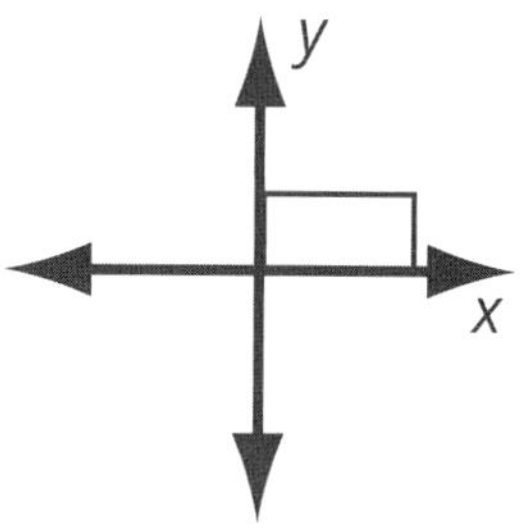

b.

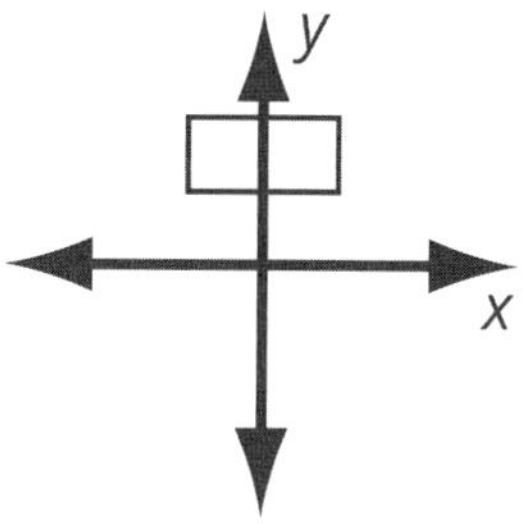

c.

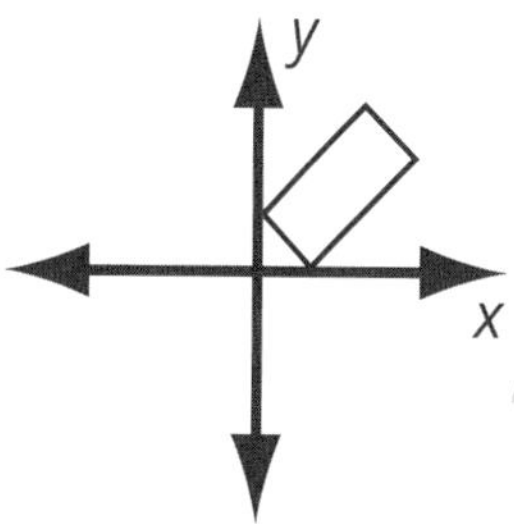

4.2 Circle ______________

a.

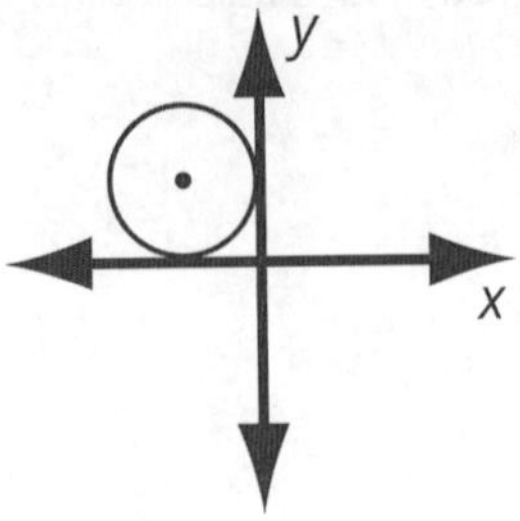

b.

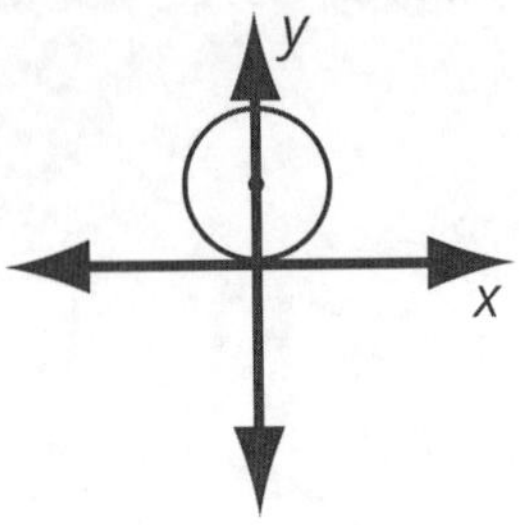

c.

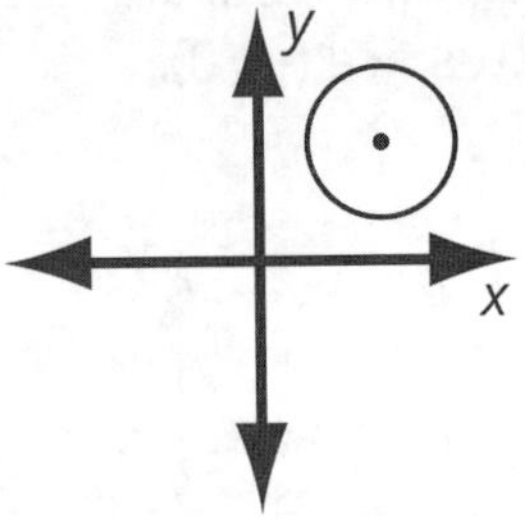

4.3 Equilateral Triangle ______________

a.

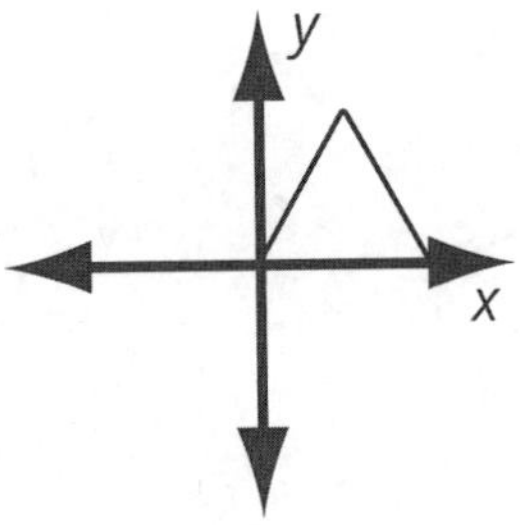

b.

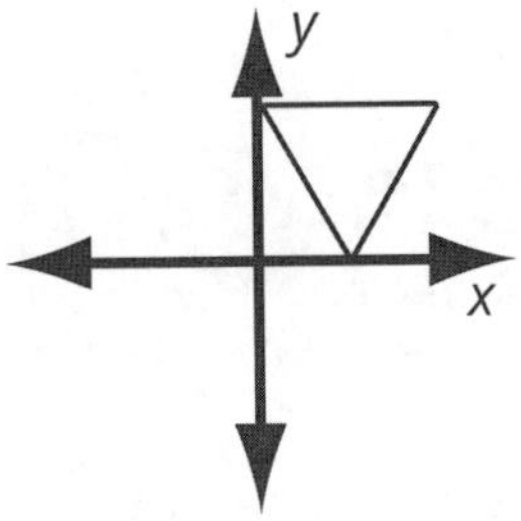

c.

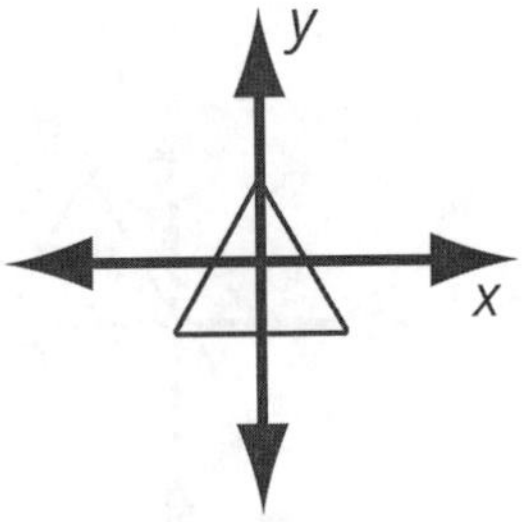

4.4 Isosceles Triangle ______________

a.

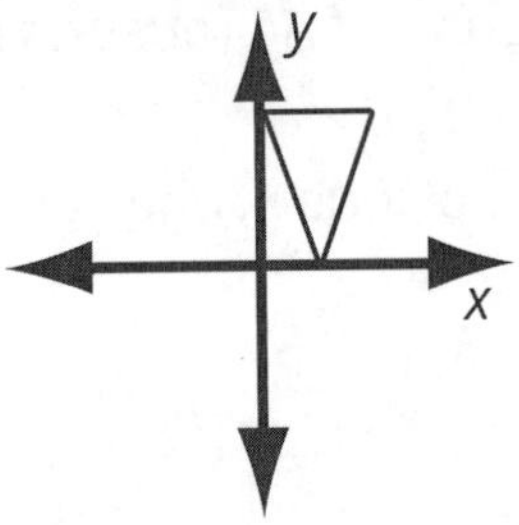

b.

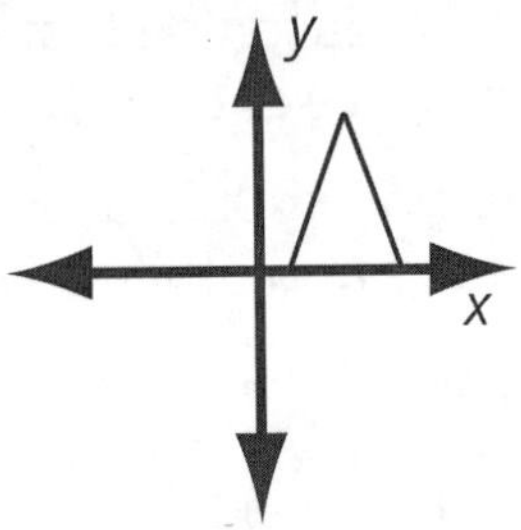

c.

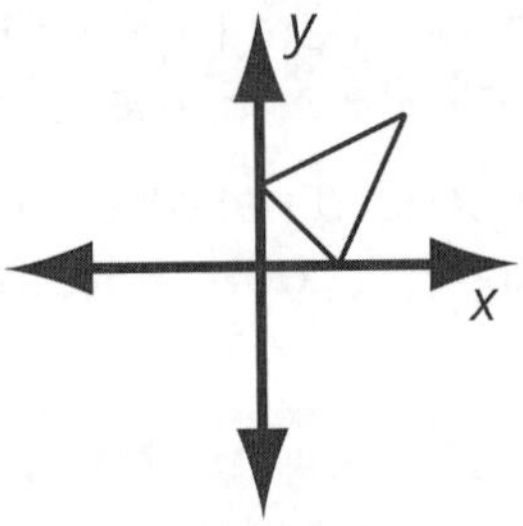

4.5 Trapezoid ______________

a.

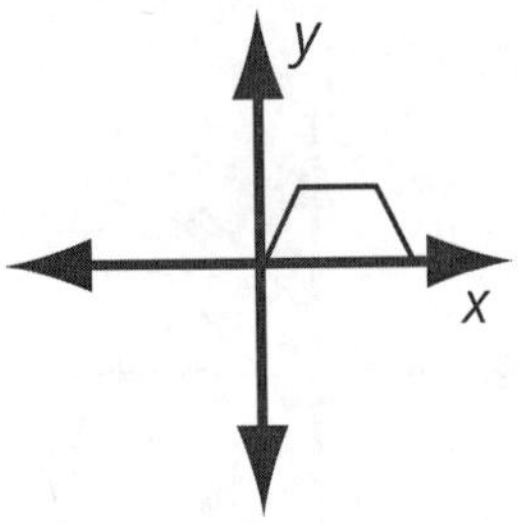

b.

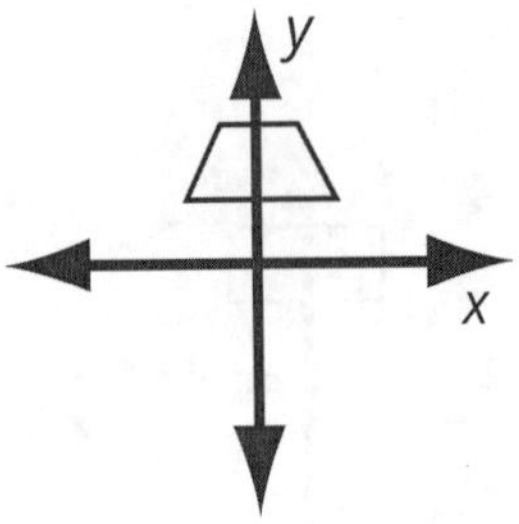

c.

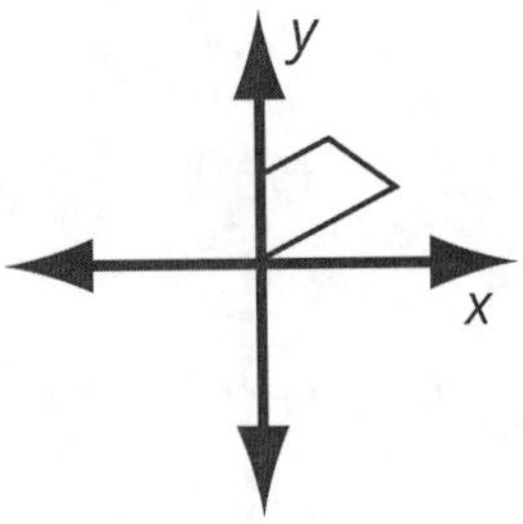

Complete the activities and sketch a graph for each problem.

4.6 The x-axis contains the base of an equilateral triangle RST. The origin is at S. Vertex T has coordinates $(2h, 0)$ and the y-coordinate of R is g, with $g > 0$.

a. Find the coordinates of the midpoint of ST. ____________________

b. Find the x-coordinate of R. ____________________

c.

4.7 The coordinate axes contain two sides of a square $ABCD$. If A $(0, a)$ and B $(0, 0)$ are two vertices of the square,

a. state the coordinates of the other two vertices so that all coordinates are > 0:

____________________;

b. so that some coordinates are < 0: ____________________.

c.

4.8 The x-axis and y-axis are lines of symmetry for a square. If one of its vertices has coordinates (a, b), find the other three vertices.

a. ____________________

b.

4.9 The base of an isosceles triangle is parallel to the x-axis. The y-axis passes through an end point of the base.

a. If the endpoints of the base are $(0, t)$ and (j, t), what is the x-coordinate of the vertex of the triangle? ____________________

b.

4.10 A base of a parallelogram is on the x-axis and the origin is located at the left endpoint of that base.

Three consecutive vertices are (h, j), $(0, 0)$, and $(k, 0)$, where $h > 0$.

a. What is the y- coordinate of the fourth vertex? ____________

b. How many units to the right of the y-axis is the point (h, j)? ____________

c. How many units to the right of a vertical line through $(k, 0)$ must the fourth vertex be?

____

d. What, in terms of k and h, is the x-coordinate of the fourth vertex? ____________

e.

APPLICATIONS IN PROOFS

To prove a statement using coordinate methods, we can use the theorems about slope of parallel and perpendicular lines, the distance and midpoint formulas, and the equations for circles and lines. In your proof, picture the placement of the figure with respect to axes and describe the location of the axes in relation to the figure. Then assign coordinates to the various points in such a way that your algebraic work will be simple and direct. Proofs may be written in paragraph form.

Model 1: Prove that a segment joining the midpoints of two sides of a triangle is half the length of the third side.

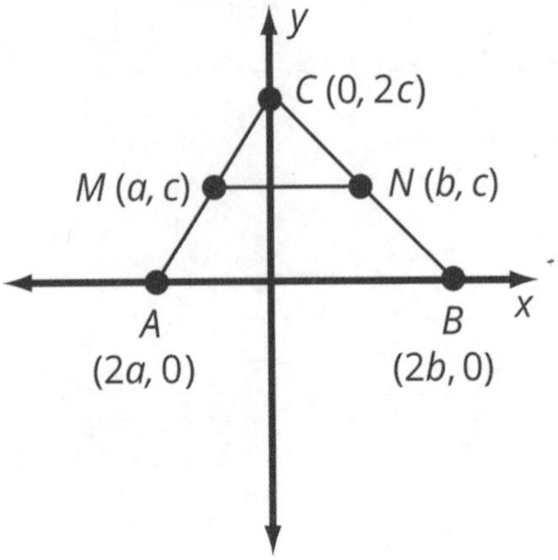

Proof: Given, triangle ABC with M and N the midpoints of AC and BC. Let the line containing AB be the x-axis and a perpendicular from C to AB be the y-axis. Let the coordinates of the points be as shown in the figure.

By the midpoint formula the coordinates of M are (a, c).
The coordinates of N are (b, c).
Then by the distance formula

$$MN = \sqrt{(a-b)^2 + (c-c)^2}$$
$$MN = \sqrt{(a-b)^2}$$
$$MN = a - b$$

Also

$$AB = \sqrt{(2a-2b)^2 + (0-0)^2}$$
$$AB = \sqrt{(2a-2b)^2}$$
$$AB = 2\,(a-b)$$
$$\frac{1}{2}AB = (a-b)$$
$$\therefore MN = \frac{1}{2}AB$$

Model 2: Prove that the diagonals of a parallelogram bisect each other.

Proof: Given, parallelogram $ABCD$. Let the line containing AB be the x-axis and let the y-axis pass through point A. Let the coordinates of the points be as shown. (Notice the x-coordinate of C. Refer to Problem 4.10.) Let M be the midpoint of AC and N be the midpoint of DB. We will show that M and N are the same point and thus AC and DB bisect each other.

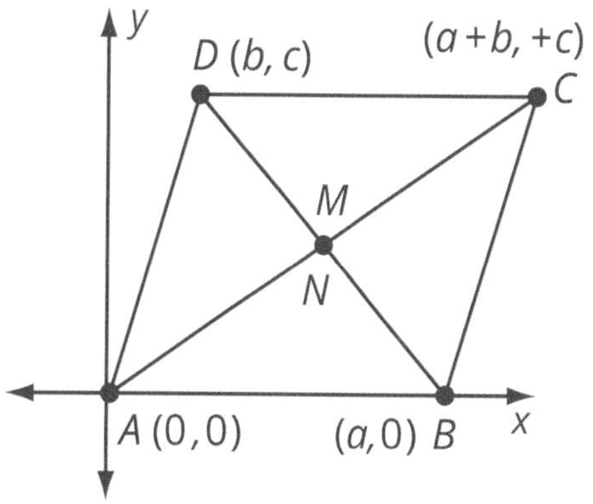

$$M = \left(\frac{a+b+0}{2}, \frac{c+0}{2}\right)$$
$$= \left(\frac{a+b}{2}, \frac{c}{2}\right)$$
$$N = \left(\frac{b+a}{2}, \frac{c+0}{2}\right)$$
$$= \left(\frac{a+b}{2}, \frac{c}{2}\right)$$

Therefore, AC bisects DB.

Complete the following proofs. Draw a figure on the coordinate axes. Label all points with their coordinates.

4.11 Prove: The segment joining the midpoints of two sides of a triangle is parallel to the third side.

4.12 Prove: The midpoint of the hypotenuse of a right triangle is equidistant from the three vertices.

4.13 Prove: In an isosceles triangle two medians are equal.

4.14 Prove: The opposite sides of a parallelogram are equal.

4.15 Prove: In an equilateral triangle the three medians are equal.

4.16 Prove: The diagonals of a rectangle are equal.

4.17 Prove: The diagonals of a square are perpendicular.

4.18 Prove: If the diagonals of a quadrilateral bisect each other, then the quadrilateral is a parallelogram.

4.19 Prove: The segments joining the midpoints of the opposite sides of a quadrilateral bisect each other.

4.20 Prove: The segment joining the midpoints of the diagonals of a trapezoid is parallel to the bases.

4.21 Prove: The median of a trapezoid equals half the sum of its bases.

4.22 Prove: If the diagonals of a parallelogram are perpendicular, then the parallelogram is a rhombus.

4.23 Prove: In a right triangle the median to the hypotenuse is $\frac{1}{2}$ the hypotenuse.

4.24 Prove: Every point on the perpendicular bisector of a segment is equidistant from the ends of the segment.

4.25 Prove: The segments joining the midpoints of the sides of a right triangle form a right triangle.

Before you take this last Self Test, you may want to do one or more of these self checks.

1. ________ Read the objectives. See if you can do them.
2. ________ Restudy the material related to any objectives that you cannot do.
3. ________ Use the **SQ3R** study procedure to review the material:
   a. **S**can the sections.
   b. **Q**uestion yourself.
   c. **R**ead to answer your questions.
   d. **R**ecite the answers to yourself.
   e. **R**eview areas you did not understand.
4. ________ Review all vocabulary, activities, and Self Tests, writing a correct answer for every wrong answer.

SELF TEST 4

Complete these items (each numbered item, 3 points).

4.01 In rectangle *ABCD*, if the coordinates of *A* are (0, 0) and of *C* are (*r*, *s*). Find the coordinates of *B* and *D*.

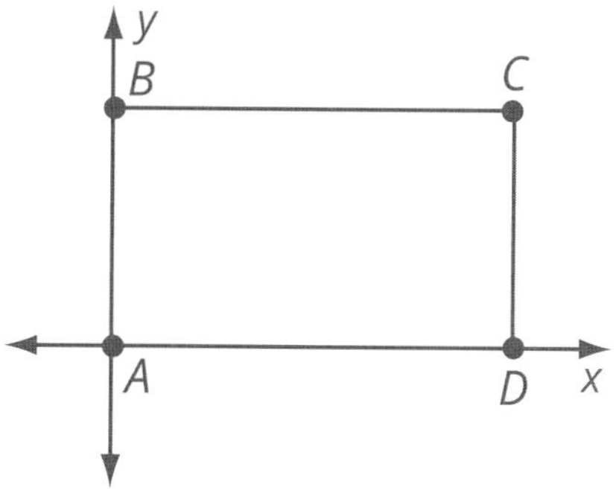

4.02 In equilateral triangle *RST*, *R* has coordinates (0, 0) and *T* has coordinates of (2*a*, 0). Find the coordinates of *S* in terms of *a*.

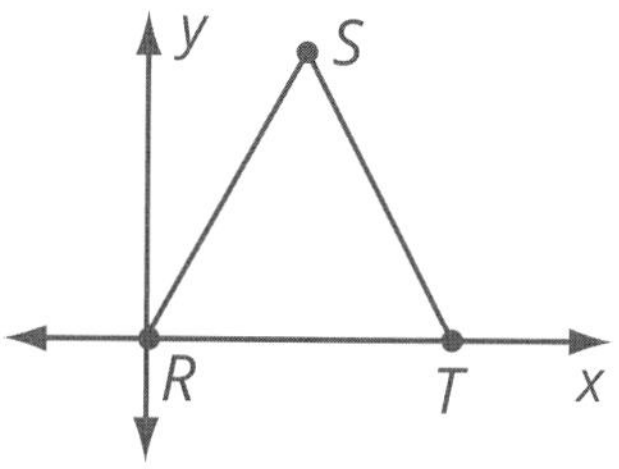

4.03 For parallelogram *ABCD*, *A* (0, 0), *B* (a, b), and *D* (c, 0) are three of its vertices. Find the coordinates of *C* in terms of *a*, *b*, *c*.

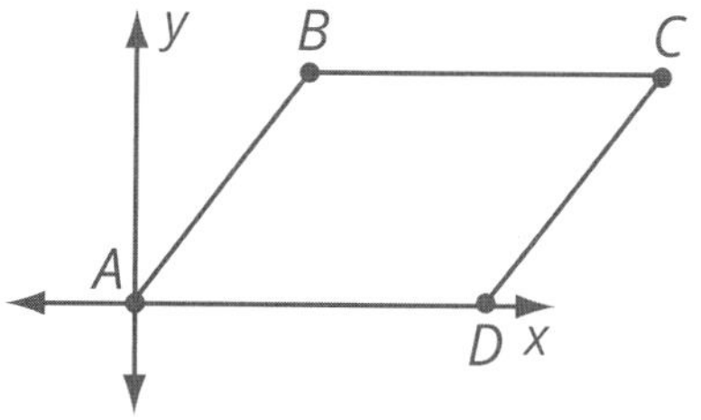

4.04 Find the slope of the diagonals *BD* and *AC* from Problem 4.03.

4.05 Which placement of the axes would be least acceptable for a rhombus?

____

a.

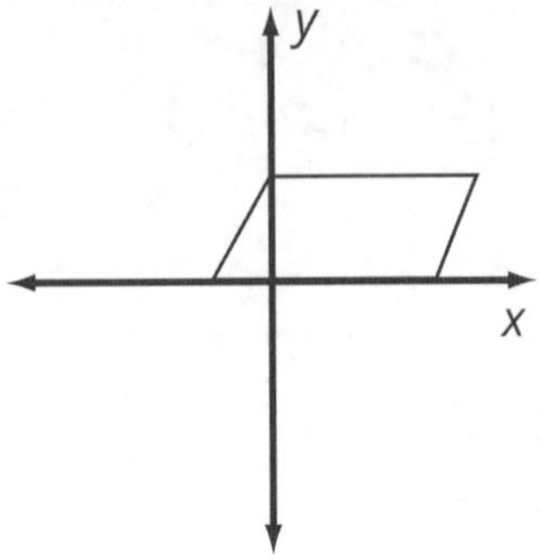

b.

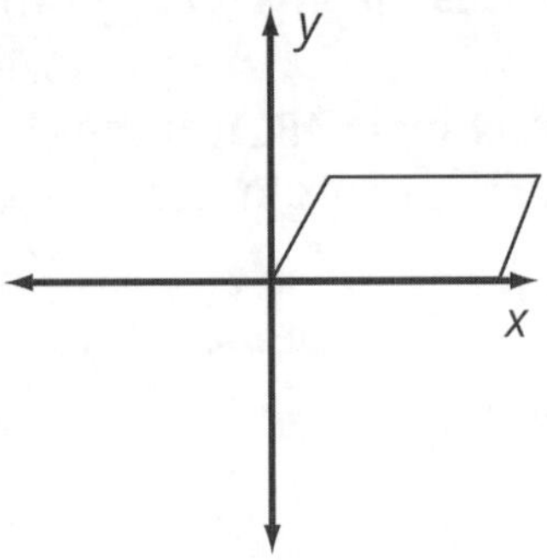

c.

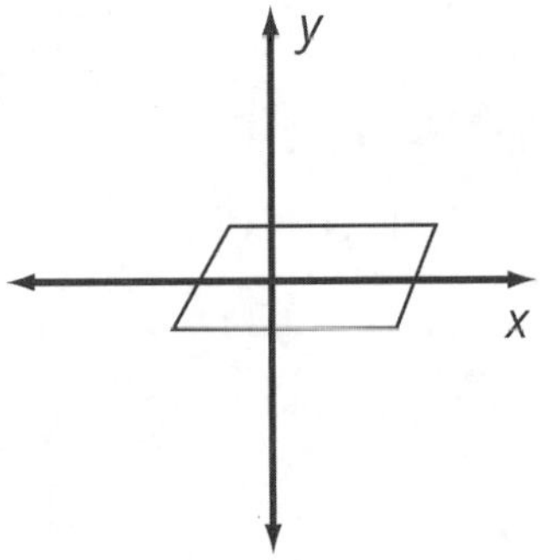

d.

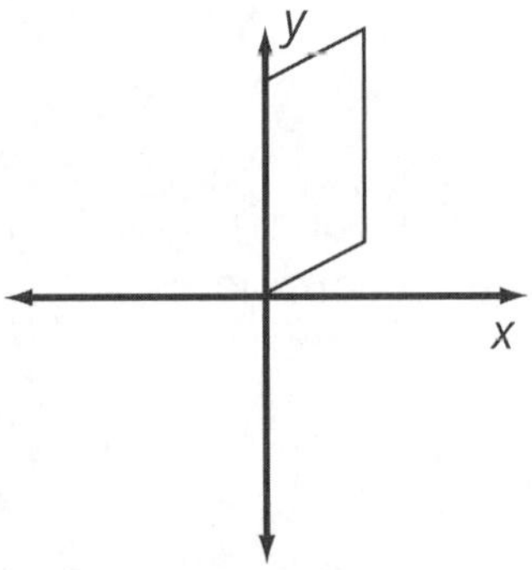

Circle *P* is tangent to the *x*-axis and the *y*-axis. If the coordinates of the center are (*r*, *r*), answer the following questions (each numbered item, 3 points).

4.06 Find the coordinates of the points of tangency. ____________; ____________

4.07 Find the length of the chord whose endpoints are the points of tangency.

____

4.08 Find the equation of the line containing the chord in Problem 4.07.

____

4.09 Find the slope of the line through the origin and the center. ________________

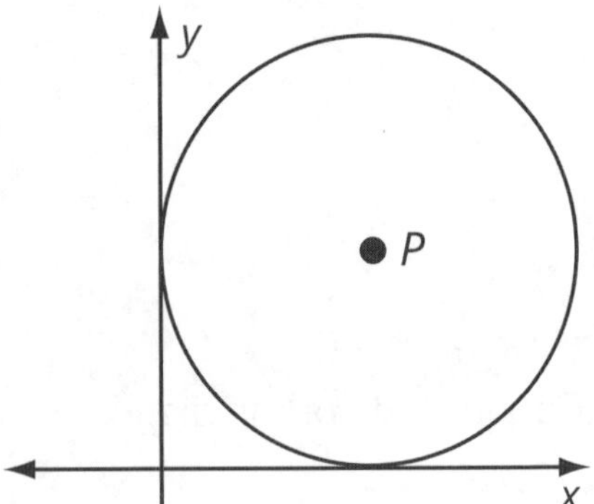

Sketch and complete the following proofs (each complete proof, 5 points).

4.010 Prove: The length of the medians to the sides of an isosceles triangle are equal.

4.011 Prove: The diagonals of a rhombus are perpendicular.

4.012 Prove: In an equilateral triangle the medians are the same length.

4.013 Prove: The length of the hypotenuse of a 45°-45°-90° triangle equals the length of a leg times $\sqrt{2}$.

4.014 Prove: The median of a trapezoid is parallel to its bases.

Write the kind(s) of symmetry: point, line, plane, or none (each answer, 2 points).

4.015 ____________________ **4.016** ____________________ **4.017** ____________________

A B C

4.018 ____________________ **4.019** ____________________ **4.020** ____________________

O 8 7

Write the equation or inequality that is shown by the graph (each answer, 4 points).

4.021 ______________________________ **4.022** ______________________________

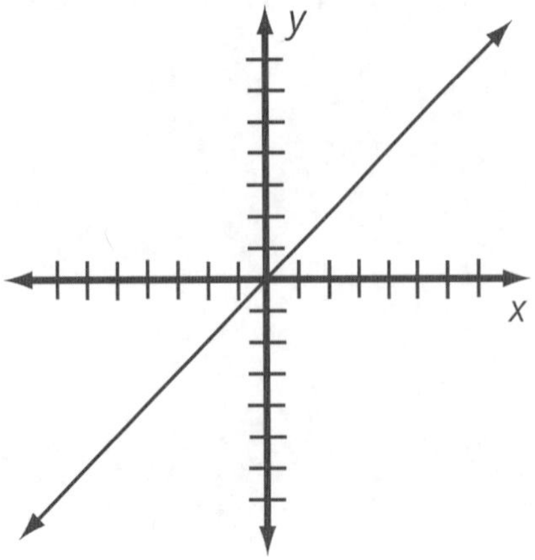

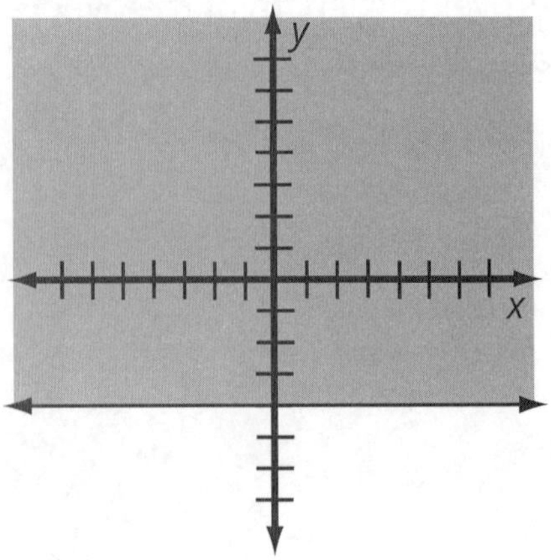

4.023 ______________________

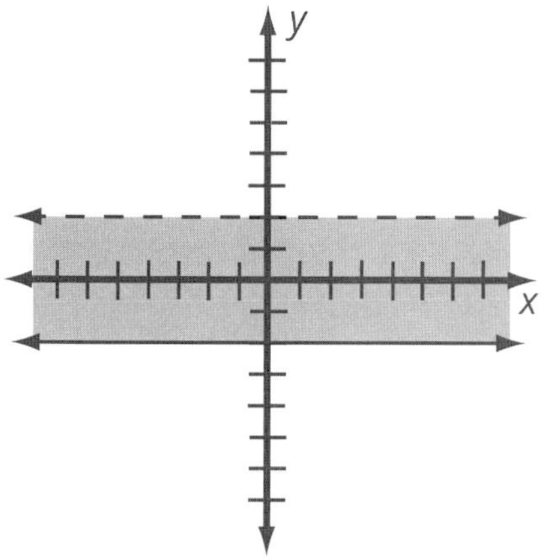

4.024 ______________________

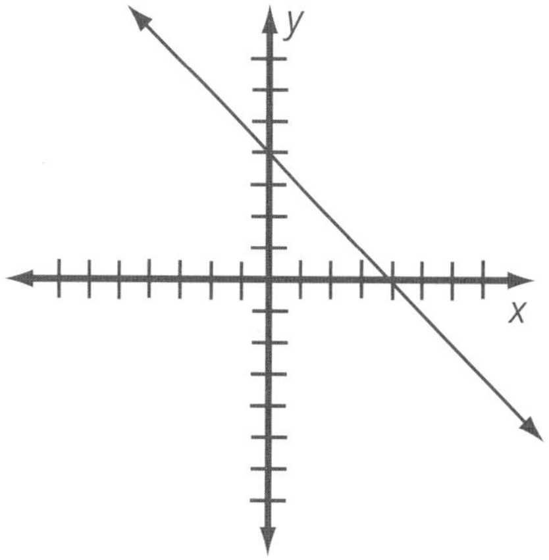

Find the coordinates of the center and the length of the radius of the given circle (each answer, 3 points).

4.025 $(x - 5)^2 + (y + 3)^2 = 25$ a. center ______________ b. radius = ______________

4.026 $(x)^2 + (y)^2 = 16$ a. center ______________ b. radius = ______________

4.027 $(x)^2 + (y - 3)^2 = 8$ a. center ______________ b. radius = ______________

Find the coordinates of the other endpoint when you are given the midpoint and one of the endpoints (each answer, 3 points).

	P_1	M	P_2
4.028	(5, 6)	(8, 2)	______________
4.029	(-16, 0)	(0, -16)	______________
4.030	(12, 4)	(2, 6)	______________

Find the distance between the points given. Simplify all irrational answers (each answer, 3 points).

4.031 (0, 6) and (5, 12) $d =$ ______________

4.032 (4, 1) and (7, 5) $d =$ ______________

4.033 (-3, 0) and $(0, \sqrt{7})$ $d =$ ______________

Find the slope of a line parallel to the line through the given points (each answer, 3 points).

4.034 *A* (3 8), *B* (-2, 5) $m =$ ______________

4.035 *R* (0, 22), *S* (-4, 2) $m =$ ______________

4.036 *X* (0, 0), *Y* (5, 10) $m =$ ______________

Find the slope of a line perpendicular to the line through the given points (each answer, 3 points).

4.037 C (13, 2), D (15, -5) m = ____________

4.038 M (2, -1), N (0, 4) m = ____________

4.039 V (3, 2), W (8, 5) m = ____________

Write in standard form the equation of the line passing through the given points (each answer, 4 points).

4.040 B (0, 0), C (4, -4) ____________

4.041 E (-2, 2), F (5, 1) ____________

4.042 M (0, 6), N (5, 6) ____________

Write in standard form the equation of the line passing through the given point and having the given slope (each answer, 4 points).

4.043 A (5, 5), m = 3 ____________

4.044 C (0, 4), m = 0 ____________

4.045 Q (3, 5), m = no slope ____________

127/158 **SCORE** ____________ **TEACHER** ____________ ____________
initials date

Before you take the LIFEPAC Test, you may want to do one or more of these self checks.

1. ______ Read the objectives. See if you can do them.
2. ______ Restudy the material related to any objectives that you cannot do.
3. ______ Use the **SQ3R** study procedure to review the material.
4. ______ Review activities, Self Tests, and LIFEPAC Glossary.
5. ______ Restudy areas of weakness indicated by the last Self Test.

GLOSSARY

coordinate axes .... The *x*-axis and the *y*-axis arranged to intersect at right angles at the zero point on each axis.

origin .... The intersection of the coordinate axes at (0, 0).

slope .... The ratio of the difference in the *y*-coordinates to the difference in *x*-coordinates of any two points on a line; $m = \frac{y_2 - y_1}{x_2 - x_1}$.

***x*-axis** .... The horizontal axis in the coordinate axes.

***y*-axis** .... The vertical axis in the coordinate axes.

NOTES

MATH 1010
Geometry Review

LIFEPAC Test is located at the back of the booklet. Please remove before starting the unit.

Author:
Milton R. Christen, M.A.

Editor-in-Chief:
Richard W. Wheeler, M.A.Ed.

Editor:
Robin Hintze Kreutzberg, M.B.A.

Consulting Editor:
Robert L. Zenor, M.A., M.S.

Revision Editor:
Alan Christopherson, M.S.

Media Credits:
Page 15: © Fuse; iStock, Thinkstock

AOP

804 N. 2nd Ave. E.
Rock Rapids, IA 51246-1759

Geometry Review

Introduction

This LIFEPAC® contains the definitions, postulates, theorems, and other information that you have studied in the previous nine LIFEPACs. Review activities for you to complete are included in each section. If you have trouble completing any of the review activities, you should go back to the original LIFEPAC and restudy the sections that you are not sure of. When you have completed this review, you will be ready to take the final examination for geometry.

Objectives

Read these objectives. The objectives tell you what you will be able to do when you have successfully completed this LIFEPAC. When you have finished this LIFEPAC, you should be able to:

1. Name, sketch, and label geometric figures.
2. Write and identify conditional sentences and their converse, inverse, and contrapositive.
3. Make and use truth tables.
4. Calculate linear and angle measures.
5. Prove geometric theorems using definitions, postulates, and properties.
6. Identify congruent figures and apply the properties of congruence.
7. Identify similar figures and apply the properties of similarity.
8. Identify and sketch parts of circles.
9. Construct geometric figures using only a compass and straightedge.
10. Sketch and name figures that meet locus conditions.
11. Calculate area and volume of geometric figures.
12. Sketch geometric figures on the coordinate axes.
13. Use algebraic notation to solve geometric distance, slope, and midpoint problems.

Survey the LIFEPAC. Ask yourself some questions about this study and write your questions here.

1. GEOMETRY, PROOF, AND ANGLES

This section contains the review of geometry as a mathematical system, proof of theorems, and basic angle relationships. Do not hesitate to go back and restudy at any time!

Section Objectives

Review these objectives. When you have completed this section, you should be able to:

1. Name, sketch, and label geometric figures.
2. Write and identify conditional sentences and their converse, inverse, and contrapositive.
3. Make and use truth tables.
4. Calculate linear and angle measures.
5. Prove geometric theorems using definitions, postulates, and properties.

GEOMETRY AS A SYSTEM

A mathematical system is a logical study of shape, arrangement, and quantity. Algebra, geometry, trigonometry, and calculus are examples of mathematical systems. Geometry is the logical study of the shape and size of things. The word comes from Greek and means *earth measurement*.

Any mathematical system contains four items:

1. Basic undefined terms;
2. All other terms, carefully defined;
3. Postulates; and
4. Theorems.

The basic undefined terms in geometry are

1. point,
2. line, and
3. plane.

Other fundamental terms are carefully defined in the Definitions box.

DEFINITIONS

Space: the set of all points.

Collinear points: a set of two or more points all on the same line.

Coplanar points: a set of points all on the same plane.

Betweenness of points: point B is *between* points A and C if A, B, and C are collinear and $AB + BC = AC$.

Line segment: the set of two different points and all points between them.

Midpoint of a segment: the point on a segment that divides the segment into two segments of equal length.

Bisector of a segment: a line or segment that intersects the first segment at its midpoint.

Ray: the set of all points $\overline{AB}$ and all points P, such that B is between A and P.

Opposite rays: two rays with a common endpoint that form a line.

Postulate: a statement accepted without proof.

Theorem: a general statement that can be proved.

Postulates will be numbered consecutively throughout this LIFEPAC. If you wish to review a postulate in more detail, it will be found in the Math LIFEPAC with the same name as the section name in this review LIFEPAC. The first five basic postulates are listed here.

POSTULATES

P1: A line contains at least two points; a plane contains at least three points not on one line; space contains at least four points not all in one plane.

P2: Through any two different points exactly one line exists.

P3: Through any three points not on one line exactly one plane exists.

P4: If two points lie in a plane, the line containing them lies in that plane.

P5: If two planes intersect, then their intersection is a line.

Theorems will be numbered exactly as they were in the first nine LIFEPACs of the Math 1000 series. You may wish to review the proof of each theorem as it is presented again.

THEOREMS

1-1 If two lines intersect, then their intersection is exactly one point.

1-2 Exactly one plane contains a given line and a given point not on the line.

1-3 If two lines intersect, then exactly one plane contains both lines.

Name the following geometric figures.

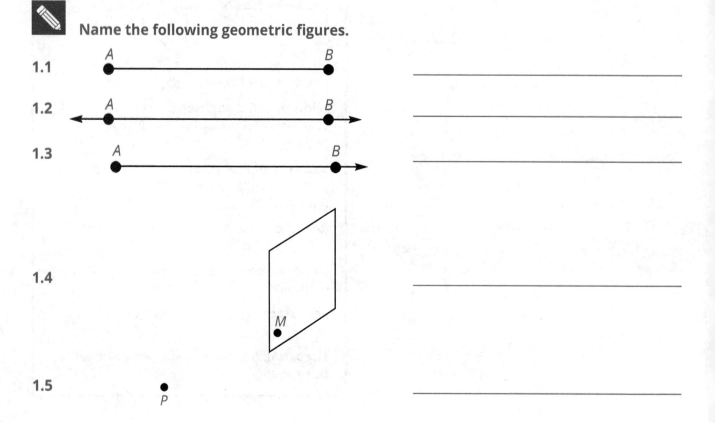

1.1 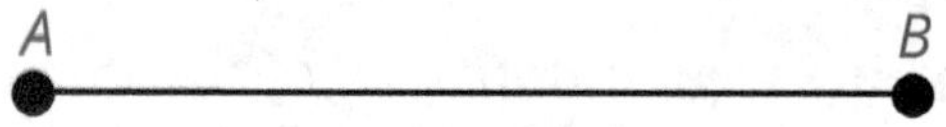

____

1.2 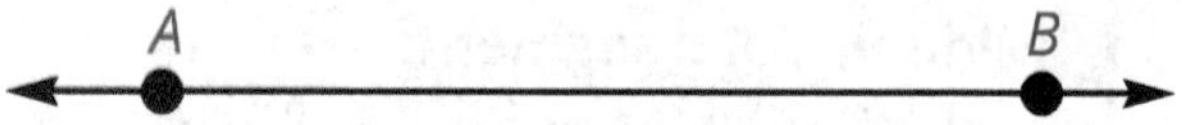

____

1.3 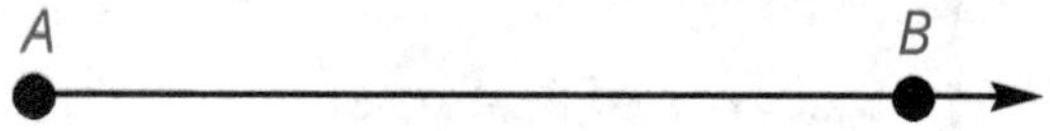

____

1.4 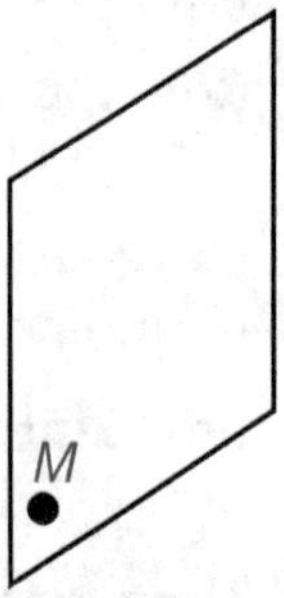

____

1.5 

____

Complete the following activities.

1.6 The set of all points is called ____________________.

1.7 The endpoint of ray $\overrightarrow{RS}$ is point ____________________.

1.8 If S is between R and T, then $RS + ST =$ ____________________.

1.9 A plane contains at least ______________ points.

1.10 A line contains at least ______________ points.

1.11 A postulate is accepted without ____________________.

1.12 If two lines intersect, their intersection is exactly ______________ point(s).

1.13 Space contains at least ______________ points.

1.14 How many lines are determined by four points, no three of which are collinear?

____

1.15 Two opposite rays form a ____________________.

Sketch and label the following conditions.

1.16 Collinear points B, U, N, T

1.17 Segment $\overline{WX}$ with midpoint M

1.18 Lines m and n, both in plane T, intersecting at point P

1.19 Opposite rays $\overrightarrow{OP}$ and $\overrightarrow{OG}$

1.20 Plane A and Plane B intersecting in line $\overleftrightarrow{PQ}$

PROOF

One of the main items of our geometric system are statements that we call theorems. Theorems are statements that we can prove to be true. We prove theorems true by using logical thinking and deductive reasoning.

DEFINITIONS

Statement: a sentence that is either true or false but not both.

Conjunction: a statement formed by combining two statements with the word *and*.

Disjunction: a statement formed by combining two statements with the word *or*.

Negation: if *p* is a statement, the new statement, not *p*, is called the negation of *p*.

Conditional: a statement formed from two statements by connecting them in the form *if* ________, *then* ________ .

Hypothesis: the *if* clause in a conditional statement.

Conclusion: the *then* clause in a conditional statement.

Converse: a statement formed by interchanging the hypothesis and the conclusion in a conditional statement.

Inverse: a statement formed by negating both the hypothesis and the conclusion of a conditional statement.

Contrapositive: a statement formed by exchanging the hypothesis and conclusion and negating both of them.

Inductive reasoning: the process of making a general conclusion based on specific examples.

Deductive reasoning: the process of making a conclusion by fitting a specific example to a general statement.

Truth table: an arrangement of truth values to determine when a statement is true or false.

Two-column proof: a formal proof of a theorem composed of six standard parts.

Indirect proof: a proof of a theorem by indirect means.

The compiled truth table for use in this geometry course is shown here for your reference.

COMPILED TRUTH TABLE

STATEMENT		NEGATION		CONDITIONAL	CONVERSE	INVERSE	CONTRAPOSITIVE
p	q	$\sim p$	$\sim q$	$p \rightarrow q$	$q \rightarrow p$	$\sim p \rightarrow \sim q$	$\sim q \rightarrow \sim p$
T	T	F	F	T	T	T	T
T	F	F	T	F	T	T	F
F	T	T	F	T	F	F	T
F	F	T	T	T	T	T	T

The six parts of a two-column proof are listed in order:

Statement: a full written statement of the theorem.

Figure: a lettered figure drawn to illustrate the given conditions of the statement.

Given: the given conditions of the statement expressed in terms of the letter and numerals used in the figure.

To Prove: the part of the statement that requires proof expressed in terms of the letters and numerals that are used in the figure.

Plan of Proof: a brief description of the plan you are going to use in the proof.

Proof: the actual proof; a series of numbered statements in one column with a like-numbered column next to it for the reasons.

The normal method of an indirect proof is to follow the three steps outlined here.

1. Suppose the negative of the conclusion is true.
2. Reason from your assumed statement until you reach a contradiction of a known fact.
3. Point out why the assumed statement must be false and that the desired conclusion must be true.

Identify the following statements as conjunction, disjunction, negation, or conditional, and tell if the statement is true or false.

1.21 If three sides of one triangle are equal to three sides of another triangle then the triangles are congruent.

________________________ (T/F) ________

1.22 A triangle has three sides and a pentagon has five sides.

________________________ (T/F) ________

1.23 It is false that $3 + 2 \neq 5$.

________________________ (T/F) ________

1.24 The sum of the angles of a triangle equals 180°, or a right triangle has two right angles.

________________________ (T/F) ________

1.25 If a triangle has at least two sides equal, then it is an isosceles triangle.

________________________ (T/F) ________

Write the converse, inverse, and contrapositive of the following theorems, and tell if the new statements are true or false.

1.26 If two lines are parallel, then the alternate interior angles are equal.

a. Converse: ______________________________

______________________________ (T/F) __________

b. Inverse: ______________________________

______________________________ (T/F) __________

c. Contrapositive: ______________________________

______________________________ (T/F) __________

1.27 If two lines intersect, then the vertical angles formed are equal.

a. Converse: ______________________________

______________________________ (T/F) __________

b. Inverse: ______________________________

______________________________ (T/F) __________

c. Contrapositive: ______________________________

______________________________ (T/F) __________

1.28 The diagonals of a parallelogram bisect each other.

a. Converse: ______________________________

______________________________ (T/F) __________

b. Inverse: ______________________________

______________________________ (T/F) __________

c. Contrapositive: ______________________________

______________________________ (T/F) __________

1.29 Base angles of isosceles triangles are equal.

a. Converse: ____

____ (T/F) __________

b. Inverse: ____

____ (T/F) __________

c. Contrapositive: ____

____ (T/F) __________

1.30 If two lines are perpendicular they meet to form right angles.

a. Converse: ____

____ (T/F) __________

b. Inverse: ____

____ (T/F) __________

c. Contrapositive: ____

____ (T/F) __________

Sketch a figure to represent the following theorems.

1.31 If two lines are perpendicular, then they form right angles.

1.32 In a plane, if two lines are perpendicular to a third line, then they are parallel to each other.

1.33 If two legs of one right triangle are equal to the legs of another right triangle, then the triangles are congruent.

1.34 If two lines are parallel, then the alternate interior angles are equal.

1.35 If two adjacent acute angles have their exterior sides in perpendicular lines, then the angles are complementary.

Complete the following truth tables.

1.36

p	$\sim p$
T	a. ________
F	b. ________

1.37

p	q	$p \rightarrow q$
T	F	a. ________
F	F	b. ________
T	T	c. ________
F	T	d. ________

1.38

p	q	$q \rightarrow p$
T	T	a. ________
T	F	b. ________
F	F	c. ________
F	T	d. ________

1.39

p	*q*	*p* or *q*
T	T	a. ________
T	F	b. ________
F	T	c. ________
F	F	d. ________

1.40

p	*q*	*p* and *q*
T	T	a. ________
F	F	b. ________
T	F	c. ________
F	T	d. ________

ANGLE RELATIONSHIPS AND PARALLELS

Lines, segments, and rays can be placed in such a way as to form angles. Angles are present everywhere and are very important in the study of geometry. Special angles are formed when parallel lines are cut by a transversal.

DEFINITIONS

Angle: the union of two noncollinear rays that have a common endpoint.

Acute angle: an angle whose measure is less than 90°.

Right angle: an angle whose measure is equal to 90°.

Obtuse angle: an angle whose measure is greater than 90° but less than 180°.

Perpendicular: two lines that intersect and form four equal angles.

Adjacent angles: two angles in the same plane that have a common vertex and a common side but no interior points in common.

Complementary angles: two angles whose measures total 90°.

Supplementary angles: two angles whose measures total 180°.

Vertical angles: two angles whose sides form two pairs of opposite rays.

Parallel lines: lines that are in the same plane and have no points in common.

Skew lines: two lines that do not lie in the same plane and will never intersect.

Transversal: a line that intersects two or more coplanar lines in different points.

Triangle: the union of three segments determined by three noncollinear points.

Exterior angle of a triangle: an angle formed by one side of a triangle and an extension of another side.

Auxiliary line: a line introduced in a figure to make a proof possible.

Regular polygon: a polygon with all angles equal and all sides equal.

Postulates about angle relationships are helpful in proving theorems about these relationships. The next five postulates are listed for your review.

POSTULATES

P6: Every angle corresponds with a unique real number greater than zero and less than 180.

P7: The set of rays on the same side of a line with a common endpoint in the line can be put into one-to-one correspondence with the real numbers from 0 to 180 inclusive in such a way that:

1. one of the two opposite rays lying in the line is paired with zero and the other is paired with 180, and
2. the measure of an angle whose sides are rays of that given set is equal to the absolute value of the difference between the numbers corresponding to its sides.

P8: If two parallel lines are cut by a transversal, then the corresponding angles have equal measure.

P9: Through a point not on a line, one and only one line can be drawn parallel to the line.

P10: If two lines are cut by a transversal so that corresponding angles are equal, then the lines are parallel.

The following theorems were discussed in detail in Math LIFEPAC 1003. You may wish to review the proofs of any or all of them.

THEOREMS

3–1 If $\overrightarrow{OA}$ lies between $\overrightarrow{OB}$ and $\overrightarrow{OC}$, then m $\angle BOA$ + m $\angle AOC$ = m $\angle BOC$. (angle addition theorem).

3–2 If the exterior sides of two adjacent angles are opposite rays, then the angles are supplementary.

3–3 If two lines are perpendicular, then they form right angles.

3–4 If two adjacent angles have their exterior sides in perpendicular lines, then the angles are complementary.

3–5 If two angles are supplementary to the same angle or to equal angles, then they are equal to each other.

3–6 If two angles are complementary to the same angle or to equal angles, then they are equal to each other.

3–7 If two lines intersect, the vertical angles formed are equal.

3–8 All right angles are equal.

3–9 If two lines meet and form right angles, then the lines are perpendicular.

3–10 If two parallel planes are cut by a third plane, then the lines of intersection are parallel.

3–11 If a transversal is perpendicular to one of two parallels, then it is perpendicular to the other one also.

3–12 If two parallel lines are cut by a transversal, then the alternate interior angles are equal.

3–13 If two parallel lines are cut by a transversal, then the alternate exterior angles are equal.

3–14 In a plane, if two lines are perpendicular to a third line, then they are parallel to each other.

3–15 If two lines are cut by a transversal so that alternate interior angles are equal, then the lines are parallel.

3–16 If two lines are cut by a transversal so that alternate exterior angles are equal, then the lines are parallel.

3–17 The sum of the measures of the angles of a triangle is 180°.

3–18 The measure of an exterior angle of a triangle is equal to the sum of the remote interior angles.

3–19 The sum of the measures of the angles of a quadrilateral is 360°.

Use this figure to complete the following activities.

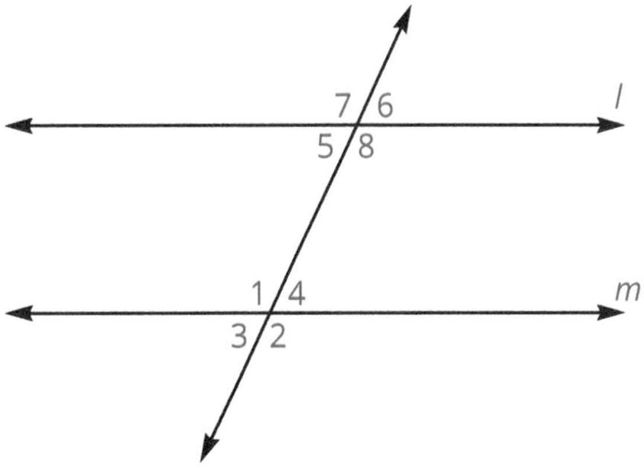

1.41 Name four pairs of corresponding angles.

______ ______ ______ ______

1.42 Name two pairs of alternate interior angles.

______ ______

1.43 Name two pairs of alternate exterior angles.

______ ______

1.44 Name four pairs of vertical angles.

______ ______ ______ ______

1.45 Name twelve pairs of supplementary angles.

______ ______ ______ ______

______ ______ ______ ______

______ ______ ______ ______

Name the following polygons.

1.46 Name the polygon that has four sides. ______________

1.47 Name the polygon that has five sides. ______________

1.48 Name the polygon that has six sides. ______________

1.49 Name the polygon that has eight sides. ______________

1.50 Name the polygon that has n sides. ______________

Complete the following proofs.

1.51 Given: $r \parallel s$

To Prove: $\angle 2$, $\angle 8$ are supplementary

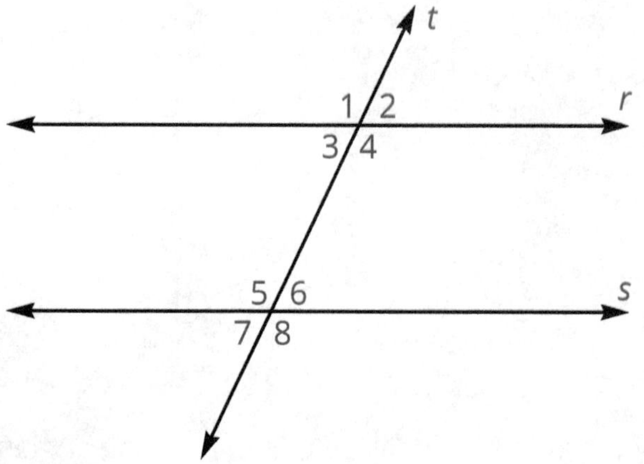

STATEMENT	REASON

1.52 Given: $l \parallel m$

$\angle 1 = \angle 4$

To Prove: $\angle 2 = \angle 3$

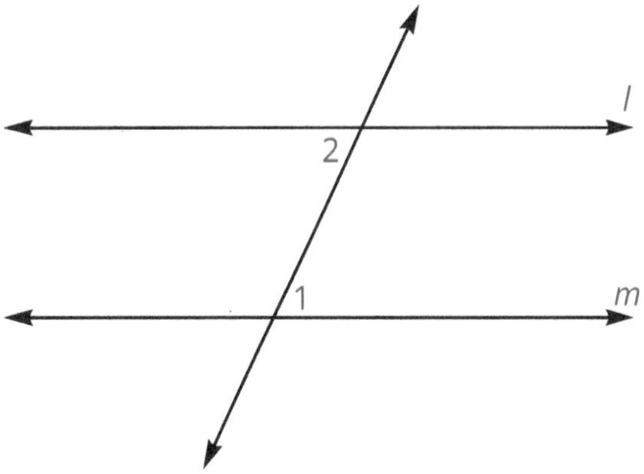

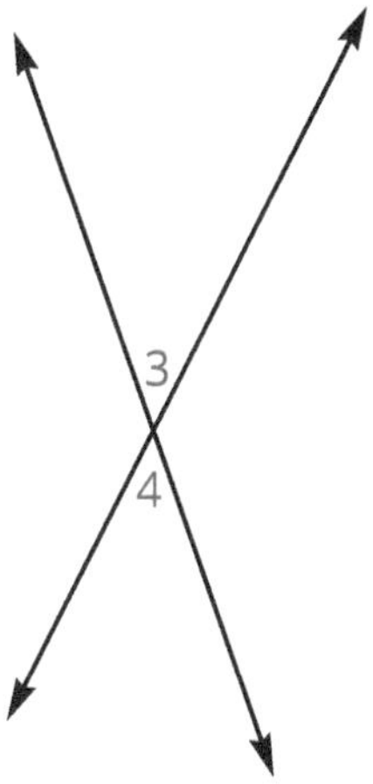

STATEMENT	REASON

1.53 Given: $\angle 1 = \angle 3$

To Prove: $a \parallel b$

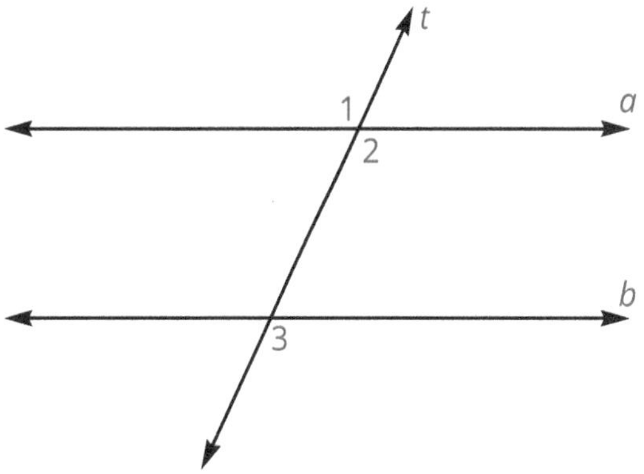

STATEMENT	REASON

Given the following diagram, find the required measures.

Given: $l \parallel m$

m $\angle 1 = 120°$

m $\angle 3 = 40°$

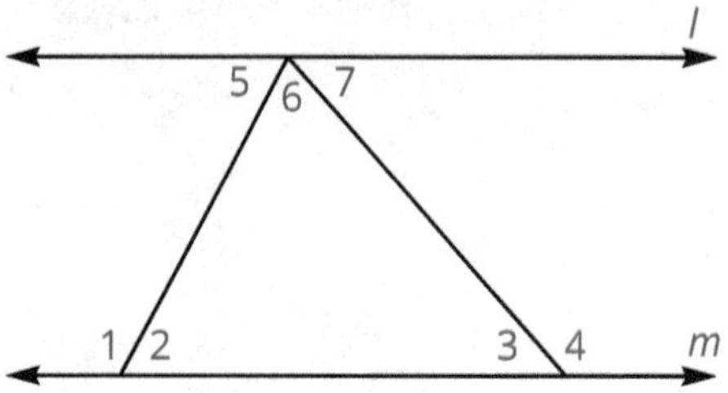

1.54 m $\angle 2$ = ______________

1.55 m $\angle 4$ = ______________

1.56 m $\angle 5$ = ______________

1.57 m $\angle 6$ = ______________

1.58 m $\angle 7$ = ______________

Find the sum of the interior angles of the following polygons.

1.59 Triangle ______________

1.60 Quadrilateral ______________

1.61 Pentagon ______________

1.62 Hexagon ______________

1.63 20-gon ______________

1.64 50-gon ______________

1.65 What is the sum of the *exterior* angles of an *n*–gon? ______________

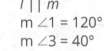

Review the material in this section in preparation for the Self Test. The Self Test will check your mastery of this particular section. The items missed on this Self Test will indicate specific areas where restudy is needed for mastery.

SELF TEST 1

Match the following items (each answer, 2 points).

1.01 ______ 

1.02 ______ 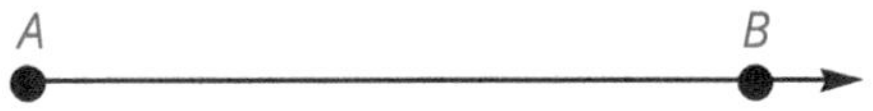

1.03 ______ 

1.04 ______ 

1.05 ______ 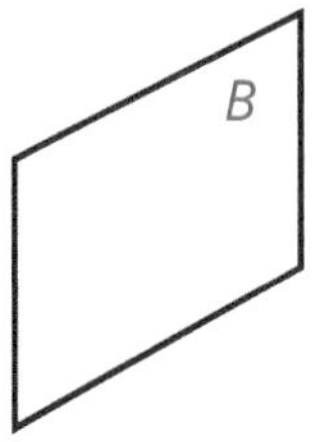

a. plane *B*
b. line *AB*
c. plane *A*
d. point *A*
e. segment *AB*
f. ray *AB*

Complete the following truth tables (each answer, 2 points).

1.06

p	*q*	$p \rightarrow q$
T	F	a. ________
F	F	b. ________
T	T	c. ________
F	T	d. ________

1.07

p	*q*	*p* and *q*
T	T	a. ________
F	F	b. ________
T	F	c. ________
F	T	d. ________

Use this diagram to find the required measures (each answer, 3 points).

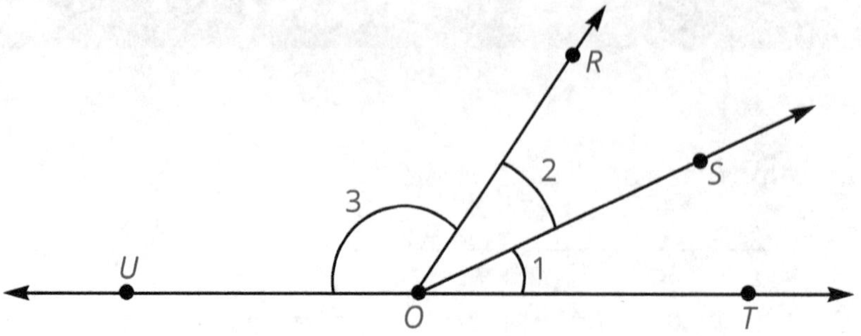

1.08	m ∠1 = 30°	m ∠2 = 30°	m ∠3 = ________
1.09	m ∠2 = 20°	m ∠3 = 130°	m ∠1 = ________
1.010	m ∠1 = 40°	m ∠3 = 110°	m ∠2 = ________
1.011	m ∠1 = 45°	m ∠2 = 45°	m ∠3 = ________
1.012	m ∠2 = 15°	m ∠3 = 118°	m ∠1 = ________

Write the correct letter for the answer on the blank (each answer, 2 points).

1.013 The sum of the interior angles of a triangle is ________________ .

a. 1,800° b. 360° c. 180° d. 3,240°

1.014 The sum of the interior angles of a quadrilateral is ________________ .

a. 540° b. 720° c. 360° d. 180°

1.015 The sum of the interior angles of a pentagon is ________________ .

a. 540° b. 720° c. 360° d. 180°

1.016 The sum of the interior angles of a 20-gon is ________________ .

a. 1,800° b. 360° c. 180° d. 3,240°

Complete the following proofs (each proof, 6 points).

1.017 Given: $\overline{JK} \perp \overline{MN}$

To Prove: ∠1, ∠2 are complementary

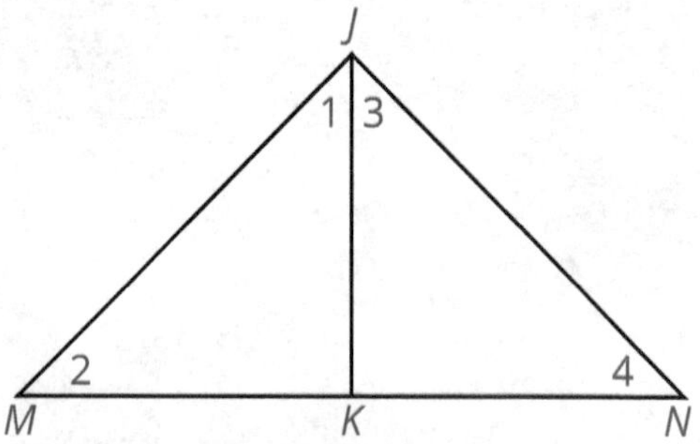

STATEMENT	REASON

1.018 Given: $m\angle 5 = m\angle 6$

To Prove: $m\angle 3 = m\angle 4$

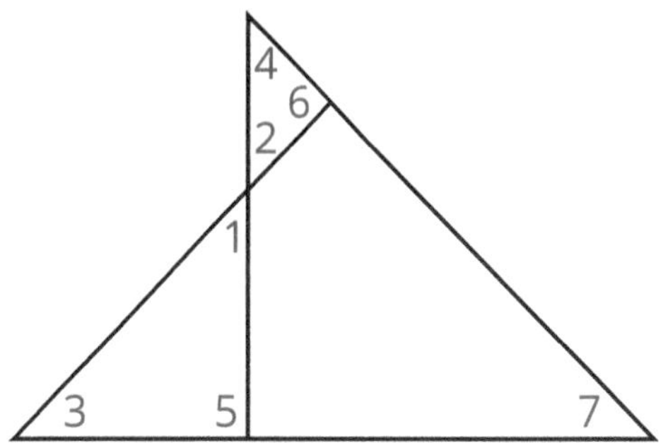

STATEMENT	REASON

1.019 Given: $\overline{AC} \perp \overline{CD}$

$\overline{DB} \perp \overline{AB}$

To Prove: $m\angle A = m\angle D$

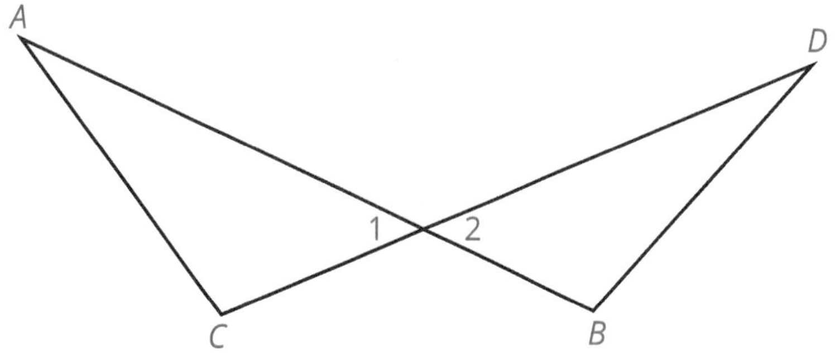

STATEMENT	REASON

54/67 **SCORE** ________ **TEACHER** ________ ________

initials date

2. TRIANGLES, QUADRILATERALS, POLYGONS, AND CIRCLES

This section will review definitions, postulates, and theorems about geometric figures and their properties. The figures will include triangles, quadrilaterals, polygons, and circles.

Section Objectives

Review these objectives. When you have completed this section, you should be able to:

5. Prove geometric theorems using definitions, postulates, and properties.
6. Identify congruent figures and apply the properties of congruence.
7. Identify similar figures and apply the properties of similarity.
8. Identify and sketch parts of circles.

CONGRUENT TRIANGLES AND QUADRILATERALS

Most of the material goods we use today are mass-produced by the thousands. They all look more or less alike; they are the same size and the same shape. Figures that are the same size and the same shape are called congruent figures.

DEFINITIONS

Congruent triangles: two triangles in which the six parts of one are equal to the corresponding six parts of the other.

Included angle: the angle formed by two sides of a triangle. The angle is included between the two sides.

Included side: the side of a triangle that is the common side of two angles. The side is included between the two angles.

Isosceles triangle: a triangle with at least two sides equal.

Altitude of a triangle: a segment from a vertex perpendicular to the opposite side.

Median of a triangle: a segment from a vertex to the midpoint of the opposite side.

Parallelogram: a quadrilateral with both pairs of opposite sides parallel.

Rectangle: a parallelogram with four right angles.

Rhombus: a parallelogram with all sides equal.

Square: a rectangle with all sides equal.

Trapezoid: a quadrilateral with exactly one pair of sides parallel.

Median of a trapezoid: the segment connecting the midpoint of the legs.

Isosceles trapezoid: a trapezoid with legs of the same length.

The next four postulates listed relate to congruent triangles.

POSTULATES

P11: If three sides of one triangle are equal to three sides of another triangle, then the triangles are congruent. (SSS)

P12: If two sides and the included angle of one triangle are equal to two sides and the included angle of another triangle, then the triangles are congruent. (SAS)

P13: If two angles and the included side of one triangle are equal to two angles and the included side of another triangle, then the triangles are congruent. (ASA)

P14: If the hypotenuse and a leg of one right triangle are equal to the hypotenuse and leg of another right triangle, then the triangles are congruent. (HL)

Theorem 4–14, included among the following theorems, is the theorem that allows triangle postulates and theorems to be applied to parallelograms. Be sure you can prove each theorem reviewed.

THEOREMS

4–1 If two angles and a not-included side of one triangle are equal to the corresponding parts of another triangle, then the triangles are congruent. (AAS)

4–2 If two legs of one right triangle are equal to two legs of another right triangle, then the triangles are congruent. (LL)

4–3 If the hypotenuse and an acute angle of one right triangle are equal to the hypotenuse and an acute angle of another right triangle, then the triangles are congruent. (HA)

4–4 If a leg and an acute angle of one right triangle are equal to a leg and an acute angle of another right triangle, then the triangles are congruent. (LA)

4–5 The altitude to the base of an isosceles triangle bisects the base.

4–6 The base angles of isosceles triangles are equal.

4–7 The altitude to the base of an isosceles triangle bisects the vertex angle of the triangle.

4–8 If two angles of a triangle are equal, then the sides opposite them are equal.

4–9 If two sides of a triangle are not equal, then the angle opposite the longer side is the larger angle.

4–10 If two angles of a triangle are not equal, then the side opposite the larger angle is the longer side.

4–11 The sum of the lengths of any two sides of a triangle is greater than the length of the third side.

4–12	If two sides of one triangle are equal to two sides of another triangle but the included angle of the first is larger than the included angle of the second, then the third side of the first triangle is longer than the third side of the second triangle.
4–13	If two sides of one triangle are equal to two sides of another triangle but the third side of the first triangle is longer than the third side of the second triangle, then the included angle of the first is larger than the included angle of the second.
4–14	If a diagonal is drawn in a parallelogram, then two congruent triangles are formed.
	Corollary 1: Opposite angles of a parallelogram are equal.
	Corollary 2: Opposite sides of a parallelogram are equal.
	Corollary 3: Two parallel lines are equidistant apart throughout.
4–15	The diagonals of a parallelogram bisect each other.
4–16	If two sides of a quadrilateral are equal and parallel, then the quadrilateral is a parallelogram.
4–17	If both pairs of opposite sides of a quadrilateral are equal, then the quadrilateral is a parallelogram.
4–18	If the diagonals of a quadrilateral bisect each other then the quadrilateral is a parallelogram.
4–19	If the midpoints of two sides of a triangle are connected, the segment is parallel to the third side and equals half the length of the third side.
4–20	The diagonals of a rectangle are equal.
4–21	The diagonals of a rhombus are perpendicular.
4–22	The diagonals of a rhombus bisect two angles of the rhombus.
4–23	The median of a trapezoid is parallel to the bases and its length is half the sum of the lengths of the bases.
4–24	Base angles of isosceles trapezoids are equal.
4–25	The diagonals of an isosceles trapezoid are equal.

Name the corresponding parts of $\triangle ABC \cong \triangle TSR$.

2.1 $\angle A$ = ________________ **2.2** $\angle C$ = ________________ **2.3** $\angle S$ = ________________

2.4 TR = ________________ **2.5** TS = ________________ **2.6** BC = ________________

Complete the following proofs.

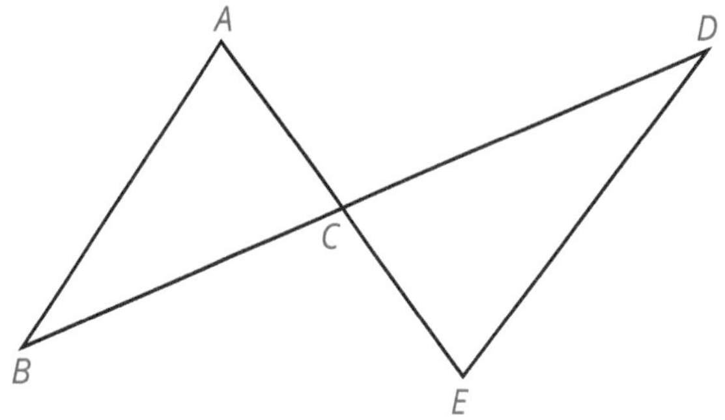

2.7 Given: $\overline{AB} \parallel \overline{DE}$, $AC = CE$

To Prove: $\triangle ABC \cong \triangle EDC$

STATEMENT	REASON

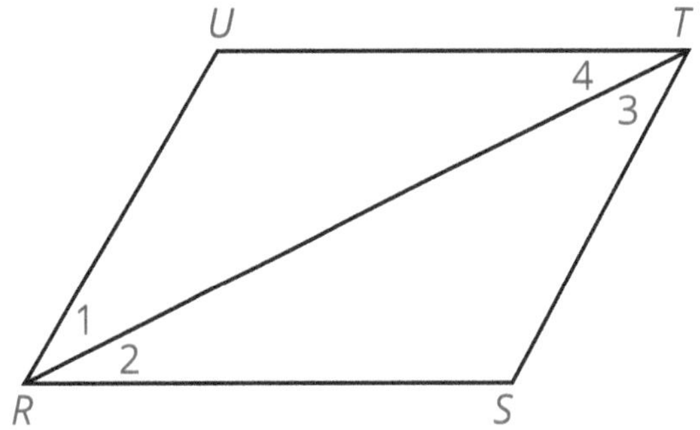

2.8 Given: $\overline{UT} \parallel \overline{RS}$, $UT = RS$

To Prove: $\angle S = \angle U$

STATEMENT	REASON

2.9 Given: $\angle B = \angle C$, $AE = DE$

To Prove: $AB = DC$

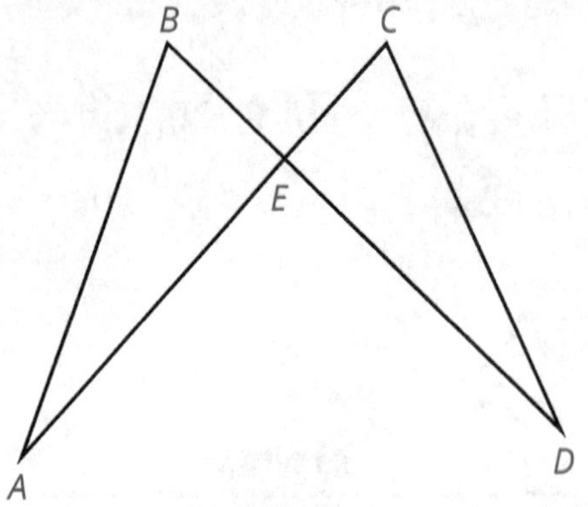

STATEMENT	REASON

2.10 Given: $AC = BC$, $MC = NC$

To Prove: $\angle ANC = \angle BMC$

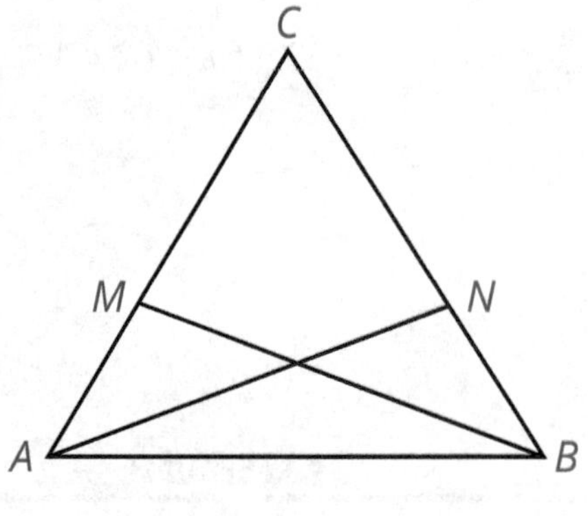

STATEMENT	REASON

Write the names of the sides according to size from large to small.

2.11 ____________________

____

____

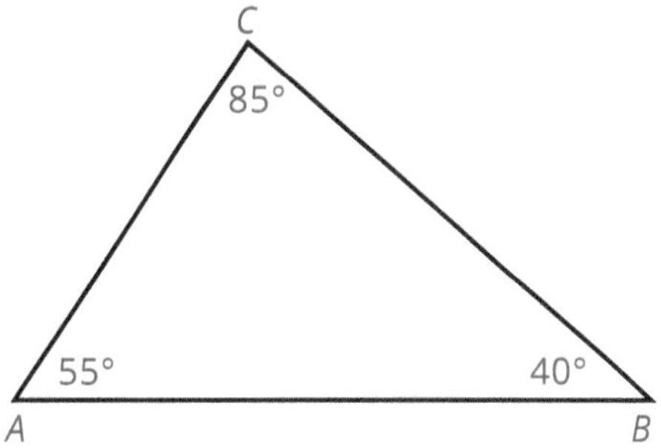

Can a triangle have sides of the following lengths? Write yes or no.

2.12 6 inches, 12 inches, 17 inches ______________

2.13 1 ft., 2 ft., 3 ft. ______________

2.14 6 cm, 8 cm, 10 cm ______________

Given: *M, N, O* are midpoints of $\overline{AC}$, $\overline{BC}$, and $\overline{AB}$. Complete the following statements.

2.15 $\overline{MO} \parallel$ ______________

2.16 $\overline{NO} \parallel$ ______________

2.17 $\overline{MN} \parallel$ ______________

2.18 $MN = \frac{1}{2}$ ______________

2.19 $NO = \frac{1}{2}$ ______________

2.20 $AC = 2$ ______________

2.21 *MNOA* is a ______________ .

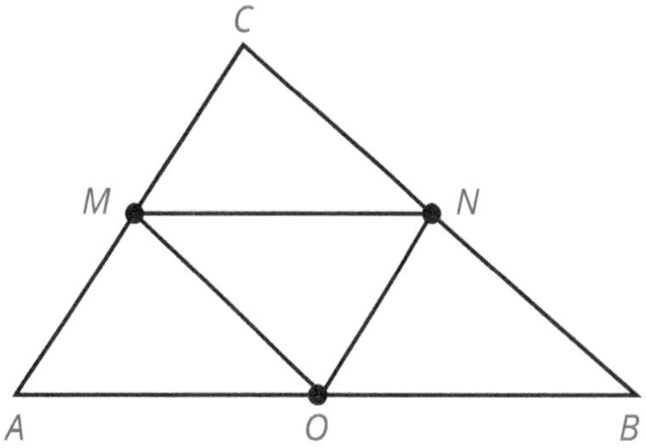

Given: *ABCD* is a parallelogram; $\angle A = x + 30°$; and $\angle D = 2x + 60°$. Find the angle measures.

2.22 $\angle A =$ _______

2.23 $\angle B =$ _______

2.24 $\angle C =$ _______

2.25 $\angle D =$ _______

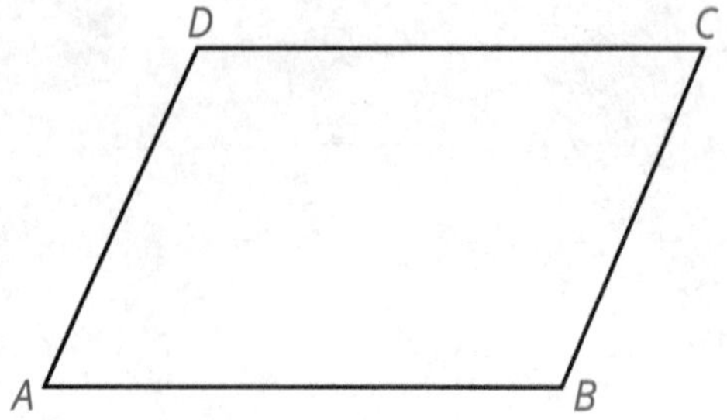

SIMILAR POLYGONS

Figures that have the same size and shape are called congruent figures. Figures that have the same shape but not necessarily the same size are called similar figures.

The following postulate is related to the SSS postulate from the previous section. Note, however, that while the SSS postulate proves congruence, the AAA postulate proves only similarity.

POSTULATE

P15: If the three angles of one triangle are equal to the three angles of another triangle, then the triangles are similar. (AAA)

DEFINITIONS

Ratio: the comparison of two numbers by division. The quotient is the ratio of the two numbers.

Proportion: an equation that states that two ratios are equal.

Similar polygons: polygons whose vertices can be matched in a one-to-one correspondence so that corresponding angles are equal and corresponding sides are in proportion.

Geometric mean: for any positive real numbers *a*, *b*, and *x*, if $\frac{a}{x} = \frac{x}{b}$, then *x* is called the geometric mean between *a* and *b*.

Projection of a point on a line: the point where a perpendicular through the point to the line intersects the line.

Projection of a segment on a line: the portion of a line with endpoints that are the projections of the endpoints of the segment.

Sine ratio: in a right triangle, the side opposite an acute angle over the hypotenuse.

Cosine ratio: in a right triangle, the side adjacent to an acute angle over the hypotenuse.

Tangent ratio: in a right triangle, the side opposite an acute angle over the side adjacent to the acute angle.

These special properties of proportions can often save time in proofs. Remember that the variables used in these statements represent nonzero numbers.

PROPERTIES OF PROPORTIONS (POP):

Cross Product property

If $\frac{a}{b} = \frac{c}{d}$, then $ad = bc$.

Equivalent Forms property

$\frac{a}{b} = \frac{c}{d}$, $\frac{a}{c} = \frac{b}{d}$, $\frac{d}{b} = \frac{c}{a}$, $\frac{b}{a} = \frac{d}{c}$ are equivalent forms. The cross product of each proportion gives the same equation, $ad = bc$.

Denominator Sum property

If $\frac{a}{b} = \frac{c}{d}$, then $\frac{(a + b)}{b} = \frac{(c + d)}{d}$.

Denominator Difference property

If $\frac{a}{b} = \frac{c}{d}$, then $\frac{(a - b)}{b} = \frac{(c - d)}{d}$.

Numerator-Denominator Sum property

If $\frac{a}{b} = \frac{c}{d} = \frac{e}{f} = \frac{g}{h} = \ldots$, then $\frac{(a + c + e + g + \ldots)}{(b + d + f + h + \ldots)} = \frac{a}{b} = \frac{c}{d} = \frac{e}{f} = \frac{g}{h} = \ldots$

THEOREMS

5-1 If two angles of one triangle are equal to two angles of another triangle, then the triangles are similar.

5-2 If two sides of one triangle are proportional to two sides of another and the included angles are equal, then the triangles are similar.

5-3 If three sides of one triangle are proportional to three sides of another, then the triangles are similar.

5-4 Similarity of polygons is reflexive, symmetric, and transitive.

5-5 If two polygons are similar, then the ratio of their perimeters is the same as the ratio of any pair of corresponding sides.

5-6 If a line is parallel to one side of a triangle and intersects the other two sides, then it divides the two sides proportionally.

5-7 If a ray bisects an angle of a triangle, then it divides the opposite side into segments with lengths proportional to the lengths of the other two sides of the triangle.

5-8 If two triangles are similar, then the lengths of corresponding altitudes have the same ratio as the lengths of any pair of corresponding sides.

5-9 If the altitude to the hypotenuse of a right triangle is drawn, then the two triangles formed are similar to each other and similar to the given triangle.

5-10 In a right triangle the sum of the squares of the length of the legs is equal to the square of the length of the hypotenuse. (Pythagorean Theorem)

5-11	If the sum of the squares of two sides of a triangle equals the square of the third side, then the triangle is a right triangle.
5-12	In a 30°-60°-90° triangle, the hypotenuse is twice the short leg, and the longer leg is the short leg times $\sqrt{3}$.
5-13	If each acute angle of a triangle is 45°, then the measure of the hypotenuse is $\sqrt{2}$ times the leg.

Solve the following proportions.

2.26 $\frac{x}{8} = \frac{5}{4}$

$x =$ ______________

2.27 $\frac{3}{x} = \frac{x}{4}$

$x =$ ______________

2.28 $\frac{x}{3} = \frac{x+2}{2}$

$x =$ ______________

Complete the following proofs.

2.29 Given: $a \parallel b$

To Prove: $\triangle MOP \sim \triangle RON$

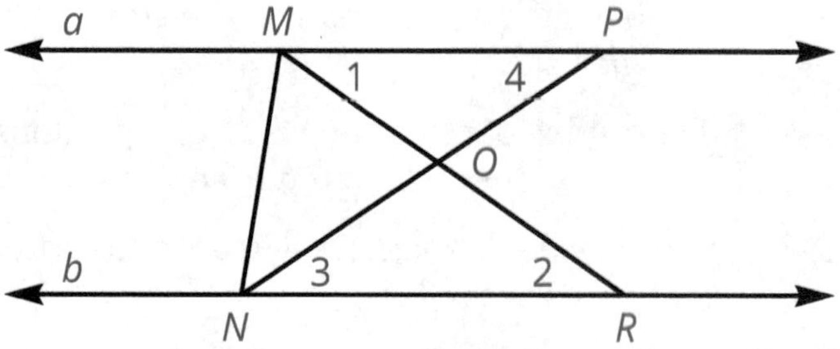

STATEMENT	REASON

2.30 Given: $\overline{EC} \perp \overline{AC}$, $\overline{DB} \perp \overline{AC}$, $\angle A = \angle F$

To Prove: $\triangle MDF \sim \triangle NCA$

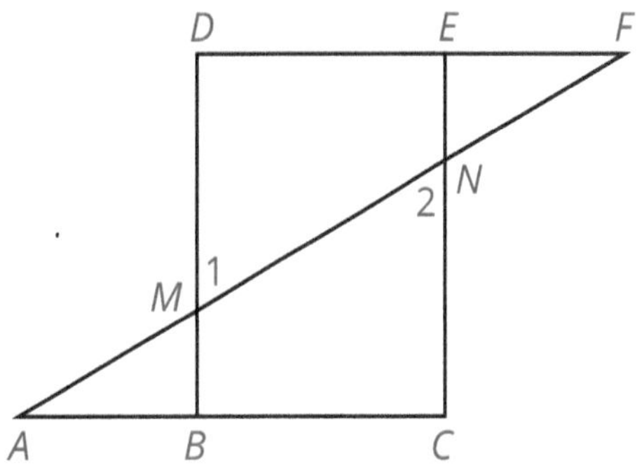

STATEMENT	REASON

2.31 Given: $AB \parallel CD$

To Prove: $\frac{MC}{MB} = \frac{CD}{AB}$

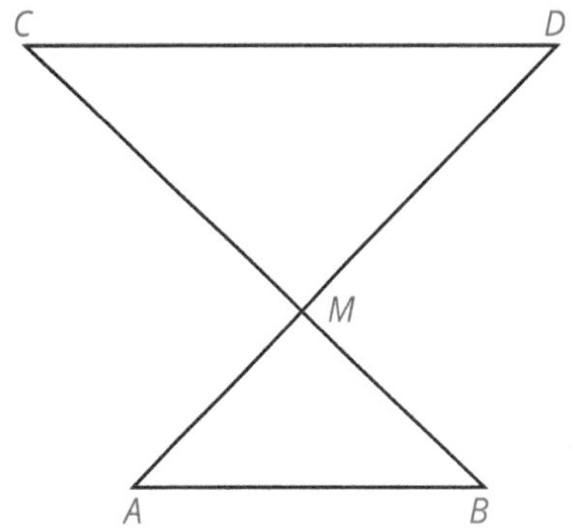

STATEMENT	REASON

2.32 Given: $\overline{RS} \parallel \overline{AB}$, $\angle 1 = \angle 2$

To Prove: $\frac{CR}{RA} = \frac{CS}{RS}$

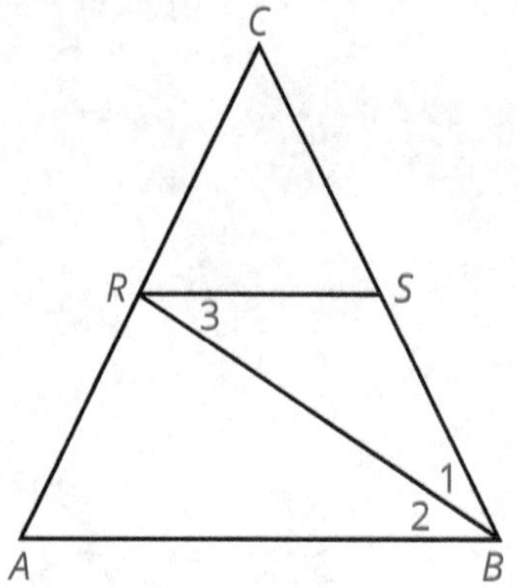

STATEMENT	REASON

2.33 Given: $\triangle ABC$ is rt. triangle

$\overline{BD} \perp \overline{AC}$

$AB = \sqrt{17}$

To Prove: $(AD)(AC) = 17$

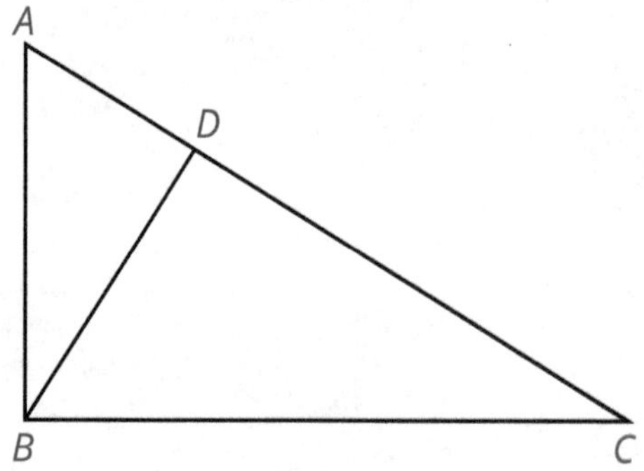

STATEMENT	REASON

Find the missing measures.

Given: $\triangle ABC$ is a right triangle

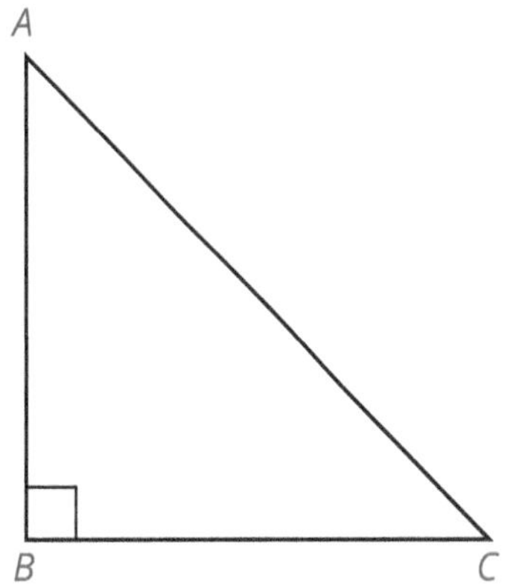

2.34 $AB = 6$, $BC = 8$, $AC =$ ________________

2.35 $AB =$ ________________, $BC = 5$, $AC = 20$

2.36 $AB = 5\sqrt{2}$, $BC =$ ________________, $AC = 10$

2.37 Find the diagonal of a cube if its side equals 5. ________________

2.38 Find the slant height of a square-base pyramid with base edge 6 and lateral edge 6.

____

Write the trigonometric equation (sin, tan, or cos) you would use to find *x* in the following right triangles. Do not solve the equations.

2.39 ________________

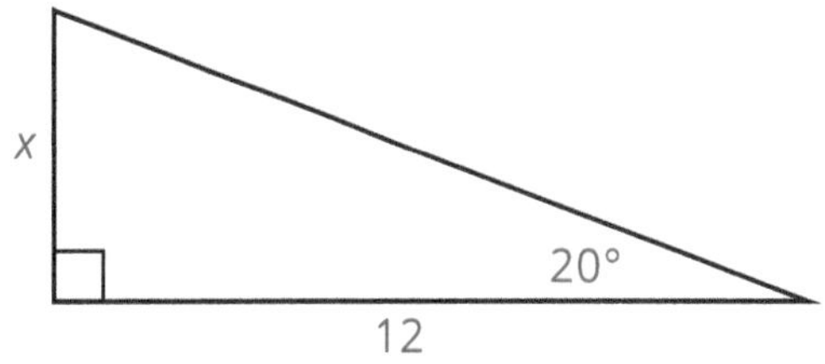

2.40 ________________

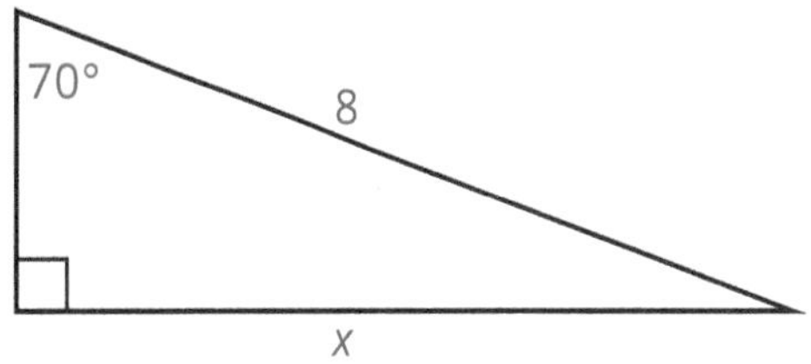

2.41 ________________

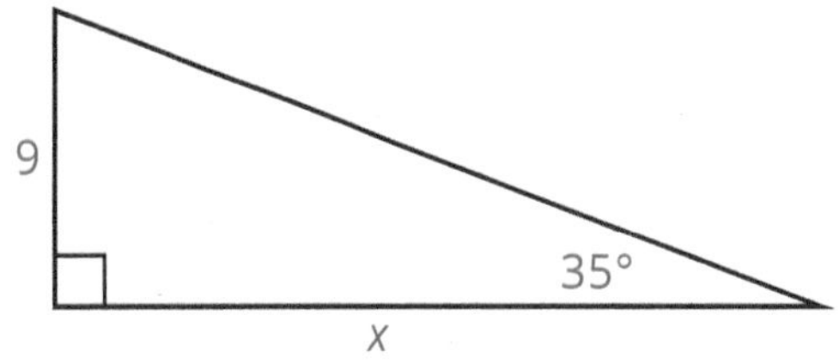

2.42 ____________________

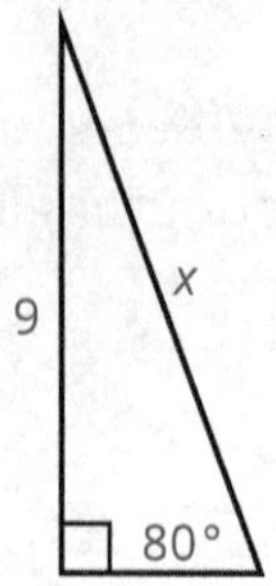

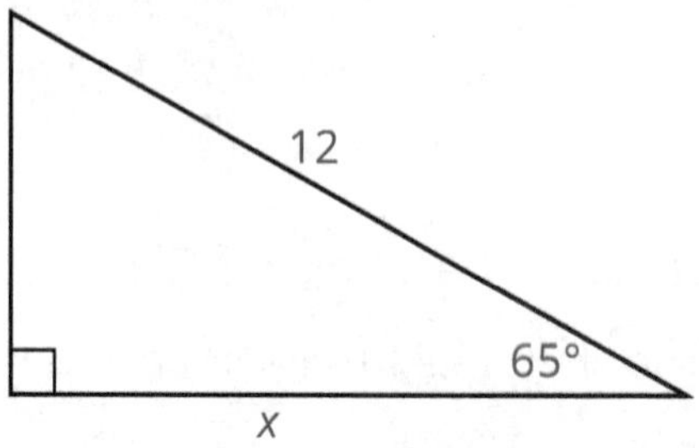

2.43 ____________________

Find *x* and *y* in these 30°-60°-90° triangles.

2.44

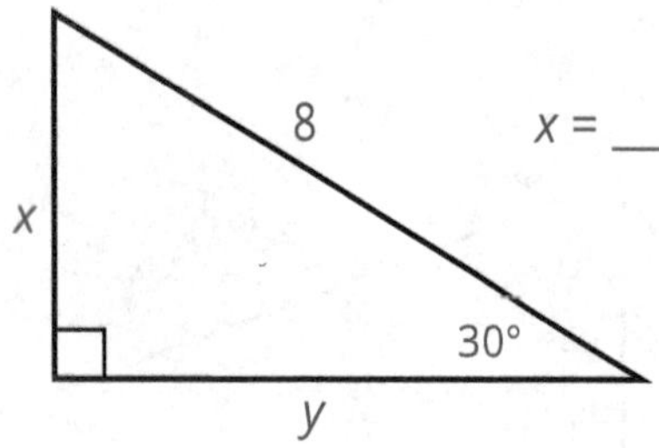

$x =$ __________ $y =$ __________

2.45

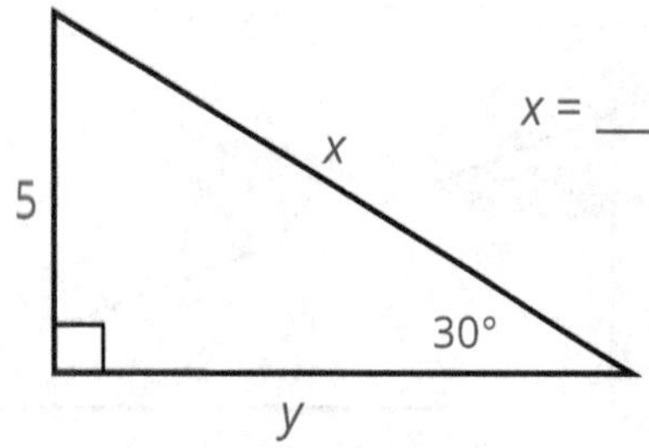

$x =$ __________ $y =$ __________

2.46

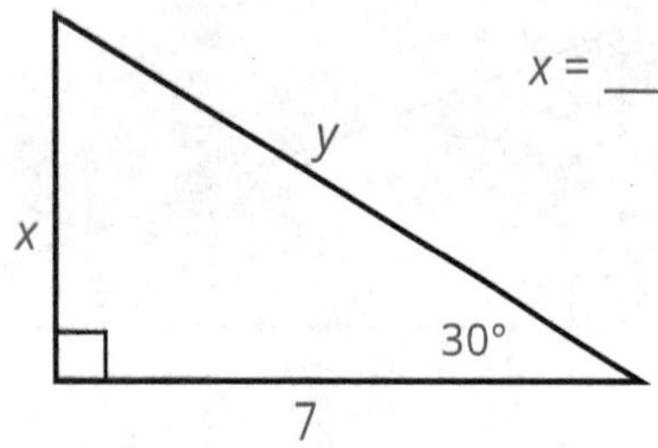

$x =$ __________ $y =$ __________

Find *x* in these 45°-45°-90° triangles.

2.47

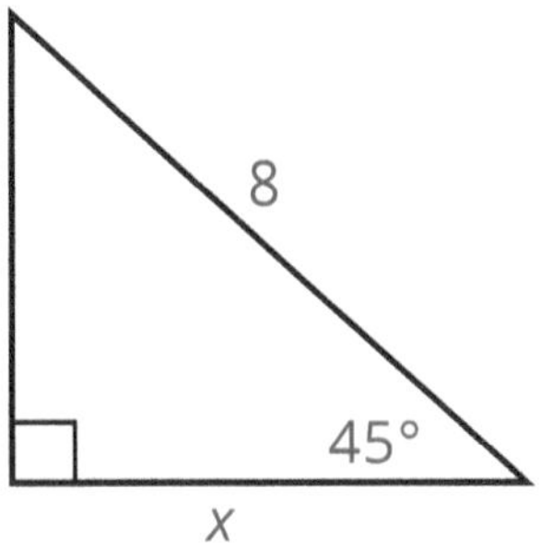

$x =$ ____________

2.48

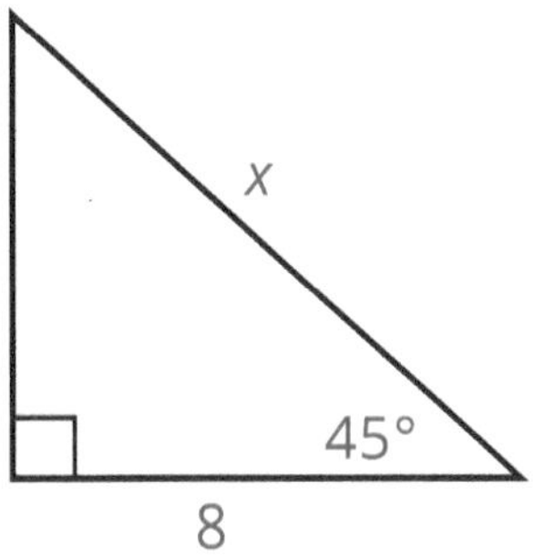

$x =$ ____________

2.49

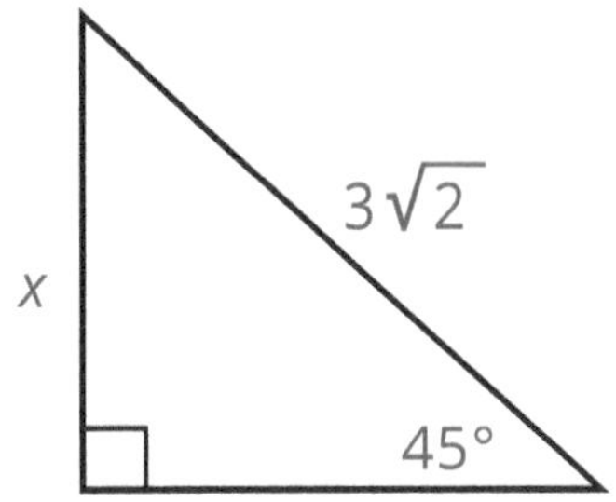

$x =$ ____________

2.50

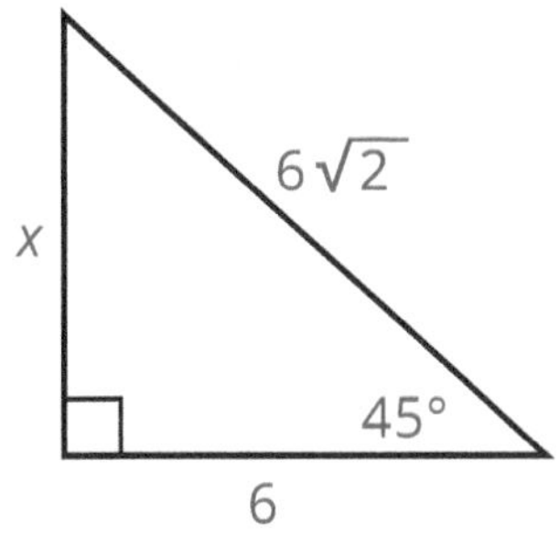

$x =$ ____________

CIRCLES

The circle and its related space partner, the sphere, play an important part in our everyday life. In Math LIFEPAC 1006 you learned how the parts of these shapes are related to each other and how they are measured.

DEFINITIONS

Circle: the set of all points in a plane that are the same distance from a given point in that plane called its center.

Radius: a segment whose endpoints are the center of a circle and a point on the circle.

Diameter: a segment passing through the center with endpoints on the circle.

Concentric circles: two or more circles that lie in the same plane and have the same center.

Sphere: the set of all points that are the same distance from a given point.

Congruent circles: circles that have equal radii.

Tangent line: a line in the plane of a circle that intersects the circle in exactly one point.

Central angle: an angle in the plane of a circle whose vertex is at the center of the circle.

Minor arc: the union of two points of the circle (not endpoints of a diameter) and all points of the circle that are in the interior of the central angle whose sides contain the two points.

Major arc: the union of two points of the circle (not endpoints of a diameter) and all points of the circle that are in the exterior of the central angle whose sides contain the two points.

Semicircle: the union of the endpoints of a diameter and all points of the circle that are on the same side of the diameter.

Chord: a segment whose endpoints are on the circle.

Secant: a line that contains a chord.

Midpoint of an arc: a point x on arc AB such that m $\overset{\frown}{AX}$ = m $\overset{\frown}{XB}$.

Center of an arc: the center of the circle that contains the arc.

Inscribed angle: an angle whose sides contain the endpoints of an arc and whose vertex is a point of the arc other than an endpoint of the arc.

In circles and spheres we are usually interested in finding or proving certain angle measures. The arc addition postulate is useful for this purpose.

POSTULATE

P16: If the intersection of $\overset{\frown}{AB}$ and $\overset{\frown}{BC}$ of a circle is the single point B, then m $\overset{\frown}{AB}$ + m $\overset{\frown}{BC}$ = m $\overset{\frown}{ABC}$. (Arc addition)

The following theorems include facts that can be proved about circles, arcs, chords, and rays. Carefully think through the proof to each theorem as you review.

THEOREMS

6–1 A radius drawn to a point of tangency is perpendicular to the tangent.

6–2 A line in the plane of a circle and perpendicular to a radius at its outer endpoint is tangent to the circle.

6–3 If in the same circle or congruent circles two central angles are equal, then their arcs are equal.

6–4 If in the same circle or congruent circles two minor arcs are equal, then their central angles are equal.

6–5 If in the same circle or congruent circles the chords are equal, then the arcs are equal.

6–6 If in the same circle or congruent circles the arcs are equal, then the chords are equal.

6–7 If a diameter is perpendicular to a chord, then it bisects the chord and its two arcs.

6–8 If in the same circle or congruent circles the chords are equidistant from the center, then their lengths are equal.

6–9 If in the same circle or congruent circles the chords have the same length, then they are equidistant from the center.

6–10 The measure of an inscribed angle is equal to half the measure of its intercepted arc.

Corollary 1: An angle inscribed in a semicircle is a right angle.

Corollary 2: The opposite angles of an inscribed quadrilateral are supplementary.

Corollary 3: If two angles intercept the same or equal arcs, then the angles are equal.

6–11 The measure of an angle formed by a secant ray and a tangent ray drawn from a point on a circle is equal to half the measure of the intercepted arc.

6–12 The measure of an angle formed by two secants that intersect inside the circle is equal to half the sum of the intercepted arcs.

6–13 The measure of the angle formed by two secants intersecting outside the circle is equal to half the difference of the intercepted arcs.

6–14 The measure of the angle formed by a tangent ray and a secant ray intersecting outside the circle is equal to half the difference of the intercepted arcs.

6–15 The measure of the angle formed by two tangent rays intersecting outside the circle is equal to half the difference of the intercepted arcs.

6–16 If two chords intersect in a circle, then the product of the lengths of the segments of one chord is equal to the product of the length of the segments of the other chord.

6–17 If two secants intersect at a point outside a circle, then the length of one secant times the length of its external segment part is equal to the length of the other secant times the length of its external segment part.

6–18 If a tangent segment and a secant segment intersect outside a circle, then the length of the tangent segment is the geometric mean between the secant segment and the external part of the secant segment.

Refer to this figure to name the following items.

2.51 A radius ______________

2.52 A tangent ______________

2.53 A chord not a diameter ______________

2.54 A secant ______________

2.55 A diameter ______________

2.56 An inscribed angle ______________

2.57 A central angle ______________

2.58 A minor arc ______________

2.59 A semicircle ______________

2.60 A right triangle ______________

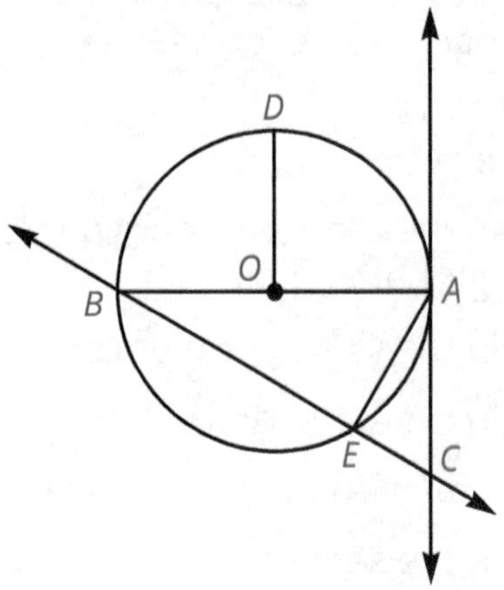

Refer to the figures to find the following measures.

2.61 If $\angle 1 = 60°$, then m $\overset{\frown}{BC}$ = ______________ .

2.62 If m $\overset{\frown}{CD} = 50°$, then $\angle 2$ = ______________ .

2.63 If $\angle 1 = 70°$, then m $\overset{\frown}{AB}$ = ______________ .

2.64 If m $\overset{\frown}{AD} = 120°$, then m $\overset{\frown}{ABD}$ = ______________ .

2.65 If m $\overset{\frown}{BC}$ = m $\overset{\frown}{CD}$ and $\angle 1 = 48°$, then m BAD = ______________ .

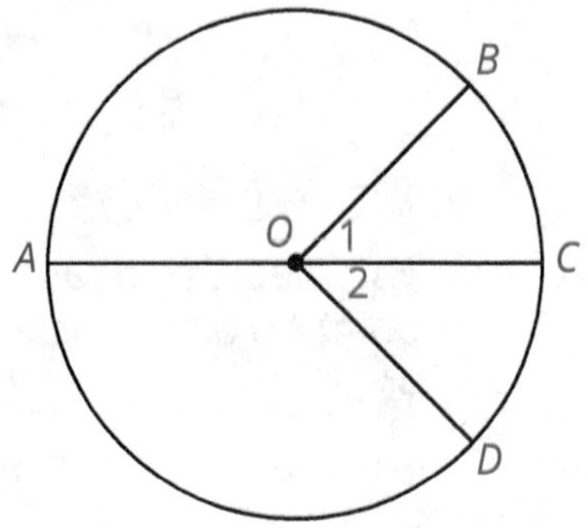

2.66 If $AP = 3$, $PC = 4$, and $DP = 6$, then BP = ______________ .

2.67 If m $\overset{\frown}{AD} = 20°$ and m $\overset{\frown}{BC} = 30°$, then m $\angle 1$ = ______________ .

2.68 If m $\overset{\frown}{DC} = 120°$ and $\angle 2 = 115°$, then m $\overset{\frown}{AB}$ = ______________ .

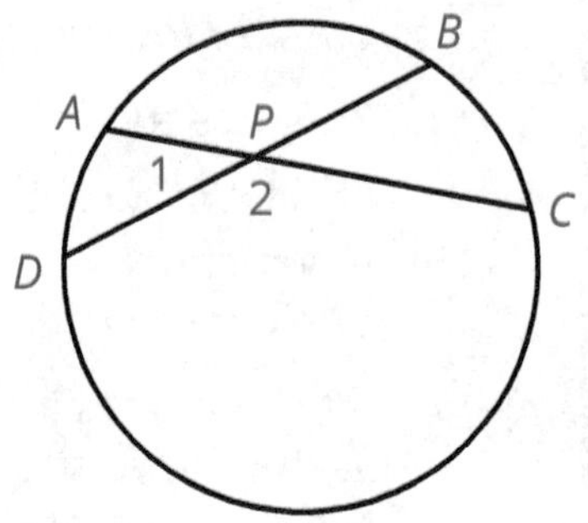

2.69 If $AB = 6$, $BC = 6$, and $DC = 4$, then EC = ____________ .

2.70 If m $\widehat{AE} = 90°$ and m $\widehat{BD} = 30°$, then $\angle C$ = ____________ .

2.71 If $\angle C = 25°$ and m $\widehat{AE} = 100°$, then m $\widehat{BD}$ = ____________ .

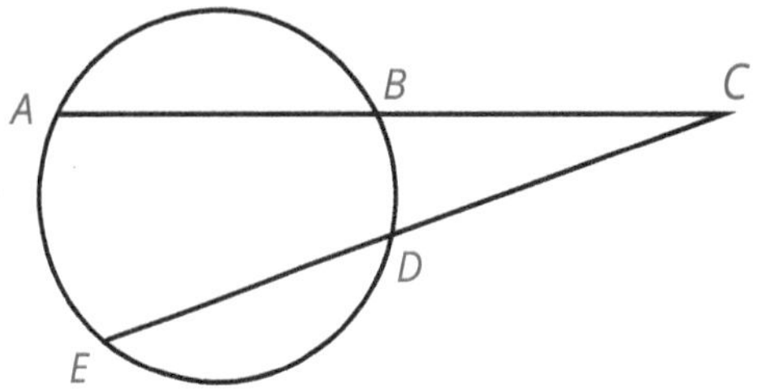

Find *x* in the following figures.

2.72 x = ____________

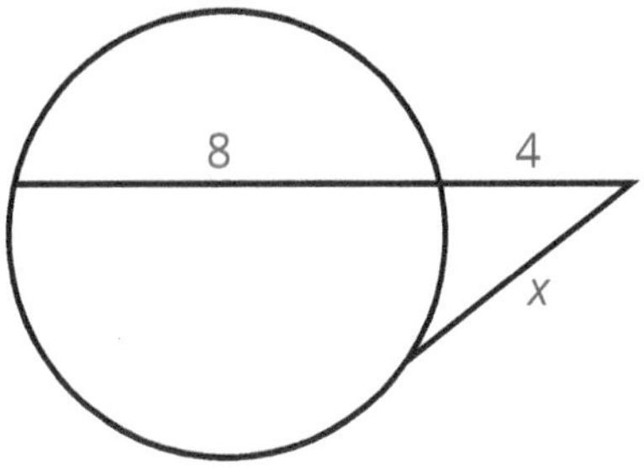

2.73 x = ____________

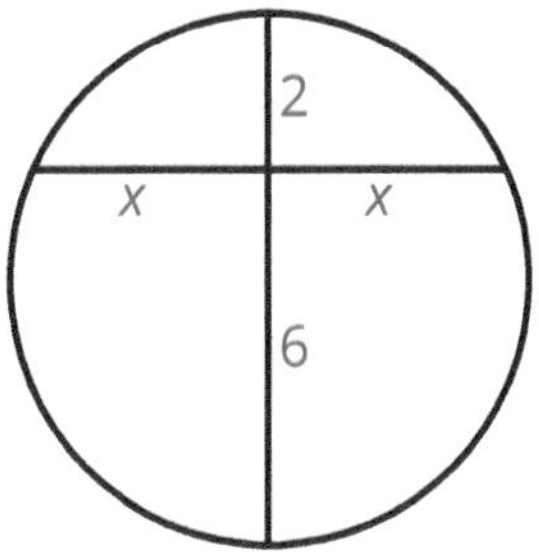

2.74 x = ____________

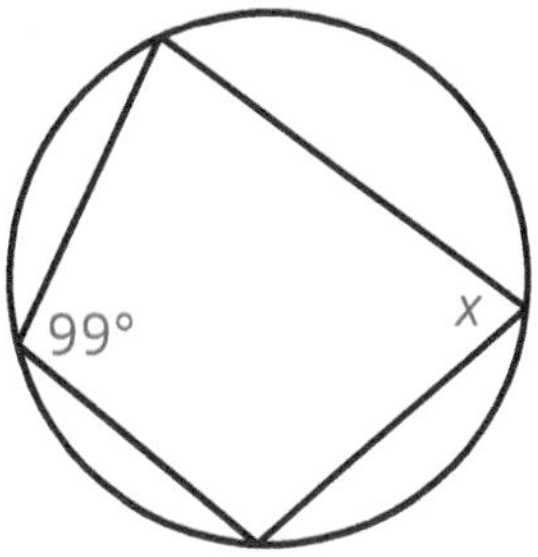

2.75 x = ____________

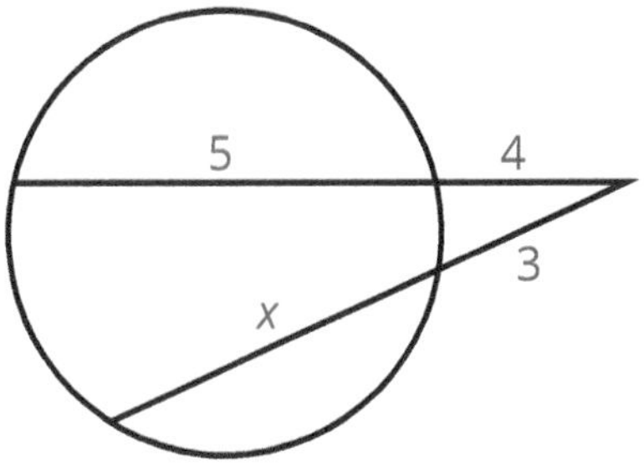

Review the material in this section in preparation for the Self Test. This Self Test will check your mastery of this particular section as well as your knowledge of the previous section.

SELF TEST 2

Name the corresponding parts if polygon *WXYZ* ≅ polygon *PQRS* (each answer, 2 points).

2.01 $\angle W =$ ________________

2.02 $XY =$ ________________

2.03 $\angle R =$ ________________

2.04 $PS =$ ________________

2.05 $\angle S =$ ________________

2.06 $YZ =$ ________________

2.07 $\angle X =$ ________________

2.08 $QP =$ ________________

Solve the following proportions (each answer, 3 points).

2.09 $\frac{x}{25} = \frac{2}{5}$ $x =$ ________________

2.010 $\frac{9}{x} = \frac{3}{12}$ $x =$ ________________

2.011 $\frac{3}{2} = \frac{x}{4}$ $x =$ ________________

2.012 $\frac{16}{x} = \frac{x}{4}$ $x =$ ________________

Find x in these 45°-45°-90° triangles (each answer, 3 points).

2.013 ________________

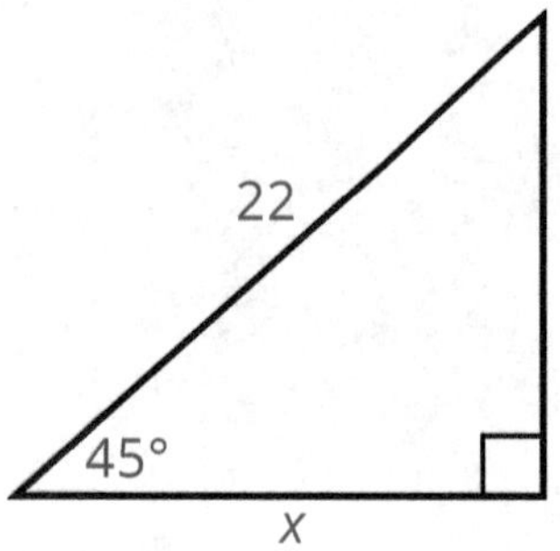

2.014 ________________

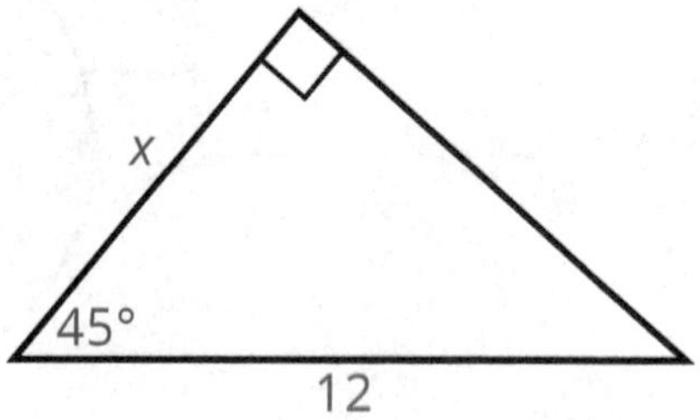

2.015 ______________________

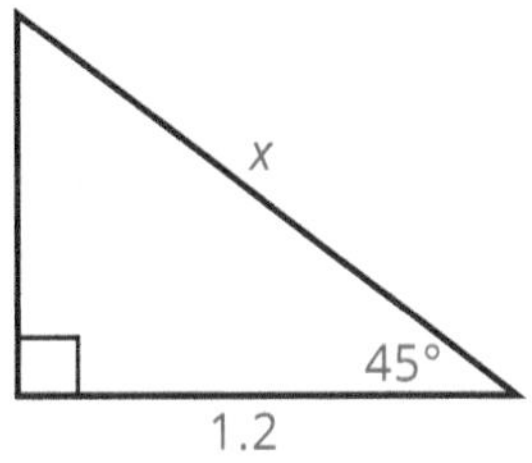

2.016 ______________________

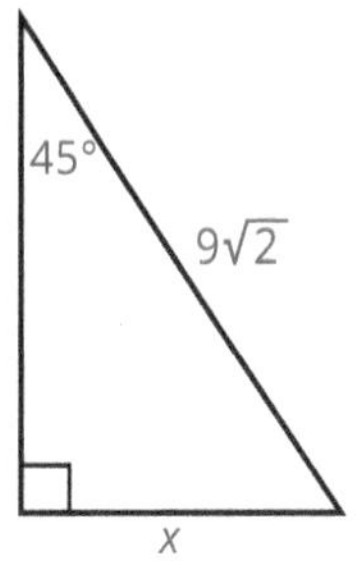

2.017 ______________________

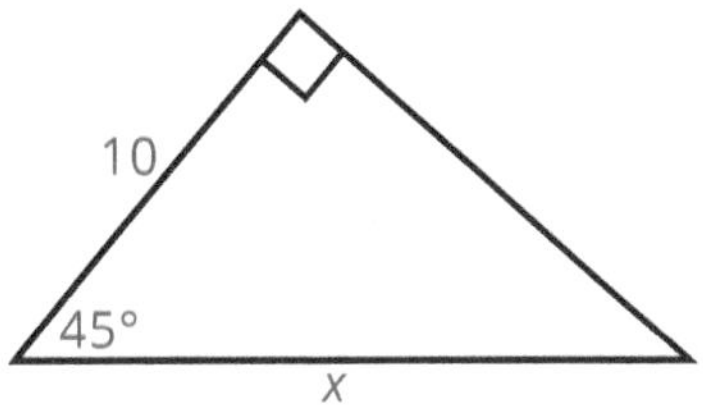

2.018 ______________________

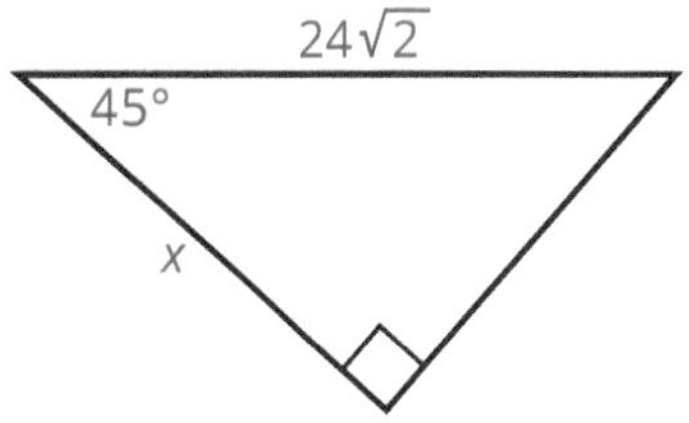

Refer to the figures to find the following measures (each answer, 3 points).

Given: $\overline{PB}$ tangent

$\overline{PV}$, $\overline{PU}$ secants

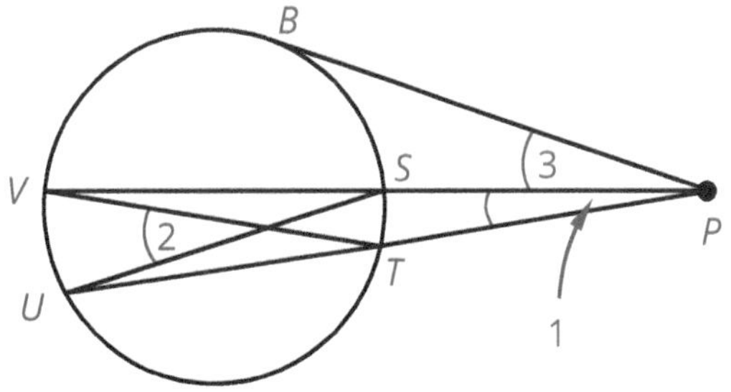

2.019 If m $\widehat{VU}$ = 80° and m $\widehat{ST}$ = 40°,

then m ∠1 = ______________ .

2.020 If m $\widehat{UV}$ = 70° and m $\widehat{ST}$ = 30°,

then m ∠2 = ______________ .

2.021 If m $\widehat{VB}$ = 60° and m $\widehat{BS}$ = 30°,

then m ∠3 = ______________ .

2.022 If m ∠1 = 30° and m $\widehat{ST}$ = 20°,

then m $\widehat{UV}$ = ______________ .

Given: t is tangent at B

$\overline{AB}$ is diameter

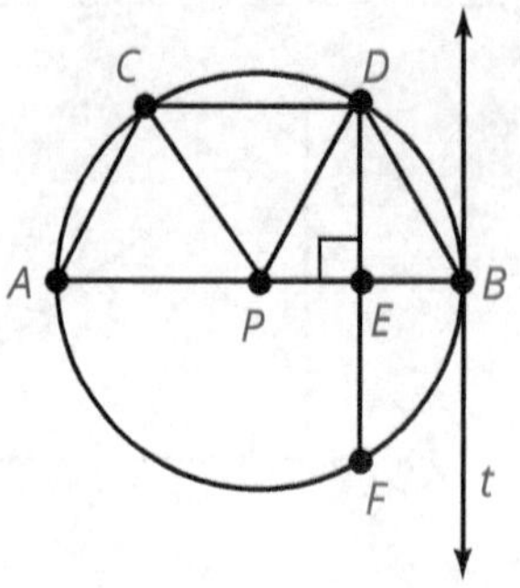

2.023 If m $\angle DPB$ = 60°, then m $\overset{\frown}{DB}$ = ______________ .

2.024 If m $\overset{\frown}{AF}$ = 110°, then m $\overset{\frown}{DB}$ = ______________ .

2.025 If $AC = CD = DB$, then m $\angle CPD$ = ______________ .

2.026 If $\overline{AB} \perp \overline{DF}$, then $\overline{DF}$ || ______________ .

2.027 If m $\overset{\frown}{DB}$ = 60° and $PE = 3$, then PB = ______________ .

Complete the following proofs (each proof, 6 points).

2.028 Given: $\overline{AE}$ tangent to ⊙R at A and to circle S at E

To Prove: $\angle R = \angle S$

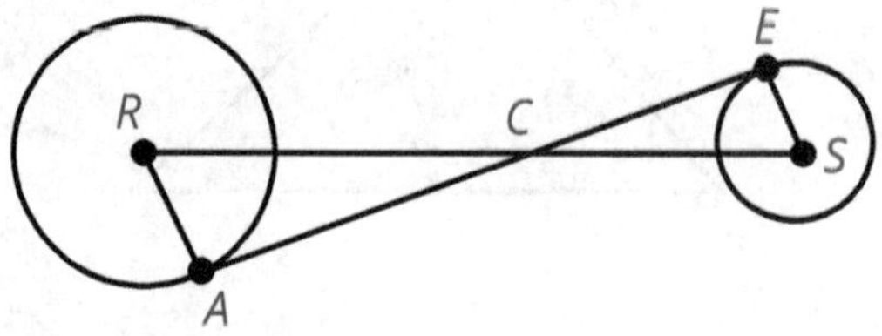

STATEMENT	REASON

2.029 Given: $\overline{XZ} \parallel \overline{BC}$

$\angle 1 = \angle 2$

To Prove: $\frac{AX}{XB} = \frac{AY}{ZC}$

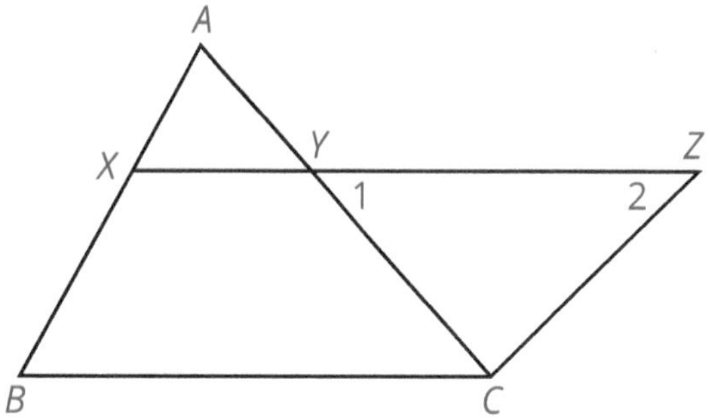

STATEMENT	REASON

2.030 Given: $\overline{RS} \parallel \overline{BC}$

$\angle 1 = \angle 2$

To Prove: $\frac{AR}{RS} = \frac{AS}{SC}$

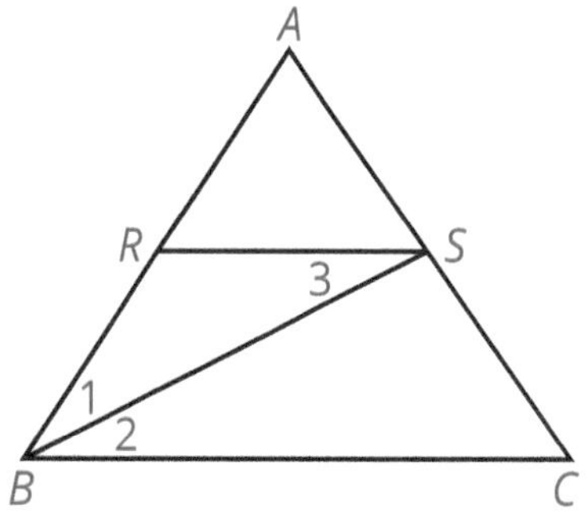

STATEMENT	REASON

73/91 **SCORE** ________ **TEACHER** ________ ________
initials date

3. CONSTRUCTION, MEASUREMENT, AND COORDINATE GEOMETRY

This section will review the material most recently presented in the Math 1000 series. The main topics included are construction of figures and the concept of locus; measurement of area and volume; and the system of coordinate geometry.

Section Objectives

Review these objectives. When you have completed this section, you should be able to:

5. Prove geometric theorems using definitions, postulates, and properties.
9. Construct geometric figures using only a compass and straightedge.
10. Sketch and name figures that meet locus conditions.
11. Calculate area and volume of geometric figures.
12. Sketch geometric figures on the coordinate axes.
13. Use algebraic notation to solve geometric distance, slope, and midpoint problems.

CONSTRUCTION AND LOCUS

Only two tools are permitted in making a geometric construction. These tools are the compass to construct circles and arcs of circles, and an unmarked straightedge to construct segments.

The following basic constructions are shown in detail in Math LIFEPAC 1007. Return to that LIFEPAC for review of any constructions you do not remember how to do.

DEFINITIONS

Locus: the set of all those points and only those points that satisfy a given condition.

Regular hexagon: a hexagon with all six sides equal and all six angles equal.

Regular octagon: an octagon with all eight sides equal and all eight angles equal.

Inscribed circle: a circle placed inside a polygon so that all sides of the polygon are tangent to the circle.

Circumscribed circle: a circle placed around a polygon so that each vertex of the polygon is on the circle.

Construction 1: Copy a segment.

Construction 2: Copy an angle.

Construction 3: Bisect a segment.

Construction 4: Bisect an angle.

Construction 5: Bisect an arc.

Construction 6: Construct a perpendicular to a line through a point on the line.

Construction 7: Construct a perpendicular to a line through a point not on the line.

Construction 8: Construct a tangent to a circle at a point on the circle.

Construction 9: Construct a tangent to a circle from a point exterior to the circle.

> **Construction 10:** Construct a parallel to a line through a point not on a line.
>
> **Construction 11:** Divide a segment into a given number of equal segments.
>
> **Construction 12:** Construct the fourth proportional given three segments.
>
> **Construction 13:** Construct the geometric mean given two segments.

Once you had mastered the thirteen basic constructions, you were able to use them to construct figures. The following constructions are presented in detail in Math LIFEPAC 1007. Make sure you either remember or review how to do each one.

> Construct triangles given measurements of sides and angles.
>
> Construct medians of triangles.
>
> Construct altitudes of triangles.
>
> Inscribe a circle in a triangle.
>
> Circumscribe a circle about a triangle.
>
> Construct polygons given their sides.
>
> Construct figures to fit locus concepts.

Do the following constructions.

3.1 Copy segment *RS*.

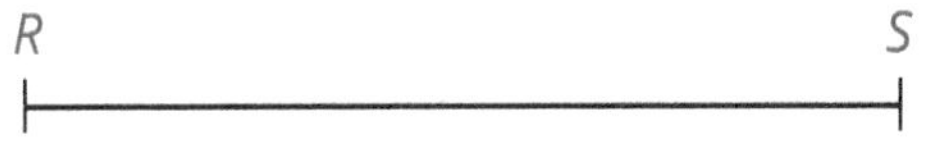

3.2 Copy $\angle RST$.

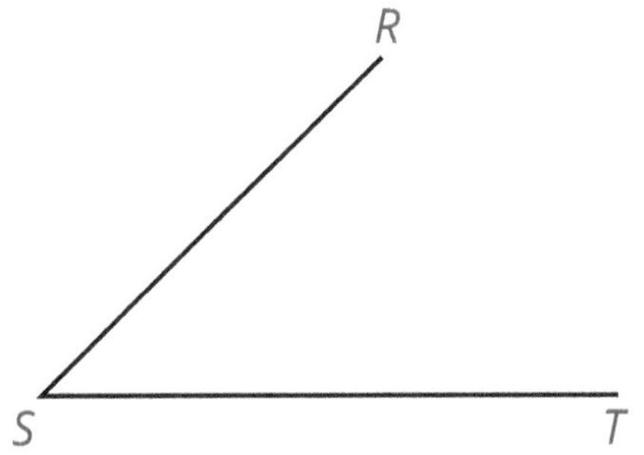

3.3 Bisect $\overline{XY}$.

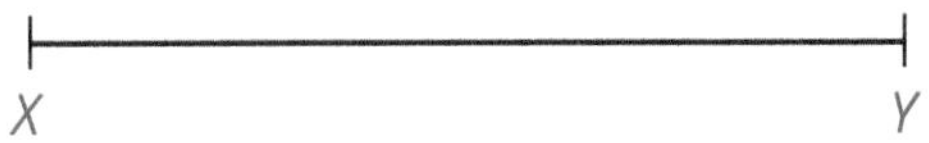

3.4 Construct a perpendicular from C to $\overleftrightarrow{AB}$.

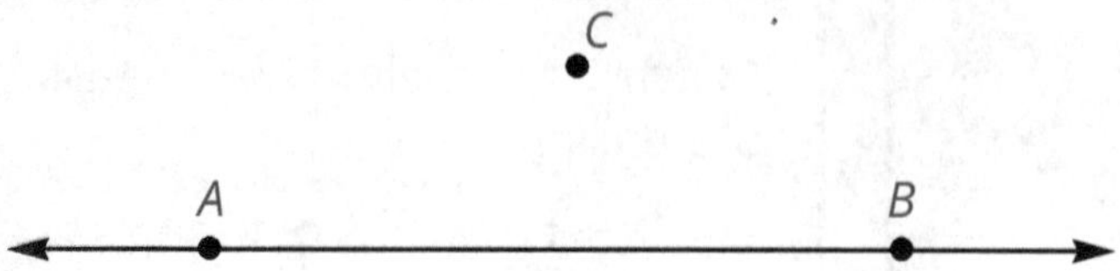

3.5 Construct a perpendicular to $\overleftrightarrow{MN}$ at Q.

3.6 Construct a tangent to the circle from point P.

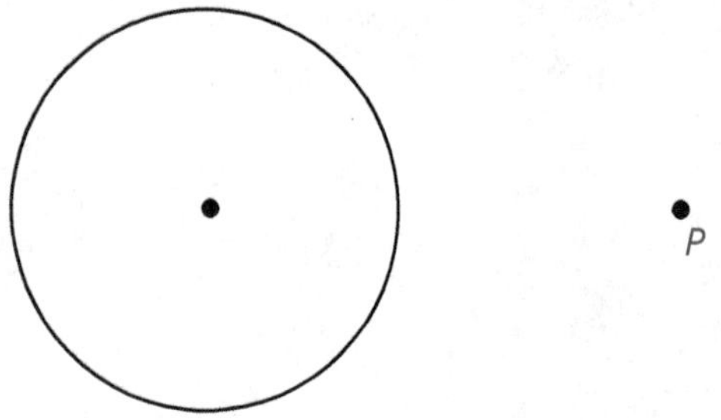

3.7 Construct a parallel to $\overleftrightarrow{AB}$ through C.

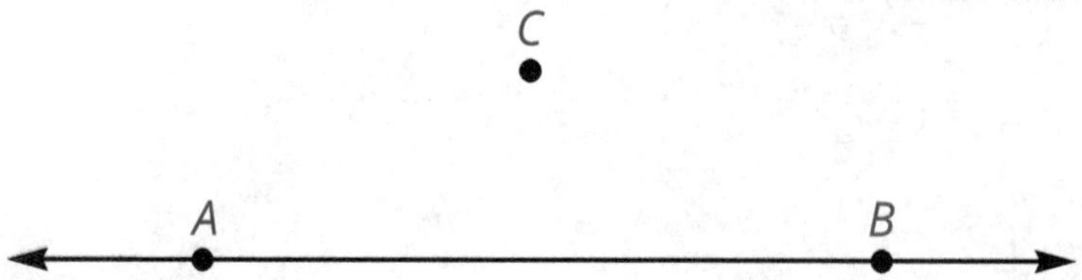

3.8 Divide $\overline{AB}$ into three equal parts.

3.9 Construct the geometric mean between *c* and *d*. Call the segment *x*.

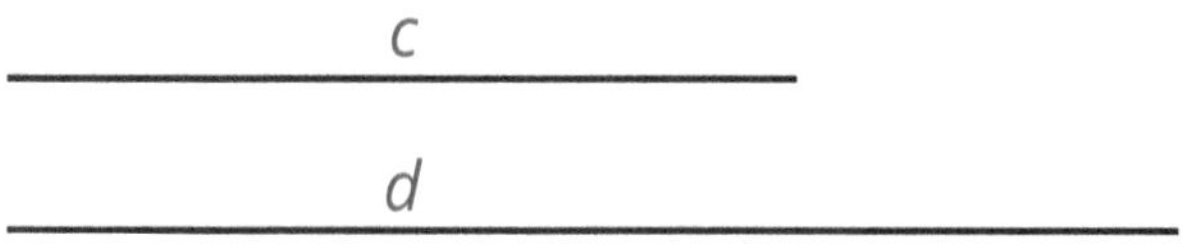

3.10 Construct the three medians in this triangle.

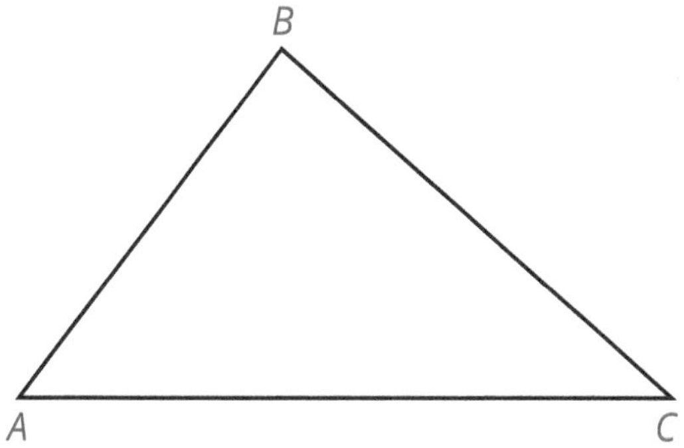

3.11 Construct a 30°-60°-90° triangle with short leg equal to *b*.

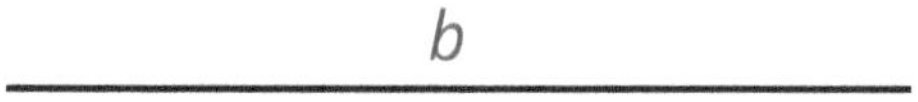

Make a sketch and answer the following questions.

3.12 What is the locus of points equidistant from two parallel lines and in their plane?

____

3.13 What is the locus of points in the plane of and equidistant from two points?

____

3.14 What is the locus of points equidistant from a given point?

____

3.15 What is the locus of points a given distance from a line *l*?

____

AREA AND VOLUME

The formulas for area and volume were developed as part of our deductive system. Instead of simply memorizing and using the formulas, you saw where the formulas actually came from.

The following postulates are used in the proofs of the area and volume theorems. The postulates again relate mostly to the basic geometric figure, the triangle.

DEFINITIONS

Center of a regular polygon: the common center of its inscribed and circumscribed circles.

Radius of a regular polygon: the distance from the center of the polygon to a vertex.

Apothem: the distance from the center of a polygon to a side.

Central angle of a regular polygon: an angle whose vertex is the center of the polygon and whose sides contain consecutive vertices of the polygon.

Circumference of a circle: is the limit of the perimeters of the inscribed regular polygons.

Area of a circle: the limit of the areas of the inscribed regular polygons.

Pi (π): the ratio of the circumference to the diameter of a circle.

Sector: the region of a circle bounded by two radii and an arc of the circle.

Segment of a circle: the region bounded by a chord and an arc of the circle.

POSTULATES

P17: For every polygonal region a unique positive number exists that is called the area of that region.

P18: If two triangles are congruent, then their areas are the same number.

P19: The area of a polygonal region is the sum of the areas of the triangular regions that form the polygonal region.

P20: The area of a rectangle is the product of the length of a base and the length of the altitude: $A = bh$.

P21: If two polygons are similar, then they can be separated into the same number of triangles similar each to each and in corresponding position.

P22: The volume of any pyramid is $\frac{1}{3}$ the product of the area of the base (B) and the length of the altitude h: ($V = \frac{1}{3}Bh$).

P23: The volume of a sphere is $\frac{4}{3}\pi r^3$.

P24: The surface area of a sphere is $4\pi r^2$.

These theorems about areas and volumes can be proved using postulates and definitions. You may recognize many of the formulas as those you have previously used without proof.

THEOREMS

8–1 The area of a parallelogram is the product of any base and the altitude to that base: $A = bh$.

8–2 The area of a triangle is $\frac{1}{2}$ the product of the base and the altitude to that base: $A = \frac{1}{2}bh$.

Corollary 1: The area of an equilateral triangle with side of length s is $\frac{1}{4}$ the product of the square of s and $\sqrt{3}$: $A = \frac{s^2\sqrt{3}}{4}$.

Corollary 2: The area of a rhombus is $\frac{1}{2}$ the product of the lengths of its diagonals: $A = \frac{d_1 \cdot d_2}{2}$.

8–3 The area of a trapezoid is $\frac{1}{2}$ the product of the length of an altitude and the sum of the length of the bases: $A = \frac{1}{2}h(b_1 + b_2)$.

8–4 The area of a regular polygon is $\frac{1}{2}$ the product of the apothem and the perimeter: $A = \frac{1}{2}ap$.

8–5 The ratio of the area of two similar triangles is equal to the square of the ratio of the lengths of any two corresponding sides.

8–6 The ratio of the areas of two similar polygons is equal to the square of the ratio of the length of any pair of corresponding sides.

8–7 The ratio of the circumference to the diameter is the same for all circles: $\pi \doteq 3.1416$.

8–8 The area of a circle is the product of π and the square of the radius of the circle: $A = \pi r^2$.

Other important formulas are derived from the theorem formulas. Be certain that you understand and can use each one.

Prism	$L.A. = ph$	$T.A. = L.A. + 2B$	$V = Bh$
Pyramid	$L.A. = \frac{1}{2}pl$	$T.A. = L.A. + B$	$V = \frac{1}{3}Bh$
Cylinder	$L.A. = 2\pi rh$	$T.A. = L.A. + 2\pi r^2$	$V = \pi r^2 h$
Cone	$L.A. = \pi rl$	$T.A. = L.A. + \pi r^2$	$V = \frac{1}{3}\pi r^2 h$
Sphere	$S = 4\pi r^2$	$V = \frac{4}{3}\pi r^3$	
Area of sector	$\frac{m\,\widehat{AB}}{360°}(\pi r^2)$		

Area of segment = area of sector – area of triangle

Use the figures to find the following measures.

3.16 Area of base ____________

3.17 Lateral area ____________

3.18 Total area ____________

3.19 Volume ____________

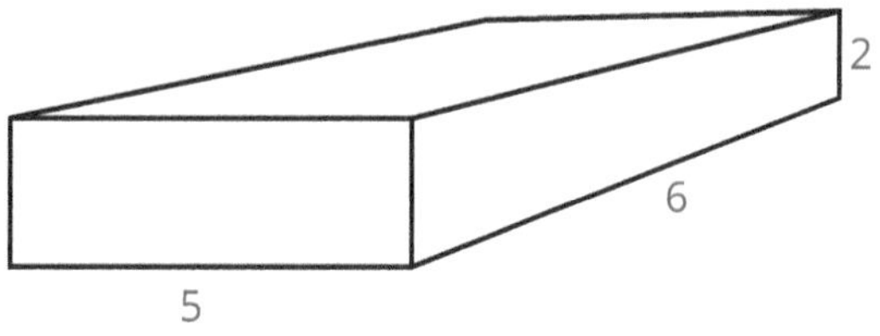

3.20 Slant height ____________

3.21 Lateral area ____________

3.22 Altitude ____________

3.23 Total area ____________

3.24 Volume ____________

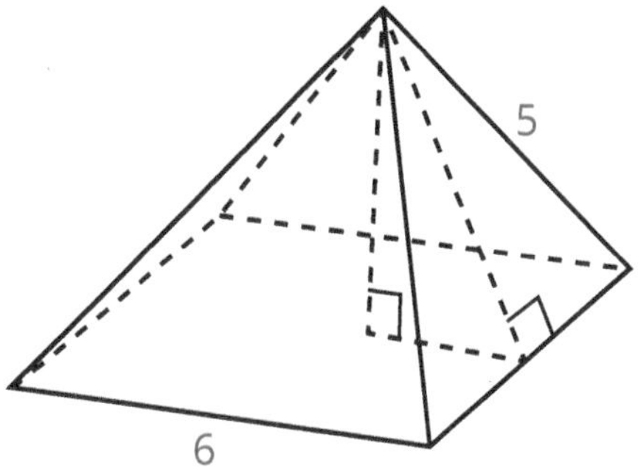

3.25 Lateral area ____________

3.26 Total area ____________

3.27 Volume ____________

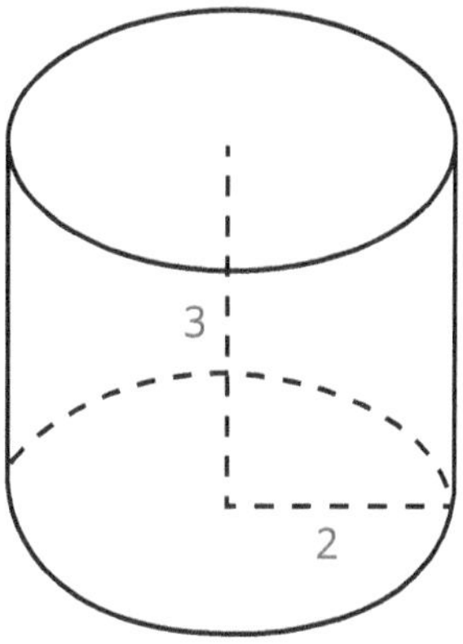

3.28 Slant height ____________

3.29 Lateral area ____________

3.30 Total area ____________

3.31 Volume ____________

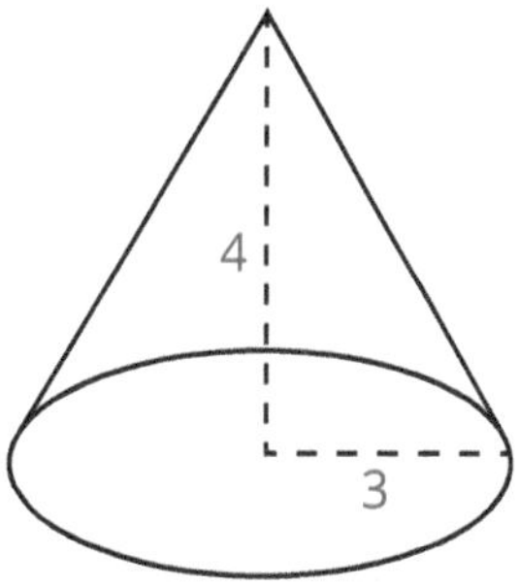

3.32 Surface area ____________

3.33 Volume ____________

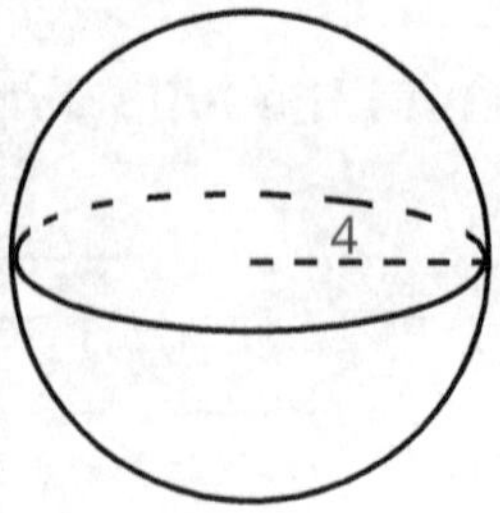

3.34 Area of circle ____________

3.35 Area of sector *O-AXB* ____________

3.36 Area of segment *AXB* ____________

3.37 Circumference of circle ____________

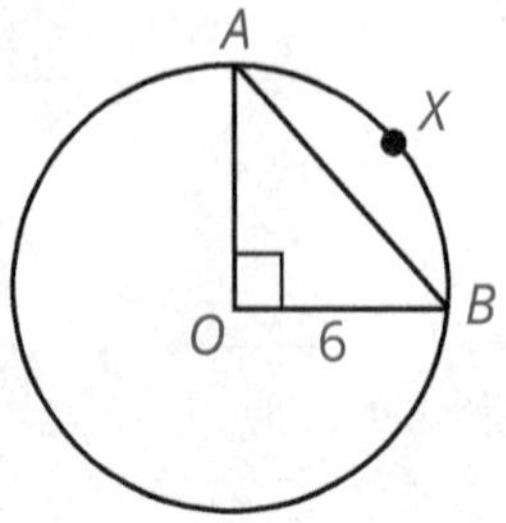

3.38 Apothem ____________

3.39 Radius ____________

3.40 Central angle ____________

3.41 Area ____________

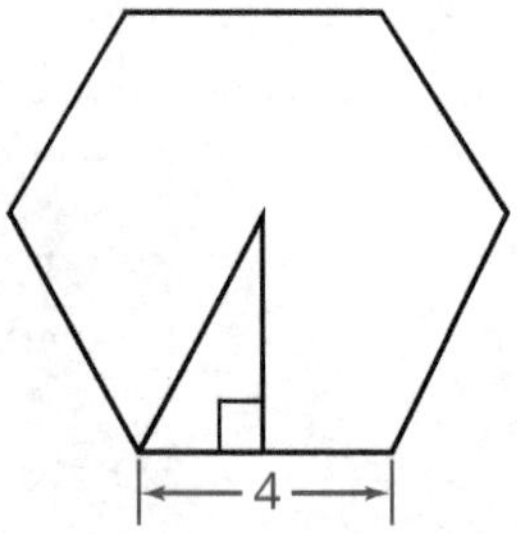

3.42 Area of triangle *DEF* = ____________

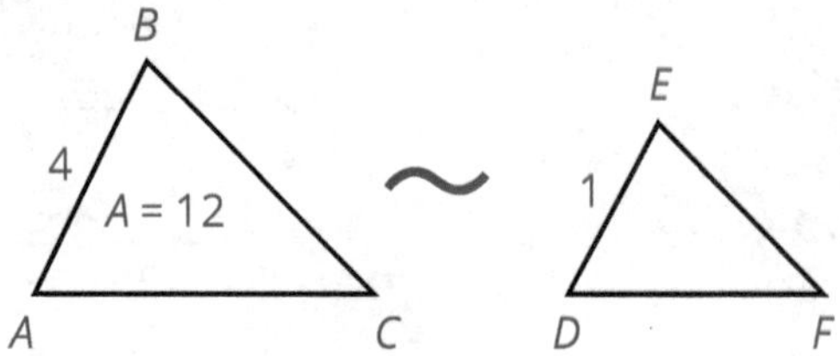

3.43 x = ____________

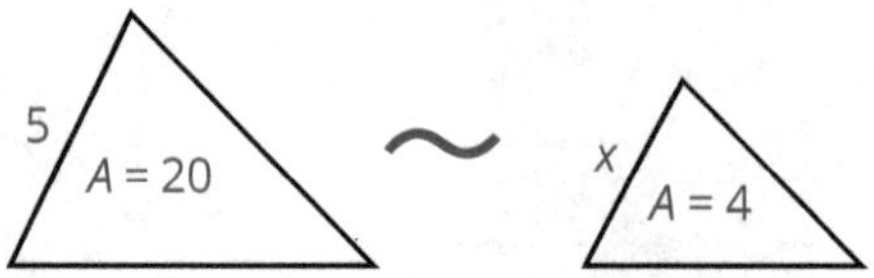

COORDINATE GEOMETRY

Coordinate geometry is the study of geometry by using algebra. Points are identified by pairs of numbers which locate them on a coordinate plane. Equations for lines, distances, circles, and other geometric ideas are then developed.

DEFINITIONS

***x*-axis:** a horizontal number line.

***y*-axis:** a vertical number line.

Coordinate axes: an *x*-axis and a *y*-axis intersecting at the zero points and perpendicular to each other.

Quadrants: the four regions of a plane formed by the coordinate axes.

Symmetry: the property of balance that a figure has with respect to a point, a line, or a plane.

Graph: a set of points in the coordinate plane that meets certain algebraic conditions.

Slope: a number identifying the slant of a line with respect to the coordinate axes and found by the formula

$$m = \frac{y_2 - y_1}{x_2 - x_1},$$

where (x_1, y_1) and (x_2, y_2) are the coordinates of two points on the line.

These last seven theorems state some important geometric concepts in basic algebraic notation. These theorems enable us to sketch and use familiar geometric figures on the coordinate axes. Be sure you can remember each proof.

THEOREMS

9–1 The distance between two points (x_1, y_1) and (x_2, y_2) is given by the formula

$$d = \sqrt{(x_1 - x_2)^2 + (y_1 - y_2)^2}.$$

9–2 The equation of a circle with center at (h, k) and having a radius of r is

$$(x - h)^2 + (y - k)^2 = r^2.$$

9–3 The coordinate of the midpoint of a segment with endpoints (x_1, y_1) and (x_2, y_2) is

$$\left(\frac{x_2 + x_1}{2}, \frac{y_2 + y_1}{2}\right).$$

9–4 Two nonvertical lines are parallel if and only if they have equal slopes.

9–5 Two nonvertical lines are perpendicular if and only if the slope of one line is the negative reciprocal of the slope of the other line.

9–6 The graph of any equation that can be written in the form $Ax + By = C$, where A and B are not both zero, is a line.

9–7 The equation of the line passing through the points (x_1, y_1) and (x_2, y_2) is given by the formula

$$y - y_1 = m(x - x_1)$$

where $m = \frac{y_2 - y_1}{x_2 - x_1}$.

Use the given axes to graph the following points.

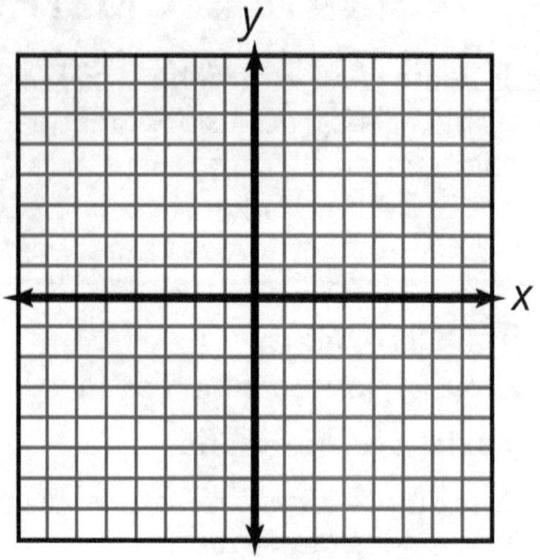

3.44 *A* (3, 3)

3.45 *B* (4, -2)

3.46 *C* (0, 5)

3.47 *D* (-3, -5)

3.48 *E* (-6, 4)

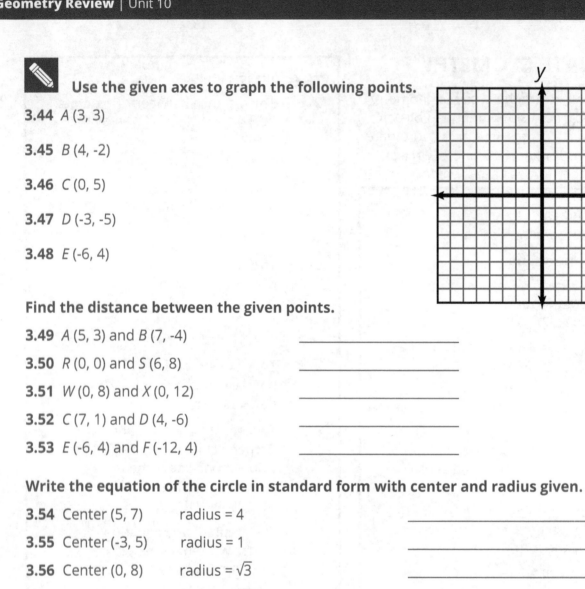

Find the distance between the given points.

3.49 *A* (5, 3) and *B* (7, -4) ________________

3.50 *R* (0, 0) and *S* (6, 8) ________________

3.51 *W* (0, 8) and *X* (0, 12) ________________

3.52 *C* (7, 1) and *D* (4, -6) ________________

3.53 *E* (-6, 4) and *F* (-12, 4) ________________

Write the equation of the circle in standard form with center and radius given.

3.54 Center (5, 7) radius = 4 ________________

3.55 Center (-3, 5) radius = 1 ________________

3.56 Center (0, 8) radius = $\sqrt{3}$ ________________

3.57 Center (0, 0) radius = $\sqrt{5}$ ________________

3.58 Center (-3, -8) radius = $2\sqrt{3}$ ________________

Write the equation of the line meeting the given conditions.

3.59 Containing *A* (1, 3) and *B* (0, 2) ________________

3.60 Containing *C* (3, 3) and *D* (-3, 2) ________________

3.61 Containing *E* (4, 3) and *F* (6, 1) ________________

3.62 Containing *A* (5, 3) and perpendicular to a line with slope of -2

____

3.63 Containing *B* (3, 1) and parallel to a line with slope of $\frac{1}{5}$

____

3.64 Write the equation of the lines containing the medians in the triangle whose vertices are A (4, 8), B (-2, 2), and C (6, 0). ________________

Sketch the graphs of the following equations.

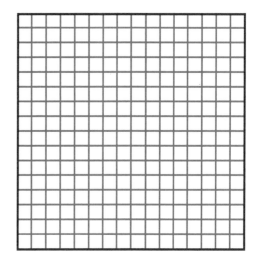

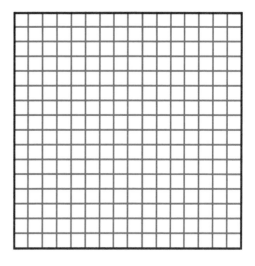

3.65 $4x - 3y = 12$

3.66 $|x| \leq 4$

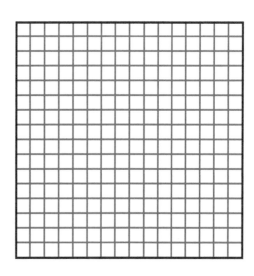

3.67 $\{(x, y): 4 \geq y > -3\}$

Prove using coordinate methods. Include a representative sketch.

3.68 A segment connecting the midpoints of two sides of a triangle equals $\frac{1}{2}$ the third side.

Before you take this last Self Test, you may want to do one or more of the following self checks.

1. ________ Read the objectives. Determine if you can do them.
2. ________ Restudy the material related to any objectives that you cannot do.
3. ________ Use the **SQ3R** study procedure to review the material:
   a. **S**can the sections.
   b. **Q**uestion yourself.
   c. **R**ead to answer your questions.
   d. **R**ecite the answers to yourself.
   e. **R**eview areas you did not understand.
4. ________ Review all activities and Self Tests, writing a correct answer for every wrong answer.

SELF TEST 3

Complete the following statements (each answer, 3 points).

3.01 Points A and A' have symmetry with respect to the line $y = 3$. A is point (2, 5).
A' is point ________________ .

3.02 Three consecutive vertices of a parallelogram are points (2, 4), (0, 0), and (6, 0).
The fourth vertex is point ________________ .

3.03 The shortest sides of two similar polygons have lengths in the ratio 2:5. The perimeter of the smaller polygon is 20. The perimeter of the larger polygon is ______________________ .

3.04 Two chords intersect inside a circle. The lengths of the segments of one chord are 4 and 6. The lengths of the segments of the other chord are 3 and ______________ .

3.05 The equation of the circle with center (3, -2) and radius 7 is ___________________ .

3.06 The equation of the line passing through the point (2, -5) and having slope $-\frac{2}{3}$ is

____________________ .

3.07 A solid metal cylinder with a 4-in. radius and a 10-in. altitude is melted and recast into solid right circular cones each with a 1-in. radius and a 2-in. altitude.
The number of cones formed is _______________ .

3.08 The slope of any line perpendicular to $\overleftrightarrow{AB}$, where A (0, -3) and B (4, 9) are two points on the line, is ____________________ .

3.09 The volume of a sphere with a 10-in. radius is ___________________ .

3.010 Point P (3, -4) and P' have symmetry with respect to the origin.
P' is point ________________ .

3.011 An angle of measure less than 90° is called a(n) __________________ angle.

3.012 The longest chord that can be drawn in a circle is a __________________ .

3.013 If points A, B, and C lie on a line, they are said to be __________________ points.

3.014 Where p and q are statements, "p or q" denotes the __________________ of p and q.

3.015 Theorems in a mathematical system are proved by __________________ reasoning.

Write the answer in the space provided (each answer, 3 points).

3.016 If l is parallel to m in this figure, find x.

x = ______________

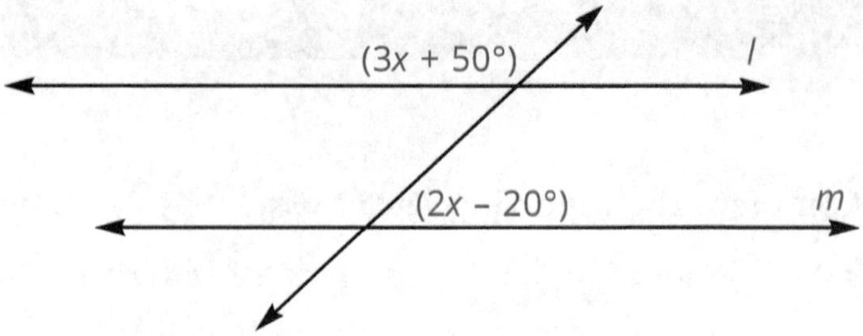

3.017 In triangle ABC, m $\angle A = 80°$. The bisectors of $\angle B$ and $\angle C$ intersect at point P. Find the measure of $\angle BPC$. ______________

3.018 A square with sides of $x + 2$ and an equilateral triangle of sides with length $2x$ have equal perimeters. Find x. ______________

3.019 The lengths of the sides of a triangle are 6, 7, and 9. Find the lengths of the sides of a similar triangle whose shortest side is 4. ______________

3.020 If the legs of a right triangle are 8 and 10, find the length of the hypotenuse. ______________

3.021 In a circle a 70° central angle and an inscribed angle both intercept the same arc. What is the measure of the inscribed angle? ______________

3.022 Find the area of a rhombus whose diagonals measure 6 and 12. ______________

Complete the following proofs (each proof, 6 points).

3.023 Given: $\angle 1 = \angle 2$

$AP = BP$

To Prove: $\triangle APD \cong \triangle BPC$

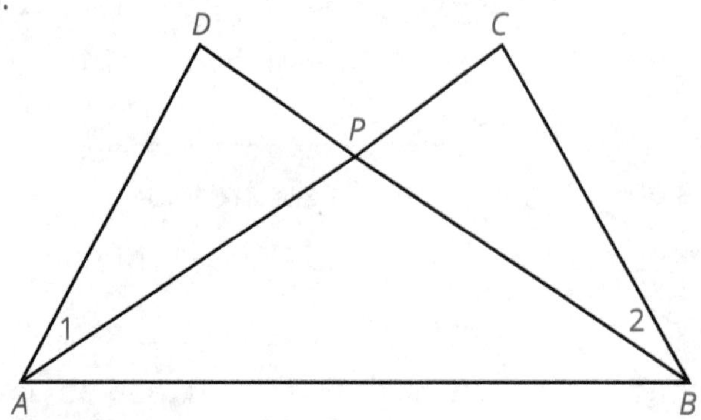

STATEMENT	REASON

3.024 Given: $\overline{AB} \perp \overline{CD}$

To Prove: $m\angle 2 + m\angle 4 + m\angle 7 = m\angle 1$

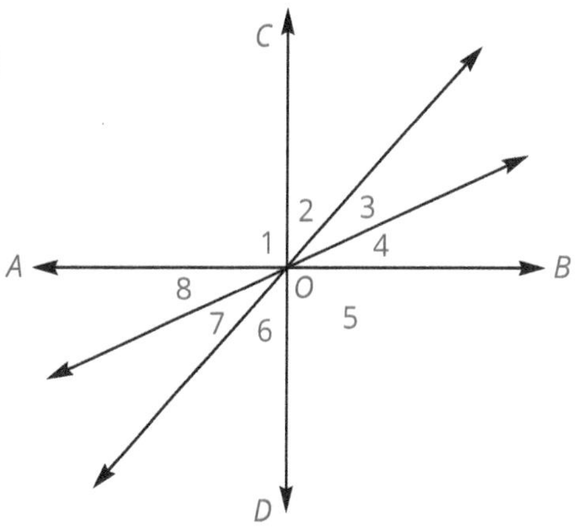

STATEMENT	REASON

3.025 Given: $\overline{XA} \perp \overleftrightarrow{RS}$

$\angle 1 = \angle 2$

To Prove: $\frac{BX}{XC} = \frac{AB}{AC}$

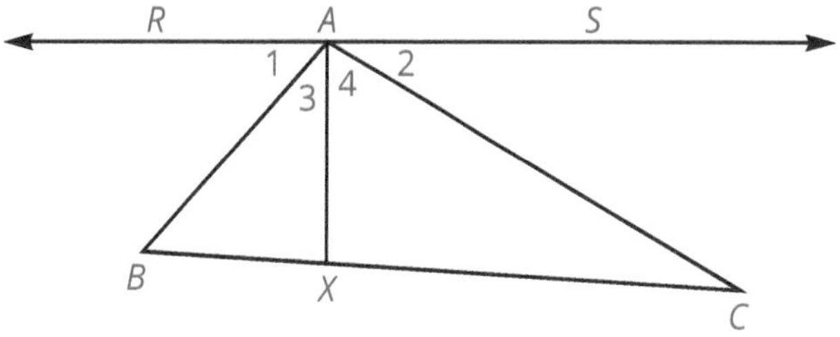

STATEMENT	REASON

3.026 Given: m $\angle 1$ = m $\angle 2$
m $\angle 5$ = m $\angle 6$

To Prove: m $\angle 7$ = m $\angle 8$

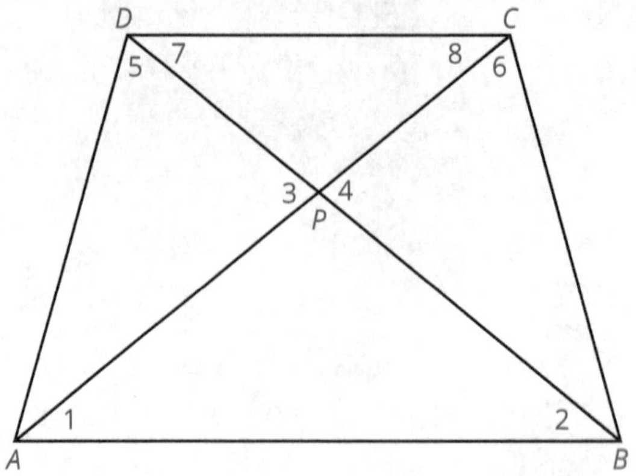

STATEMENT	REASON

3.027 Given: $\overline{AB}$ diameter,
$\overline{BC}$ is tangent to circle O.

To Prove: $\triangle AXB \sim \triangle ABC$

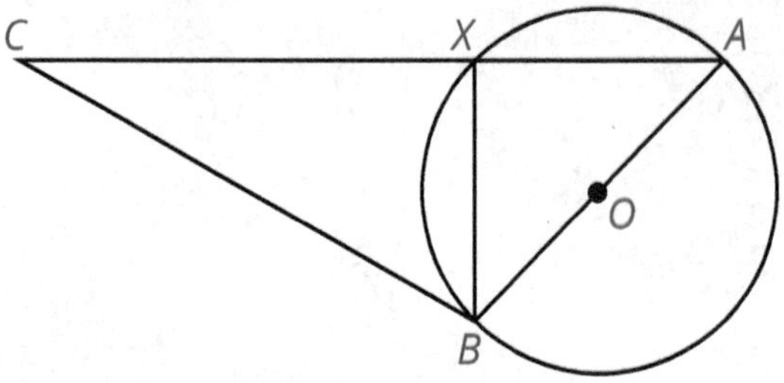

STATEMENT	REASON

3.028 Given: $\overline{AB} \parallel \overline{CD}$
$\angle 1 = \angle 2$
To Prove: $m\angle 1 = m\angle 2 + m\angle 3$

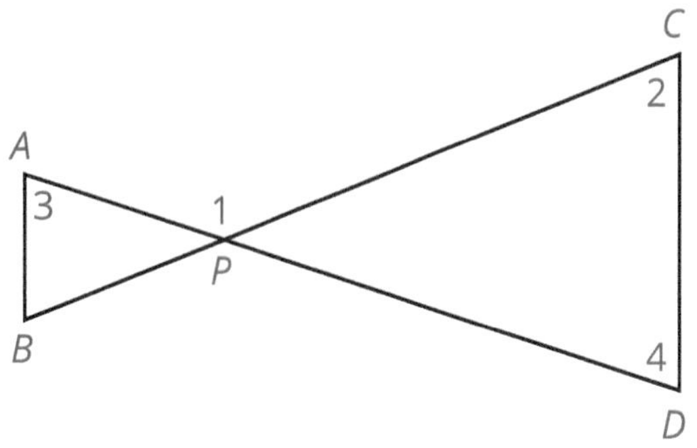

STATEMENT	REASON

82/102 **SCORE** ________ **TEACHER** ________ ________
initials date

Before taking the LIFEPAC Test, you may want to do one or more of these self checks.

1. ________ Read the objectives. Check to see if you can do them.
2. ________ Restudy the material related to any objectives that you cannot do.
3. ________ Use the **SQ3R** study procedure to review the material.
4. ________ Review activities, Self Tests, and LIFEPAC Glossary.
5. ________ Restudy areas of weakness indicated by the last Self Test.

GLOSSARY

Acute angle .... an angle whose measure is less than 90°.

Adjacent angles .... two angles in the same plane that have a common vertex and a common side but no interior points in common.

Altitude of a triangle .... a segment from a vertex perpendicular to the opposite side.

Angle .... the union of two noncollinear rays that have a common endpoint.

Apothem .... the distance from the center of a polygon to a side.

Area of a circle .... the limit of the areas of the inscribed regular polygons.

Auxiliary line .... a line introduced in a figure to make a proof possible.

Betweenness of points .... point B is between points A and C if A, B, and C are collinear and AB + BC = AC.

Bisector of a segment .... a line or segment that intersects the first segment at its midpoint.

Center of an arc .... the center of the circle that contains the arc.

Center of a regular polygon .... the common center of its inscribed and circumscribed circles.

Central angle .... an angle in the plane of a circle whose vertex is at the center of the circle.

Central angle of a regular polygon .... an angle whose vertex is the center of the polygon and whose sides contain consecutive vertices of the polygon.

Chord .... a segment whose endpoints are on the circle.

Circle .... the set of all points in a plane that are the same distance from a given point in that plane called its center.

Circumference of a circle .... is the limit of the perimeters of the inscribed regular polygons.

Circumscribed circle .... a circle placed around a polygon so that each vertex of the polygon is on the circle.

Collinear points .... a set of two or more points all on the same line.

Complementary angles .... two angles whose measures total 90°.

Concentric circles .... two or more circles that lie in the same plane and have the same center.

Conclusion .... the then clause in a conditional statement.

Conditional .... a statement formed from two statements by connecting them in the form *if* ________ , *then* ________ .

Congruent circles .... circles that have equal radii.

Congruent triangles .... two triangles in which the six parts of one are equal to the corresponding six parts of the other.

Conjunction .... a statement formed by combining two statements with the word and.

Contrapositive .... a statement formed by exchanging the hypothesis and conclusion and negating both of them.

Converse .... a statement formed by interchanging the hypothesis and the conclusion in a conditional statement.

Coordinate axes .... an x-axis and a y-axis intersecting at the zero points and perpendicular to each other.

Coplanar points .... a set of points all on the same plane.

Cosine ratio .... in a right triangle, the side adjacent to an acute angle over the hypotenuse.

Deductive reasoning .... the process of making a conclusion by fitting a specific example to a general statement.

Diameter .... a segment passing through the center with endpoints on the circle.

Disjunction .... a statement formed by combining two statements with the word or.

Exterior angle of a triangle .... an angle formed by one side of a triangle and an extension of another side.

Figure .... a lettered figure drawn to illustrate the given conditions of the statement.

Geometric mean .... for any positive real numbers a, b, and x, if $\frac{a}{x} = \frac{x}{b}$, then x is called the geometric mean between a and b.

Given .... the given conditions of the statement expressed in terms of the letter and numerals used in the figure.

Graph .... a set of points in the coordinate plane that meets certain algebraic conditions.

Hypothesis .... the if clause in a conditional statement.

Included angle .... the angle formed by two sides of a triangle. The angle is included between the two sides.

Included side .... the side of a triangle that is the common side of two angles. The side is included between the two angles.

Indirect proof .... a proof of a theorem by indirect means.

Inductive reasoning .... the process of making a general conclusion based on specific examples.

Inscribed angle .... an angle whose sides contain the endpoints of an arc and whose vertex is a point of the arc other than an endpoint of the arc.

Inscribed circle .... a circle placed inside a polygon so that all sides of the polygon are tangent to the circle.

Inverse .... a statement formed by negating both the hypothesis and the conclusion of a conditional statement.

Isosceles trapezoid .... a trapezoid with legs of the same length.

Isosceles triangle .... a triangle with at least two sides equal.

Line segment .... the set of two different points and all points between them.

Locus .... the set of all those points and only those points that satisfy a given condition.

Major arc .... the union of two points of the circle (not endpoints of a diameter) and all points of the circle that are in the exterior of the central angle whose sides contain the two points.

Median of a trapezoid .... the segment connecting the midpoint of the legs.

Median of a triangle .... a segment from a vertex to the midpoint of the opposite side.

Midpoint of an arc .... a point x on arc AB such that $m\,\widehat{AX} = m\,\widehat{XB}$.

Midpoint of a segment .... the point on a segment that divides the segment into two segments of equal length.

Minor arc .... the union of two points of the circle (not endpoints of a diameter) and all points of the circle that are in the interior of the central angle whose sides contain the two points.

Negation .... if p is a statement, the new statement, not p, is called the negation of p.

Obtuse angle .... an angle whose measure is greater than 90° but less than 180°.

Opposite rays .... two rays with a common endpoint that form a line.

Parallel lines .... lines that are in the same plane and have no points in common.

Parallelogram .... a quadrilateral with both pairs of opposite sides parallel.

Perpendicular .... two lines that intersect and form four equal angles.

Pi (π) .... the ratio of the circumference to the diameter of a circle.

Plan of Proof .... a brief description of the plan you are going to use in the proof.

Postulate .... a statement accepted without proof.

Projection of a point on a line .... the point where a perpendicular through the point to the line intersects the line.

Projection of a segment on a line .... the portion of a line with endpoints that are the projections of the endpoints of the segment.

Proof .... the actual proof; a series of numbered statements in one column with a like-numbered column next to it for the reasons.

Proportion .... an equation that states that two ratios are equal.

Quadrants .... the four regions of a plane formed by the coordinate axes.

Radius .... a segment whose endpoints are the center of a circle and a point on the circle.

Radius of a regular polygon .... the distance from the center of the polygon to a vertex.

Ratio .... the comparison of two numbers by division. The quotient is the ratio of the two numbers.

Ray .... the set of all points $\overline{AB}$ and all points P, such that B is between A and P.

Rectangle .... a parallelogram with four right angles.

Regular hexagon .... a hexagon with all six sides equal and all six angles equal.

Regular octagon .... an octagon with all eight sides equal and all eight angles equal.

Regular polygon .... a polygon with all angles equal and all sides equal.

Rhombus .... a parallelogram with all sides equal.

Right angle .... an angle whose measure is equal to 90°.

Secant .... a line that contains a chord.

Sector .... the region of a circle bounded by two radii and an arc of the circle.

Segment of a circle .... the region bounded by a chord and an arc of the circle.

Semicircle .... the union of the endpoints of a diameter and all points of the circle that are on the same side of the diameter.

Similar polygons .... polygons whose vertices can be matched in a one-to-one correspondence so that corresponding angles are equal and corresponding sides are in proportion.

Sine ratio .... in a right triangle, the side opposite an acute angle over the hypotenuse.

Skew lines .... two lines that do not lie in the same plane and will never intersect.

Space .... the set of all points.

Sphere .... the set of all points that are the same distance from a given point.

Square .... a rectangle with all sides equal.

Statement .... a full written statement of the theorem.

Statement .... a sentence that is either true or false but not both.

Supplementary angles .... two angles whose measures total 180°.

Symmetry .... the property of balance that a figure has with respect to a point, a line, or a plane.

Tangent line .... a line in the plane of a circle that intersects the circle in exactly one point.

Tangent ratio .... in a right triangle, the side opposite an acute angle over the side adjacent to the acute angle.

Theorem .... a general statement that can be proved.

To Prove .... the part of the statement that requires proof expressed in terms of the letters and numerals that are used in the figure.

Transversal .... a line that intersects two or more coplanar lines in different points.

Trapezoid .... a quadrilateral with exactly one pair of sides parallel.

Triangle .... the union of three segments determined by three noncollinear points.

Truth table .... an arrangement of truth values to determine when a statement is true or false.

Two-column proof .... a formal proof of a theorem composed of six standard parts.

Vertical angles .... two angles whose sides form two pairs of opposite rays.

***x*-axis** .... a horizontal number line.

***y*-axis** .... a vertical number line.

MATH 1010

LIFEPAC TEST

NAME ______________________________

DATE ______________________________

SCORE ______________________________

Write the correct letter and answer on the blank (each answer, 2 points).

1. For any circle, π is exactly equal to ________________ .
   a. $\frac{22}{7}$ b. 3.14 c. $\frac{C}{d}$ d. $\frac{d}{C}$
2. The line containing points (-1, 3) and (3, 8) has slope ________________ .
   a. $\frac{5}{2}$ b. $\frac{5}{4}$ c. $\frac{2}{5}$ d. $\frac{4}{5}$
3. The midpoint of the segment joining points (a, b) and (j, k) is ________________ .
   a. $(j - a, k - b)$ b. $(\frac{j-a}{2}, \frac{k-b}{2})$ c. $(j + a, k + b)$ d. $(\frac{j+a}{2}, \frac{k+b}{2})$
4. The altitude of an equilateral triangle is $7\sqrt{3}$ units long. The length of one side of the triangle is ________________ .
   a. 7 b. 14 c. $14\sqrt{3}$ d. $\frac{7\sqrt{3}}{2}$
5. The area of a square is 36. The length of the diagonal of the square is __________ .
   a. $36\sqrt{2}$ b. $6\sqrt{2}$ c. $3\sqrt{2}$ d. 6
6. The only defined term of those listed is ________________ .
   a. line b. angle c. plane d. point
7. The intersection of two planes is a ________________ .
   a. line b. segment c. point d. ray
8. Which of the following items can be measured? ________________
   a. plane b. line c. ray d. segment
9. Ray $\overrightarrow{OX}$ bisects AOC and m $\angle AOX = 42°$. m $\angle AOC$ = ________________ .
   a. 42° b. 84° c. 21° d. 68°
10. In triangle ABC, m $\angle A = 47°$, m $\angle B = 62°$. m $\angle C$ = ________________ .
    a. 81° b. 61° c. 71° d. 51°
11. In triangle ABC, $AC = BC$ and m $\angle C = 62°$. The longest side of the triangle is ________ .
    a. AC b. BC c. AB d. AM

12. Point T is the midpoint of $\overline{JH}$. The coordinate of T is (0, 5) and the coordinate of J is (0, 2). The coordinate of H is ________________ .

a. (0, 8) b. (0, 3) c. (0, 7) d. (0, 11)

13. In a certain n-gon, the sum of the measures of the interior angles is 1,260°; n = __________ .

a. 7 b. 12 c. 9 d. 8

14. Four angles of a pentagon have measures of 85°, 90°, 95°, and 110°. The smallest of all the exterior angles measures ________________ .

a. 5° b. 20° c. 70° d. 85°

15. The measures of the angles of a quadrilateral are x, x, x + 15°, and x + 45°; x = __________ .

a. 75° b. 65° c. 71° d. 55°

Answer true or false (each answer, 2 points).

16. ____________ All diagonals from a single vertex of a hexagon are drawn. Four triangles will result.

17. ____________ A person who looks at a sequence of 14, 12, 10, 8 and decides that the next two terms are 6 and 4 is doing deductive thinking.

18. ____________ If "if p, then q" is the conditional statement, then "if q, then p" is the converse.

19. ____________ A square is a rhombus.

20. ____________ An equilateral triangle is an isosceles triangle.

21. ____________ The legs of a trapezoid are parallel.

22. ____________ The complement of an acute angle is an obtuse angle.

23. ____________ Vertical angles can never be complementary.

24. ____________ If $RX = SX$, then X must be the midpoint of RS.

25. ____________ The sum of the measures of the interior angles of a pentagon is 540°.

26. ____________ If $\frac{a}{b} = \frac{2}{5}$, then $\frac{b}{a} = \frac{5}{2}$.

27. ____________ An equilateral triangle and square are similar polygons.

28. ____________ A circle with circumference of 10 has area of 100.

29. ____________ If $\triangle ABC \sim \triangle RST$, then $\triangle STR \sim \triangle BCA$.

30. ____________ The length of each lateral edge of a regular pyramid is greater than the slant height.

Write the answer in the space provided (each answer, 3 points).

31. The coordinate of the midpoint of segment *AB* is (-3, 2). Find the coordinate of *A* if the coordinate of *B* is (0, 2). ______________

32. In triangle *ABC*, m $\angle A = 38°$ and m $\angle B$ = m $\angle C$. Find m $\angle B$. ______________

33. Find the measure of each exterior angle of a regular hexagon. ______________

34. For statements *p* and *q*, "$p \rightarrow q$" is false; "*p* or *q*" is true. Which of the two statements, *p* or *q*, must be false? ______________

35. Find the number of sides of a regular polygon for which the sum of the measures of the interior angles is 900°. ______________

36. Write the equation of a line through point (2, 5) and having slope $\frac{3}{7}$. ______________

37. Find the area of a 120° sector of a circle whose radius is 6. ______________

38. The vertices of a trapezoid are points (0, *a*), (0, 0), (*b*, 0), and (*c*, *a*). Find the area in terms of *a*, *b*, and *c*. ______________

Sketch the following graphs (each graph, 4 points).

39. Sketch the graph of $\{x: x^2 < 4\}$ on the number line.

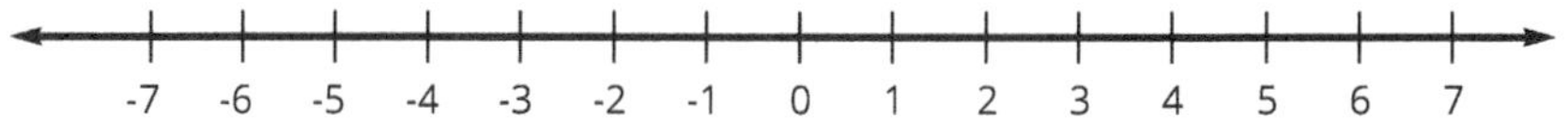

40. Sketch the graph of $\{(x, y): x = 2 \text{ and } y \leq 1\}$ on the coordinate axes.

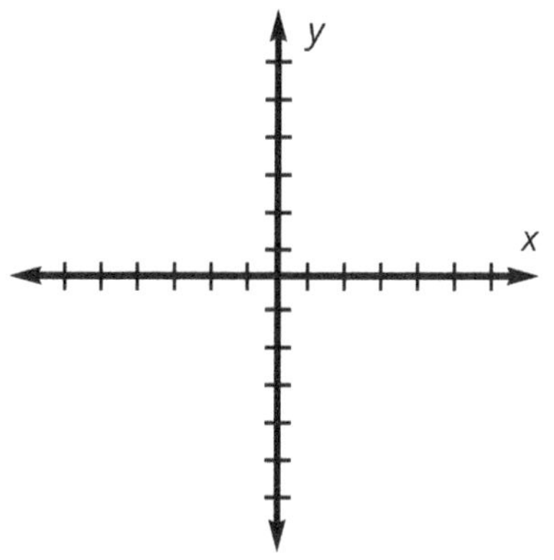

Complete the following proofs (each proof, 6 points).

41. Given: $m\angle 1 = m\angle 2$, $m\angle 5 = m\angle 6$

To Prove: $m\angle 7 = m\angle 8$

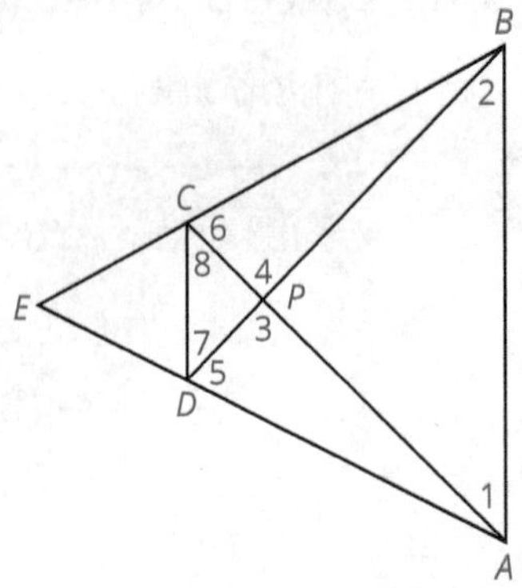

STATEMENT	REASON

42. Given: $\angle 1 = \angle 2$, $AP = BP$

To Prove: $\triangle APD \cong \triangle BPC$

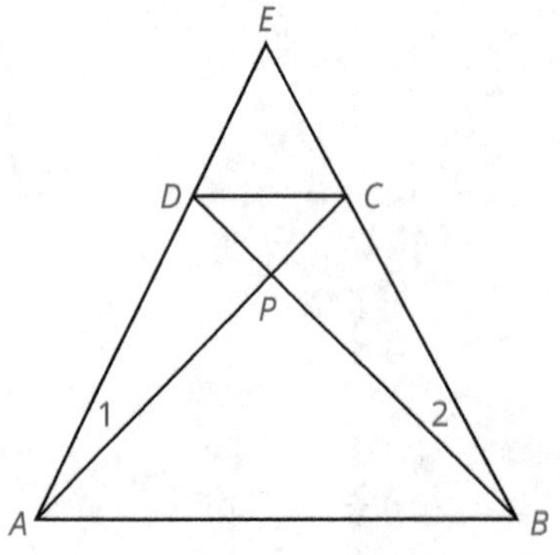

STATEMENT	REASON